Heterocyclic Systems with BRIDGEHEAD NITROGEN ATOMS

In Two Parts

PART ONE

This is Part One of the fifteenth volume published in the series

THE CHEMISTRY OF HETEROCYCLIC COMPOUNDS

THE CHEMISTRY OF HETEROCYCLIC COMPOUNDS

A SERIES OF MONOGRAPHS

ARNOLD WEISSBERGER, *Consulting Editor*

Heterocyclic Systems with BRIDGEHEAD NITROGEN ATOMS

Part One

William L. Mosby
American Cyanamid Company
Bound Brook, New Jersey

1961
INTERSCIENCE PUBLISHERS, INC., NEW YORK
INTERSCIENCE PUBLISHERS LTD., LONDON

Library of Congress Catalog Card Number 60–13118

INTERSCIENCE PUBLISHERS, INC., 250 Fifth Avenue, New York 1, N. Y.

For Great Britain and Northern Ireland:

Interscience Publishers, Ltd., 88/90 Chancery Lane, London, W.C. 2

PRINTED IN THE UNITED STATES OF AMERICA

The Chemistry of Heterocyclic Compounds

The chemistry of heterocyclic compounds is one of the most complex branches of organic chemistry. It is equally interesting for its theoretical implications, for the diversity of its synthetic procedures, and for the physiological and industrial significance of heterocyclic compounds.

A field of such importance and intrinsic difficulty should be made as readily accessible as possible, and the lack of a modern detailed and comprehensive presentation of heterocyclic chemistry is therefore keenly felt. It is the intention of the present series to fill this gap by expert presentations of the various branches of heterocyclic chemistry. The subdivisions have been designed to cover the field in its entirety by monographs which reflect the importance and the interrelations of the various compounds and accommodate the specific interests of the authors.

Research Laboratories
Eastman Kodak Company
Rochester, New York

ARNOLD WEISSBERGER

Rochester 4, New York

Arnold Weissberger

Preface

The generous assistance of several others has greatly facilitated the completion of this book, and the author gratefully acknowledges their contribution. Initially, this work was begun in collaboration with Dr. L. E. Craig, who, before he was obliged to withdraw from participation, supplied a preliminary literature survey and draft of a manuscript covering approximately fifty ring systems, and contributed to discussions on the organization of the material.

Dr. Leonard T. Capell gave most liberally of his time in checking and correcting the names proposed for approximately 350 ring systems which lacked systematic names. Instruction in the rules of nomenclature and assistance in naming many complex structures were provided by Mrs. Marie Cline.

Many authors, particularly those abroad, kindly supplied reprints of their publications. Drs. J. J. Leavitt and A. P. Paul read critically portions of the manuscript, and the former is responsible for bringing to the author's attention numerous references from the current literature. The author is especially grateful to the American Cyanamid Company for providing freely of excellent library and secretarial facilities.

Bound Brook, New Jersey William L. Mosby

Contents

Part One

Introduction 1

A. FUSED RING SYSTEMS

I. Fused 3-Membered Ring Systems 7
II. Fused 4-Membered Ring Systems 35
III. Fused 5/5 Ring Systems 63
IV. Fused 5/6 Ring Systems with No Extra Heteroatom 239
V. Fused 5/6 Ring Systems with One Extra Heteroatom 451

Part Two

VI. Fused 5/6 Ring Systems with Two Extra Heteroatoms
VII. Fused 5/6 Ring Systems with Three Extra Heteroatoms
VIII. Fused 5/6 Ring Systems with Four or More Extra Heteroatoms
IX. Fused 5/6 Ring Systems with Two Bridgehead Nitrogen Atoms
X. Fused 5/7 and Larger Ring Systems
XI. Fused 6/6 Ring Systems with No Extra Heteroatom
XII. Fused 6/6 Ring Systems with One Extra Heteroatom
XIII. Fused 6/6 Ring Systems with Two or More Extra Heteroatoms.
XIV. Fused 6/6 Ring Systems with Two Bridgehead Nitrogen Atoms
XV. Fused 6/7 and Larger Ring Systems

B. BRIDGED RING SYSTEMS

XVI. Bridged 3/4 through 5/6 Ring Systems
XVII. Bridged 6/6 Ring Systems
XVIII. Bridged 6/7 and Larger Ring Systems
Ring Index
Subject Index

Introduction

One might, initially, consider the number of ring systems having bridgehead nitrogen atoms to be rather small, and further, that such systems could be of only limited importance. There are, however, nearly eleven hundred such nuclei, and many of them are of considerable importance, particularly to the dyestuff and pharmaceutical industries, and in the study of natural products. No comprehensive review of bridgehead nitrogen systems has appeared thus far, and it is hoped that the present work will help to stimulate interest in such systems as a class, and to provide a convenient source of information on the individual members of this class.

In accordance with the precepts of the "Definitive Rules for the Nomenclature of Organic Chemistry" issued by the Commission on Nomenclature of Organic Chemistry of the International Union of Pure and Applied Chemistry, defining a "bridge" and "bridgehead" atoms, both atom-bridged and valence bond-bridged systems have been included in this book. Generally, only covalent nitrogen ring systems have been considered, although some exceptions to this practice have been admitted, particularly when they were included in the *Ring Index*. Systems in which the bridgehead nitrogen is necessarily quaternary (as in certain spiranes, betaines, etc.), have usually been omitted.

It was the author's intention to review *all* references to every ring system discussed. Every effort has been made to achieve this goal in all areas save one: natural products having bridgehead nitrogen atoms. It was impracticable to review exhaustively in the manner chosen, an additional area as extensive, progressive and contentious as that of natural products. Consequently, such highly important topics as penicillin, gliotoxin and the lupine, strychnos, reserpine and quinine alkaloids have been given scanty attention. Fortunately, these lacunae can be filled admirably by a number of recent reviews, and frequent reference to these works has been made in the appropriate places.

For each ring system included, the literature has been surveyed systematically through Volume 50 (1956) of *Chemical Abstracts*. In addition, the major occidental journals have been searched through the first half of 1958. New compounds and ring systems are being reported daily and, while every effort was expended to insure complete coverage, undoubtedly a few have been overlooked.

In this survey, emphasis has been placed upon the critical presentation of information rather than mere compilation of data. The author has speculated freely (sometimes, possibly, tenuously) upon the structures of controversial products, partly to encourage discussion and work in areas requiring elucidation.

One of the most difficult problems encountered in the preparation of this book was that of organization. Two major divisions were immediately apparent: A, valence bond-bridged systems as typified by pyrrocoline, etc. and B, atom-bridged systems such as quinuclidine. The problem was to achieve optimum juxtaposition of the nine hundred ring systems in category A. There are obvious advantages in placing together systems which form a homologous series (e.g., pyrrole, indole, carbazole, etc.). However, the complex interrelationships of the present ring systems make such an arrangement impractical. It was finally decided to arrange the ring systems in the manner described below, employing some of the principles used by the *Ring Index* and by *Chemical Abstracts*.

For organizational purposes, each ring system was examined for what was termed the "operative bicycle," namely, the two rings sharing the bridgehead nitrogen atom(s). The sequence of ring systems was then determined by the character of the operative bicycle. Three-membered rings were considered first with a 3/3 operative bicycle preceding a 3/4 system, etc., as in the *Ring Index*. To determine the proper sequence, the ring system was redrawn arbitrarily so that, in the operative bicycle, the nitrogen was at the bottom and the smaller ring on the right (as in A-235). The operative bicycle

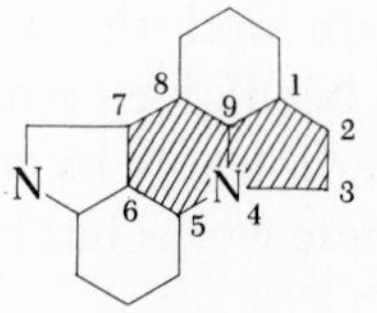

(A-235)

(shaded) was then numbered (as shown) by the accepted method. The operative bicycle itself (if known) was then listed first, followed by homologs of increasing substitution numbers and increasing complexity.

Following these were listed nuclei in which the operative bicycles contained additional heteroatoms (other than the original bridgehead nitrogen). The heteroatoms were accorded the precedence recommended by the *Ring Index* (O, S, Se, N, etc.), and ring systems with a heteroatom at position 1 of the operative bicycle were placed first, etc. Strict numerical sequence was followed, with, for example, a nucleus containing additional nitrogen atoms at positions 1, 5 and 7 of the operative bicycle preceding one with similar nitrogen atoms in positions 2, 3 and 6. The principle of "earliest entry" was followed, with A-77 listed as a 5/5 (not 5/6) system, and A-121 considered to have one "extra" nitrogen in the 3-position of the operative bicycle (rather than two in positions 1 and 5). Nuclei containing two bridgehead nitrogen atoms were placed last in the group of systems of that particular ring size.

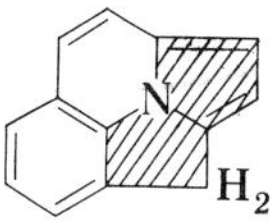

(A-77) 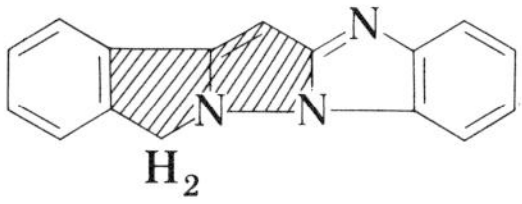 (A-121)

So much then for the mode of organization. A little practice should enable those interested to make use of the system in finding particular nuclei. However, in view of the complexity of the nuclei covered, many will prefer to make use of the indices, especially the "Index of Ring Systems" when seeking particular ring systems. The latter, arranged according to the system employed by *Chemical Abstracts* and the *Ring Index*, enables one with no knowledge of nomenclature or of the organization of this book, to locate rapidly all the known ring systems of a particular size and specification.

A little should be said concerning the incidence of various types of ring systems. Valence bond-bridged systems having a 5/6 operative bicycle constitute the greatest single group (46%) of the systems considered. Next in numbers come the atom-bridged systems (all together) and the valence bond-bridged 6/6 systems, each amounting to 15% of the total. Of the remaining 24%, those valence bond-bridged systems having a 5/5 operative bicycle account for 11%. Amongst the more extensively studied individual ring systems are found pyrrocoline (A-183), imidazo[1,2-*a*]pyridine (A-271), 3*H*-pyrrolo[1,2-*a*]pyrrole (A-64), 9*aH*-quinolizine (A-721), 2*H*-pyrido-[1,2-*a*]pyridine (A-780) and quinuclidine (B-87).

Numerous tables have been used to summarize the data on individual compounds, and in these simple esters, amides, etc., are often, but not exclusively, listed under the parent acid. The colors of compounds are usually mentioned only when they are other than colorless or pale yellow.

Every effort was made to consult the original references quoted. In certain cases (oriental and some Slavic journals) it was necessary to refer only to abstracts of the original papers, and these secondary sources are cited in those cases. However, the listing of a secondary reference should not necessarily be taken to imply that the original was not consulted, since, as a matter of convenience, references to abstracts of articles in some of the less accessible journals have often been included. Following many of the references to German patents are the letters *Frdl.*, referring to the appropriate volume and page number of Friedländer, *Fortschritte der Teerfarbenfabrikation*, Springer, Berlin, 1882–1942.

Frequent reference has been made to work done in various laboratories in Germany, the only description of which appears in the so-called "PB Reports." These reports, in microfilm form, are published by the Office of Technical Service of the United States Department of Commerce, Washington, D. C. Further information on these reports, and on the related BIOS and FIAT reports, is summarized by Maynard in Lubs (Editor), *The Chemistry of Synthetic Dyes and Pigments*, Reinhold Publishing Corp., New York, 1955, p. 692.

An attempt has been made to follow the nomenclature system adopted by *Chemical Abstracts* and/or the *Ring Index*, though doubtless some deviations have crept in. An asterisk following the title of a ring system indicates that the name was either approved of, or devised by Dr. L. T. Capell of *Chemical Abstracts*. His generous assistance has made it possible to name correctly some 340 previously innominate nuclei.

A. FUSED RING SYSTEMS

CHAPTER I

Fused 3-Membered Ring Systems

A-1. 2-Oxa-1-azabicyclo[1.1.0]butane. R.I. 425

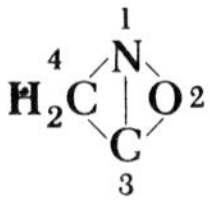

Kolb obtained[1] four products from the reaction of 1-bromophenylacetone with alcoholic ammonia, including a substance (C_9H_9NO, m. 89–90°) easily soluble in ethanol or hydrochloric acid, but difficultly soluble in benzene or water. It gives a yellow chloroplatinate, but does not react with nitrous acid. Kolb assigned the product structure I or II, but an alternative structure (possibly III) would seem more acceptable.

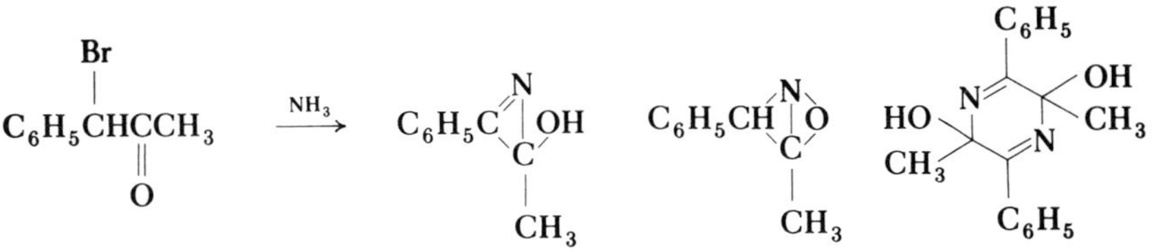

$C_6H_5CHBrCOCH_3 \xrightarrow{NH_3}$

(I) (II) (III)

Reference

1. Kolb, *Ann.*, **291,** 253 (1896).

A-2. 1,2-Diazabicyclo[1.1.0]butane.
R.I. 426

H_2C N NH C H (ring positions 1, 2, 3, 4)

Treatment[1] of I with alcoholic potassium hydroxide gave a substance (m. 133°), which, largely because it was different from the known and expected 7-methyl-2-phenylquinoxaline, was assigned structure II, which now seems highly improbable.

CH_3 NH CH HONH C C_6H_5 $\xrightarrow[C_2H_5OH]{KOH}$ C_6H_5C N N$-C_6H_4CH_3$ C

(I) (II)

Reference

1. Busch and Kämmerer, *Ber.*, **63,** 649 (1930).

A-3. 2-Oxa-1,4-diazabicyclo[1.1.0]butane.
R.I. 424

HN N O C (ring positions 1, 2, 3, 4)

A number of products thought to have structure I, and named *1,3-endoxyhydrazomethylenes*, were described by Busch and Schmidt.[1] These compounds are discussed in Section A-11.

R′–N N O C N=N–R

(I)

Reference

1. Busch and Schmidt, *Ber.*, **62,** 1449 (1929).

A-4. 2-Oxa-1,3-diazabicyclo[1.1.0]butane. R.I. 427

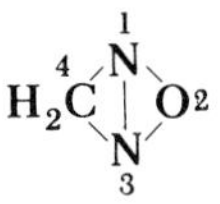

By treating malonic ester with nitric oxide, Traube[1,2] isolated (as the sodium and barium salts) a product which he formulated as I. Other possibilities exist, and further work on these products would seem indicated.

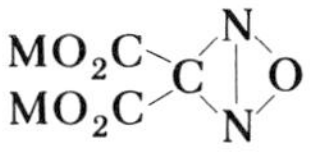

(I)

References

1. Traube, *Ber.*, **28,** 1795 (1895).
2. Traube, *Ann.*, **300,** 81 (1898).

A-5. Anthranil. R.I. 729

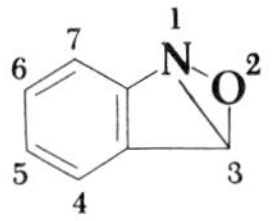

and

A-6. Thioanthranil. R.I. 737

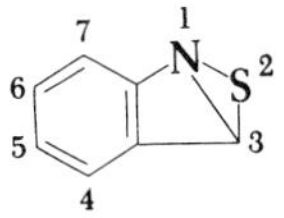

The *Ring Index* numbers cited belong to the names, but not the structures shown.

Structures I and II, respectively, were once assigned to these substances, which are now thought[1] to be represented best by a mesoionic structure such as III (X = O or S).

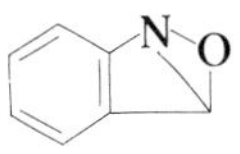

(I) 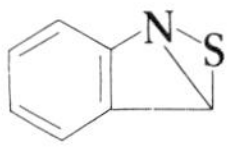 (II) 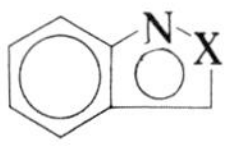 (III)

Reference

1. Abramovich, *Proc. Chem. Soc.*, **1957,** 8.

A-7. 2-Oxa-1,5-diazabicyclo[2.1.0]-pentane*

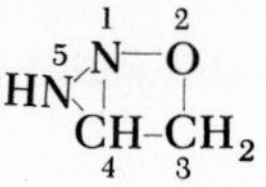

Structure I was originally assigned[1] to the sydnones, which are now known to be represented by a mesoionic structure such as II (see review of mesoionic compounds[2]).

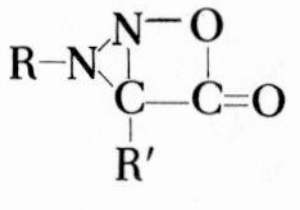

(I) 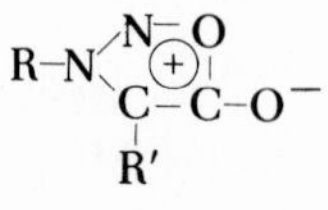 (II)

References

1. Earl and Mackney, *J. Chem. Soc.*, **1935,** 899.
2. Baker and Ollis, *Quart. Revs.*, **11,** 15 (1957).

A-8. 1,4,5-Triazabicyclo[2.1.0]pentane. R.I. 438

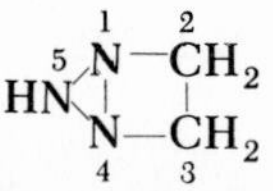

The name *3,4-dihydro-1,2,5-triazole* and the numbering shown in I have also been used.

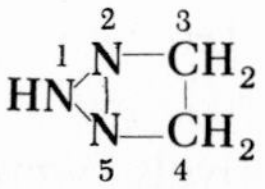

(I)

From the reaction of phenylhydrazine with (*a*) meso-α,β-dibromohydrocinnamic acid, (*b*) α-bromocinnamic ester (II), or (*c*) α-bromocinnamoylphenylhydrazide, Ruhemann[1] isolated the same product (orange needles, m. 172°), to which he assigned structure V. He postulated the existence of III and IV as intermediates in the formation of V. Further work is required to demonstrate the true structure of the product.

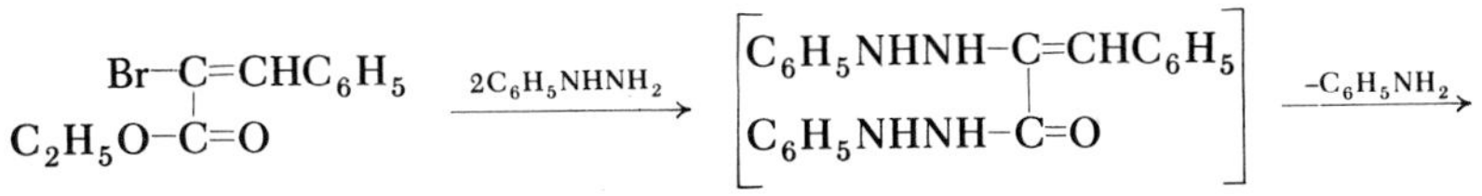

$$\begin{array}{l} Br-C=CHC_6H_5 \\ C_2H_5O-C=O \end{array} \xrightarrow{2C_6H_5NHNH_2} \left[\begin{array}{l} C_6H_5NHNH-C=CHC_6H_5 \\ C_6H_5NHNH-C=O \end{array}\right] \xrightarrow{-C_6H_5NH_2}$$

(II) (III)

$$\left[C_6H_5N\begin{array}{l} NH-C=CHC_6H_5 \\ NH-C=O \end{array}\right] \xrightarrow[C_6H_5NHNH_2]{-H_2} C_6H_5N\begin{array}{l} N-C=CHC_6H_5 \\ N-C=O \end{array}$$

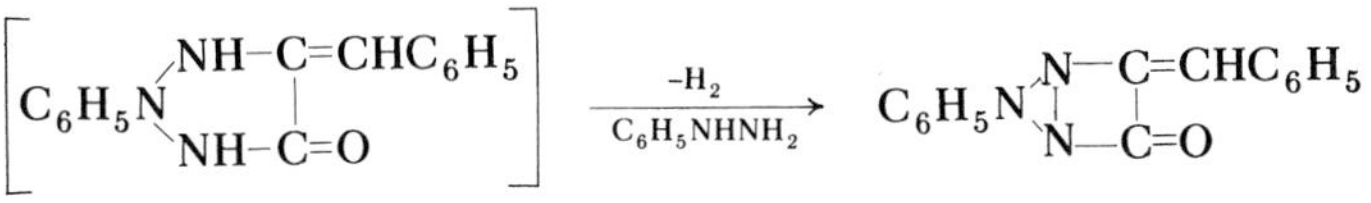

(IV) (V)

Reference

1. Ruhemann, *J. Chem. Soc.*, **61,** 278 (1891).

A-9. Benzo[1,2,3,4]bistriazole.
R.I. 2853

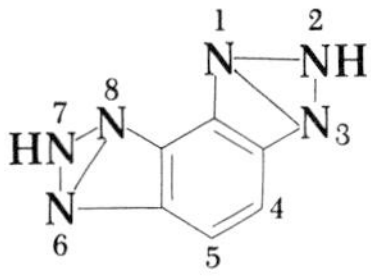

and

A-10. Benzo[1,2,4,5]bistriazole.
R.I. 2852

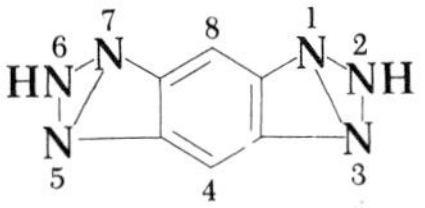

These nuclei (as tricyclic systems) also were given, respectively, *R.I.* 1320 and 1319.

By coupling into *m*-phenylenediamine, Schmidt and Hagenböcker[1] and others claimed to have obtained bisazo compounds (I, R = H), which could be oxidized to *linear* benzobistriazoles (II). These products were shown[2,3] to be trisazo compounds (I, R = —N=N—Ar), which led to *angular* benzobistriazoles, for which structure III was proposed. It seems, therefore, that no authentic examples of the linear system are known, although it has not been demonstrated that none can be made.

It seems probable that the angular benzobistriazoles may not possess the 3/5 system shown in III. An alternative *o*-quinonoid structure, IV, has certain merits (e.g., the seeming nonexistence of *linear* benzobistriazoles, for which a quinonoid structure cannot be

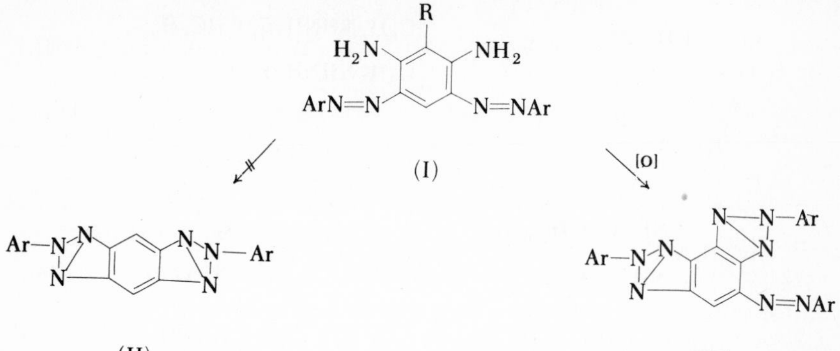

(I)

(II)

(III)

written), but dipolar or mesoionic structures[4,5] such as V must also be considered. Further work is needed to establish the precise structure of these products, and to ascertain if *linear* benzobistriazoles can exist.

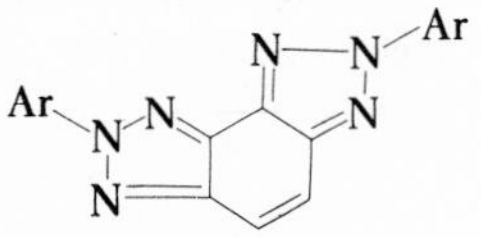

(IV)

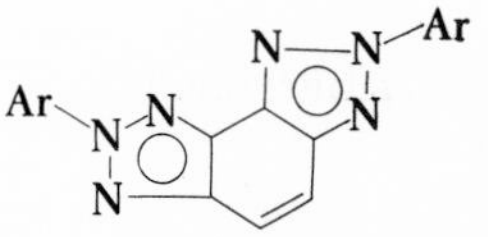

(V)

This same structural problem, of course, applies to the simpler 2-substituted benzotriazoles, naphthotriazoles, etc., which have been formulated both as 3/5 systems and as *o*-quinonoid systems (cf. *R.I.* 715, 1507, and 1509).

References

1. Schmidt and Hagenböcker, *Ber.*, **54**, 2191 and 2201 (1921).
2. Fries and Waltnitzki, *Ann.*, **511**, 267 (1934).
3. Mužík and Allan, *Collection Czechoslov. Chem. Communs.*, **18**, 388 (1953).
4. Johnson, *Ann. Repts. Chem. Soc.*, **48**, 213 (1951).
5. Baker and Ollis, *Quart. Revs.*, **11**, 15 (1957).

A-11. Isotetrazole. R.I. 437

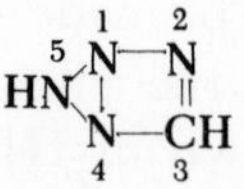

The numbering shown in I was proposed originally.

Whereas diphenylsemicarbazide reacts with nitrous acid to give

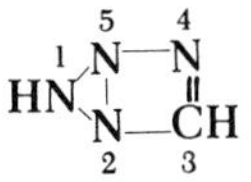

(I)

only an unstable *N*-nitroso derivative, Busch and Becker[1] found that diphenylthiosemicarbazide (II, R = R′ = C_6H_5) afforded, in nearly quantitative yield, a dark red crystalline (m. 110°) sulfur-free product, to which they gave the "isotetrazole" structure III. Later, dissatisfied with structure III, Busch and Schmidt[2] proposed structure IV (R = R′ = C_6H_5), and prepared from various thiosemicarbazides a series of alkyl and aryl homologs.

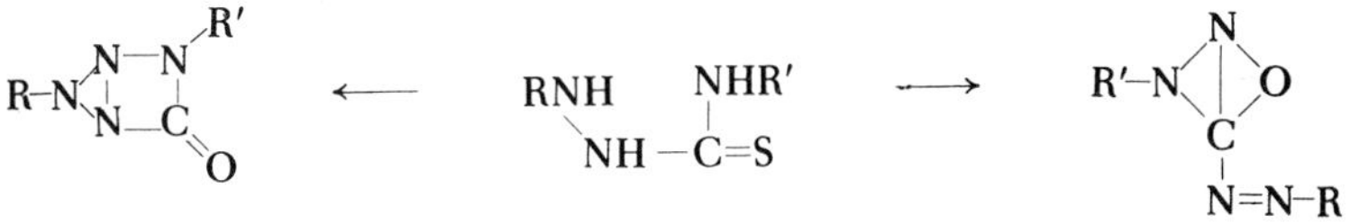

(III) (II) (IV)

The diphenyl compound dyes silk golden-orange from an acid bath and forms yellow salts, including an unusually insoluble nitrate. This latter property recalls the similar behavior of "Nitron" ("triphenylendoiminotriazoline") also discovered by Busch, and for which a mesoionic structure is now accepted.[3] However, the deep color and the rearrangement (v.i.) undergone by these products make the assignment of a mesoionic structure questionable. Similarly, the basicity of these substances and the preparation[2] of a yellow, amphoteric homolog (colorless salts) from phenylthiosemicarbazide (II, R = C_6H_5, R′ = H) would seem to exclude structure V. Hydrolysis of the diphenyl compound with dilute mineral acid yielded[1,2] nitrogen and diphenylazocarbonamide, while very mild reduction gave the latter

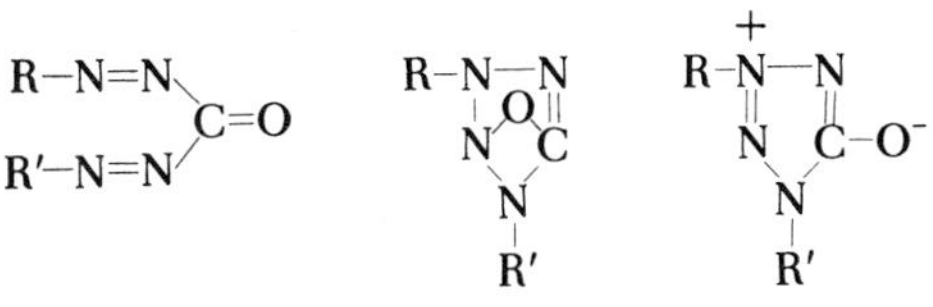

(V) (VI) (VII)

compound together with phenylazocarbonamide, ammonia, and diphenylsemicarbazide. The diaryl compounds of this group (but not those in which R′ = H or alkyl) were converted[2] by treatment with alcoholic potassium hydroxide into colorless, higher-melting, isomeric substances. The products of this rearrangement were thought[2] to have structure VI (or, less likely, III). The colorless diphenyl compound (VI, R = R′ = C_6H_5) so obtained was recently shown[4] (by mixed melting point determination) to be identical with a product obtained by Backer[5] from the coupling of benzenediazonium chloride with dimethylsulfonylmethane, and considered by him to be V (R = R′ = C_6H_5).

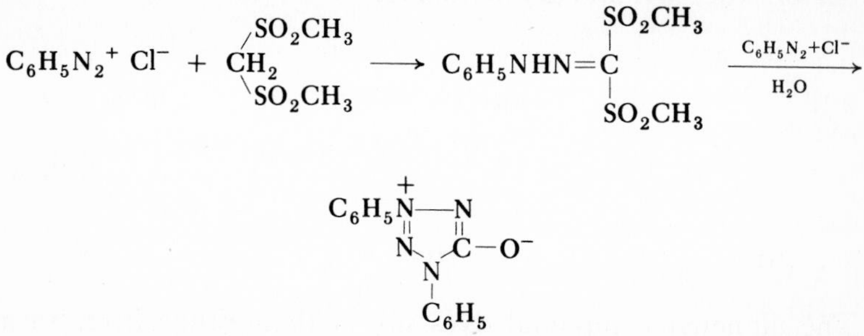

$$C_6H_5N_2^+\,Cl^- + CH_2(SO_2CH_3)_2 \longrightarrow C_6H_5NHN{=}C(SO_2CH_3)_2 \xrightarrow[H_2O]{C_6H_5N_2^+Cl^-}$$

$$\text{(1-}C_6H_5\text{-triazolium betaine: } C_6H_5\overset{+}{N}{-}N{=}C(O^-){-}N(C_6H_5){-}N{=})$$

It is interesting that diarylcarbadiazones, so often discussed, are still, evidently, unknown. Cazeneuve[6] believed he had prepared V (R = R′ = C_6H_5) by oxidation of diphenylcarbazone (VIII), but Bamberger[7,8] showed that the product was the diphenyltetrazolium betaine X (or IX, in more modern formulation). The thio analog was similarly obtained from diphenylthiocarbazone.

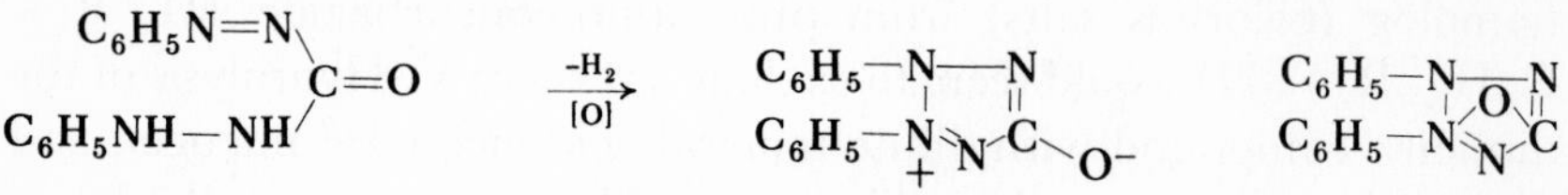

$$\underset{\text{(VIII)}}{C_6H_5N{=}N{-}C({=}O){-}NH{-}NHC_6H_5} \xrightarrow[{[O]}]{-H_2} \underset{\text{(IX)}}{C_6H_5{-}N{-}N{=}C(O^-){-}\overset{+}{N}{=}N(C_6H_5)} \quad \underset{\text{(X)}}{C_6H_5{-}N{-}N{=}C{-}N{=}N{-}C_6H_5 \text{ (O-bridged)}}$$

In summary, then, the exact structure of Busch's red products (IV ?)[1,2] is uncertain. It would seem that modern physical methods of analysis could quickly settle this question. The compounds originally given the endoxy structures VI and X have been formulated as betaines (VII and IX) although possibly a mesoionic structure (e.g.,

XI or XII) would be more precise. Finally, no representatives of the isotetrazole class have been authenticated.

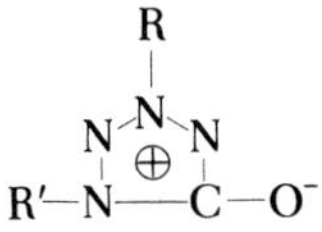

(XI) 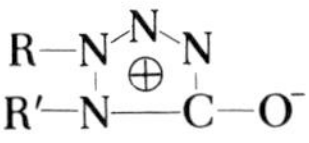 (XII)

References

1. Busch and Becker, *Ber.*, **29,** 1686 (1896).
2. Busch and Schmidt, *Ber.*, **62,** 1449 (1929).
3. Baker and Ollis, *Quart. Revs.*, **11,** 15 (1957).
4. Hünig and Boes, *Ann.*, **579,** 28 (1953).
5. Backer, *Rec. trav. chim.*, **70,** 733 (1951).
6. Cazeneuve, *Bull. soc. chim. France*, [3] **25,** 375 (1901).
7. Bamberger, *Ber.*, **44,** 3743 (1911).
8. Bamberger, Padova and Ormerod, *Ann.*, **446,** 260 (1926).

A-12. 1-Azabicyclo[3.1.0]hexane. R.I. 451.

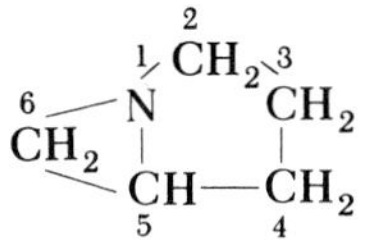

Dehydration of the acid I yielded a product thought[1] to be II, but later (see Section A-433) shown to be III.

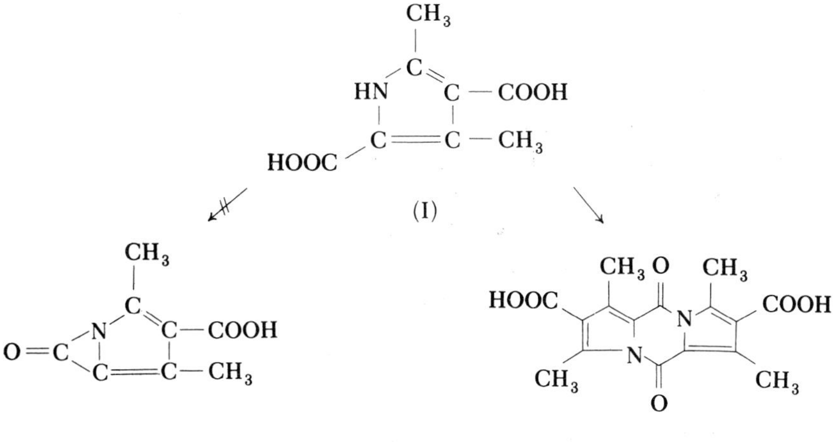

(I)

(II) (III)

Hydrolysis of pyrrolephthalein (IV) gave an acid assigned[2] either structure V or VI. The former would seem preferable.

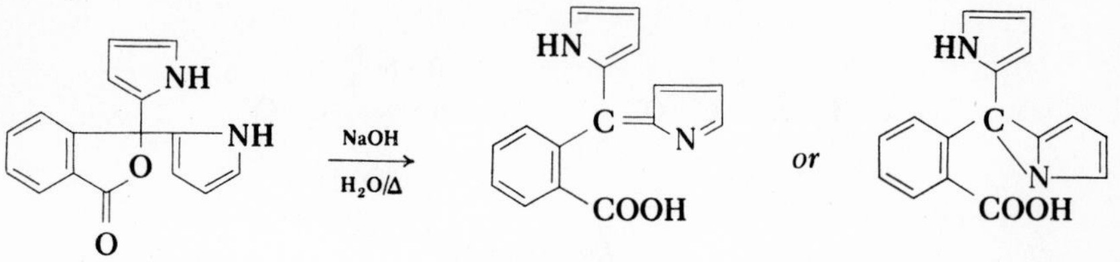

(IV) (V) (VI)

References

1. Magnanini, *Ber.*, **21,** 2874 (1888).
2. Oddo and Tognacchini, *Gazz. chim. ital.*, **53,** 265 (1923).

A-13. Tricycloindole. R.I. 1212

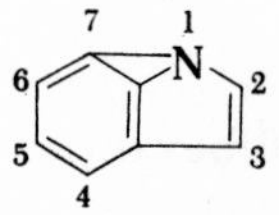

and

A-14. 2-Pyrano[2,3-*b*]tricycloindole. R.I. 2190

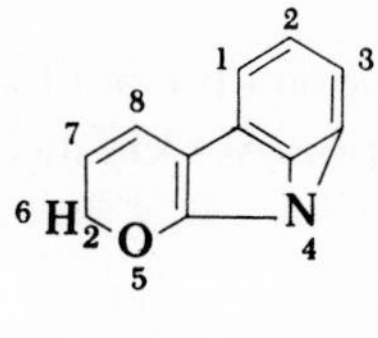

The first of these two nuclei may also be named azir[*hi*]indole.

Dehydrobromination of a tribromo acid thought to be I yielded a product claimed[1] to be II, but which, because of the absence of acidic properties, was said to exist in the lactone form III.

Since the tribromo acid was later found[2] to have structure IV, the dehydrohalogenation product can be formulated as V without recourse to the improbable azirindole structures.

References

1. Kendall, Osterberg, and MacKenzie, *J. Am. Chem. Soc.*, **48,** 1384 (1926).
2. Kendall and Osterberg, *J. Am. Chem. Soc.*, **49,** 2047 (1927).

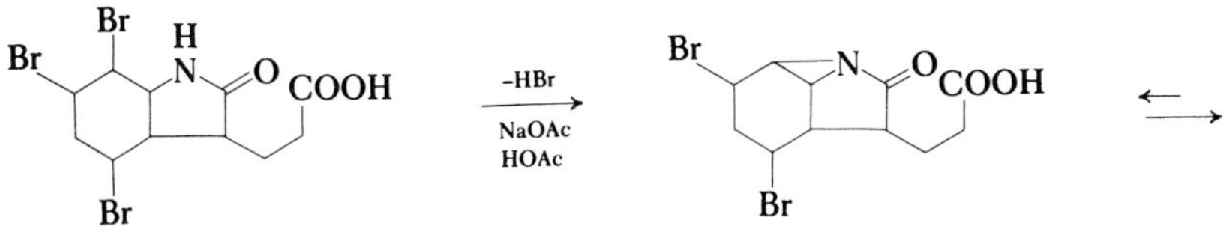

(I) (II)

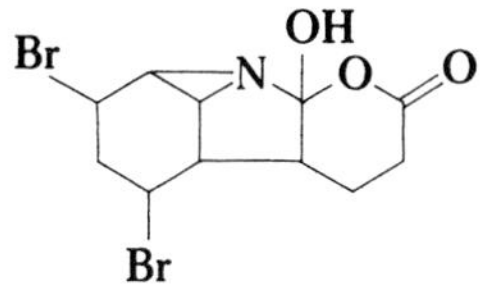

(III)

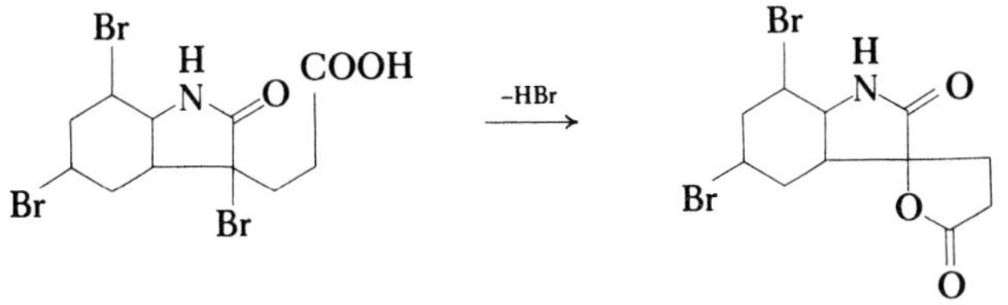

(IV) (V)

A-15. Spiro[1-azabicyclo (3.1.0)-2,4-hexadiene-6,1′(3′*H*)-isobenzofuran]. R.I. 2188

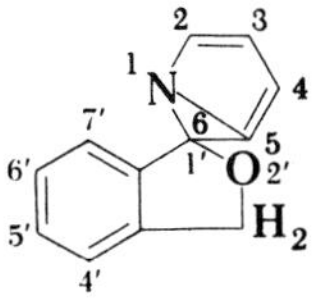

The pyrrole phthalides, obtained from the reaction of phthalic anhydride and pyrrole magnesium bromides, were originally assigned structure I, but this was later amended[2] to II.

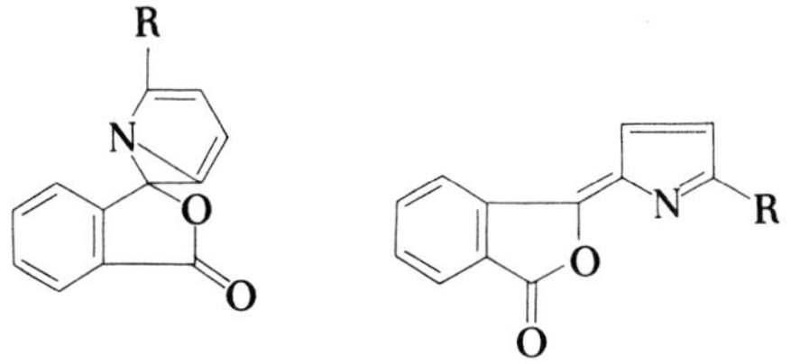

(I) (II)

References

1. Oddo and Mingoia, *Gazz. chim. ital.*, **55**, 235 (1925); *Chem. Zentr.*, **II**, 1428 (1925).
2. Oddo, *Gazz. chim. ital.*, **55**, 242 (1925).

A-16. 6-Oxa-1-azabicyclo[3.1.0]hexane. R.I. 442

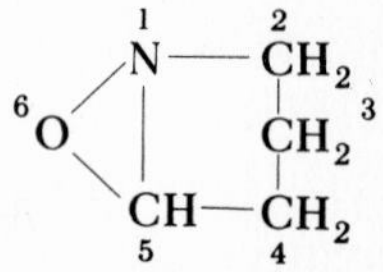

Hydrogenation of I (R = various alkoxyphenyl groups) over a palladium charcoal catalyst in pyridine consumed two moles of hydrogen and gave products assigned[1] structure II or III. It was not found possible, however, to remove the hydroxyl group by further reduction or to replace it by chlorine. Another structure (possibly an *N*-oxide) would seem indicated, and infrared spectra should be of assistance.

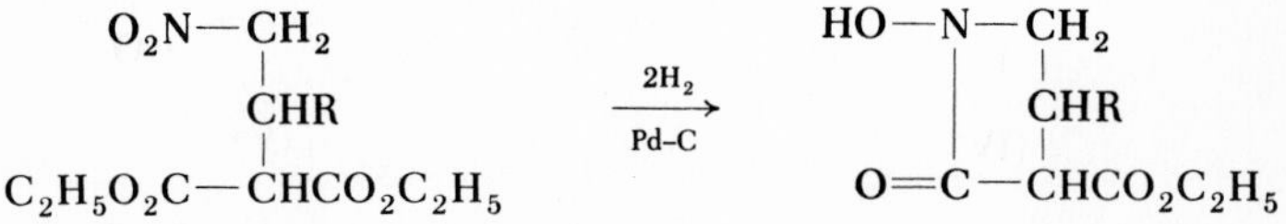

$$O_2N-CH_2-CHR-CH(CO_2C_2H_5)-CO_2C_2H_5 \xrightarrow[\text{Pd-C}]{2H_2} \text{HO}-N(CH_2-CHR-CH(CO_2C_2H_5)-C{=}O)$$

(I) (II)

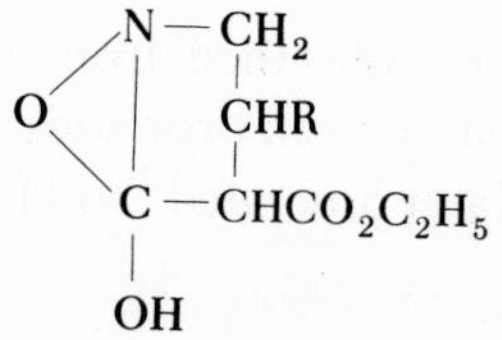

(III): bicyclic N–O–C with CH_2, CHR, $C(OH)-CHCO_2C_2H_5$

Reference

1. Reichert and Wegner, *Ber.*, **71**, 1254 (1938).

A-17. Oxazir[*a*]indole. R.I. 1211

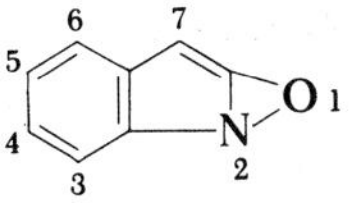

In 1880 Baeyer found[1,2] that I (R = $COOC_2H_5$) was isomerized by cold sulfuric acid to a product which he first considered to have structure II (R = $COOC_2H_5$) and later amended to III (R = $COOC_2H_5$). He proposed the name *isatogen* for this class of products. Pfeiffer[3] greatly extended the knowledge concerning isatogens and concluded that they were best represented by a "meta quinonoid" structure (with a pentacovalent nitrogen), which today would be written as the nitrone IV. The isatogens, investigated so extensively by Ruggli, have been reviewed.[4]

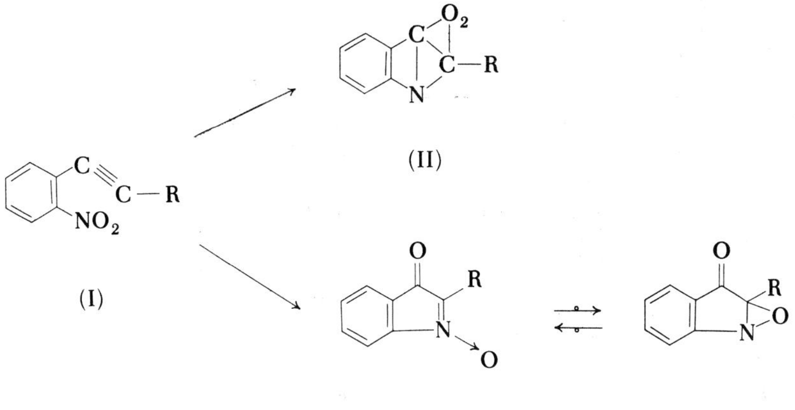

(II)

(I)

(IV) (III)

However, structure III was not long in exile. Ruggli[5] found that the isatogens could be isomerized by the action of heat and acids to a new class of products, which he named *isoisatogens*. It should be noted that while I, III, and IV are isomeric, they differ greatly in their appearance and properties. The color of a given trio of isomers increases in the order I < III < IV, and the isatogens are often highly colored. The isoisatogens do not react[6] with bromine, diazonium salts, etc., they do not show the oxidizing power of the isatogens, and, unlike the latter, they do not react with acetic anhydride or benzoyl chloride. The isoisatogens may be reconverted[6] into isatogens by the action of heat (with or without solvents, although best in phenyl isocyanate) and, like isatogens, are reduced readily to the same indoxyl. These (and other) data led Ruggli to suggest formula III for the isoisatogens, and no evidence to refute this proposition has yet been adduced. In fact, the existence of oxazirane rings, for many years in doubt, just recently has been authenticated.[7,8] Heller suggested[9] that Ruggli's isoisatogens were not true isomers but resulted from the addition of a molecule of alcohol to IV, but this suggestion was easily dismissed.[10] A number of isoisatogens have been obtained[5,6,10-14] from the corresponding isatogens.

Oxazir[*a*]indoles

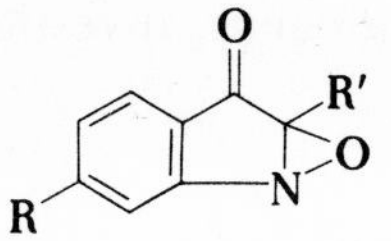

R	R′	Properties	Ref.
H	$COOCH_3$	Yel., m. ~165 °d.	5
H	$COOC_2H_5$	Yel., m. 146°.	6
H	α-Pyridyl	Yel., m. 105–7°.	13
H	2,4-Cl_2-6-$NO_2C_6H_2$	Yel., m. 177–8°.	11
H	4-$C_6H_4NO_2$	Or.-yel., m. 199–202°.	14
NO_2	C_6H_5	Yel., m. 152–3°. Oxime, brn., m. ~290 °.	5,10
H	C_6H_5	Or.-yel., m. 94°.	12
$COOCH_3$	C_6H_5	Yel., m. 100.5–1.5°.	5
$COOC_2H_5$	C_6H_5	Yel., m. 100.5°.	12

References

1. Baeyer, *Ber.*, **14,** 1741 (1881).
2. Baeyer, *Ber.*, **15,** 775 (1882).
3. Pfeiffer, *Ann.*, **411,** 148 (1916).
4. Smith, *Chem. Rev.*, **23,** 223 (1938).
5. Ruggli, *Ber.*, **52,** 1 (1919).
6. Ruggli and Bolliger, *Helv. Chim. Acta*, **4,** 626 (1921).
7. Farbenfabriken Bayer A. G., Brit. Pat. 743,940.
8. Emmons, *J. Am. Chem. Soc.*, **78,** 6208 (1956).
9. Heller and Boessneck, *Ber.*, **55,** 474 (1922).

10. Ruggli, Bolliger and Leonhardt, *Helv. Chim. Acta*, **6,** 594 (1923).
11. Ruggli and Zaeslin, *Helv. Chim. Acta*, **22,** 134 (1939).
12. Ruggli, Caspar and Hegedüs, *Helv. Chim. Acta*, **22,** 140 (1939).
13. Ruggli, and Cuenin, *Helv. Chim. Acta*, **27,** 649 (1944).
14. Kröhnke, Kröhnke and Vogt, *Chem. Ber.*, **86,** 1500 (1953).

A-18. 5*a*,11*a*(6*H*,12*H*)-Epoxydiindolo-[1,2-*a*,1′,2′-*c*]urete. R.I. 3443

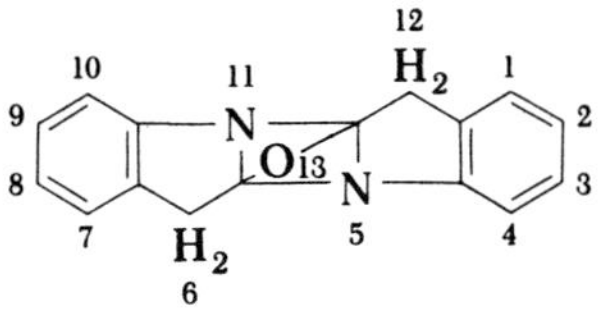

See Section A-46.

A-19. 6-Oxa-1,2-diazabicyclo[3.1.0]-hexane. R.I. 441

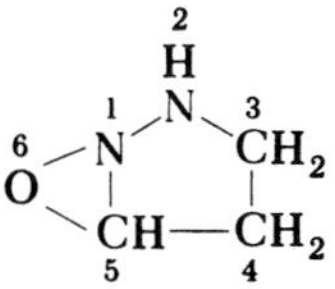

and

A-20. 6-Thia-1,2-diazabicyclo[3.1.0]-hexane. R.I. 443

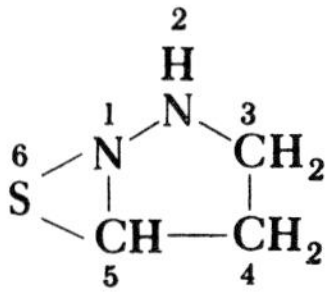

and

A-21. 6-Selena-1,2-diazabicyclo[3.1.0]-hexane. R.I. 444

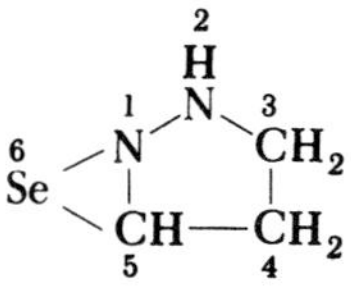

A group of compounds was obtained[1,2] by treating I with, respectively, sodium hydroxide, sodium sulfhydrate, and sodium selenhydrate and was assigned structure II (X = O, S, or Se). There seems no reason, however, to eschew structure III for these products, and the pentacovalent nitrogen atom of II is unquestionably wrong.

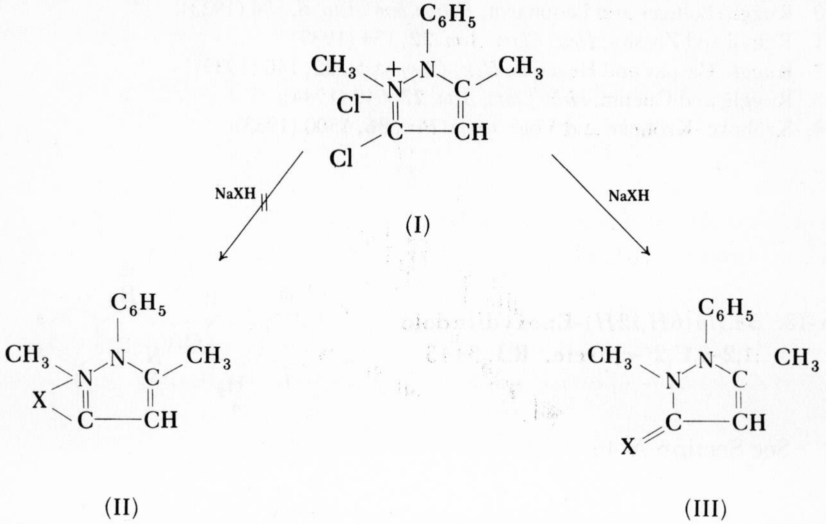

(I)

(II)

(III)

References

1. Mayer, *Ber.*, **36,** 717 (1903).
2. Michaelis, *Ann.*, **338,** 267 (1904).

A-22. 1,2,6-Triazabicyclo[3.1.0]hexane. R.I. 446

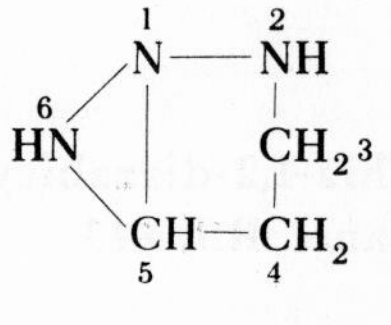

The name *pyrazole-2(2),3-imine* has been used.

Treatment of I with ammonia yielded[1] a product, which was formulated as III, and for which the unlikely alternative structure II has been offered.[2]

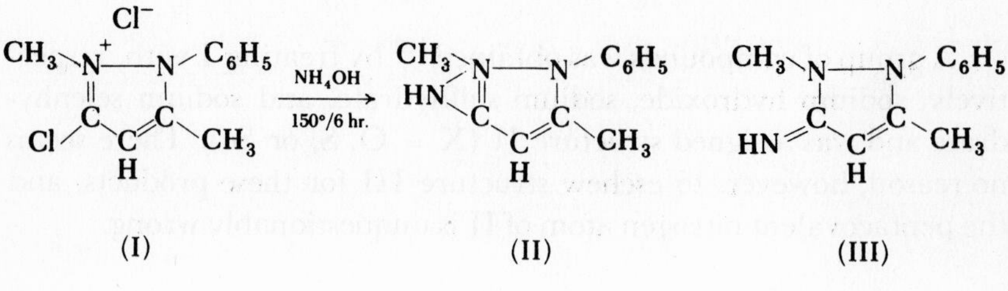

NH_4OH, 150°/6 hr.

(I) (II) (III)

References

1. Stolz, *Ber.*, **36,** 3279 (1903).
2. Beilstein, *Handbuch der organischen Chemie*, 4th ed., Springer, Berlin, 1936, Vol. 24, p. 36.

A-23. 2,6-Dioxa-1,3-diazabicyclo[3.1.0]-hexane. R.I. 439

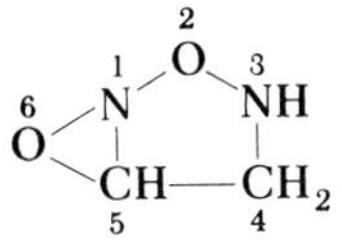

Furoxanes, such as those assigned[1] structure I, are now preferably formulated as *N*-oxides (II). See Sections B-12 and B-13.

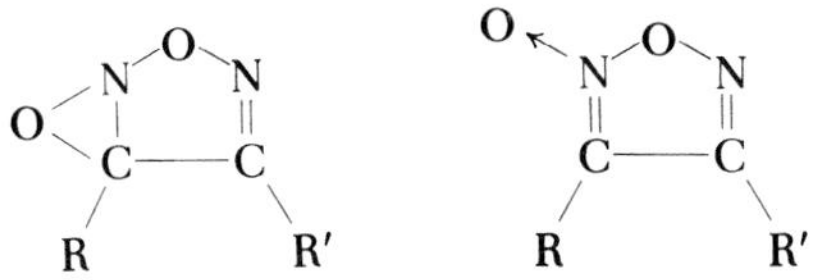

(I) (II)

Reference

1. Wieland and Semper, *Ann.*, **358,** 36 (1907).

A-24. 6-Oxa-1,2,3-triazabicyclo[3.1.0]-hexane. R.I. 440

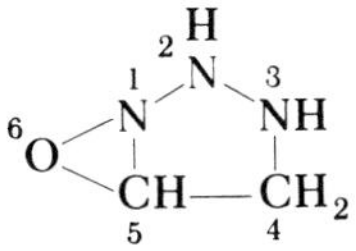

The $\Delta^{3,4}$-dehydro derivatives have been called *4,5-oxyosotriazoles*, *1,2-oxypyrro-1,4-diazoles*, and *3,4-endooxytriazolines*.

By oxidizing I with mercuric oxide or nitrogen tetroxide, Ponzio[1-3] obtained products which he thought to have structure II, since they were readily reduced to III. However, structure IV now seems more appropriate for these compounds.

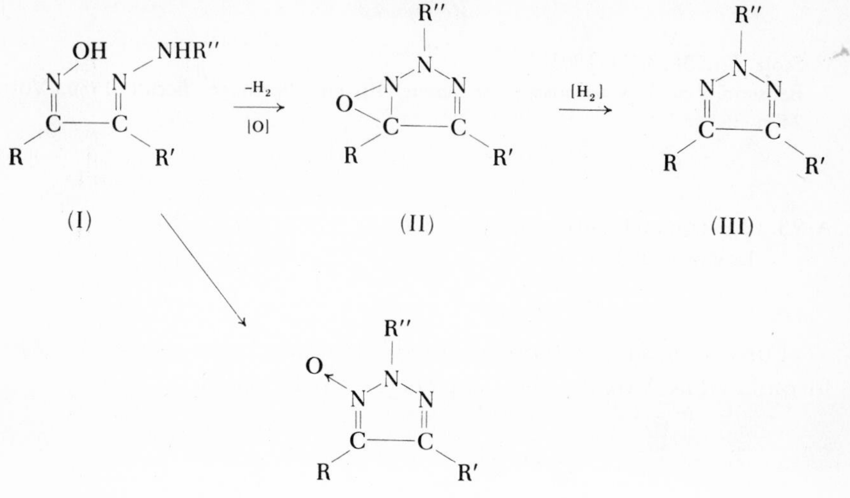

(I) (II) (III) (IV)

References

1. Ponzio, *J. prakt. Chem.*, **57,** 160 (1898).
2. Ponzio, *Gazz. chim. ital.*, **29,** I, 284 (1899).
3. Ponzio, *Gazz. chim. ital.*, **30,** II, 460 (1900).

A-25. 2-Oxa-1,3,6-triazabicyclo[3.1.0]-hexane. R.I. 445

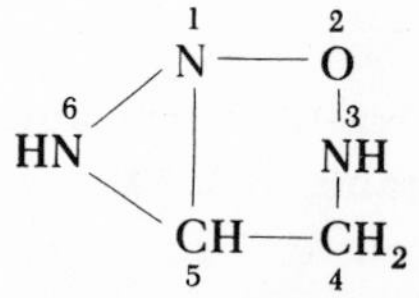

Hydrolysis of I yielded a product (m. 175°) which was called *β-fulminuric acid amide* and was formulated as II. The corresponding acid (III, m. 196°) was called *imidofuroxanecarboxylic acid* or *4,5-endo-imino-1,2,5-oxadiazoline-3-carboxylic acid.* Compound III was a strong acid, which, by the Fischer-Speyer method, gave an ethyl ester (m. 103–4°) and, with nitrous acid, yielded a nitroso derivative (explodes at 133°) thought to be IV. These structures are almost certainly incorrect, and further work is needed to clarify the issue.

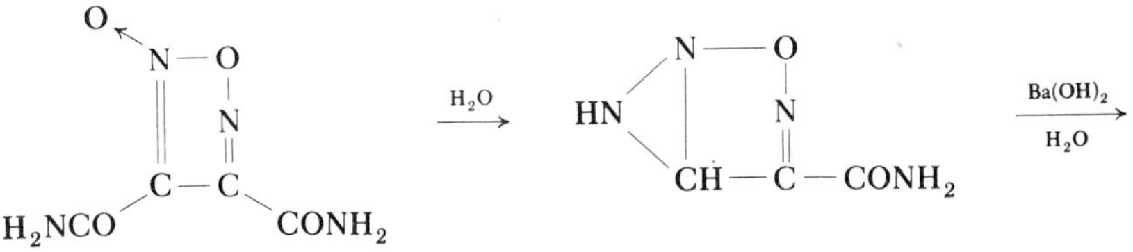

(I) $\xrightarrow{H_2O}$ (II) $\xrightarrow[H_2O]{Ba(OH)_2}$

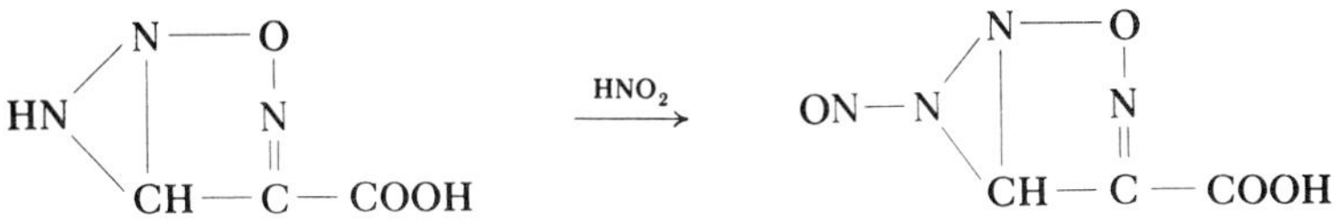

(III) $\xrightarrow{HNO_2}$ (IV)

Reference

1. Ulpiani, *Gazz. chim. ital.*, **42,** I, 375 (1912); *Chem. Zentr.*, **II,** 235 (1912).

A-26. Triaziroindiazole. R.I. 1223

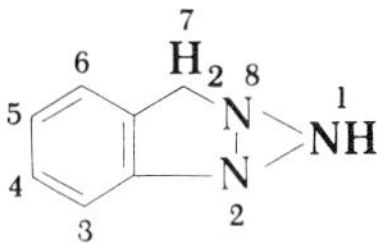

The names *7H-triaziroindiazene*, *cycloazibentriazine*, and *endoiminodihydrobenzisodiazole* have also been applied to this nucleus.

Chattaway and his coworkers[1-6] found that dehydrohalogenation of I (prepared by halogenating the benzalhydrazone) yielded products thought to be of type II, and that reduction of these gave new products assigned structure IV. Recrystallization of I from ethanol yielded explosive substances formulated as III (although, if the 3/5 bicyclic formulation is correct, these would now be written as *N*-oxide derivatives). Reduction of III again yielded compounds thought to have structure IV. These products (IV) are unaffected by nitric or nitrous acid, halogens, or acetic anhydride and may be distilled without decomposition. Extensive reduction with stannous chloride gave anthranilic acid and a hydrazine ($R'NHNH_2$). Hydrolysis of IV with alcoholic potassium hydroxide gave *N*-arylazoanthranilic acids.

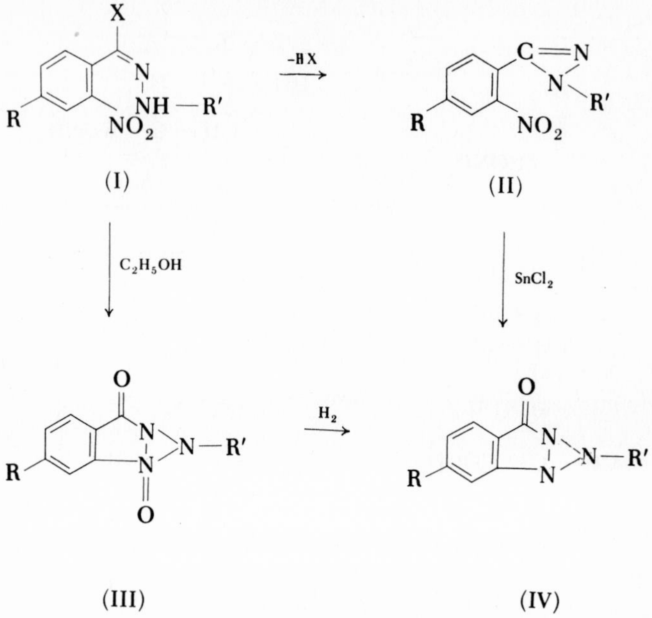

Derivatives of Type III

R	R′	Properties	Refs.
H	C_6Br_5	Yel., expl. 157°.	6
H	C_6Cl_5	Yel., expl. 128°.	6
H	C_6HBr_4	Yel., expl. 155°.	6
H	4-Br-2-(NO_2)-C_6H_3-	Yel., expl. 142°.	4
NO_2	2,6-Br_2-4-CH_3-C_6H_2-	Yel., expl. 142°.	5
NO_2	2-Br-4-CH_3-C_6H_3-	Yel., expl. 133°.	5
H	2,6-Br_2-4-CH_3-C_6H_2-	Yel., expl. 167°.	2
H	4,6-Br_2-2-CH_3-C_6H_2-	Yel., expl. 145°.	4
H	4,6-Br_2-3-CH_3-C_6H_2-	—	7
H	2,6-Cl_2-4-CH_3-C_6H_2-	Yel., expl. 155°.	3
H	2-Br-4-CH_3-C_6H_3-	Yel., expl. 139°.	2
H	4-Br-2-CH_3-C_6H_3-	Yel., expl. 151°.	4
H	2-Cl-4-CH_3-C_6H_3-	Yel., expl. 134°.	3

Derivatives of Type IV

R	R′	Properties	Refs.
H	2,4,6-Cl_3-C_6H_2-	m. 258°.	1
H	2,4-Br_2-C_6H_3-	m. 178°.	1
H	2,4-Cl_2-C_6H_3-	Two forms: labile prisms, m. 167°; stable needles, m. 157°	1
H	4-Br-C_6H_4-	Pale yel., m. 197°.	1
NO_2	2,6-Br_2-4-CH_3-C_6H_2-	m. 279°.	5
H	2,6-Br_2-4-CH_3-C_6H_2-	Yel., m. 190°.	2
H	2,6-Cl_2-4-CH_3-C_6H_2-	m. 202°.	3
NO_2	2-Br-4-CH_3-C_6H_3-	m. 250°.	5
H	2-Br-4-CH_3-C_6H_3-	Yel., m. 166°.	2
H	4-Br-2-CH_3-C_6H_3-	Pale yel., m. 181°.	4
H	2-Cl-4-CH_3-C_6H_3-	m. 173°.	3

Further support for these structures would seem welcome, and both infrared and ultraviolet spectra should be of assistance with this problem.

References

1. Chattaway and Walker, *J. Chem. Soc.*, **1927,** 323.
2. Chattaway and Adamson, *J. Chem. Soc.*, **1930,** 157.
3. Chattaway and Adamson, *J. Chem. Soc.*, **1930,** 843.
4. Chattaway and Adamson, *J. Chem. Soc.*, **1931,** 2787.
5. Chattaway and Adamson, *J. Chem. Soc.*, **1931,** 2792.
6. Chattaway and Parkes, *J. Chem. Soc.*, **1935,** 1005.
7. Parkes and Burney, *J. Chem. Soc.*, **1935,** 1619.

A-27. 7-Oxa-1-azabicyclo[4.1.0]heptane*

7 O — 1 N — 2 CH_2 — 3 CH_2; 6 CH — 5 CH_2 — 4 CH_2

and

A-28. 7-Thia-1-azabicyclo[4.1.0]heptane*

7 S — 1 N — 2 CH_2 — 3 CH_2; 6 CH — 5 CH_2 — 4 CH_2

and

A-29. 7-Selena-1-azabicyclo[4.1.0]heptane*

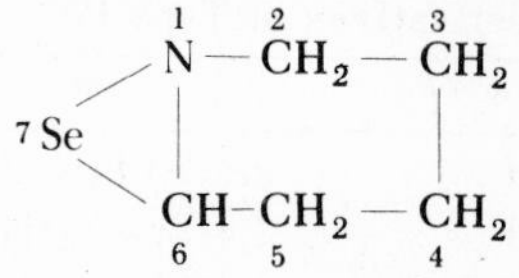

The 1-alkyl-2-pyridones (I) and their sulfur and selenium homologs were once[1] depicted as II (X = O, S, or Se).

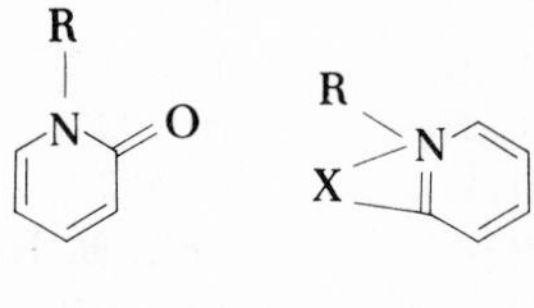

(I) (II)

Reference

1. Michaelis and Hölken, *Ann.*, **331,** 245 (1904).

A-30. 1*aH*-Oxaziro[*a*]quinoline. R.I. 1225

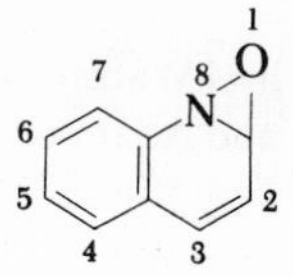

and

A-31. Spiro[1*aH*-oxaziro[*a*]quinoline-2(3*H*),3′(4′*H*)-quinoline].* R.I. 2860

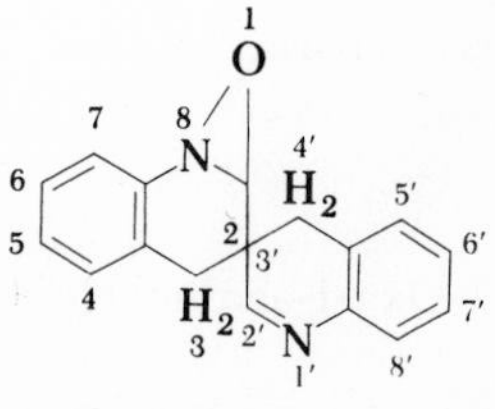

A single example of these nuclei has been reported. Reduction of I with stannous chloride-hydrochloric acid gave[1] a base, ($C_{18}H_{16}N_2O_2$, m. 184° with sintering at 178°), formulated as II. Reduction with hydriodic acid liberated carbon dioxide and yielded a new base thought to be 3-(2-aminobenzyl)quinaldine.

An alternative structure, possibly III, seems likely.

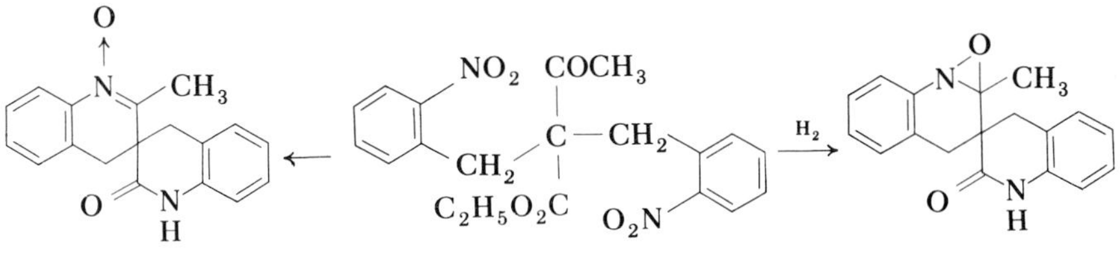

(III) (I) (II)

Reference

1. Gabriel and Wolter, *Ber.*, **56**, 2445 (1923).

A-32. 1,4-Diazabicyclo[4.1.0]heptane*

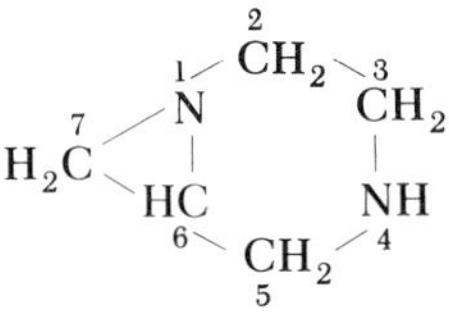

Having previously found that α-halo-α,β-unsaturated esters condensed with amines to yield 1,2-disubstituted azirane-3-carboxylic acid esters, Moureu, Chovin, and Petit treated[1,2] α-bromocinnamic ester with ethylenediamine and obtained, along with much tar, a 16% yield of a product (m. 134°) which they considered to be I and named *5-keto-7-phenyl-1,4-diazanorcarane*. Treatment of I in acetone with dry hydrogen chloride ruptured the azirane ring and gave II.

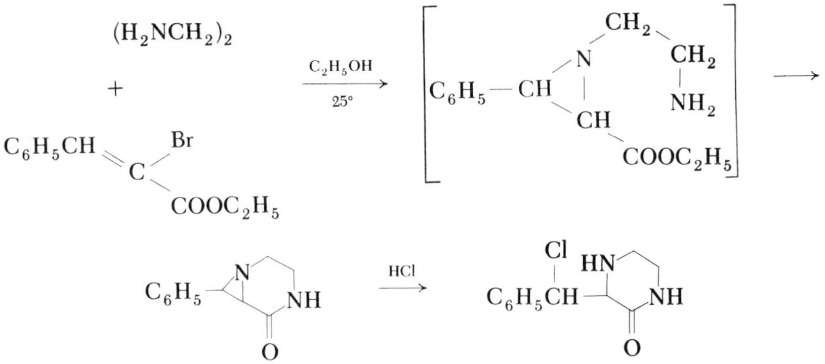

$(H_2NCH_2)_2$ + $C_6H_5CH{=}C(Br)COOC_2H_5$ $\xrightarrow[25°]{C_2H_5OH}$ [ ] → (I) $\xrightarrow{HCl}$ (II)

(I) (II)

References

1. Moureu, Chovin, and Petit, *Compt. rend.*, **143,** 910 (1956).
2. Moureu, Chovin, and Petit, *Bull. soc. chim. France*, **1956,** 1785.

A-33. 1*aH*-Oxaziro[*a*]quinoxaline. R.I. 1224

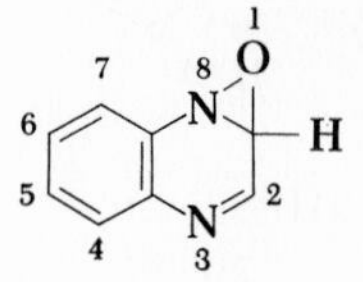

1 O, 8 N, H, 2, N 3, 4, 5, 6, 7

Among the products resulting from the action of nitrosyl chloride upon the moist bismethylanilide of malonic acid (I), was found[1] a substance ($C_{17}H_{15}N_3O_3$, m. 191°) assigned structure II. Structure III, however, is probably more accurate. See Section A-863.

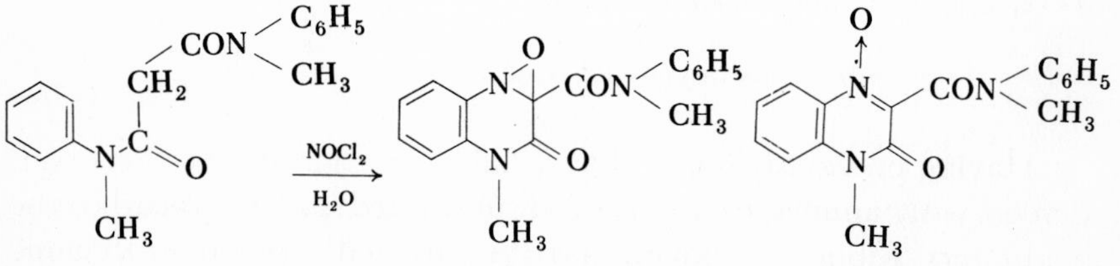

CON C_6H_5 CH_3, CH_2, N C=O, CH_3 — $NOCl_2$ / H_2O → O, N, CON C_6H_5 CH_3, N O, CH_3 — O ↑ N, CON C_6H_5 CH_3, N O, CH_3

(I) (II) (III)

Reference

1. Usherwood and Whiteley, *J. Chem. Soc.*, **123,** 1069 (1923).

A-34. 6*H*-Bisaziro[*c,e*]diaziro[*a*]-*s*-tetrazine*

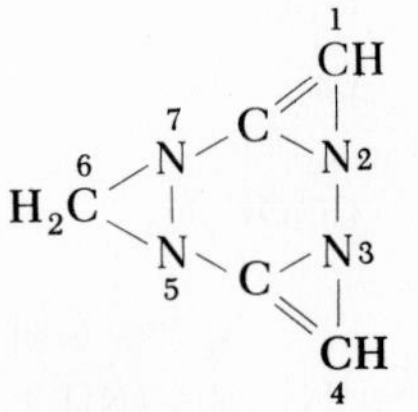

1 CH, C, N2, N3, C, CH 4, 7 N, 6 H_2C, N 5

Treatment of tetrazine with diazomethane yielded[1] a yellowish brown product thought to have structure I and named *trimethylene-*

tetrazine. It was decomposed to formaldehyde and hydrazine by warming with dilute sulfuric acid.

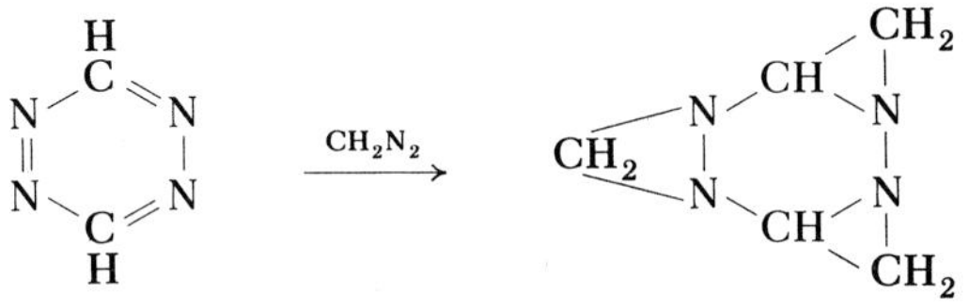

(I)

Reference

1. Müller, *Ber.*, **47,** 3001 (1914).

A-35. 3-Thia-1,6-diazabicyclo[4.1.0]heptane

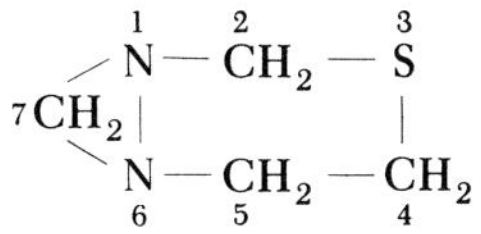

While studying the structure of the 2-amino-1,3,4-thiadiazines (I), Traverso[1] obtained several products from the reaction of I with *p*-nitrobenzaldehyde. With the work of Cornelius and Homolka[2] and of Rassow and Lummerzheim[3] as precedents, the products were assigned structure II (R = R′ = H, R″ = CH_3, m. 164–5°, *N*-acetyl derivative, m. 195–6°; R = R′ = CH_3, R″ = H, m. 146–7°; R = R′ = R″ = CH_3, m. 173–4°; R = CH_3, R′ = C_2H_5, R″ = H, m. 135°).

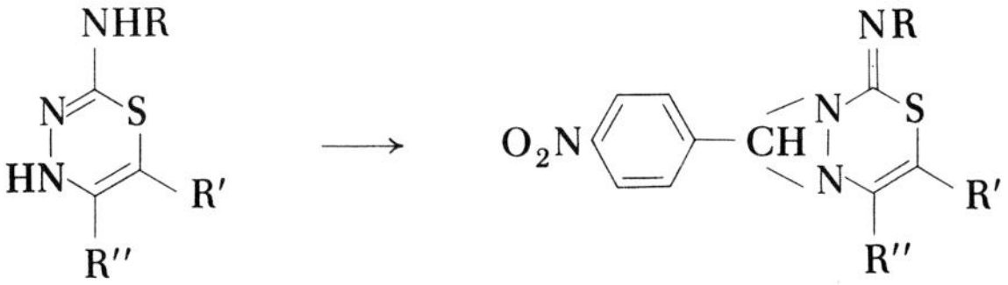

(I) (II)

However, Cornelius and Homolka's diaziridines[2] were shown[3] to have other structures, and, as only a few authentic diaziridines have been described[3] (none containing a fused diaziridine system), structure II appears dubious. Other structures such as III or IV may merit consideration.

(III)

(IV)

References

1. Traverso, *Gazz. chim. ital.*, **83,** 296 (1953); *Chem. Abstracts*, **47,** 12368 (1953).
2. Cornelius and Homolka, *Ber.*, **19,** 2239 (1886).
3. Rassow and Lummerzheim, *J. prakt. Chem.*, **64,** 136 (1901).

A-36. 1,3,4,6-Tetrazabicyclo[4.1.0]heptane. R.I. 465

and

A-37. 1,3,5,7-Tetrazatricyclo[5.1.0.0^{3,5}]-octane*

By condensing *p*-urazine, which was thought to have structure I, with (*a*) benzaldehyde[1] and (*b*) various ketones,[2] products assigned, respectively, structures II and III were obtained. However, Stollé[3] and others have shown that the *p*-urazine used actually was 4-aminourazole (IV).

Similarly, utilizing what they thought to be V, Purgotti and Vignano[2] prepared derivatives which they formulated as VI. Presumably authentic V has subsequently been prepared[4,5] and is reported[4] not to react with aldehydes. Therefore, the nature of the substance used by Purgotti and Vignano remains obscure. Structure

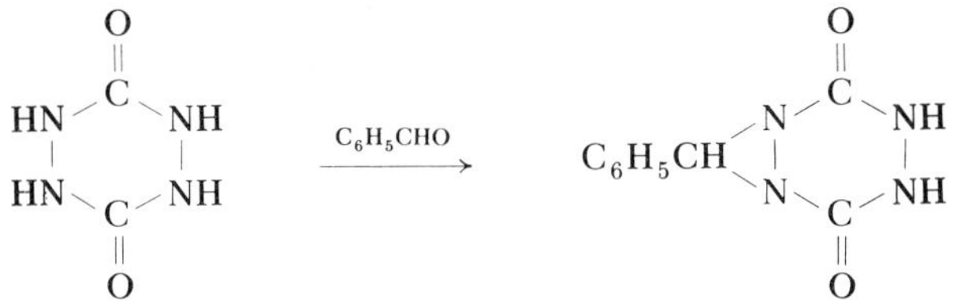

C_6H_5CHO

(I) (II)

RR′CO

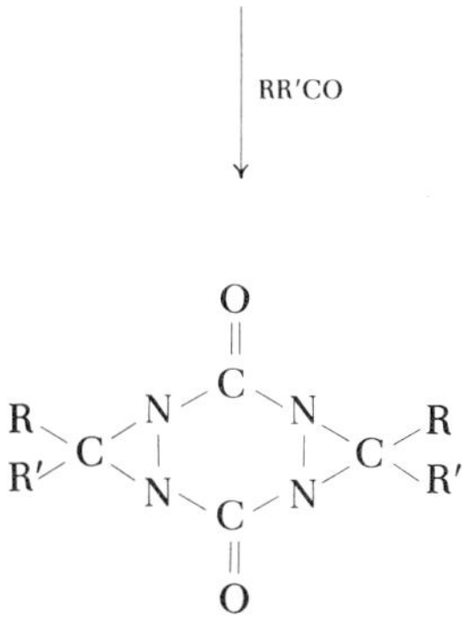

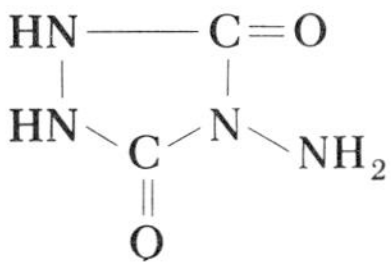

(III) (IV)

VII was proposed[3] for this material, but, when synthesized,[6] VII proved to be different from Purgotti and Vignano's substance.

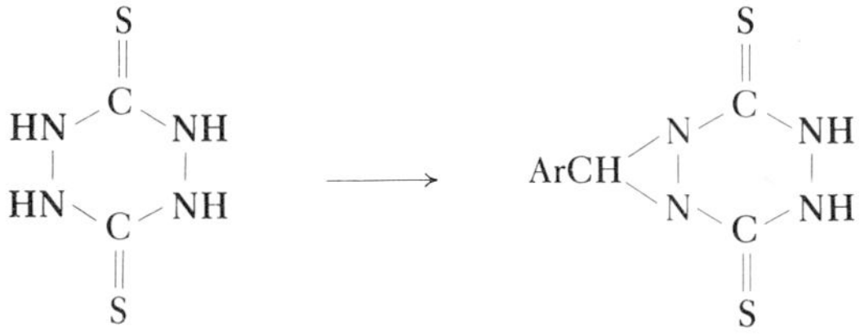

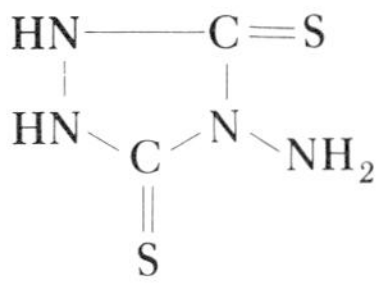

(V) (VI) (VII)

References

1. Curtius and Heidenreich, *J. prakt. Chem.*, **52,** 485 (1895).
2. Purgotti and Vignano, *Gazz. chim. ital.*, **31,** II, 550 (1901); *Chem. Zentr.*, **I,** 480 (1902).

3. Stollé, *J. prakt. Chem.*, **75,** 416 (1907).
4. Guha and De, *Quart. J. Indian Chem. Soc.*, **1,** 141 (1924); *Chem. Zentr.*, **I,** 1999 (1925).
5. Beckett and Dyson, *J. Chem. Soc.*, **1937,** 1358.
6. Arndt and Bielich, *Ber.*, **56,** 809 (1923).

A-38. 1,4,7,8-Tetrazabicyclo[5.1.0]octane. R.I. 483

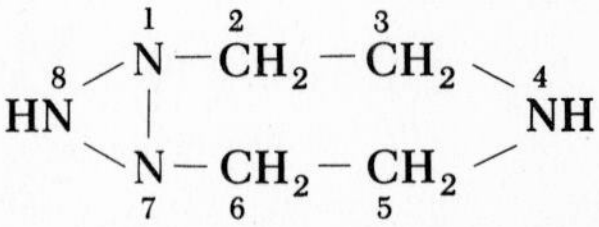

$$\begin{array}{ccccc} & {}^{1}N & -{}^{2}CH_2 & -{}^{3}CH_2 & \\ {}^{8}HN & | & & & {}^{4}NH \\ & {}_{7}N & -{}_{6}CH_2 & -{}_{5}CH_2 & \end{array}$$

Reduction of a substance thought to be I (see Section A-8) yielded[1] a product to which structure II was given. Since structure I is undoubtedly incorrect, the nature of the reduction product is uncertain.

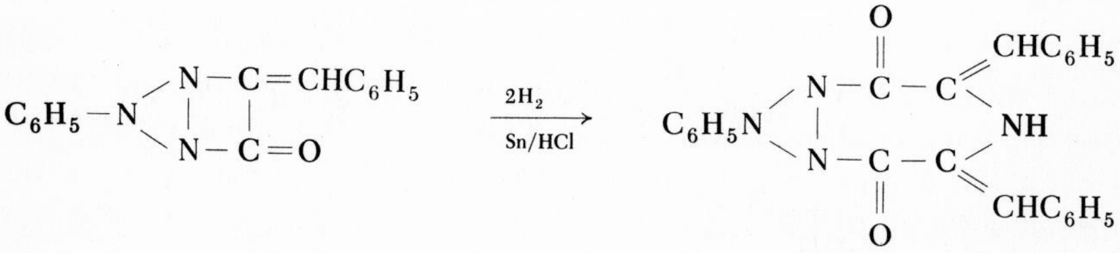

$$C_6H_5-N\begin{array}{l} N-C=CHC_6H_5 \\ |\quad\ \ | \\ N-C=O \end{array} \xrightarrow[Sn/HCl]{2H_2} C_6H_5N\begin{array}{l} N-\overset{O}{\overset{\|}{C}}-C{=}CHC_6H_5 \\ |\qquad\qquad\ \ NH \\ N-\underset{O}{\underset{\|}{C}}-C{=}CHC_6H_5 \end{array}$$

(I) (II)

Reference

1. Ruhemann, *J. Chem. Soc.*, **61,** 278 (1891).

CHAPTER II

Fused 4-Membered Ring Systems

A-39. 1,3-Diazabicyclo[2.2.0]hexane

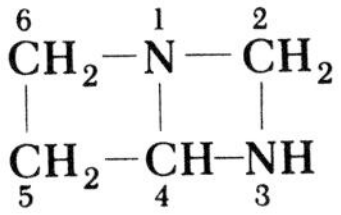

```
6      1    2
CH2—N—CH2
|      |     |
CH2—CH—NH
5      4     3
```

Derivatives of this nucleus are claimed to have been obtained as shown by Ghosh.[1,2] Structures such as II and III, if correct, are quite unique, possessing, as they do, two fused 4-membered rings, one of which contains a double bond. It would be expected that the ring strain would be quite large.[3] Compound II is reported[2] to be "unaffected by 10.15% alcoholic potash," although the details of the experiment are not given. This casts doubt upon the assigned structure, since, in general, the simpler (i.e., not heavily substituted) β-lactams are quite readily cleaved by alcoholic alkali.

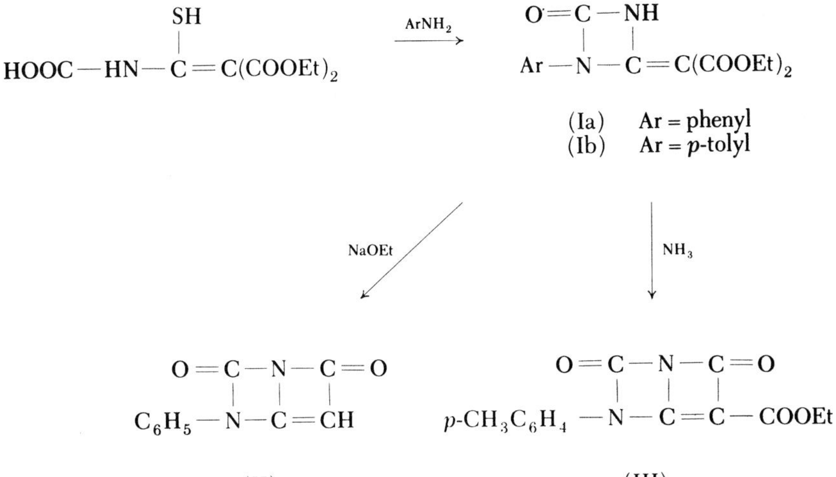

```
                SH                             O=C—NH
                |           ArNH2               |   |
HOOC—HN—C=C(COOEt)2     ——————>      Ar—N—C=C(COOEt)2

                                      (Ia)  Ar = phenyl
                                      (Ib)  Ar = p-tolyl

                        NaOEt ↙                ↓ NH3

   O=C—N—C=O                         O=C—N—C=O
     |   |   |                          |   |   |
C6H5—N—C=CH              p-CH3C6H4—N—C=C—COOEt

      (II)                                 (III)
```

Compound II[2] crystallizes in colorless plates, m. 245–6°; it is readily soluble in acetic acid, and the resulting solution decolorizes potassium permanganate. Compound III[1] melts at 90–91°, is readily soluble in dilute hydrochloric acid, but is insoluble in alkali.

References

1. Ghosh, *Science and Culture*, **5,** 494 (1940); *Chem. Abstracts*, **34,** 4068 (1940).
2. Ghosh and DasGupta, *J. Indian Chem. Soc.*, **19,** 41 (1942).
3. Woodward in Clarke, Johnson, and Robinson, *The Chemistry of Penicillin*, Princeton University Press, Princeton, N. J., 1949, pp. 443–4.

A-40. 1,3,5-Triazabicyclo[2.2.0]hexane. R.I. 489

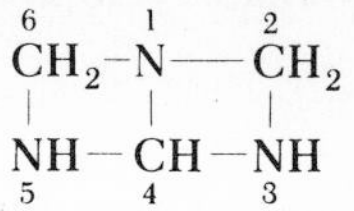

$$\begin{array}{ccccc} ^{6} & & ^{1} & & ^{2} \\ CH_2 & - & N & - & CH_2 \\ | & & | & & | \\ NH & - & CH & - & NH \\ _{5} & & _{4} & & _{3} \end{array}$$

Treatment of the two polymorphic forms of trimeric chloralimide (I) with bromine in chloroform yielded[1] the corresponding two forms of a product assigned structure II, but which probably has,[2] instead, structure III. Structure III previously had been considered and rejected.[1]

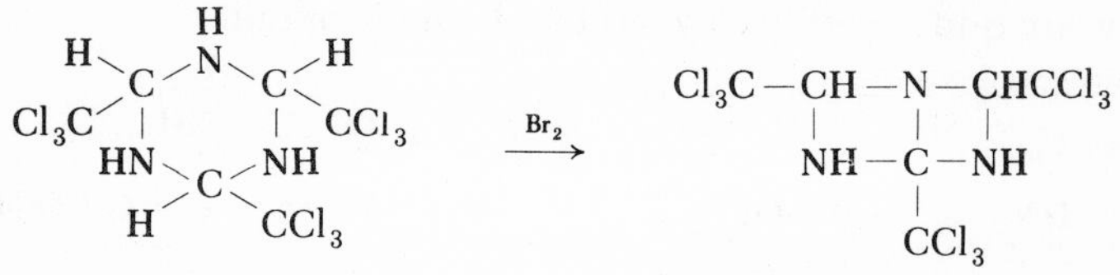

$$\begin{array}{ccccc} & & H & & \\ H & & N & & H \\ & C & & C & \\ Cl_3C & | & & | & CCl_3 \\ & HN & & NH & \\ & & C & & \\ & H & & CCl_3 & \end{array} \xrightarrow{Br_2} \begin{array}{ccccccc} Cl_3C & - & CH & - & N & - & CHCCl_3 \\ & & | & & | & & | \\ & & NH & - & C & - & NH \\ & & & & | & & \\ & & & & CCl_3 & & \end{array}$$

(I) (II)

$$\begin{array}{ccccc} H & & H & & \\ & C & & C & - CCl_3 \\ Cl_3C & | & & | & \\ & HN & & NH & \\ & & C & & \\ & H & & CCl_3 & \end{array}$$

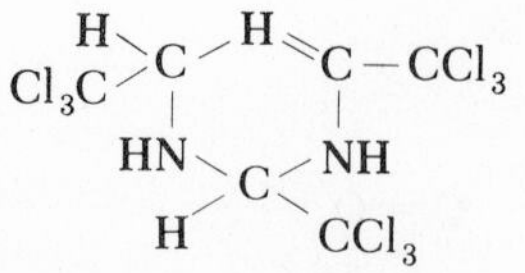

(III)

References

1. Béhal and Choay, *Ann. chim. et phys.*, [6]**26,** 15 (1892).
2. Beilstein, *Handbuch der organischen Chemie*, 4th Ed., Springer, Berlin, 1937, Vol. 26, p. 10.

A-41. 2,3-Dioxa-1,4,5-triazabicyclo-[2.2.0]hexane. R.I. 487

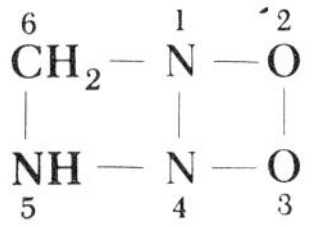

By treating I with nitric acid, Jovitschitsch obtained products he thought[1] had structure II (R = H or $COOC_2H_5$). However, these products were shown [2] to be impure samples of III (R = H or $COOC_2H_5$).

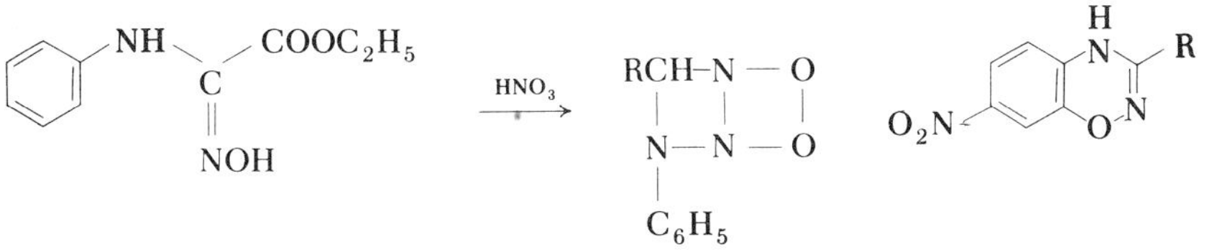

(I) (II) (III)

References

1. Jovitschitsch, *Ber.*, **30,** 2426 (1897); **31,** 3036 (1898); **35,** 151 (1902); **39,** 3821 (1906).
2. Semper and Lichtenstadt, *Ann.*, **400,** 302 (1913).

A-42. 6*H*-Azeto[1,2-*a*, 4,3-*b*′]diindole. R.I. 2873

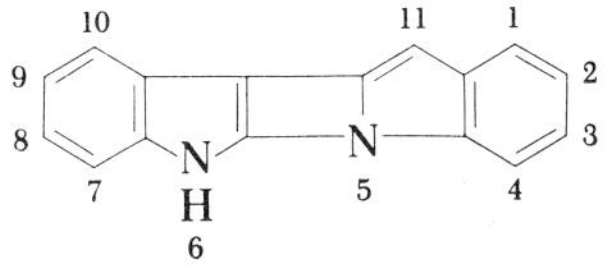

In the presence of acids, indole and skatole (I, R = H and CH_3, respectively) polymerize, and from the mixture of products may be isolated dimers, which Oddo and Crippa[1] considered to have structure II (R = H and CH_3, respectively). Several derivatives of these nuclei also were described.[2,3] However, considerable evidence supports a linear structure such as III for the dimers[4,5] as well as the trimers (see Sections A-262 and A-444).

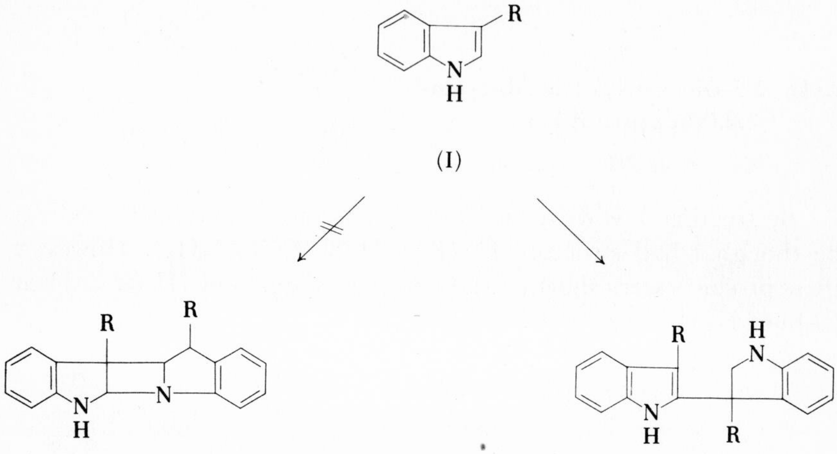

(I)

(II)

(III)

References

1. Oddo and Crippa, *Atti reale accad. naz. Lincei*, [5]**33 I,** 31 (1924); *Gazz. chim. ital.*, **54,** 339 (1924); *Chem. Zentr.*, **I,** 2364 (1924); *Chem. Abstracts*, **19,** 65 (1925).
2. Oddo and Mingoia, *Gazz. chim. ital.*, **57,** 480 (1927); *Chem. Zentr.*, **II,** 1697 (1927); *Chem. Abstracts*, **22,** 78 (1928).
3. Diels, Alder, and Lübbert, *Ann.*, **490,** 277 (1931).
4. Schmitz-Dumont, Hamann, and Geller, *Ann.*, **504,** 1 (1933).
5. Schmitz-Dumont, *Ann.*, **514,** 267 (1934).

A-43. 7-Ox-1-azabicyclo[3.2.0]heptane. R.I. 510

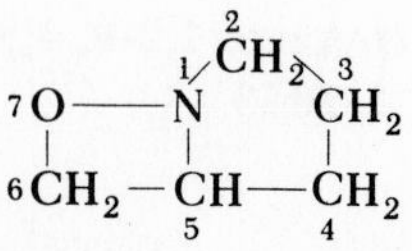

The alkaloids[1] stachydrine (I, R = H) and betonicine (I, R = OH) are the closest approach to examples of this nucleus.

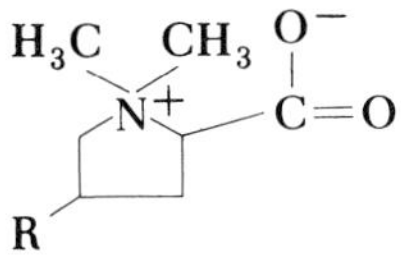

(I)

Reference

1. Marion, "The Pyrrolidine Alkaloids," in Manske and Holmes, *The Alkaloids*, Academic Press, New York, Vol. 1, 1950, p. 91.

A-44. 4-Thia-1-azabicyclo[3.2.0]heptane

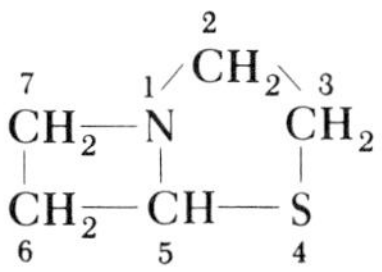

All of the examples of this ring system were prepared in connection with work upon the penicillins, and all contain a 6-oxo group. These compounds may be viewed as the β-lactams of 2-thiazoline-acetic acids, and Sheehan[1] has proposed the trivial names *penam* (I) and *penicillamic acid* (II), with the numbering shown.

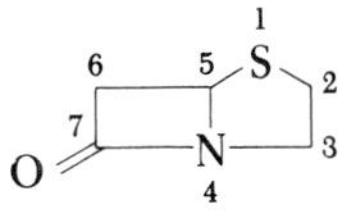

(I) 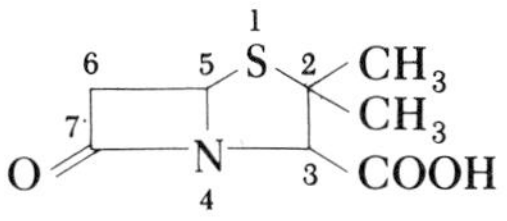 (II)

Before World War II examples of this nucleus were unknown. At that time, as a result of the importance of antibiotic therapy, it became mandatory to elucidate the structure of that group of antibiotics known as the "penicillins." As a result of the concerted collaboration of several research teams in the United States and in England, the penicillins were shown to contain the nucleus III. While one of them ($R = C_6H_5CH_2$) was synthesized[2] earlier in infinitesimal quantities, only recently was a practical synthesis for penicillin

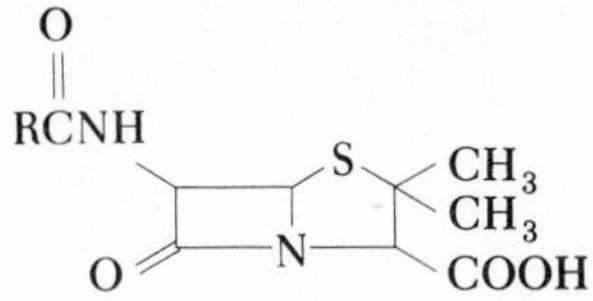

$$\begin{array}{c}O \\ \| \\ RCNH\end{array}$$
S, N, CH_3, CH_3, COOH, O

(III)

(R = $C_6H_5OCH_2$) devised.[17] Some of the complexities involved in synthetic work in this field may be appreciated by noting that III is capable of existing in eight stereochemical modifications, only one of which is identical with the natural product. Elaboration of the chemistry of these compounds was made more difficult by the obscure and bewildering reactions and rearrangements undergone by the penicillin molecule, and by the lack of sufficient knowledge regarding the chemistry of various heterocyclic systems which necessitated much collateral work on systems such as the oxazolidones, thiazolidines, β-lactams, etc. The results of all of this work have been reported admirably in an extensive monograph[3] and in much smaller degree in several reviews (*inter alia* 4). Since the only representatives of the 4-thia-1-azabicyclo[3.2.0]heptane nucleus are the penicillins and their synthetic precursors, which have been reviewed in detail,[3,4] it is not proposed to discuss the chemistry of the penicillins, but merely to report in brief detail the various syntheses of the parent ring system. Also, no attempt has been made to give a complete bibliography of the myriad books and papers concerning the penicillins and their derivatives.

The first synthesis of a compound of type I was reported by Ballard, Melstrom, and Smith,[5] who condensed diphenyl ketene with 2-phenyl-2-thiazoline. The choice of the reactants was par-

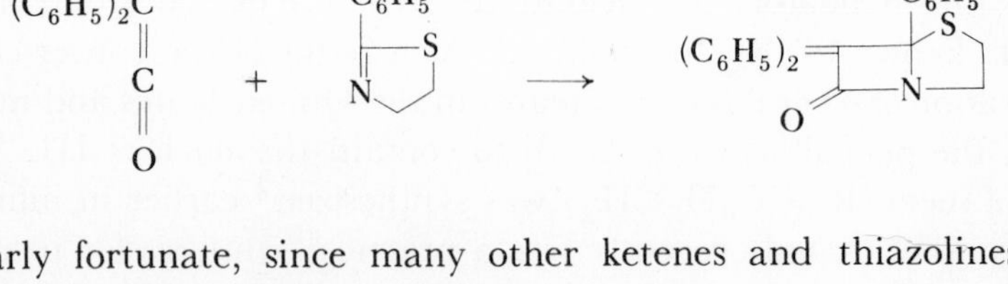

$$(C_6H_5)_2C{=}C{=}O \quad + \quad \text{2-}C_6H_5\text{-thiazoline (S, N)} \quad \longrightarrow \quad (C_6H_5)_2,\ C_6H_5,\ S,\ N,\ O$$

ticularly fortunate, since many other ketenes and thiazolines react to give thiazolidinepiperidinediones (IV). It was later found that these diones (IV) could be converted into the thiazolidine β-

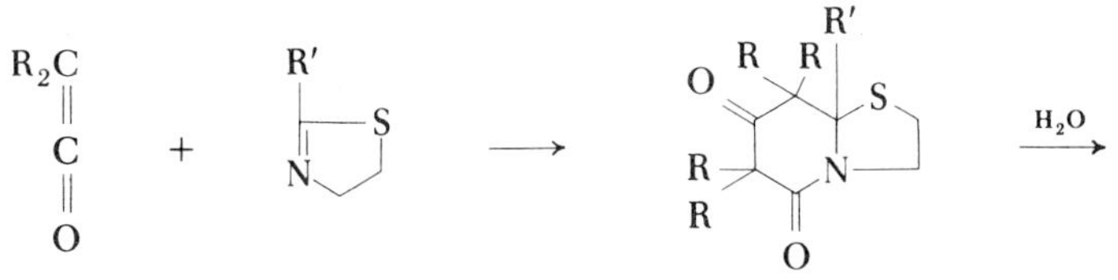

$$R_2C{=}C{=}O + \text{(thiazoline, R')} \longrightarrow \text{(IV)} \xrightarrow{H_2O}$$

(IV)

$$\text{HOOC, RRCH–C(=O)–N (thiazolidine, R', R, R)} \xrightarrow{\Delta} \text{(β-lactam, R, R, R', S, N, O)}$$

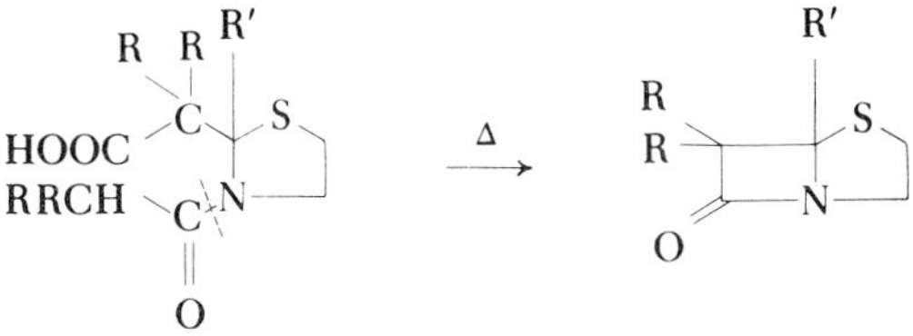

lactams by hydrolysis and pyrolytic cleavage. The reaction of ketenes with thiazolines was recently studied further, and three new penam derivatives were reported.[18]

As previously mentioned, du Vigneaud *et al.*[2,6] obtained traces of benzyl penicillin (VII) by the reaction of D-penicillamine hydrochloride (VI) with 2-benzyl-4-methoxymethylene-5(4)-oxazolone (V), although the method is not of practical value. A second syn-

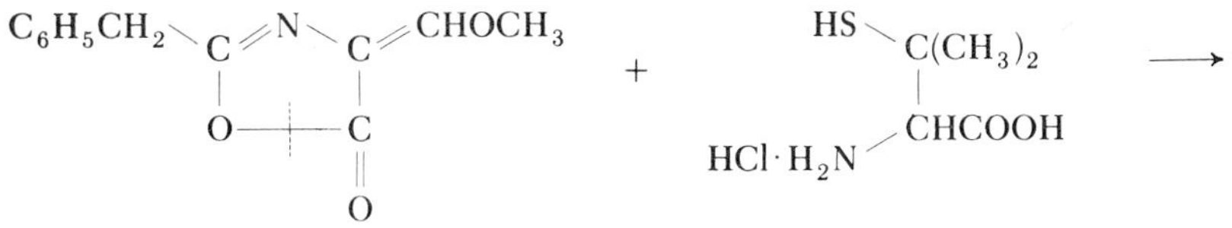

$$C_6H_5CH_2\text{–(oxazolone)}{=}CHOCH_3 + HS\text{–}C(CH_3)_2\text{–}CHCOOH\text{–}HCl\cdot H_2N \longrightarrow$$

(V) (VI)

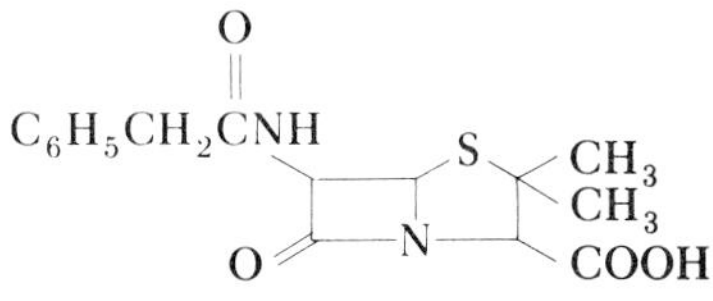

$$C_6H_5CH_2CONH\text{–(penam)–}(CH_3)_2,\ COOH$$

(VII)

thesis of VII was reported by Süs,[7] who treated VIII with phosphorus trichloride. Unsuccessful efforts to cyclize compounds similar

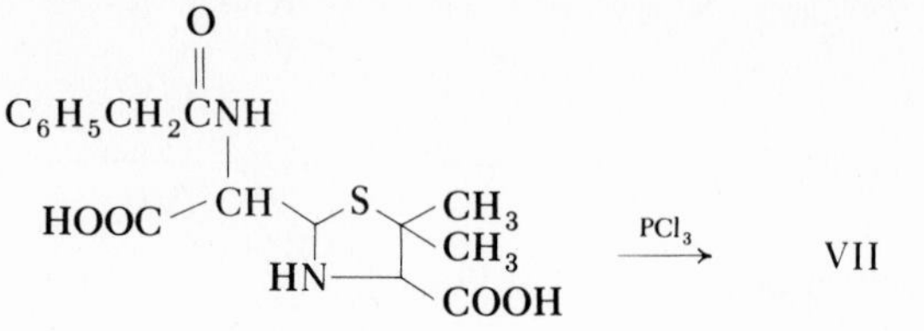

(VIII) $\xrightarrow{PCl_3}$ VII

to VIII were previously recorded,[1,8] although Sheehan reports the preparation of X by the treatment of IX with thionyl chloride.[1]

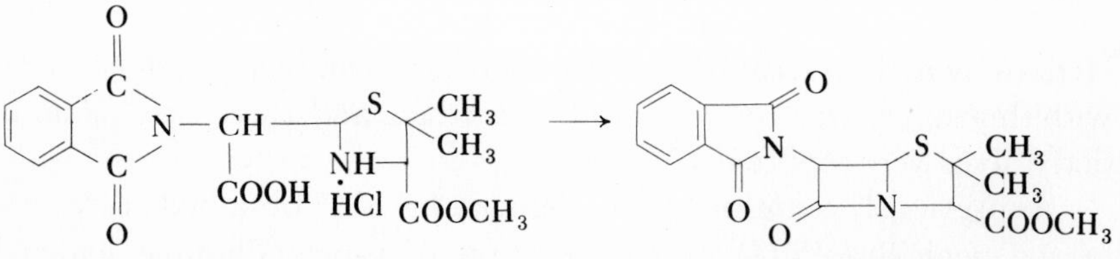

(IX) → (X)

Considerable work has been done by Sheehan and his co-workers[9-16] on the elaboration of two general methods for the synthesis of compounds of types I and II. The first of these methods[9-12] involves the condensation of 2-phenyl-2-thiazolines with succinimido- or phthalimidoacetyl chlorides. The second method condenses 2-phenyl-2-thiazoline with compounds of type XI.

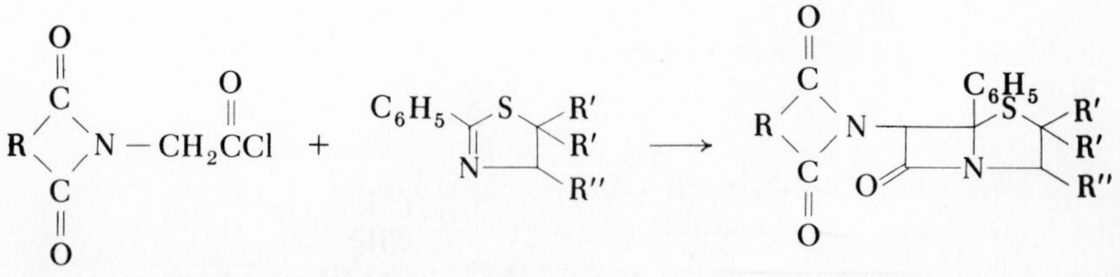

R = $(CH_2)_2$ *or* C_6H_4 R′ = H *or* CH_3 R″ = H *or* $COOCH_3$

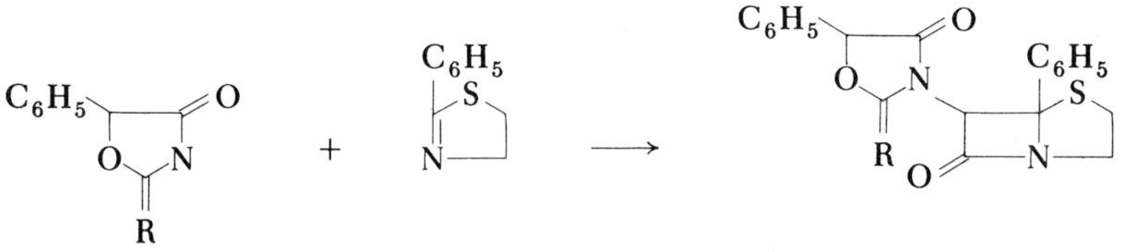

(XIa) R = O
(XIb) R = CHC_6H_5

References

1. Sheehan, Henery-Logan, and Johnson, *J. Am. Chem. Soc.*, **75,** 3292 (1953).
2. du Vigneaud, Carpenter, Holley, Livermore, and Rachele, *Science*, **104,** 431, 450 (1946).
3. Clarke, Johnson, and Robinson, *The Chemistry of Penicillin*, Princeton University Press, Princeton, N. J., 1949.
4. Cook, *Quart. Revs.*, **2,** 203 (1948).
5. Reference 3, pp. 984 ff.
6. Reference 3, pp. 1018 ff.
7. Süs, *Ann.*, **571,** 201 (1951).
8. Reference 3, p. 852.
9. Sheehan, Buhle, Corey, Laubach, and Ryan, *J. Am. Chem. Soc.*, **72,** 3828 (1950).
10. Sheehan and Ryan, *J. Am. Chem. Soc.*, **73,** 4367 (1951).
11. Sheehan, Hill and Buhle, *J. Am. Chem. Soc.*, **73,** 4373 (1951).
12. Sheehan and Laubach, *J. Am. Chem. Soc.*, **73,** 4376 (1951).
13. Sheehan and Laubach, *J. Am. Chem. Soc.*, **73,** 4752 (1951).
14. Sheehan and Corey, *J. Am. Chem. Soc.*, **73,** 4756 (1951).
15. Sheehan and Cruickshank, *J. Am. Chem. Soc.*, **78,** 3680 and 3683 (1956).
16. Sheehan and Hoff, *J. Am. Chem. Soc.*, **79,** 237 (1957).
17. Sheehan and Henery-Logan, *J. Am. Chem. Soc.*, **79,** 1262 (1957).
18. Pfleger and Jäger, *Chem. Ber.*, **90,** 2460 (1957).

A-45. Azeto[2,1-*b*]benzothiazole

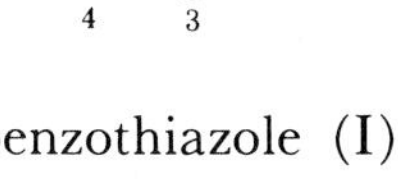

By treating 2-(2-hydroxyethyl)benzothiazole (I) with hydrogen bromide, a compound of structure II was obtained, and this, when heated, gave a cyclic quaternary salt.[1] A similar sequence of reactions is mentioned (no details given) by Bavley,[2] who treated I with phosphorus trichloride and cyclized the intermediate chlorine

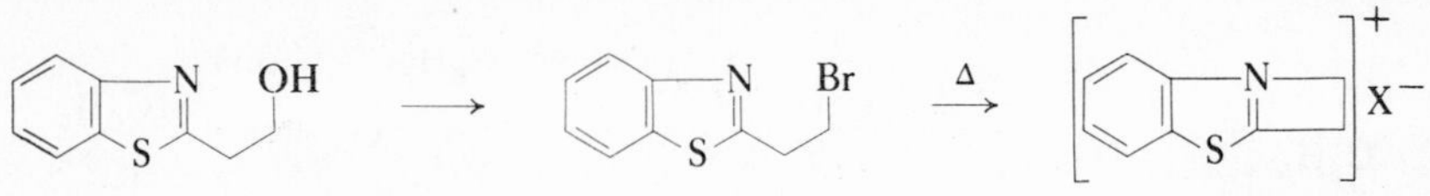

(I) (II) (III)

analog of II to a product assigned structure III. The nature of these cyclic quaternary salts has not been demonstrated, and they may well have some other structure, such as IV. Their use in color photography has been patented.[2]

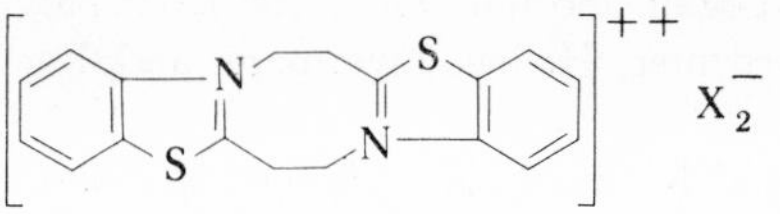

(IV)

References

1. Takahashi, Nishigaki, and Taniyama, *J. Pharm. Soc. Japan*, **64,** 237 (1944); *Chem. Abstracts*, **45,** 1997 (1951).
2. Bavley, U. S. Pat. 2,418,748.

A-46. Diindolo[1,2-*a*, 1′2′-*c*]urete. R.I. 2871

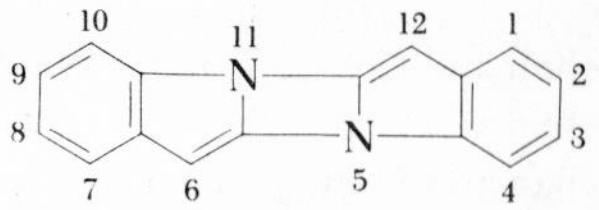

The only compounds for which this ring system has been suggested are those substances, variously called "isatols" or "isatoids," derived from *O*-alkylisatins upon exposure to light or moisture. The earliest reference to such compounds occurs in the work of Baeyer and Oekonomides,[1] who, however, suggested no structure for the substances. The compounds were investigated extensively by Hantzsch[2-6] and by Heller[7-19] and coworkers and were the subject of extensive polemics between the two schools. Much of Heller's work was shown by Hantzsch to be invalid as a result of working with impure substances, and the use of confusing nomenclature has not simplified the problem.

It is not proposed to discuss these compounds at length, since there is evidence that the structure (I) proposed is inaccurate, and that another structure, such as II, may be the correct one. Un-

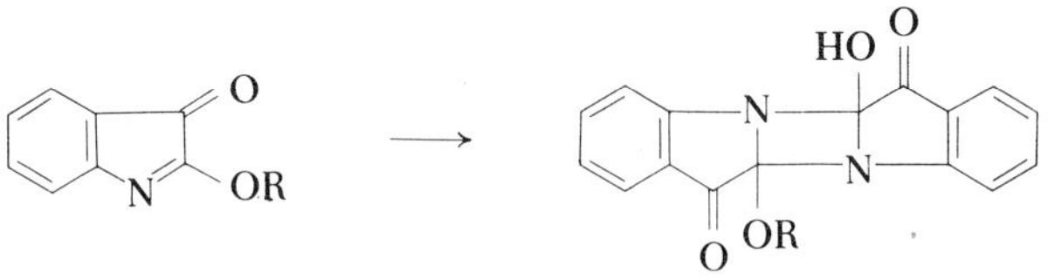

(I)

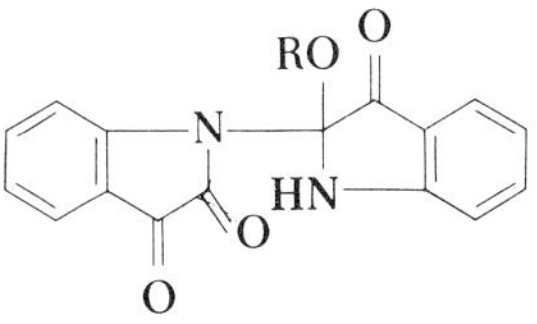

(II)

expected differences in the reactions of various members of the homologous series of isatoids also cast doubt upon the accuracy of structure I. Methylisatoid, for example, is claimed to exist in three interconvertible modifications (α-, β-, and γ-), whereas the ethyl analog yields only a single form. Crystallographic and X-ray studies[20] on methylisatoid seem to show that it is not merely a 1:1 complex of isatin and isatin *O*-methyl ether. β-Methylisatoid (IIIa) or methyl tetramethylisatoid (IIIb) are claimed by Heller[12,15,16] to yield a substance of structure IV (see Section A-460), whereas treatment of IIIb with hot acetic acid is reported by Hantzsch[4] to give an anhydride for which he proposed structure V. Treatment of IIIa, or of ethylisatoid in acetic acid, with 48% hydrobromic acid gives a product thought by Heller[12,15,16] to have structure VI. Under these conditions, methyl- or ethyldibromoisatoids undergo similar rearrangements to products of type VI, although methyl tetrachloroisatoid (III, R = Cl) gives only dichloroisatin. While β-methylisatoid is reported to yield a crystalline phenylhydrazone, methyl dichloroisatoid gives only 5-chloroisatinphenylhydrazone.

These and other data, equally inconclusive, raise the doubt that a uniform species is at hand. Only a careful reworking of the prob-

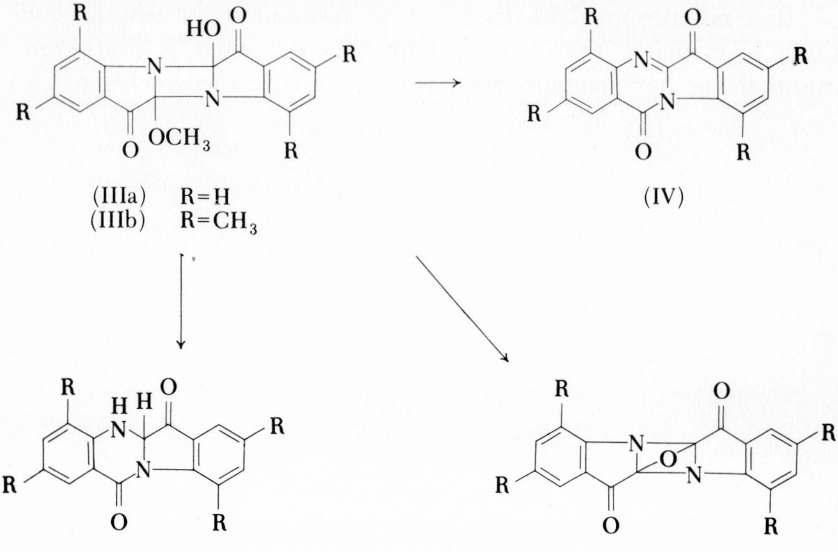

(IIIa) R=H
(IIIb) R=CH_3

(IV)

(VI)

(V)

lem, with scrupulous attention to the purity of the products, will clarify the matter. It would seem that the application of ultraviolet and infrared spectroscopic techniques would do much to simplify the solution of this problem.

Isatoids

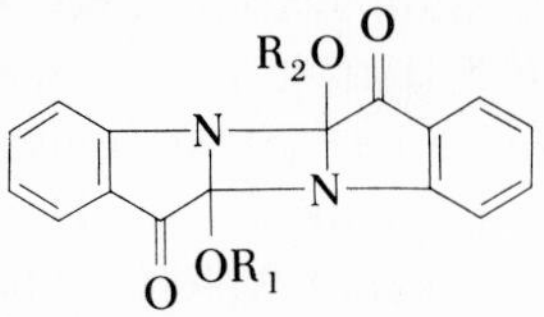

Empirical formula	R_1	R_2	Substituents	Properties	Refs.
$C_{16}H_{10}N_2O_4$	H	H	None	Or.-yel., m. 178–82° (163–4°).	6,18
$C_{17}H_8Cl_4N_2O_4$	H	Me	2,4,8,10-Tetra-chloro-	m. 127°, resolidifies at ~180° and remelts at ~222°.	16
$C_{17}H_{10}Br_2N_2O_4$	H	Me	2,8-Dibromo-	*β-Isomer:* or.-red., darkens at 225°, sinters at 240°, m. 262° d. (246° d.). Recryst. from C_6H_6 gives a product m. 259–60°.	3,17
				γ-Isomer: red flocs. m. 306–7°.	17

Isatoids (*continued*)

Empirical formula	R_1	R_2	Substituents	Properties	Refs.
$C_{17}H_{10}Cl_2N_2O_4$	H	Me	2,8-Dichloro-	Or.-red, m. 239°.	3
$C_{17}H_{12}N_2O_4$	H	Me	None	α-*Isomer:* m. 244° d. (238–40°).	2,15
				β-*Isomer:* m. 226° (219°).	1,3,12
				γ-*Isomer:* Or.-yel., m. ~255°.	12,14
$C_{18}H_{12}Br_2N_2O_4$	H	Et	2-8-Dibromo-	Or.-yel., m 244–5°.	1,17
$C_{18}H_{14}N_2O_4$	H	Et	None	m. 228°.	3,17
$C_{19}H_{14}Br_2N_2O_4$	H	*n*-Pr	2,8-Dibromo-	m. 227–32° d.	17
$C_{19}H_{16}N_2O_4$	H	*n*-Pr	None	m. 189° (187°).	3,15
$C_{20}H_{16}Br_2N_2O_4$	H	*i*-Bu	2,8-Dibromo-	m. 210°.	1
$C_{21}H_{18}N_2O_4$	H	*i*-Bu	None	m. 147–8°.	15
$C_{21}H_{20}N_2O_4$	H	Me	2,4,8,10-Tetramethyl-	Red, m. 247° (245°, 232°).	3,4,16,17

References

1. Baeyer and Oekonomides, *Ber.*, **15,** 2093 (1882).
2. Hantzsch, *Ber.*, **54,** 1221 (1921).
3. Hantzsch, *Ber.*, **55,** 3180 (1922).
4. Hantzsch, *Ber.*, **56,** 2110 (1923).
5. Hantzsch, *Ber.*, **58,** 680 (1925).
6. Hantzsch, *Ber.*, **58,** 686 (1925).
7. Heller, *Ber.*, **40,** 1291 (1907).
8. Heller, *Ber.*, **49,** 2757 (1916).
9. Heller, *Ber.*, **50,** 1199 (1917).
10. Heller, *Ber.*, **51,** 180 (1918).
11. Heller, *Ber.*, **51,** 1270 (1918).
12. Heller, *Ber.*, **52,** 437 (1919).
13. Heller, *Ber.*, **53,** 1545 (1920).
14. Heller, *Ber.*, **54,** 2214 (1921).
15. Heller and Benade, *Ber.*, **55,** 1006 (1922).
16. Heller, *Ber.*, **55,** 2681 (1922).
17. Heller and Lauth, *Ber.*, **56,** 1591 (1923).
18. Heller and Fuchs, *J. prakt. Chem.*, **110,** 283 (1925).
19. Heller and Lauth, *J. prakt. Chem.*, **112,** 331 (1926).
20. Cox, Goodwin, and Wagstaff, *Proc. Roy. Soc. (London)*, **A157,** 399 (1936); *Brit. Chem. Abstracts*, **AII,** 166 (1937); *Chem. Zentr.*, **I,** 3458 (1938); *Chem. Abstracts*, **31,** 1803 (1937).

A-47. Diisoindolo[2,1-*b*, 1′,2′-*d*][1.2]-diazete. R.I. 2872

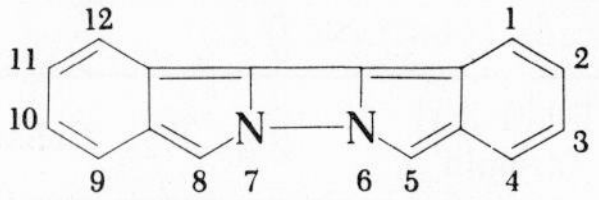

In 1895, Bistrzycki and Fink[1] found that treatment of compounds of type I with phosphorus oxychloride removed the elements of one mole of water, and they established that the products so formed were dimeric. Although unable to prove the exact nature of these dimeric compounds, they considered them probably to have structure II. Compound IIa is a pale brown and IIb a yellow-orange color; both melt above 325°.

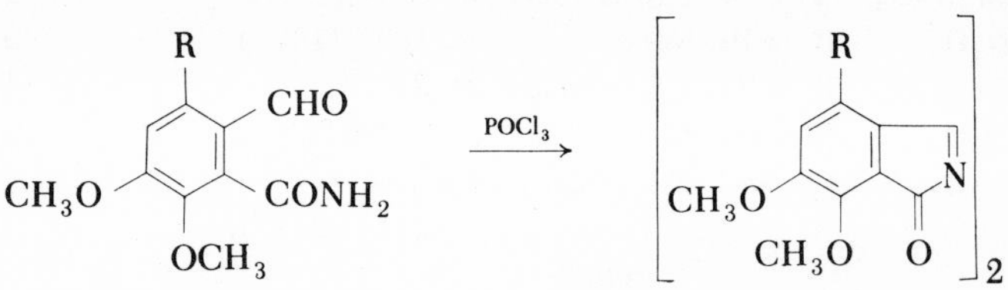

(Ia) R = Br
(Ib) R = NO_2

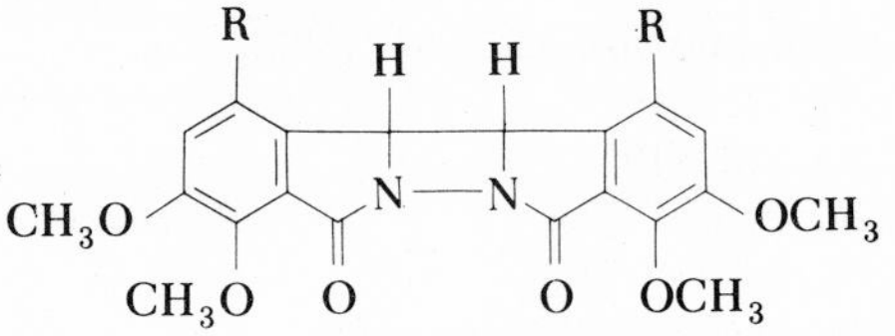

(IIa) R = Br
(IIb) R = NO_2

More recently, by heating compounds of type IIIa, Dunet and Willemart[2] obtained a substance (m. 302°) with the formula $C_{16}H_{10}N_2O_2$. The same product was obtained by treating IIIb with thionyl chloride, but was not formed by merely heating IIIb. As the new product is converted by heat into *β*-isoindigo (V, with which it is isomeric), structure IV was proposed for it.

Further confirmation of structures II and IV would be desirable, and it would seem that here again infrared and ultraviolet spectroscopy would be of considerable aid.

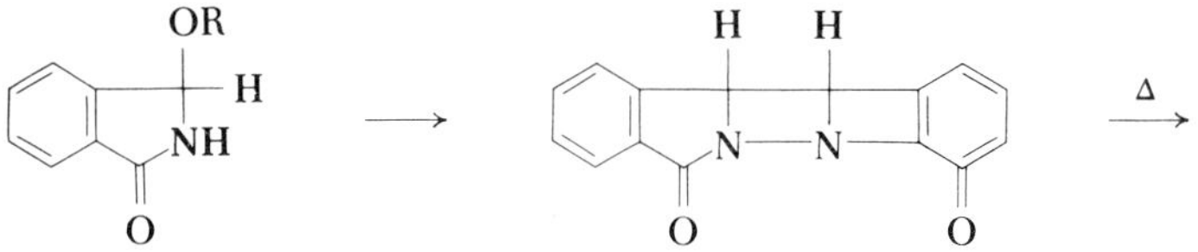

OR H NH O → H H N—N O O Δ→

(IIIa) R = CH_3 *or* C_2H_5
(IIIb) R = H

(IV)

NH HN O O

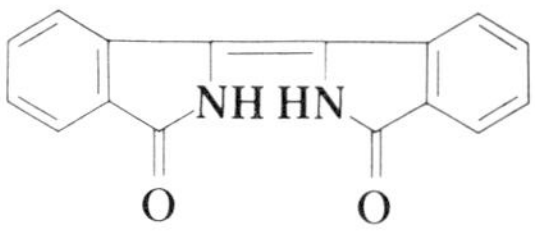

(V)

References

1. Bistryzycki and Fink, *Ber.*, **31,** 930 (1895).
2. Dunet and Willemart, *Compt. rend.*, **226,** 1286 (1948).

A-48. 1,2-Diazabicyclo[3.2.0]heptane*

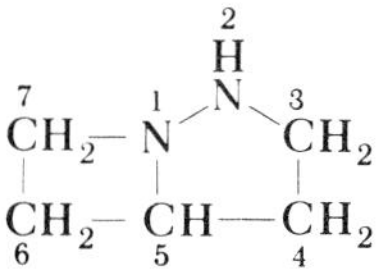

CH_2(7)—N(1)—N(2)H—CH_2(3); CH_2(6)—CH(5)—CH_2(4)

An intermediate of structure II was postulated[1] in the conversion of I into III by treatment with acetic acid.

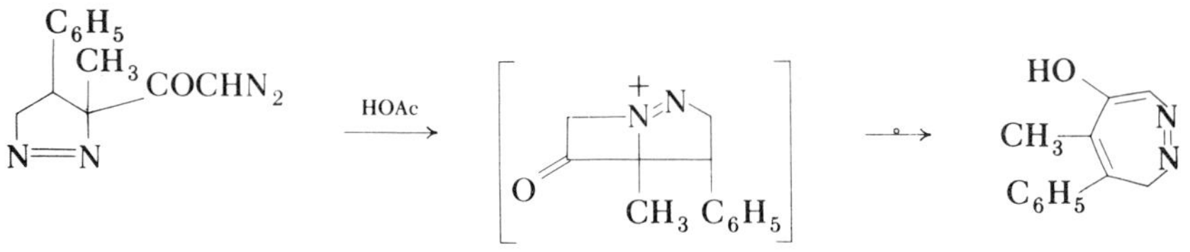

C_6H_5 CH_3 $COCHN_2$ N=N →(HOAc) [$\overset{+}{N}$=N O CH_3 C_6H_5] → HO CH_3 C_6H_5 N=N

(I) (II) (III)

Reference

1. Moore, *J. Am. Chem. Soc.*, **77,** 3417 (1955).

A-49. 6-Oxa-1,4-diazabicyclo[3.2.0]-heptane. R.I. 508

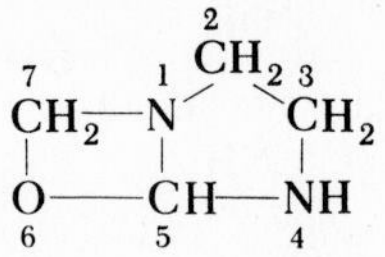

Treatment of a group of compounds of structure I with formic acid yielded products, which, because no formyl group cleavage occurred under alkaline conditions, were considered[1] to have structure II. However, treatment with hydrobromic acid did effect hydrolysis of the formyl group, and it seems probable that these substances are merely the normal *N*-formyl derivatives (III or, more likely, IV).

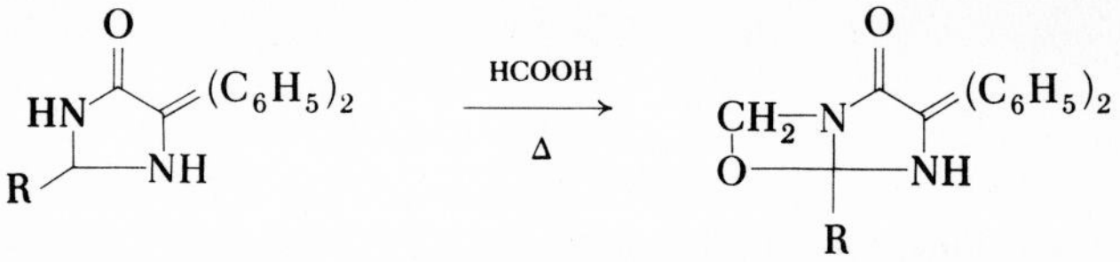

(I) (II)

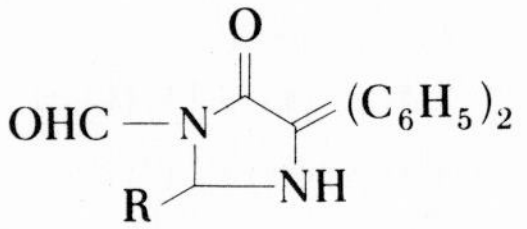

(III) 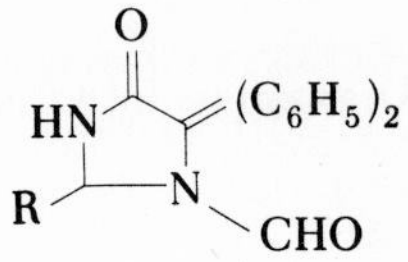 (IV)

Reference

1. Biltz, Seydel, and Hamburger-Glaser, *Ann.*, **428,** 198 (1922).

A-50. 2*H*,8*aH*-[1,3]-Thiazeto-[2,3-*b*]benzothiazole*

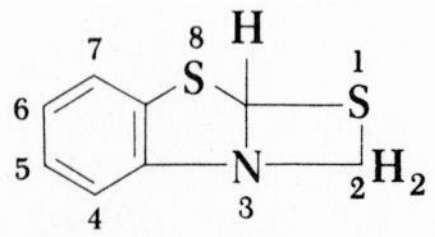

During the preparation of benzothiazole by heating dimethylaniline with sulfur, there was obtained a by-product, which was thought[1-3] to have structure I. However, the same substance was prepared[4] by treating II with thiophosgene, a synthesis which confirms structure III for this product.

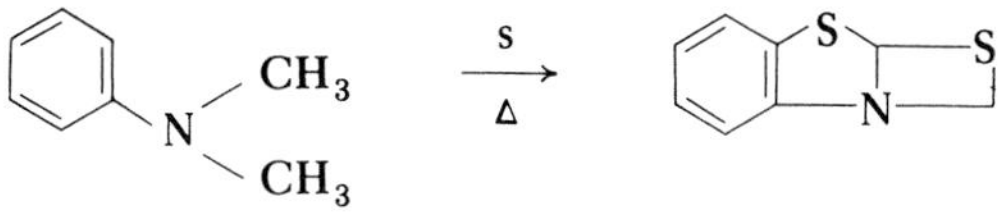

N CH_3 CH_3 $\xrightarrow[\Delta]{S}$ S S N

(I)

SH $NHCH_3$ $\xrightarrow{CSCl_2}$ S S N — CH_3

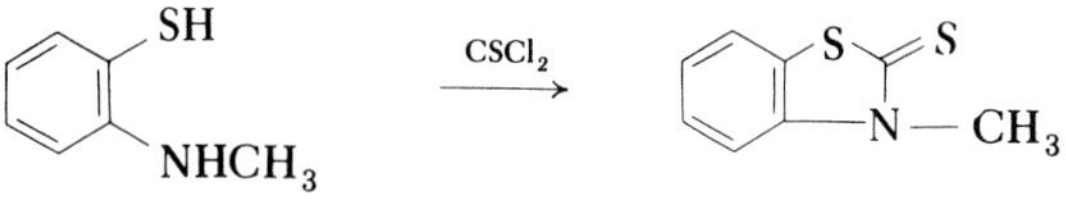

(II) (III)

References

1. Möhlau and Krohn, *Ber.*, **21,** 59 (1888).
2. Möhlau and Klopfer, *Ber.*, **31,** 3164 (1898).
3. Rassow, Döhle and Reim, *J. prakt. Chem.*, **93,** 183 (1916).
4. Mills, Clark and Aeschlimann, *J. Chem. Soc.*, **123,** 2362 (1923).

A-51. 1*H*-Triazeto[4,1-*c*]pyrrocoline. R. I. 1249

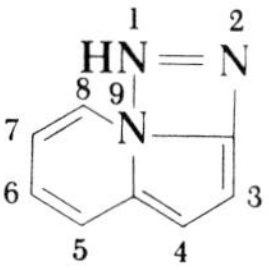

1 2 HN = N 8 9 N 7 6 5 4 3

The reaction of I with collidine gave[1] a product (red-brown, d. vigorously at 180°) thought to be either II or III. Neither is, of course, a true representative of this nucleus (see Section A-183).

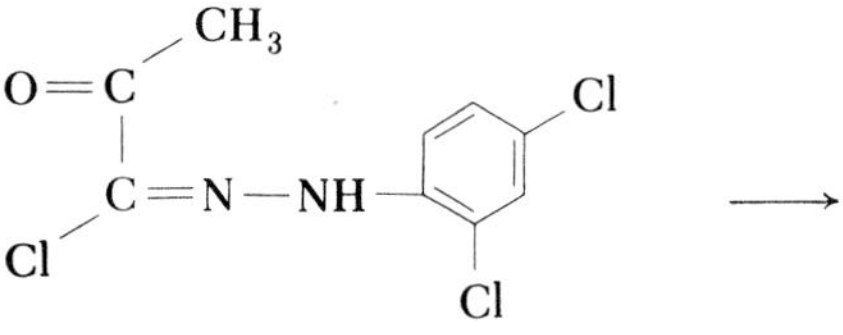

CH_3 O = C C = N — NH Cl Cl Cl

(I)

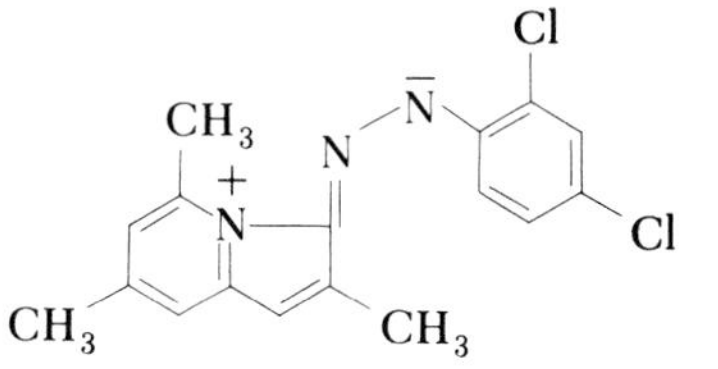

$\longrightarrow$

CH_3 + N N N Cl Cl CH_3 CH_3

(II)

or

CH_3 N N = N Cl Cl CH_3 CH_3

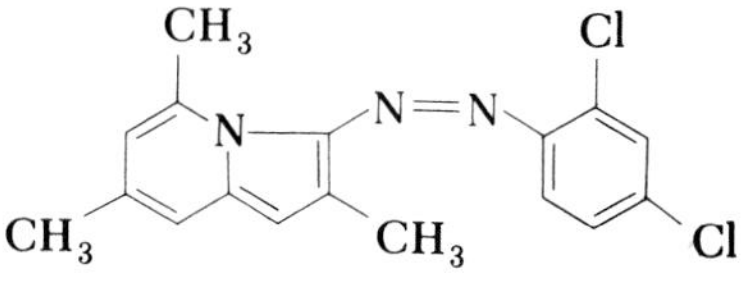

(III)

Reference

1. Neber and Wörner, *Ann.*, **526,** 173 (1936).

A-52. Diindazolo[2,3-*a*, 2′,3′-*c*]urete*

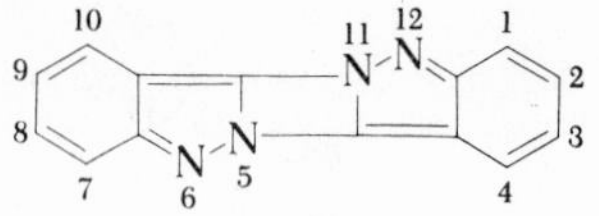

The only compound for which this nucleus has been proposed is the product (I) obtained by Hantzsch[1] from anthranilic acid hydrazide. Compound I forms a dihydrochloride (m. 255°d.) and a diacetate (d. 186°). Treatment of I with acetic anhydride removes a mole of water giving a product (m. 188°) which Hantzsch considered to be II. A reinvestigation of these compounds would be desirable.

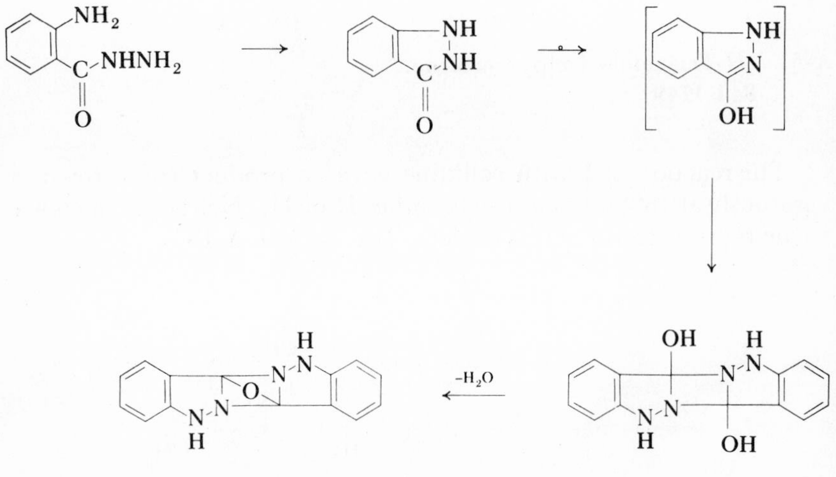

$-H_2O$

(II) (I)

Reference

1. Hantzsch, *Ber.*, **58,** 680 (1925).

A-53. Diphenylenepyrrodiazoline. R.I. 2868

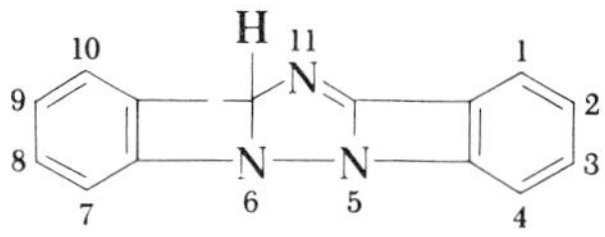

The reduction of *o*-nitrobenzonitrile (I) with zinc and acetic acid is reported[1] to give, among other products, a base ($C_{14}H_{10}N_4$) to which structure II was assigned. The product forms yellow needles (m. 221°) and yields acetyl (m. 269–70°) and benzoyl (m. 255–6°) derivatives and a hydrochloride (m. 277°). Replacement of the amino group by hydroxyl to give III occurs when II is heated at 180° with hydrochloric acid, whereas diazotization replaces the amino group with hydroxyl and also introduces a nitro (?) group. Methylation of III (m. >320°) gives a methyl ether (m. 214°, unc.). Further evidence for the accuracy of the structures proposed would be highly desirable.

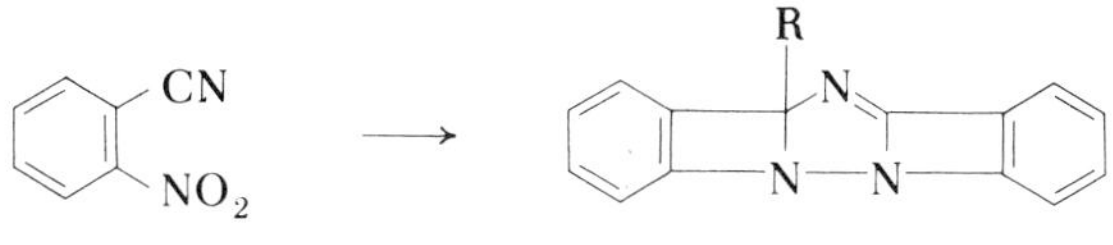

(I)

(II) R = NH_2
(III) R = OH

Reference

1. Pinnow and Müller, *Ber.*, **28,** 152 (1895).

A-54. Triazetindazole

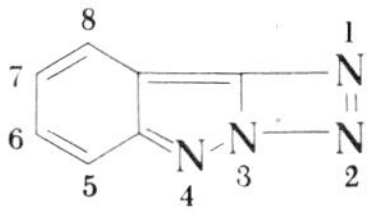

The name *indazoltriazolene* also has been used.

Diazotization of I in weakly acid solution afforded[1] (in 72% yield) a yellow substance (m. 137–45°d.) assigned structure II. It could not be recrystallized, but was purified by solution in hydrochloric acid and precipitation with sodium acetate. While readily soluble in alcohols, ether, acetone, or acetic acid, it was difficultly soluble in benzene and insoluble in ligroin or cold caustic solution (hot caustic solution caused decomposition). In dilute mineral acid solutions, II readily coupled with phenolic components.

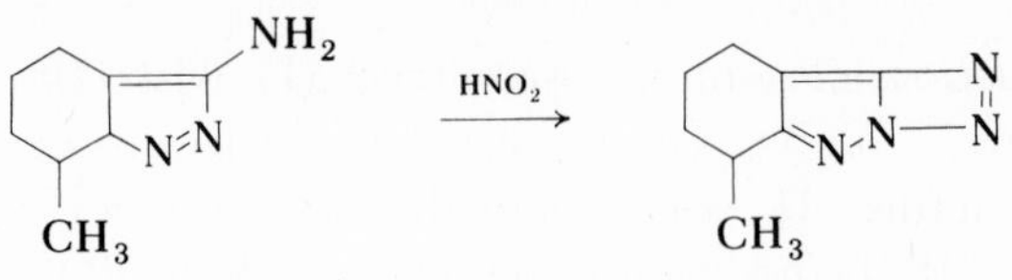

(I) $\xrightarrow{HNO_2}$ (II)

Reference

1. v. Auwers, Bahr, and Frese, *Ann.*, **441,** 68 (1925).

A-55. 1-Azabicyclo[4.2.0]octane. R.I. 551

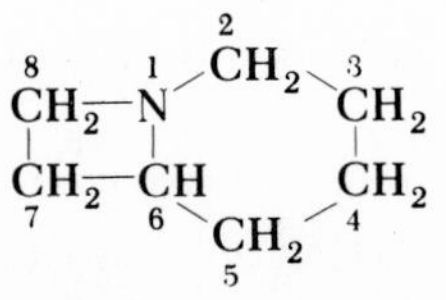

The trivial name of *conidine* has been given to this nucleus, and the numbering shown in I has been used[1] most often in describing these compounds. The action of hydrohalic acids upon the alkaloid

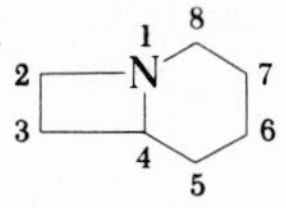

(I)

conhydrine [2-(α-hydroxypropyl)piperidine] causes dehydration to yield several isomeric bases called *coniceines*, and *ε-coniceine* is 8-methyl-1-azabicyclo[4.2.0]octane[4] or, as it is called in Löffler's papers,[4-8] *2-methylconidine*. Synthetic ε-coniceine having the L-configuration at C_6 (from *l*-2-propenylpiperidine, also called *l*-β-coniceine) has been resolved into optical isomers, and Löffler has suggested that the *ld*-form be called *2-methylconidine* and the *ll*-form *iso-2-methylconidine*.

Conidine and its methyl derivatives have been prepared by treating various alkenyl- or hydroxyalkyl-2-piperidines with hydrohalic acids alone or in the presence of red phosphorus. They are rather strongly basic oils, which yield crystalline salts. The methylconidines are highly toxic, with an action similar to that of coniine.

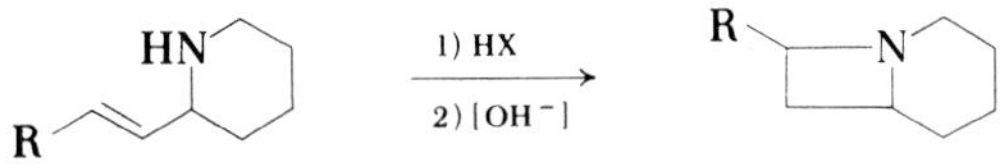

Upon standing, or when heated, 2-(2-haloalkyl)pyridines (II) rearrange to a cyclic quaternary salt to which structure III has been assigned.[1,2,4,5,9-11] Recently, however, the product thus obtained from 2-(2-bromoethyl)pyridine was shown[12] to have structure IV, and it seems probable that the other products similarly obtained are also of this type (see Section A-893).

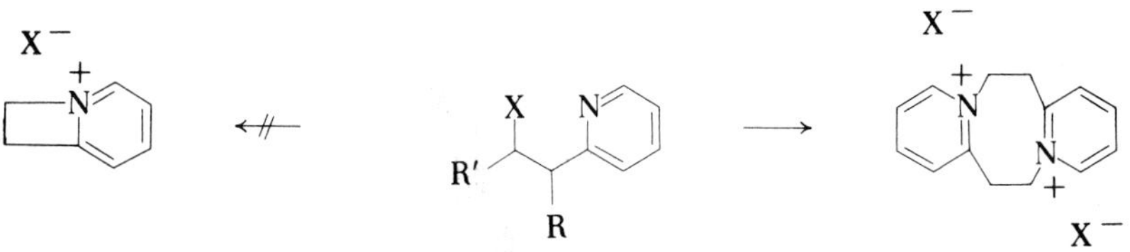

(III) (II) (IV)

Derivatives of Conidine

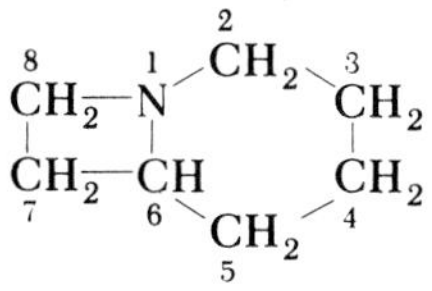

Empirical formula	Substituents	Properties	Refs.
$C_7H_{13}N$	None	Oil, b. 152–8°; HBr salt; chloroplatinate of *N*-ethyl deriv., dk. red, m. 178° d.	3,6
$C_8H_{15}N$	2-Methyl-	Oil, b. 156°; d_4^{15} 0.8931; HCl salt; picrate, m. 237°; chloroaurate, m. 191–2°; chloroplatinate, m. 198°; ethiodide, m. 202° d.; *N*-ethyl chloroplatinate, m. 210.5°.	8
	7-Methyl-(*dl*-)	Oil, b. 158°; d_4^{15} 0.8946; picrate, m. 194–5°; chloroaurate, yel., m. 151°; chloroplatinate, m. 197–9°; $HgCl_2$ complex, m. 205–6°; ethiodide, m. 169°; chloroplatinate of *N*-ethyl deriv., or., m. 185–7°.	5

Derivatives of Conidine (*continued*)

Empirical formula	Substituents	Properties	Refs.
$C_8H_{15}N$ (*cont.*)	7-Methyl-(*l*-)	$[\alpha]_D^{17}$ −17.13°; *d*-tartrate · $2H_2O$ salt, m. 93–4°.	5
	7-Methyl-(*d*-)	$[\alpha]_D^{8}$ +16.0°; *d*-tartrate salt, oily; *l*-tartrate salt, m. 93–4°.	5
	8-Methyl-(*dl*-)	Oil, b. 151–2°; picrate, m. 221–2° d.; HCl salt; aurichloride, m. 172–3° after previous sintering; methiodide, m. 185–6°; ethiodide, m. 176–7°; chloroplatinate of *N*-ethyl deriv., m. 198–200° d.	3
	8-Methyl-(*ld*-)	Oil, b. 151.5–4°; d_4^{15} 0.8856; $[\alpha]_D^{15}$ +67.4°; acid *d*-tartrate salt · $2H_2O$, m. 72–3°; chloroaurate, m. 167–8°; chloroplatinate, m. 184–5°; ethiodide, m. 165° d.	7
	8-Methyl-(*l l*-)	Oil, b. 143–5°; d_{15} 0.8624; $[\alpha]_D^{15}$ −87.34°; HCl salt; acid-*d*-tartrate salt·$2H_2O$, m. 91–2°; picrate, m. 220–1°; chloroaurate, m. 198–9°; chloroplatinate, m. 185°; ethiodide, m. 180–1° d.	7
$C_9H_{17}N$	8-Ethyl-	Oil, b. 176–83°; HCl salt; picrate, m. 198°; aurichloride, m. 132–5°; chloroplatinate, blackens at 205°, m. 210° d.; $HgCl_2$ complex, m. 220–1°; ethiodide, m. 222° d.	1

References

1. Löffler and Plöcker, *Ber.*, **40,** 1310 (1907).
2. Löffler, *Ber.*, **37,** 161 (1904).
3. Löffler, *Ber.*, **37,** 1879 (1904).
4. Löffler, and Kirschner, *Ber.*, **38,** 3329 (1905).
5. Löffler and Grosse, *Ber.*, **40,** 1325 (1907).
6. Löffler and Grosse, *Ber.*, **40,** 1336 (1907).
7. Löffler, *Ber.*, **42,** 948 (1909).
8. Löffler and Remmler, *Ber.*, **43,** 2048 (1910).
9. Takahashi, Nishigaki, and Taniyama, *J. Pharm. Soc. Japan*, **64,** 237 (1944); *Chem. Abstracts*, **45,** 1997 (1951).
10. Ohki and Noike, *J. Pharm. Soc. Japan*, **72,** 490 (1952); *Chem. Abstracts*, **47,** 6419 (1953).

11. Bohlmann, Ottawa, Keller, Nebel, and Politt, *Ann.*, **587,** 162 (1954).
12. Boekelheide and Feely, *J. Am. Chem. Soc.*, **80,** 2217 (1958).

A-56. Azeto[1,2-*a*]quinoline*

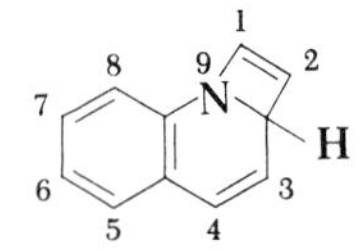

Takahashi, Nishigaki, and Taniyama[1] treated 2-(2-hydroxyethyl)quinoline (I) with hydrogen bromide and the resulting bromoethyl compound (II) was converted by heat into a cyclic quaternary salt, probably either III or IV. Structure III, which represents a violation of Bredt's rule, is analogous to the structures incorrectly proposed for the products obtained similarly from 2-(2-bromoethyl)pyridine (Section A-55).

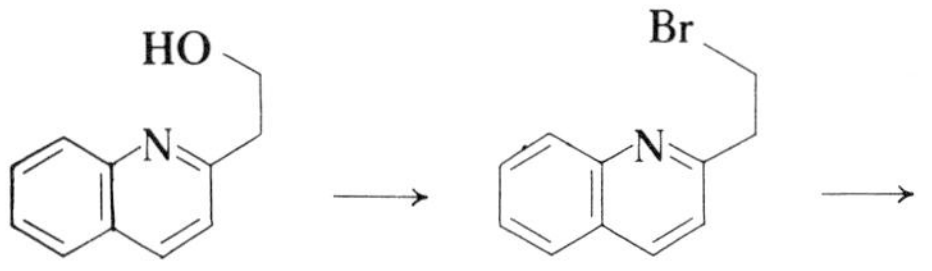

(I) (II)

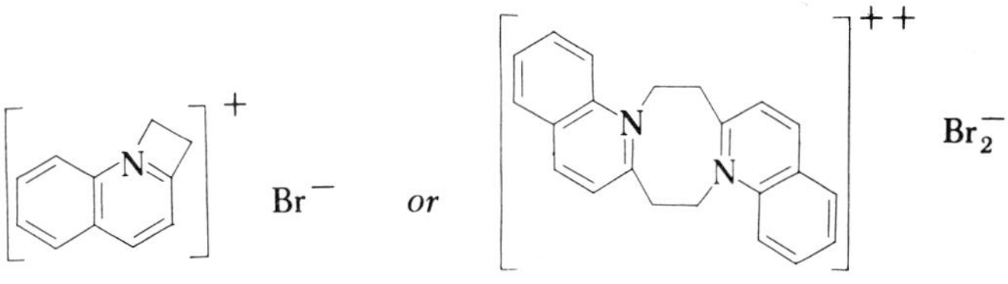

(III) or (IV)

A structure having the azeto[1,2-*a*]quinoline nucleus has recently been proposed[2] and discussed[3] as an intermediate in the alkaline rearrangement of chloralquinaldine.

References

1. Takahashi, Nishigaki, and Taniyama, *J. Pharm. Soc. Japan*, **64,** 237 (1944); *Chem. Abstracts*, **45,** 1997 (1951).
2. Brown, Hammick, and Robinson, *J. Chem. Soc.*, **1950,** 78.
3. Dauben and Vaughan, *J. Am. Chem. Soc.*, **75,** 4651 (1953).

A-57. 8-Oxa-1-azabicyclo[4.2.0]-octane. R.I. 541

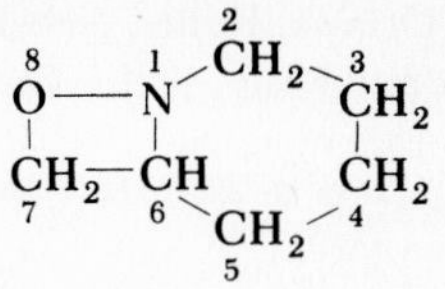

The betaines[1] I were considered by the *Ring Index* to be examples of this nucleus.

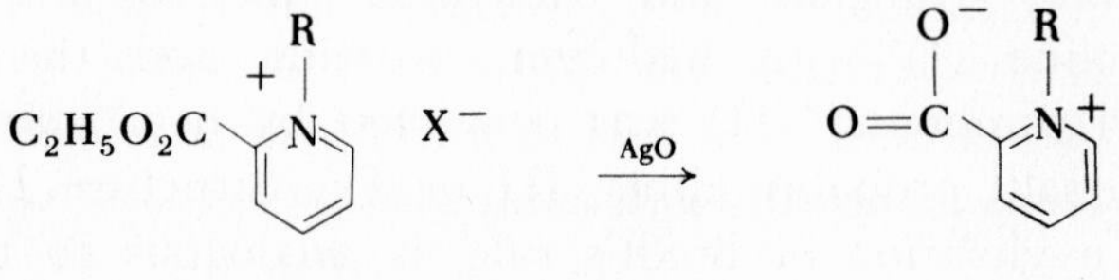

(I)

Reference

1. Meyer, *Monatsh.*, **15,** 164 (1894).

A-58. [1,2]Oxazeto[3,2-*a*]isoquinoline. R.I. 1258

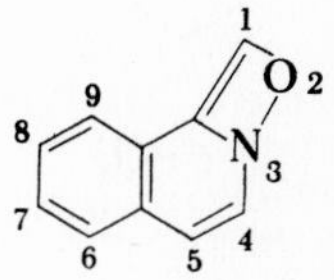

Betaines such as I[1] were cited by the *Ring Index* as examples of this ring system, but no true representatives have been reported.

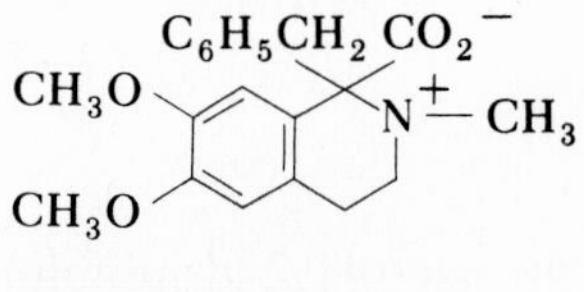

(I)

Reference

1. Hahn and Stiehl, *Ber.*, **69,** 2627 (1936).

A-59. Azeto[1,2-*a*]benzo[*de*]quinazoline*

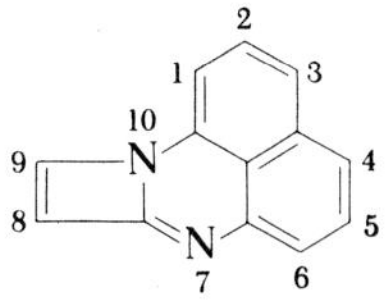

A compound (I), reported probably to be a derivative of this nucleus was described by Sachs,[1] who obtained it together with II by melting malonic acid with 1,8-naphthylenediamine. Compound I forms colorless crystals (m. 210°d.). It is stable to hot concentrated hydrochloric acid and dissolves with a red color in sulfuric acid, but gives no salts with dilute acids.

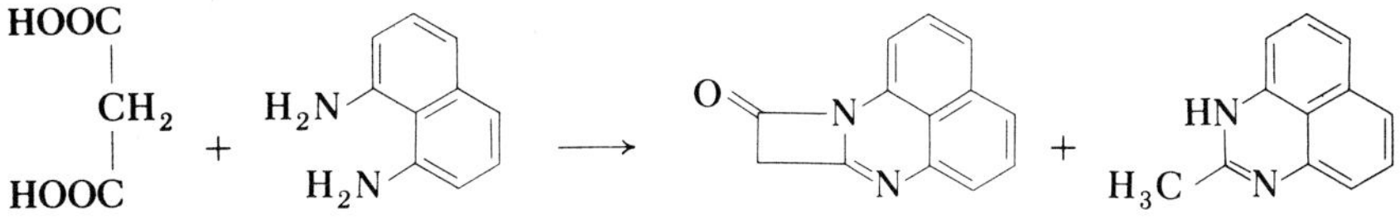

(I) (II)

The elemental analysis of Sachs' compound agrees well with the formula $C_{13}H_8ON_2$ (e.g., I), but the molecular weight determinations were 242 and 264 as contrasted with a theoretical value of 208. A study of the ultraviolet and infrared spectra of I should throw further light upon the accuracy of the assigned structure.

Reference

1. Sachs, *Ann.*, **365**, 53 (1909).

A-60. 10,11-Epoxy-10*H*-indeno[1,2-*b*]-quinoxaline.* R.I. 2879

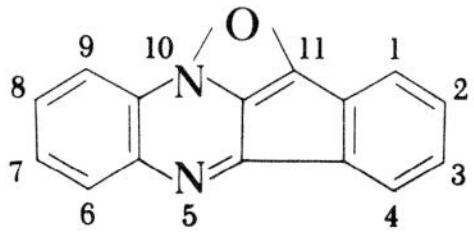

Rosindonic acid[1,2] (I) was given by the *Ring Index* as an example of this nucleus.

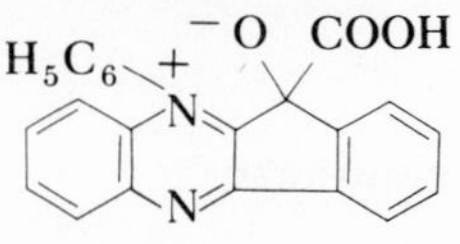

(I)

References

1. Fischer and Hepp, *Ann.*, **262,** 237 (1891).
2. Fischer, *Ber.*, **36,** 3622 (1903).

A-61. 1,6,7-Triazabicyclo[4.2.0]octane. R.I. 535

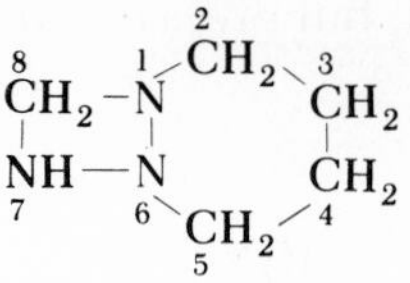

The aromatic system has been called *triazeto*[1,2-*a*]*pyridazine* and numbered as shown in I.

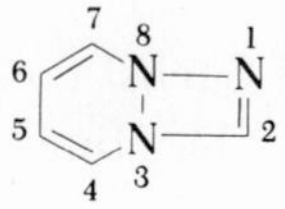

(I)

Treatment of ω-chloroacetophenone semicarbazone (II) with sodium bicarbonate yielded[1] a colorless, nonbasic product (m. 221.5°) having the formula $C_{17}H_{17}N_3O$. Boiling dilute acids were without effect upon the product, but it was converted by hot ethanolic sodium ethoxide solution into a substance considered (because of its conversion into 3,6-diphenylpyridazine) to be 3,4,5,6-tetrahydro-3,6-diphenylpyridazine. Structure III, proposed[1] for this product, seems improbable, and further work is needed to establish the correct structure.

Reference

1. Hoogeveen and Van Hoogstraten, *Rec. trav. chim.*, **52,** 378 (1933).

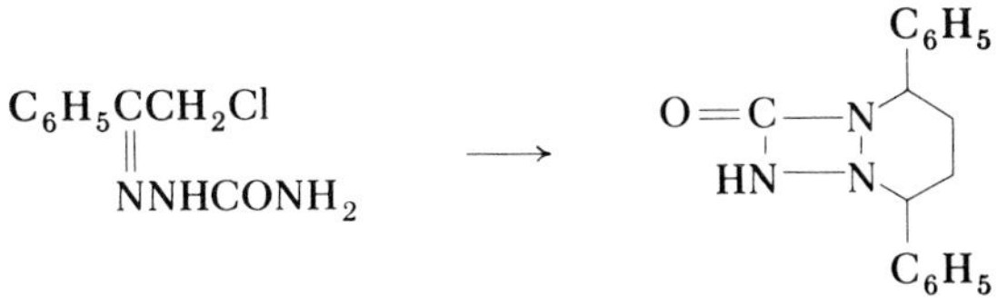

$C_6H_5C(=NNHCONH_2)CH_2Cl$ ⟶ (III)

(II) (III)

A-62. *7H*,16*H*-Bis-*s*-tetrazino[1′,2′,3,4]-tetrazeto[1,2-*a*, 1′,2′-*d*]-*s*-tetrazine*

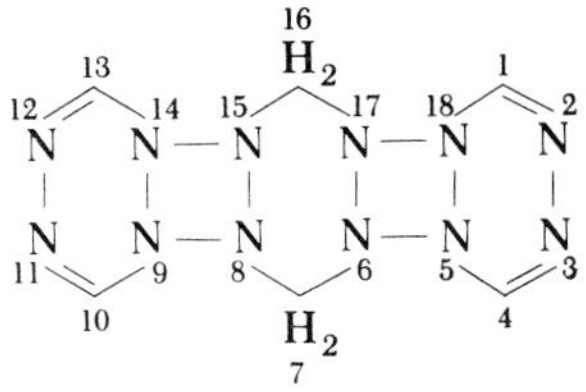

Polymerization of diazoacetic ester yields a dimer thought to be I, and treatment of this with alcoholic potassium hydroxide gave a product (m. 183°) called *trisbisdiazomethanetetracarboxylic acid* and assigned[1] structure II. This substance also is produced when diazoacetic ester is heated with aqueous caustic. Further evidence for this unusual structure would be welcome.

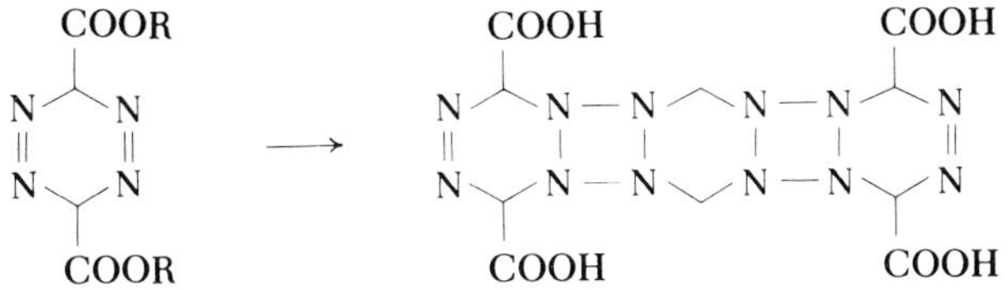

(I) (II)

Reference

1. Hantzsch and Silberrad, *Ber.*, **33**, 58 (1900).

A-63. 1,6-Diazabicyclo[7.2.0]-undecane*

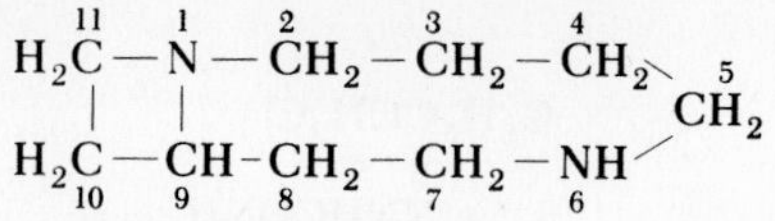

$$\begin{array}{l} \overset{11}{H_2C}-\overset{1}{N}-\overset{2}{CH_2}-\overset{3}{CH_2}-\overset{4}{CH_2}\diagdown \overset{5}{CH_2} \\ \quad | \qquad | \\ \underset{10}{H_2C}-\underset{9}{CH}-\underset{8}{CH_2}-\underset{7}{CH_2}-\underset{6}{NH}\diagup \end{array}$$

An antibiotic ($C_9H_{14}O_3N_2$, m. 183–4°) isolated by chemists of the Sandoz laboratories from Actinomycetaceae Buchanan, was named *nocardamine* and assigned structure I.

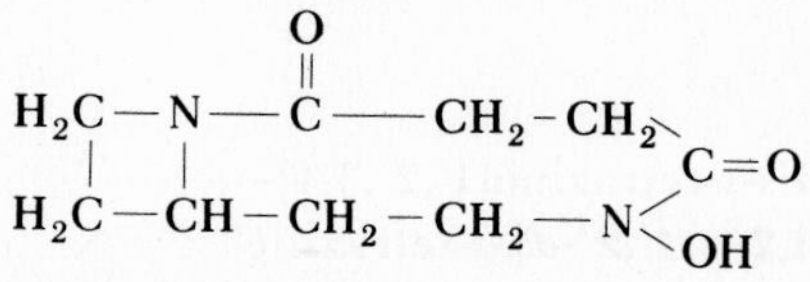

$$\begin{array}{l} \qquad\qquad\quad O \\ \qquad\qquad\quad \| \\ H_2C-N-C-CH_2-CH_2\diagdown \\ \quad | \qquad | \qquad\qquad\qquad\quad C=O \\ H_2C-CH-CH_2-CH_2-N\diagup \\ \qquad\qquad\qquad\qquad\qquad\quad \diagdown OH \end{array}$$

(I)

Reference

1. Stoll, Renz, and Brack, *Helv. Chim. Acta*, **34,** 862 (1951).

CHAPTER III

Fused 5/5 Ring Systems

A-64. 3*H*-Pyrrolo[1,2-*a*]pyrrole. R.I. 635

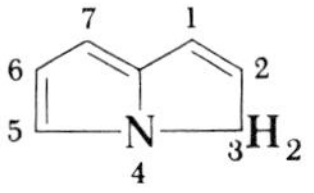

The following names and numbering also have been used: *pyrrolizine* (I), *di-(1:2)-pyrrole* (II), and *4,3-pyrrolopyrrole*. The perhydro system has been called *pyrrolizidine* and *1-azabicyclo[0.3.3]octane* (III). The 7*a* position in pyrrolizidine has often been designated as the 8-position.

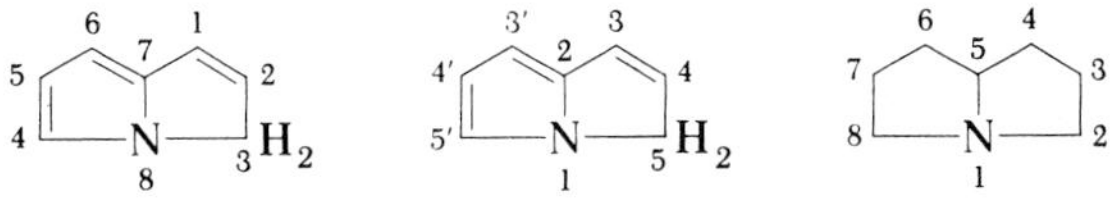

(I) (II) (III)

Interest in this nucleus derives chiefly from the presence of the perhydro system in a number of widely distributed alkaloids. However, these alkaloids have been reviewed[1-4] recently, and will not be considered in the present discussion.

It is interesting that the first examples of this ring system are the most unsaturated, and subsequent work has been directed entirely towards more saturated derivatives. The first representative (V) of this nucleus was prepared[5] by heating IV in methanol. About a

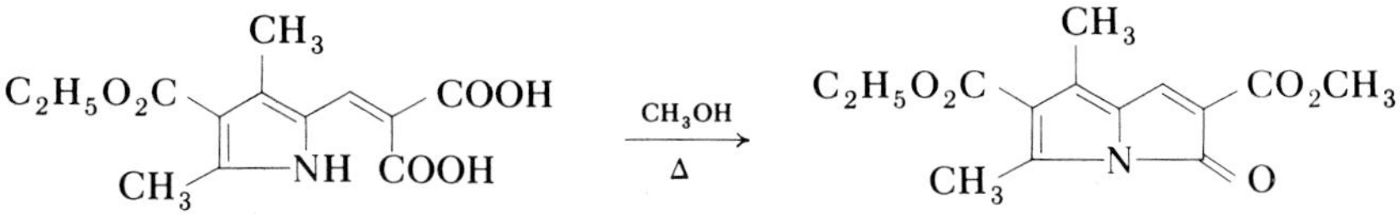

CH_3OH, Δ

(IV) (V)

decade later, Micheel and Kimpel[6] treated the related acid VI with hot acetic anhydride, and obtained a substance formulated as VII. The reaction of VII with alcoholic caustic gave products having two active hydrogens and a titratable carboxylic acid group. These were given structure VIII (R = CH_3, m. 242°; R = C_2H_5, m.

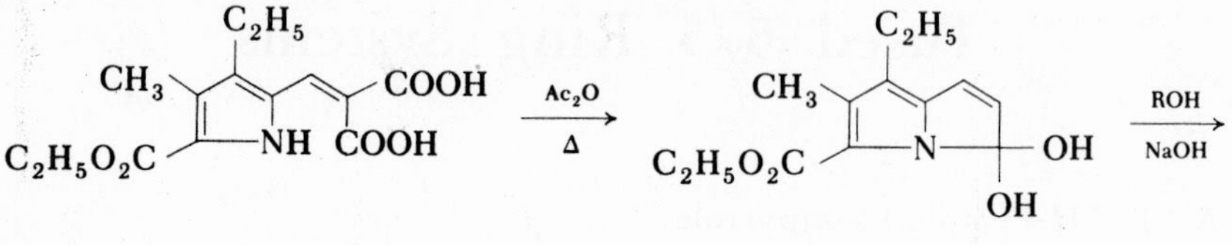

C_2H_5 CH_3 COOH $C_2H_5O_2C$ NH COOH $\xrightarrow[\Delta]{Ac_2O}$ C_2H_5 CH_3 $C_2H_5O_2C$ N OH OH $\xrightarrow[NaOH]{ROH}$

(VI) (VII)

C_2H_5 CH_3 HO_2C N OH OR

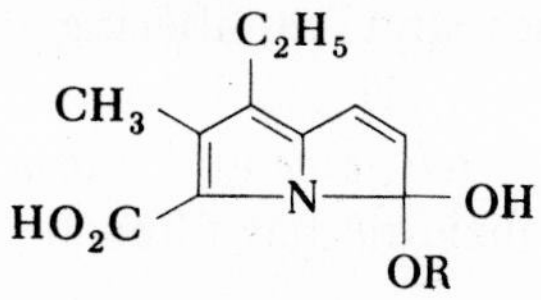

(VIII)

127.5°), but the wide difference in melting points is surprising, and both structures VII and VIII seem unlikely. It is possible that these products are merely solvated 3-oxo compounds

The only reported 1,2-dihydro-1-oxo derivative is IX, prepared[7,8] by the Hoesch reaction upon 1-cyanoethylpyrrole via the intermediate ketimine. The 1,2-dihydro-3-oxo compound XI was obtained[9] by dehydrating X.

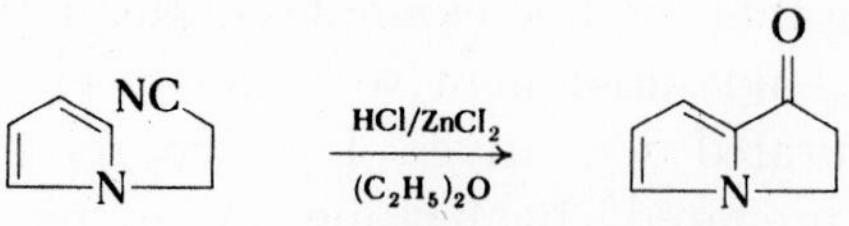

NC N $\xrightarrow[(C_2H_5)_2O]{HCl/ZnCl_2}$ O N

(IX)

$CO_2C_2H_5$ CH_3 NH COOH $\xrightarrow[\Delta]{Ac_2O}$ $CO_2C_2H_5$ CH_3 N O

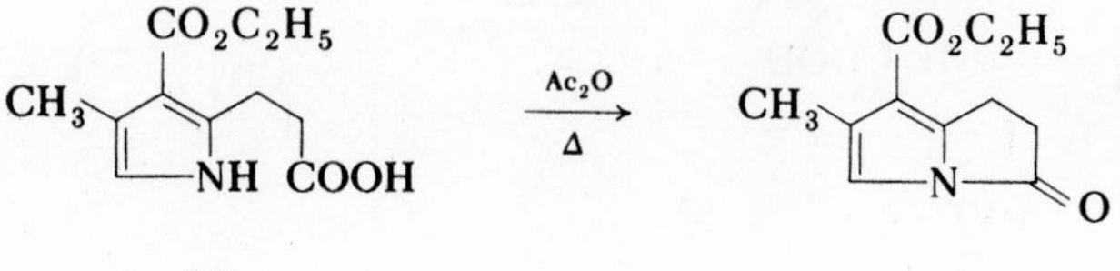

(X) (XI)

When dimethylaminomethylpyrrole was substituted for gramine in the reaction with acylaminomalonic esters, cyclization of the expected alkylation product XII occurred, giving[10-12] XIII in 70–80% yields. With malonic ester, traces of a product thought to be XIV were obtained.[10]

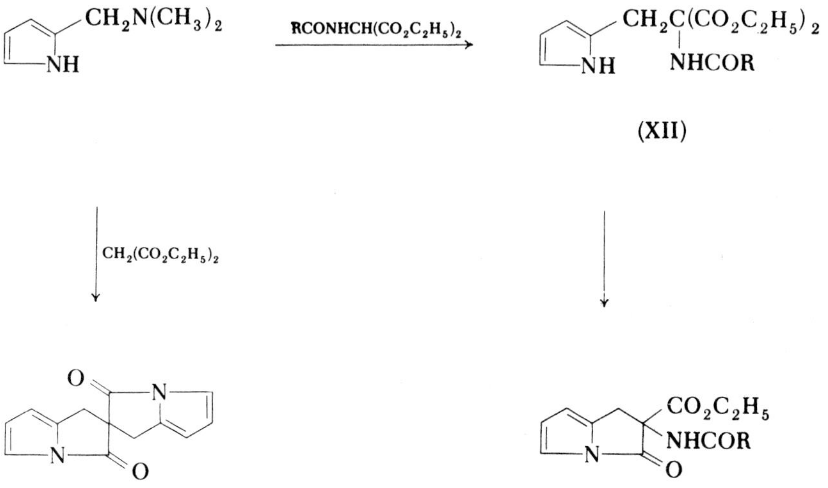

$CH_2N(CH_3)_2$ NH $\xrightarrow{RCONHCH(CO_2C_2H_5)_2}$ $CH_2C(CO_2C_2H_5)_2$ NH NHCOR

(XII)

$CH_2(CO_2C_2H_5)_2$

O N N O

(XIV)

$CO_2C_2H_5$ NHCOR N O

(XIII)

Two syntheses of 1,2-dihydro compounds have been reported. Šorm and Arnold[13] prepared the prototype XV by dehydrating 2-(3-aminopropyl)furan, and Bersch[14] reported the isolation of XVII from the Hofmann degradation of XVI.

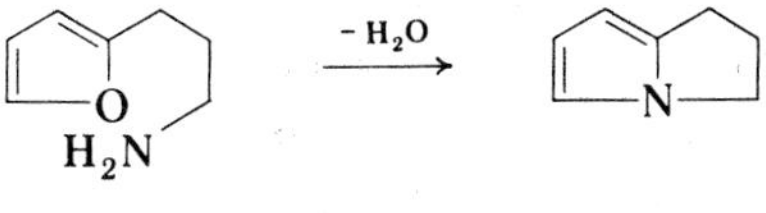

O H_2N $\xrightarrow{-H_2O}$ N

(XV)

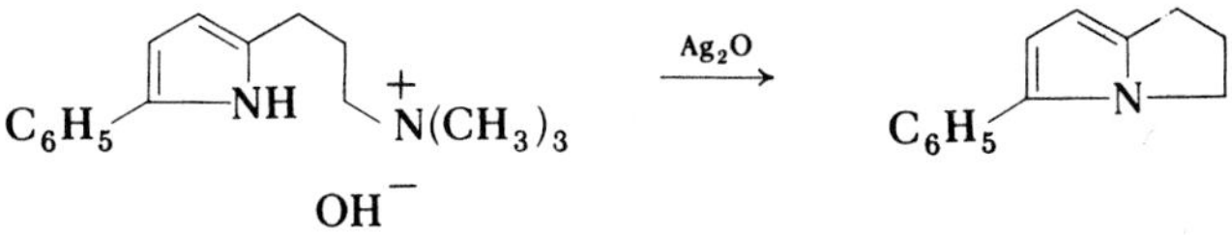

C_6H_5 NH $\overset{+}{N}(CH_3)_3$ OH^- $\xrightarrow{Ag_2O}$ C_6H_5 N

(XVI) (XVII)

Several perhydro-3,5-dioxo derivatives have been prepared by rather similar syntheses. Nitropimelic esters such as XVIII, which are readily accessible from the condensation of nitroalkanes with acrylonitrile, may be hydrogenated over platinum oxide to yield[15-17] XIX or XXI. The aminoester XIX may also be obtained[18] from the ketoester XX by the Leuckart reaction. Saponification of XX followed by hydrogenation over Raney nickel in the presence of ammonia yielded[19] XXIII, which could be dehydrated to form

R'OOC NO$_2$ COOR' (XVIII) → R'OOC NH$_2$ COOR' (XIX) ← R'OOC O COOR' (XX)

(XXI) → (XXII) ← (XXIII)

XXII, as could XIX (R' = H)[18] and XXI (R' = H).[16,17] Hydrogenation of XVIII[20] or of XXI[15] (under mild conditions) using a copper chromite catalyst may be used to prepare XXII directly.

A somewhat different synthesis was recently reported,[21] in which XXV was formed by alkylating malonic ester with XXIV.

(XXIV) $\xrightarrow{CH_2(CO_2C_2H_5)_2}$ (XXV)

Compounds of type XXII may be reduced to perhydro homologs catalytically, electrolytically[18] or by treatment with lithium aluminum hydride.[16] Treatment of XXII with alcohols (and an acid catalyst), methanolic ammonia or aqueous caustic results in scission of one of the two lactam bonds, yielding[22] pyrrolidone propionic esters, amide or acid, respectively. Benzyl magnesium bromide reacted[16] with only one carbonyl group of XXII (R = H), but several other Grignard reagents react[16] with both groups. A Reformatsky reaction upon XXII (R = H) also involved only one carbonyl group.[16] Treatment of XXII (R = H) with phosphorus pentasulfide gave the blueish green dithio homolog.

Perhydro-1-oxo compounds of structure XXVII (R or R′ = CH_3) were obtained[23,24] via the Dieckmann cyclization of XXVI. Catalytic hydrogenation of XXVII with platinum oxide gave[23] the carbinol, while the Wolff-Kishner reduction afforded[24] 1-methylpyrrolizidine. The perhydro-2-oxo derivatives XXIX (R = H or CH_3) were obtained[8,25] in a similar manner from XXVIII and underwent reductions analogous to those of XXVII. The perhydro-3-oxo compound was obtained[26] by pyrolysis of ethyl 2-pyrrolidyl-2-propionate, and hydrogenation over platinum oxide (or electrolytic reduction) produced pyrrolizidine.

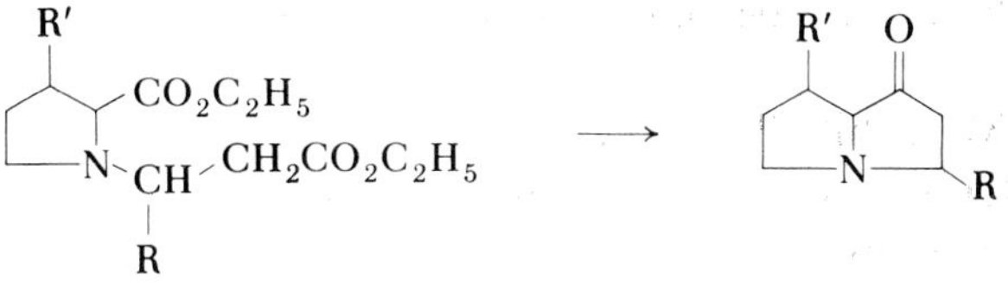

(XXVI) (XXVII)

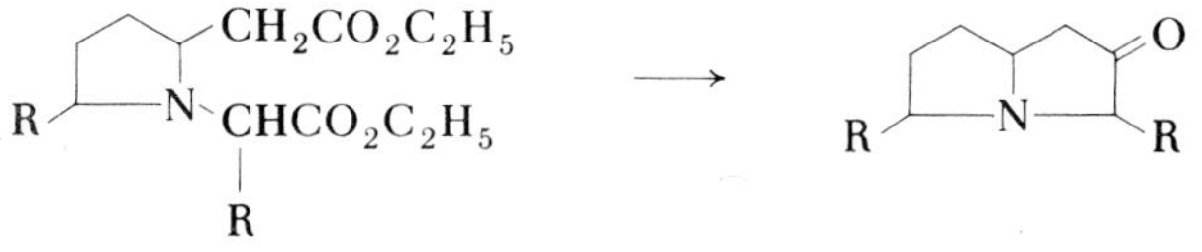

(XXVIII) (XXIX)

The synthesis of pyrrolizidines by the reductive cyclization of γ-nitropimelic esters (XVIII) has been studied in some detail by Leonard and his coworkers.[15,20,27–31] Mono-, di-, and trialkyl homologs have been prepared by this route. The high-pressure hydrogenation of compounds XXX,[32] XXXI,[33] XXXII[11] over a copper chromite catalyst has also been utilized to prepare pyrrolizidines.

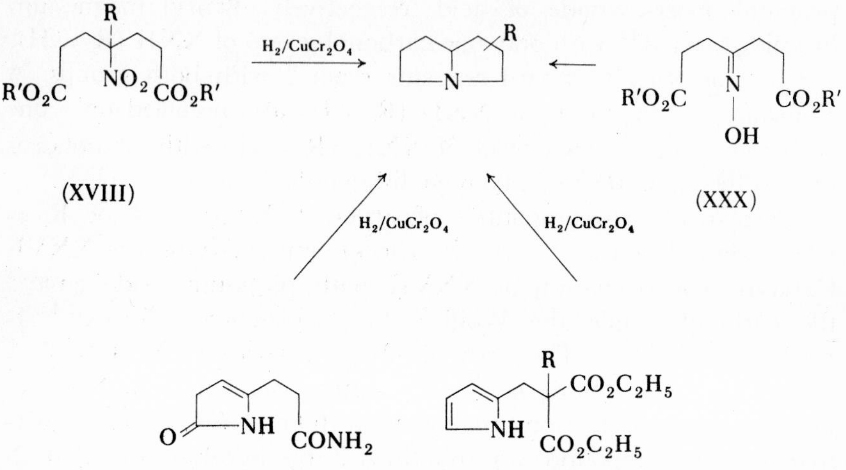

R
$H_2/CuCr_2O_4$
$R'O_2C$ NO_2 CO_2R'
(XVIII)
N R
$R'O_2C$ N OH CO_2R'
(XXX)
$H_2/CuCr_2O_4$ $H_2/CuCr_2O_4$
O NH $CONH_2$
(XXXI)
R $CO_2C_2H_5$ NH $CO_2C_2H_5$
(XXXII)

Cyclodehydrohalogenation of *N*-haloamines by the action of sulfuric acid (the Löffler-Freytag reaction) was first applied in this series by Menschikoff,[34] who thus prepared 3-methylpyrrolizidine from XXXIII, and who, incidentally, first proposed the name *pyrrolizidine*. Attempts to extend the reaction to the preparation of

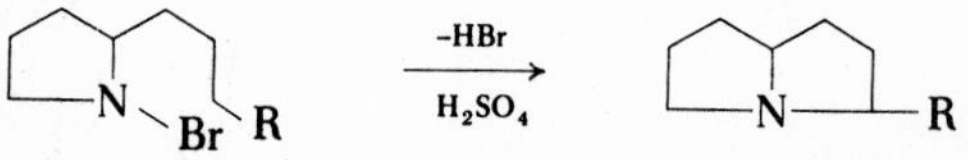

N Br R
-HBr
H_2SO_4
N R
(XXXIII)

pyrrolizidine[34] and 1-methylpyrrolizidine[35] gave only resinous materials, although recently the synthesis by this method of pyrrolizidine was reported.[36]

Pyrrolizidines have also been prepared by various double cyclization reactions. Dehydrohalogenation of amines having structures XXXIV[37,38] and XXXV[13] has been used to prepare pyrrolizidine[13,37] and its 1-methyl homolog.[38] Ammonolysis of tribromoalkanes (XXXVI) has been used by Seiwerth for the preparation of pyr-

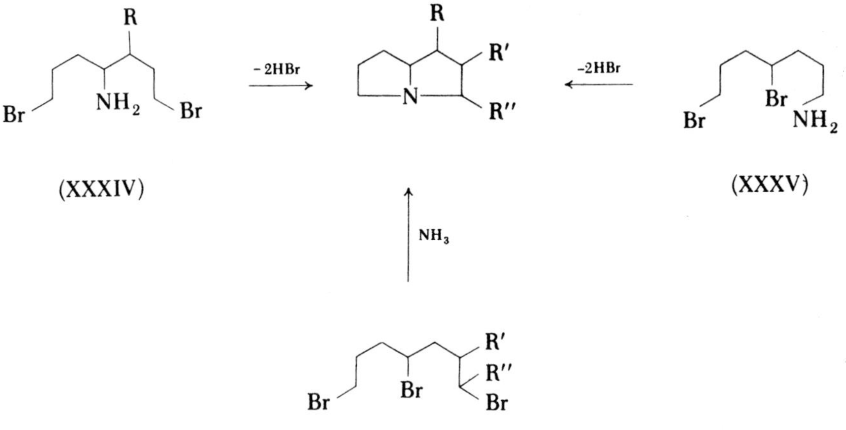

R
NH2
Br
Br
- 2HBr
R
R'
N
R''
-2HBr
Br
Br
NH2

(XXXIV)

(XXXV)

NH3

R'
R''
Br
Br
Br

(XXXVI)

rolizidine[39] and its 2-[41] and 3-methyl[40] and 3-carbomethoxy[45] homologs.

Cyclization of XXXVII yielded[17] the unusual compound (XXXVIII) *1-azoniatricyclo[3.3.3.0]undecane*, the Hofmann degradation of which gave XXXIX.

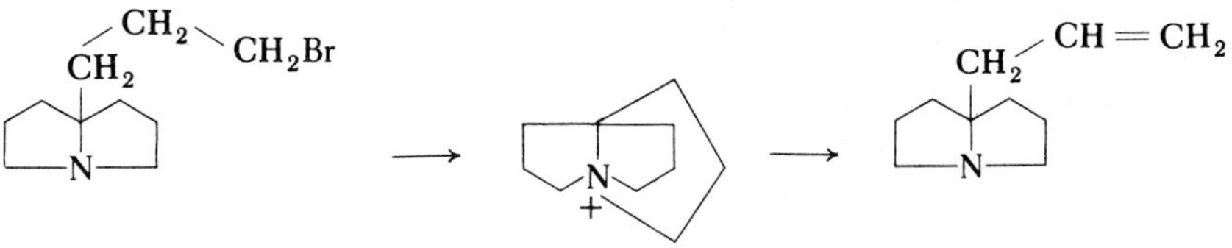

CH_2 CH_2Br
CH_2
N

N
+

$CH=CH_2$
CH_2
N

(XXXVII)

(XXXVIII)

(XXXIX)

Oxidation with chromic acid of two different epimers (*iso-retronecanol*[43] and *laburnine*[44]) of 1-hydroxymethylpyrrolizidine yielded the corresponding 1-carboxy compounds, indicating the stability of the nucleus to oxidation. However, attempts to dehydrogenate pyrrolizidine by heating it at 320° for ten hours with palladium–charcoal, gave[42] only traces of basic products.

3H-Pyrrolo[1,2-*a*]pyrroles

Empirical formula	Substituents or structure	Properties	Refs.
C_7H_7NO	1,2-Dihydro-1-oxo-	Pale yel., m. 54°. Semicarbazone, m. 211°. Piperonylidene deriv., m. 194°.	7,8
C_7H_9N	1,2-Dihydro-	b_6 58.5°.	13
$C_7H_9NO_2$	Perhydro-3,5-dioxo-	m. 181° (176°, 176–7°).	15,16,18,19
$C_7H_9NS_2$	Perhydro-3,5-dithio-	Bl.-grn., m. 167° d.	16
$C_7H_{11}NO$	Perhydro-2-oxo-	b_1 78°. Picrolonate, m. 212–3°.	8
	Perhydro-3-oxo-		26
$C_7H_{13}N$	Perhydro-	b_{740} 142–5°, b_{748} 140–3°, b. 148° (146°,143°, 135°); n_D^{20} 1.4561. Picrate, m. 258° d. (256–8°,257°,255–7°, 255–6°,253°,245°, 239–42°). Picrolonate, m. 228° (227°) d. Chloroaurate, m. 235°. Chloroplatinate, m. 205° (204–5°). Methiodide, m. > 340°.	13,15,16, 18,26,32–34,36,37, 39
$C_8H_{11}NO_2$	Perhydro-7*a*-methyl-3,5-dioxo-	b_3 160–5°; m. 160–1°.	20
$C_8H_{13}N$	$\Delta^{1,2}$- or $\Delta^{2,3}$-Perhydro-2-methyl-	Oil. Picrolonate, m. 169–70°.	8
$C_8H_{13}NO$	Perhydro-3-methyl-1-oxo-	Picrate, m. 189–90° d. Picrolonate, m. 206–7° d.	24
	Perhydro-7-methyl-1-oxo-	b_8 79–80°, b_{18} 96.5–8°; n_D^{20} 1.4770. Picrate, m. 189–90°. Methiodide, m. 149.5–50.5°. Oxime, m. 166–7°.	23
$C_8H_{13}NO_2$	1-Carboxyperhydro-	One form: m. 228–9°. Picrate, m. 220–1° d.	43
		An epimer: m. 216°.	44
$C_8H_{14}ClN$	7*a*-Chloromethylperhydro-	HCl salt, m. 210–2°. Picrate, m. 227–8°.	30

$C_8H_{15}N$	Perhydro-1-methyl-	Two racemic forms. One form: b_{749} 161–2°; n_D^{20} 1.4638. Picrate, m. 234–6° (233–4°). Picrolonate, m. 167–9° (162–3°). Styphnate, m. 196–7°. Chloroaurate, m. 200–1° d.	20,28,38
		An epimer: picrate, m. 243–4°.	20
	Perhydro-2-methyl-	Two forms? One form: b_{10} 52°, b_{20} 58–60°; n_D^{20} 1.4619 (1.4602); d_4^{20} 0.897. Picrate, m. 183–4° (183°). Picrolonate, m. 153°.	11,29,41
		An epimer (?): b_{25} 62°; pK_H 10.49. Picrate, m. 169–70°.	8,27
	Perhydro-3-methyl-	Two forms? One form: b. 158–9°. Picrate, m. 261.5° (251–2°). Picrolonate, m. 176.5°.	24,40
		An epimer (?): b. 162–3°. Picrate, m. 182–4°. Methiodide, m. 225–6°.	34
	Perhydro-7*a*-methyl-	b_{740} 152°; n_D^{20} 1.4610; pK_H 10.69. Picrate, m. 281° d. (277–80°). Picrolonate, m. 198° (197–8°).	15,27,30
$C_8H_{15}NO$	Perhydro-3-hydroxymethyl-	b_{16} 76–80°. HCl salt, subl. 100–120°/14 mm.	45
	Perhydro-7*a*-hydroxymethyl-	$b_{2.8}$ 70–1°; n_D^{20} 1.4882; d_4^{20} 1.0150. HCl salt, m. 282–3°. Picrate, m. 292–3° d.	30
	Perhydro-2-hydroxy-2-methyl-	b_1 95°. Picrolonate, m. 198°.	8
	Perhydro-1-hydroxy-7-methyl-	Picrate, m. 218.5–9.5° d. Picrolonate, m. 182.5–3.5°.	23
$C_9H_{13}NO_6$	3,5-Dicarboxyperhydro-3,5-dihydroxy-	Oil. Anhydride, oily. Amide, cryst.	16
$C_9H_{15}NO$	Perhydro-3,5-dimethyl-2-oxo-	b_1 65°. Picrate, m. 186°. Picrolonate, m. 217°.	25
$C_9H_{15}NO_2$	3-Carbomethoxyperhydro-	b_{14} 111–2°. HCl salt, m. 120–5°.	45

(*continued*)

3H-Pyrrolo[1,2-*a*]pyrroles (*continued*)

Empirical formula	Substituents or structure	Properties	Refs.
$C_9H_{16}NO_2$	Perhydro-3,5-dihydroxy-3,5-dimethyl-	m. 94°.	16
$C_9H_{17}N$	7*a*-Ethylperhydro-	b_{740} 170–2°; n_D^{20} 1.4670; pK_H 10.67. Picrate, m. 238° d. Picrolonate, m. 222° d.	15,27
	Perhydro-2,6-dimethyl-	b_{44} 83–5°; n_D^{20} 1.4559; d_4^{20} 0.868. Picrate, m. 124.6–5.0°. Picrolonate, m. 167–8°.	29
	Perhydro-2,7*a*-dimethyl-	b_{42} 76–7°; n_D^{20} 1.4542; d_4^{20} 0.878. Picrate, m. 193–4.5°. Picrolonate, m. 155–6°.	29
	Perhydro-3,5-dimethyl-	b_1 25°. Picrate, m. 249°. Picrolonate, brn., m. 180°.	25
$C_9H_{17}NO$	Perhydro-2-hydroxymethyl-2-methyl-	$b_{0.5}$ 78–9°; n_D^{20} 1.4818; d_4^{20} 1.000.	11
	Perhydro-2-hydroxy-3,5-dimethyl-	b_1 68–70°. Picrolonate, m. 205°.	25
$C_{10}H_{13}NO_4$	2-Carbethoxyperhydro-3,5-dioxo-	m. 88°; $[\alpha]_D$ + 54° (EtOH).	21
$C_{10}H_{17}N$	7*a*-Allylperhydro-	b_{12} 72°, b. 191–3°; n_D^{20} 1.4802; d_4^{20} 0.9322. Picrate, m. 163°.	17
$C_{10}H_{18}N$	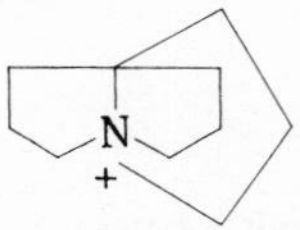 N^+	Bromide, m. > 350°. Picrate, m. 318° d.	17
$C_{10}H_{18}BrN$	7*a*-(3-Bromopropyl)-perhydro-	HBr salt, m. 123°.	17
$C_{10}H_{19}N$	Perhydro-1-propyl-	b_{30} 94–5°; n_D^{20} 1.4639; d_4^{20} 0.895. Picrate, m. 143–5°. Picrolonate, m. 164–6°.	31

Formula	Name	Properties	Ref.
	Perhydro-7*a*-propyl-	b_{745} 192°, b. 190°; n_D^{20} 1.4632 (1.4646); d_4^{20} 0.8918; pK_H 10.61. Picrate, m. 156–7° (155–6°).	17,27
	Perhydro-7*a*-*i*-propyl-	b_{745} 191°; n_D^{20} 1.4692; d_4^{20} 0.8899; pK_H 10.70. Picrate, m. 228–9° d.	27
	7*a*-Ethylperhydro-2-methyl-	b_{38} 90–3°; n_D^{20} 1.4612; d_4^{20} 0.887. Picrate, m. 154.5–5.5°. Picrolonate, m. 171.5–2.0°.	29
	Perhydro-2,6,7*a*-trimethyl-	b_{40} 86–8°; n_D^{20} 1.4502; d_4^{20} 0.867. Picrate, m. 165.5–7.0°. Picrolonate, m. 177–8°.	29
$C_{10}H_{19}NO$	Perhydro-7*a*-(3-hydroxypropyl)-	b_{12} 132–3°; n_D^{20} 1.4965; d_4^{20} 1.0354. Picrate, m. 146–7°.	17
$C_{11}H_{12}NO_3$	7-Carbethoxy-1,2-dihydro-6-methyl-3-oxo-	m. 110°.	9
$C_{11}H_{15}NO_3$	O, N, $CHCO_2C_2H_5$	m. 84°.	16
$C_{11}H_{17}NO_4$	O, N, $CH_2CO_2C_2H_5$, OH	m. 52°.	16
$C_{11}H_{20}NO_2$	3,5-Diethylperhydro-3,5-dihydroxy-	m. 124°.	16
$C_{11}H_{21}N$	7*a*-Ethylperhydro-2,6-dimethyl-	b_{43} 106–8°; n_D^{20} 1.4579; d_4^{20} 0.877. Picrate, m. 136–7°. Picrolonate, m. 184.0–5.5°.	29
$C_{12}H_{14}N_2O_4$	2-Acetamido-2-carbethoxy-1,2-dihydro-3-oxo-	m. 151°.	10
$C_{12}H_{15}NO_4$	5-Carboxy-7-ethyl-3-hydroxy-3-methoxy-6-methyl-	m. 242°	6

(continued)

3*H*-Pyrrolo[1,2-*a*]pyrroles (*continued*)

Empirical formula	Substituents or structure	Properties	Refs.
$C_{12}H_{17}NO_4$	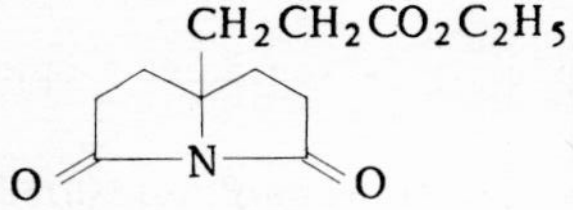 $CH_2CH_2CO_2C_2H_5$; O, N, O	$b_{0.9}$ 220–4°; m. 103°.	17
$C_{13}H_{10}N_2O_2$	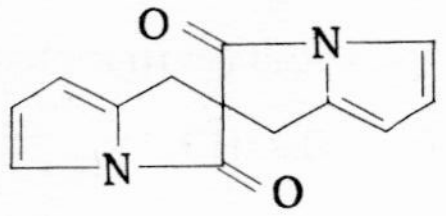 O, N, N, O	m. 157°.	10
$C_{13}H_{13}N$	1,2-Dihydro-5-phenyl-		14
$C_{13}H_{17}NO_4$	5-Carbethoxy-7-ethyl-3,3-dihydroxy-6-methyl-	Yel., m. 234–5°.	6
	5-Carboxy-3-ethoxy-7-ethyl-3-hydroxy-6-methyl-	m. 127.5°.	6
$C_{13}H_{19}NO_5$	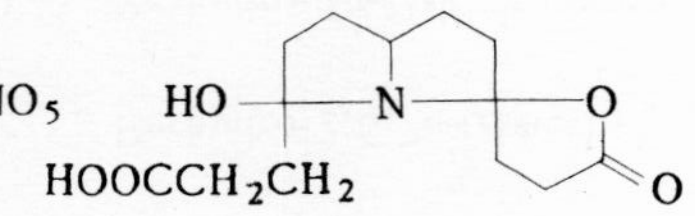 HO, N, O; $HOOCCH_2CH_2$; O	Oil. Methyl ester, oily.	16
$C_{14}H_{17}NO_2$	3-Benzylperhydro-3-hydroxy-5-oxo-	m. 133°.	16

$C_{15}H_{15}NO_5$	6-Carbethoxy-2-carbomethoxy-5,7-dimethyl-3-oxo-	Yel.-grn., darkens > 260°; no m.p.	5
$C_{15}H_{25}NO_2$	HO / N / OH; $CH_2=CHCH_2CH_2$ / $CH_2CH_2CH=CH_2$	Oil.	16
$C_{16}H_{22}N$	N^+; CH—CH=CH_2 / CH_2—CH=CH_2 / CH—CH=CH_2	Bromide, m. 131°.	16
$C_{17}H_{16}N_2O_4$	2-Benzamido-2-carbethoxy-1,2-dihydro-3-oxo-	m. 136–7°.	11
$C_{18}H_{18}N_2O_4$	2-Carbethoxy-1,2-dihydro-3-oxo-2-phenylacetamido-	m. 125°.	12
$C_{19}H_{21}NO_2$	Perhydro-3,5-dihydroxy-3,5-diphenyl-	m. 182°.	16
$C_{23}H_{21}NO_2$	Perhydro-3,5-dihydroxy-3,5-bis(phenylethinyl)-	m. 172.5°.	16

References

1. Leonard, "Senescio Alkaloids" in Manske and Holmes, *The Alkaloids*, Academic Press, New York, 1950, Vol. I.
2. Henry, *The Plant Alkaloids*, 4th ed., The Blakiston Co., Philadelphia, 1949, p. 601.
3. Warren, "Pyrrolizidine Alkaloids" in *Fortschritte der Chemie organischer Naturstoffe*, Springer, Wien, 1955, Vol. XII, p. 198.
4. Adams, *Angew. Chem.*, **69**, 5 (1957).
5. Küster, Brudi, and Koppenhöfer, *Ber.*, **58**, 1014 (1925).
6. Micheel and Kimpel, *Ber.*, **69**, 1990 (1936).
7. Clemo and Ramage, *J. Chem. Soc.*, **1931**, 49.
8. Clemo and Melrose, *J. Chem. Soc.*, **1942**, 424.
9. Fischer and Neber, *Ann.*, **496**, 1 (1932).
10. Herz, Dittmer, and Cristol, *J. Am. Chem. Soc.*, **70**, 504 (1948).
11. Leonard and Burk, *J. Am. Chem. Soc.*, **72**, 2543 (1950).
12. Kutscher and Klamerth, *Chem. Ber.*, **86**, 352 (1953).
13. Šorm and Arnold, *Collection Czechoslov. Chem. Communs.*, **12**, 467 (1947).
14. Bersch, *Angew. Chem.*, **69**, 237 (1957).
15. Leonard, Hruda, and Long, *J. Am. Chem. Soc.*, **69**, 690 (1947).
16. Micheel and Albers, *Ann.*, **581**, 225 (1953).
17. Šorm and Beránek, *Collection Czechoslov. Chem. Communs.*, **19**, 298 (1954); *Chem. listy*, **47**, 1359 (1953); *Chem. Abstracts*, **49**, 292 (1955).
18. Lukeš and Šorm, *Collection Czechoslov. Chem. Communs.*, **12**, 278 (1947).
19. Micheel and Flitsch, *Chem. Ber.*, **88**, 509 (1955).
20. Leonard and Felley, *J. Am. Chem. Soc.*, **72**, 2537 (1950).
21. Hardegger and Ott, *Helv. Chim. Acta*, **38**, 312 (1955).
22. Micheel and Flitsch, *Chem. Ber.*, **89**, 129 (1956).
23. Adams and Leonard, *J. Am. Chem. Soc.*, **66**, 257 (1944).
24. Leonard, Fischer, Barthel, Figueras, and Wildman, *J. Am. Chem. Soc.*, **73**, 2371 (1951).
25. Clemo and Metcalfe, *J. Chem. Soc.*, **1936**, 606.
26. Galinovsky and Reichard, *Ber.*, **77**, 138 (1944).
27. Leonard and Beck, *J. Am. Chem. Soc.*, **70**, 2504 (1948).
28. Leonard and Felley, *J. Am. Chem. Soc.*, **71**, 1758 (1949).
29. Leonard and Schoemaker, *J. Am. Chem. Soc.*, **71**, 1760 (1949).
30. Leonard and Schoemaker, *J. Am. Chem. Soc.*, **71**, 1762 (1949).
31. Leonard, Felley, and Nicolaides, *J. Am. Chem. Soc.*, **74**, 1700 (1952).
32. Leonard and Goode, *J. Am. Chem. Soc.*, **72**, 5404 (1950).
33. Tsuda and Saeki, *J. Org. Chem.*, **23**, 91 (1958).
34. Menschikoff, *Ber.*, **69**, 1802 (1936).
35. Menschikoff, *Bull. acad. sci. U.R.S.S.*, 1035 (1937); *Chem. Zentr.*, **I**, 2780 (1939).
36. Šorm and Brandejs, *Collection Czechoslov. Chem. Communs.*, **12**, 444 (1947); *Chem. Obzor.*, **18**, 102 (1943).
37. Prelog and Heimbach, *Ber.*, **72**, 1101 (1939).
38. Prelog and Zalan, *Helv. Chim. Acta*, **27**, 531 (1944).

39. Seiwerth, *Arhiv Kem.*, **23,** 77 (1951); *Chem. Abstracts*, **46,** 10183 (1952).
40. Oreščanin-Majhofer and Seiwerth, *Monatsh.*, **83,** 1298 (1952); *Chem. Abstracts*, **48,** 668 (1954).
41. Oreščanin-Majhofer and Seiwerth, *Arhiv Kem.*, **25,** 131 (1953); *Chem. Abstracts*, **49,** 2415 (1955).
42. Prelog and Balenović, *Ber.*, **74,** 1508 (1941).
43. Adams and Hamlin, *J. Am. Chem. Soc.*, **64,** 2597 (1942).
44. Galinovsky and Vogl, *125th National Meeting, American Chemical Society*, Kansas City, Mo., March 23–April 1, 1954; Abstracts, p. 32N.
45. Seiwerth and Djokić, *Croat. Chem. Acta*, **29,** 403 (1957).

A-65. Furo[2,3,4-*gh*]pyrrolizine

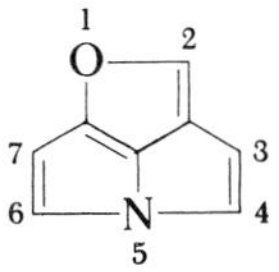

Derivatives of some of the *Senecio* alkaloids are known to contain this nucleus.[1-3]

References

1. Leonard and Felley, *J. Am. Chem. Soc.*, **72,** 2537 (1950).
2. Adams and Van Duuren, *J. Am. Chem. Soc.*, **76,** 6379 (1954).
3. Dry, Koekemoer, and Warren, *J. Chem. Soc.*, **1955,** 59.

A-66. 3*H*-Imidazo[2,1,5-*cd*]pyrrolizine*

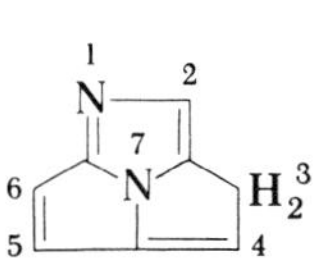

Treatment of the sulfate of the alkaloid *chaksine* with acetic anhydride yielded a product, which was assigned[1] structure I. Further evidence for the structure would be welcome.

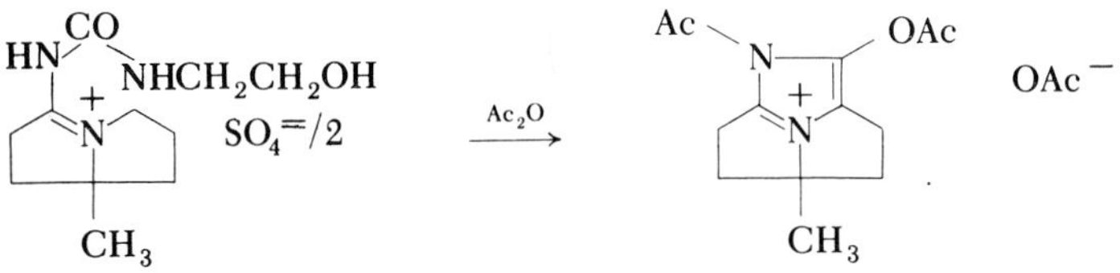

(I)

Reference

1. Guha and Ray, *J. Indian Chem. Soc.*, **33**, 225 (1956); *Chem. Abstracts*, **51**, 1211 (1957).

A-67. *5H*-Pyrrolo[2,1-*a*]isoindole.
R.I. 1404

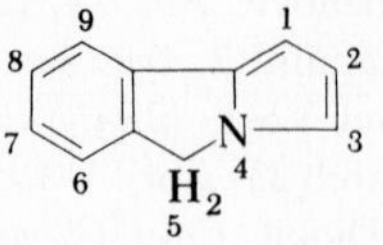

While preparing II by the condensation of I with malonic ester, Gabriel[1] obtained a by-product which he identified as III, and named as a derivative of *o-benzoylenedimethylpyrrolone*. A number of related compounds were described by Pfaehler.[2] The cyano analog of III, compound IV, was similarly obtained[3] from I and cyanoacetic

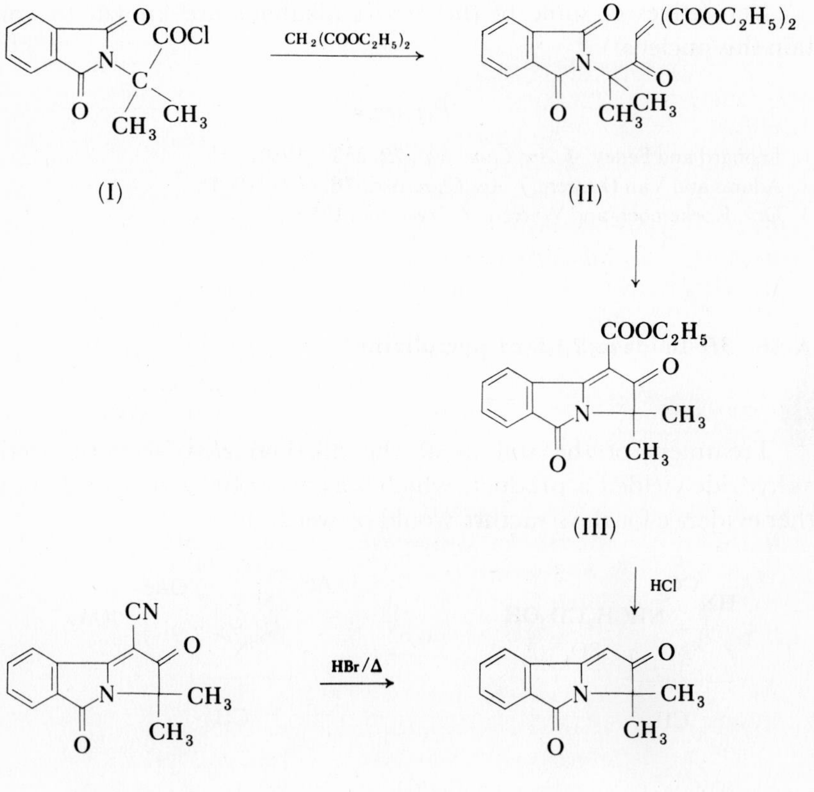

$CH_2(COOC_2H_5)_2$

(I) (II)

(III)

HCl

HBr/Δ

(IV) (V)

ester. Both III and IV were converted into V by heating with aqueous acid, and reduction of V with phosphorus and hydriodic acid gave the 1,9*b*-dihydro analog of V. Treatment of V with nitric acid gave a mononitro derivative, thought[1] to be VIa (R = NO_2). The

(VIa) R = NO_2
(VIb) R = NH_2

Derivatives of

Empirical formula	Substituents	Properties	Refs.
$C_{13}H_{10}N_2O_4$	3,3-Dimethyl-1-nitro-	Yel., m. 264–5°.	1
$C_{13}H_{11}NO_2$	3,3-Dimethyl-	m.125–6°.	1,3
$C_{13}H_{12}N_2O_2$	1-Amino-3,3-dimethyl-	Or.-red, m. 212°.	1
$C_{13}H_{12}N_2O_4$	1,9*b*-Dihydro-3,3-dimethyl-*x*-nitro-	m. 172–3°.	1
$C_{13}H_{13}NO_2$	1,9*b*-Dihydro-3,3-diemthyl-	m. 172–3°. Oxime, m. 220.0–1.5°. Phenylhydrazone, yel.; m. 215.0–7.5°.	1
$C_{14}H_{10}N_2O_2$	1-Cyano-3,3-dimethyl-	Yel., m. 273°.	3
$C_{14}H_{12}N_2O_3$	1-Carboxamido-3,3-dimethyl-	Yel., m. 217°	3
$C_{14}H_{13}NO_2$	3-Ethyl-3-methyl-	m. 94–5°.	2
$C_{15}H_{15}NO_2$	3,3-Diethyl-	m. 71°.	2
$C_{16}H_{15}NO_4$	1-Carbomethoxy-3-ethyl-3-3-methyl-	Yel., m. 130–1°.	2
	1-Carbethoxy-3,3-diemthyl-	m. 176–7°.	1
$C_{17}H_{17}NO_4$	1-Carbethoxy-3-ethyl-3-methyl-	m. 112°.	2
	1-Carbomethoxy-3,3-diethyl-	Yel., m. 109–10°.	2
$C_{18}H_{19}NO_4$	1-Carbethoxy-3,3-diethyl-	Yel., m. 85.0–5.5°.	2

basis for this structure was the observation that the reduction of VIa gave, in addition to the corresponding amine VIb (R = NH_2), also the 1,9*b*-dihydro derivative of V, evidently formed by the reductive cleavage of the nitro (or amino) group from VI. Nitration of this dihydro analog of V gave a mononitrodihydro compound presumably having the nitro group in the phenyl ring. The lactam ring of V is cleaved by alkali to a substituted pyrrolylbenzoic acid, which reverts to V on thermal dehydration.

References

1. Gabriel, *Ber.*, **44,** 70 (1911).
2. Pfaehler, *Ber.*, **46,** 1702 (1913).
3. Gabriel, *Ber.*, **46,** 1319 (1913).

A-68. *3H*-Pyrrolo[1,2-*a*]indole. R.I. 1399

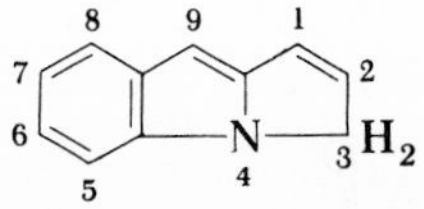

The *1H* analog of this nucleus has *R.I.* 1398. This ring system has been called *4,3-pyrroloindole*, while the name *propenylene-2.1-indole* and the numbering shown in I were assigned to it by Scholtz.[1]

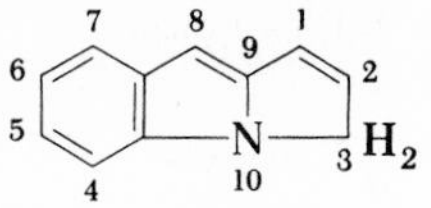

(I)

Anthranilic acid reacts with phenacyl bromide to produce II, which, when heated with acetic anhydride, gives a product (m. 288°) thought[1] to have structure III. Treatment of III with bromine yields a yellow dibromide (m. 265°), while alcoholic potassium hydroxide cleaves the lactam ring of III to form IV.

Treatment[2] of 1-phenylpyrrole (V) with one equivalent of butyllithium, followed by carbonation and hydrolysis gives chiefly VI. However, if two or three equivalents of butyllithium are used, the

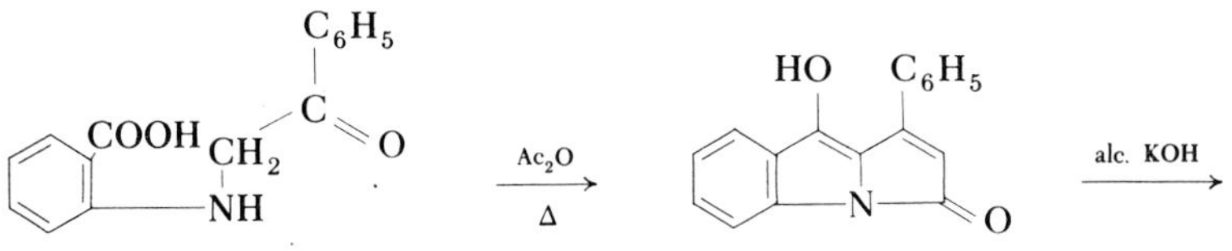

(II) $\xrightarrow[\Delta]{Ac_2O}$ (III) $\xrightarrow{\text{alc. KOH}}$

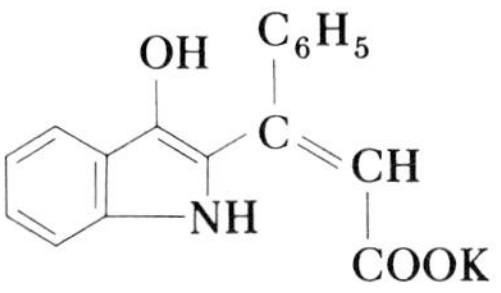

(IV)

major product is the ketone VII (bright yellow, m. 121–2°; oxime, m. 192–3°). 1-Phenylindole behaves similarly (see Section A-76).

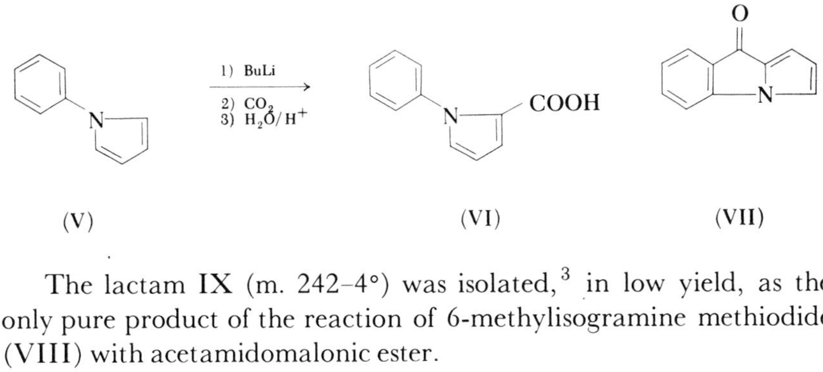

(V) $\xrightarrow[\text{2) } CO_2 \text{ 3) } H_2O/H^+]{\text{1) BuLi}}$ (VI) (VII)

The lactam IX (m. 242–4°) was isolated,[3] in low yield, as the only pure product of the reaction of 6-methylisogramine methiodide (VIII) with acetamidomalonic ester.

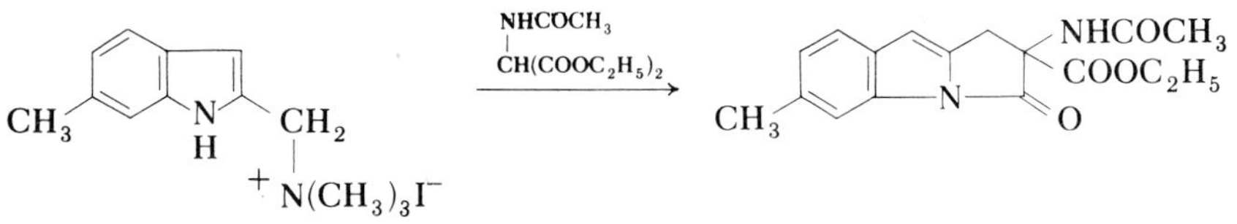

(VIII) $\xrightarrow{NHCOCH_3-CH(COOC_2H_5)_2}$ (IX)

References

1. Scholtz, *Ber.*, **51,** 1645 (1918).
2. Shirley, Gross and Roussel, *J. Org. Chem.*, **20,** 225 (1955).
3. Snyder and Cook, *J. Am. Chem. Soc.*, **78,** 969 (1956).

A-69. Pyrrolo[*cd*]indolizine*

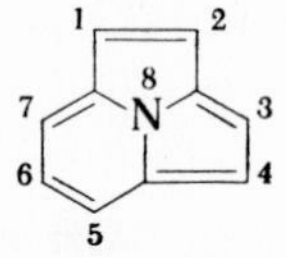

The trivial name *cycl[3.2.2]azine* was proposed for this ring system.

The prototype II (R = R′ = H, yellow, m. 65–6°) and two homologs II (R = H, R′ = C_6H_5, yellow, m. 98–9°) and II (R = R′ = C_6H_5, yellow, m. 143.5–4°) of this unique ring system were recently prepared[1] by heating pyrrocolines of structure I (see Section A-183) in acetic acid.

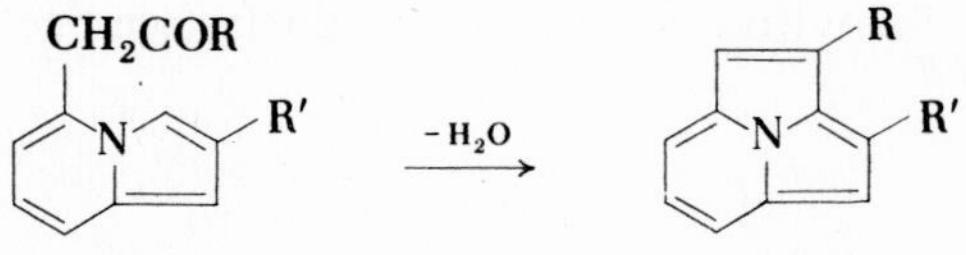

CH_2COR R′ $-H_2O$ → R R′

(I) (II)

Unlike the pyrrocolines, products of structure II are nonbasic and stable to heat, light and air.

Reference

1. Boekelheide and Windgassen, *J. Am. Chem. Soc.*, **80,** 2020 (1958).

A-70. Pyrido[3,4,5-*gh*]pyrrolizine*

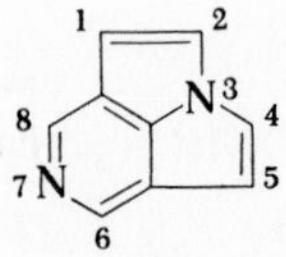

High-pressure hydrogenation of I over a copper chromite catalyst afforded[1] a 40% yield of II (oil, b_4 70–2°; monohydrate, m. 160°; sulfamate salt, m. 127°). See Sections A-64, A-183, A-198, A-721, and A-733.

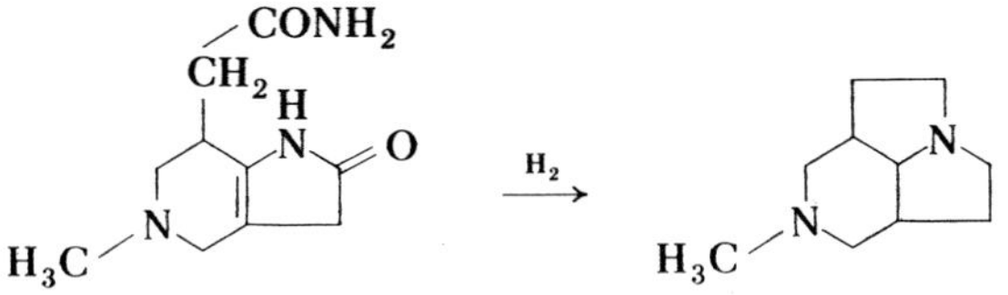

$CONH_2$ CH_2 H N O H_3C N $\xrightarrow{H_2}$ N H_3C N

(I) (II)

Reference

1. Tsuda and Saeki, *J. Org. Chem.*, **23,** 91 (1958).

A-71. 1*H*-*p*-Oxazino[3,4,5-*cd*]pyrrolizine

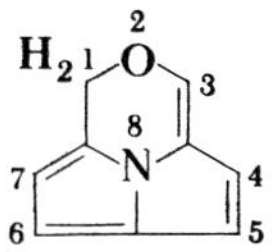

H_2 1 O 2 3 8 N 7 4 6 5

See Section A-64.

A-72. 2*H*-[1,3,5]-Oxadiazino[2,3,4-*cd*]-pyrrolizine*

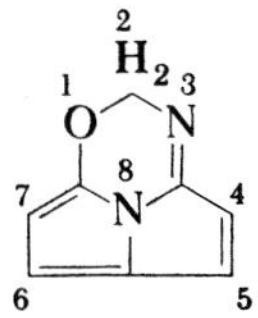

2 H_2 1 3 O N 8 N 7 4 6 5

Treatment of the chloride of the alkaloid *chaksine* with nitrous acid yielded, *inter alia*, a product thought to have structure I. Additional support for this structure would be welcome.

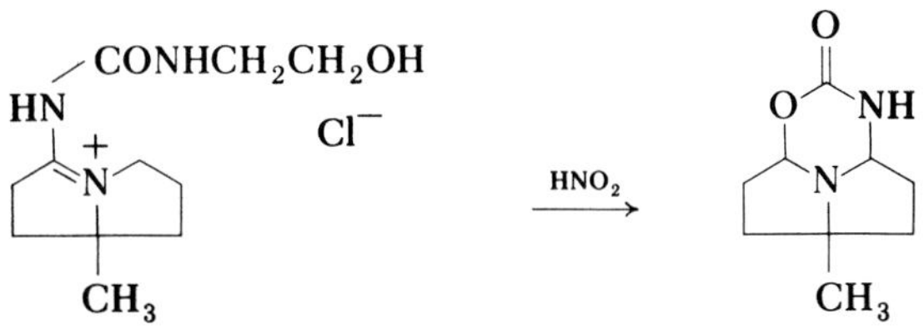

$CONHCH_2CH_2OH$ HN Cl^- + N CH_3 $\xrightarrow{HNO_2}$ O O NH N CH_3

(I)

Reference

1. Guha and Ray, *J. Indian Chem. Soc.*, **33,** 225 (1956); *Chem. Abstracts,* **51,** 1211 (1957).

A-73. *s*-Triazino[*cd*]pyrrolizine*

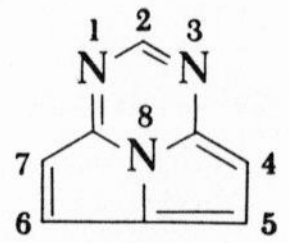

Treatment of the nitrate of the alkaloid *chaksine* with sulfuric acid followed by sodium bicarbonate yielded a product assigned[1] structure I. Further evidence to support this structure would seem needed.

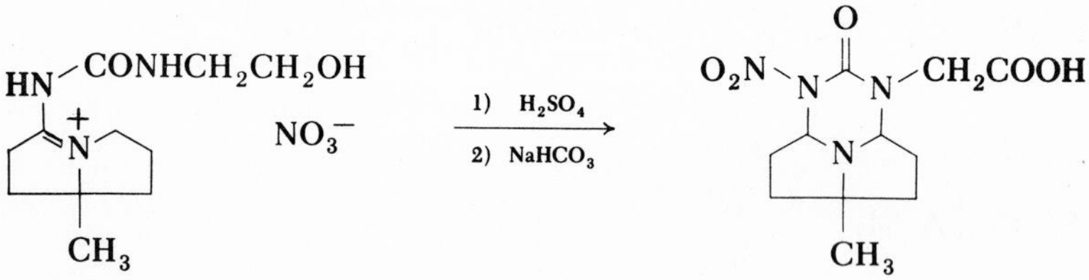

1) H_2SO_4
2) $NaHCO_3$

(I)

Reference

1. Guha and Ray, *J. Indian Chem. Soc.*, **33,** 225 (1956); *Chem. Abstracts,* **51,** 1211 (1957).

A-74. 6*H*-Indolo[2,1-*a*]isoindole

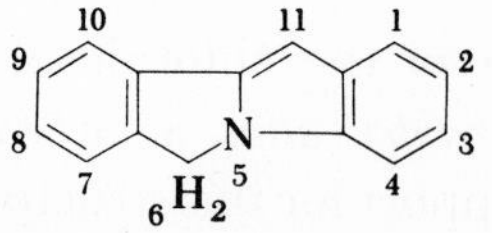

When Höchst Yellow R (I, see Section A-210) was heated for six hours at 140–50° with 15% aqueous potassium hydroxide solution, among the products formed was a yellow compound (m. 218°; benzoyl derivative, yellow, m. 228°), thought[1] to have structure II (R = OH). Alkaline fusion of this material yielded indigo, and anthranilic and benzoic acids. Treatment of I with methanolic ammonia yielded,[5] *inter alia*, a yellow substance (m. 216°) assigned structure II (R = H).

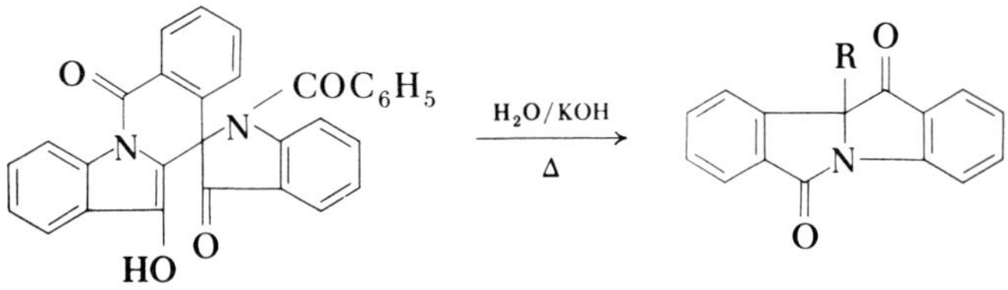

(I) (II)

The condensation of phthalide with nitrobenzaldehydes yielded[2] III, which isomerized to IV by the action of sodium methoxide. Reduction of III, accompanied by simultaneous dehydration, gave V (Va, R = H, HCl salt, m. 261–2°; Vb, R = NH_2, HCl salt, m. 287–9°). An alternative route to V involved heating the phthalimides VI with dimethylaniline to form VII (R = H, yellow, m. 232°; R = NO_2, pale yellow, m. 241–3°) followed by reduction of the nitro groups. The name *o-benzoylene-1,2-indole* has been applied[2] to the nucleus of V and VII.

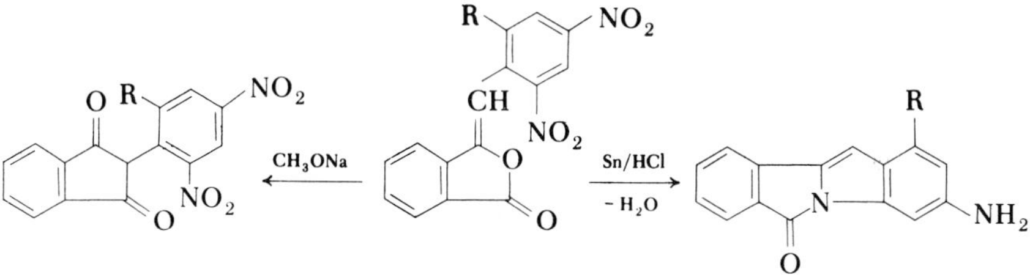

(IV) (III) (V)

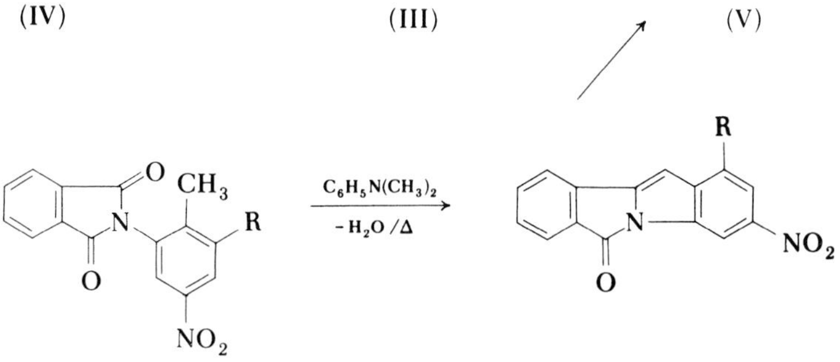

(VI) (VII)

The oxidation of VIII in ethanol and potassium acetate with chloranil, followed by methylation of the hydroxyl groups yielded[3] a product (m. 202–3°; λ_{max} 330 and 347.4 mμ with log ϵ = 4.48 and 4.47) thought to be IX.

OH NH OH

1) chloranil / C_2H_5OH / KOAc
2) $(CH_3)_2SO_4$ / KOH

OCH_3 N OCH_3

(VIII) (IX)

The ring system X (*5H-1,3-dioxolo[f]indolo[2,1-a]isoindole*) may appropriately be considered here. The Pschorr cyclization of XI yielded[4] XII (yellow, m. 214–6°; λ_{max} 248, 274, 301, 314, 352, 365 mμ (ϵ = 22,500, 30,000, 26,000, 28,000, 6,000, 6,000); lactam carbonyl absorption at 1712 cm.$^{-1}$).

10 11 12 1 O 2 9 8 N O 3 7 6 H_2 4 5

(X)

H_2N N O O O

Pschorr

N O O O

(XI) (XII)

References

1. de Diesbach, Heppner and Siegwart, *Helv. Chim. Acta*, **31,** 724 (1948).
2. Poraĭ-Koshits and Chizhevskaya, *J. Gen. Chem. (U.S.S.R.)*, **26,** 842 (1956); *Chem. Abstracts*, **50,** 14720 (1956).
3. Sugasawa and Kanaoka, *Pharm. Bull. (Japan)*, **3,** 266 (1955); *Chem. Abstracts*, **50,** 12016 (1956).
4. Humber *et al.*, *J. Chem. Soc.*, **1954,** 4622.
5. de Diesbach and Frossard, *Helv. Chim. Acta*, **37,** 701 (1954).

A-75. 5*H*-1,3-Dioxolo[*f*]indolo[2,1-*a*]-isoindole

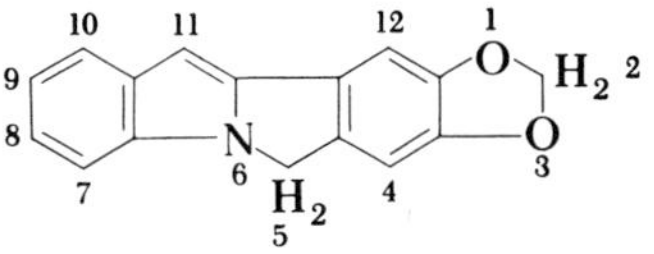

See 6*H*-indolo[2,1-*a*]isoindole (Section A-74).

A-76. 10*H*-Indolo[1,2-*a*]indole

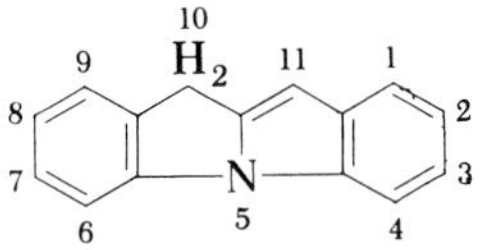

Shirley and Roussel[1] found that metallation of 1-phenylindole with butyl lithium followed by treatment with carbon dioxide gave, surprisingly, a 42% yield of I (orange-yellow, m. 169.0–70.5°; oxime, m. 235.5–7.5°d.) and 15% of II. Similar reactions occur with 1-phenylpyrrole (see Section A-68).

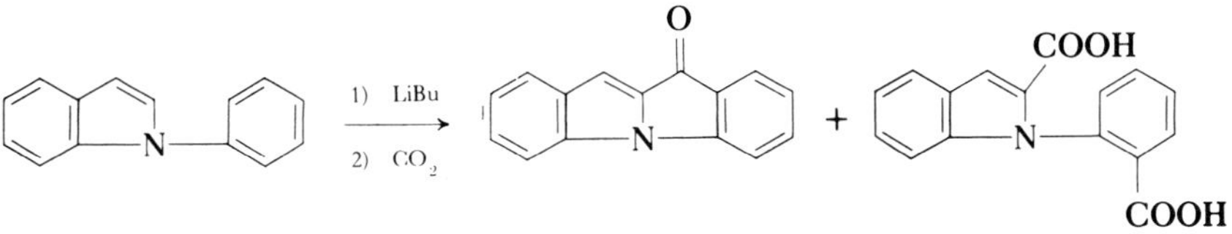

1) LiBu
2) CO_2

(I) (II)

Reference

1. Shirley and Roussel, *J. Am. Chem. Soc.*, **75**, 375 (1953).

A-77. 3*H*-Indolo[2,1,7-*cde*]pyrrocoline. R.I. 2285

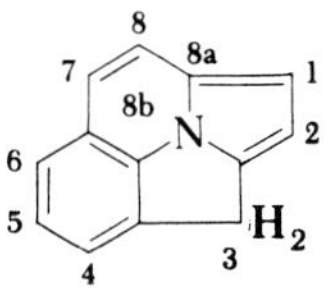

This nucleus was given the above name and number by the *Ring Index*; however, the formula shown there has been transposed inadvertently with that of *benzofuro[3,2-b]indole* (*R.I.* 2289).

The reaction of quinaldine with acetylene dicarboxylic ester was found by Diels and Alder[1] to yield a labile, yellow adduct ($C_{22}H_{21}NO_8$, m. 174–5°) and a stable, red adduct ($C_{22}H_{21}NO_8$, m. 204° d.). A third reaction product (see Section A-761) was subsequently[2] isolated from the mother liquors of this reaction. The labile, yellow adduct was transformed by heat into the stable, red adduct, which had not the expected structure I (see Section A-729), but was thought to have structure II.

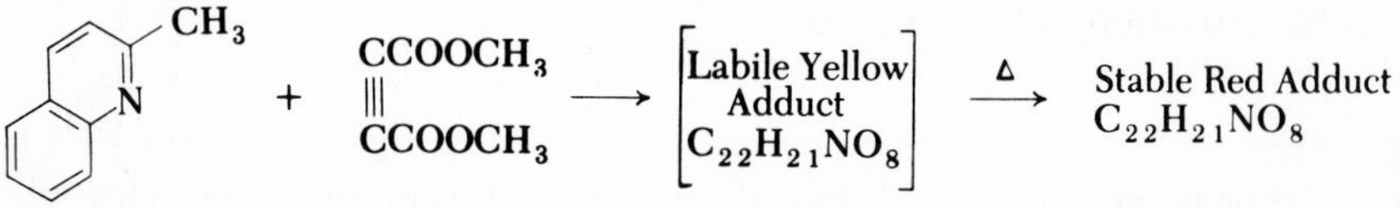

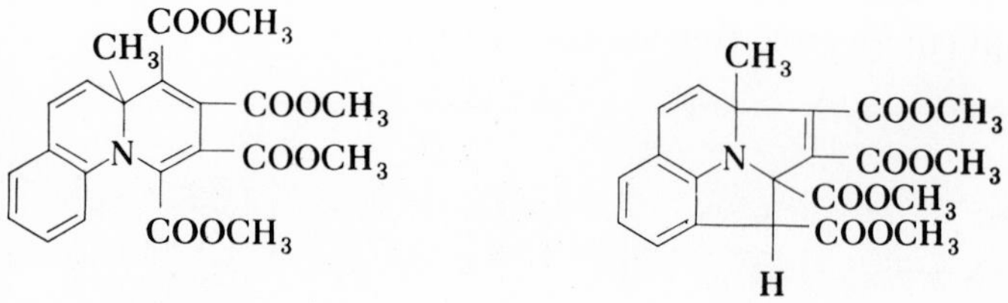

Quinaldine (CH_3, N) + $CCOOCH_3 \equiv CCOOCH_3$ ⟶ [Labile Yellow Adduct $C_{22}H_{21}NO_8$] $\xrightarrow{\Delta}$ Stable Red Adduct $C_{22}H_{21}NO_8$

(I) — structure with CH_3, N, and four $COOCH_3$ groups

(II) — structure with CH_3, N, H, and four $COOCH_3$ groups

Treatment of II with bromine gave a yellow tetrabromide[3] ($C_{22}H_{21}Br_4NO_8$, m. 145–7°), which could be reconverted into II by warming with zinc dust in aqueous acetone. Perchloric acid converted the tetrabromide into $C_{22}H_{21}BrNO_8 \cdot ClO_4$ (white, m. 217°d.), while formic acid gave $C_{22}H_{21}Br_2NO_8$ (m. 145°), and this in turn gave back II when heated with aniline.[3] Heating II with hydrochloric acid gave,[3] chiefly, a tribasic acid $C_{17}H_{13}NO_6$ (d. 245°). Hydrogenation[3] of II, using Adams catalyst, gave a dihydro derivative ($C_{22}H_{23}NO_8$, yellow, m. 164°), which on treatment with alcoholic potash gave a compound (m. 247–8°) containing three methoxyl groups: either $C_{21}H_{21}NO_8$ or $C_{21}H_{23}NO_8$. Treatment[2] of II with nitrous gases yielded III (nitrate, d. 162°), which gave red crystals of IV (d. 224°) when heated with water or methanol. Oxidation[2,3] of II with either nitric or chromic acid yielded V (m. 138°; nitrate, m. 215°d.), which was hydrogenated over Adams catalyst to $C_{22}H_{31}NO_8$ (m. 181°), presumably VI. When V was treated with diazomethane, two isomeric compounds (m. 167° and m. 157°, respectively) of the formula $C_{23}H_{23}N_3O_9$ were obtained.[2]

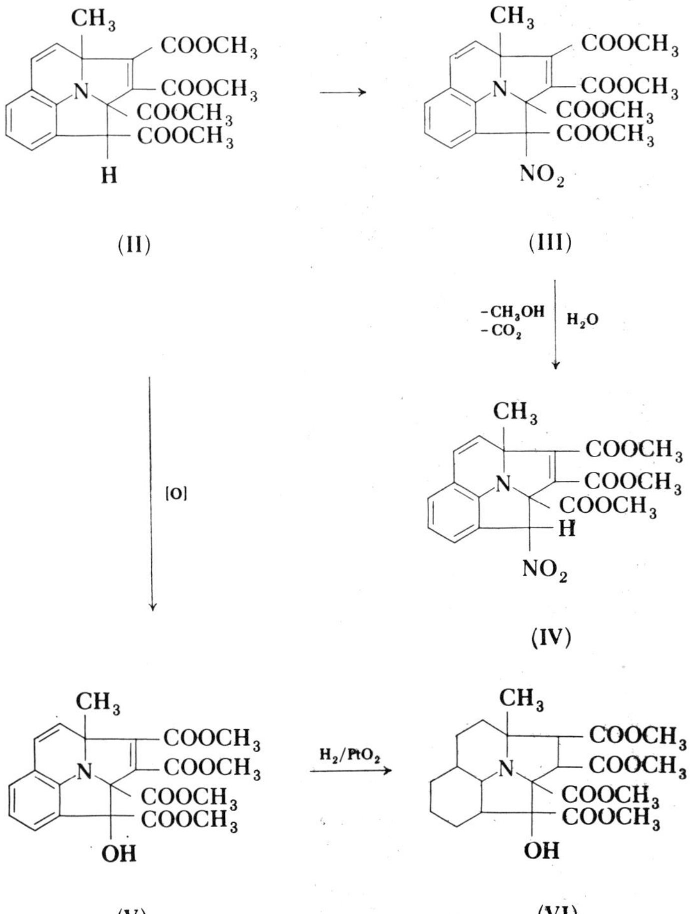

CH3 COOCH3 COOCH3 COOCH3 COOCH3 N H

(II)

CH3 COOCH3 COOCH3 COOCH3 COOCH3 N NO2

(III)

-CH3OH -CO2 H2O

CH3 COOCH3 COOCH3 COOCH3 H N NO2

(IV)

[O]

CH3 COOCH3 COOCH3 COOCH3 COOCH3 N OH

(V)

H2/PtO2

CH3 COOCH3 COOCH3 COOCH3 COOCH3 N OH

(VI)

References

1. Diels and Alder, *Ann.*, **498,** 16 (1932).
2. Diels and Kech, *Ann.*, **519,** 140 (1935).
3. Diels, Alder, Friedrichsen, Petersen, Brodersen, and Kech, *Ann.*, **510,** 87 (1934).

A-78. Pyrrolo[1,2,3-*lm*]carbazole

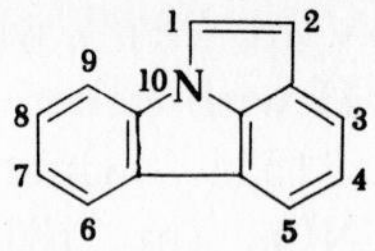

The treatment of 2,3-dihydro-*N*-nitrosoindole with cyclohexanone in the presence of zinc dust and acetic acid is reported[1] to yield a compound (m. 154°), thought to be II, presumably by indolization of the intermediate I (see Section A-79.).

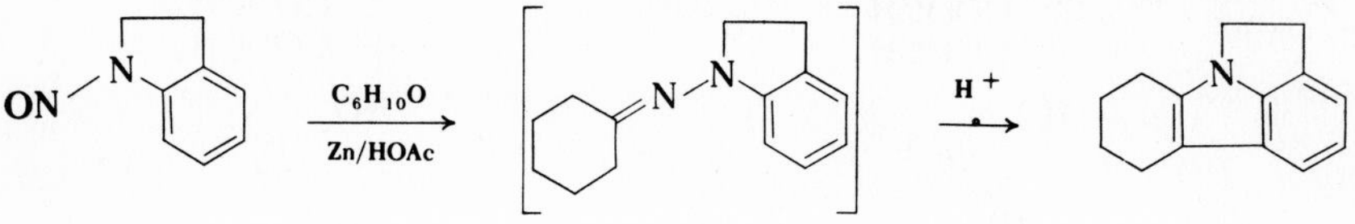

$C_6H_{10}O$

Zn/HOAc

H^+

(I) (II)

Reference

1. Lions and Ritchie, *J. Am. Chem. Soc.*, **61,** 1927 (1939).

A-79. Indolo[3,2,1-*jk*]carbazole. R.I. 2969

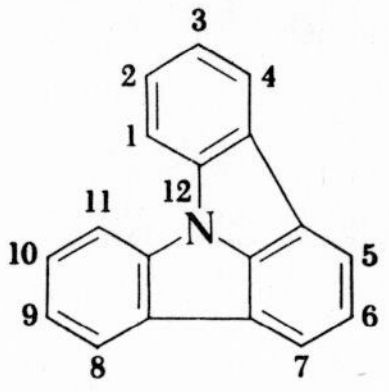

This nucleus has also been called *periindolocarbazole* and *1,9-phenylenecarbazole* (numbered as shown in I).

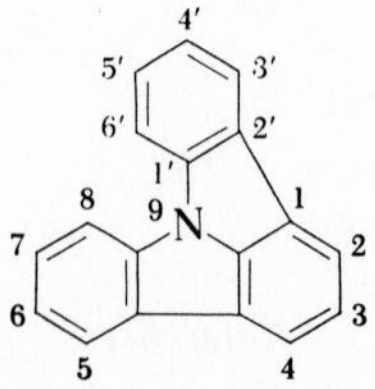

(I)

In 1927 Manjunath[1] treated I with zinc dust and cyclohexanone and obtained products (*a*, R = H, m. 83°; b_{13} 230–40°; picrate, d. 138°; *b*, R = CH_3, b_{13} 240–50°; picrate, d. 118°), which he called *8,9-(1,2-cyclohexyl)-tetrahydrocarbazoles*. Lions and Ritchie[2] confirmed Manjunath's synthesis of these compounds and suggested for them structures IIa and IIb. No similar reaction product could be obtained[2] from III, in which the position of cyclization is blocked with a methyl group. Electrolytic reduction of IIa gave[1] the dihydro derivative (m. 144°; b_{15} 235–45°; HCl salt, m. 225°d.; picrate, m. 160°; methiodide, m. 187°d.).

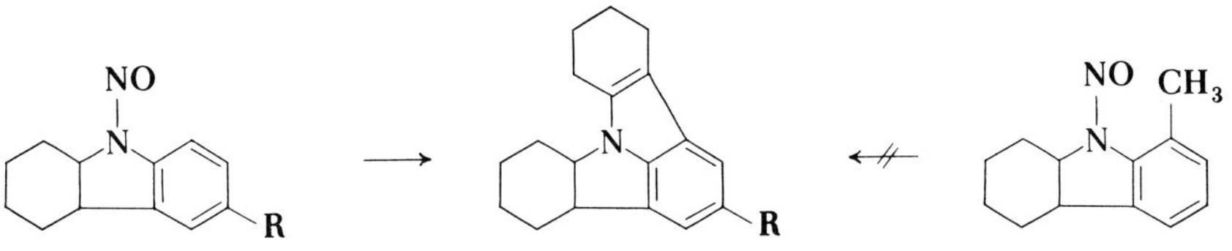

(I) (IIa) R = H (IIb) R = CH_3 (III)

Similar products (V) were obtained by Dunlop and Tucker[3] from IV via the Pschorr reaction: Va (R = R′ = R″ = H, m. 136.5–8.5°; picrate, red, m. 165–9°; TNB complex, yellow, m. 192–4°), Vb (R = R′ = H, R″ = CH_3, m. 109–11°; picrate, red, m. 145–50°; TNB complex, yellow, m. 170–2°), Vc (R = R′ = H, R″ = COOH, m. 240°; methyl ester, m. 155–62°), Vd (R = COOH, R′ = R″ = H, softens at 240°, m. 305°) and Ve (R = R′ = COOH, R″ = H, m. >360°; diethyl ester, m. 185–7°).

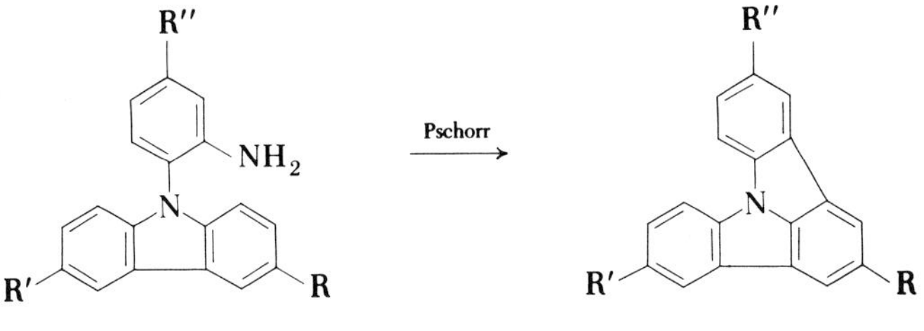

Pschorr

(IV) (V)

Preston and Tucker[4] were able to prepare VI from 9-aminocarbazole and cyclohexanone, and they subjected it to the Fischer indole reaction, obtaining VII (m. 99–100°; TNB derivative, orange-red, m. 164–6°; picrate, bronze, m. 159–60°). Dehydrogenation of VII by heating with sulfur in quinoline gave Va, the identity of which was confirmed by its synthesis from VIII via the Pschorr reaction.

HCl 160°

(VI) (VII)

S $-H_2$

NH_2

Pschorr

(VIII) (Va)

References

1. Manjunath, *J. Indian Chem. Soc.*, **4,** 271 (1927); *Chem. Abstracts*, **21,** 3199 (1927); *Chem. Zentr.*, **II,** 1698 (1927).
2. Lions and Ritchie, *J. Am. Chem. Soc.*, **61,** 1927 (1939).
3. Dunlop and Tucker, *J. Chem. Soc.*, **1939,** 1945.
4. Preston and Tucker, *J. Chem. Soc.*, **1943,** 659.

A-80. Anthr[10,4-*cd*]indolo[1,2-*a*]pyrrole. R.I. 3474

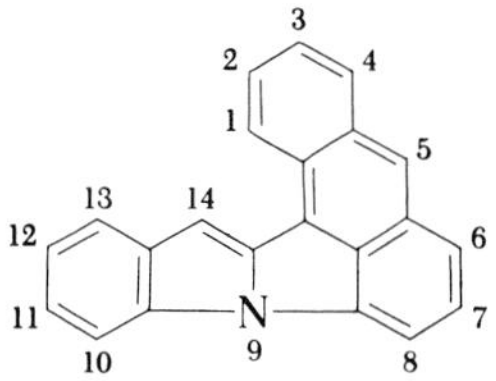

Schirmacher and Voss[1] described the preparation of a red dye (dark blue vat; red-violet sulfuric acid solution), thought to have structure I and referred to as an *isatanthrene* dye.

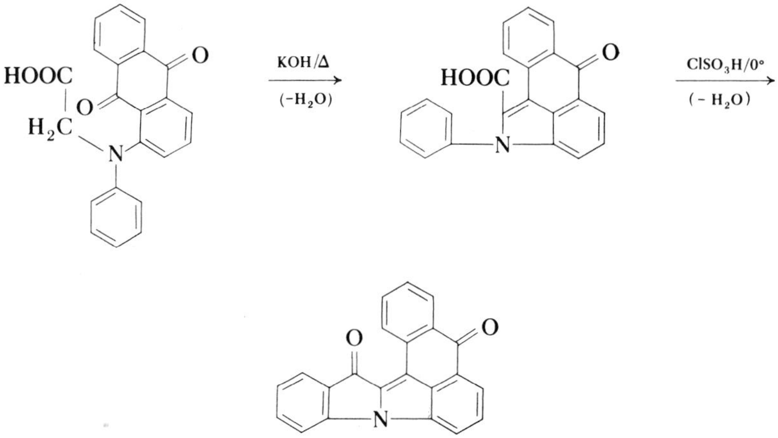

$\xrightarrow[(-H_2O)]{KOH/\Delta}$ $\xrightarrow[(-H_2O)]{ClSO_3H/0°}$

(I)

Reference

1. Schirmacher and Voss, Ger. Pat. 284,208; *Frdl.*, **12,** 423 (1917); U. S. Pat. 1,123,390.

A-81. 9*H*-Isoindolo[7,1,2-*ghi*]naphtho-[2,3-*b*]quinoxalino[2,3-*e*]indole*

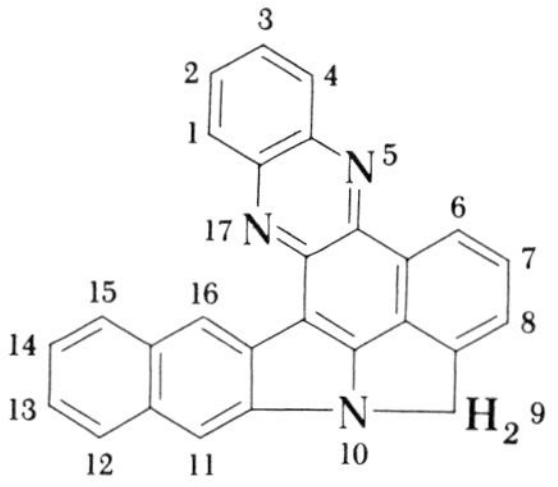

A compound thought to possess this ring system was obtained by Ritter[1,2] in the course of his efforts to prepare analogs of the dye

Indanthrene Yellow 6GD (see Section A-88). Naphthostyrilquinone (I) reacts with *o*-phenylenediamine to yield the azine II, which was treated with three moles of 2,3-dichloronaphthoquinone (a 1:1 ratio of quinone to azine failed to give the product) or with "excess" naphthoquinone to obtain the product thought to have structure III. Compound III formed yellow crystals, and exhibited the expected chemical and physical properties, but had no substantivity for cotton and was readily washed off of the fiber by soap, possibly as a result of cleavage of the lactam ring.

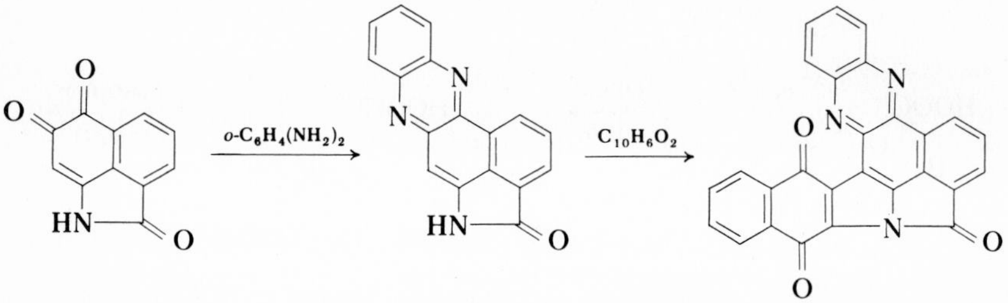

o-$C_6H_4(NH_2)_2$ → $C_{10}H_6O_2$ →

(I) (II) (III)

An attempt to condense II with 1,2-dichloranthraquinone was not successful.

References

1. Ritter, *I.G. Farbenindustrie A.G., 21 Tätigkeitsbericht*, 1938; *PB Report No.* 74203, frames 6700–4.
2. Ritter, *I.G. Farbenindustrie A. G., 41 Wissenschaftlicher Austausch der Gruppe IX*, Leverkusen, June 16 and 17, 1939; *PB Report No.* 70343, frames 15310–4.

A-82. Oxazolo[2,3-*a*]isoindole. R.I. 1337

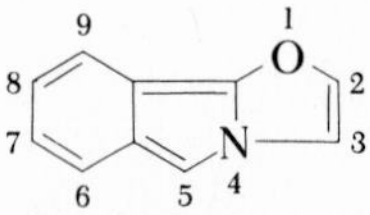

When compound I was treated with benzene and aluminum chloride, Freytag[1] obtained a product (m. 133–4°) to which he assigned structure II. Acid hydrolysis of II yielded α,α-diethylglycine and *o*-benzoylbenzoic acid, while basic hydrolysis gave an acid of either structure III or IV.

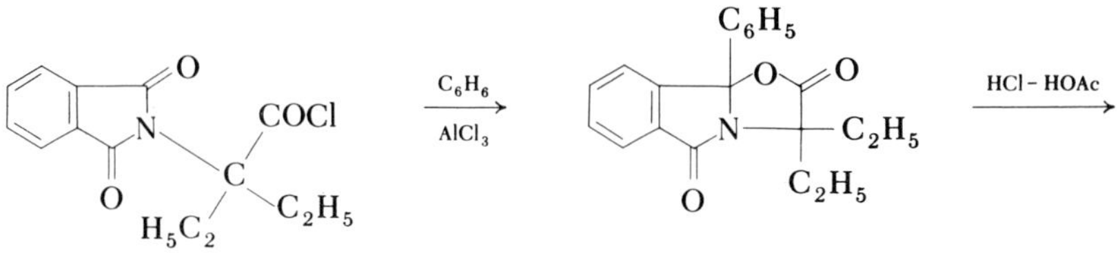

(I) $\xrightarrow[AlCl_3]{C_6H_6}$ (II) $\xrightarrow{HCl-HOAc}$ [o-benzoylbenzoic acid] + $H_2N-C(C_2H_5)_2-COOH$

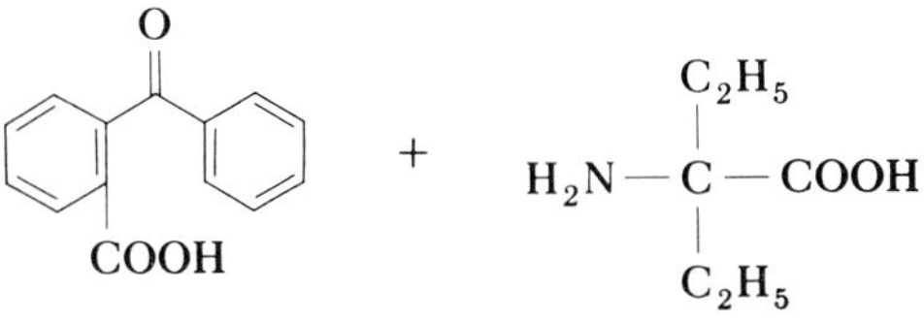

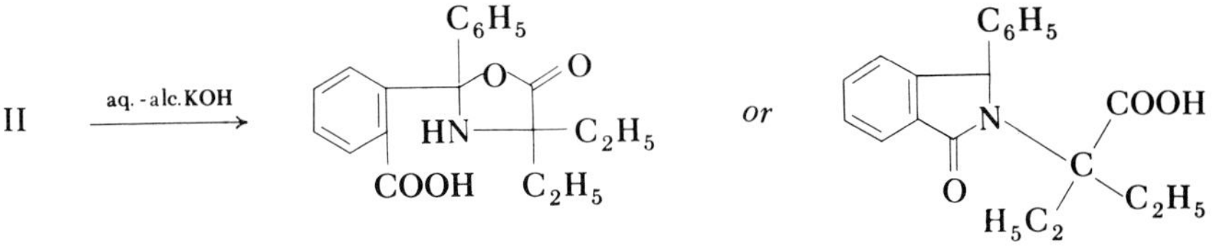

II $\xrightarrow{aq.-alc.KOH}$ (III) *or* (IV)

Gabriel[2] condensed phthalidylideneacetic acid (V) with α-aminoisobutyric acid, and obtained a neutral product thought to be VII (VIIa, $R_1 = R_2 = CH_3$, m. 112–4°). Honzl[3] thus prepared other examples of VII (VIIb, $R_1 = CH_3$, $R_2 = C_6H_5$, m. 97–9°; VIIc, $R_1 + R_2 = (CH_2)_5$, m. 113–4°) and showed that products of this type resulted only from the condensation of V with α,α-disubstituted glycines, while with α-monosubstituted glycines, acids of structure VI were formed.

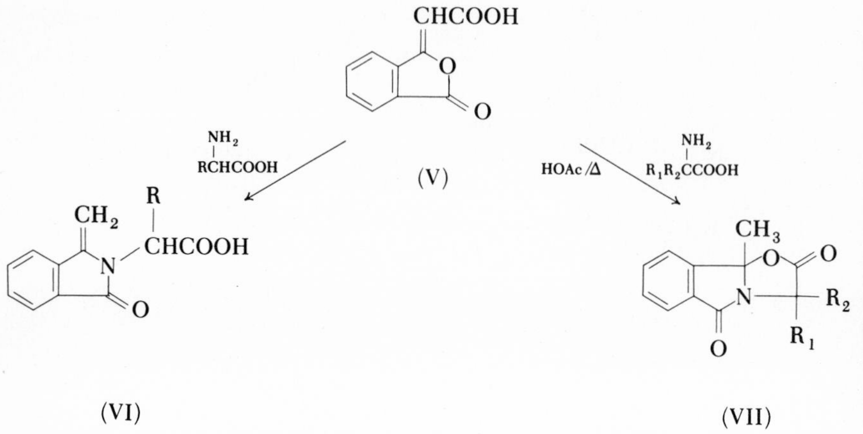

(V)

(VI)

(VII)

Treatment of VIIa with bromine gave the acid VIII, which was converted by dilute caustic solutions into IX (m. 123°). Catalytic

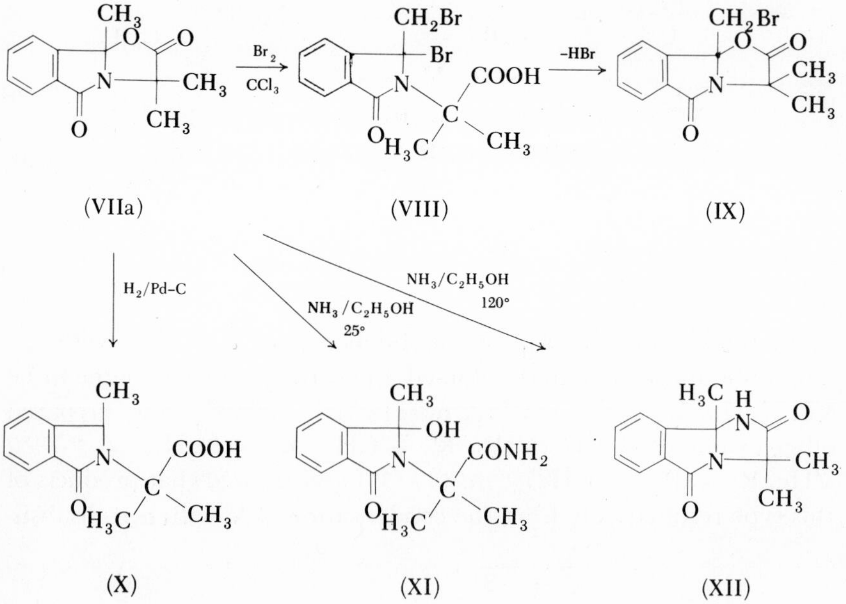

(VIIa)

(VIII)

(IX)

(X)

(XI)

(XII)

hydrogenation of VIIa yielded X. With ammonia, under mild conditions, products of type XI are formed, whereas more vigorous conditions produce the lactam XII (see Section A-93). The reaction of VIIa with methylamine yields a homolog of XI in which the hydroxyl group also is replaced by a methylimino group. The reaction of VIIa with hydrazine yields 1-hydroxy-4-methylphthalazine by extrusion of the elements of aminoisobutyric acid.

References

1. Freytag, *Ber.*, **48,** 648 (1915).
2. Gabriel, *Ber.*, **44,** 70 (1911).
3. Honzl, *Collection Czechoslov. Chem. Communs.*, **21,** 725 (1956); *Chem. listy*, **49,** 1671 (1955); *Chem. Abstracts*, **50,** 5621 (1956).

A-83. Pyrrolo[2,1-*b*]thiazole. R.I. 600

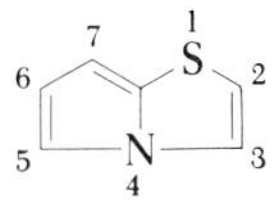

This nucleus also has been named *thiazolo-2′,3′,2,1-pyrrole.*

While studying the reactivity of the methyl group of 2-methylthiazoles (e.g., I), Kondo and Nagasawa[1] obtained compound III by treating I with phenacyl bromide. Several related thiazoles have been treated[2-4] similarly, and under mild reaction conditions it is often possible to isolate the intermediate thiazolium salt (II).

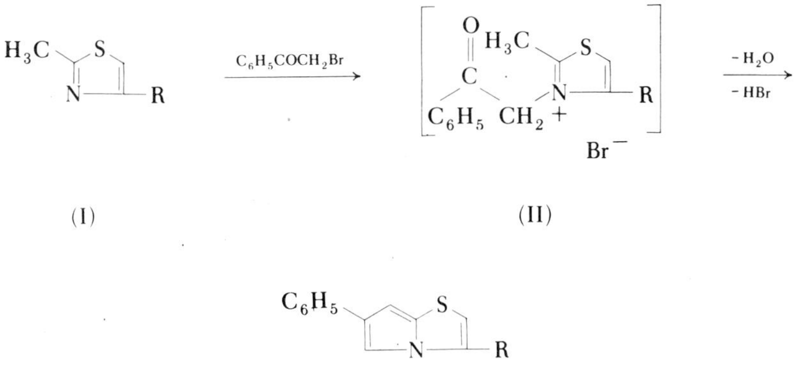

$C_6H_5COCH_2Br$; $-H_2O$, $-HBr$

(I) (II) Br^-

(III)

Efforts to prepare homologs and analogs of penicillin produced a number of pyrrolo[2,1-*b*]thiazoles. Suitable thiazolidine intermediates (VI) are obtained[5] by the condensation of aldehydes such as IV (R = H or C_6H_5CONH or $C_6H_5CH_2CONH$, etc.) with mercaptoamino acids such as V (cysteine, R′ = H or penicillamine, R′ = CH_3). The resulting thiazolidine derivatives (VI) are then converted[5-7] into the corresponding γ-lactams (VII). Compounds

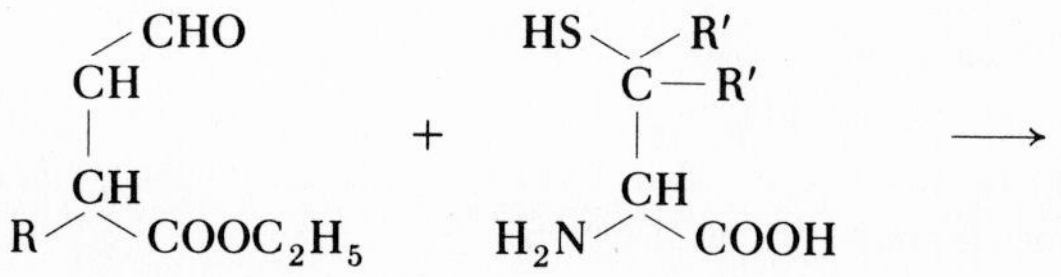

(IV) $OHC\text{-}CH_2\text{-}CH(R)COOC_2H_5$ + (V) $HS\text{-}C(R')_2\text{-}CH(NH_2)COOH$ →

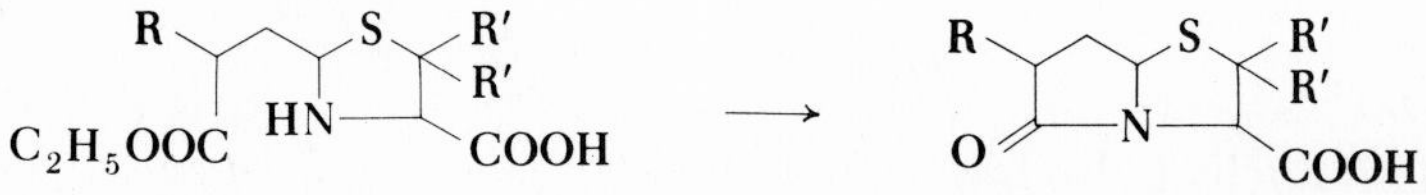

(VI) → (VII)

such as VII are converted[5,6] by mild oxidizing agents (e.g., metaperiodates) into the corresponding sulfoxides (e.g., VIII). Alkaline hydrolysis of VIII causes destruction of both rings to yield the fragments IX and X.

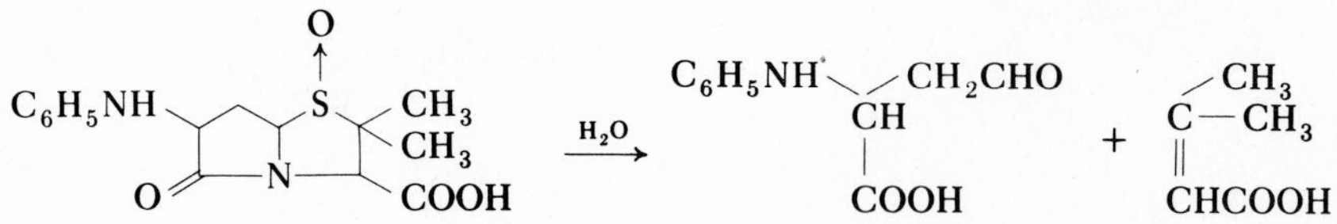

(VIII) $\xrightarrow{H_2O}$ (IX) $C_6H_5NH\text{-}CH(CH_2CHO)\text{-}COOH$ + (X) $(CH_3)_2C{=}CHCOOH$

A similar synthesis was recently described[8] in which the mucohalic acids (XI) replace IV, and products such as XII are obtained.

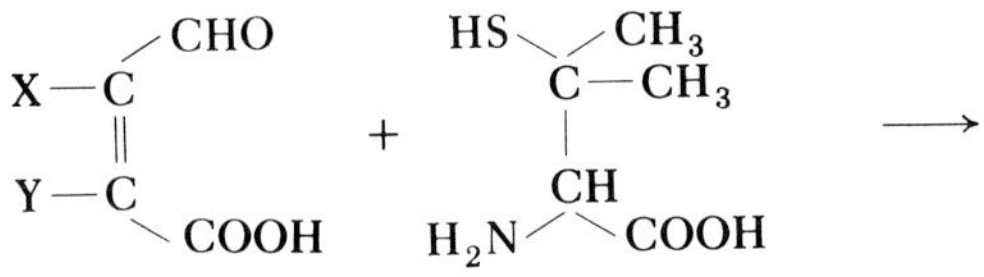

(XI)

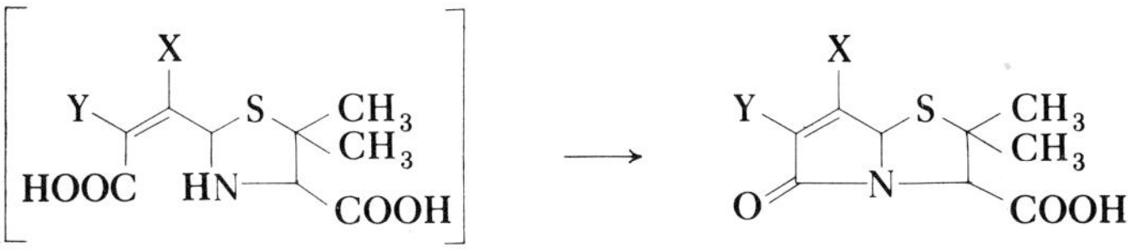

(XII)

Treatment of XIII with ethylene bromide produced[11] XIV.

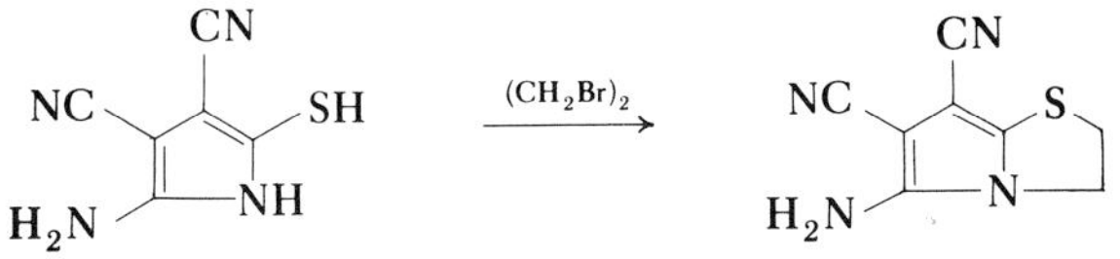

(XIII) $\xrightarrow{(CH_2Br)_2}$ (XIV)

Derivatives of Pyrrolo[2,1-*b*]thiazole

Empirical formula	Structure	Properties	Refs.
$C_7H_9N_2O_3S$	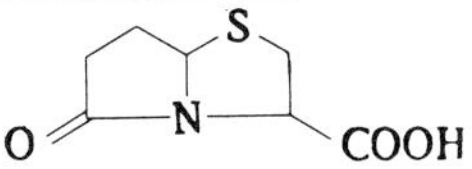	m. 137.0–7.5°	7
$C_7H_{10}NS$	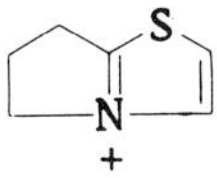	Bromide	2
$C_7H_{11}NOS$	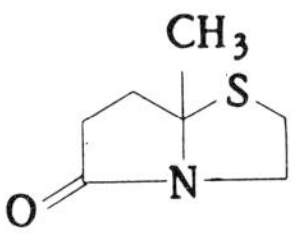	b_2 86°	10

(continued)

Derivatives of Pyrrolo[2, 1-*b*]thiazole (*continued*)

Empirical formula	Structure	Properties	Refs.
$C_8H_6N_4S$		m. > 300 °	11
$C_8H_9N_2O_5S$		d. 134–5°	7
$C_8H_{11}NO_3S$		m. 198–9°	10
$C_9H_9Cl_2NOS$		m. 153–4° d. Methyl ester, m. 99–100°	8
$C_{10}H_{11}Br_2NOS$		m. 96–8°	8
$C_{10}H_{13}N_2O_5S$		Oil	7
$C_{12}H_{17}N_2O_5S$		Oil. Corresponding *acid*, m. 217–22° d. Disodium salt, m. 250–5° d. Hydrazide and azide known.	5,9
$C_{12}H_{18}N_3O_5S$		m. 158°. Methyl ester m. 101.0-1.5°.	9
$C_{14}H_{14}N_2O_4S$		m. 242–5°	5
$C_{16}H_{16}ClNO_2S$		m. 90.5–2°	8

Derivatives of Pyrrolo[2,1-*b*]thiazole (*continued*)

Empirical formula	Structure	Properties	Refs.
$C_{16}H_{18}N_2O_4S$	$C_6H_5C(=O)NH$; S; N; CH_3; CH_3; COOH; O	m. 241°	5
$C_{16}H_{18}N_2O_5S$	$C_6H_5C(=O)NH$; S→O; N; CH_3; CH_3; COOH; O	m. 164° (or 201° anhydr.)	5,6
$C_{17}H_{20}N_2O_4S$	$C_6H_5CH_2C(=O)NH$; S; N; CH_3; CH_3; COOH; O	m. 255–8°	5
$C_{17}H_{20}N_2O_5S$	$C_6H_5OCH_2C(=O)NH$; S; N; CH_3; CH_3; COOH; O	m. 187.0–7.5°	9
$C_{26}H_{20}N_2S_2$	[C_6H_5; $-CH_2$; S; N]$_2$	m. 124°	4
$C_{28}H_{24}N_2S_2$	[C_6H_5; $-CH_2$; S; N; CH_3]$_2$	m. 185°	3

References

1. Kondo and Nagasawa, *J. Pharm. Soc. Japan*, **57,** 1050 (1937); *Chem. Zentr.*, **II,** 859 (1938); *Chem. Abstracts*, **32,** 3398 (1938).
2. deSmet and Schwarz, *Natuurw. Tijdschr. (Ghent)*, **21,** 271 (1940); *Chem. Abstracts*, **34,** 3603 (1940).
3. Erlenmeyer, Weber, Schmidt, Küng, Zinsstag, and Prijs, *Helv. Chim. Acta*, **31,** 1142 (1948).
4. Traupel, Erne, and Sorkin, *Helv. Chim. Acta*, **33,** 1960 (1950).
5. du Vigneaud and Carpenter in Clarke *et al.*, *The Chemistry of Penicillin*, Princeton University Press, Princeton, N. J., 1949, p. 1004.
6. Peck and Folkers in Clarke *et al.*, *The Chemistry of Penicillin*, Princeton University Press, Princeton, N. J., 1949, pp. 157, 188.
7. Strukov, *J. Gen. Chem.*, **22,** 521 (1952).
8. Wasserman, Precopio and Liu, *J. Am. Chem. Soc.*, **74,** 4093 (1952).

9. Wasserman, Suryanarayana, Koch and Tse, *Chem. and Ind.*, **1956,** 1022.
10. Oliver, Dann and Gates, *J. Am. Chem. Soc.*, **80,** 702 (1958).
11. Middleton, Engelhardt, and Fisher, *J. Am. Chem. Soc.*, **80,** 2822 (1958).

A-84. Pyrrolo[2,1-*b*]benzothiazole

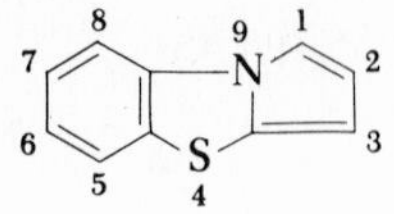

DeSmet and Schwarz[1] claim to have obtained the quaternary salt II by the reaction of I (R = H or CH_3) with ethylene dibromide. Compound II was treated further to produce photographic sensitizers.

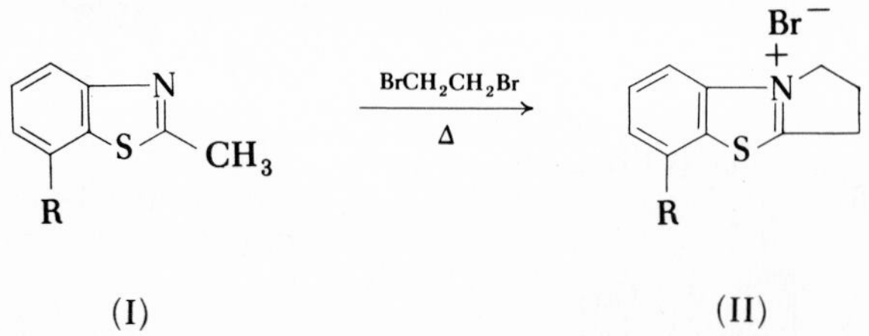

$BrCH_2CH_2Br$, Δ

(I) (II)

Condensation of 2-mercaptoaniline with levulinic ester yielded[2] the lactam III (b_3 172–6°).

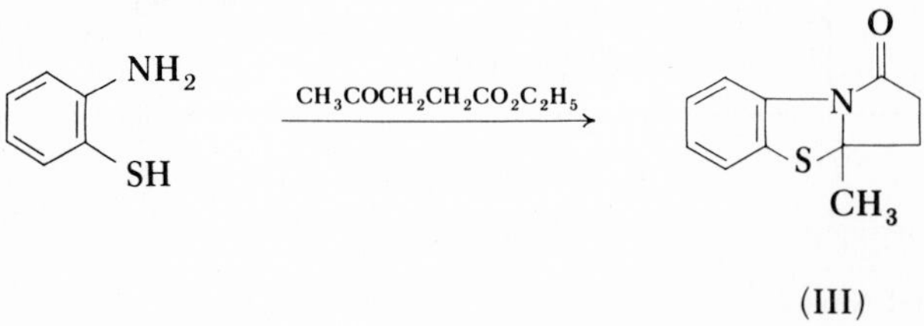

$CH_3COCH_2CH_2CO_2C_2H_5$

(III)

References

1. deSmet and Schwarz, *Natuurw. Tijdschr.* (*Ghent*), **21,** 271 (1940); *Chem. Abstracts*, **34,** 3603 (1940).
2. Oliver, Dann, and Gates, *J. Am. Chem. Soc.*, **80,** 702 (1958).

A-85. Thiazolo[2,3-*a*]isoindole*

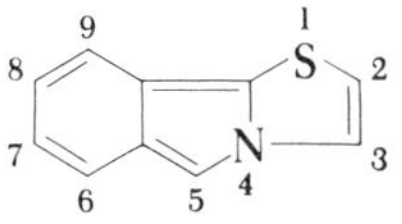

Condensation of 2-mercaptoethylamine (I, R = H) or of cysteine (I, R = COOH) with phthalaldehydic acid yielded[1] II (R = H, m. 97–100°; R = COOH, m. 218–20°), while with *o*-cyanobenzaldehyde, III (R = H, hydrochloride, m. 242–5°d.; R = COOH, m. 185–90°d.) was formed. When R = H, compound III was stable only as the salt, but the carboxylic acid (III, R = COOH) was stabilized by internal salt (zwitterion) formation. See Sections A-83, A-84, A-86, and A-452.

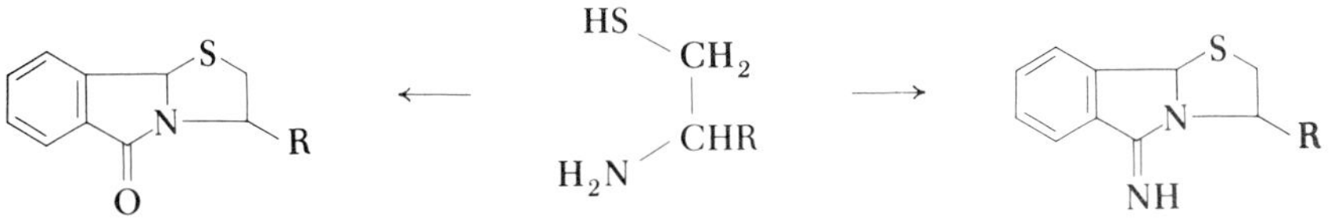

(II) (I) (III)

Reference

1. Oliver, Dann, and Gates, *J. Am. Chem. Soc.*, **80**, 702 (1958).

A-86. Isoindolo[1,2-*b*]benzothiazole*

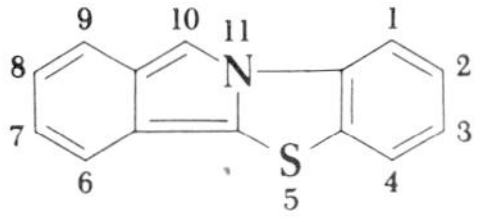

Condensation of 2-mercaptoaniline with phthalaldehydic acid yielded[1] I (m. 172–4°), while with 2-cyanobenzaldehyde, II (hydrochloride, m. 192–3°) was formed. Compound II was stable only in the form of its salt. See Sections A-83, A-84, A-85, and A-452.

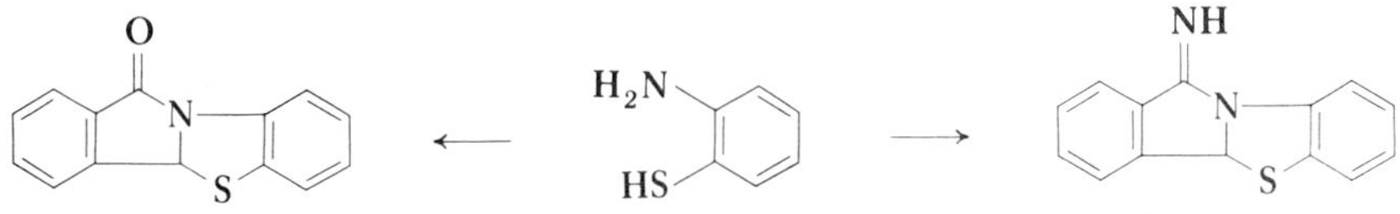

(I) (II)

Reference

1. Oliver, Dann, and Gates, *J. Am. Chem. Soc.*, **80,** 702 (1958).

A-87. Naphtho[2,1-*d*]pyrrolo-[2,1-*b*]thiazole

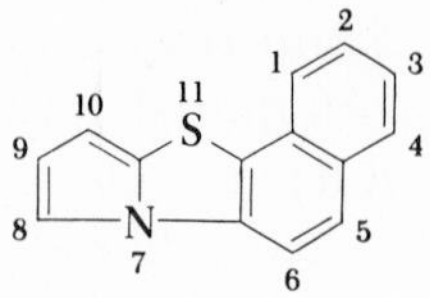

Schwarz and deSmet obtained[1,2] compound I (m. ~220°d.), which was then used[2,3] for the preparation of photographic sensitizing agents.

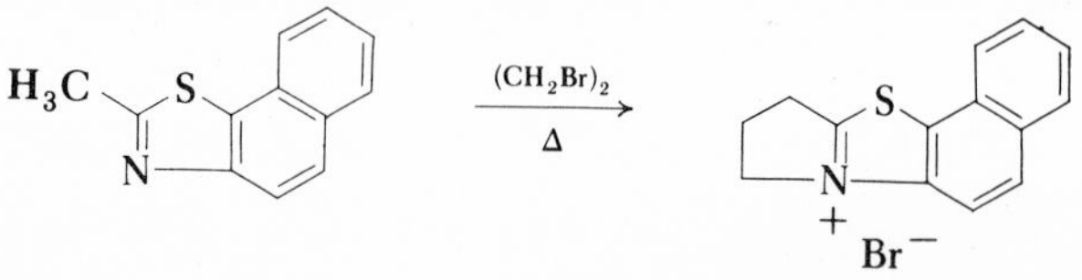

$(CH_2Br)_2$, Δ

(I)

References

1. Schwarz and deSmet, Brit. Pat. 587,434; *Chem. Abstracts*, **42,** 619 (1948).
2. deSmet and Schwarz, *Natuurw. Tijdschr.*, **21,** 271 (1940); *Chem. Abstracts*, **34,** 3603 (1940).
3. Schwarz and deSmet, Brit. Pat. 615,205; *Chem. Abstracts*, **43,** 8293 (1949).

A-88. Benzisothiazolo[4,3,2-*ghi*]naphtho-[2,3-*b*]quinoxalino[2,3-*e*]indole*

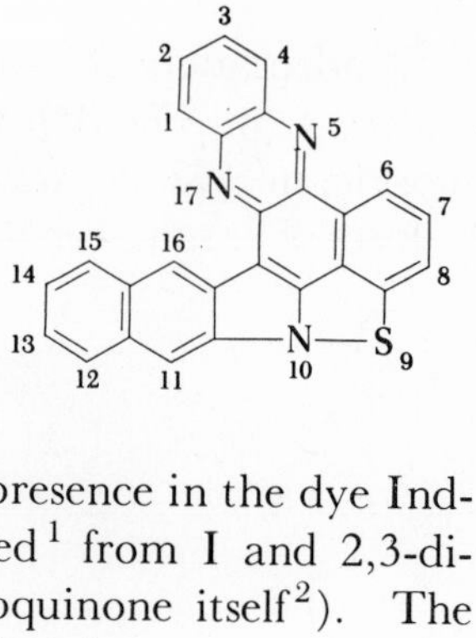

Interest in this ring system arises from its presence in the dye Indanthrene Yellow 6GD, which is manufactured[1] from I and 2,3-dichloro-1,4-naphthoquinone[7] (or 1,4-naphthoquinone itself[2]). The dye is a nontendering[3] greenish yellow (yellow-brown vat; orange solution in sulfuric acid) of fairly good fastness. Although the structure of the dye has never been ascertained with certainty, it is generally accorded structure II; however, Bruck[4] favored structure III.

Chlorination of Indanthrene Yellow 6GD in weak oleum yielded a dichloro derivative considered[5] to have structure IV, since it was also prepared from 2,3,5,8-tetrachloronaphthoquinone. This product dyed increasingly greener with increasing temperature and was of no value.

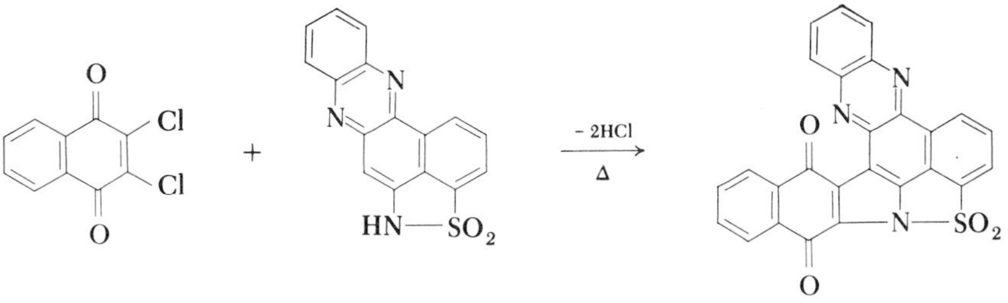

(I)

(II)

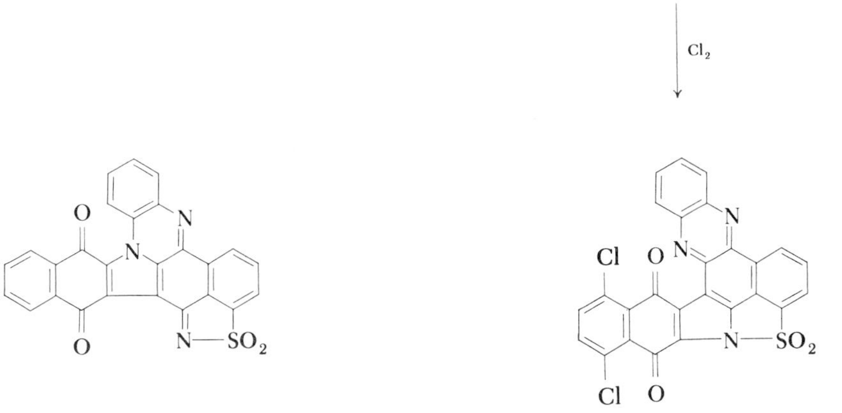

(III)

(IV)

A variety of substituents was introduced[6] into the quinoxaline moiety of II in an effort to improve the light- and soda-boil fastness. The resulting dyes were all inferior to II, however, and the introduction[6] of an aroylamino group into the naphthoquinone ring was similarly fruitless.

For the sake of brevity, three related systems (V–VII), which showed no advantages as dyes, but were briefly mentioned,[6] are included here.

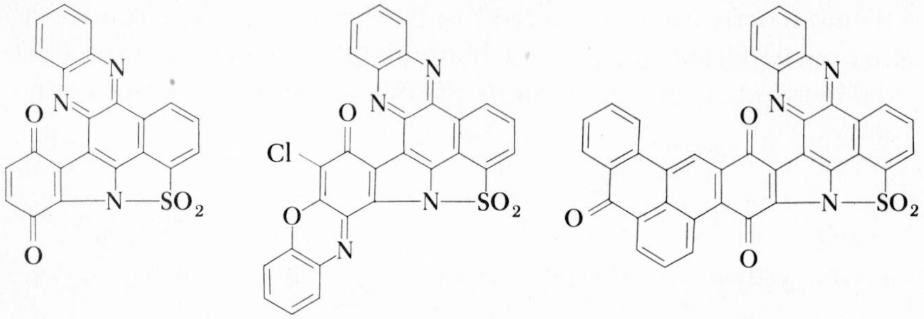

(V) (VI) (VII)

References

1. I. G. Farbenindustrie A.-G., *B.I.O.S. Report No.* 987, p. 125.
2. Kränzlein, Greune and Vollmann, Ger. Pat. 433,192; *Frdl.*, **15,** 437 (1928).
3. I. G. Farbenindustrie A.-G., *FIAT Report No.* 1313, Vol. III, p. 35.
4. Bruck, *I. G. Farbenindustrie A.-G., 41 Wissenschaftlicher Austausch der Gruppe IX*, Ludwigshafen, June 6, 1939; *PB Report No.* 70342, frames 14412–7.
5. Bruck, *I. G. Farbenindustrie A.-G.*; *PB Report No.* 70341, frame 13632.
6. Ritter, *I. G. Farbenindustrie A.-G.*; *PB Report No.* 74203, frames 6700–4.
7. Herzberg and Hoppe, Ger. Pat. 368,172; *Frdl.*, **14,** 742 (1926).

A-89. Pyrrolo[2,1-*b*]benzoselenazole

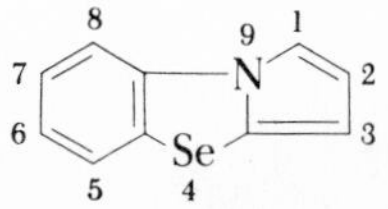

By treating I with ethylene dibromide, deSmet and Schwarz[1] obtained the quaternary salt II, which was treated further to produce a sensitizer for photographic emulsions.

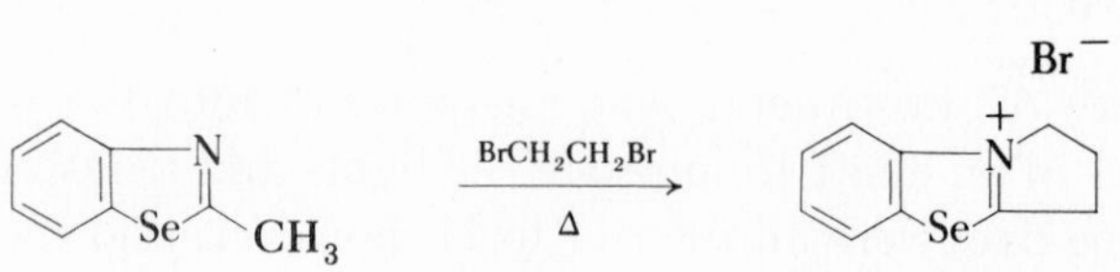

$\xrightarrow[\Delta]{BrCH_2CH_2Br}$

(I) (II)

Reference

1. deSmet and Schwarz, *Natuurw. Tijdschr.*, **21,** 271 (1940); *Chem. Abstracts*, **34,** 3603 (1940).

A-90. 1*H*-Imidazo[1,2-*a*]pyrrole

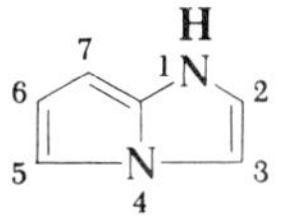

Two other names are encountered for this ring system: *2,4,1-imidazopyrrole* and *pyrrolo(1′:2′–1:2)glyoxaline.*

Treatment of I with sodium ethoxide yielded[1,2] II (IIa, R = $COOC_2H_5$, R′ = CH_3, m. 187°; IIb, R = CN, R′ = H, d. >280°; IIc, R = CN, R′ = CH_3, m. 165–6°). These compounds give no

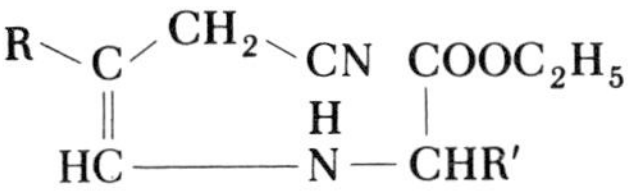

(I)

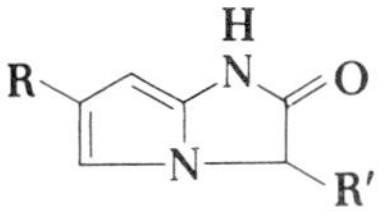

(IIa) R = $COOC_2H_5$, R′ = CH_3
(IIb) R = CN, R′ = H
(IIc) R = CN, R′ = CH_3

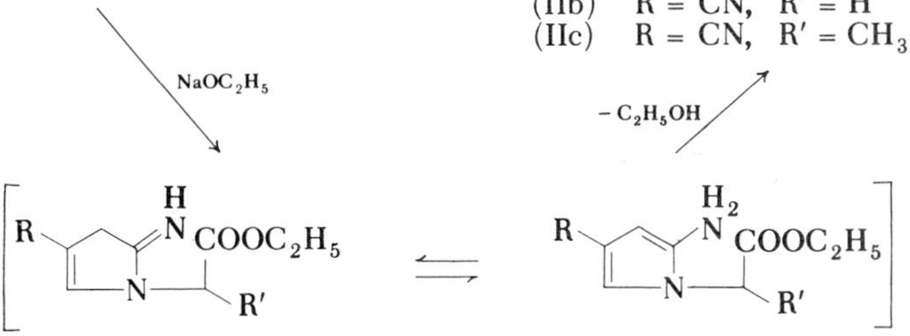

$NaOC_2H_5$

$- C_2H_5OH$

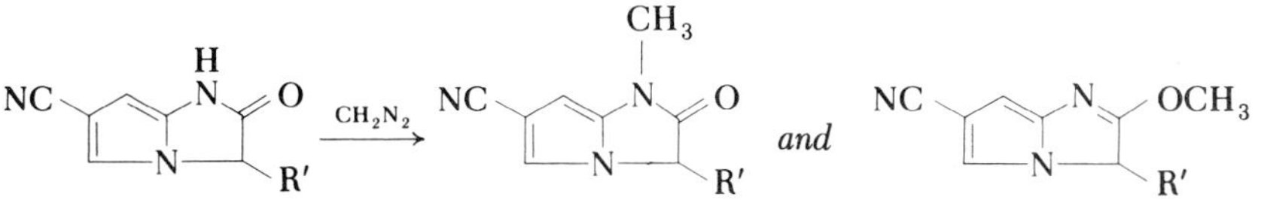

CH_2N_2

(IIb) R′=H
(IIc) R′=CH_3

(III)

and

(IV)

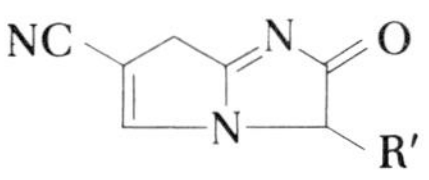

(V)

salts with acids, even in anhydrous media, but are soluble in dilute alkali carbonates. They do not give a ferric chloride test, but do give a positive Ehrlich test. Methylation of IIb or IIc with diazomethane gave[2] a mixture of 80% III (IIIa, R = H, m. 210°; IIIb, R = CH_3, m. 178–9°) and 20% IV (IVa, R = H, m. 151°; IVb, R = CH_3, m. 133–4°). This further confirms structure II for the cyclization product of I, and eliminates V from consideration. The nitrile group of compounds IIc and IIIb is very resistant to hydrolysis and only traces of the ethyl ester (m. 134°) corresponding to IIIb could be obtained.[3]

Bromination of IIc and IIIb yielded[3] VIa (R = H, decomposes above 158° without melting) and VIb (R = CH_3, m. ~160°d.). The chlorine analog of VIa (m. 229–31°) and the corresponding dibromo analog of IVb (d. ~150°) were also obtained.[3] Sulfuric acid converted IIc into the corresponding 5-sulfonic acid (d. ~180°, sodium salt, m. 230–40° d.).

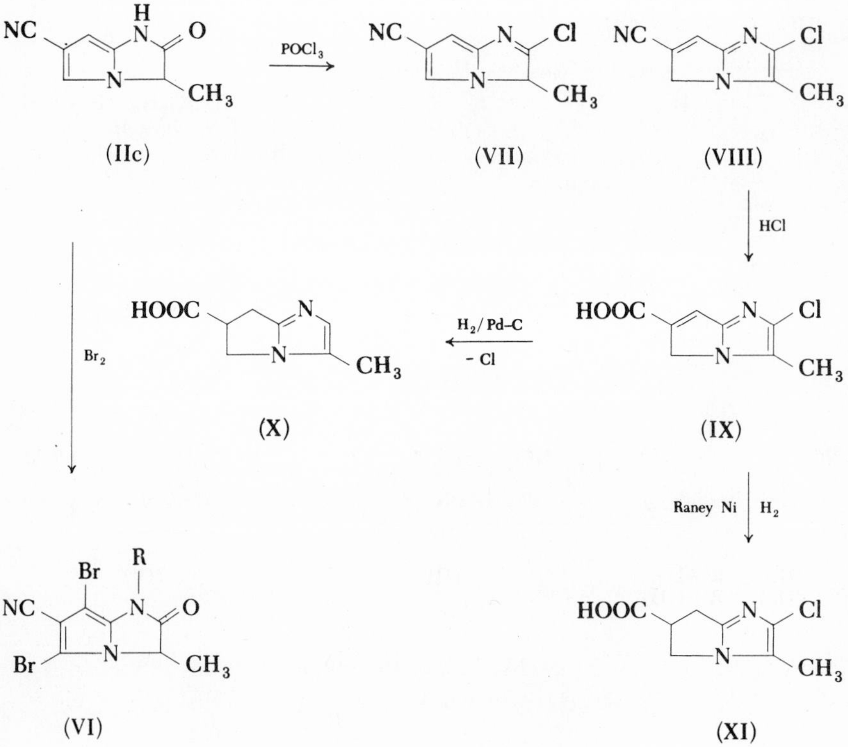

(IIc) —$POCl_3$→ (VII) (VIII)

(VIII) —HCl→ (IX)

(IX) —H_2/Pd–C, - Cl→ (X)

(IX) —Raney Ni, H_2→ (XI)

(IIc) —Br_2→ (VI)

When IIc was treated with phosphorus oxychloride, a product (m. 177–82°d.) $C_8H_6N_3Cl$ was obtained. Since this product was basic and stable to aqueous alkali and showed an ultraviolet absorption spectrum quite different from that of IVb, it was evidently not compound VII, and structure VIII was assigned to it.[3] The nitrile group of VIII was readily saponified[3] giving IX (m. 242–5°; ethyl ester, m. 142°), which was hydrogenated to XI (m. 258–60°) over a Raney nickel catalyst, and to X (m. 250–2°) with palladium-charcoal. The ultraviolet absorption spectra of many of these compounds have been measured.[3]

Efforts by Grob and Utzinger[4] to obtain compound XIII by the cyclization of XII were not successful.

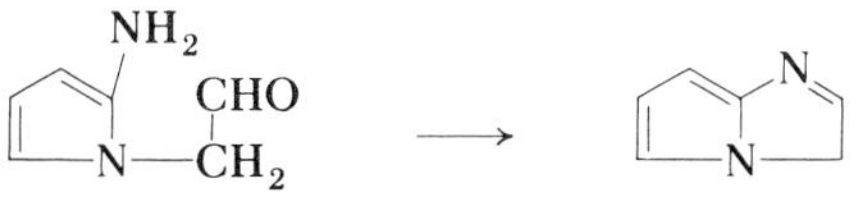

NH_2 CHO CH_2 N → N N

(XII) (XIII)

References

1. Grob and Ankli, *Helv. Chim. Acta*, **33,** 273 (1950).
2. Cohen, *J. Chem. Soc.*, **1950,** 3005.
3. Grob and Ankli, *Helv. Chim. Acta*, **33,** 658 (1950).
4. Grob and Utzinger, *Helv. Chim. Acta*, **37,** 1256 (1954).

A-91. 1*H*-Pyrrolo[1,2-*a*]benzimidazole. R.I. 1374

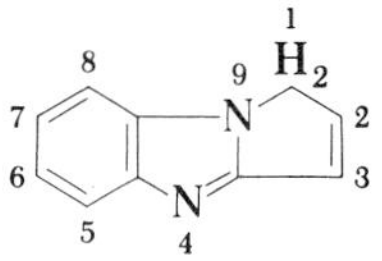

1 H_2 9 N 2 3 N 4 5 6 7 8

Anderlini[1,2] studied the reaction of *o*-phenylenediamine with succinic anhydride and isolated a product which he thought had structure I. It was shown by Meyer and Lüders,[3] and later by Betrabet and Chakravarti,[4] that this product was actually II, and that on dehydration it was converted into III (m. 171° or 172–5°). Compound III, which was called *propionylenebenzimidazole* or $\alpha,(\beta)$-*dihydroacrylenene-1,3-benzimidazole*, was also obtained[3] directly by heating at 230–40° a mixture of *o*-phenylenediamine and succinic anhy-

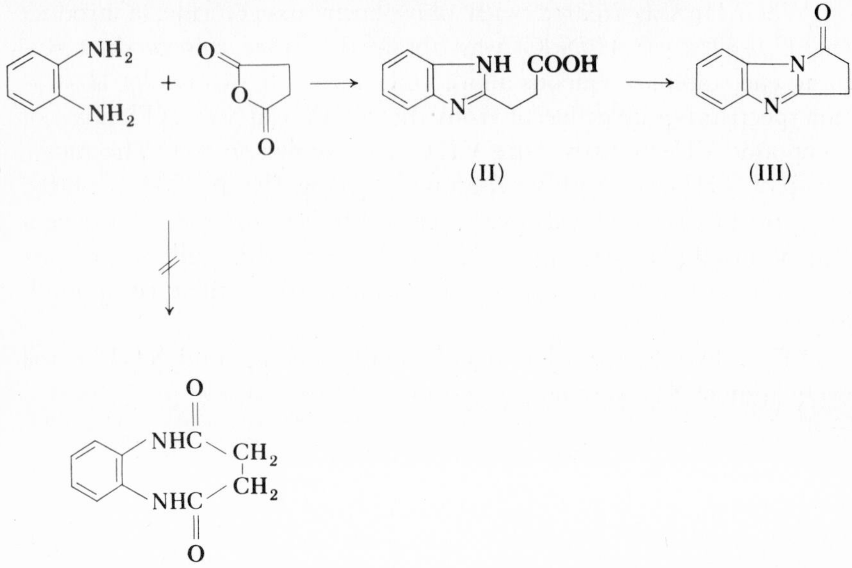

(II) (III)

(I)

dride. In a similar fashion diphenylmaleic anhydride yielded[5] 2,3-diphenylpyrrolo[1,2-*a*]benzimidazol-1-one (brown, m. 186°).

A further synthesis of this ring system has been described by Bistrzycki and Schmutz,[6] who heated *o*-phenylenediamine with γ-valerolactone and obtained IV (R = CH_3) as a brown oil (picrate, yellow, m. 222–4°). Recently Reppe *et al.*[7] described the desmethyl

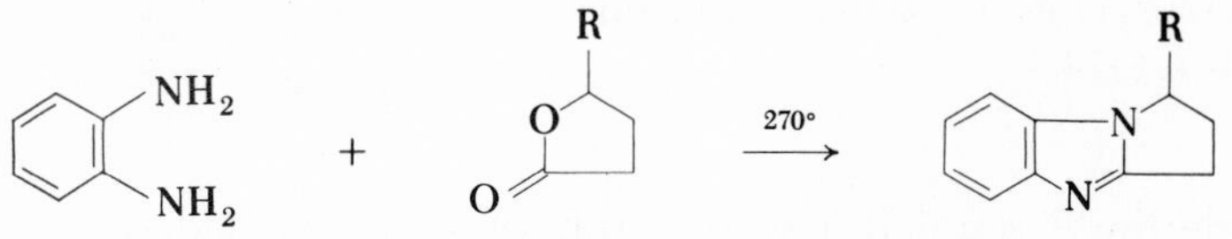

270°

(IV)

homolog (IV, R = H, $b_{0.2}$ 130°, m. 115°), obtained similarly from γ-butyrolactone. It yielded a nitro derivative (m. 173°), which was reduced catalytically to an amine (m. 205°; acetyl derivative, m. 266°).

References

1. Anderlini, *Atti reale accad. Lincei*, **I,** 425 (1893).
2. Anderlini, *Gazz. chim. ital.*, **24,** 140 (1894).
3. Meyer and Lüders, *Ann.*, **415,** 29 (1917).
4. Betrabet and Chakravarti, *J. Indian Chem. Soc.*, **7,** 191 (1930); *Chem. Zentr.*, **II,** 240 (1930); *Chem. Abstracts*, **24,** 4516 (1930); **25,** 701 (1931).
5. Bistrzycki and Fässler, *Helv. chim. Acta*, **6,** 519 (1923).
6. Bistrzycki and Schmutz, *Ann.*, **415,** 1 (1917).
7. Reppe *et al.*, *Ann.*, **596,** 176, 209 (1955).

A-92. 9*H*-Imidazo[1,2-*a*]indole*

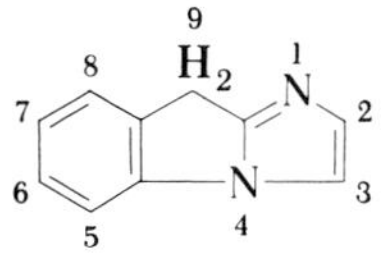

Metallation of 1-phenylimidazole (I) and carbonation of the resulting dilithium derivative (II) gave a 5% yield of bright yellow III (m. 162–3°, after sublimation).

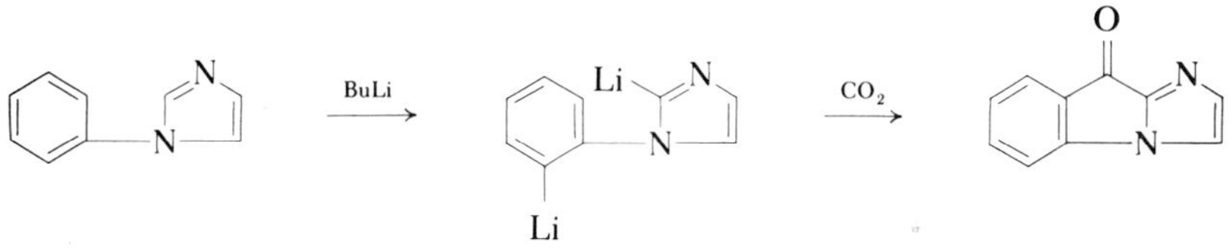

BuLi → CO_2 →

(I) (II) (III)

Reference

1. Shirley and Alley, *J. Am. Chem. Soc.*, **79,** 4922 (1957).

A-93. 5*H*-Imidazo[2,1-*a*]isoindole. R.I. 1373

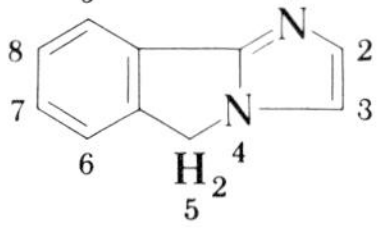

The alternative name *o-benzylenebenzimidazole* given by the *Ring Index* for this nucleus is, obviously, an error.

Betrabet and Chakravarti[1] described the condensation of phthalide (I) with ethylenediamine to yield, ultimately, II (m. 152–3°). Oxidation of II with potassium permanganate gave III (m. 229–30°), which was also obtained from the condensation of phthalic anhydride with ethylenediamine.

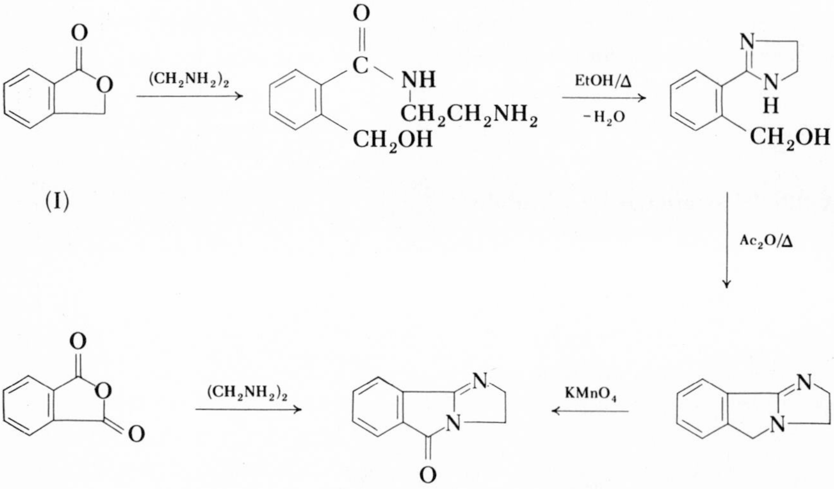

O
$(CH_2NH_2)_2$
O
C
NH
$CH_2CH_2NH_2$
CH_2OH
EtOH/Δ
$-H_2O$
N
N
H
CH_2OH
(I)
$Ac_2O/Δ$
O
O
O
$(CH_2NH_2)_2$
N
N
O
$KMnO_4$
N
N

(III) (II)

Treatment of the lactones IV (see Section A-82) with ammonia yielded[2] V ($R_1 = R_2 = CH_3$, m. 219°; $R_1 + R_2 = (CH_2)_5$, m. 206°).

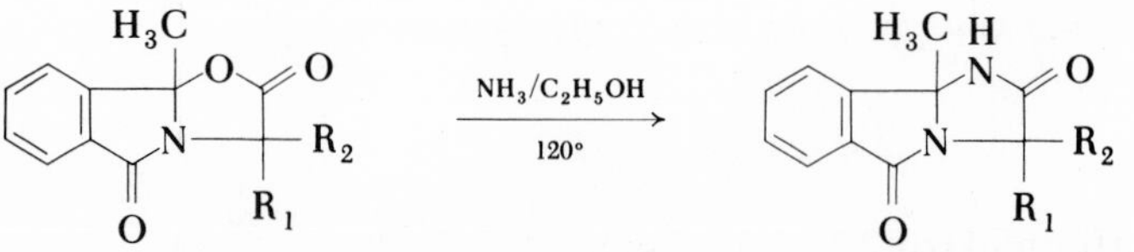

H_3C
O
O
N
R_2
R_1
O
NH_3/C_2H_5OH
120°
H_3C H
N
O
N
R_2
R_1
O

(IV) (V)

References

1. Betrabet and Chakravarti, *J. Indian Chem. Soc.*, **7,** 495 (1930); *Chem. Zentr.*, **II,** 3025 (1930); *Chem. Abstracts*, **25,** 701 (1931).
2. Honzl, *Collection Czechoslov. Chem. Communs.*, **21,** 725 (1956); *Chem. listy*, **49,** 1671 (1955); *Chem. Abstracts*, **50,** 5622 (1956).

A-94. 11*H*-Isoindolo[2,1-*a*]benzimidazole. R.I. 2271

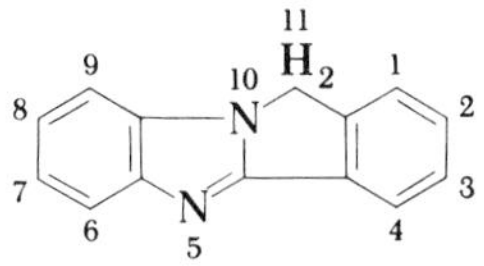

Alternative names encountered for this nucleus are: *pseudoisoindolobenzimidazole*, *o-benzolylene-2,1-benzimidazole*, and *phenylenephthalamidone*.

This type of ring system was first investigated by Bistrzycki,[1-4] who was interested, initially, in identifying the product formed from the condensation of opianic acid with toluenediamine.[1] Subsequently he showed that, in general, phthalaldehydic acids (I) condense with 1,2-diamines to yield benzimidazoles such as II, which can then be dehydrated to products of type III.

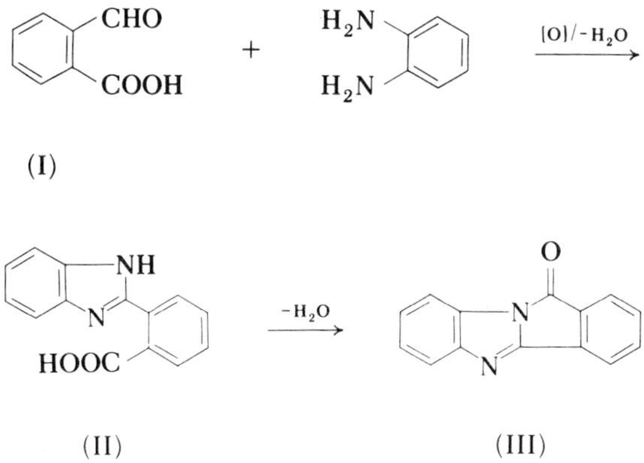

(I)

(II) (III)

The reaction of phthalic anhydride with *o*-phenylenediamine in ethanol solution was studied by Anderlini[5] and by Meyer,[6] who obtained products such as II, IV, and V. However, when these reactants are fused at elevated temperatures, a good yield of III can be

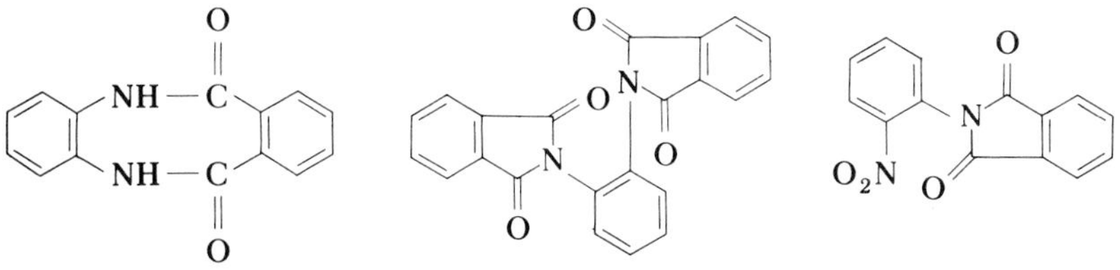

(IV) (V) (VI)

obtained directly,[7] together with some V and other products.[8] Compounds of type III have also been prepared by the reduction and dehydration of *o*-phenylazophenylphthalimides[9] or *o*-nitrophenylphthalimides[10] (e.g., VI).

Thiele and Falk[11] treated phthalaldehyde with *o*-phenylenediamine and isolated a product ($C_{14}H_{10}N_2$) which they considered to be either VII or VIII. Controlled oxidation of this product gave III,

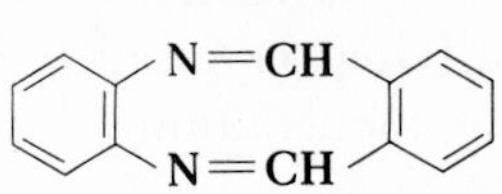

(VII) 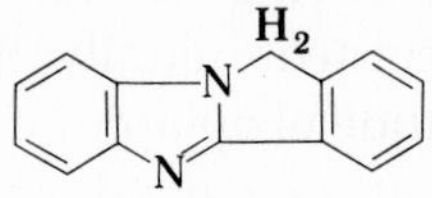 (VIII)

and additional evidence in favor of structure VIII was provided by the fact that the product was a monoacidic base. Bistrzycki and Schmutz[12] prepared VIII from phthalide and *o*-phenylenediamine, and the properties of their product agreed with those of Thiele and Falk's product. In spite of this evidence, Betrabet and Chakravarti reopened the problem and, presumably because they had difficulty in obtaining VIII by various routes, concluded[13] that Thiele and Falk's product was VII, which rearranged under oxidizing conditions to yield III. Rowe and his co-workers[14, 15] also obtained VIII by an unusual series of rearrangements.

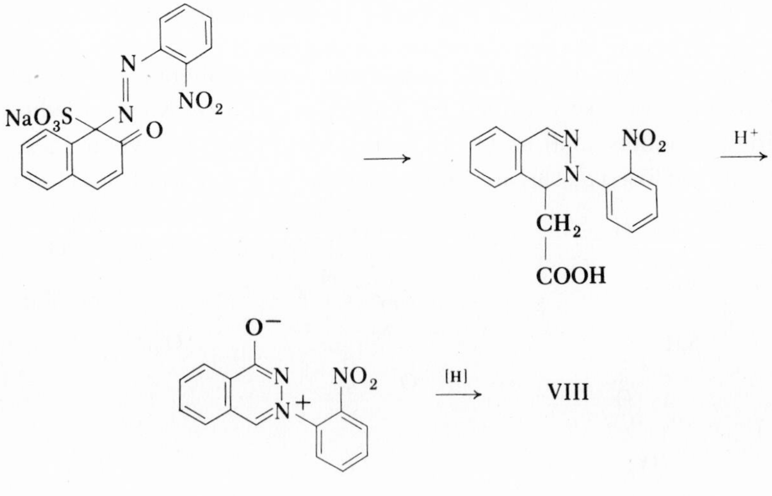

$\xrightarrow{H^+}$

$\xrightarrow{[H]}$ VIII

Beckmann rearrangement of the *cis-trans* dioxime of 1,5-dichloroanthraquinone (IX) yielded[22] a dichloro compound considered to be either X or XI because of the elemental analysis and the similarity of the ultraviolet absorption spectrum to that of III.

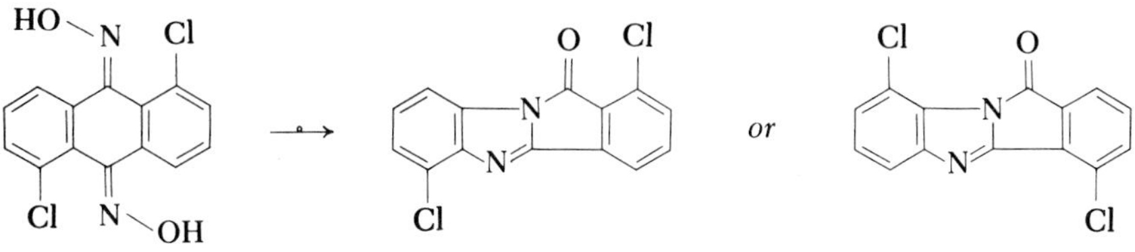

(IX) → (X) *or* (XI)

The nitration of III has been reported[10] to yield two different (probably the 6-, 7-, 8-, or 9-) mononitro derivatives of III, depending upon the mode of nitration. One of these was reduced readily to an amine whereas the other resisted reduction. The condensation of 3- and 4-nitrophthalic anhydrides with *o*-phenylenediamine has been claimed,[20] but no effort was made to relate these products to the above nitro compounds. Treatment of III with alkyl halides yielded[10] quaternary salts which were reconverted by heat into their components. The amide linkage of III is readily cleaved both by acidic and (especially) by basic reagents; for example, with aniline, III yields 2-(2-benzimidazolyl)benzanilide. The zinc reduction of certain homologs of III is reported[4] to yield tetrahydro derivatives, but the structure of these substances is unknown.

Derivatives of 11*H*-Isoindolo[2,1-*a*]benzimidazole

Empirical formula	Substituents or structure	Properties and comments	Refs.
$C_{14}H_4Cl_4N_2O$	1,2,3,4-Tetrachloro-11-oxo-	Grn.-yel., m. 290–1°.	7
$C_{14}H_6Cl_2N_2O$	1,6-(or 4,9 ?)-Dichloro-11-oxo-	Yel., m. 282°.	22
$C_{14}H_6N_4O_5$	1,4-Dinitro-11-oxo-	Brn.-yel.	20
$C_{14}H_7ClN_2O$	2-Chloro-11-oxo-	Yel., m. 156°.	14
$C_{14}H_7N_3O_3$	*x*-Nitro-11-oxo-	Yel.-grn., m. 239°.	10
	y-Nitro-11-oxo-	Brn., m. 280° d.	10
	1(or 4)-Nitro-11-oxo	—	20
	2(or 3)-Nitro-11-oxo-	Yel.-brn.	20
$C_{14}H_8N_2O$	11-Oxo-	Yel., m. 211–2°(209–10°; 211°). Methiodide and methochloride, m. ~200°.	4,7,8,10, 11,13, 14,15, 18–20, 22
$C_{14}H_8N_2O_2$	8-Hydroxy-11-oxo	m. 320°.	21
$C_{14}H_9ClN_2$	2-Chloro-	m. 242°.	14,15
$C_{14}H_9N_3O$	*x*-Amino-11-oxo-	Red, m. 298–305°. Acetyl der., d. 253°.	10
$C_{14}H_{10}N_2$	Unsubstituted	m. 212–3° (210°; 212°). Picrate, yel., m. 243.5°.	11–15
$C_{14}H_{14}N_2O$	1,2,3,4,4a,11a-Hexahydro-11-oxo-	m. 175–6°.	19
$C_{15}H_9BrN_2O$	6(or 9)-Bromo-8(or 7)-methyl-11-oxo-	Yel., m. 234–5°.	4
$C_{15}H_{10}N_2O$	7(or 8)-methyl-11-oxo-	Yel., m. 188° (166°).	4,16
$C_{15}H_{12}N_2$	7(or 8)-Methyl-	m. 192–3°.	11
$C_{15}H_{14}N_2O$	*x*,*x*,*x*,*x*-Tetrahydro-7(or 8)-methyl-11-oxo-	m. 186–7°.	4
$C_{15}H_{16}N_2O$	1,2,3,4,4a,11a-Hexahydro-7(or 8)-methyl-11-oxo-	m. 186–7°.	19
$C_{17}H_{13}BrN_2O_3$	6(or 9)-Bromo-3,4-dimethoxy-7(or 8)-methyl-11-oxo-	Yel., m. 212–3°.	4
$C_{17}H_{14}N_2O_3$	3,4-Dimethoxy-7(or 8)-methyl-11-oxo-	Yel., m. 228°.	3
$C_{17}H_{22}N_2O_3$	*x*,*x*,*x*,*x*-Tetrahydro-3,4-dimethoxy-7(or 8)-methyl-11-oxo-	m. 248°.	4

Derivatives of 11*H*-Isoindolo [2,1-*a*] benzimidazole (*continued*)

Empirical formula	Substituents or structure	Properties and comments	Refs.
$C_{22}H_{11}N_3O_3$	8-Phthalimido-11-oxo-	Yel., m. 295°.	9
$C_{26}H_{18}N_2O_2$	11,11-Bis(4-hydroxyphenyl)-	m. 354-5°. Picrate, yel., m. 203-4°. *O,O*-Diacetate picrate, yel., d. 285.5-6°.	12
$C_{28}H_6Cl_8N_4O_2$	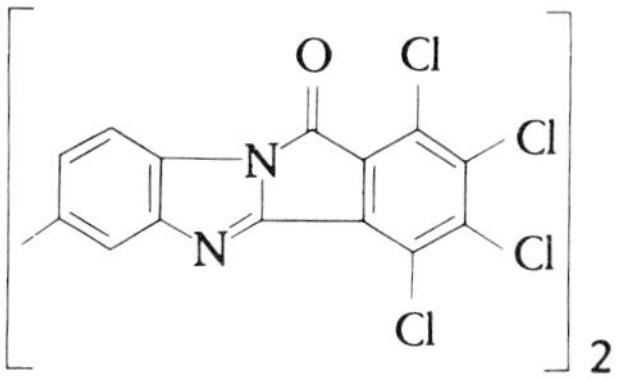	—	20
$C_{28}H_{14}N_4O_2$	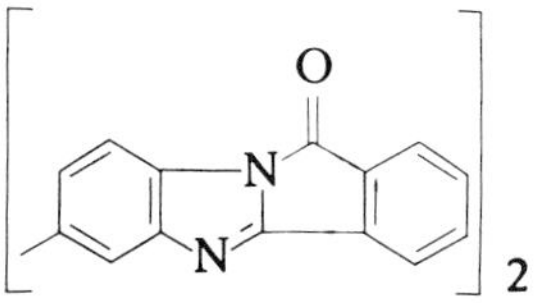	Grn.-yel., m. >300°.	17,20

References

1. Bistrzycki, *Ber.*, **21,** 2518 (1888).
2. Bistrzycki, *Ber.*, **23,** 1042 (1890).
3. Bistrzycki, *Ber.*, **24,** 627 (1891).
4. Bistrzycki, and Cybulski, *Ber.*, **25,** 1984 (1892).
5. Anderlini, *Gazz. chim. ital.*, **24,** 140 (1894).
6. Meyer, *Ann.*, **327,** 1 (1903).
7. Bistrzycki and Lecco, *Helv. Chim. Acta*, **4,** 425 (1921).
8. Poraĭ-Koshits and Antoshul'skaya, *J. Gen. Chem.* (*U.S.S.R.*), **13,** 339 (1943); *Chem. Abstracts*, **38,** 1234 (1944).
9. Crippa and Galimberti, *Gazz. chim. ital.*, **59,** 825 (1929); *Chem. Zentr.*, **I,** 1307 (1930); *Chem. Abstracts*, **24,** 2115 (1930).
10. Rupe and Thiess, *Ber.*, **42,** 4287 (1909).
11. Thiele and Falk, *Ann.*, **347,** 112 (1906).
12. Bistrzycki and Schmutz, *Ann.*, **415,** 1 (1917).
13. Betrabet and Chakravarti, *J. Indian Chem. Soc.*, **7,** 495 (1930); *Chem. Zentr.*, **II,** 3025 (1930); *Chem. Abstracts*, **25,** 701 (1931).
14. Rowe, Dovey, Garforth, Levin, Pask and Peters, *J. Chem. Soc.*, **1935,** 1796.
15. Rowe, Adams, Peters and Gillam, *J. Chem. Soc.*, **1937,** 90.

16. Chakravarti, *Quart. J. Indian Chem. Soc.*, **1**, 19 (1924); *Chem. Zentr.*, **I**, 518 (1925); *Chem. Abstracts*, **19**, 830 (1925).
17. Crippa and Galimberti, *Gazz. chim. ital.*, **63**, 81 (1933).
18. Syrkin and Shott-L'vova, *Acta Physicochem U.R.S.S.*, *20*, 397 (1945); *Bull. acad. sci. U.R.S.S., Classe sci. chim.*, No. 4, 314 (1945); *Chem. Abstracts*, **40**, 5310 (1946).
19. Betrabet and Chakravarti, *J. Indian Chem. Soc.*, **7**, 191 (1930); *Chem. Zentr.*, **II**, 240 (1930); *Chem. Abstracts*, **25**, 701 (1931) and **24**, 4516 (1930).
20. d'Ennequin, *Teintex*, **20**, 879 (1955).
21. Guarneri, *Ann. chim. (Rome)*, **47**, 163 (1957).
22. Rydon, Smith and Williams, *J. Chem. Soc.*, **1957**, 1900.

A-95. 1,4-Epoxy-1*H*-isoindolo[2,1-*a*]-benzimidazole. R.I. 2889

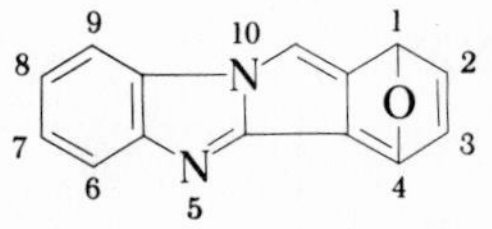

Anderlini[1] treated cantharidin (I) with *o*-phenylenediamine and with 3,4-toluenediamine, and obtained products (m. 165–6° and 180–1°, respectively), to which Gadamer[2] assigned structure II (R = H or CH_3). The 8-substituted isomer of II would seem to be an equally possible structure for these products.

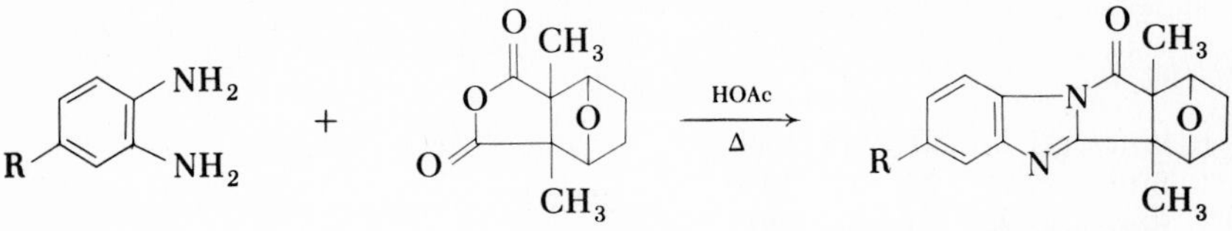

(I) (II)

References

1. Anderlini, *Gazz. chim. ital.*, **23, I**, 138 (1893).
2. Gadamer, *Arch. Pharm.*, **260**, 199 (1922); *Chem. Zentr.*, **I**, 687 (1923).

A-96. 5*H*-Benzimidazo[1,2-*a*]pyrido-[2,3-*c*]pyrrole. R.I. 2270

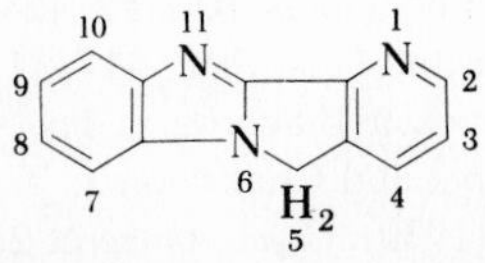

This nucleus has also been named *benzimidazopyrrolopyridine* and *nicotinoylenebenzimidazole*. In 1921 Bistrzycki and Leko[1] treated quinolinic acid (I) with *o*-phenylenediamine and obtained a product (yellow crystals, m. 221–2°), which they recognized might have either structure II or III. Since picolinic acid is a weaker acid than nicotinic acid, these authors reasoned that the 3-carboxyl group of I would be more apt to react initially with the diamine and therefore they considered their product to have structure III.

In reinvestigating this problem, Leko and Ivkovich[2] degraded the product (by hydrolysis and decarboxylation) to a 2-(pyridyl)benzimidazole. This was identified as 2-(2-pyridyl)benzimidazole by comparison with authentic samples of the two possible benzimidazoles, thus showing the original product to be II, not III.

NH_2 NH_2 + HOOC HOOC N →

(I)

N N N O *or* N N N O

(II) (III)

It has been suggested[3] that shielding of the 3-carboxyl group of I, such as by inner salt formation, is responsible for the formation of II instead of III. Even when the 2-carboxyl group is blocked, for example as in the case of the 2-monoamide[3] or 2-monoester[4] derivatives of I, only compound II results.

References

1. Bistrzycki and Leko, *Helv. chim. Acta*, **4,** 425 (1921).
2. Leko and Ivkovich, *Bull. soc. chim. roy. Jugoslav.*, **1,** No. 1, 3 (1930); *Chem. Zentr.*, **I,** 1100 (1932); *Chem. Abstracts*, **25,** 4269 (1931).
3. Leko and Bastić, *Bull. soc. chim. Belgrade*, **13,** 203 (1948); *Chem. Abstracts*, **46,** 8655 (1952).
4. Leko and Bastić, *Bull. soc. chim. Belgrade*, **14,** 105 (1949); *Chem. Abstracts*, **46,** 8656 (1952).
5. Bastić and Golubović, *Bull. soc. chim. Belgrade*, **21,** 95 (1956).

A-97. 5*H*-Benzimidazo[1,2-*a*]pyrido-[4,3-*c*]pyrrole

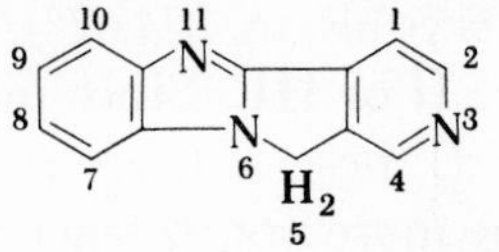

Compound I (m. 208–9°), the only example of this nucleus, was obtained[1] from cinchomeronic acid as shown. Its structure was demonstrated by degradation to 2-(4-pyridyl)benzimidazole (II).

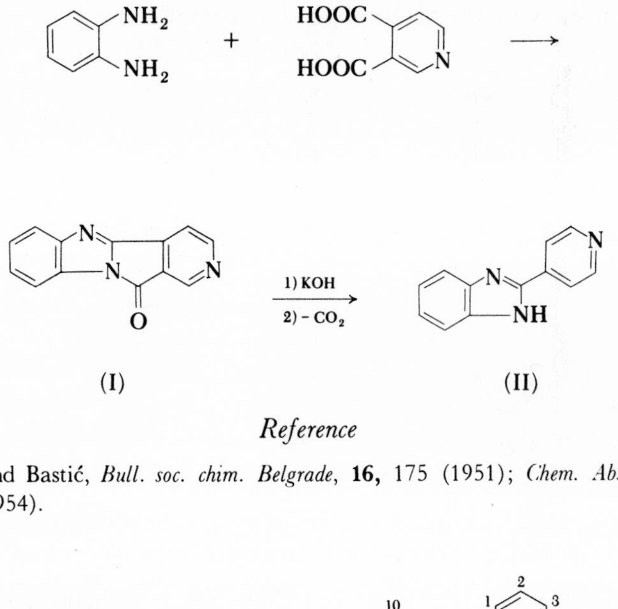

1) KOH

2) - CO_2

(I) (II)

Reference

1. Leko and Bastić, *Bull. soc. chim. Belgrade*, **16,** 175 (1951); *Chem. Abstracts*, **48,** 9366 (1954).

A-98. 10*H*-Naphtho[1,2-*d*]pyrrol-[1,2-*a*]imidazole*

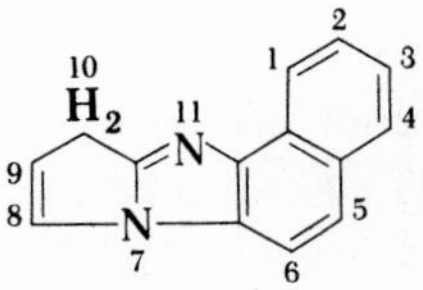

or

A-99. 10*H*-Naphtho[2,1-*d*]pyrrol-[1,2-*a*]imidazole*

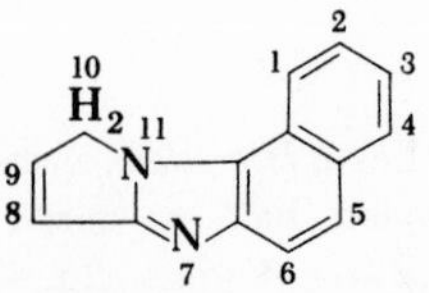

By the reaction of 1,2-naphthylenediamine with γ-butyrolactone, Reppe *et al.*[1] obtained a product (m. 168–70°), which probably has either structure I or II, probably the former, if the reaction is analogous to that of the diamine with δ-valerolactone (see Section A-283).

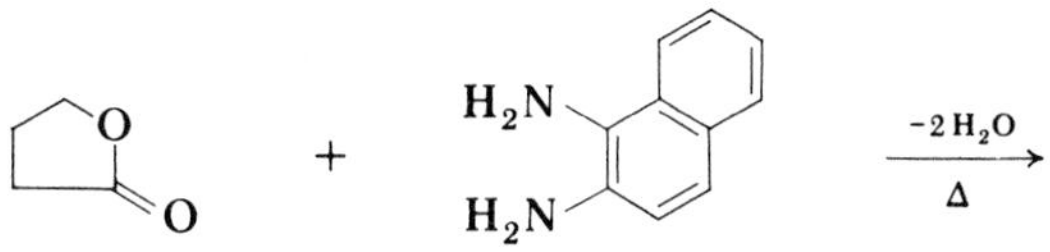

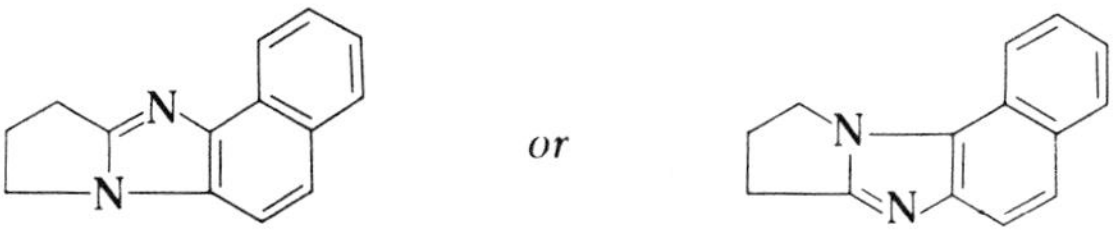

H_2N H_2N $-2H_2O$ Δ

(I) or (II)

Reference

1. Reppe *et al.*, *Ann.*, **596,** 209 (1955).

A-100. Cyclohepta[3,4]pyrrolo[1,2-*a*]-benzimidazole*

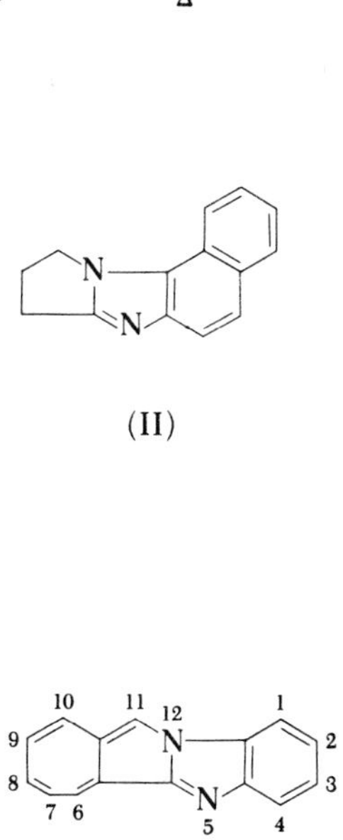

One of the metabolites isolated from cultures of various *Penicillia* molds is the compound $C_9H_4O_7$, which was named *puberulonic acid.* On the basis of incomplete information, puberulonic acid was considered[1] to have structure I or II, and its reaction with *o*-phenylenediamine was thought[1] to yield a quinoxaline derivative. Recently, however, the structure of the acid was shown[2] to be III, and the con-

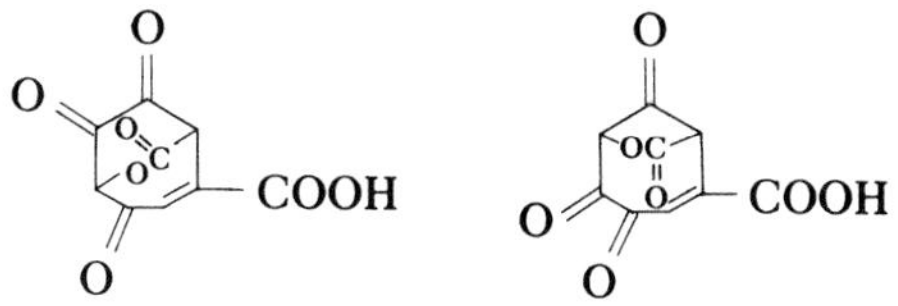

COOH COOH

(I) (II)

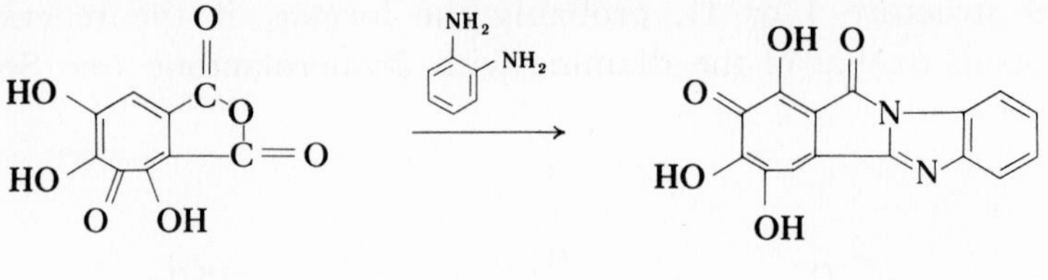

(III) (IV)

densation product (vermilion, chars but does not melt below 350°) with *o*-phenylenediamine is considered[3] to be IV.

References

1. Corbett, Hassall, Johnson, and Todd, *J. Chem. Soc.*, **1950,** 1.
2. Aulin-Erdtman, *Acta Chem. Scand.*, **5,** 301 (1951).
3. Johnson, Sheppard, and Todd, *J. Chem. Soc.*, **1951,** 1139.

A-101. 8*H*-Isoindolo[2,1-*a*]naphth-[1,2-*d*]imidazole. R.I. 2942

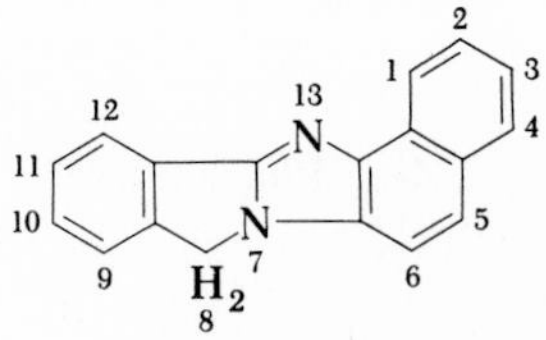

and

A-102. 12*H*-Isoindolo[2,1-*a*]naphth-[2,1-*d*]imidazole. R.I. 2943

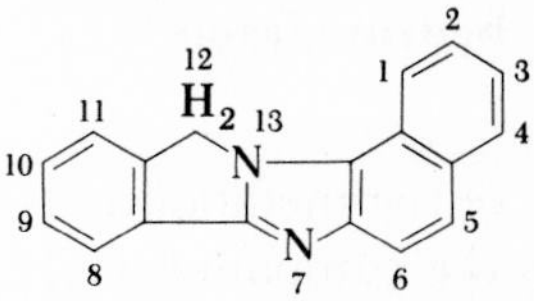

These nuclei have also been named *1,2-o-benzoylene-1,3-naphthodiazole* and *1′,2′-benzoylene-α-naphthimidazole-1,2* and *1(CO)-2-benzoylene-[naphtho-1′,2′:4,5-imidazole]*, and they are examples of the larger class of products, formed from the condensation of phthalic anhydride with vicinal aromatic diamines, which Bistrzycki has called *phthalamidones.* As these ring systems have a common origin they are discussed together here.

In 1892 Bistrzycki and Cybulski[1] described the product (yellow, m. 191–2°) obtained from the condensation of 1,2-naphthylenediamine (I) with opianic acid and assigned to it structure III. It is apparent that the carbonyl group could be attached to the nitrogen at either the α- or β-position of the naphthalene nucleus. To help settle

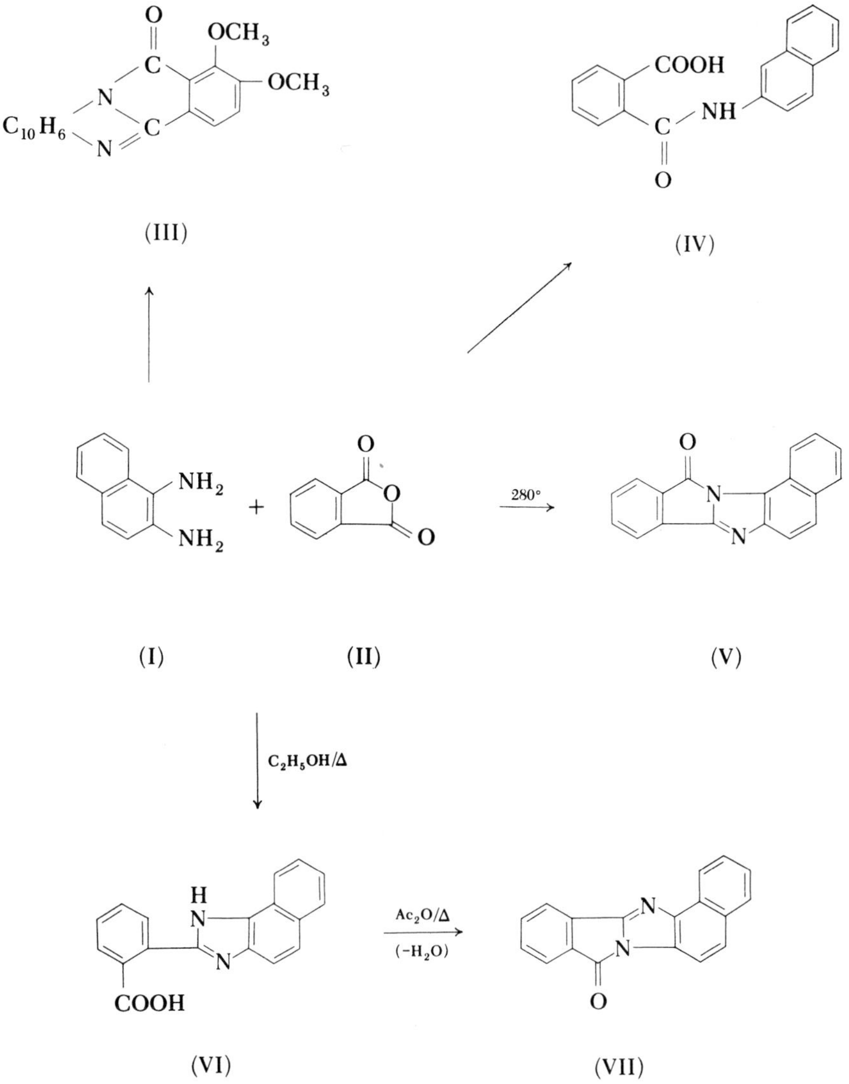

$C_{10}H_6$ N N C C O OCH_3 OCH_3

(III)

COOH NH C O

(IV)

NH_2 NH_2 + O O O 280° O N N

(I) (II) (V)

C_2H_5OH/Δ

H N N COOH Ac_2O/Δ $(-H_2O)$ N N O

(VI) (VII)

this question of structure, Bistrzycki and Risi[2] treated phthalic anhydride (II) with 1,2-naphthylenediamine (I) to obtain a phthalamic acid. The free amino group of this phthalamic acid was eliminated by diazotization and reduction to give a product, which might be either a 1- or 2-naphthylphthalamic acid. By synthesis of these two possible isomers it was shown that the product was the 2-isomer (IV). On the basis of this information Bistrzycki and Risi assigned structure

V to the product (yellowish orange, m. 213°) obtained from the fusion of I and II. This same product was obtained by Lieb,[7] who also assigned to it structure V. Chakravarti[3] claimed to have obtained VI by reacting I with II in ethanol and that dehydration of VI gave VII. No properties of VII, or other evidence to support this claim were

NH_2 NO_2 II → O N O NO_2

O N N

I + II 270–280° (V)

140–170° N N O

(VII)

NO_2 NH_2 II → O NO_2 N O

mentioned. The reaction of tetrahydrophthalic anhydride with I was reported[4] to give a product (m. 223–4°), which might be the tetrahydro analog of either V or VII.

An unequivocal solution to this problem was finally offered by Crippa and Galimberti,[5] who found that the nature of product formed by the fusion of I and II depended upon the temperature of the reaction. Lower temperatures gave VII, whereas at higher temperatures V was obtained. Each compound was synthesized independently from the appropriate nitronaphthylamine by condensation with II followed by reduction of the nitro group and dehydration. The properties of V agreed with those reported by Bistrzycki and Risi, and VII was found to melt at 299–300°.

In a further synthesis, IX (straw colored, m. 246°) was obtained[6] as shown from VIII.

II + H_2N ... $N=N-C_6H_5$ ... Br → O, N, O, Br, $N=N-C_6H_5$ →

(VIII)

O, N, N, Br

(IX)

References

1. Bistrzycki and Cybulski, *Ber.*, **25,** 1984 (1892).
2. Bistrzycki and Risi, *Helv. Chim. Acta*, **8,** 810 (1925).
3. Chakravarti, *Quart. J. Indian Chem. Soc.*, **1,** 19 (1924); *Chem. Zentr.*, **I,** 518 (1925); *Chem. Abstracts*, **19,** 830 (1925).
4. Betrabet and Chakravarti, *J. Indian Chem. Soc.*, **7,** 191 (1930); *Chem. Zentr.*, **II,** 240 (1930); *Chem. Abstracts*, **24,** 4516 (1930); **25,** 701 (1931).
5. Crippa and Galimberti, *Gazz. chim. ital.*, **59,** 510 (1929).
6. Crippa and Perroncito, *Gazz. chim. ital.*, **65,** 678 (1935).
7. Lieb, *Monatsh.*, **39,** 883 (1918).

A-103. 5*H*-Naphth[2′,3′,4,5]imidazo-[1,2-*a*]pyrido[2,3-*c*]pyrrole*

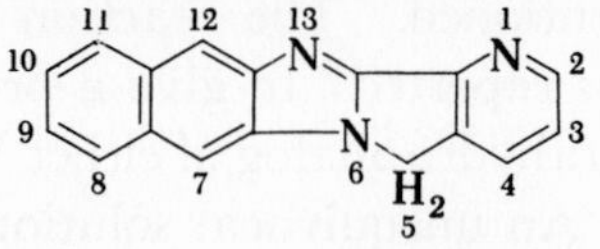

Condensation of quinolinic anhydride with 2,3-naphthylenediamine yielded[1] I (m. 320°); the structure of which was demonstrated by degradation to II, which also was prepared by the condensation of picolinic acid with 2,3-naphthylenediamine. See Sections A-96/97.

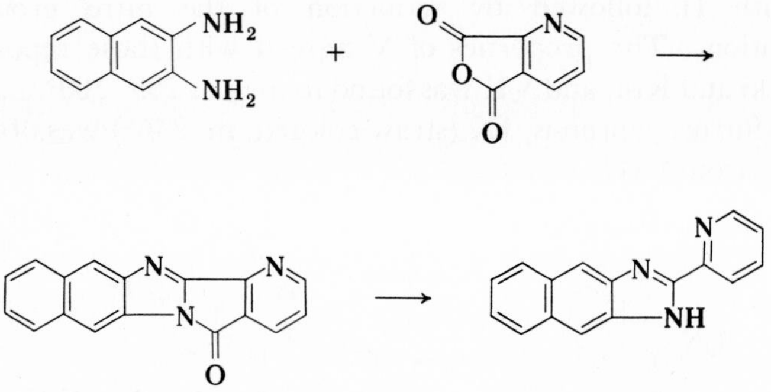

(I) (II)

Reference

1. Bastić and Golubović, *Glasnik Khem. Drushtva, Beograd*, **18,** No. 4, 235 (1953); *Chem. Abstracts*, **52,** 2005 (1958).

A-104. 13*H*-Isoindolo[2,1-*a*]quinoxalo-[2′,3′-*d*]imidazole. R.I. 2941

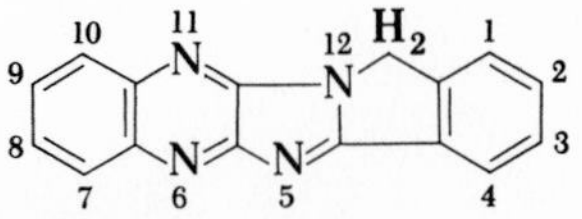

While investigating the reaction of 2,3-diaminoquinoxaline (I) with various acid anhydrides, Sircar and Pal[1] obtained II (light yellow, m. >300°), which was called *o-benzoylenequinoxalino(2,3)imidazole.*

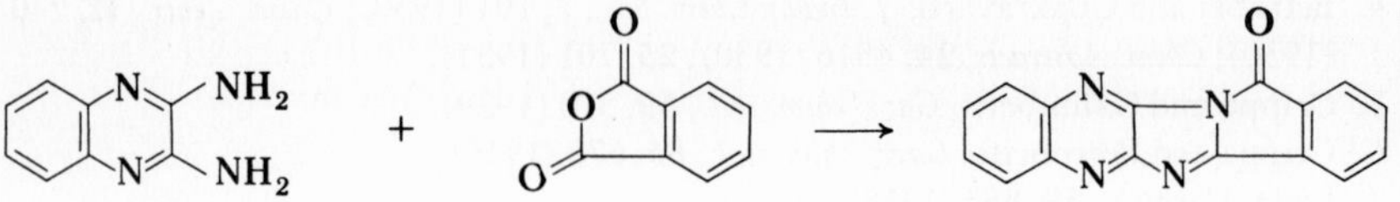

(I) (II)

Reference

1. Sircar and Pal, *J. Indian Chem. Soc.*, **9,** 527 (1932); *Chem. Zentr.*, **I,** 1947 (1933); *Chem. Abstracts*, **27,** 1882 (1932).

A-105. 12*H*-Acenaphth[4,5-*d*]isoindolo-[2,1-*a*]imidazole. R.I. 3455

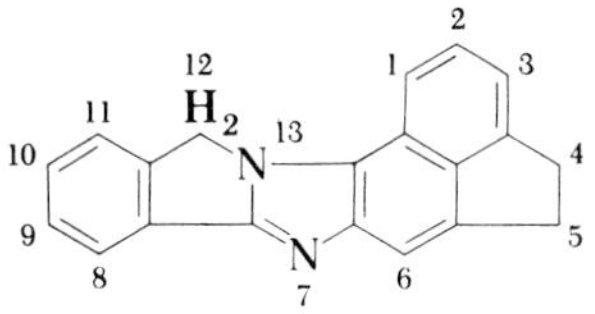

This nucleus has also been called *1′,2′-benzyleneacenaphtho-4,5-imidazole.* By heating compound I with zinc dust and acetic acid, Crippa and Perroncito[1] obtained II (m. 280°).

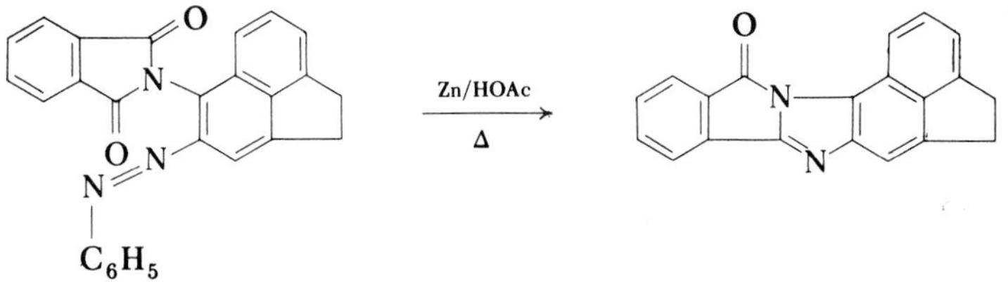

Zn/HOAc
Δ

(I) (II)

Reference

1. Crippa and Perroncito, *Gazz. chim. ital.*, **64,** 415 (1934); *Chem. Abstracts*, **28,** 6433 (1934); *Chem. Zentr.*, **II,** 3620 (1934).

A-106. 13*H*-Anthra[2,1-*d*]isoindolo-[2,1-*a*]imidazole. R.I. 3465

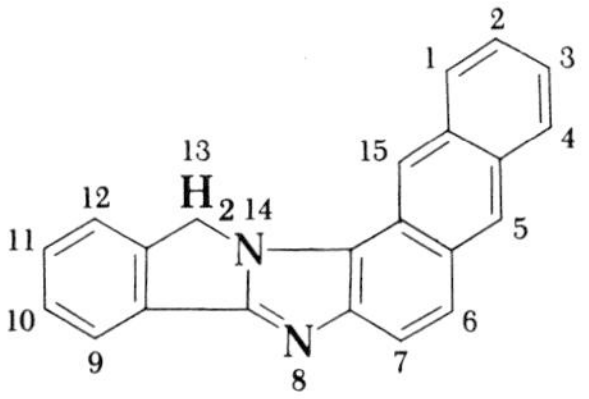

This nucleus was also called *isoindoloanthrimidazole.* The single representative, I (yellow needles, m. 354°d.), was prepared by Lieb and Schwarzer[1,2] from the reaction of 1,2-diaminoanthraquinone with phthalic anhydride. The lactam ring is readily split when I is warmed with alkaline solutions.

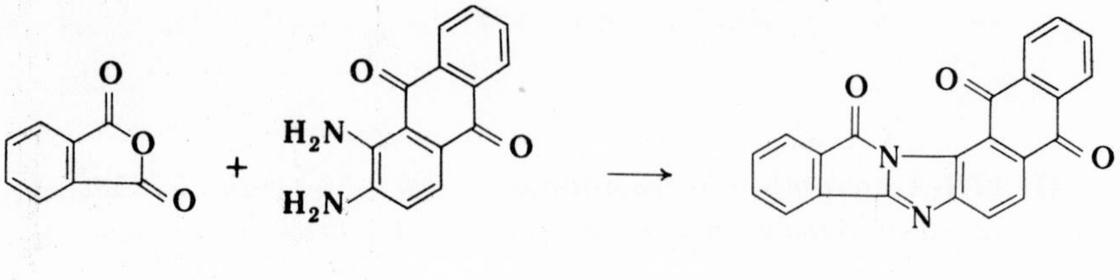

(I)

References

1. Lieb and Schwarzer, *Monatsh.*, **41,** 573 (1921).
2. Lieb and Schwarzer, *Sitzber. Akad. Wiss. Wien, Math. naturw. Kl., Abt. IIb*, **129,** 573 (1920).

A-107. 12*H*-Isoindolo[2,1-*a*]phenazino-[2,3-*d*]imidazole. R.I. 3464

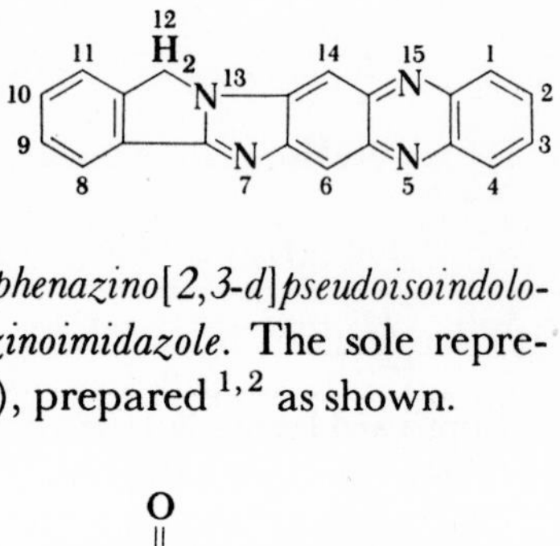

This nucleus has also been called *phenazino[2,3-d]pseudoisoindolo-[2,3-a]imidazole* and *o-benzoylene-2,3-phenazinoimidazole*. The sole representative is compound I (yellow, m. 358°), prepared[1,2] as shown.

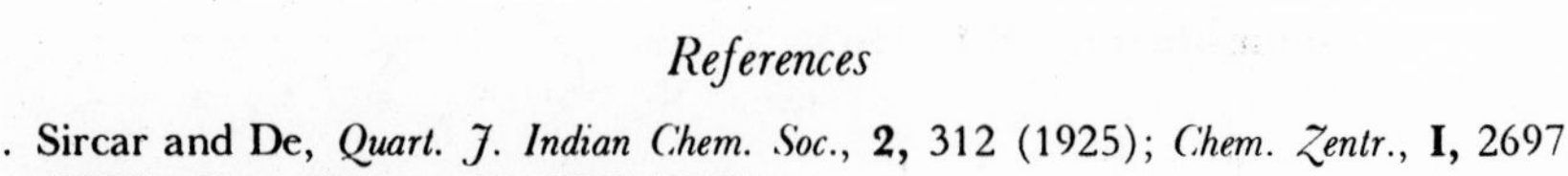

(I)

References

1. Sircar and De, *Quart. J. Indian Chem. Soc.*, **2,** 312 (1925); *Chem. Zentr.*, **I,** 2697 (1926); *Chem. Abstracts*, **20,** 1805 (1926).
2. Crippa and Galimberti, *Gazz. chim. ital.*, **61,** 91 (1931); *Chem. Zentr.*, **I,** 3349 (1931); *Chem. Abstracts*, **25,** 3343 (1931).

A-108. 16*H*-Benzimidazo[2,1-*a*]phenanthro[9,10-*f*]isoindole. R.I. 3693

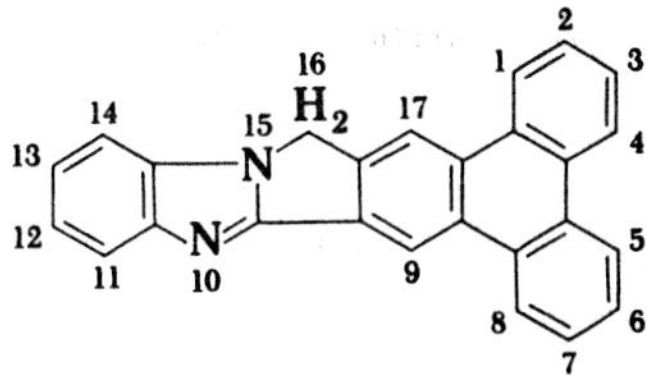

While investigating the reactions of the anhydride I, Dilthey, ter Horst and Schaefer[1] prepared compound II (yellow crystals, m. 312°; gives a red sulfuric acid solution).

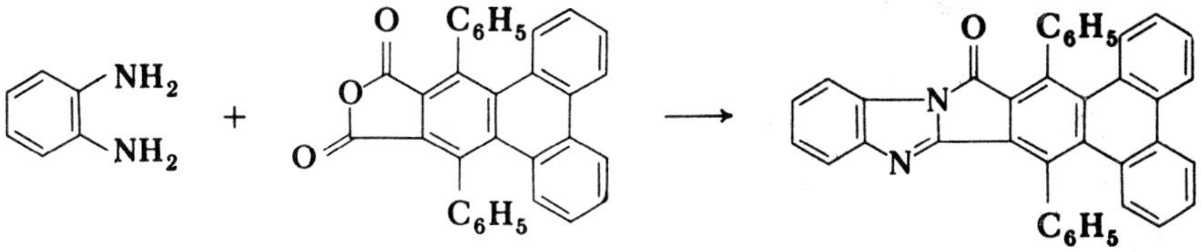

(I) (II)

Reference

1. Dilthey, ter Horst, and Schaefer, *J. prakt. Chem.*, **148,** 53 (1937).

A-109. 12*H*,16*H*-Diisoindolo-[2,1-*a*, 1,2-*h*]*m*-benzobisimidazole. R.I. 3680.

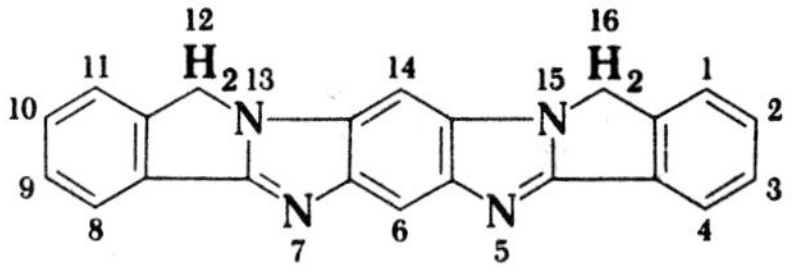

Crippa and Galimberti[1] obtained compound II (red-brown, m. >300°), which they called *sym-bisbenzoylenebenzimidazole*, by reduction of I (R = NO_2) and cyclodehydration of the resulting diamine

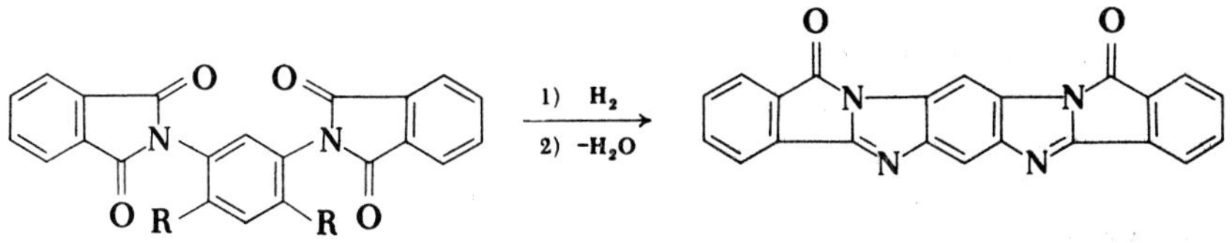

1) H_2 2) $-H_2O$

(I) (II)

by treatment with hot acetic anhydride. Efforts to prepare I ($R = C_6H_5N{=}N$) by the condensation of 4,6-bisphenylazo-*m*-phenylenediamine with phthalic anhydride were not successful, since the phenylazo groups were eliminated during the reaction.

Reference

1. Crippa and Galimberti, *Gazz. chim. ital.*, **61**, 91 (1931).

A-110. Benzobis[1″,2″-*c*, 4″,5″-*c*′]-benzimidazo[1,2-*a*]pyrrole

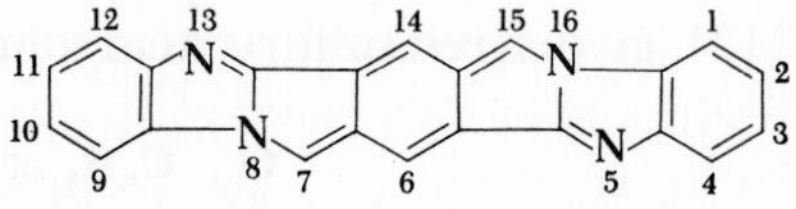

The single representative (II) of this ring system has been obtained[1,2] by the condensation of pyromellitic acid (or anhydride, I) with *o*-phenylenediamine. Compound II is golden yellow, m. ~300°d., and the lactam rings are readily cleaved by caustic.

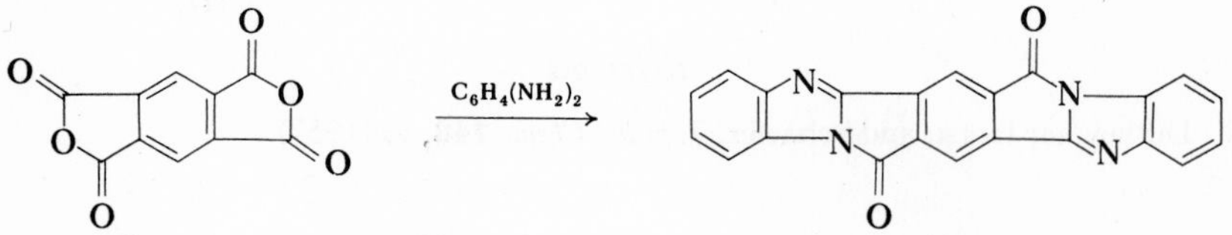

$C_6H_4(NH_2)_2$

(I) (II)

References

1. Bayer, *I. G. Farbenindustrie A.-G.*, *8 Wissenschaftlicher Austausch der Gruppe IX*, May 23, and June 28, 1933, Höchst; *PB Report No.* 25630, frame 683.
2. de Diesbach and Riat, *Helv. Chim. Acta*, **24**, 1306 (1941).

A-111. Bisbenzimidazo-[1,2-*a*, 1′,2′-*a*′]naphtho-[2,1-*c*, 6,5-*c*′]dipyrrole*

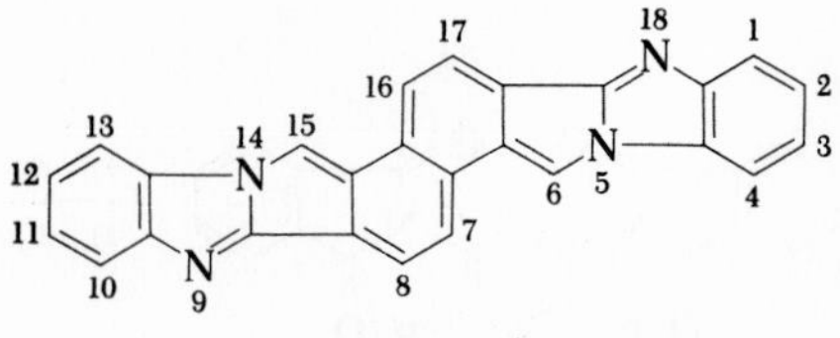

and/or

A-112. Bisbenzimidazo-[1,2-*a*, 1′,2′-*a*′]naphtho-[1,2-*c*, 6,5-*c*′]dipyrrole*

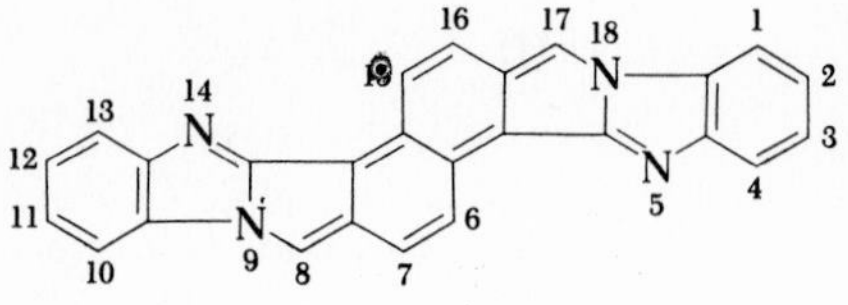

and/or

A-113. 14*H*,17*H*-Bisbenzimidazo-[1,2-*a*, 1′,2′-*a*′]naphtho-[1,2-*c*, 6,5-*c*′]dipyrrole*

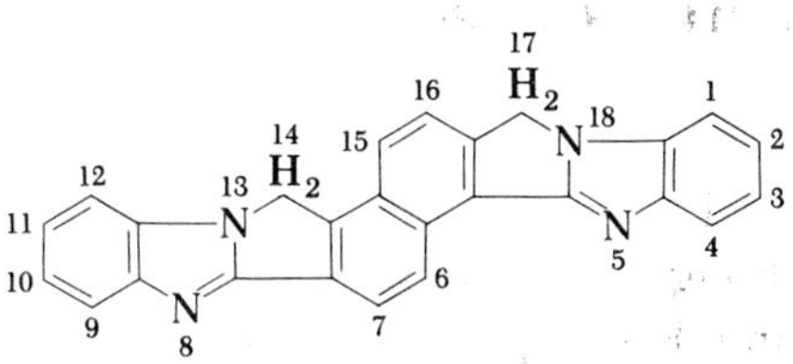

The preparation of the dianhydride I has been described by Vollmann and Boedeker,[1] who treated I with *o*-phenylenediamine in acetic acid and obtained a pale orange "di-imidazole derivative" (m. >400°). This product, which vats (only in the presence of pyridine) to a greenish yellow solution exhibiting no affinity for cotton, must be represented by either structure II or III or a mixture of both. A third possibility, structure IV, seems excluded by the fact that the compound does vat, albeit reluctantly.

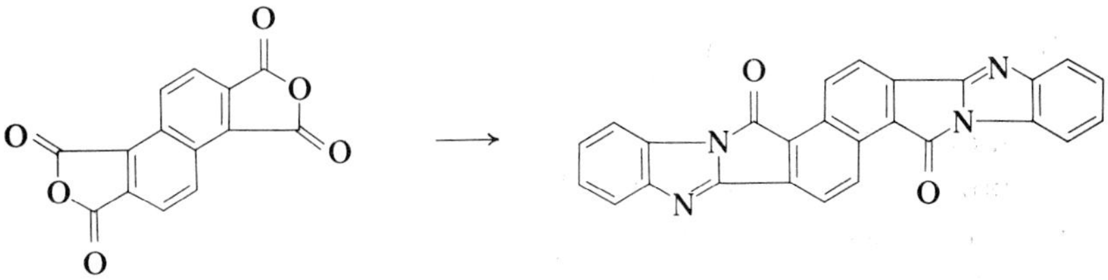

(I) (II)

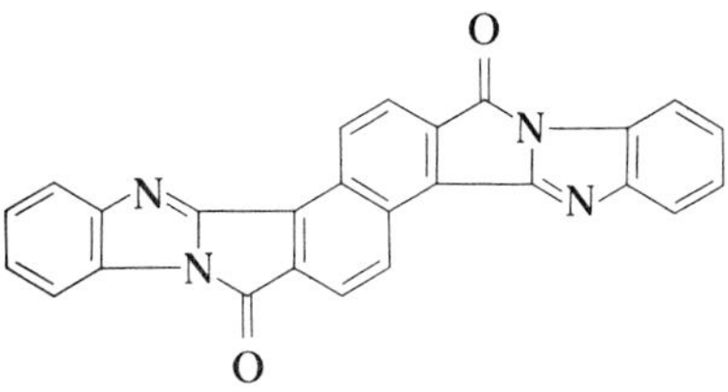

(III) 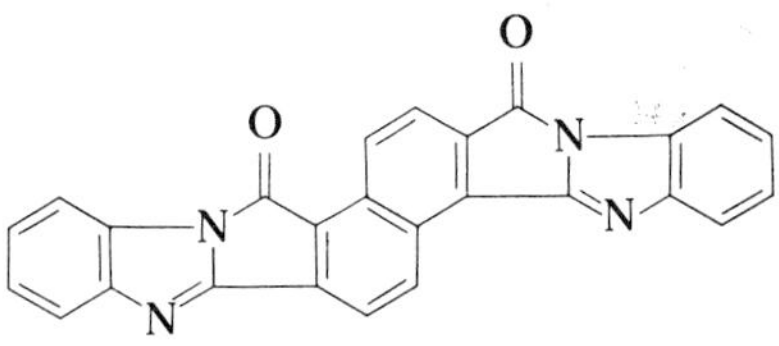 (IV)

Reference

1. Vollmann and Boedeker, *I. G. Farbenindustrie A.-G., 38 Zetko-Sitzung*, Feb. 23, 1934; *PB Report No*. 17657, frames 1466–76.

A-114. 1*H*,3*H*-Pyrrolo[1,2-*c*]oxazole

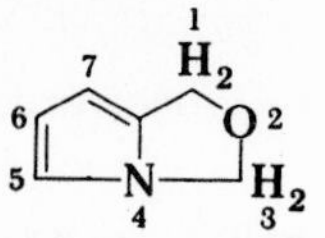

It has been claimed by Clemo and Vipond[1] that the product thought to be IV by Leonard and Ruyle,[2] is, in fact, III. Leonard and Ruyle prepared their product by the method of Hess,[3] who treated I with formaldehyde and acid. Hess suggested that the intermediate II underwent an internal oxidation-reduction, and that the product had structure IV. Instead, it appears dehydration to III (b_{12} 70–2°; n_D^{20} 1.4611; picrate, m. 103–4°; aurichloride, m. 106°) occurs.

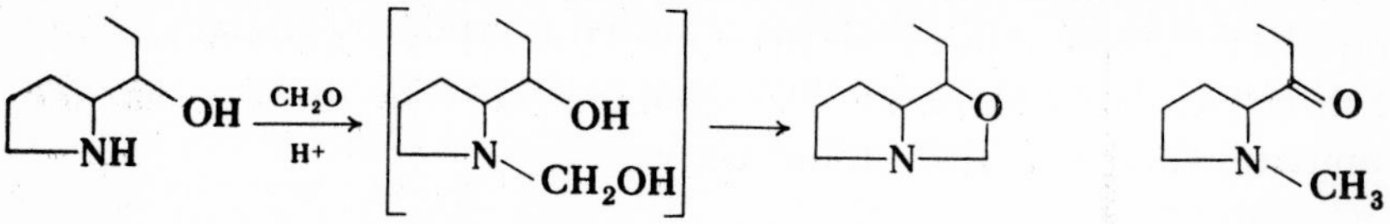

(I) (II) (III) (IV)

Compound V, prepared as shown from proline by Petri and Staverman,[4] might be considered a member of this ring system. Compound V was also obtained[5] by treating *N*-carbobenzoxy-L-proline with phosphorus pentachloride, and was converted, with loss of carbon dioxide, into poly-L-proline.

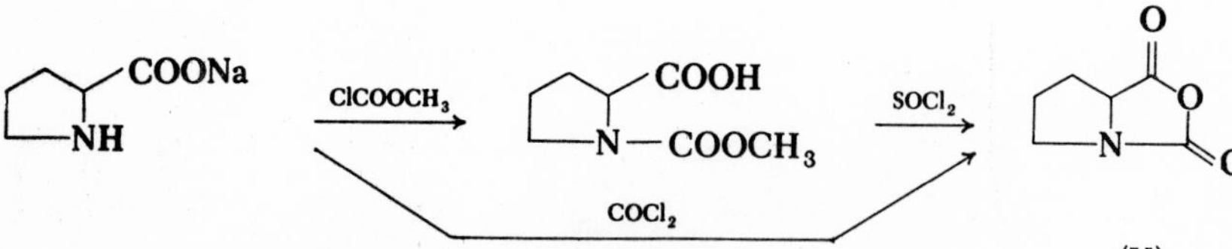

(V)

References

1. Clemo and Vipond, *Chem. and Ind.*, **1949,** 856.
2. Leonard and Ruyle, *J. Am. Chem. Soc.*, **71,** 3094 (1949).
3. Hess, *Ber.*, **46,** 4104 (1913).
4. Petri and Stavermann, *Rec. trav. chim.*, **71,** 385 (1952).
5. Berger, Kurtz, and Katchalski, *J. Am. Chem. Soc.*, **76,** 5552 (1954).

A-115. 1*H*-Imidazo[1,5-*a*]pyrrole.
R.I. 616

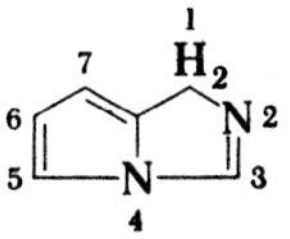

A number of derivatives of this nucleus have been prepared by the reaction of cyanic acid and its derivatives (e.g., phenyl isocyanate, thiocyanic acid, etc.) with the amino acid proline (I) and its derivatives (e.g., hydroxyproline, pyrrolidonecarboxylic acid, etc.).[1-13] These products of type II have been called (where R = H and X = O) *proline hydantoin*, and (where R = C_6H_5 and X = S) *1-oxo-2-phenyl-3-thio-1-imidazolino[1,5-a]pyrrolidine*, and where R = H and X = S) *pyrrolidino(1′:2′-1:5)-2-thiohydantoin*. They are of interest in the identification and isolation of amino acids.[9,12,19,20] A different synthesis of II (R = C_6H_5) was reported recently by Gaudry,[13] who built up stepwise, as shown, both rings of the system.

(I) —RNCX→ (II) X = O *or* S

C_6H_5NCO; 1. HBr 2. $[OH^-]$

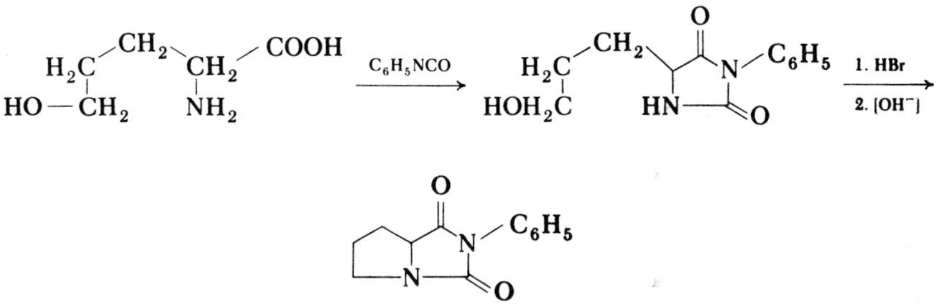

Burke and Hammer[14] found that while pyrrole itself underwent the Mannich reaction to yield only α-alkylaminomethylpyrroles, 3-carbethoxy-2,4-dimethylpyrrole reacted further to give III. In contrast to many pyrrole derivatives, the ring system of III was stable to acids and to alcoholic alkali. The pyrrole ring was also found stable to lithium aluminum hydride reduction.

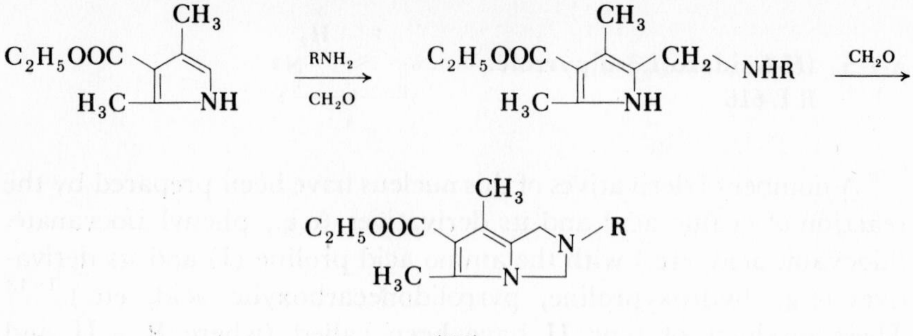

$$C_2H_5OOC\text{-(3-}CH_3\text{, 2-}H_3C\text{-pyrrole)} \xrightarrow[CH_2O]{RNH_2} C_2H_5OOC\text{-(3-}CH_3\text{, 2-}H_3C\text{-pyrrole)-}CH_2NHR \xrightarrow{CH_2O}$$

(III)

A recent synthesis of this nucleus, unique in that it begins with an intact imidazole ring, was described by Bullerwell, Lawson, and Morley,[15] who obtained V from the dehydration of IV. The acetyl group was cleaved by boiling water and then the lactam ring was opened by treatment with a base. Compound V was named as a derivative of *glyoxalino(1′:5′-1:5)pyrrolid-2-one.*

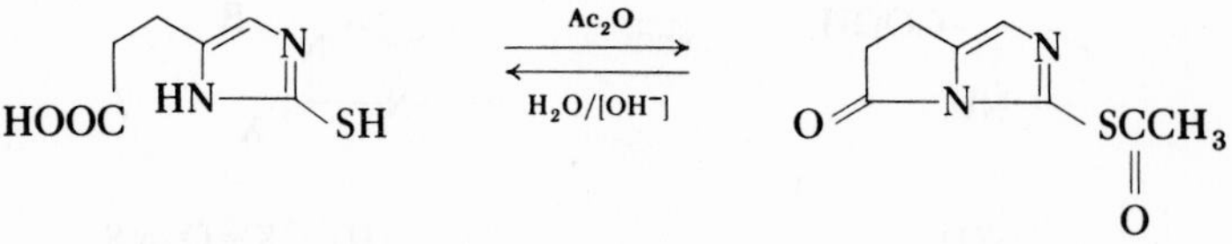

$$\text{(IV)} \underset{H_2O/[OH^-]}{\overset{Ac_2O}{\rightleftharpoons}} \text{(V)}$$

(IV) (V)

Derivatives of Imidazo[1,5-*a*]pyrrole

Empirical formula	Structure	Properties and comments	Refs.
$C_6H_6N_2OS$	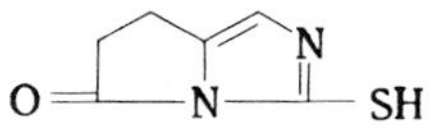	m. 228°. *S*-Acetyl deriv., m. 192 °	15
$C_6H_6N_2O_2S$	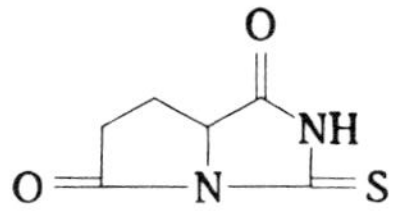	m. 206–7°	3,4,10,17
$C_6H_6N_2O_3$	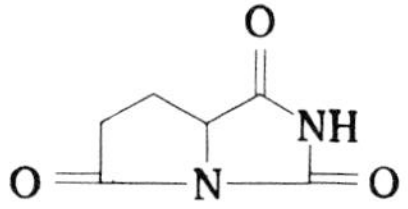	m. 201°. *N*-Acetyl deriv., m. 147–8°.	10
$C_6H_8N_2OS$	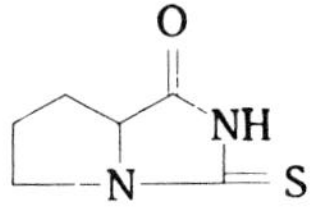	m. 161–3°.	17
$C_6H_8N_2O_2$	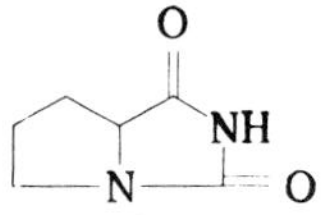	*dl*-Isomer, m. 142–3°. *l*-Isomer, m. 165–7°; $[\alpha]_D^{20}$ – 232 to – 238.5 (C = 2).	5,7,9
$C_6H_8N_2O_3$	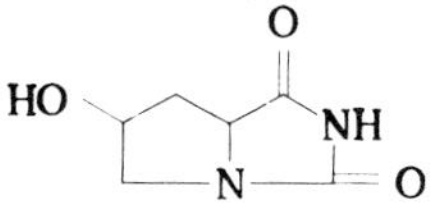		9

(continued)

Derivatives of Imidazo[1,5-*a*]pyrrole (*continued*)

Empirical formula	Structure	Properties and comments	Refs.
$C_{12}H_{11}N_2O_3S$	O, N, N, S, NO_2	*l*-Isomer, m. 168–9°.	18
$C_{12}H_{12}NOS$	O, N, N, S, C_6H_5	*dl*-Isomer, m. 146–8°. *l*-Isomer, m. 179°.	6,11,12,16,21
$C_{12}H_{12}NO_2$	O, N, N, O, C_6H_5	*dl*-Isomer, m. 118° (114–6°). *l*-Isomer, m. 143°.	1,2,13
$C_{12}H_{12}NO_2S$	HO, O, N, N, S, C_6H_5	m. 145–8°.	11
$C_{12}H_{12}NO_3$	HO, O, N, N, O, C_6H_5	*d*-Isomer, m. 130–1°. Dihydrate, m. 70°. $[\alpha]_D^{25°}$ + 49.2°.	6

$C_{13}H_{14}NO_2$	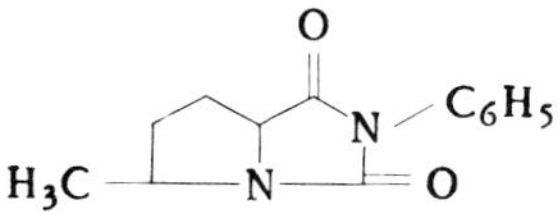 O; H_3C; N; C_6H_5; O	m. 130°.	8
$C_{14}H_{22}N_2O_2$	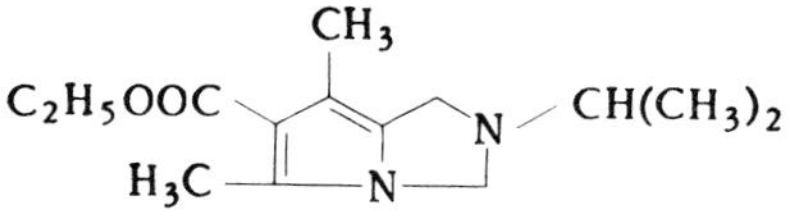 CH_3; C_2H_5OOC; H_3C; N; N; $CH(CH_3)_2$	m. 86.5–7.5°. HCl salt, m. 159–60°.	14
$C_{15}H_{22}N_2O_2$	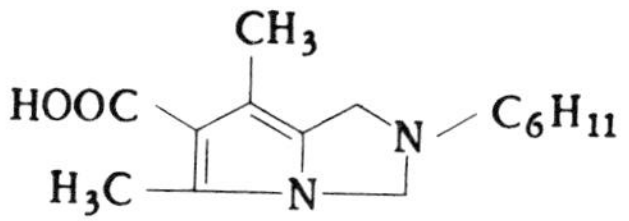 CH_3; HOOC; H_3C; N; N; C_6H_{11}	m. 183°. Ethyl ester, m. 88.5°-9°; HCl salt, m. 184-6°.	14
$C_{15}H_{24}N_2O$	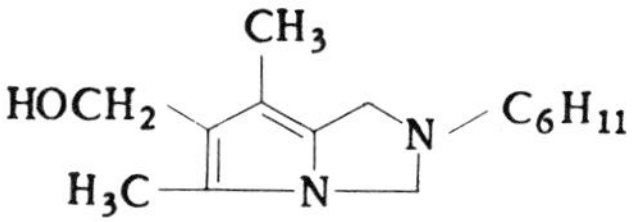 CH_3; $HOCH_2$; H_3C; N; N; C_6H_{11}	m. 94.5–5.5°.	14
$C_{15}H_{24}N_2O_2$	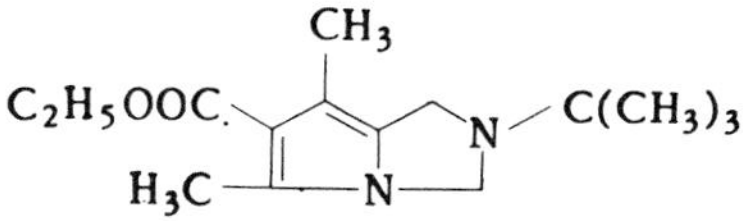 CH_3; C_2H_5OOC; H_3C; N; N; $C(CH_3)_3$	m. 187–9°.	14

References

1. Fischer, *Z. physiol. Chem.*, **33,** 151 (1901).
2. Fischer, *Ber.*, **34,** 460 (1901).
3. Johnson and Guest, *Am. Chem. J.*, **47,** 242 (1912).
4. Johnson and Nicolet, *Am. Chem. J.*, **49,** 197 (1913).
5. Dakin, *Biochem. J.*, **12,** 290 (1918).
6. Leuchs and Bormann, *Ber.*, **52,** 2086 (1919).
7. Dakin, *J. Biol. Chem.*, **44,** 499 (1920).
8. Winterfeld and Rönsberg, *Arch. Pharm.*, **274,** 40 (1936).
9. Boyd, *Biochem. J.*, **27,** 1838 (1937).
10. Szabo and Karabinos, *J. Am. Chem. Soc.*, **66,** 650 (1944).
11. Edman, *Acta Chem. Scand.*, **4,** 277 (1950).
12. Sjöquist, *Acta Chem. Scand.*, **7,** 447 (1953).
13. Gaudry, *Can. J. Chem.*, **29,** 544 (1951).
14. Burke and Hammer, *J. Am. Chem. Soc.*, **76,** 1294 (1954).
15. Bullerwell, Lawson, and Morley, *J. Chem. Soc.*, **1954,** 3283.
16. Landmann, Drake, and Dillaha, *J. Am. Chem. Soc.*, **75,** 3638 (1953).
17. Elmore, Ogle, and Toseland, *J. Chem. Soc.*, **1956,** 192.
18. Ramachandran and McConnell, *J. Am. Chem. Soc.*, **78,** 1255 (1956).
19. Levy, *Biochim. et Biophys. Acta*, **15,** 589 (1954); *Chem. Abstracts*, **49,** 5547 (1955).
20. Levy and Chung, *Biochim. et Biophys. Acta*, **17,** 454 (1955); *Chem. Abstracts*, **49,** 14839 (1955).
21. Ramachandran and McConnell, *Anal. Chem.*, **27,** 1734 (1955).

A-116. 1*H*-Imidazo[3,4-*a*]indole

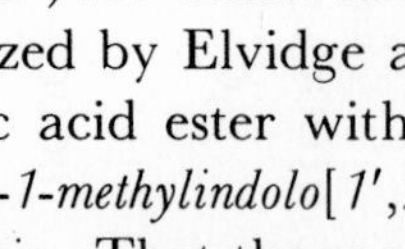

Alkaline hydrolysis of the mold metabolite *gliotoxin* yielded a product $C_{11}H_8N_2OS$ (m. 189°, 188°) for which structure I was suggested.[1] Compound I was synthesized by Elvidge and Spring[2,3] by the reaction of indole-2-carboxylic acid ester with methyl isothiocyanate, and named by them *2-thio-1-methylindolo[1′,2′,3,4]hydantoin* or *2-thio-3-methylindolo-1′:2′-1:5-hydantoin.* That the reaction had indeed occurred to give product I, and not, for example, II, was shown by evidence that 1-methylindole-3-carboxylic acid ester failed to react with methyl isothiocyanate, whereas 3-methylindole-2-carboxylic acid ester gave a compound (the 9-methyl homolog of I, orange-yellow, m. 222°) having an ultraviolet absorption spectrum virtually identical with that of I.

Further evidence in favor of the assignment of structure I to the gliotoxin hydrolysis product was adduced by Johnson and

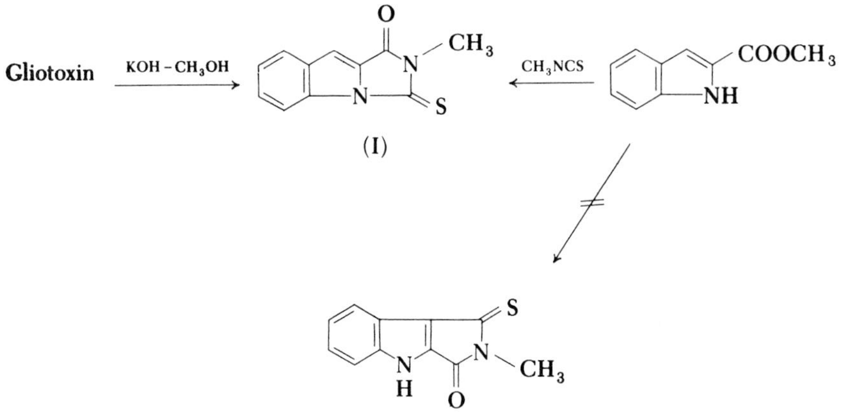

Gliotoxin $\xrightarrow{KOH-CH_3OH}$ (I) $\xleftarrow{CH_3NCS}$ indole-2-$COOCH_3$ (NH) $\nrightarrow$ (II)

(I): O, N–CH_3, N, S

(II): S, N–CH_3, N H, O

Buchanan,[4] who synthesized I by the reaction of III with *o*-brombenzaldehyde to give IV, which was cyclized to I. Also, indole-2-carboxylic acid ester was converted[5] into V (m. 263–4°), and .this was methylated to yield VI (m. 181.5–2°), a product readily obtained from the oxidative hydrolysis of I.

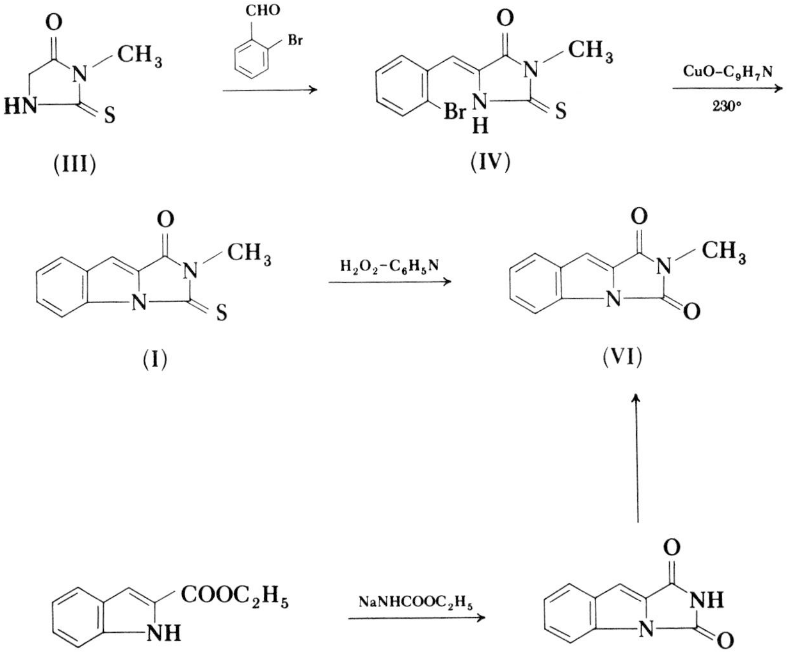

(III) (O, N–CH_3, HN, S) + CHO, Br (*o*-bromobenzaldehyde) $\longrightarrow$ (IV) (O, N–CH_3, Br, N H, S) $\xrightarrow[230°]{CuO-C_9H_7N}$

(I) (O, N–CH_3, N, S) $\xrightarrow{H_2O_2-C_6H_5N}$ (VI) (O, N–CH_3, N, O)

indole-2-$COOC_2H_5$ (NH) $\xrightarrow{NaNHCOOC_2H_5}$ (V) (O, NH, N, O) $\longrightarrow$ (VI)

References

1. Dutcher, Johnson, and Bruce, *J. Am. Chem. Soc.*, **67,** 1736 (1945).
2. Elvidge and Spring, *Nature*, **163,** 94 (1949).
3. Elvidge and Spring, *J. Chem. Soc.*, **1949,** S 134.
4. Johnson and Buchanan, *J. Am. Chem. Soc.*, **73,** 3749 (1951).
5. Dutcher and Kjaer, *J. Am. Chem. Soc.*, **73,** 4139 (1951).

A-117. 1*H*,4a*H*-Pyrrolo[1′,2′-3,4]imidazo-[1,2-*a*]pyridine*

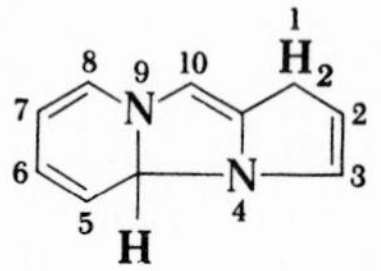

Treatment of quaternary salts of structure I (see Section A-271) with base did not yield the expected "enol-betaine" II, but gave[1] instead dehydration products of structure III (R = R′ = CH_3, red, m. 190°; R = CH_3, R′ = C_6H_5, red, m. ~192°; R = C_6H_5, R′ = CH_3, golden, m. 210–2°, HBr salt, m. ~280°; R = R′ = C_6H_5, red, m. 225°, HBr salt, m. ~250°d.), probably a resonance hybrid of forms such as IIIa–IIId, and others.

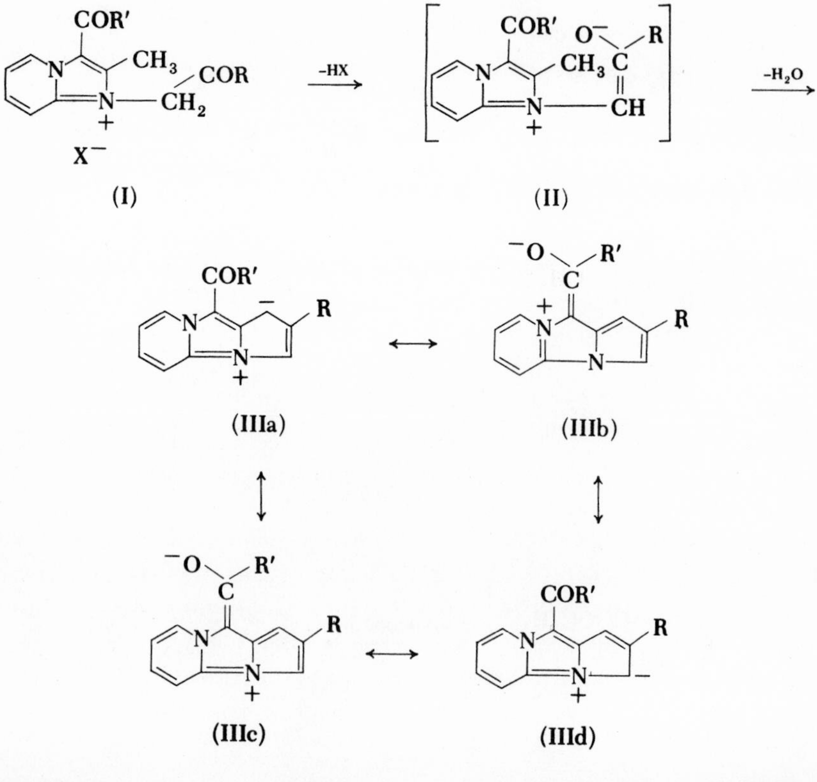

-HX

-H_2O

(I)

(II)

(IIIa)

(IIIb)

(IIIc)

(IIId)

Reference

1. Schilling, Kröhnke, and Kickhöfen, *Chem. Ber.*, **88,** 1093 (1955).

A-118. 6*H*-Diindolo[1,2-*c*, 2′,1′-*e*]-imidazole. R.I. 2906

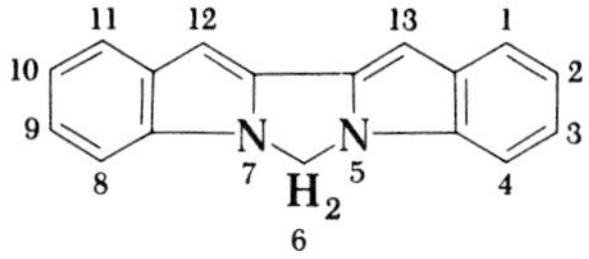

By warming 2,2′-diindolyl (I) with acetic anhydride, Madelung and Hager[1] obtained, among other products, a material (colorless crystals, m. 212°) which they called *N-cycloacetyldiindolyl* and to which they assigned structure II. Some further evidence for this structure would be welcome.

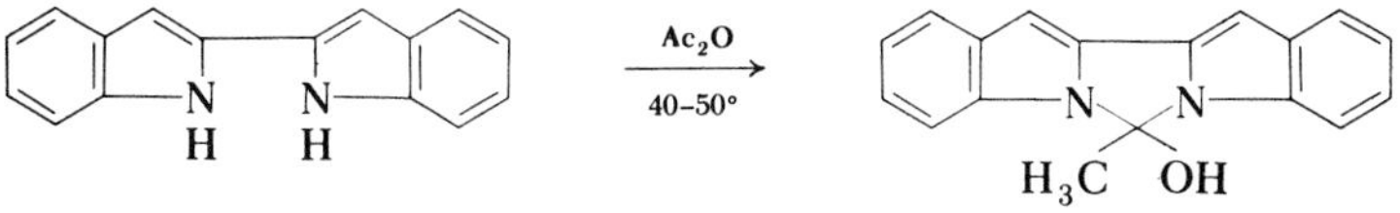

(I) (II)

Reference

1. Madelung and Hager, *Ber.*, **49,** 2039 (1916).

A-119. Pyrrolo[1,2-*b*]isoxazole. R.I. 596

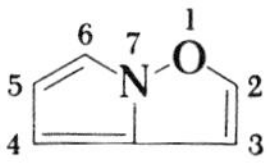

The only representative is a betaine of the 3,6-ethano compound (see Section B-24).

A-120. 1*H*-Pyrazolo[5,1-*a*]isoindole. R.I. 1372

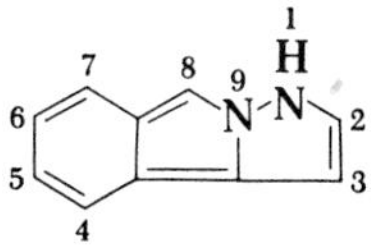

All of the known derivatives of this nucleus have been prepared by Rowe and his coworkers[1-7] during their investigation of the complex chemistry of the products derived from the diazonium coupling into 2-naphthol-1-sulfonic acid. They refer to the compounds as *isoindolinopyrazolidocolines* and number the nucleus as shown in I.

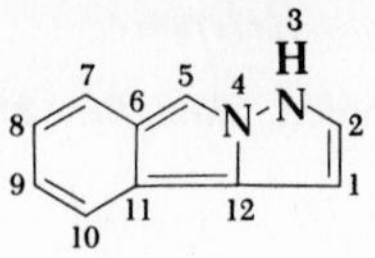

(I)

When 2-naphthol-1-sulfonic acid is treated with an aryldiazonium salt under alkaline conditions, the primary addition product (II) rearranges rapidly, via the intermediate III, into IV. Under acidic conditions IV rearranges further to V, which yields VI on dehydration with acetic anhydride. This cyclodehydration is reversible, and treatment of VI with an acetic-hydrochloric acid mixture causes cleavage to V. Nitration of VI when Ar = phenyl or 2- or 4-nitro-

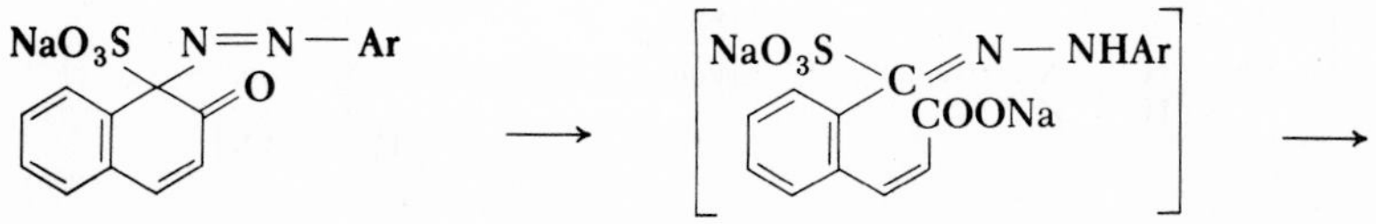

(II)

(III)

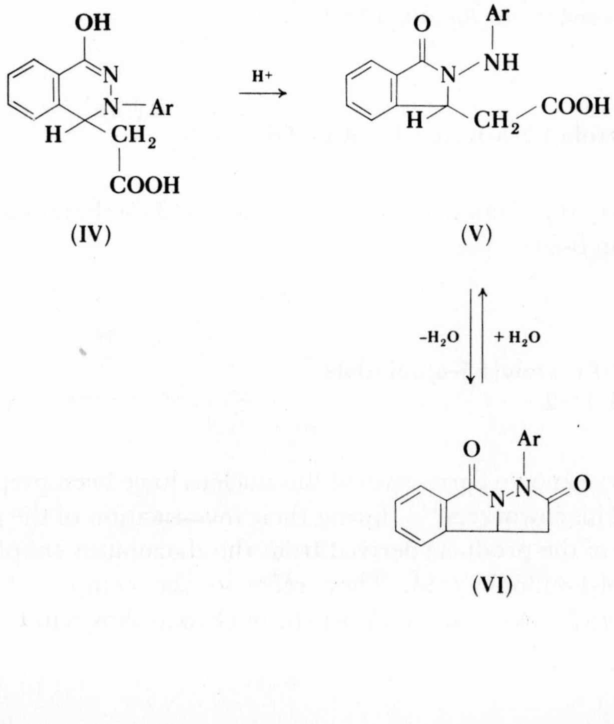

(IV)

(V)

$-H_2O$ $+H_2O$

(VI)

phenyl, yielded[5,7] the 2,4-dinitrophenyl analog, indicating the deactivation of the "benz" ring in VI.

Dehydration of VI (Ar = 2-$C_6H_4NH_2$) yielded a pentacyclic system (see Section A-121).

Derivatives of

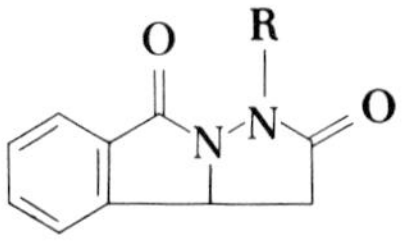

R = substituted phenyl with substituents as below	Properties	Ref.
2,6-Dibromo-4-nitro-	m. 290°.	4
2,6-Dichloro-4-nitro-	m. 256°.	4
2,4-Dinitro-	Lt. yel., m. 239°.	5,7
2-Bromo-4-nitro-	m. 272–3°.	4
2-Chloro-4-nitro-	m. 244°.	4
4-Chloro-2-nitro-	m. 248–9° .	1
5-Chloro-2-nitro-	m. 209°.	1
2-Nitro-	m. 209°.	1
4-Nitro-	m. 250°.	4
Unsubstituted	m. 220–1°.	7
4-Amino-2-nitro-	Or., m. 276°.	5
2-Amino-4-chloro-	m. 253–4°. *N*-Acetyl deriv., m. 242–3°.	1
4-Amino-2-chloro-	m. 240°. *N*–Acetyl deriv., m. 245°.	4
2-Amino-	m. 234–6°. *N*-Acetyl deriv., m. 175–6°.	1
4-Amino-	m. 213–5°. *N*-Acetyl deriv., m. 263–4°.	4
2-Methyl-4-nitro-	m. 213–4°.	4
4-Methyl-2-nitro-	m. 233°.	2
2-Amino-4-methyl-	m. 233°. Diacetyl deriv., m. 194°.	2
2-Methoxy-4-nitro-	m. 227–8°.	3
2,5-Dimethoxy-4-nitro-	m. 208°.	6
4-Amino-2,5-dimethoxy-	m. 174°. *N*–Acetyl deriv., m. 259°.	6

References

1. Rowe, Dovey, Garforth, Levin, Pask, and Peters, *J. Chem. Soc.*, **1935,** 1796.
2. Rowe, Haigh, and Peters, *J. Chem. Soc.*, **1936,** 1098.
3. Rowe and Cross, *J. Chem. Soc.*, **1947,** 461.
4. Rowe, McFadyen, and Peters, *J. Chem. Soc.*, **1947,** 468.
5. Rowe and Osborn, *J. Chem. Soc.*, **1947,** 829.
6. Rowe, Desai, and Peters, *J. Chem. Soc.*, **1948,** 281.
7. Peters, Rowe, and Brodrick, *J. Chem. Soc.*, **1948,** 1249.

A-121. *7H*-Benzimidazo[1,2-*b*]isoindolo-[1',2'-*e*]pyrazole. R.I. 2904

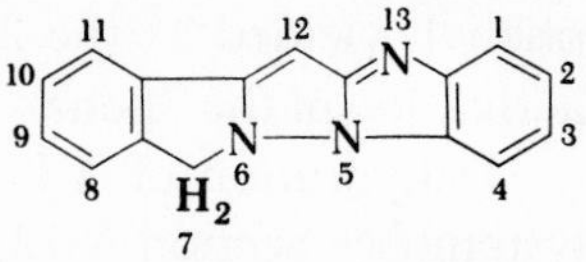

The only representatives of this nucleus are those of type IV, which have been called *2:2'-anhydro-2:5-diketo-3-(2'-aminophenyl)iso-indolinopyrazolidocoline*, and numbered as shown in I.

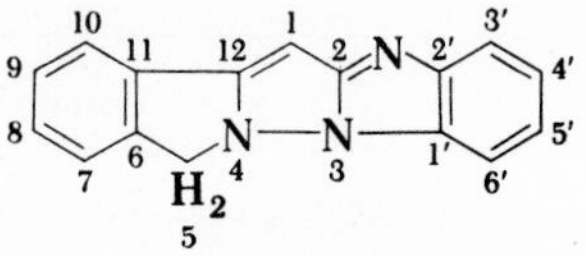

(I)

While investigating the quite complex rearrangements undergone by compounds such as II, Rowe and his coworkers[1,2] obtained III.

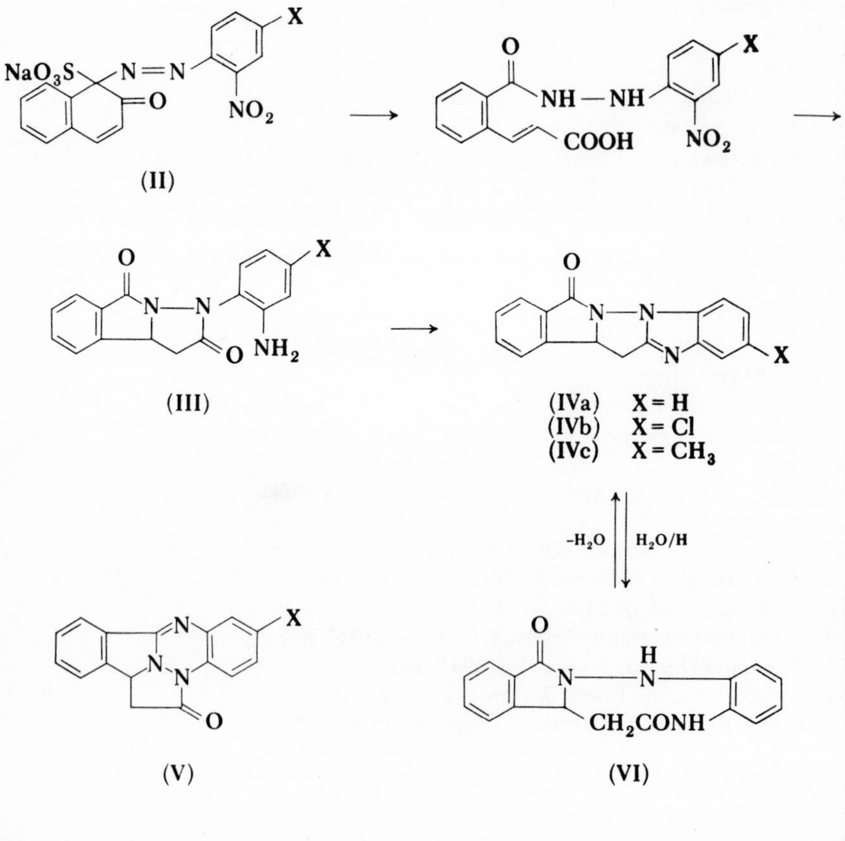

(II)

(III)

(IVa) X = H
(IVb) X = Cl
(IVc) X = CH_3

(V)

(VI)

When III was heated with 50% sulfuric acid, dehydration occurred to give a product thought to be IV (IVa, X = H, m. 219–21°; picrate, m. 234–6°; IVb, R = Cl, m. 238–9°; sulfate, m. 278°; IVc, R = CH_3, m. 242°; sulfate, m. 269°d.; picrate, m. 239°). The alternative structure V, which would result from cyclization to the other carbonyl group of III, was rejected[2] for reasons inadequately disclosed. When heated in dilute acid, IVc was hydrated to a compound thought to be VI, and this, in turn, could be reconverted into IVc by heating it in toluene with phosphorus trichloride.

References

1. Rowe, Dovey, Garforth, Levin, Pask, and Peters, *J. Chem. Soc.*, **1935,** 1796.
2. Rowe, Haigh, and Peters, *J. Chem. Soc.*, **1936,** 1098.

A-122. Pyrazolo[1′,2′,3′-5,6,7]-*as*-benzotriazino[3,2-*a*]isoindole

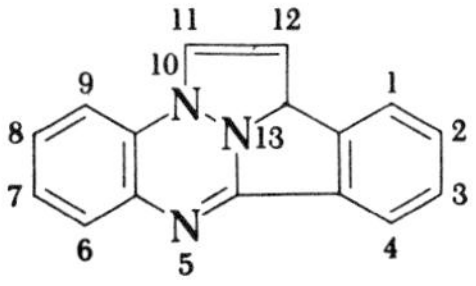

See Section A-121.

A-123. 7*aH*-Oxazolo[2,3-*b*]thiazole. R.I. 593

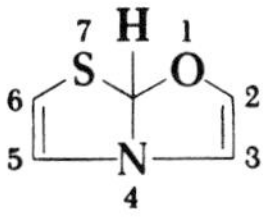

Groth and Holmberg[1] reported the treatment of I with nitric acid to yield II (m. 165°; acid sulfate, m. 114–5°), which is the only example of this ring system.

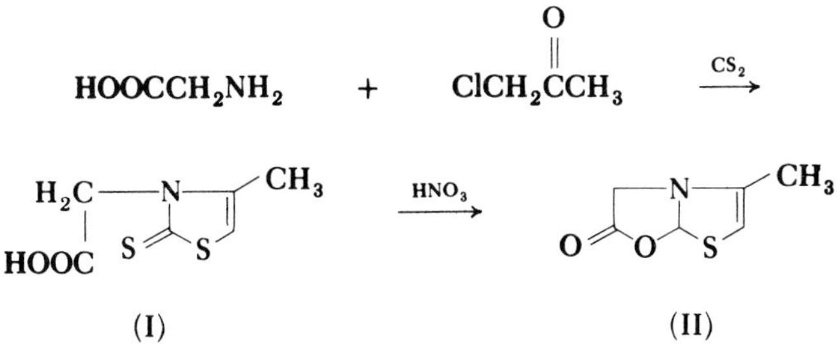

$$HOOCCH_2NH_2 + ClCH_2C(=O)CH_3 \xrightarrow{CS_2} \text{(I)} \xrightarrow{HNO_3} \text{(II)}$$

(I) (II)

Reference

1. Groth and Holmberg, *Ber.*, **56,** 289 (1923).

A-124. 2*H*-Isothiazolo[3,2-*b*]benzothiazole

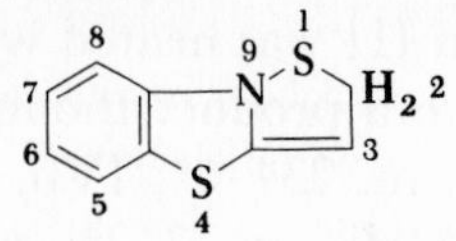

See 9*aH*-thiazolo[2,3-*b*]benzothiazole (Section A-128.)

A-125. 5*H*-Thiazolo[4,3-*b*]thiazole

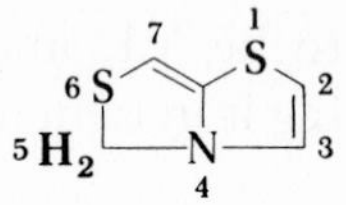

The only examples of this nucleus were discussed[1] in connection with the investigations upon the structure of penicillin. When the thiazolidines Ia (R = H) and Ib (R = $COOCH_3$) were refluxed with carbon disulfide, in each case, two isomeric products were obtained. Differences in their physical properties made it unlikely that they were merely stereoisomeric, and they were assigned,[1] respectively, structures IIa and IIb, and IIIa (m. 187–8°) and IIIb (m. 219°). It was shown further that both IIa and IIIa underwent mild acid or alkaline hydrolysis to give the *same* acid (m. 197–8°, corresponding to the ester IIIa). See Section A-130.

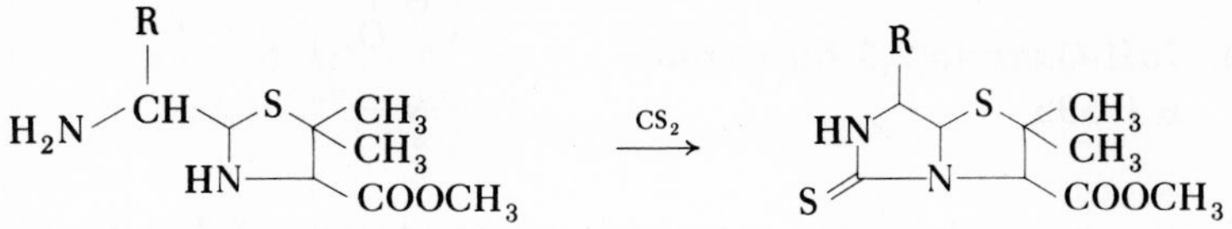

(Ia) R = H
(Ib) R = $COOCH_3$

(IIa) R = H
(IIb) R = $COOCH_3$

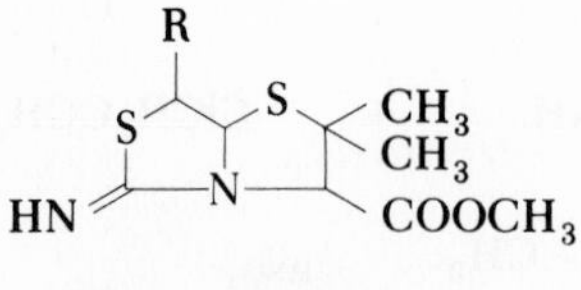

(IIIa) R = H
(IIIb) R = $COOCH_3$

Reference

1. Cook and Heilbron, in Clarke *et al.*, *The Chemistry of Penicillin*, Princeton University Press, Princeton, N. J., 1949, pp. 921–72.

A-126. 1,3,5-Trithia-6*b*-azacyclopenta-[*cd*]pentalene*

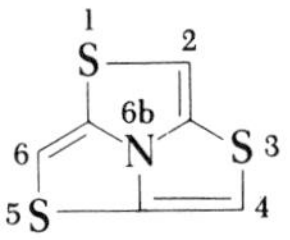

1 S, 2, 6b N, S 3, 4, 5 S, 6

The perhydro compound has been called *2,5,8-trithia-10-azatricyclo*$[5.2.1.0^{4,10}]$*decane* (I) and *1,4,7-trithia-2,5,8-endazacyclononane* (II).

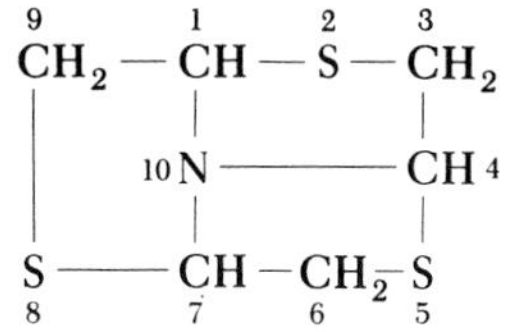

9 CH_2 — 1 CH — 2 S — 3 CH_2

10 N — CH 4

8 S — 7 CH — 6 CH_2 — 5 S

(I)

The reaction of mercaptoacetaldehyde with ammonia in dimethylformamide (but not in ether) afforded[1] a 36% yield of a product (b_2 122°, m. 144°, d_4^{20} 1.565) assigned structure II. Hydrogenation of II over Raney nickel gave a 70% yield of triethylamine.

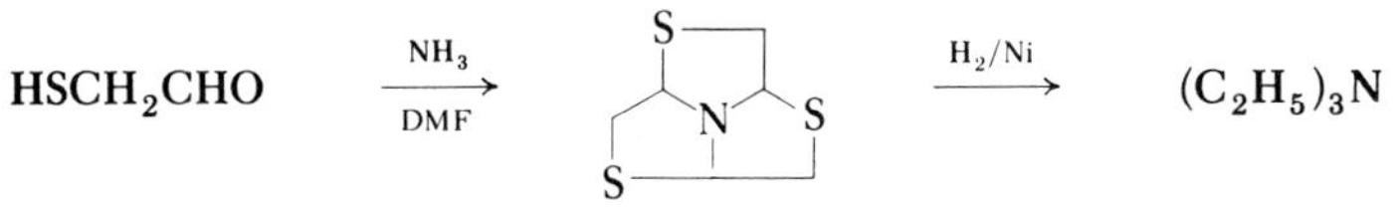

$HSCH_2CHO \xrightarrow[DMF]{NH_3}$ (II) $\xrightarrow{H_2/Ni} (C_2H_5)_3N$

(II)

Reference

1. Thiel, Asinger, and Schmiedel, *Ann.*, **611,** 121 (1958).

A-127. 7*aH*-Thiazolo[2,3-*b*]thiazole

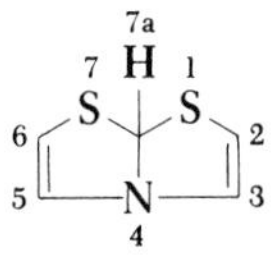

7a H, 7 S, 1 S, 2, 3, 4 N, 5, 6

When the acid I was heated with acetic anhydride, there was produced a dark blue substance (m. 237°), thought,[1] at first, to have structure II in analogy with the thioindigoid dyes. Recent work on related compounds (see Section A-128) suggests that structure III is more probable. It is of interest that the nonaromatic acid IV gives, as might be expected, a less deeply colored dye (V, brick-red, m. 290°).

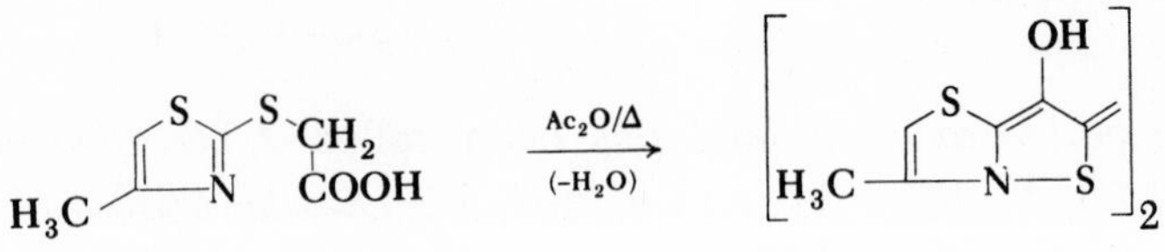

(I) $\xrightarrow[(-H_2O)]{Ac_2O/\Delta}$ (II)

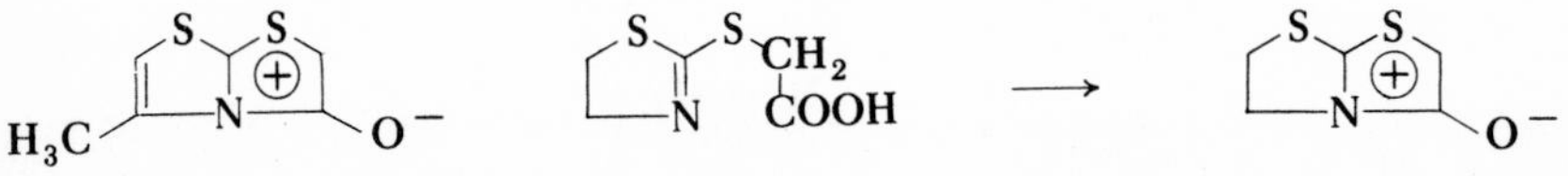

(III) (IV) → (V)

Reference

1. Duffin and Kendall, U.S. Pat. 2,513,923.

A-128. 9*aH*-Thiazolo[2,3-*b*]benzothiazole

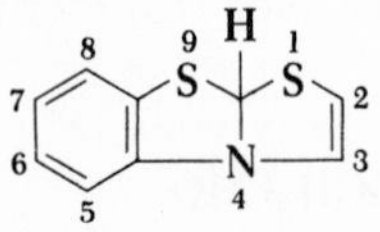

Duffin and Kendall[1] found that 2-benzothiazolylthioacetic acids (I) underwent dehydration upon treatment with acetic anhydride and yielded dark blue products for which they proposed structure II, in analogy to the thioindigoid dyes. The formation of this ring system was, presumably, to have occurred as a result of migration, then cyclication of the thioacetic acid side chain. Subsequently, Duffin and Kendall investigated a related group of compounds (see Section A-133) and proposed for them dipolar or mesoionic[2] structures. By analogy, it seems probable that the structure of the dyes obtained from I is probably best represented by a resonance hydride of type III.

In the cyclodehydration of I to III, the presence in the reaction mixture of traces of organic bases such as pyridine or triethylamine is beneficial, while acids have distinctly the opposite effect.[1] Benzothiazolylthioacetic acids with substituents in the 4-position required[1] more vigorous conditions to effect ring closure, possibly because of steric screening of the ring nitrogen atom.

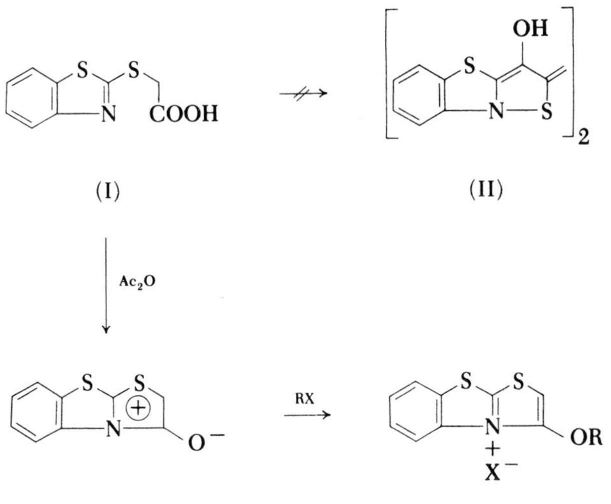

(I) —/→ (II)

(I) —Ac_2O→ (III) —RX→ (IV)

Compound III reacts with salts of metals such as silver, copper, zinc, etc., to give colored metal salts of the dye,[3] and with alkylating agents to give dark blue, high melting quaternary ethers,[4] which presumably have structure IV.

Derivatives of Thiazolo[2,3-*b*]benzothiazole

Empirical formula	Structure	Properties	Refs.
$C_9H_4BrNOS_2$	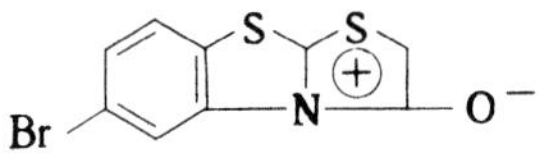	Blue, m >300°.	1
$C_9H_5NOS_2$	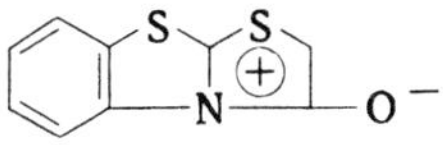	Blue, m. 284°. H_2SO_4 solution blue. Methiodide, dk. blue, m. >300°. Methyl methosulfate, dk. blue. Ethiodide, dk. blue, m. >300°.	1,3,4

(continued)

Derivatives of Thiazolo[2,3-*b*]benzothiazole (*continued*)

Empirical formula	Structure	Properties	Refs.
$C_9H_6N_2OS_2$	[structure: H_2N-substituted]	Blue, m. 297°.	1
$C_{10}H_6ClNOS_2$	[structure: Cl, CH_3-substituted]	Blue, m. 300°.	1
$C_{10}H_7NOS_2$	[structure: CH_3-substituted]	Blue, m. ~292°.	1
$C_{11}H_9NO_2S_2$	[structure: C_2H_5O-substituted]	Blue, m. 300°.	1
$C_{11}H_9NO_3S_2$	[structure: CH_3O, CH_3O-substituted]	Blue, m. >300°.	1

References

1. Duffin and Kendall, U.S. Pat. 2,513,923.
2. Katritzky, *Chem. and Ind.*, **1955,** 521.
3. Duffin and Kendall, U.S. Pat. 2,556,526.
4. Duffin and Kendall, U.S. Pat. 2,556,527; Brit. Pat. 654,346.

A-129. 10*aH*-Thiazolo[2,3-*b*]naphtho-[2,1-*d*]thiazole

Duffin and Kendall[1] treated the acid I with acetic anhydride to remove a molecule of water, and obtained a product (dark blue crystals with a bronze luster, m. >300°) which they considered to have structure II, formed as a result of a rearrangement of the thio-acid side chain. Later they proposed more reasonable structures for some related compounds (see Section A-133), and it seems likely that this product has the mesoionic structure III.

(I)

Ac_2O/Δ $(-H_2O)$

(II)

(III)

Reference

1. Duffin and Kendall, U. S. Pat. 2,513,923.

A-130. Imidazo[5,1-*b*]thiazole

Before interest developed in the structure of penicillin, this nucleus was unknown, and even today the only examples which have been described are those prepared in connection with penicillin studies.

Very mild acid hydrolysis (e.g., in aqueous solution at 25° and pH 2.0) converts the penicillins (I, where R = *n*-amyl, benzyl, 2-pentenyl, etc., depending upon the particular penicillin involved) into dicarboxylic acids of type II, which have been named *penillic acids.*[1,2] The mechanism shown for this rearrangement was suggested by Woodward.[3] The synthesis of benzyl penillic acid (V) by the condensation of III with penicillamine (IV) has been described by du Vigneaud and his collaborators.[2,4] While V is capable of existing in four diastereoisomeric forms, it is noteworthy that the condensa-

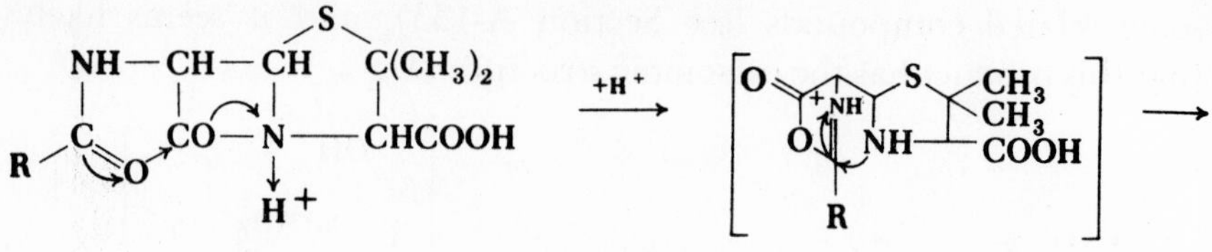

S
NH—CH—CH C$(CH_3)_2$
C CO—N—CHCOOH
R O
H+

$+H^+$ →

[O NH S CH_3 CH_3 O NH COOH R] →

(I)

[O NH S CH_3 CH_3 O N+ COOH H R]

$-H^+$ →

COOH
N S CH_3
CH_3
R N COOH

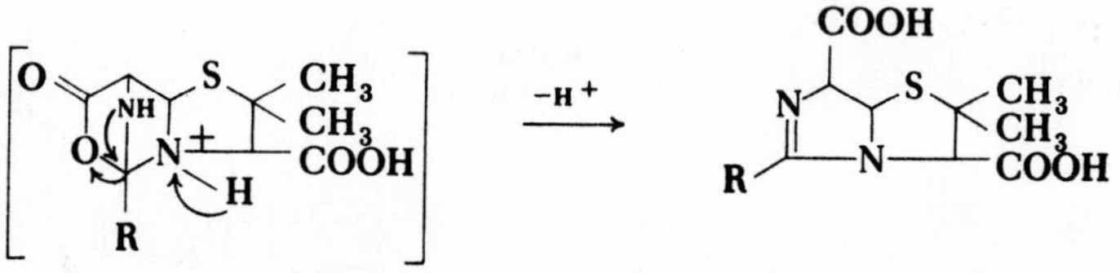

(II)

tion of III with D-penicillamine yielded a single modification, and one identical with the material prepared from benzyl penicillin.

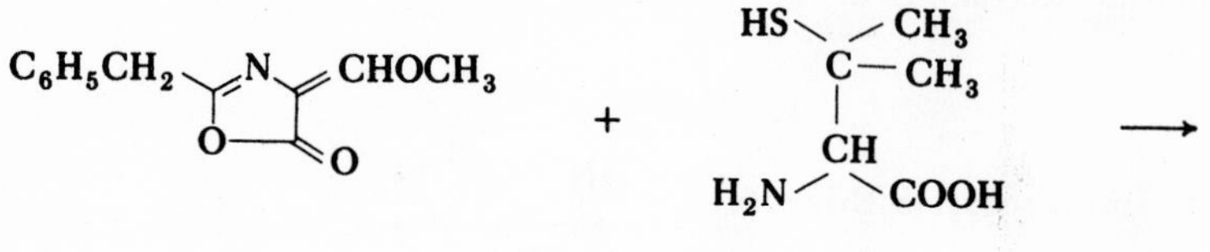

$C_6H_5CH_2$ N $CHOCH_3$
O O

+

HS CH_3
C—CH_3
CH
H_2N COOH

→

(III)

(IV)

[O—C=O
$C_6H_5CH_2$ N C HS
CH C$(CH_3)_2$
NH—CHCOOH]

→

COOH
N S CH_3
CH_3
$C_6H_5CH_2$ N COOH

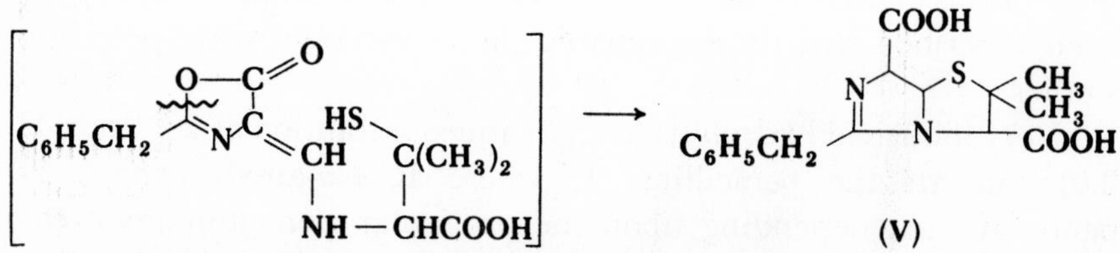

(V)

Stavely[5] found that penaldic acid derivatives such as VI, when heated with penicillamine in acetic acid solution, gave homologs (such as VIII) of penillic acid. However, fusion of VI with D-penicillamine yielded the penicilloic acid derivative VII, which was converted into VIII by hot acetic acid. Sheehan and Tishler[6] prepared dimethyl penillate (X) by the reaction of IX with ethyl phenyl-

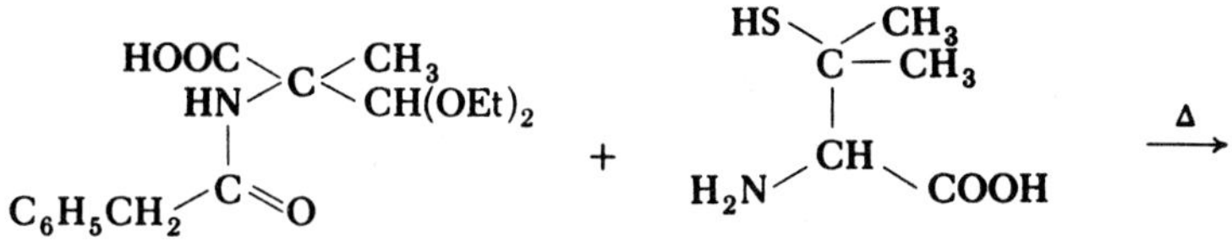

HOOC C CH_3 HN $CH(OEt)_2$ $C_6H_5CH_2$ C=O + HS C CH_3 CH_3 H_2N CH COOH $\xrightarrow{\Delta}$

(VI) (IV)

HOOC CH_3 HN S CH_3 CH_3 C HN COOH $C_6H_5CH_2$ O $\xrightarrow[\Delta]{HOAc}$ HOOC CH_3 N S CH_3 CH_3 $C_6H_5CH_2$ N $COOCH_3$

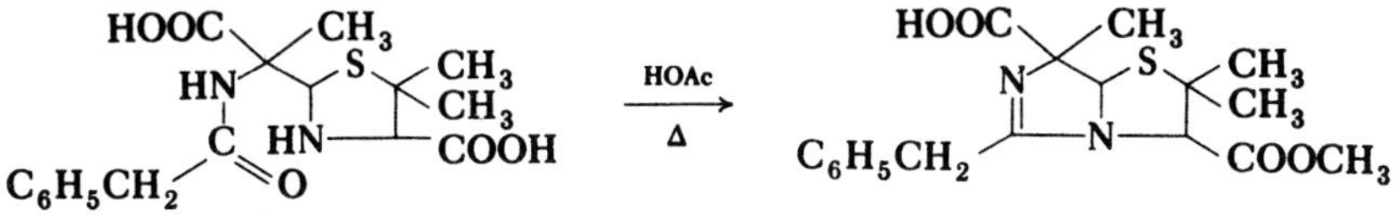

(VII) (VIII)

acetimidate at room temperature in ethylene dichloride. The related acid XII was obtained by Heilbron, Cook, and Elvidge[7] by treating XI with a phosphoric acid-phosphorus oxychloride mixture (essentially polyphosphoric acid).

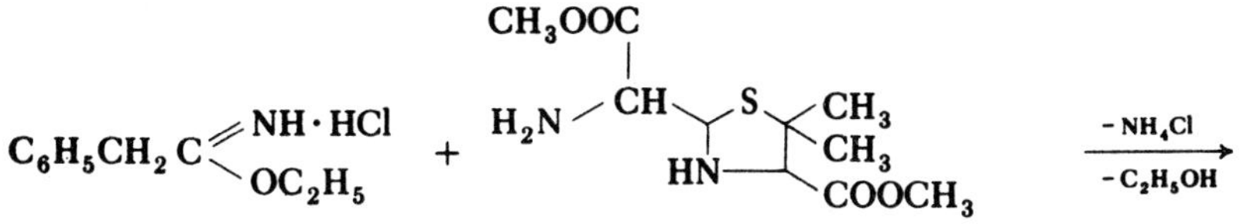

$C_6H_5CH_2C$ $NH \cdot HCl$ OC_2H_5 + CH_3OOC H_2N CH S CH_3 CH_3 HN $COOCH_3$ $\xrightarrow[-C_2H_5OH]{-NH_4Cl}$

(IX)

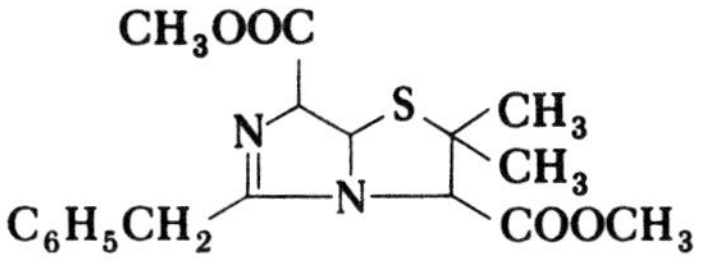

CH_3OOC N S CH_3 CH_3 $C_6H_5CH_2$ N $COOCH_3$

(X)

HN S CH_3 CH_3 C HN COOH C_5H_{11} O $\xrightarrow[(-H_2O)]{POCl_3 - H_3PO_4}$ N S CH_3 CH_3 C_5H_{11} N COOH

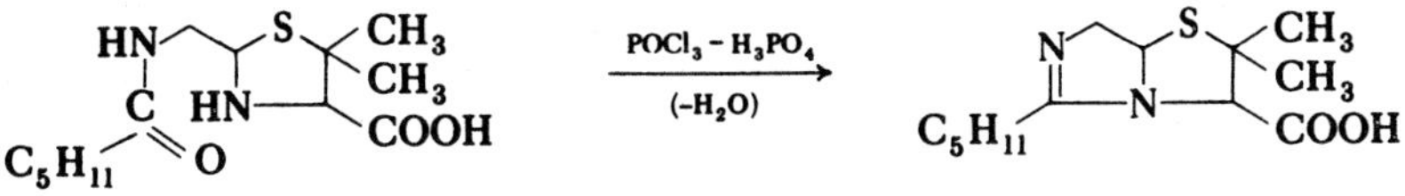

(XI) (XII)

Compound XIII (where R = H or COOR′) reacts[8,9] normally with phosgene to yield XIV. However, with carbon disulfide, in each case, a mixture of two isomeric esters was obtained.[9] These esters, thought to have structures XV and XVI, are converted by mild alkaline or acid hydrolysis into the same carboxylic acid, considered[9] to be XVII.

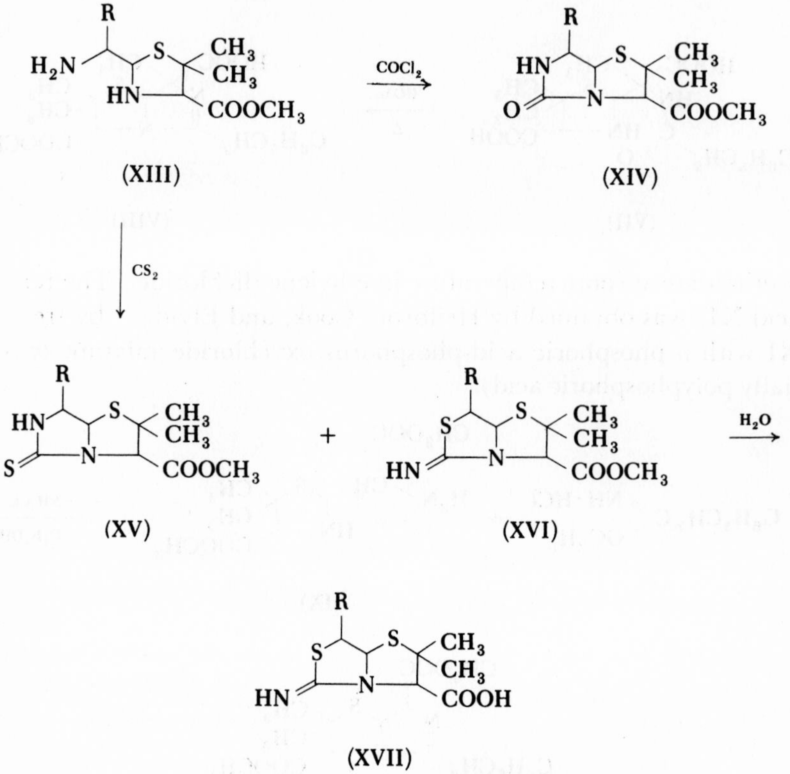

(XIII) —$COCl_2$→ (XIV)

(XIII) —CS_2→ (XV) + (XVI) —H_2O→ (XVII)

Aromatic, or at least fully conjugated representatives of this nucleus have not been described. The saturated compounds such as those mentioned above show reactions similar to the thiazolines (e.g., desulfurization on treatment with mercuric chloride, etc.). The reactions of these compounds have been discussed in detail,[1,3,8,9] and will not be reviewed here. The "retarding" action of penillic acids and other penicillin decomposition products upon photographic emulsions has been studied by Koseki and Ishida.[10]

Derivatives of Imidazo[5,1-*b*]thiazole

Empirical formula	Structure	Properties	Refs.
$C_9H_{14}N_2O_2S_2$	HN; S; N; S=; CH_3; CH_3; $COOCH_3$	m. 117–8°.	9
$C_9H_{14}N_2O_3S$	HN; S; N; O=; CH_3; CH_3; $COOCH_3$	m. 124–5°.	9
$C_{10}H_{14}N_2O_5S$	COOH; HN; S; N; O=; CH_3; CH_3; $COOCH_3$	m. 168–9° d.; $[\alpha]_D^{23°}$ + 215° (C_2H_5OH).	8
$C_{11}H_{16}N_2O_4S_2$	$COOCH_3$; HN; S; N; S=; CH_3; CH_3; $COOCH_3$	m. 162°.	9
$C_{14}H_{20}N_2O_4S$	COOH; N; S; N; C_5H_9; CH_3; CH_3; COOH	m. 173° d.; $[\alpha]_D^{16.5°}$ +527° (± 10°).	1
$C_{15}H_{18}N_2O_2S$	N; S; N; $C_6H_5CH_2$; CH_3; CH_3; COOH	—	1,7
$C_{16}H_{18}N_2O_4S$	COOH; N; S; N; $C_6H_5CH_2$; CH_3; CH_3; COOH	m. 189° (180–2°); λ_{max} 239 mμ. ($E_{1 cm.}^{1\%}$ 148.5).	1,2,4
$C_{16}H_{18}N_2O_5S$	COOH; N; S; N; *p*-$HOC_6H_4CH_2$; CH_3; CH_3; COOH	m. 218°; $[\alpha]_D^{17.5°}$ + 478°; λ_{max} 278 mμ.	1
$C_{17}H_{20}N_2O_4S$	HOOC; CH_3; N; S; N; $C_6H_5CH_2$; CH_3; CH_3; COOH	m. 197.8°.	5

(*continued*)

Derivatives of Imidazo[5,1-*b*]thiazole (*continued*)

Empirical formula	Structure	Properties	Refs.
$C_{17}H_{21}N_3O_3S$	H_2NOC, CH_3; N, S; CH_3, CH_3, COOH; $C_6H_5CH_2$, N	$[\alpha]_D^{25°}$ 383° (C = 0.61 in CH_3OH).	5
$C_{18}H_{22}N_2O_4S$	CH_3OOC, CH_3; N, S; CH_3, CH_3, COOH; $C_6H_5CH_2$, N	$[\alpha]_D^{25°}$ 292° (C = 1.02 in C_2H_5OH).	5
	$COOCH_3$; N, S; CH_3, CH_3, $COOCH_3$; $C_6H_5CH_2$, N	m. 133–5°; $[\alpha_D^{23°}]$ 411°.	6
$C_{18}H_{23}N_3O_3S$	H_2NOC, CH_3; N, S; CH_3, CH_3, $COOCH_3$; $C_6H_5CH_2$, N	m. 212–4°.	5

References

1. Cook in Clarke, Johnson, and Robinson, *The Chemistry of Penicillin*, Princeton University Press, Princeton, N. J., 1949, pp. 106 ff.
2. Carpenter, Turner, and du Vigneaud, *J. Biol. Chem.*, **176,** 893 (1948).
3. Woodward in Clarke, Johnson, and Robinson, *The Chemistry of Penicillin*, Princeton University Press, Princeton, N. J., 1949, pp. 445, 453.
4. Holley, Carpenter, Livermore, and du Vigneaud, *Science*, **108,** 136 (1948).
5. Stavely, *J. Am. Chem. Soc.*, **73,** 3450 (1951).
6. Sheehan and Tishler, U.S. Pat. 2,492, 243.
7. Heilbron, Cook, and Elvidge, Brit. Pat. 600,245.
8. Bachmann and Cronyn in Clarke, Johnson, and Robinson, *The Chemistry of Penicillin*, Princeton University Press, Princeton, N. J., 1949, pp. 859, 891.
9. Cook and Heilbron in Clarke, Johnson, and Robinson, *The Chemistry of Penicillin*, Princeton University Press, Princeton, N. J., 1949, pp. 929 and 949.
10. Koseki and Ishida, *Bull. Soc. Sci. Phot., Japan*, August, p. 17 (1951); *Chem. Abstracts*, **46,** 6977 (1952). *J. Chem. Soc. Japan, Ind. Chem. Sect.*, **54,** 648 (1951); *Chem. Abstracts*, **47,** 6803 (1953).

A-131. Imidazo[2,1-*b*]thiazole. R.I. 599

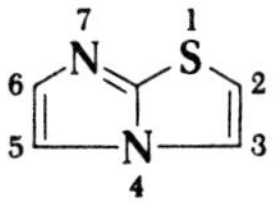

English authors often use the name *glyoxalino(2′:1′-2:3)thiazole*, and the name *1-thia-3a,6-diazapentalene* has also been advanced.

This nucleus may be prepared, alternatively, by building a thiazole ring onto an imidazole derivative, or vice versa. The former route was that first employed. Stephen and Wilson[1,2] found that treatment of I with chloracetic ester readily gave II, but they were unable to cyclize II to III. Finally they obtained a low yield of III directly from I by heating the reactants in pyridine. Benzaldehydes react with III to give 2-benzylidene derivatives.[14]

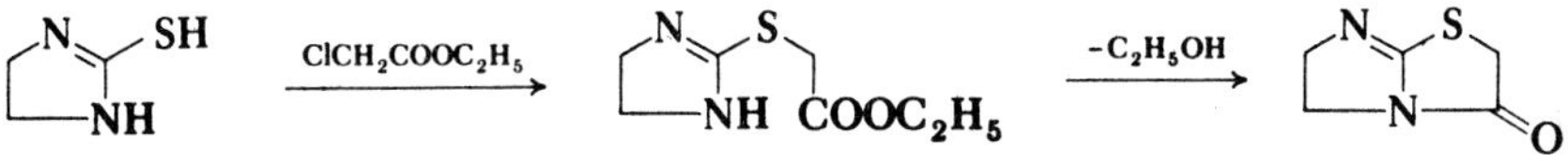

$ClCH_2COOC_2H_5$; $-C_2H_5OH$

(I) (II) (III)

A decade later Ochiai[3] found that IV, on treatment with chloracetone, readily gave V, but to obtain VI it was necessary to heat V

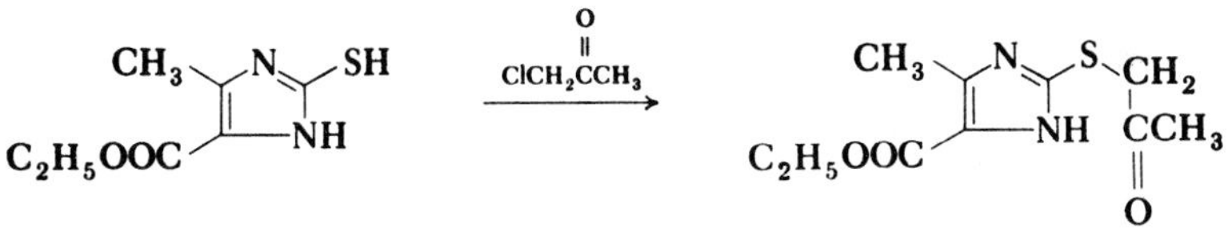

$ClCH_2COCH_3$; $POCl_3$; Ac_2O

(IV) (V) 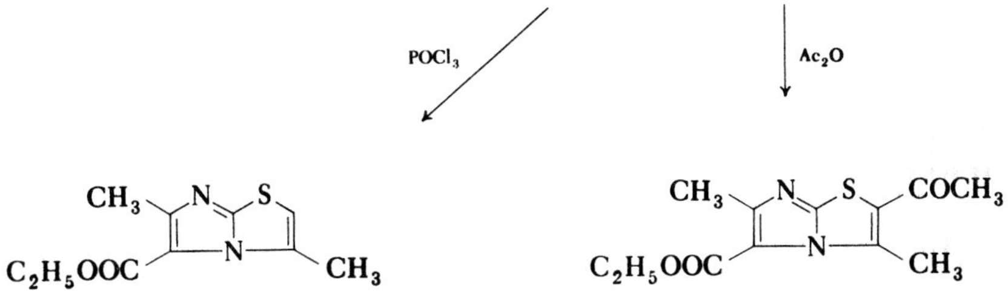 (VI) (VII)

with phosphorus oxychloride. When V was heated with acetic anhydride the ketone VII was formed by acetylation of the ring >NH followed by cyclodehydration. In the case of compounds similar to V, cyclization was accomplished[4, 17] by treatment with sulfuric acid. Acetals obtained from 2-mercaptoimidazoles and bromoacetals were cyclized by phosphorus oxychloride to 3-alkoxy-2,3-dihydroimidazo-[1,2-*b*]thiazoles.[19] Heating the closely related compounds of structure VIII with hydrochloric acid gave[11, 16, 21] the cyclized products IX.

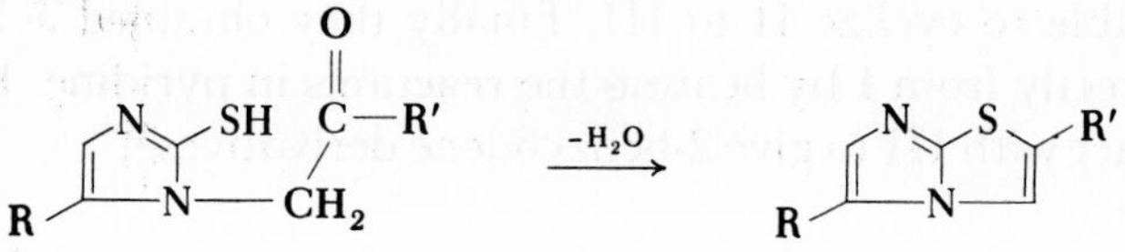

(VIII) $\xrightarrow{-H_2O}$ (IX)

The alternative route previously mentioned was employed by Kondo and Nagasawa[6] and by Matsukawa and Ban.[7, 8] By treating 2-aminothiazoles with phenacyl halides, a group of imidazo[2,1-*b*]-thiazoles were prepared.

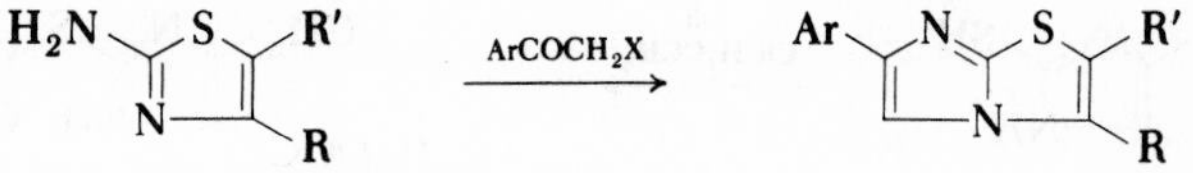

$\xrightarrow{ArCOCH_2X}$

The location of the aryl group in the 6-position was demonstrated by Kickhöfen and Kröhnke,[12] who showed that XI was formed from either 2-aminothiazole or 2-acetylaminothiazole. Unlike the pyridine analogs, X could not be cyclized in "basic" media.[12]

During investigations upon the structure of penicillin, it was found that when benzyl penicillin methyl ester (XII) was heated in hydrocarbon solvents for short periods, a new product ($C_{17}H_{20}N_2O_4S$) was produced. Studies leading to the establishment of structure XIII for this product, and its synthesis from XIV, have been described.[9]

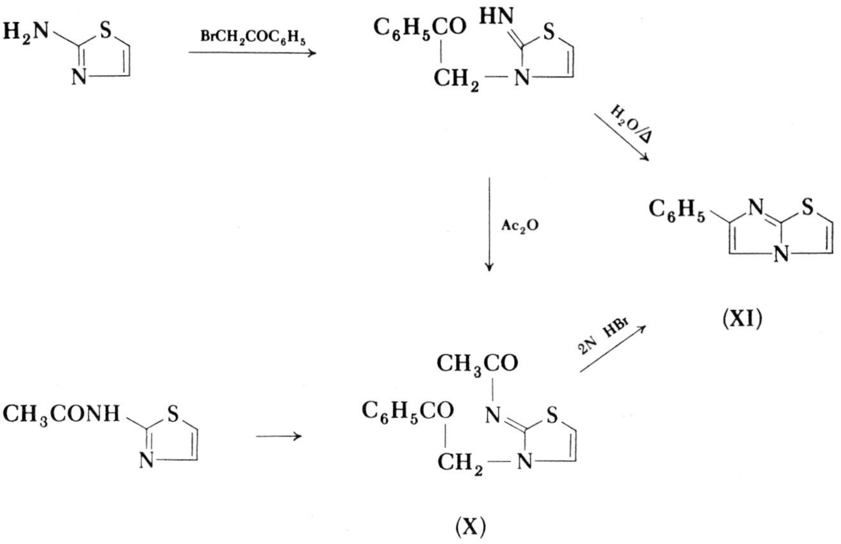

(XI)

(X)

The mechanisms for the conversion of XII and XIV into XIII were proposed by Woodward.[10] Compound XIII is named methyl benzyl *penillonate*.

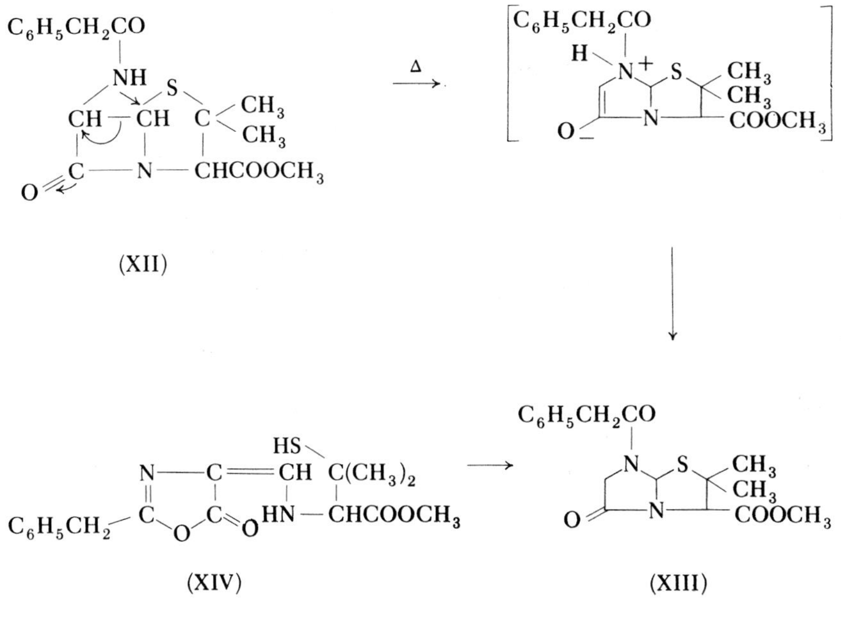

(XII)

(XIV)

(XIII)

The ultraviolet absorption spectra of some 5,6-dihydroimidazo-[2,1-*b*]thiazolium salts were examined by Wilson and Woodger.[13] A bathochromic shift of 8–13 mμ with respect to analogous monocyclic thiazolium salts was explained tentatively on the basis of ring strain in the bicyclic systems.

The antithyroid activity of the 3,5-dimethyl compound has been assayed and found to be slight.[22]

Derivatives of Imidazo[2,1-*b*]thiazole

Empirical formula	Substituents or structure	Properties	Refs.
$C_5H_6N_2S$	5,6-Dihydro-	m. 84–6°; λ_{max} 264 mμ (ε 7100) in EtOH. HCl salt, m. 183–6°; λ_{max} 270 mμ (ε 7400) in EtOH.	13
$C_5H_6N_2OS$	5,6-Dihydro-3(2*H*)-oxo-	m. 159°. Benzylidene derivative, m. 180°, and its methiodide, m. 238°. Anisylidene derivative, m. 214–5°, and its methiodide, m. 243–5°.	1,2,14, 15
$C_6H_8N_2S$	5,6-Dihydro-3-methyl-	m. 90–2°; λ_{max} 268 mμ (ε 6700) in EtOH. HCl salt, m. 258–9°; λ_{max} 270 mμ (ε 8000) in EtOH.	13
$C_7H_8N_2S$	2,5-Dimethyl-	m. 88–9°; λ_{max} 248 mμ (ε 5400) in EtOH.	11
	3,5-Dimethyl-	b_3 150–60°. HCl salt, m. 242°.	4,22
$C_9H_{12}N_2S$	2,5-Diethyl-	Oil. Picrate, yel., m. 238–40° d.	11
$C_{10}H_{12}N_2O_2S$	5-Carbethoxy-3,6-dimethyl-	m. 146–7°.	3
$C_{11}H_7N_3O_2S$	6-(4-Nitrophenyl)-	m. 238–9°.	19

Derivatives of Imidazo[2,1-*b*]thiazole (*continued*)

Empirical formula	Substituents or structure	Properties	Refs.
$C_{11}H_8N_2S$	6-Phenyl-	m. 146.0–6.5° (145–6°). HBr salt, m. 123–4° (114–6°). HCl salt, m. 153–4°. Picrate, m. 223–3.5° (224–6°). Sulfate, m. 210–1°. Methiodide, m. 213–4°.	12,19
$C_{11}H_8N_2O_3S_2$	6-(4-Sulfophenyl)-	m. >360°.	19
$C_{11}H_9N_3O_3S$	2,3-Dihydro-3-hydroxy-6-(4-nitrophenyl)-	d. 203–4°.	19
$C_{11}H_{10}N_2S$	5,6-Dihydro-3-phenyl-	m. 111–3°; λ_{max} 269 mμ (ε 13,200) in EtOH. HBr salt, m. 243–4°; λ_{max} 264 mμ (ε 8400) in EtOH.	13
$C_{11}H_{10}N_2OS$	2,3-Dihydro-3-hydroxy-6-phenyl-	d. 160–1°. HCl salt d. 163–5°. Picrate d. 145–6°.	19
$C_{12}H_9N_3O_2S$	3-Methyl-6-(4-nitrophenyl)-	m. 246°.	7,18
$C_{12}H_{10}N_2S$	3-Methyl-6-phenyl-	m. 113.5°. HCl salt, m. 228–32°. HBr salt, m. 198–224°. Picrate, m. 241°. Perchlorate, m. 201°. Methiodide, m. 115–7°. $HgCl_2$ complex, m. 264°. Sulfate, m. 217–8°.	6,16–18
	2-Methyl-5-phenyl-	m. 181°.	21
$C_{12}H_{10}N_2O_3S_2$	3-Methyl-6-(4-sulfophenyl)-	m. >360°.	17

(*continued*)

Derivatives of Imidazo[2,1-*b*]thiazole (*continued*)

Empirical formula	Substituents or structure	Properties	Refs.
$C_{12}H_{11}N_3S$	3-Methyl-6-(4-aminophenyl)-	m. 183–4°. DiHCl salt, m. >300°. *N*-Acetyl deriv., m. 195–6°.	7
$C_{12}H_{12}N_2S$	3-Benzyl-5,6-dihydro-	Oil, λ_{max} 267 mμ (ε 7400) in EtOH. HBr salt, m. 181–3°, λ_{max} 268 (ε 8700) and 234 mμ (ε 23,300) in EtOH.	13
	5,6-Dihydro-2-methyl-3-phenyl-	m. 90.5–1.5°; λ_{max} 272 mμ (ε 10,600) in EtOH. HBr salt, m. 236–9°; λ_{max} 234 (ε 27,000) and 293 mμ (ε 7,500) in EtOH.	13
	5,6-Dihydro-3-methyl-2-phenyl-	m. 121–4°; λ_{max} 288 mμ (ε 12,800) in EtOH. HBr salt, m. 246–8°; λ_{max} 282 (ε 8100) and 325 mμ (ε 9800) in EtOH.	13
$C_{12}H_{12}N_2OS$	2,3-Dihydro-3-methoxy-6-phenyl-	m. 71.5–2.5°. Picrate, d. 172–3°.	19
$C_{12}H_{14}N_2O_3S$	2-Acetyl-5-carbethoxy-3,6-dimethyl-	m. 205°. Oxime, d. 256°. *p*-Nitrophenylhydrazone, or., d. >280°.	3
$C_{13}H_{10}N_2OS$	2-Acetyl-5-phenyl-	m. 150–1°.	20
	2-Benzoyl-3-methyl-	m. 227–8°.	20
$C_{13}H_{11}N_3O_2S$	2,3-Dimethyl-6-(4-nitrophenyl)-	m. 248.0–8.5°.	18
$C_{13}H_{12}N_2S$	2,3-Dimethyl-6-phenyl-	m. 157–8°. HCl salt, m. 237–9°.	16–18
$C_{13}H_{12}N_2O_2S$	2-Methyl-5-(4-methoxyphenyl)-	HCl salt, m. 217°. Picrate, m. 223° d.	21

Derivatives of Imidazo[2,1-*b*]thiazole (*continued*)

Empirical formula	Substituents or structure	Properties	Refs.
$C_{13}H_{12}N_2O_3S_2$	2,3-Dimethyl-6-(4-sulfophenyl)-	m. > 360°.	17
$C_{13}H_{14}N_2OS$	3-Ethoxy-1,3-dihydro-6-phenyl-	m. 122°. Picrate, d. 197–8°.	19
$C_{13}H_{20}N_2S$	2,5-Di-*n*-butyl-	Oil. Picrate, yel., m. 185–6°.	11
	2,5-Diisobutyl-	m. 96–8°.	11
$C_{14}H_{11}N_3O_3S$	2-Acetyl-3-methyl-5-(4-nitrophenyl)-	m. 186–7°.	20
	2-Acetyl-3-methyl-6-(4-nitrophenyl)-	m. 281–1.5°:	20
$C_{14}H_{11}N_3O_4S$	2-Carbomethoxy-3-methyl-6-(4-nitrophenyl)-	m. 238–9°.	7
$C_{14}H_{12}N_2OS$	2-Acetyl-3-methyl-6-phenyl-	m. 203–3.5°. HCl salt, m. 232–4°.	20
$C_{14}H_{13}N_3O_2S$	2-Carbomethoxy-3-methoxy-6-(4-aminophenyl)-	m. 195–205°. *N*-Acetyl deriv., m. 246°.	7
	5-Carbethoxy-3-methyl-6-(3-pyridyl)-	m. 138°.	5
$C_{14}H_{13}N_3O_3S$	2-(2-Hydroxyethyl)-3-methyl-6-(4-nitrophenyl)-	m. 213–4°.	7
$C_{14}H_{14}N_2O_2S$	2-Methyl-5-(3,4-dimethoxyphenyl)-	m. 169–70°. HCl salt, m. 230°.	21
$C_{14}H_{15}N_3OS$	2-(2-Hydroxyethyl)-3-methyl-6-(4-aminophenyl)-	m. 217°. Picrate, d. 227°. *N*-Acetyl deriv., m. 110°.	7
$C_{16}H_{14}N_3O_4S$	2-Carbethoxymethyl-3-methyl-6-(4-nitrophenyl)-	m. 171°.	7
$C_{16}H_{15}N_3O_4S$	2-(2-Acetoxyethyl)-3-methyl-6-(4-nitrophenyl)-	m. 169–70°.	7
$C_{16}H_{16}N_3O_2S$	2-Carbethoxymethyl-3-methyl-6-(4-aminophenyl)-	m. 183–5°. *N*-Acetyl deriv., m 236–7°.	7

(*continued*)

Derivatives of Imidazo[2,1-*b*]thiazole (*continued*)

Empirical formula	Substituents or structure	Properties	Refs.
$C_{16}H_{18}N_2O_4S$	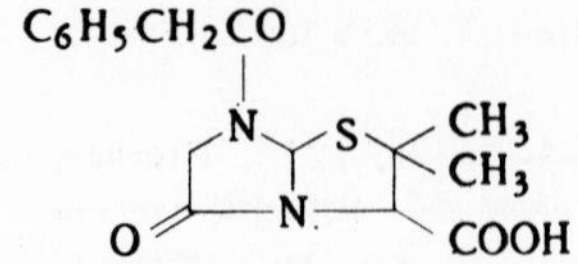 $C_6H_5CH_2CO$ (structure: N-acyl bicyclic, CH_3, CH_3, COOH, O) (benzylpenillonic acid)	m. 185–7°; $[\alpha]_D$ + 342° (in MeOH, C = 0.451). Methyl ester, m. 152–4°; $[\alpha]_D^{22}$ + 318° (in MeOH) or + 298° (in $CHCl_3$).	9
$C_{17}H_{11}N_3O_2S$	6-(3-Nitrophenyl)-3-phenyl-	m. 156.5–7.0°.	18
	6-(4-Nitrophenyl)-3-phenyl-	m. 210.5–1.5°.	18
$C_{17}H_{12}N_2S$	3,6-Diphenyl-	m. 125.0–5.5°. HCl salt, m. 201–2°.	18
	2,5-Diphenyl-	m. 124°.	21
$C_{17}H_{13}N_3S$	3-(3-Aminophenyl)-6-phenyl-	d. 257–60°.	18
$C_{18}H_{16}N_2S$	3-Benzyl-5,6-dihydro-2-phenyl-	m. 102–3°; λ_{max} 286 mμ (ε 12,600) in EtOH. HBr salt, m. 193–4°; λ_{max} 280 and 324 mμ (ε 7300 and 9200) in EtOH.	13
$C_{19}H_{13}N_3O_3S$	3-Methyl-2-(3-nitrobenzoyl)-5-phenyl-	m. 144–5°.	20
	3-Methyl-2-(4-nitrobenzoyl)-5-phenyl-	m. 190°.	20
$C_{19}H_{14}N_2OS$	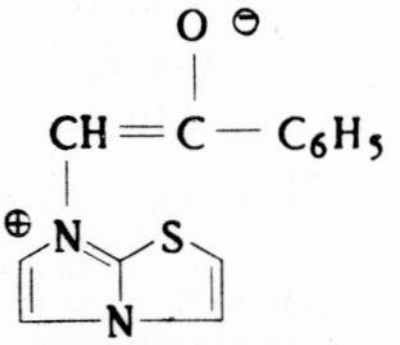 (structure: $CH=C(O^\ominus)-C_6H_5$ on $N^\oplus$ of imidazo[2,1-b]thiazole) (an "enol-betaine")	Yel., m. 90–4° d. HBr salt, m. 197–8°.	12
$C_{21}H_{20}N_2O_4S$	2,5-Bis-(3,4-dimethoxyphenyl)-	m. 233°.	21

References

1. Stephen and Wilson, *J. Chem. Soc.*, **1926,** 2531.
2. Wilson, Baird, Burns, Munro, and Stephen, *J. Roy. Tech. Coll.* (*Glasgow*), **2,** No. 1, 56 (1929); *Chem. Abstracts*, **23,** 5164 (1929).
3. Ochiai, *Ber.*, **69,** 1650 (1936).
4. Andersag and Westphal, *Ber.*, **70,** 2035 (1937).
5. Ochiai and Hou, *J. Pharm. Soc. Japan*, **58,** 236 (in German, p. 33) (1938); *Chem. Zentr.*, **II,** 859 (1938); *Chem. Abstracts*, **32,** 4161 (1938).
6. Kondo and Nagasawa, *J. Pharm. Soc. Japan*, **57,** 1050 (in German, p. 308) (1937); *Chem. Zentr.*, **II,** 859 (1938); *Chem. Abstracts*, **32,** 3398 (1938).
7. Matsukawa and Ban, *J. Pharm. Soc. Japan*, **71,** 756 (1951); *Chem. Abstracts*, **46,** 8094 (1952).
8. Matsukawa and Ban, *J. Pharm. Soc. Japan*, **72,** 884 (1952); *Chem. Abstracts*, **47,** 6410 (1953).
9. Peck and Folkers in Clarke, Johnson, and Robinson, *The Chemistry of Penicillin*, Princeton University Press, Princeton, N. J., 1949, pp. 158–161 and 188–193.
10. Woodward in Clarke, Johnson, and Robinson, *The Chemistry of Penicillin*, Princeton University Press, Princeton, N. J., 1949, p. 447.
11. Lawson and Morley, *J. Chem. Soc.*, **1955,** 1695.
12. Kickhöfen and Kröhnke, *Chem. Ber.*, **88,** 1109 (1955).
13. Wilson and Woodger, *J. Chem. Soc.*. **1955,** 2943.
14. Van Allen, *J. Org. Chem.*, **21,** 24 (1956).
15. Van Allen, *J. Org. Chem.*, **21,** 193 (1956).
16. Kochergin and Shchukina, *J. Gen. Chem.*, **26,** 458 (1956); *Chem. Abstracts*, **50,** 13883 (1956).
17. Kochergin and Shchukina, *J. Gen. Chem.*, **26,** 1723 (1956); *Chem. Abstracts*, **51,** 1942 (1957).
18. Kochergin, *J. Gen. Chem.*, **26,** 2493 (1956); *Chem. Abstracts*, **51,** 5050 (1957).
19. Kochergin and Shchukina, *J. Gen. Chem.*, **26,** 2905 (1956); *Chem. Abstracts*, **51,** 8077 (1957).
20. Kochergin, *J. Gen. Chem.*, **26,** 2916 (1956); *Chem. Abstracts*, **51,** 8078 (1957).
21. Lawson and Morley, *J. Chem. Soc.*, **1957,** 566.
22. Lawson and Searle, *Biochem. J.*, **59,** 345 (1955); *Chem. Abstracts*, **50,** 2039 (1956).

A-132. Imidazo[2,1-*b*]benzothiazole

Compound I (m. 100°, HBr salt, m. 263°) was prepared as shown by Ochiai and Nisizawa.[1] It was named *benzothiazole*[*2′,3′,2,1*]-*4-phenylbenzimidazole*.

$C_6H_5COCH_2Br$

C_2H_5OH / 100°

(I)

Similarly, IV (m. 169°; sulfate, m. 232–4°; HCl salt, m. 273–4°) was prepared[2-4] both from II and III, and the *p*-nitrophenyl analog of IV (m. 233–4°) was obtained[4] from II.

(II) (IV) (III)

The condensation of 2-mercaptoimidazoline with 2-chlorocyclohexanone and with spiro[4.5]-7-chloro-6-decanone yielded,[5] respectively, 5,6,7,8-tetrahydroimidazo[2,1-*b*]benzothiazole (m. 158–60°) and its 5,5-tetramethylene homolog (hydrobromide, m. 254–5°).

References

1. Ochiai and Nisizawa, *J. Pharm. Soc. Japan*, **60**, 132 (1940); *Chem. Abstracts*, **34**, 5082 (1940).
2. Kochergin and Shchukina, *J. Gen. Chem.*, **26**, 458 (1956); *Chem. Abstracts*, **50**, 13883 (1956).
3. Kochergin and Shchukina, *J. Gen. Chem.*, **26**, 1723 (1956); *Chem. Abstracts*, **51**, 1942 (1957).
4. Kochergin, *J. Gen. Chem.*, **26**, 2493 (1956); *Chem. Abstracts*, **51**, 5050 (1957).
5. De Stevens and Halamandaris, *J. Am. Chem. Soc.*, **79**, 5710 (1957).

A-133. Thiazolo[3,2-*a*]benzimidazole.
R.I. 1347

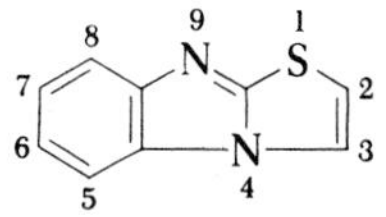

The alternative names *benzimidazo[2,1-b]thiazole*, *benziminazo-(2′:1′-2,3)thiazole* and *thiazolo(2′.3′:2.1)benzimidazole* are also encountered.

Compound II was first obtained[1,2] by treatment of the ester I ($R = C_2H_5$) in benzene solution with sodium metal. It is more conveniently obtained,[3,4] however, by dehydration of the acid I ($R = H$) with an acetic anhydride-pyridine mixture. Various reagents condense with the activated 2-position of II, and a number of derivatives have so been obtained.[4,5]

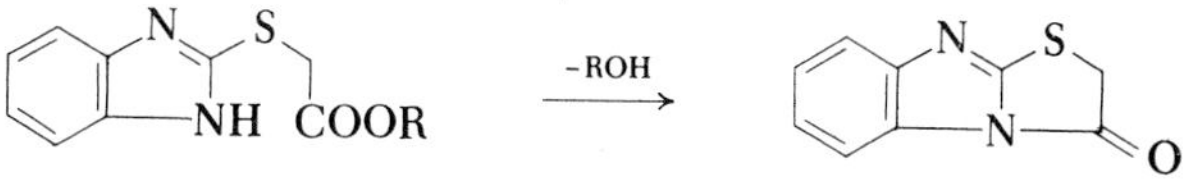

(I) —ROH→ (II)

N-Substituted derivatives of I, such as III (where $R = CH_3$ or C_6H_5), may be cyclized to mesoionic anhydro compounds (IV). However, the presence of substituents (e.g., CH_3 or C_2H_5) on the methylene group of III seems to prevent cyclization and other (non-cyclic) products are produced. While IV is stable to boiling water, the thiazole ring readily undergoes scission to give various products when IV is treated with dilute acid or with zinc and acid or dilute caustic.

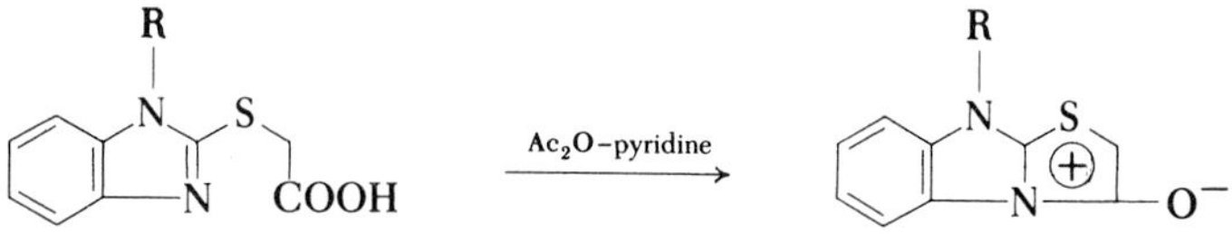

(III) —Ac_2O–pyridine→ (IV)

The reaction of chloroacetone with 2-mercaptobenzimidazole (V) yields VI.[6,7] The possibility that the product in this case is the isomeric 2-methyl compound would seem to be excluded by evidence[4] that V reacts with chloroacetic acid to give I (R = H). The 2,3-dimethyl homolog results[13] from the reaction of V with 3-bromobutanone-2.

$$\text{(V)} \xrightarrow{ClCH_2COCH_3} \text{(VI)}$$

(V) (VI)

The condensation of quinone with 2-aminothiazole is reported[12] to yield the 6- or 7-hydroxy compound, but no details were given.

Thiazolo[3,2-*a*]benzimidazoles

Empirical formula	Structure	Properties	Refs.
$C_9H_6N_2SO$	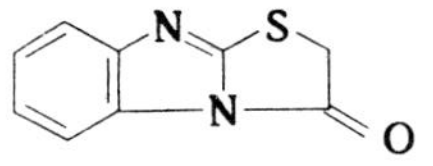 N, S, N, O	m. 182° (179–81°)	1–3,5,8
	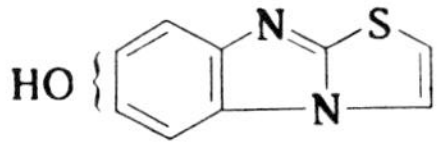 HO, N, S, N	—	12
$C_{10}H_8N_2S$	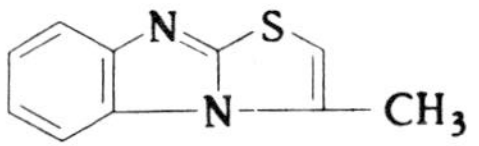 N, S, N, CH_3	m. 165°.	6,7
$C_{10}H_8N_2OS$	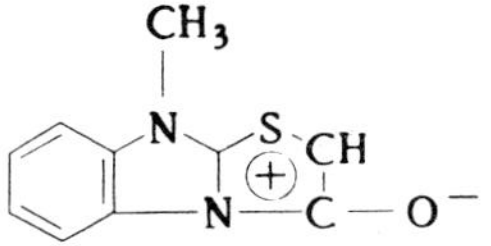 CH_3, N, S, CH, +, N, C, O^-	Yel., m. 255°.	4
$C_{11}H_{10}N_2S$	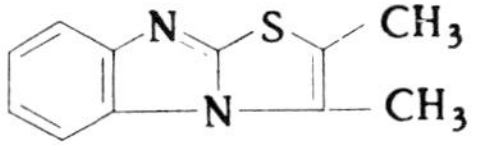 N, S, CH_3, N, CH_3	m. 154–6°. HBr salt, m. 273–5°. Methiodide, m. 303–4°.	13
$C_{12}H_{10}N_2O_2S$	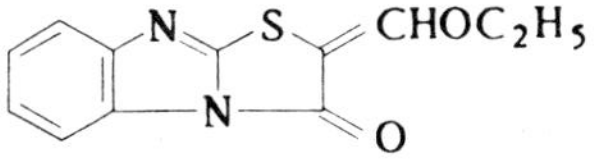 N, S, $CHOC_2H_5$, N, O	Yel., m. 167–9°.	4,9
$C_{15}H_{10}N_2OS$	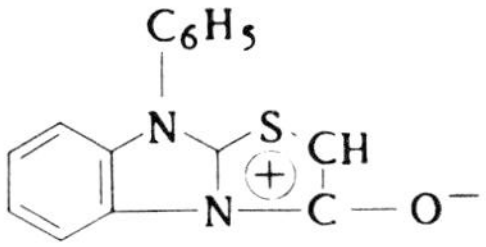 C_6H_5, N, S, CH, +, N, C, O^-	Yel., m. 222°.	4

(*continued*)

Thiazolo[3,2-*a*]benzimidazoles (*continued*)

Empirical formula	Structure	Properties	Refs.
$C_{16}H_{10}N_2OS$	2-(CHC_6H_5)-3-oxo derivative	Yel., m. 226° (219°).	4,8
$C_{16}H_{16}N_4OS$	2-substituted (N—CH_3, CH_3, $(CH_3)_2$)-3-oxo derivative	Pale yel., m. 272°.	11
$C_{16}H_{16}N_4OS_2$	2-substituted (CH_3, SCH_3, $(CH_3)_2$)-3-oxo derivative	Yel., m. 222°; λ_{max} 440 mμ.	15
$C_{16}H_{19}N_2S$	1-($CH_2CH_2COOC_2H_5$)-2,3-di-CH_3 cation (+)	Iodide, m. 250–3°.	13
$C_{17}H_{11}N_3OS_2$	2-(3-CH_3-benzothiazolinylidene)-3-oxo derivative	Yel., m. 330° (300°).	4,5
$C_{17}H_{12}N_2O_2S$	2-(CH-C$_6$H$_4$-OCH_3)-3-oxo derivative	Yel., m. 210°.	8
$C_{18}H_{15}N_3OS$	2-(CH-C$_6$H$_4$-$N(CH_3)_2$)-3-oxo derivative	Or., m. 269°.	4

Formula	Structure	Properties	Ref.
$C_{18}H_{18}N_4OS_2$	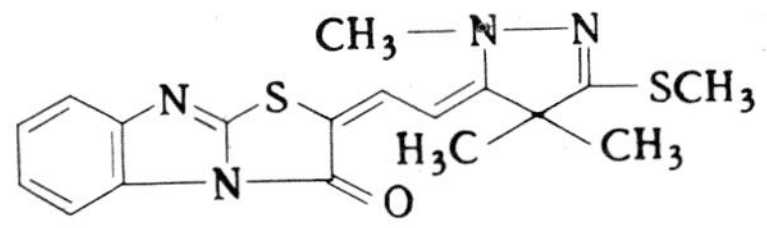	Red, m. 225°, λ_{max} 530 mμ.	9
	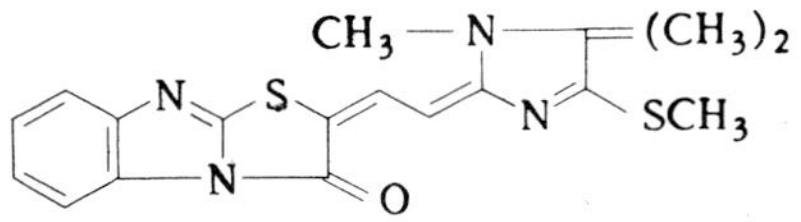	Or., m. 269°.	10
$C_{19}H_{13}N_3OS_2$	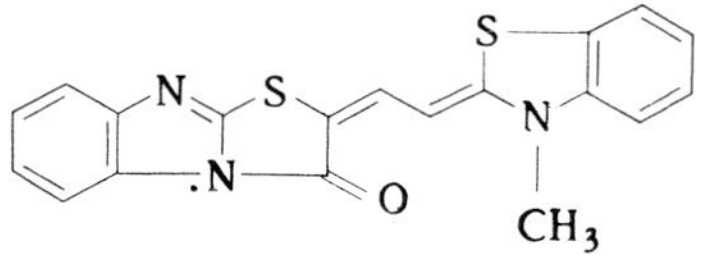	Red, m. 290° (284°).	4,5
$C_{19}H_{13}N_3O_2S$	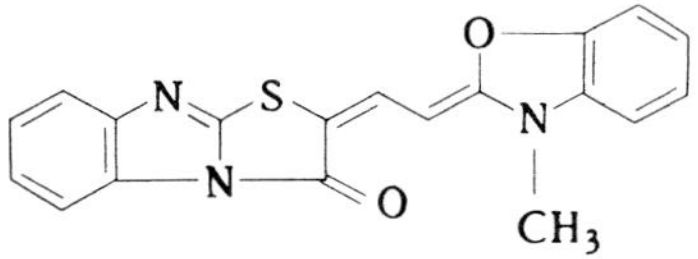	Or., m. 318° (302°).	4,5
$C_{19}H_{14}N_6OS$	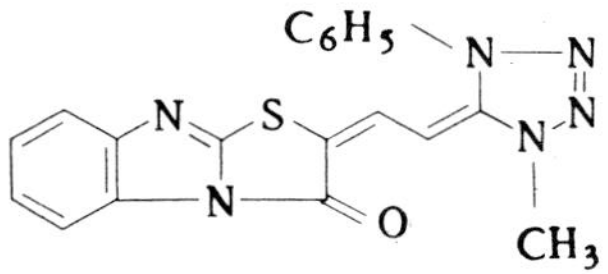	m. 258° d.	14
$C_{21}H_{15}N_3OS$	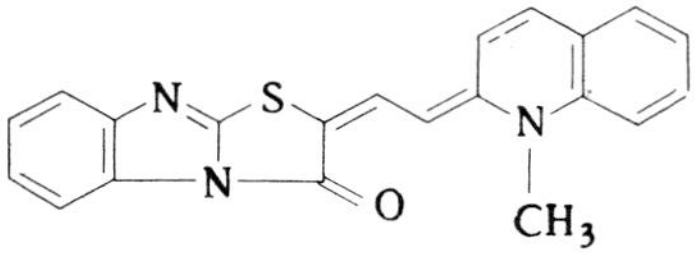	Dk. red, m. 339°.	4

(continued)

Thiazolo[3,2-*a*]benzimidazoles (*continued*)

Empirical formula	Structure	Properties	Refs.
	N S N O N—CH_3	Dk. bl., m. 295°.	4
$C_{22}H_{19}N_3OS$	CH_3 CH_3 N S N O N CH_3	Or., m. 252° (246°).	4,5
$C_{24}H_{21}N_5OS_2$	$(CH_3)_2$ N CH_3 S N S N O N CH N CH_3	m. 320°.	16
$C_{25}H_{23}N_5OS_2$	CH_3 N $(CH_3)_2$ S N S N O N CH N C_2H_5	Or., m. 244°; λ_{max} 440 mμ.	15
$C_{27}H_{25}N_5OS$	CH_3 N $(CH_3)_2$ N S N O N CH N C_2H_5	Red, m. 260°; λ_{max} 495 and 570 mμ.	15

References

1. Stephen and Wilson, *J. Chem. Soc.*, **1926,** 2531.
2. Wilson, Baird, Burns, Munro and Stephen, *J. Roy. Tech. Coll. (Glasgow)*, **2,** No. 1, 56 (1929); *Chem. Abstracts*, **23,** 5164 (1929).
3. Kendall and Duffin, U.S. Pat. 2,527,265; Brit. Pat. 634,951; *Chem. Abstracts*, **44,** 9287 (1950).
4. Duffin and Kendall, *J. Chem. Soc.*, **1956,** 361.
5. Kendall and Duffin, Brit. Pat. 634,952; *Chem. Abstracts*, **44,** 9287 (1950). U.S. Pat. 2,527,266.
6. Todd, Bergel and Karimullah, *Ber.*, **69,** 217 (1936).
7. Andersag and Westphal, *Ber.*, **70,** 2035 (1937).
8. Van Allen, *J. Org. Chem.*, **21,** 24 (1956).
9. Kendall and Duffin, Brit. Pat. 730,489; *Chem. Abstracts*, **49,** 15580 (1955).
10. Kendall and Duffin, Brit. Pat. 749,189; *Chem. Abstracts*, **51,** 904 (1957).
11. Kendall and Duffin, Brit. Pat. 749,190; *Chem. Abstracts*, **51,** 902 (1957).
12. Rudner, U.S. Pat. 2,790,172.
13. De Stevens and Halamandaris, *J. Am. Chem. Soc.*, **79,** 5710 (1957).
14. Waddington, Duffin and Kendall, Brit. Pat. 785,334; *Chem. Abstracts*, **52,** 6030 (1958).
15. Kendall and Duffin, Brit. Pats. 734,792/3; *Chem. Abstracts*, **50,** 1503 (1956).
16. Kendall and Duffin, Brit. Pat. 749,192; *Chem. Abstracts*, **50,** 16492 (1956).

A-134. Thiazolo[2,3-*f*]purine. R.I. 1346

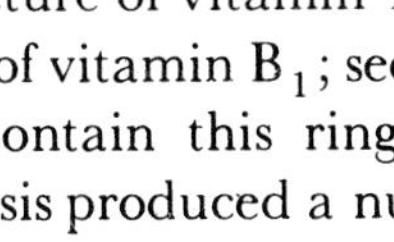

The alternative name *thiazolo-2′,3′:8,7-purine* is encountered.

During the investigations upon the structure of vitamin B_1, thiochrome (a product of the alkaline oxidation of vitamin B_1; see Section A-508) was, for a period, considered to contain this ring system. Efforts[1-3] to confirm this erroneous hypothesis produced a number of thiazolo[2,3-*f*]purines. Recently, some further examples were synthesized[4] as purine antagonists in the search for cancer-inhibiting drugs.

Most of the examples of this nucleus were prepared by treating mercaptopurines (e.g., I) with α-halocarbonyl compounds. In some cases the intermediate II was stable and required treatment with phosphorus oxychloride or hydrogen chloride to accomplish the cyclization to III, while in other cases ring closure occurred spon-

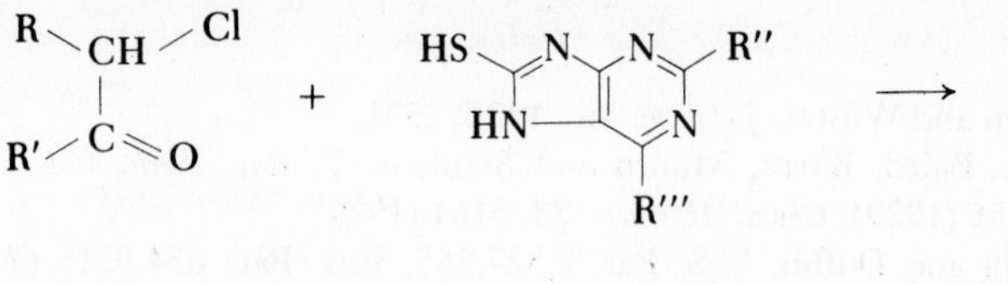

R–CH(Cl)–C(=O)–R′ + HS, HN, N, N, N, R″, R‴ ⟶

(I)

[R, S, N, N, R″, R′, O, HN, N, R‴] ⟶ R, S, N, N, R″, R′, N, N, R‴

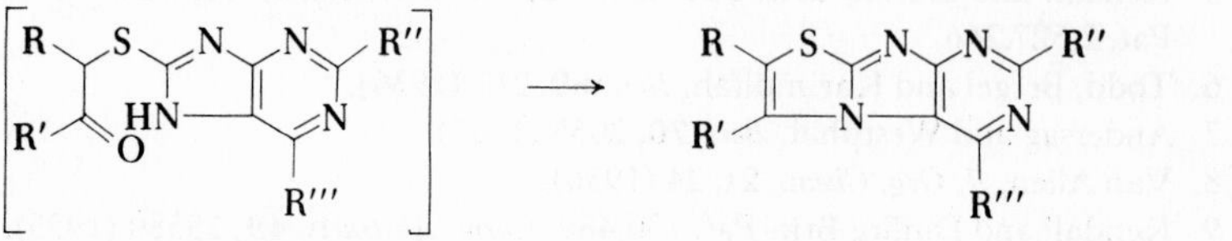

(II) (III)

taneously. These compounds are colorless, and (in contrast to thiochrome) do not fluoresce. The ultraviolet absorption spectra of some thiazolo[2,3-*f*]purines have been measured.[4]

By cyclizing the theophylline derivatives IV and V, compound VI was recently obtained.[5]

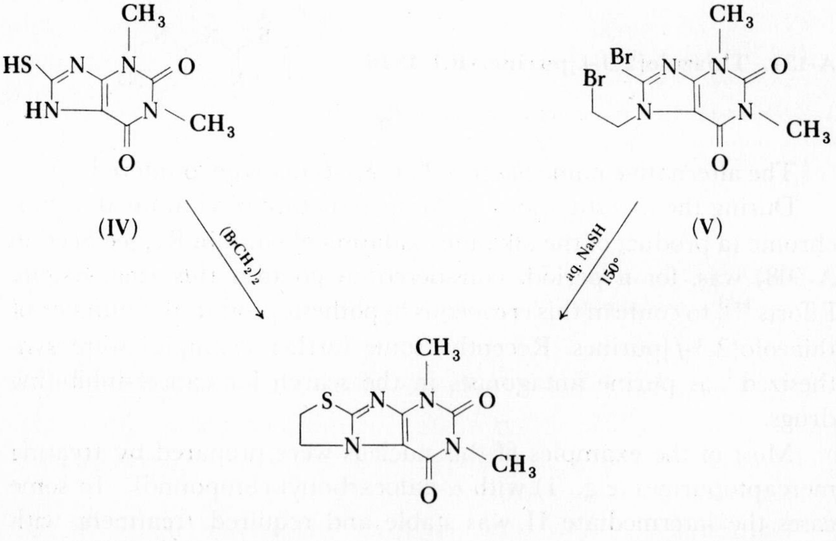

CH_3, HS, N, N, O, HN, N, CH_3, O

(IV)

$(BrCH_2)_2$

CH_3, Br, Br, N, N, O, N, N, CH_3, O

(V)

aq. NaSH 150°

CH_3, S, N, N, O, N, N, CH_3, O

(VI)

Derivatives of Thiazolo[2,3-*f*]purine

Empirical formula	Substituents	Properties	Refs.
$C_7H_6N_6S$	2,4-Diamino-	Not obtained pure.	4
$C_8H_6N_4O_2S$	2,4-Dihydroxy-6-methyl-	m. >250°.	3
$C_8H_8N_6S$	2,4-Diamino-6-methyl-	m. 288–9° d. HCl salt, m. 291–3° d.	4
$C_9H_8N_4S$	4,6-Dimethyl-	m. 241°.	2,3
$C_9H_{10}N_4O_2S$	1,2,3,4,6,7-Hexahydro-1,3-dimethyl-2,4-dioxo-	m. 256.5° d.	5
$C_{10}H_{10}N_4S$	4-Ethyl-6-methyl-	Not actually isolated.	3
$C_{10}H_{10}N_4O_2S$	1,3,6-Trimethyl-2,4-dioxo-	m. 263°.	1
$C_{11}H_{12}N_4OS$	7-(2-Hydroxyethyl)-4,6-dimethyl-	Not actually isolated.	3
$C_{12}H_{14}N_4OS$	4-Ethyl-7-(2-hydroxy ethyl)-6-methyl-	Not actually isolated.	3

References

1. Ochiai and Kitagawa, *J. Pharm. Soc. Japan*, **56,** 177 (1936); *Chem. Zentr.*, **I,** 2974 (1937); *Chem. Abstracts*, **32,** 8418 (1937).
2. Ochiai, *Ber.*, **69,** 1650 (1936).
3. Todd and Bergel, *J. Chem. Soc.*, **1936,** 1559.
4. Gordon, *J. Am. Chem. Soc.*, **73,** 984 (1951).
5. Cacace and Masironi, *Ann. chim.* (*Rome*), **46,** 806 (1956).

A-135. Benzothiazolo[3,2-*a*]-benzimidazole

Treatment[1] of I with picryl chloride gave II, which lost the elements of nitrous acid when heated in nitrobenzene solution, and yielded III (m. 243–4°). Compound III was named *benzothiazole-[2′,3′,2,1]-4,6-dinitrobenzimidazole.*

The reaction of IV with 2-chlorocyclohexanone yields[2] V (m. 153–4°; methiodide, m. 225–6°).

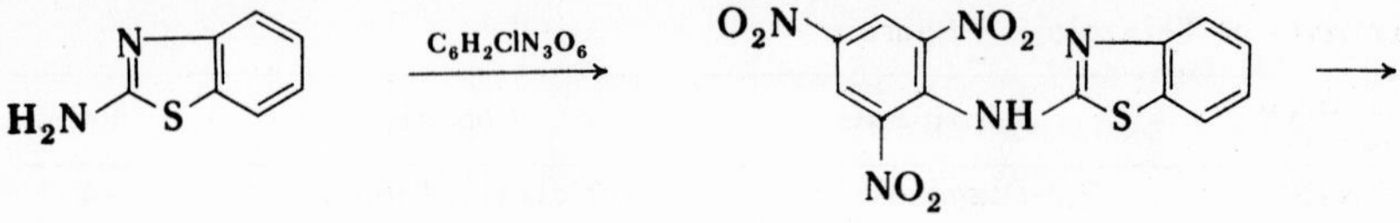

$C_6H_2ClN_3O_6$

(I) (II)

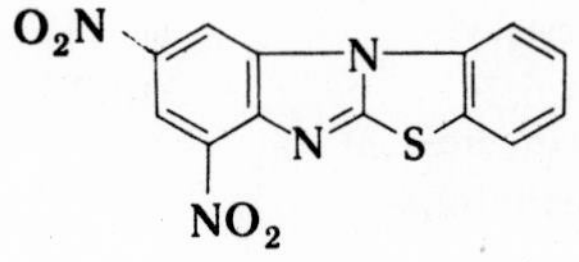

(III)

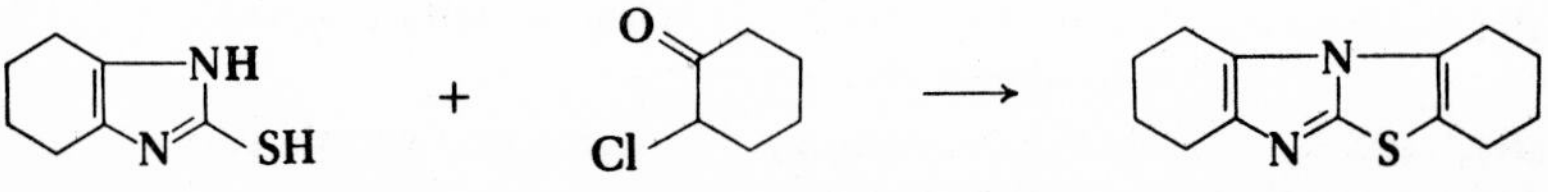

(IV) (V)

References

1. Ochiai and Nisizawa, *J. Pharm. Soc. Japan*, **60,** 132 (1940); *Chem. Abstracts*, **34,** 5082 (1940).
2. De Stevens and Halamandaris, *J. Am. Chem. Soc.*, **79,** 5710 (1957).

A-136. Naphtho[2',3',4,5]imidazo-[2,3-*b*]thiazole*

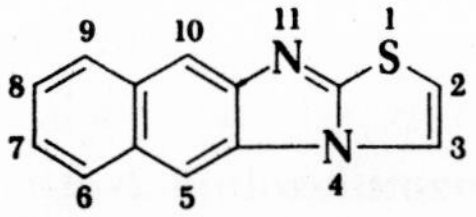

Dehydration of I produced[1] II (m. 236°) (see Sections A-131 and A-133).

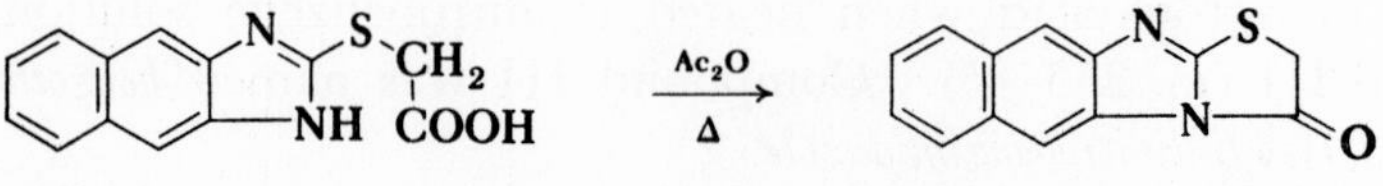

Ac_2O, Δ

(I) (II)

Reference

1. Brown, *J. Chem. Soc.*, **1958,** 1974.

A-137. 7*H*-Indeno[1′,2′,4,5]thiazolo-[3,2-*a*]benzimidazole*

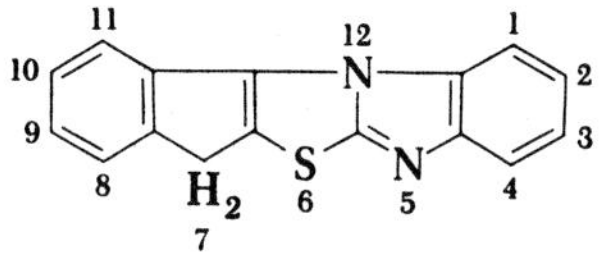

Condensation of I with 2-bromoindanone yields[1] II (hydrobromide, m. 215–6°).

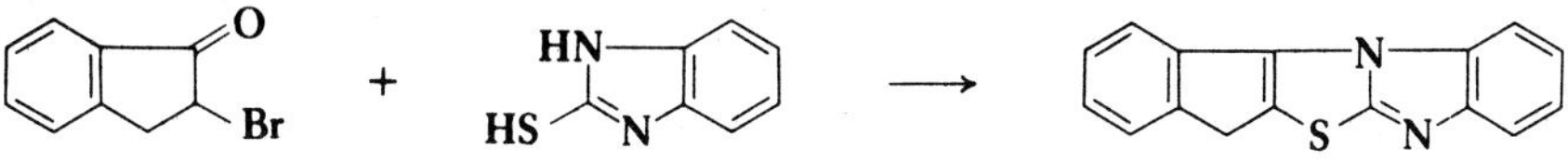

(I) (II)

Reference

1. De Stevens and Halamandaris, *J. Am. Chem. Soc.*, **79**, 5710 (1957).

A-138. Naphth[1′,2′,4,5]imidazo-[2,1-*b*]benzothiazole*

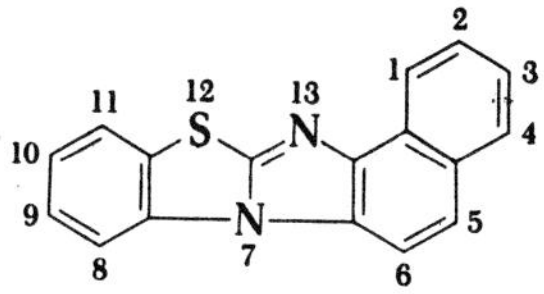

or

A-139. Naphth[2′,1′,4,5]imidazo-[2,1-*b*]benzothiazole*

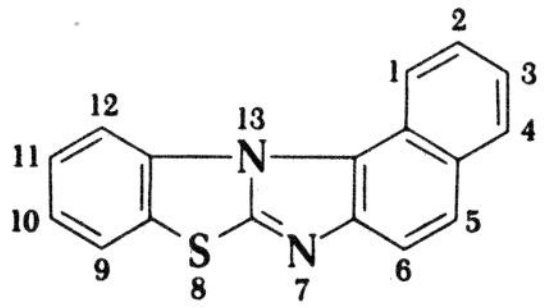

The reaction of naphthoquinone with 2-amino-6-ethoxybenzothiazole was reported to yield a product thought[1] to be either I or II, but no further details were given.

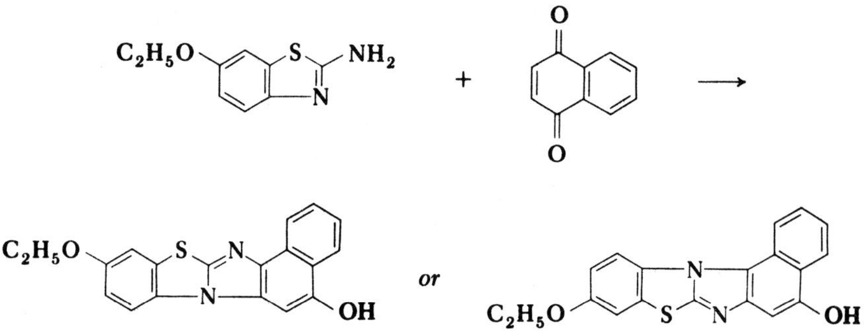

or

(I) (II)

Reference

1. Rudner, U.S. Pat. 2,790,172.

A-140. Naphtho[1′,2′,4,5]thiazolo-[3,2-*a*]benzimidazole*

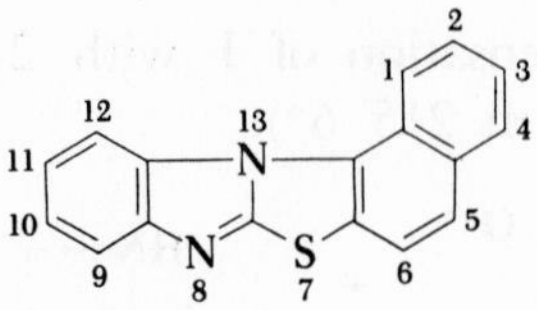

The reaction of I with 2-bromotetralone yielded[1] II (HBr salt, m. 203–5°).

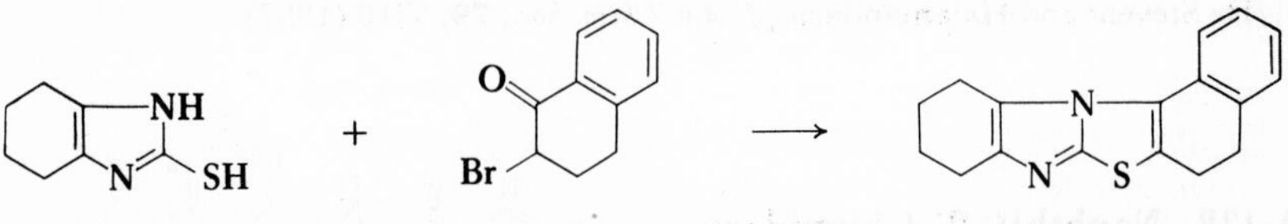

(I) (II)

Reference

1. De Stevens and Halamandaris, *J. Am. Chem. Soc.*, **79,** 5710 (1957).

A-141. Anthra[2,1-*d*]anthra[2′,1′,4,5]-imidazo[2,1-*b*]thiazole*

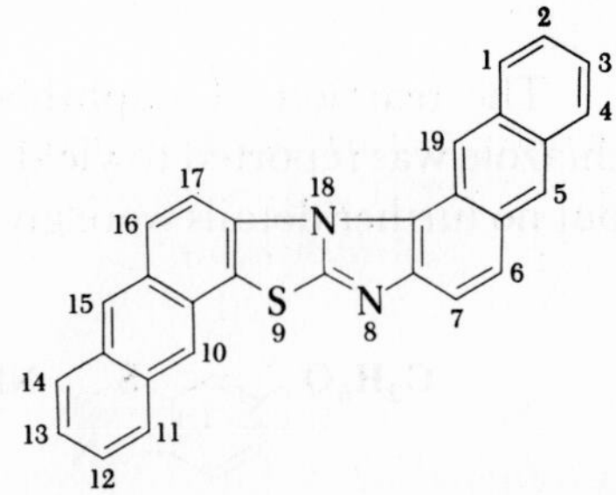

A yellow dye thought to have structure IV was prepared by Scheyer and Schwamberger,[1,2] via the intermediate III, from the condensation of I and II.

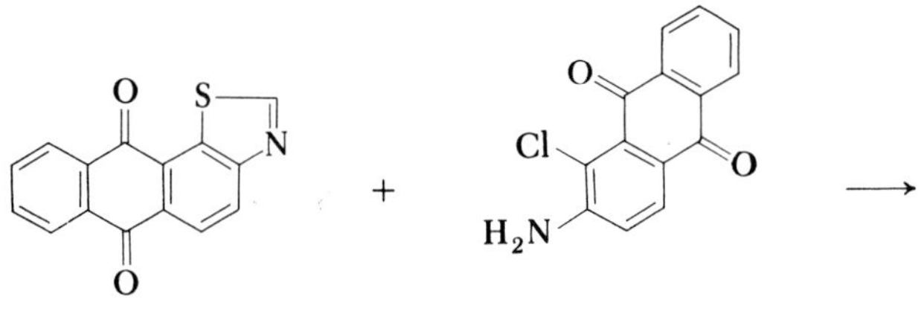

(I) (II)

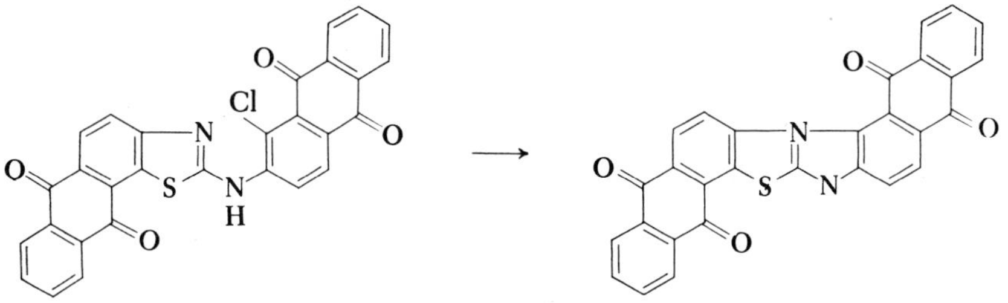

(III) (IV)

References

1. Scheyer and Schwamberger, *I. G. Farbenindustrie A.-G., 34 Wissenchaftlicher Austausch der Gruppe IX*, Leverkusen, Oct. 25, 1935; *PB Report No.* 70342, frame 15017.
2. Scheyer and Schwamberger, U.S. Pat. 2,108,413; Fr. Pat. 803,279; Ger. Pat. 642,339; *Frdl.*, **23,** 1017 (1940).

A-142. Anthra[2,1-*d*]anthra-[2′,3′,4,5]imidazo-[2,1-*b*]thiazole*

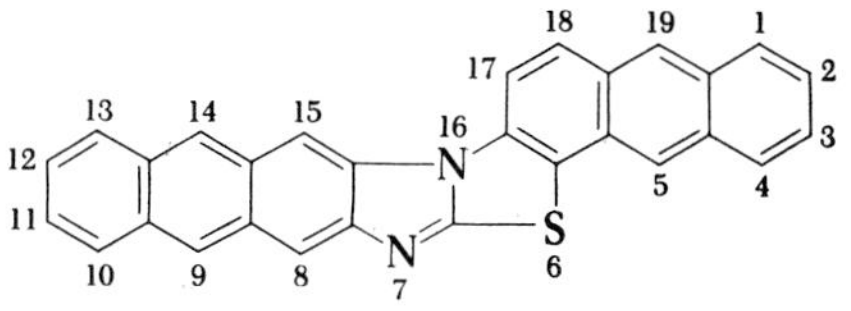

Scheyer and Schwamberger[1,2] found that the anthrimid III was produced when I and II were heated in nitrobenzene in the presence of a base. On further heating, with the addition of copper, III was converted into a new product thought to be IV. This product is a greenish yellow dye (olive-green vat) of good chlorine- and boil-fastness but only fair light fastness.

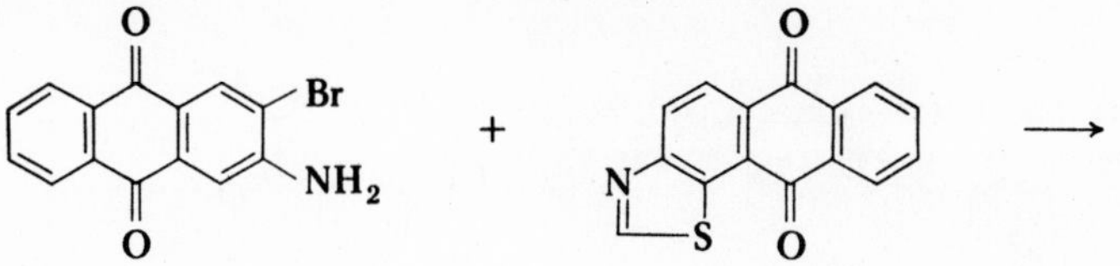

(I) (II)

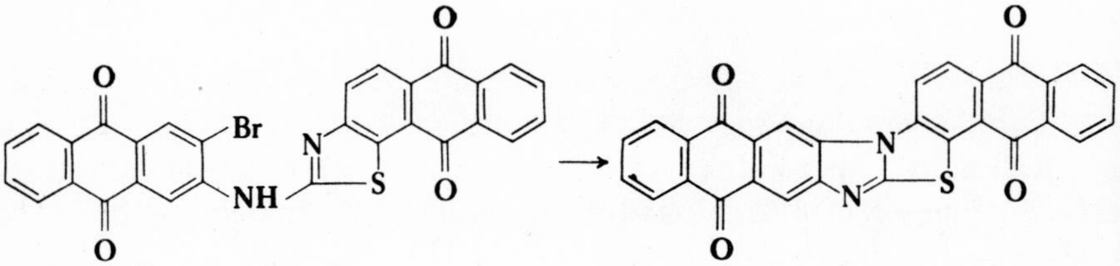

(III) (IV)

References

1. Scheyer and Schwamberger, *I. G. Farbenindustrie, A.-G., 34 Wissenschaftlicher Austausch der Gruppe IX*, Leverkusen, Oct. 25, 1935; *PB Report No.* 70342, frame 15017.
2. Scheyer and Schwamberger, U.S. Pat. 2,108,413; Fr. Pat. 803,279; Ger. Pat. 642,339; *Frdl.*, **23,** 1017 (1940).

A-143. *5H*-Pyrrolo[2,1-*c*]-*s*-triazole*

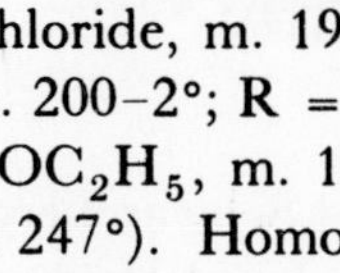

Condensation of the lactim ether I with various hydrazines yielded amidrazones (II), which were readily dehydrated to III (R = H, $b_{0.6}$ 200–2°, m. ~65°, hydrochloride, m. 196°; R = CH_3, $b_{1.2}$ 194–6°, m. 60–3°, hydrochloride, m. 200–2°; R = OH, m. 179°; R = $CONH_2$, m. 182–3° (181°); R = OC_2H_5, m. 150–1°; R = 4-pyridyl, m. 186°; R = —$(CH_2)_4$—, m. 247°). Homologous systems have been obtained from lactim ethers related to I (see Sections A-476, A-696 and A-716).

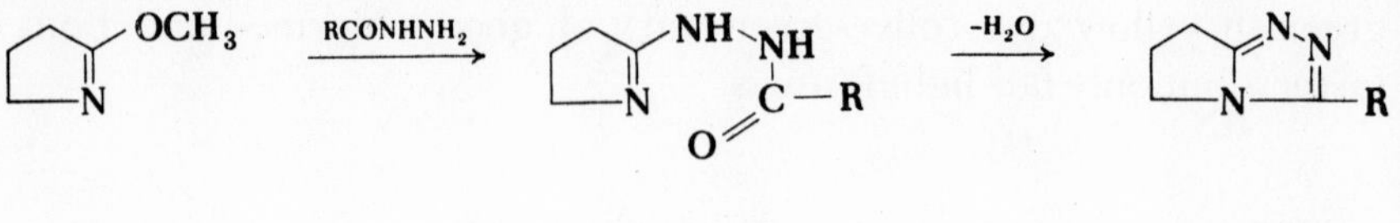

$\xrightarrow{RCONHNH_2}$ $\xrightarrow{-H_2O}$

(I) (II) (III)

References

1. Petersen and Tietze, *Chem. Ber.*, **90,** 909 (1957).
2. Petersen, Tietze and Wirth, Ger. Pat. 1,025,881.

A-144. *3H*-Pyrazolo[2,3-*a*]benzimidazole. R.I. 1361M

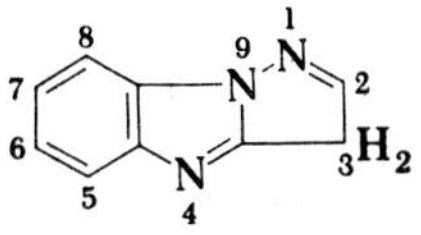

This nucleus has also been called *pyrazolino-benzimidazole.*

Refluxing I in alcoholic hydrochloric acid gave a product (m. 216–7°; picrate, m. 182–3°; hydrazide, m. 198–9°) thought[1] to be II.

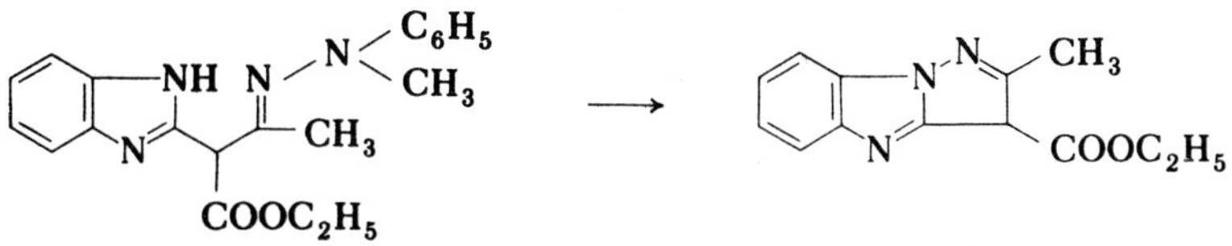

(I) (II)

Reference

1. Das Gupta and Ghosh, *Science and Culture,* **4,** 739 (1939); *Chem. Zentr.*, **II,** 2924 (1939); *Chem. Abstracts,* **33,** 7299 (1939).

A-145. *1H*-Imidaz[3,4-*a*]imidazole. R.I. 605

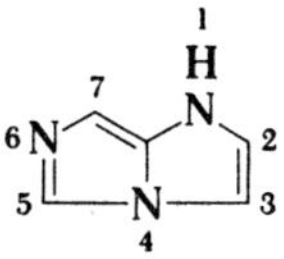

The preparation of II by heating I with an excess of phenyl isocyanate has been mentioned[1] briefly.

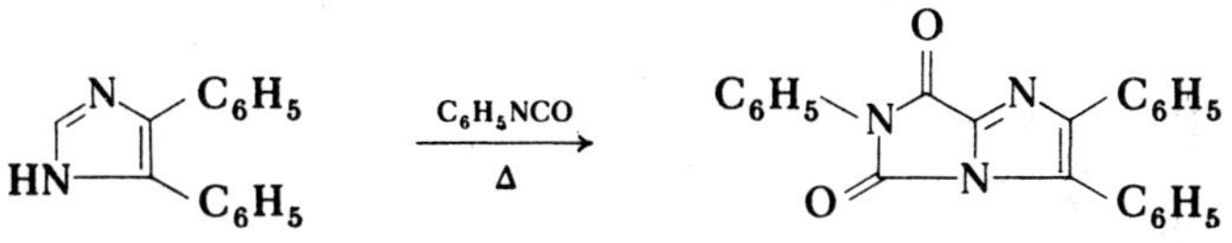

C_6H_5NCO, Δ

(I) (II)

The possibility of an equilibrium such as III ⇆ IV, which would involve derivatives of this ring system, was considered, but supporting evidence could not be adduced.[2]

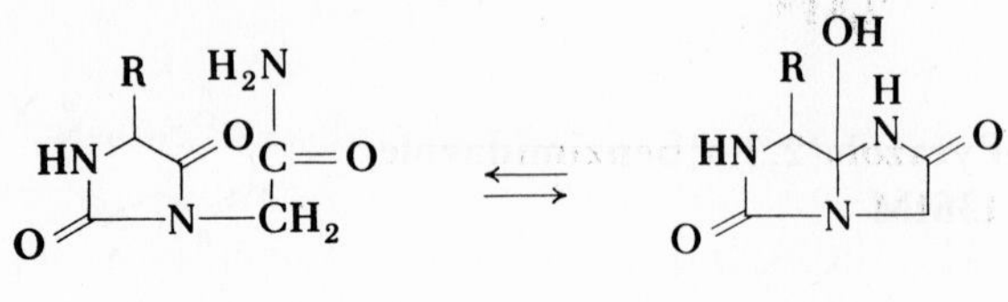

(III) (IV)

The 1,5-methano derivative is discussed in Section B-32.

References

1. Gompper, *Angew. Chem.*, **69,** 729 (1957).
2. Cohen and Fry, *J. Am. Chem. Soc.*, **78,** 5863 (1956).

A-146. 1*H*-Imidaz[1,2-*a*]imidazole.
R.I. 606

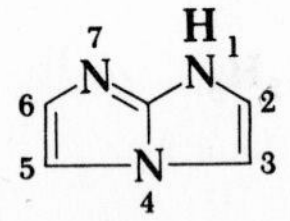

British literature uses the name *glyoxalino(1′:2′-1:2)glyoxaline.*

Compound I was mentioned initially by Pierron,[1] who gave it the name *diethyleneguanidine*, and who thought he had obtained it from the reaction of cyanogen bromide with ethylenediamine. However, McKay, who obtained I both by dehydrochlorinating[8] II, and by

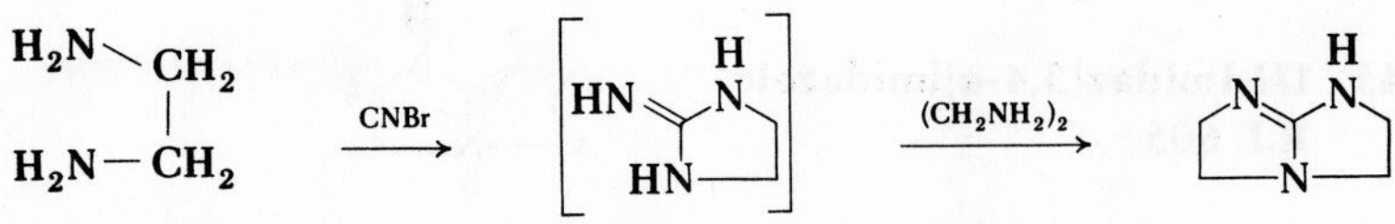

CNBr $(CH_2NH_2)_2$

(I)

treating III with silver nitrate or mercuric oxide, or (preferably[11,12]) chloroacetic acid, showed[11] that Pierron's product was actually 2-(β-aminoethylamino)-imidazoline. Compound I is slowly hydrolyzed to 1-(β-aminoethyl)-2-imidazolidone. Reaction with nitric acid gives the 1-nitro derivative.[8,11]

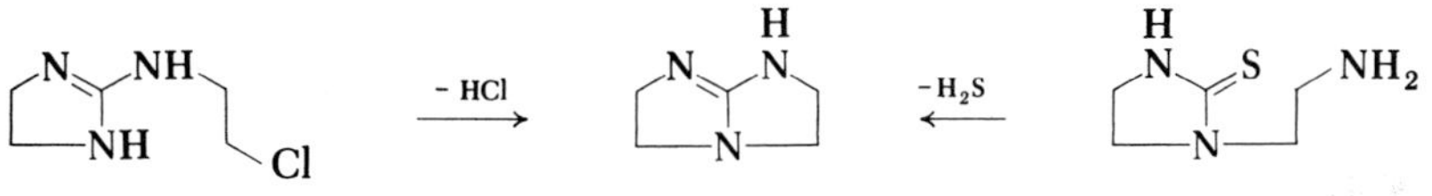

(II) (I) (III)

Lawson[2] showed that, under controlled conditions, α-amino-aldehydes react with cyanamide to give, ultimately, V. Where R is other than CH_3, the aminoketone IV is obtained instead of V, but in these cases IV is readily dehydrated to V.

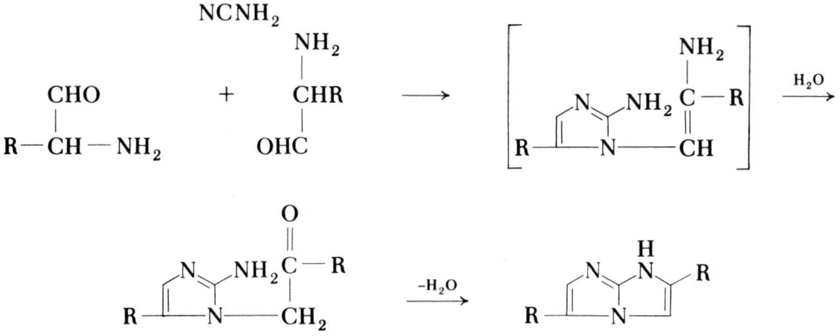

(IV) (V)

By a reaction combining features of both of the preceding syntheses, VI was obtained[3] from the condensation of an α-aminoester and a substituted cyanamide.

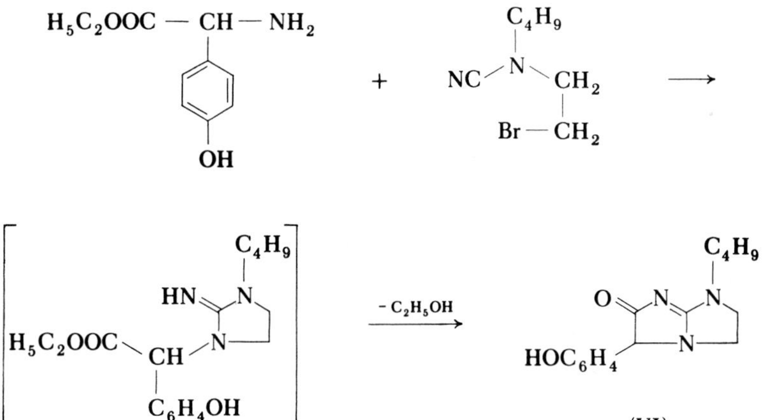

(VI)

Treatment of the nitrimine VII with amines is reported[4] to yield 1-substituted tetrahydroimidazo[1,2-*a*]imidazoles (VIII), which were also obtained[9] in good over-all yield from IX.

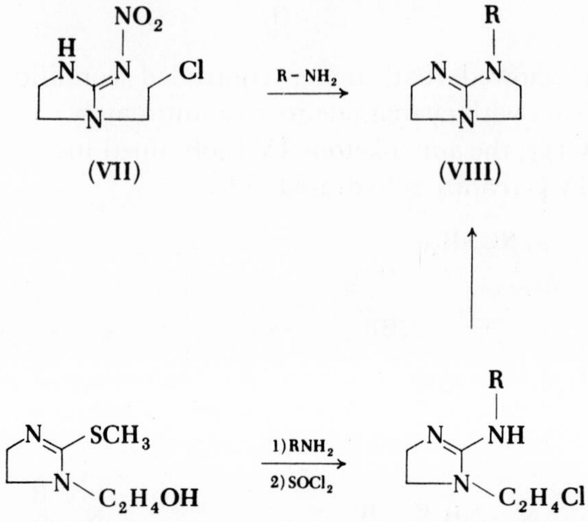

NO_2 H N N Cl N $\xrightarrow{R-NH_2}$ R N N N

(VII) (VIII)

N SCH_3 N C_2H_4OH $\xrightarrow[2)\ SOCl_2]{1)\ RNH_2}$ R N NH N C_2H_4Cl

(IX)

The ester hydrochloride X reacts with silver oxide to yield XI, which is readily hydrolyzed to the acid corresponding to X.[5]

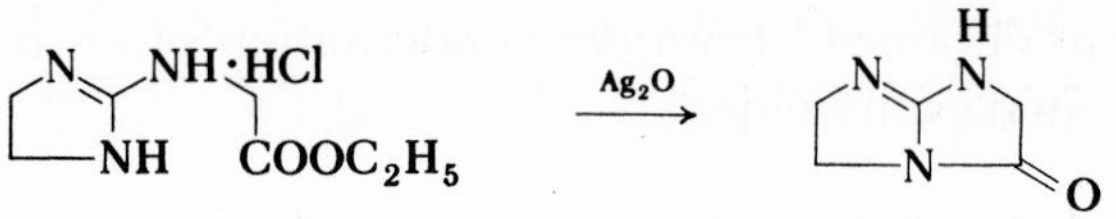

N NH·HCl NH $COOC_2H_5$ $\xrightarrow{Ag_2O}$ H N N N O

(X) (XI)

In connection with the investigations upon penicillin, it was learned[6] that XII (see Section A-149) underwent desulfurization when treated with mercuric acetate, and the product was thought to have structure XIII.

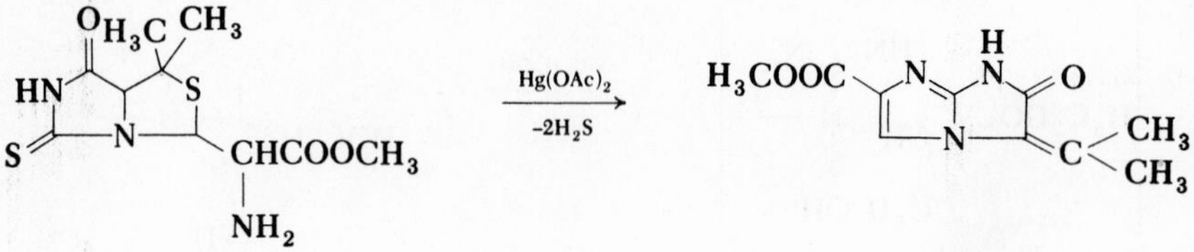

O H_3C CH_3 HN S S N $CHCOOCH_3$ NH_2 $\xrightarrow[-2H_2S]{Hg(OAc)_2}$ H_3COOC N H N O N C CH_3 CH_3

(XII) (XIII)

Certain saturated imidaz[1,2-*a*]imidazole derivatives have been patented[7] as coating compounds to improve the penetration of paints and varnishes into wood, and the 2,3,5,6-tetrahydro-1-vinyl compound has been claimed[13] as a monomer.

1*H*-Imidazo[1,2-*a*]imidazoles

Empirical formula	Substituents	Properties	Refs.
$C_5H_7N_3O$	2,3,5,6-Tetrahydro-3-oxo-	Picrate, m. 235–6°.	5
$C_5H_9N_3$	2,3,5,6-Tetrahydro-	m. 158.5–9.5°. Monopicrate, m. 219.5–20°.	1,8,11, 12
$C_5H_8N_4O_2$	2,3,5,6-Tetrahydro-1-nitro-	Nitrate salt, m. 148.5–50°.	8,11
$C_7H_9N_3$	2,5-Dimethyl-	m. 125°. HCl salt, m. 272°d. Picrate, m. 226°.	2
$C_7H_{11}N_3$	2,3,5,6-Tetrahydro-1-vinyl-	$b_{0.28}$ 85.5–6° ($b_{0.25}$ 84–5°). Picrate, m. 171.5–2.5° (170–1°).	11,13
$C_7H_{12}ClN_3$	1-(2-Chloroethyl)-2,3,5,6-tetrahydro-	Oil. Picrate, m. 120–1°.	11,13
$C_7H_{13}N_3O$	2,3,5,6-Tetrahydro-1-(2-hydroxyethyl)-	$b_{0.2}$ 135°, m. 68.5–9.5°. Picrate, m. 110.5–1.5°.	11,13
$C_8H_{15}N_3$	2,3,5,6-Tetrahydro-1-*n*-propyl-	$b_{0.15}$ 86–8°. Picrate, m. 85–6°.	10
$C_9H_{18}N_4$	1-(2-Dimethylaminoethyl)-2,3,5,6-tetrahydro-	$b_{0.05}$ 91–2°, $n_D^{25°}$ 1.5008, $d_{4°}^{22°}$ 1.018. Picrate, m. 172–3°.	9,10
$C_{10}H_{10}N_3O_3$	6-Carbomethoxy-2(3*H*)-oxo-3-*i*-propylidene-	m. 304–7°, λ_{max} 225 mμ (ε 26,000).	6
$C_{10}H_{20}N_4$	1-(3-Dimethylaminopropyl)-2,3,5,6-tetrahydro-	$b_{0.25}$ 119–21°, $n_D^{25°}$ 1.5033, $d_{4°}^{22°}$ 1.013. Picrate, m. 157–8°.	9,10
$C_{11}H_{22}N_4$	1-(2-Diethylaminoethyl)-2,3,5,6-tetrahydro-	$b_{0.05}$ 100–2°, $n_D^{25°}$ 1.4984, $d_{4°}^{22°}$ 1.002. Picrate, m. 172–3°.	9,10
$C_{12}H_{15}N_3$	1-Benzyl-2,3,5,6-tetrahydro-	$b_{0.11}$ 128–31°, $n_D^{26°}$ 1.56963, m. 39.0–40.5°. Picrate (dimorphic), m. 109–9.5° and 123–4°.	4,9,10

(*continued*)

1*H*-Imidazo[1,2-*a*]imidazoles (*continued*)

Empirical formula	Substituents	Properties	Refs.
$C_{12}H_{24}N_4$	1-(3-Diethylamino-propyl)-2,3,5,6-tetrahydro-	$b_{0.2}$ 121–3°, $n_D^{25°}$ 1.4942, $d_{4°}^{22°}$ 0.980. Picrate, m. 139–40°.	9,10
$C_{13}H_{17}N_3$	2,3,5,6-Tetrahydro-1-(2-phenylethyl)-	$b_{0.05}$ 122–214°, $n_D^{25°}$ 1.5609, $d_{4°}^{22°}$ 1.101. Picrate, m. 145–6°.	9,10
$C_{13}H_{21}N_3$	2,6-Di-*n*-butyl-	HCl salt, m. 111°. Picrate, m. 131°.	2
	2,6-Di-*i*-butyl-	HCl salt, m. 113°. Picrate, m. 128°.	2
$C_{13}H_{25}N_3$	2,3,5,6-Tetrahydro-1-octyl-	$b_{0.05}$ 115–7°, $n_D^{25°}$ 1.4857, $d_{4°}^{22°}$ 0.959. Picrate, m. 75–6°.	9,10
$C_{13}H_{26}N_4$	2,3,5,6-Tetrahydro-1-(2-dipropyl-aminoethyl)-	$b_{0.05}$ 106–8° ($b_{0.5}$ 119°), $n_D^{25°}$ 1.4968. Picrate, m. 185.5–7° (169–70°?).	4,9
$C_{15}H_{19}N_3O_2$	1-Butyl-2,3,5,6-tetrahydro-5-(4-hydroxyphenyl)-6-oxo-	Two forms: m. 116.5–7° and 139–40°. HCl salt, m. 179–80°.	3
$C_{17}H_{33}N_3$	1-Dodecyl-2,3,5,6-tetrahydro-	$b_{0.08}$ 143–5°, $n_D^{25°}$ 1.4842, $d_{4°}^{22°}$ 0.945. Picrate, m. 65–6°.	9,10
$C_{19}H_{17}N_3$	2,5-Dibenzyl-	m. 164°. Picrate, m. 182°.	2
$C_{19}H_{37}N_3$	2,3,5,6-Tetrahydro-1-tetradecyl-	$b_{0.08}$ 172–3°, $n_D^{25°}$ 1.4832, $d_{4°}^{22°}$ 0.937. Picrate, m. 75–6°.	9,10
$C_{21}H_{41}N_3$	1-Hexadecyl-2,3,5,6-tetrahydro-	$b_{0.07}$ 188–90°, m. 33–4°. Picrate, m. 78–9°.	9,10
$C_{23}H_{45}N_3$	2,3,5,6-Tetrahydro-1-octadecyl-	$b_{0.2}$ 227–8°, m. 36–7°. Picrate, m. 86–7°.	9,10

References

1. Pierron, *Ann. chim.*, [9]**11,** 361 (1919); *Chem. Zentr.*, **III,** 781 (1919); *Chem. Abstracts*, **13,** 2022 (1919).
2. Lawson, *J. Chem. Soc.*, **1956,** 307.
3. Elderfield and Green, *J. Org. Chem.*, **17,** 442 (1952).
4. McKay and Gilpin, *J. Am. Chem. Soc.*, **78,** 486 (1956).
5. McKay and Hatton, *J. Am. Chem. Soc.*, **78,** 1618 (1956).
6. du Vigneaud and Melville in Clarke *et al.*, *The Chemistry of Penicillin,* Princeton University Press, Princeton, N. J., 1949, pp. 269–309.
7. Mannheimer, U.S. Pat. 2,541,825.
8. McKay, Hatton and Braun, *J. Am. Chem. Soc.*, **78,** 6144 (1956).
9. McKay and Garmaise, *Can. J. Chem.*, **35,** 8 (1957).

10. McKay and Garmaise, U.S. Pat. 2,782,205.
11. McKay, Kreling, Paris, Braun and Whittingham, *Can. J. Chem.*, **35,** 843 (1957).
12. McKay, Braun and Paris, U.S. Pat. 2,816,896.
13. McKay and Kreling, U.S. Pat. 2,824,879.

A-147. 1*H*-Oxazolo[3,4-*c*]oxazole

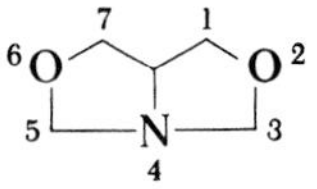

This nucleus also has been named *1-aza-3,7-dioxabicyclo*[*3,3,0*]-*octane*, and *3,4-dimethyleneoxy-4-oxazolidine*.

The reaction of 1,3-dihydroxy-2-propylamine and its homologs (I) with aldehydes was found by Johnston[1] and Senkus[2] to yield

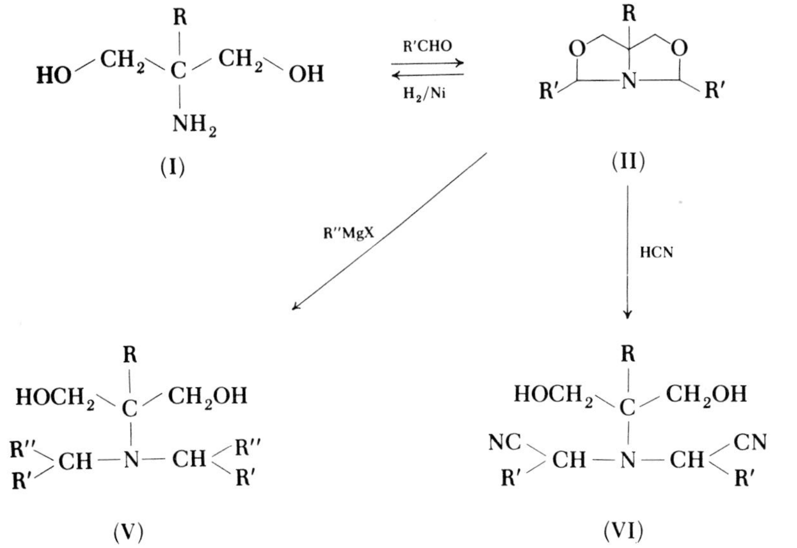

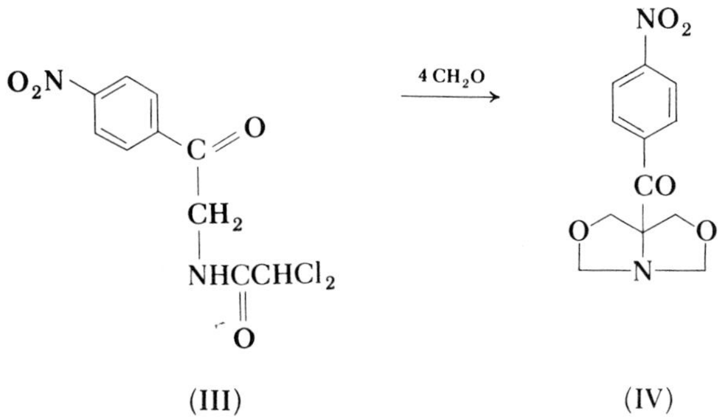

R'CHO

H_2/Ni

(I)

(II)

R''MgX

HCN

(V)

(VI)

$4\,CH_2O$

(III)

(IV)

products of structure II. In a related reaction, Gut, *et al.*[3] found III to react with four moles of formaldehyde to yield IV. Aldehydes also condense with 2-amino-1-arylpropane-1,3-diol (I, R = aryl) to give[11] derivatives of type II.

Compounds of type II are rather readily cleaved by various reagents. For example, hydrogenolysis over a Raney nickel catalyst[4] reconverts II into I, while with Grignard reagents, glycols such as V are formed,[5] and with hydrocyanic acid, II is converted[6] into VI.

Derivatives of Tetrahydrooxazolo[3,4-*c*]oxazole

R	R′	Properties	Refs.
7a-*H*	H	b_{10} 66.5°; n_D^{20} 1.4715; d_{20}^{20} 1.1850	2
7a-CH_3	H	b_{10} 60.0° (b_{760} 178–80°); n_D^{20} 1.4590 (n_D^{25} 1.4556); d_{20}^{20} 1.1088	1,2
7a-CH_2OH	H	m. 65° (62–3°, 59–60°); *p*-Nitrobenzoate, HCl salt. 1-Phenylcyclohexanecarboxylate, HCl salt, m. 166–8°.	1,2,7–9
7a-C_2H_5	H	b_{10} 74.5° (b_{1-2} 75–7°); n_D^{20} 1.4618 (n_D^{25} 1.4582); d_{20}^{20} 1.0829	1,2
7a-*n*-C_3H_7	H	b_{10} 90–1°; n_D^{20} 1.4604; d_{20}^{20} 1.0522	2
7a-*i*-C_3H_7	H	b_{10} 84–5°; n_D^{20} 1.4631; d_{20}^{20} 1.0602	2
7a-CH_3	*n*-C_3H_7	b_{10} 94–5°; n_D^{20} 1.4494; d_{20}^{20} 0.9594	2
7a-CH_2OH	*n*-C_3H_7	b_2 112.5–3.5°	7
7a-(*p*-$NO_2C_6H_4CO$)	H	m. 109°. Picrate, m. 121–2°.	3
7a-C_2H_5	*n*-C_3H_7	b_{10} 104.5°; n_D^{20} 1.4544; d_{20}^{20} 0.9599	2
7a-CH_2OH	*n*-C_5H_{11}	$b_{0.3}$ 151–3° (b_{32} 216–7°).	7
7a-CH_3	C_6H_5	m. 123°	2
7a-CH_2OH	C_6H_5	m. 93–5°. HCl salt, m. 130–1°.	7
7a-CH_3	$C_4H_9CHC_2H_5$	$b_{0.5}$ 114–8°; n_D^{20} 1.4601; d_{20}^{20} 0.9276	2
7a-CH_2OH	$C_6H_5CH_2$	b_1 238–40°.	7

Derivatives of Tetrahydrooxazolo[3,4-*c*]oxazole (*continued*)

R	R′	Properties	Refs.
1-(*p*-$NO_2C_6H_5$)	C_6H_5	Obtained from stereoisomeric forms of *p*-$NO_2C_6H_4CH(OH)$-$CH(NH_2)CH_2OH$: L-(+)-threo-, m. 93–4°, $[\alpha]_D^{20}$ – 45° (CH_3OH); D-(–)-threo, m. 93–4°, $[\alpha]_D^{20}$ + 45° (CH_3OH); DL-threo, m. 110–2°; DL-erythro-, m. 121.5–2.5°.	11,14, 15
1-(*p*-$NO_2C_6H_5$)	*p*-$CH_3C_6H_4$-	As above, L-(+)-threo, m. 115.7–6.5°, $[\alpha]_D^{20}$ – 50° (CH_3OH) D-(–)-threo, m. 115–6°, $[\alpha]_D^{20}$ + 50° (CH_3OH).	11
1-(*p*-$NO_2C_6H_5$)	H	D-(+)-Threo form, m. 77°; $[\alpha]_D^{26°}$ + 38.5° (EtOAc).	12,13
1-C_6H_5	H	D-(+)-Threo form, $b_{3.3}$ 138°.	12,13
1-(*p*-$NO_2C_6H_5$)	*p*-$NO_2C_6H_5$	D-(–)-Threo form, m. 152–5°; $[\alpha]_D^{26°}$ – 46°.	12,13
1-C_6H_5	*p*-$NO_2C_6H_5$	D-(+)-Threo form, m. 157–8°; $[\alpha]_D^{26°}$ + 58°.	12,13
1-C_6H_5	C_6H_5	D-(+)-Threo form, m. 74–5°; $[\alpha]_D^{26°}$ + 45°.	12,13
1-C_6H_5	*n*-C_6H_{13}	D-(–)-Threo form, $b_{1.5-1.8}$ 198–204°.	12,13

References

1. Johnston, U.S. Pat. 2,448,890; Brit. Pat. 564,506; *Chem. Abstracts*, **40,** 4084 (1946).
2. Senkus, *J. Am. Chem. Soc.*, **67,** 1515 (1945).
3. Gut, Sicher, Svoboda, Šneberg and Šorm, *Chem. listy*, **46,** 274 (1952); *Chem. Abstracts*, **47,** 6902 (1953).
4. Hodge, U.S. Pat. 2,433,609.
5. Senkus, U. S. Pat. 2,363,465.
6. Senkus, U. S. Pat. 2,401,196.
7. Pierce, Lunsford, Raiford, Rush and Riley, *J. Am. Chem. Soc.*, **73,** 2595 (1951).
8. Pierce and Lunsford, *J. Am. Chem. Soc.*, **73,** 2596 (1951).
9. Tilford, Van Campen and Shelton, *J. Am. Chem. Soc.*, **69,** 2902 (1947).
10. Van Campen and Tilford, U.S. Pat. 2,474,796.
11. Pedrazzoli and Tricerri, *Helv. Chim. Acta*, **39,** 965 (1956).

12. Edgerton, Woods and Fisher, U.S. Pat. 2,777,854.
13. Edgerton, Fisher and Moersch, *J. Am. Chem. Soc.*, **79,** 6487 (1957).
14. Nagawa and Shimizu, *Ann. Rept. Takamine Lab.*, **7,** 11 (1955); *Chem. Abstracts*, **50,** 14764 (1956).
15. Okajima, *Ann. Rept. Takamine Lab.*, **7,** 21 (1955); *Chem. Abstracts*, **50,** 14711 (1956).

A-148. 1*H*,3*H*-Imidaz[3,4-*c*]oxazole

The single example of this nucleus, compound I (m. 187°), was prepared as shown by Davis and Levy,[1] who named it *2:3:4:5-tetrahydro-4-keto-2:2-dimethyl-2':5'-diphenyloxazolidino(3':4' - 1:5)glyoxaline.* Cold hydrochloric acid caused scission of the oxazole ring of I with loss of benzaldehyde.

Reference

1. Davis and Levy, *J. Chem. Soc.*, **1951,** 3479.

A-149. 1*H*,3*H*-Imidazo[1,5-*c*]thiazole

During the investigations upon the structure of penicillin it was found that benzylpenicillin methyl ester (I) and β-methyl-D-α-benzylpenicilloate (II) yielded compound IV (see Section A-487) on treatment with thiocyanic acid, while α-methyl-D-α-benzylpenicil-

(I) (III)

HSCN HSCN

alc. NaOH

(IV) (V)

HSCN HCl HCl $(C_6H_5CH_2CO)_2O$

(II) (VI)

loate (III) gave[1] a different substance (V). Alcoholic alkali caused IV to rearrange to V, and both IV and V were converted[1] into VI by hydrochloric acid. By acylation of VI with phenylacetic anhydride, compound V could be reconstituted.[1] A simpler analog (VII) of IV was transformed into compound VIII by treatment with alcoholic caustic.[1]

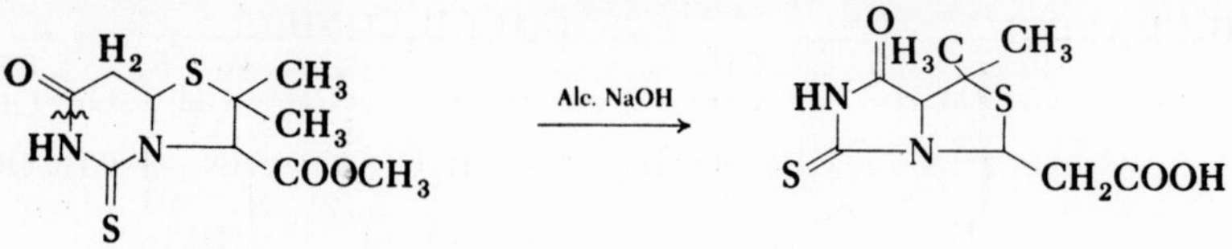

(VII) —Alc. NaOH→ (VIII)

Certain other thiazolidine-4-carboxylic acid derivatives have been converted similarly into imidazo[1,5-*c*]thiazoles. Thus IX readily yielded X on reaction with thiocyanic acid, while XI reacted with phenyl isothiocyanate to give either XII or XIII depending upon the conditions.[2]

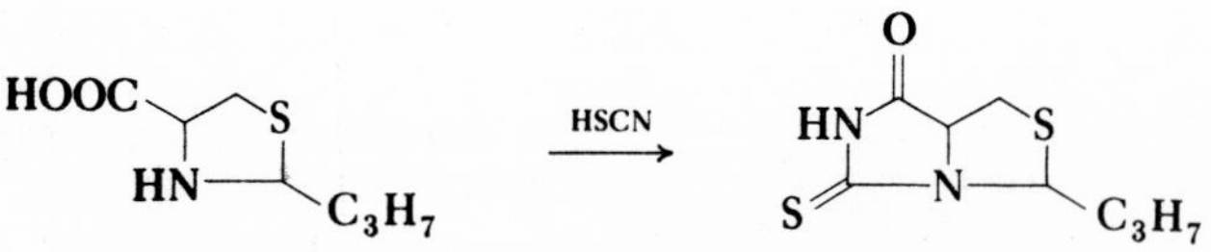

(IX) —HSCN→ (X)

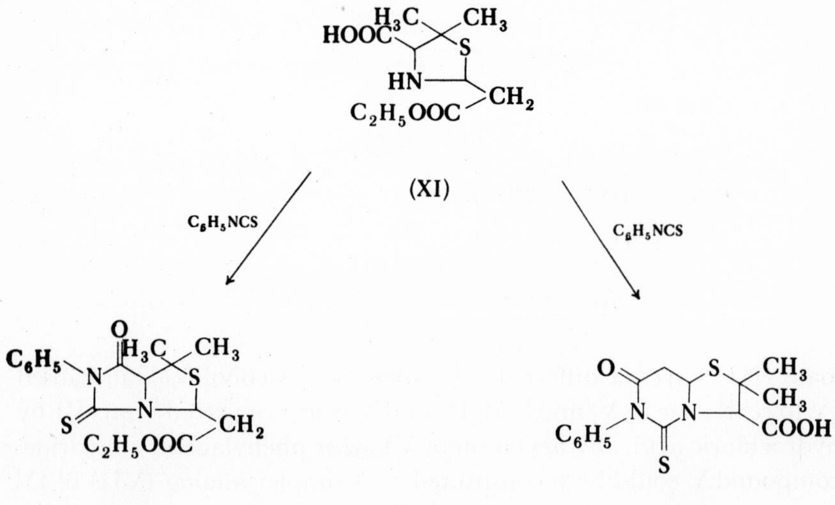

(XI)

C_6H_5NCS → (XII)

C_6H_5NCS → (XIII)

Derivatives of Imidazo[1,5-*c*]thiazole

Structure	Properties	Refs.
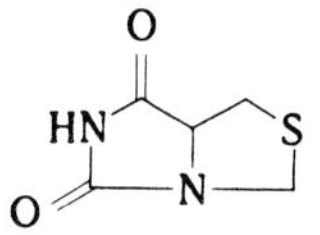 O; HN; S; N; O	m. 167°; $[\alpha]_D^{20}$ 115°.	5
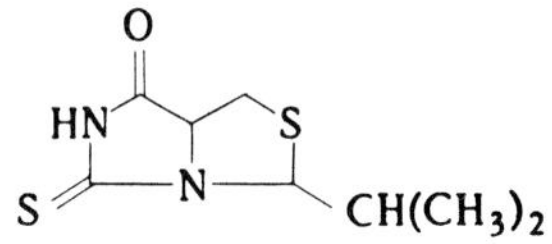 O; HN; S; N; S; $CH(CH_3)_2$	m. 118–9°.	1
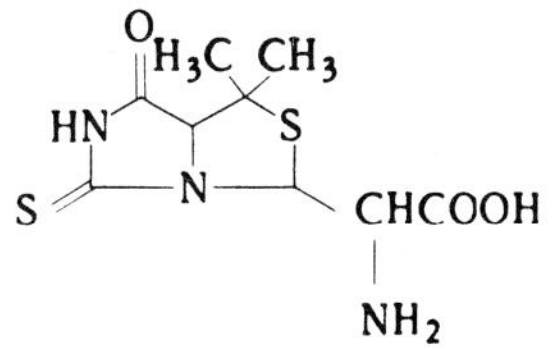 O; H_3C CH_3; HN; S; N; S; CHCOOH, NH_2	m. 206–8°. Methyl ester, m. 150–60°. *N*-Phenylacetyl deriv., m. 158–60°.	1
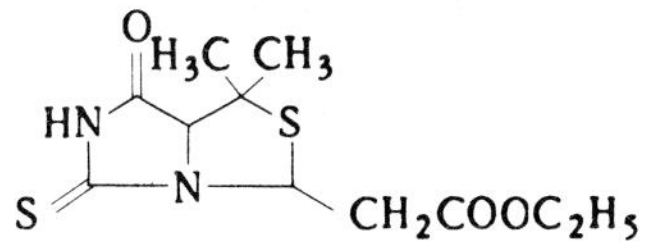 O; H_3C CH_3; HN; S; N; S; $CH_2COOC_2H_5$	Two stereoisomeric forms: I, m. 151–2°; II, exists in polymorphic modifications, m. 106–7° and 120–2°.	1
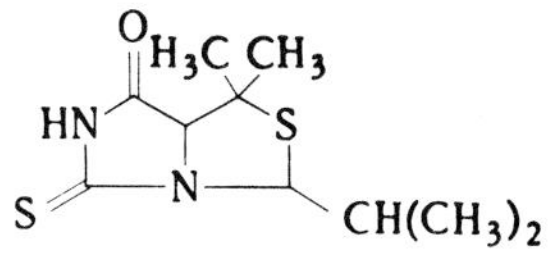 O; H_3C CH_3; HN; S; N; S; $CH(CH_3)_2$	m. 104–5°.	1
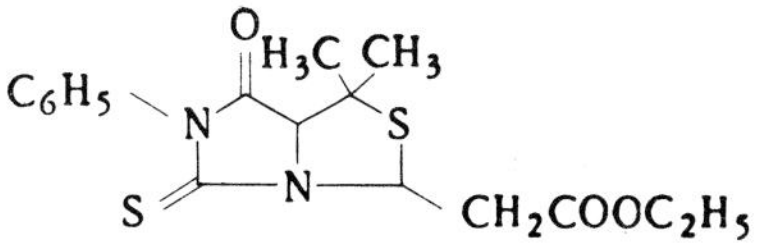 O; H_3C CH_3; C_6H_5–N; S; N; S; $CH_2COOC_2H_5$	m. 123°.	2
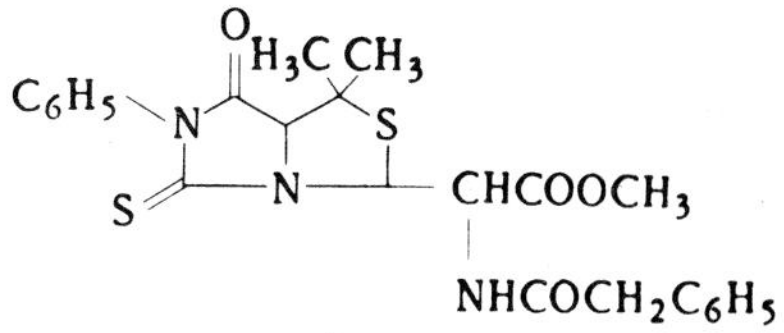 O; H_3C CH_3; C_6H_5–N; S; N; S; $CHCOOCH_3$, $NHCOCH_2C_6H_5$	m. 178–80°.	3
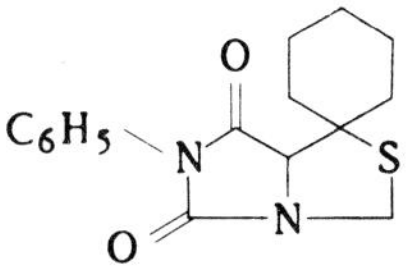 O; C_6H_5–N; S (spiro-cyclohexane); N; O	m. 143–5°.	4

(*continued*)

Derivatives of Imidazo[1,5-*c*]thiazole (*continued*)

Structure	Properties	Refs.
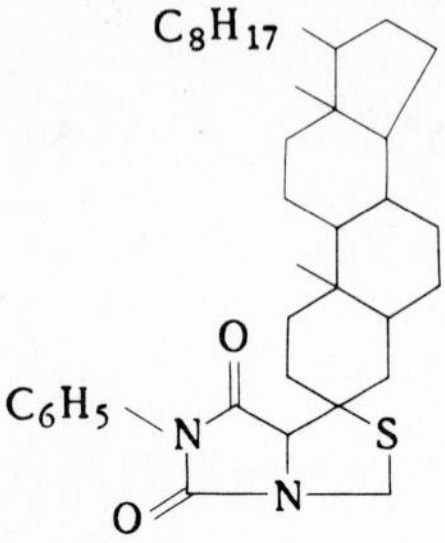 [structure: C_8H_{17} steroid spiro-imidazothiazole with C_6H_5–N, O, O, N, S]	m. 216–7°.	4

References

1. du Vigneaud and Melville in Clarke *et al.*, *The Chemistry of Penicillin*, Princeton University Press, Princeton, N. J., 1949, pp. 269–309.
2. Cook and Heilbron in Clarke *et al.*, *The Chemistry of Penicillin*, Princeton University Press, Princeton, N. J., 1949, pp. 921–972.
3. Mozingo and Folkers in Clarke *et al.*, *The Chemistry of Penicillin*, Princeton University Press, Princeton, N. J., 1949, p. 541.
4. Lieberman, Brazeau and Hariton, *J. Am. Chem. Soc.*, **70**, 3094 (1948).
5. Armstrong, *J. Am. Chem. Soc.*, **77**, 6049 (1955).

A-150. 6*H*-[1,2,3]Triazolo[1,5-*a*, 3,4-*a*′]-diindole. R.I. 2903

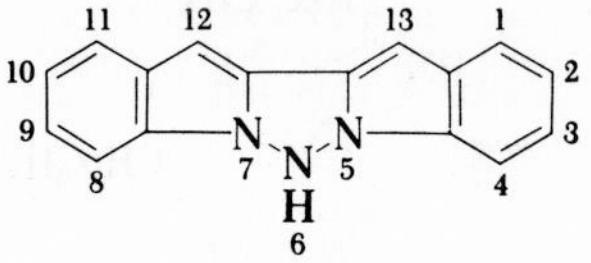

11 12 13 1 10 2 9 3 8 N 7 N 5 N 4 H 6

The only example of this ring system is compound I, which has been named *1,1′-iminoindigo*, and also *1,5(CO);3,4(CO)dibenzoylene-1,2,3-triazoline*. As a result of the series of reactions shown, Albert[1,2] obtained I (violet, d. 185°; *N*-acetyl derivative, pale violet, m. 212°; oxime, d. 290°), which dyes cotton and wool blue from a yellowish-green vat. Further evidence for these structures would be welcome.

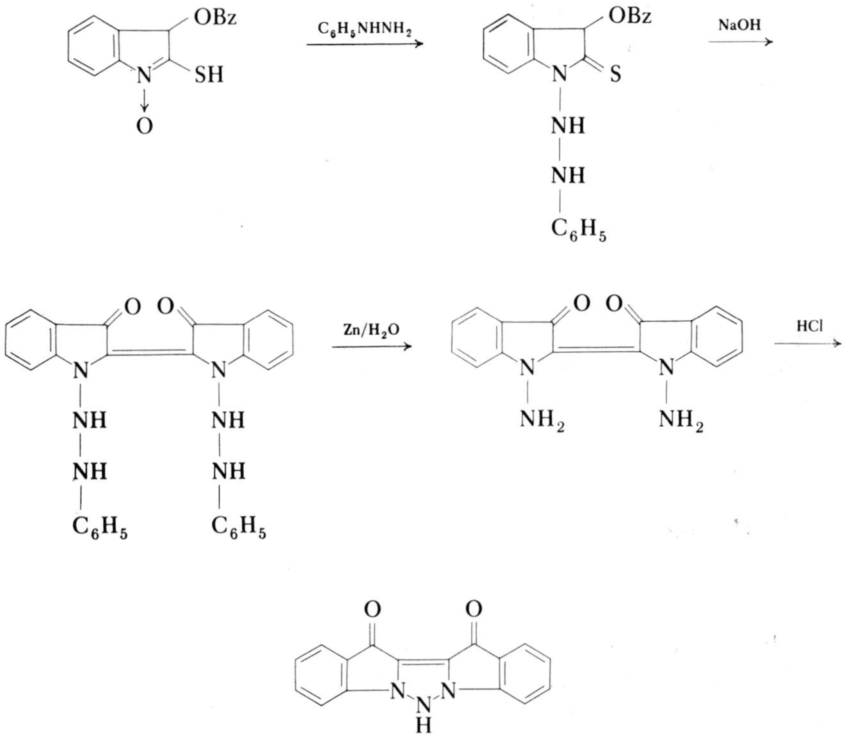

(I)

References

1. Albert, *Ann.*, **416,** 240 (1918).
2. Albert and Hurtzig, *Ber.*, **52,** 530 (1919).

A-151. 5*H*-Imidazo[4,5,1-*hi*]naphth-[1,2,3-*cd*]indazole*

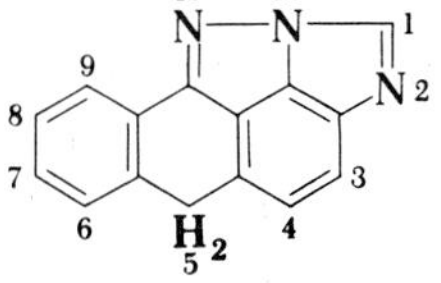

Efforts[1] to prepare II by the dehydration of I, were not successful.

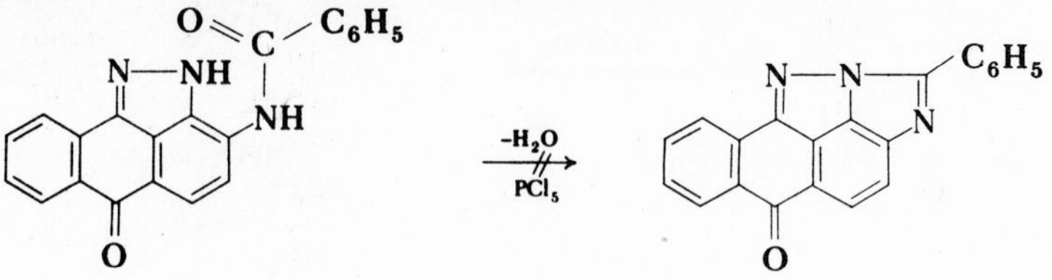

(I) (II)

Reference

1. Baumann and Schwechten, *I. G. Farbenindustrie, A.-G., 34 Wissenschaftlicher Austausch der Gruppe IX*, Leverkusen, October 25/6, 1935; *PB Report No.* 70339, frames 11319–24.

A-152. 1*H*-Imidaz[1,5-*c*]imidazole.
R.I. 607

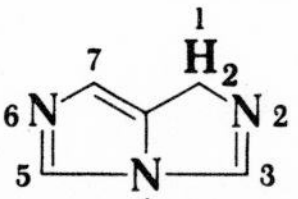

The perhydro derivatives of this nucleus have been named as *1,3,7-triazabicyclo[3.3.0]nonanes*, and numbered as shown in I, while the 1,3,5,7-tetraoxo derivatives were called *hydantoino-1′,5′:1,5-hydantoins* and numbered as shown in II.

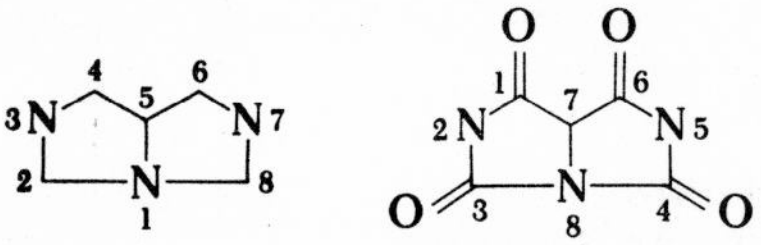

(I) (II)

While investigating the reactions of III, Biltz and Krzikalla[1] found that solution of III in dilute acids caused the hydrolytic elimination of methylamine, and formation of IV (sinters >240°, d. 262°). Further hydrolysis, giving V, resulted when IV was heated with water. Treatment of IV with diazomethane gave VI (m. 198–200°d.).

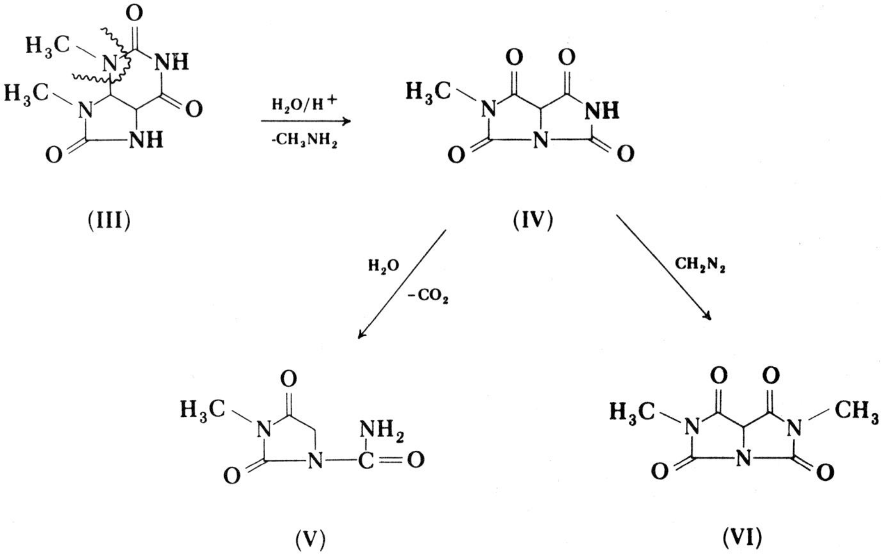

(III) $\xrightarrow[-CH_3NH_2]{H_2O/H^+}$ (IV)

(IV) $\xrightarrow[-CO_2]{H_2O}$ (V)

(IV) $\xrightarrow{CH_2N_2}$ (VI)

Senkus[2] has patented the production of compounds of structure VII by the condensation of aldehydes with certain vicinal aliphatic triamines.

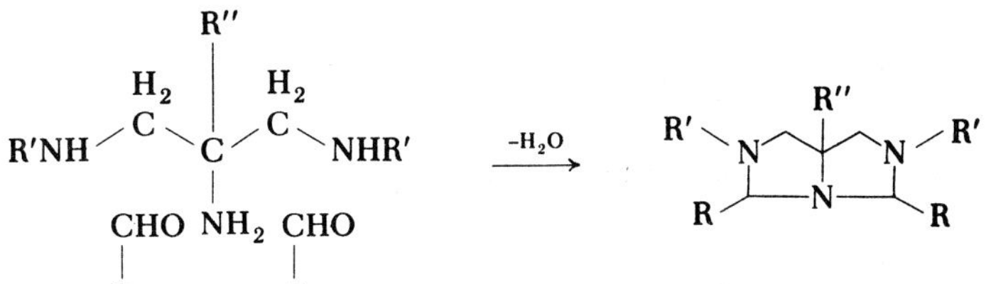

$\xrightarrow{-H_2O}$ (VII)

Derivatives of VII

R	R′	R″	Properties
-H	$-CH(CH_3)_2$	$-CH_3$	b_3 86.0–6.5°, n_D^{20} 1.4662.
-H	$-C_6H_5$	$-CH_3$	m. 122.1°.
$-C_6H_5$	$-CH(CH_3)_2$	$-CH_3$	m. 65°.
$-CH(CH_2CH_3)(CH_2)_3CH_3$	$-CH(CH_3)_2$	$-CH_3$	$b_{0.9}$ 173°, n_D^{20} 1.4736.

References

1. Biltz and Krzikalla, *Ann.*, **457,** 131 (1927).
2. Senkus, U.S. Pat. 2,393,826.

A-153. Imidazo[1,5,4-*cd*]benzimidazole

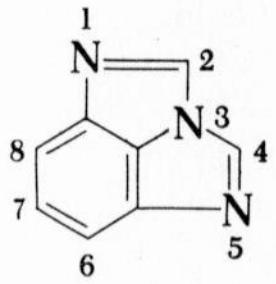

v. Auwers and Frese[1] found that neither 1,2,3-triaminobenzene nor 1,2,3-tris(acetamino)benzene could be converted into I (R = CH_3). However, Efros[2] recently heated 1,2,3-triaminobenzene at 180° with two moles of benzoic or phenylacetic acid, and obtained products stable to dilute acid hydrolysis, which he considered to be I (R = C_6H_5 or $C_6H_5CH_2$).

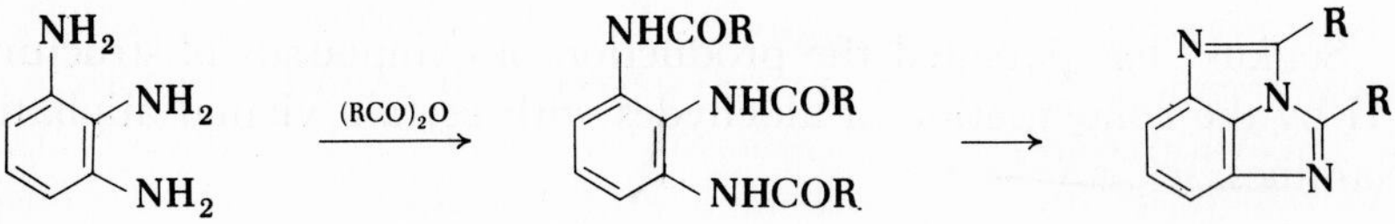

(I)

References

1. v. Auwers and Frese, *Ber.*, **59,** 554 (1926).
2. Efros, *Zhur. Obshcheĭ Khim.*, **23,** 957 (1953).

A-154. Benzimidazo[1,2-*b*]-1,2-benzisoxazole

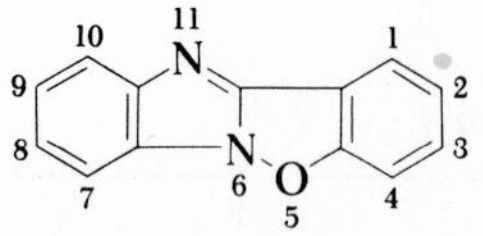

An unusual synthesis of this nucleus was discovered by Freiser and Walter,[1] who obtained II (yellow-brown m. 182–5°) from the bromination of I.

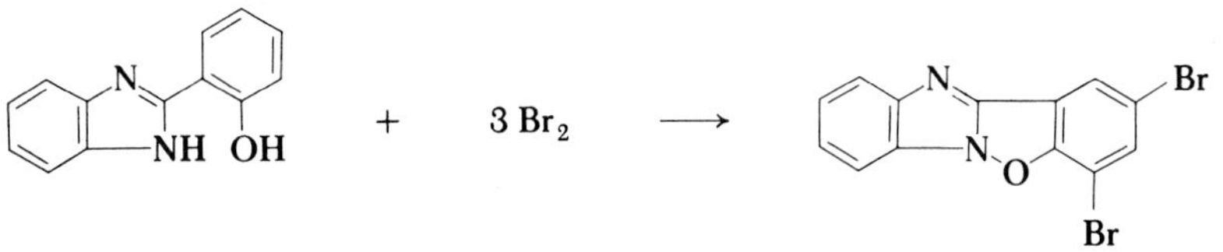

(I) + 3 Br_2 ⟶ (II)

Reference

1. Freiser and Walter, *J. Org. Chem.*, **18**, 256 (1953).

A-155. Benz[*d*]imidazo[1,2-*b*]isothiazole. R.I. 1348

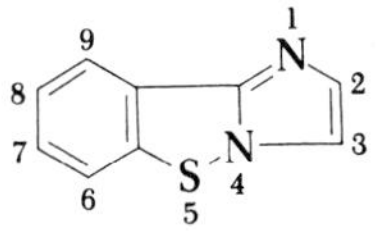

McClelland and Warren[1,2] studied the reactions of I with different amines. With ethylenediamine II results, and on treatment of this with bromine it may be converted stepwise, through III and IV, into V (hydrobromide, m. 259°; picrate, m. 241–2°). Efforts to prepare the free base of V, by treatment of the hydrobromide with bases, caused cleavage of the isothiazole ring and gave III. Compound V formed a complex (orange, m. 139–40°) with one mole of bromine, which reverted to V in the presence of water, and which could also be produced by treatment of II or III with excess bromine.

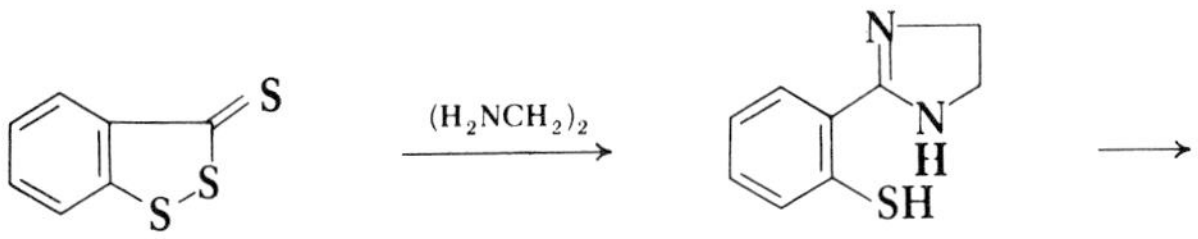

(I) $\xrightarrow{(H_2NCH_2)_2}$ (II) ⟶

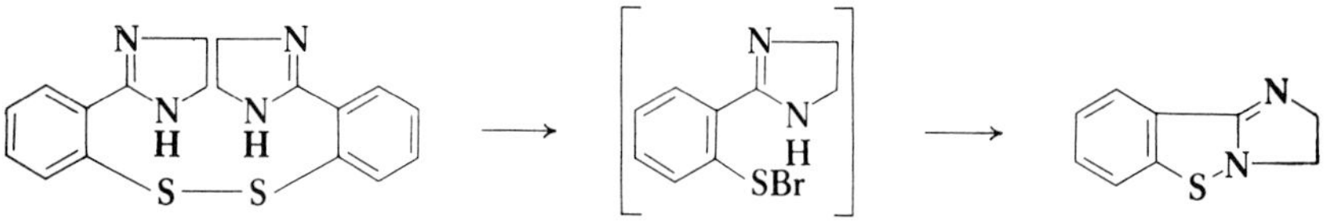

(III) ⟶ [(IV)] ⟶ (V)

References

1. McClelland and Warren, *J. Chem. Soc.*, **1929,** 2621.
2. McClelland and Warren, *J. Chem. Soc.*, **1930,** 1095.

A-156. 1*H*,3*H*-Pyrazolo[5,1-*c*][1,2,4]-oxadiazole

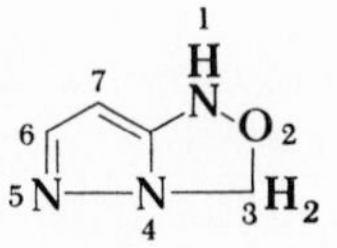

A product (m. 274°) assigned structure II was described by Cusmano and Sprio[1] as being formed by the dehydration (!) of I. Further evidence for these structures would seem desirable.

(I) (II)

Reference

1. Cusmano and Sprio, *Gazz. chim. ital.*, **82,** 373 (1952); *Chem. Abstracts*, **47,** 11152 (1953).

A-157. 3*H*-[1,2,4]Thiadiazolo[3,4-*b*]-benzothiazole

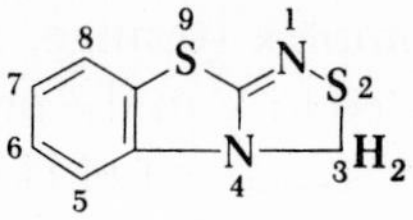

The polarography of compounds I and II has been discussed,[1] but apparently no other information concerning this ring system has been published.

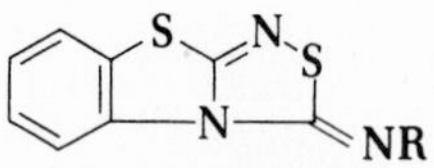

(I) R = H
(II) R = SCN

Reference

1. Sturm and Hans, *Angew. Chem.*, **67,** 743 (1955).

A-158. Imidazo[2,1-*b*][1,3,4]-thiadiazole

A number of compounds containing this nucleus have been prepared by Ban and his co-workers.[1-5] A 2-amino-1,3,4-thiadiazole (e.g. I) was condensed with a suitably constituted α-halocarbonyl component to build up the imidazole ring via intermediates such as II (formed by substitution on the tautomeric ring >NH rather than on the —NH_2 group).

(I)

(II) (III)

Derivatives of Imidazo[2,1-*b*] [1,3,4]thiadiazole

Empirical formula	Substituents	Properties and derivatives	Refs.
$C_5H_5N_3S$	6-Methyl-	Brn., m. 49–51°. HCl salt, m. 212° d. Picrate, m. 196–7°.	3
$C_6H_7N_3S$	2,6-Dimethyl-	b_{17} 133°; m. 68–70°. HCl salt, m. 213° d. Picrate, m. 205–7°.	3
$C_7H_9N_3S$	6-Ethyl-2-methyl-	b_{17} 144°; m. ~30°. Picrate, m. 161–2°.	3
$C_8H_9N_3O_2S$	5-Carbethoxy-6-methyl-	m. 199–200°. Picrate, m. 186–8°. Hydrazide, m. 260° d.	3

(continued)

Derivatives of Imidazo[2,1-*b*][1,3,4]thiadiazole (*continued*)

Empirical formula	Substituents	Properties and derivatives	Refs.
$C_9H_{11}N_3O_2S$	5-Carbethoxy-2,6-dimethyl-	m. 120°. Picrate, m. 177-80°. Hydrazide, m. 310°d.	3
$C_{10}H_6N_4O_2S$	6-(4-Nitrophenyl)-	m. 273-4°d.	1,4
$C_{10}H_7N_3S$	6-Phenyl-	Yel., m. 131-2°. Picrate, m. 213-4°.	1,4
$C_{10}H_8N_4S$	6-(4-Aminophenyl)-	m. 165°. HCl salt, m. > 300° d. *N*-Acetyl deriv., m. 205°.	2
$C_{10}H_{13}N_3O_2S$	5-Carbethoxy-2-ethyl-6-methyl-	b_2 185-90°. Picrate, m. 157°. Hydrazide, m. 275°d.	3
$C_{11}H_8N_4O_2S$	2-Methyl-6-(4-nitrophenyl)-	Yel., m. 241-2°	1,4,5
$C_{11}H_9N_3S$	2-Methyl-6-phenyl-	m. 137-9°. HCl salt, d. 250°. Perchlorate, d. 247-52°. Picrate, m. 211°. Picrolonate, d. 210°.	1,4,5
	6-Methyl-2-phenyl-	m. 117°. HCl salt, m. 213°d. Picrate, m. 233-4°.	3
$C_{11}H_{10}N_4S$	2-Methyl-6-(4-aminophenyl)-	m. 203°. *N*-Acetyl deriv., m. 260°.	2
$C_{12}H_{10}N_4O_2S$	2-Ethyl-6-(4-nitrophenyl)-	d. 193-5°.	1,4
$C_{12}H_{11}N_3S$	2-Ethyl-6-phenyl-	m. 127-8°.	1,4
$C_{12}H_{12}N_4S$	2-Ethyl-6-(4-aminophenyl)-	m. 180°. *N*-Acetyl deriv., m. 238-9°.	2
$C_{16}H_{10}N_4O_2S$	2-Phenyl-6-(4-nitrophenyl)-	Yel. m. 278°.	1,4
$C_{16}H_{11}N_3S$	2,6-Diphenyl-	m. 200°.	1,4

References

1. Matsukawa and Ban, *J. Pharm. Soc. Japan*, **72,** 610 (1952); *Chem. Abstracts*, **47,** 6409 (1953).
2. Matsukawa, Ban, Shirakawa and Yoneda, *J. Pharm. Soc. Japan*, **73,** 159 (1953); *Chem. Abstracts*, **47,** 11185 (1953).
3. Ban, *J. Pharm. Soc. Japan*, **74,** 658 (1954); *Chem. Abstracts*, **48,** 10740 (1954).
4. Matsukawa and Ban, Jap. Pat. 5879 (1953); *Chem. Abstracts*, **49,** 4725 (1955).
5. Ban, *J. Pharm. Soc. Japan*, **74,** 1044 (1954); *Chem. Abstracts*, **49,** 11630 (1955).

A-159. Thiazolo[3,2-*b*]-*s*-triazole.
R.I. 583

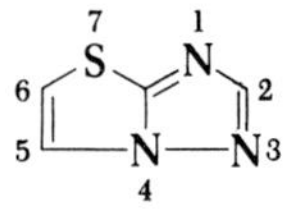

This ring system was first mentioned (and named *thiazoletriazole*) by Näf[1] in 1891, who thought that he had prepared compound II by the route shown. However, he describes the product as being unstable and reverting to I on treatment with nitrous acid, properties seemingly unlikely for a nucleus such as II. Further study of these products would be desirable.

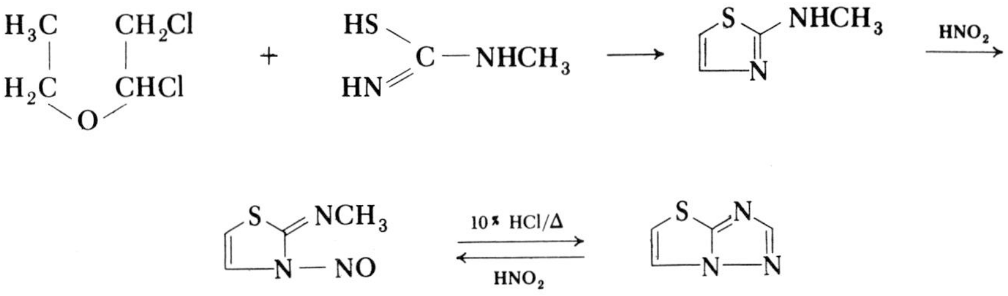

(I) (II)

Recently, the cyclization of III to IV or (possibly) V was mentioned by Kendall and Duffin,[2] but no details were offered.

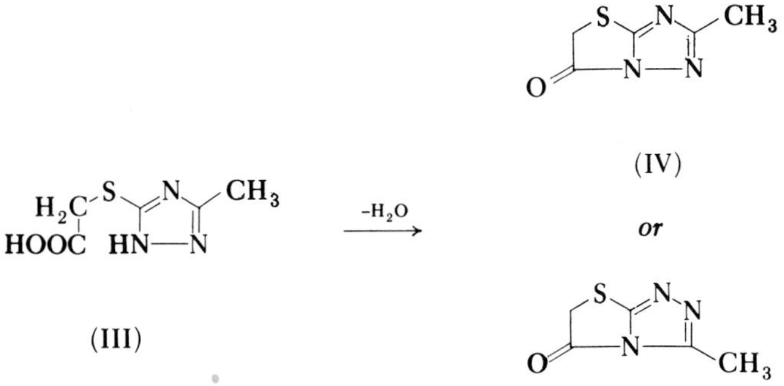

(IV)

or

(III)

(V)

References

1. Näf, *Ann.*, **265,** 108 (1891).
2. Kendall and Duffin, Brit. Pat. 634,951/2; *Chem. Abstracts*, **44,** 9287 (1950); U. S. Pat. 2,527,265/6.

A-160. Thiazolo[2,3-*c*]-*s*-triazole

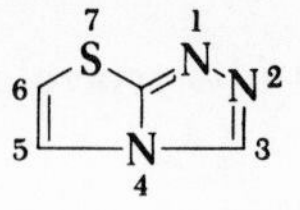

See Thiazolo[3,2-*b*]-*s*-triazole (Section A-159).

A-161. *s*-Triazolo[3,4-*b*]benzothiazole*

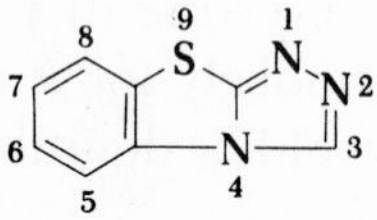

Condensation of the hydrazine I with benzaldehyde formed the corresponding hydrazone, and oxidation of this with lead tetracetate produced[1] II. Similarly, condensation of I with carbon disulfide yielded[1] the mercaptan III.

When heated with acetic anhydride in acetic acid, I yielded[2] an acetyl derivative, which could be dehydrated to IV by hot acetic anhydride containing a little phosphoric acid. A number of photographic sensitizing dyes have been prepared[2] from IV, and several derivatives of this nucleus have been claimed[3] as photographic fog inhibitors.

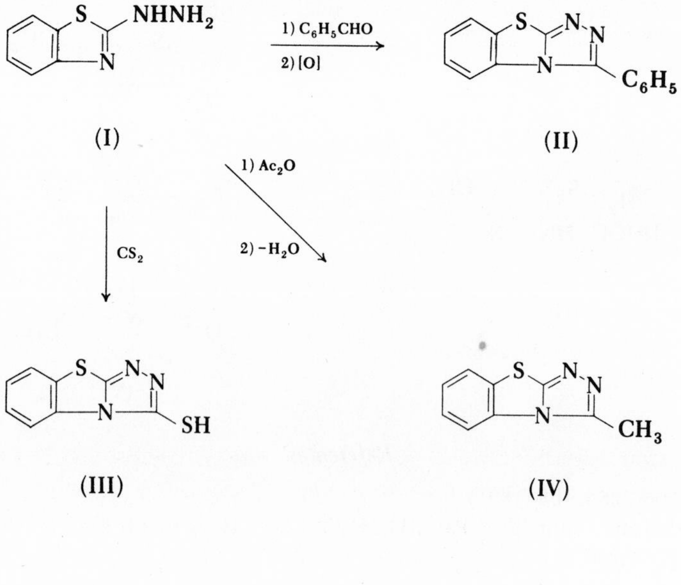

s-Triazolo[3,4-*b*]benzothiazoles

Substituents or structure	Properties	Refs.
3-Mercapto-	m. 255°.	1
3-Methyl-	m. 142–4°.	2
3-(4-Bromophenyl)-	m. 240°.	1
3-Phenyl-	m. 229°.	1
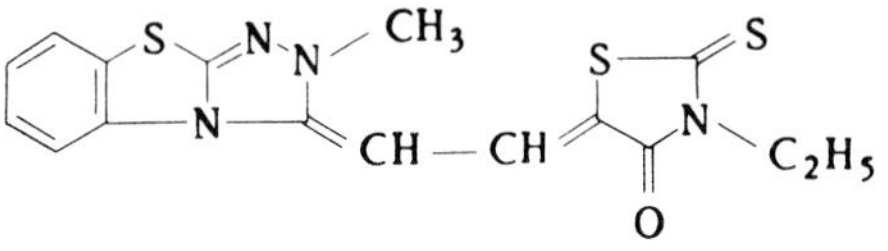 S, N, N, CH_3, N, CH—CH, S, S, N, C_2H_5, O	Scarlet, m. 276–7°d.	2
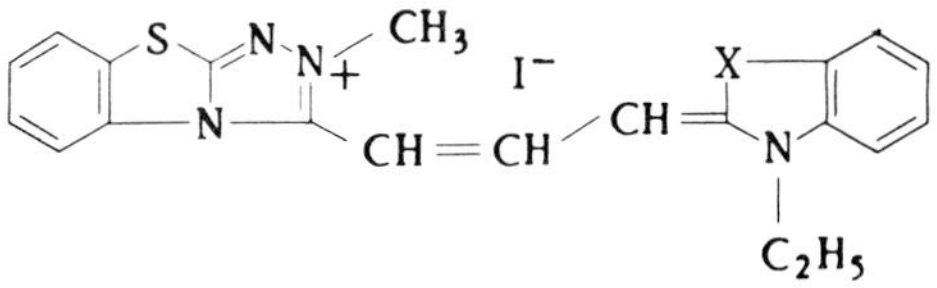 S, N, N^+, CH_3, I^-, N, CH=CH, CH=, X, N, C_2H_5	X = O, scarlet, m. 259–60° d. X = S, dk. red, m. 270–1° d. X = Se, red, m. 262–3° d.	2
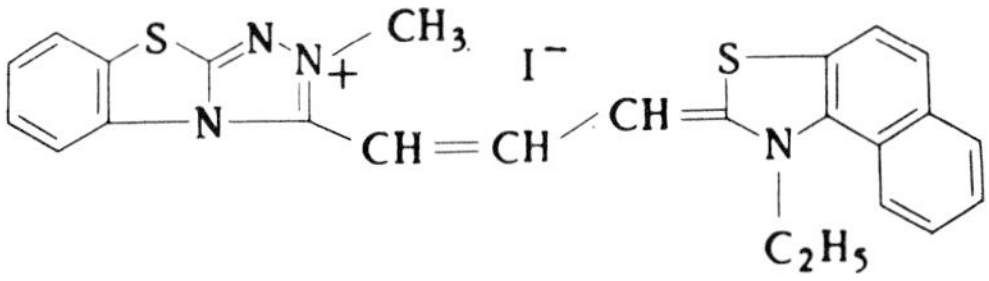 S, N, N^+, CH_3, I^-, N, CH=CH, CH=, S, N, C_2H_5	Red, m. 238–9° d.	2
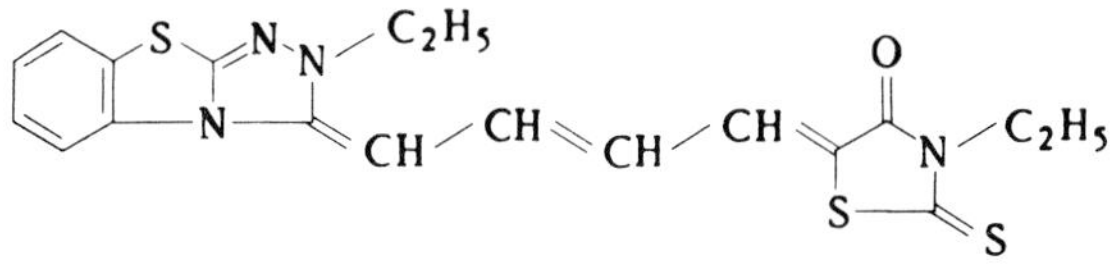 S, N, N, C_2H_5, N, CH, CH, CH, CH, O, N, C_2H_5, S, S	Grn., m. 218–9°.	2

References

1. Bower and Doyle, *J. Chem. Soc.*, **1957**, 727.
2. Brooker and VanLare, U. S. Pat. 2,786,054. Brit. Pat. 783,021.
3. Kodak, S. A., Belg. Pat. 562,142.

A-162. 5*H*-Pyrrolotetrazole.
R.I. 574

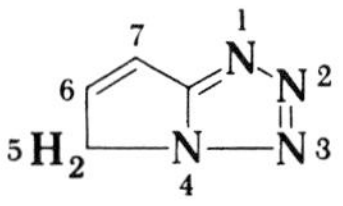

7, 1, N, N 2, 6, $_5H_2$, N, N 3, 4

Two compounds, both 6,7-dihydro derivatives of this nucleus (alternatively called *trimethylenetetrazoles*), have been reported. Treatment of γ-azidobutyronitriles (I) with chlorosulfonic acid is claimed[1] to yield trimethylenetetrazole (II, m. 110°). The 5-ethyl-7-methyl homolog (oil) was similarly prepared[1] from γ-azido-α-methylcapronitrile. The effect of II upon heart action has been studied.[2-5] See Sections A-568 and A-703.

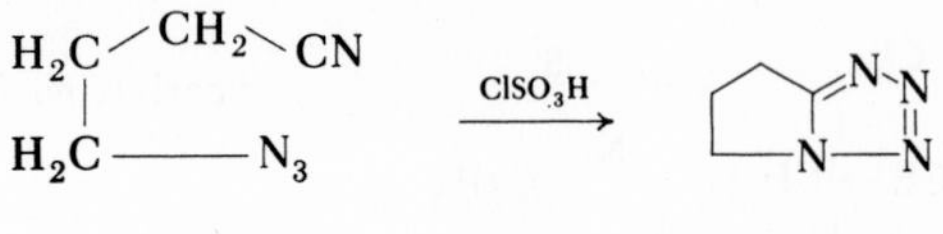

(I) (II)

References

1. Chinoin Gyógyszer és Vegyészeti Termékek Gyára R. T. (Kereszty és Wolf), Hung. Pat., 111,703; *Chem. Abstracts*, **29**, 3783 (1935). Ger. Pat. 611,692; *Frdl.*, **21,** 673 (1937). U. S. Pat., 2,020,937.
2. de Châtel, *Orvosi Hetilap*, **78,** 813 (1934); *Chem. Abstracts*, **29,** 1877 (1935).
3. Issekutz, *Arch. exptl. Path. Pharmakol.*, **177,** 415 (1935); *Chem. Abstracts*, **29,** 3721 (1935).
4. Dîrner, *Arch. exptl. Path. Pharmakol.*, **180,** 581 (1936); *Chem. Abstracts*, **30,** 6821 (1936).
5. Issekutz, Leinzinger and Novák, *Arch. exptl. Path. Pharmakol.*, **177,** 397 (1935); *Chem. Zentr.*, **II,** 1207 (1935).

A-163. 9*H*-*s*-Triazolo[4,3-*a*]-benzimidazole*

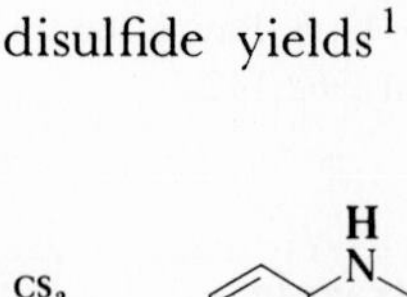

The name *s-triazolo[3,4-b]benziminazole* has been used.

Reaction of I with carbon disulfide yields[1] the mercaptan II (m. 284°).

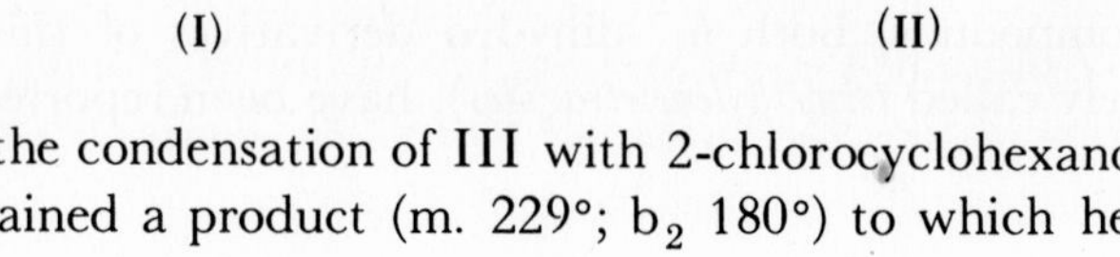

(I) (II)

From the condensation of III with 2-chlorocyclohexanone, Reitmann obtained a product (m. 229°; b_2 180°) to which he assigned structure IV. While structure IV (or one of its tautomers) is probably correct, other structures (and tautomers) such as V must also be considered.

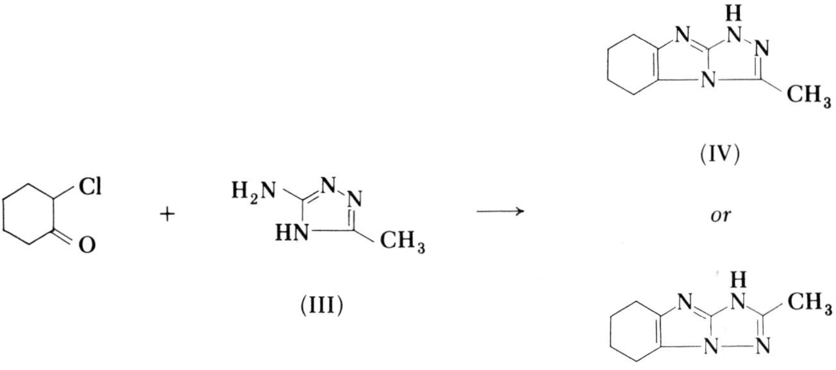

(IV)

or

(III)

(V)

References

1. Bower and Doyle, *J. Chem. Soc.*, **1957**, 727.
2. Reitmann, Ger. Pat. 547,985; *Frdl.*, **18**, 2782 (1933); U. S. Pat. 2,057,978; Brit. Pat. 360,027.

A-164. 3*H*-*s*-Triazolo[1,5-*a*]-benzimidazole

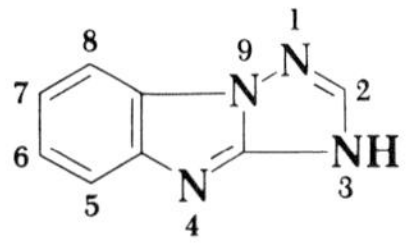

See Section A-163.

A-165. 10*aH*-(4-Aza)pyrido[1,2-*a*]triazolo-[*c,d*]benzimidazole

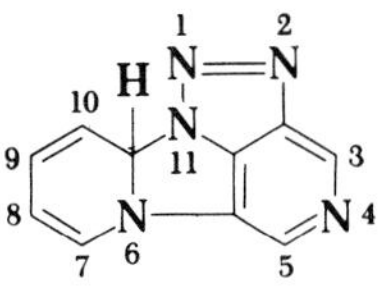

By the diazotization of I (see Section A-275), and heating of the acidic diazo solution, Petrow and Saper[1] obtained a compound (m. 314°) to which they assigned structure II, and the name *13-hydroxy-3:12-diaza-12:13-dihydrocarbazole-1:9-diazole*.

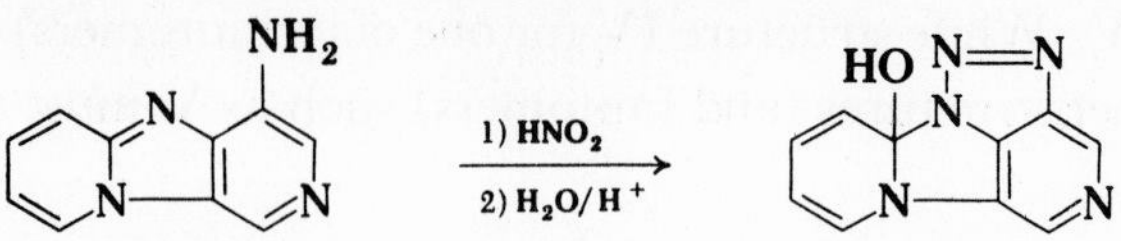

NH2 HO N=N N N 1) HNO2 2) H2O/H+ (I) (II)

Reference

1. Petrow and Saper, *J. Chem. Soc.*, **1946,** 588.

A-166. *s*-Triazolo[3,4-*b*][1,3,4]-thiadiazole*

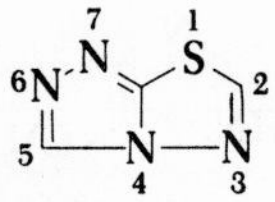

Various derivatives of this nucleus were prepared by Kanaoka as potential anti-tumor drugs, as they bear a formal resemblance to the biologically active purines.

Two routes to this ring system have been explored. Condensation[1] of the ester I with hydrazine yielded II, which was acylated to give III, dehydration of which produced IV. Compound IV (R = CH_3) also could be obtained by refluxing II with acetic anhydride, and IV (R = H) was prepared (via III) by treating II with formic acid.

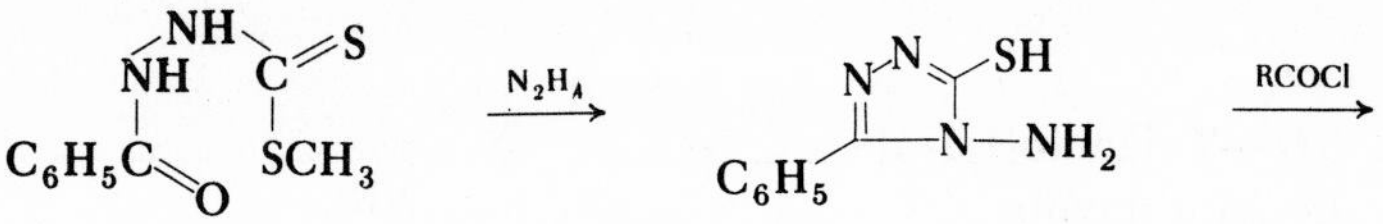

(I) $\xrightarrow{N_2H_4}$ (II) $\xrightarrow{RCOCl}$

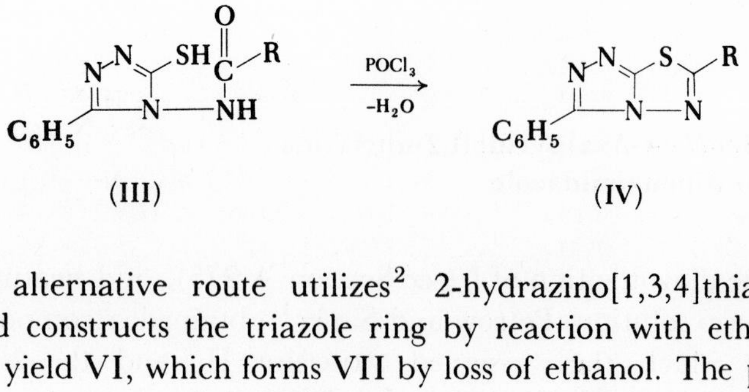

(III) $\xrightarrow[-H_2O]{POCl_3}$ (IV)

The alternative route utilizes[2] 2-hydrazino[1,3,4]thiadiazoles (V), and constructs the triazole ring by reaction with ethyl *ortho*-esters to yield VI, which forms VII by loss of ethanol. The preparation, by each route, of the 2-*i*-butyl-5-phenyl homolog provides evidence for structure VII and demonstrates the equivalence of the two routes.

(V) $\xrightarrow{R'C(OC_2H_5)_3}$ (VI) $\longrightarrow$ (VII)

Products of Structure VII

R	R′	Properties	Refs.
CH_3	H	m. 144°.	2
C_2H_5	H	m. 62°.	2
CH_3	CH_3	m. 102°.	2
C_3H_7	H	b_2 143–4°. Picrate, m. 135–6°.	2
C_2H_5	CH_3	m. 104°.	2
CH_3	C_2H_5	m. 79°.	2
$CH(CH_3)C_2H_5$	H	b_2 146°. Picrate, m. 132–5°.	2
C_2H_5	C_2H_5	m. 81°.	2
CH_3	C_3H_7	b_1 142–4°. Picrate, m. 157–9°	2
C_3H_7	CH_3	m. 67°.	2
C_2H_5	C_3H_7	b_1 150–2°. Picrate, m. 140–1°.	2
C_3H_7	C_2H_5	m. 28°.	2
CH_3	C_4H_9	m. 57°.	2
$CH(CH_3)C_2H_5$	CH_3	m. 77–8°.	2
C_6H_5	H	m. 191.5°.	2
H	C_6H_5	m. 198–9°.	1
C_2H_5	C_4H_9	b_2 156–8°. Picrate, m. 122–3°.	2
$CH(CH_3)C_2H_5$	C_2H_5	b_2 166–9°. Picrate, m. 116–7°.	2
C_3H_7	C_3H_7	b_1 150–2°. Picrate, m. 140–1°.	2
CH_3	C_6H_5	m. 186°.	1
C_6H_5	CH_3	m. 176–7°.	2
$CH(CH_3)C_2H_5$	C_3H_7	b_2 156–7°. Picrate, m. 107–9°.	2
C_3H_7	C_4H_9	b_2 172°. Picrate, m. 122–3°.	2
C_2H_5	C_6H_5	m. 124–5°.	1
C_6H_5	C_2H_5	m. 121–2°.	2
$CH(CH_3)C_2H_5$	C_4H_9	b_3 169°. Picrate, m. 120–1°	2
C_3H_7	C_6H_5	m. 110–1°.	1
$CH(CH_3)C_2H_5$	C_6H_5	m. 104° (103.5°).	1,2
C_6H_5	C_4H_9	m. 118.5°.	2
p-$NO_2C_6H_4$	C_6H_5	m. 249–50°.	1
C_6H_5	C_6H_5	m. 199–200°.	1

References

1. Kanaoka, *J. Pharm. Soc. Japan*, **76,** 113 (1956); *Chem. Abstracts*, **51,** 3579 (1957).
2. Kanaoka, *Pharm. Bull.* (Tokyo), **5,** 385 (1957); *Chem. Abstracts*, **52,** 5390 (1958).

A-167. Thiazolo[2,3]tetrazole

1 N, 2 N, 3 N, 4 S, 5, 6, 7 N

Treatment of I with nitrous acid was found by Fodor and Wilheim[1] to yield II (m. 114–115°). This synthesis was confirmed by Beyer, Lässig and Ruhlig,[2] who also prepared II by treating III with nitrous acid.

CH_3, N, S, $NHNH_2$ $\xrightarrow{HNO_2}$ CH_3, N, N, N, N, S $\xleftarrow{HNO_2}$ CH_3, N, NH_2, S, NH

(I) (II) (III)

References

1. Fodor and Wilheim, *Acta. Chim. Acad. Sci. Hung.*, **2,** 189 (1952).
2. Beyer, Lässig and Ruhlig, *Chem. Ber.*, **86,** 764 (1953).

A-168. Tetrazolo[5,1-*b*]benzothiazole

1 N, 2 N, 3 N, 4 S, 5, 6, 7, 8, 9 N

When 2-chlorobenzothiazoles are treated with hydrazine, the corresponding 2-benzothiazylhydrazines are obtained and these, upon reaction[1] with nitrous acid, yield I (R = H, m. 109°,[3] (m. 110–1.5°[1]); R = NO_2, yellow, d. 158°[1]; R = CH_3, m. 121–2°[2]; R = CH_3O, m. 163–4°[2]). Alternatively,[2] the 2-chlorobenzothiazole may be treated with aqueous sodium azide in the presence of acetic acid, or 2-aminobenzothiazoles can be diazotized and treated with sodium azide. It was shown that compounds of type I undergo ring scission on reaction with Grignard reagents, forming triazenes such as II.

Compounds of type I have been claimed[4] as photographic fog inhibitors.

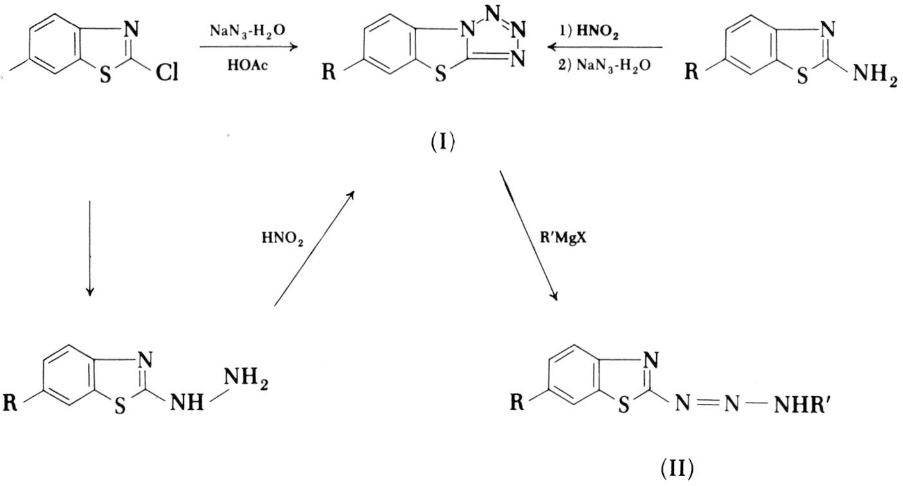

NaN_3-H_2O, HOAc; 1) HNO_2 2) NaN_3-H_2O; HNO_2; R'MgX

(I)

N=N—NHR'

(II)

References

1. Colonna and Andrisano, *Pubbl. ist. chim. ind. univ. Bologna*, **No. 5,** 3; **No. 6,** 3; (1943); *Chem. Abstracts*, **41,** 754 (1947).
2. Pochinok, Zaïtseva and El'gort, *Ukrain. Khim. Zhur.*, **17,** 509 (1951); *Chem. Abstracts*, **48,** 11392 (1954).
3. Bower and Doyle, *J. Chem. Soc.*, **1957,** 727.
4. Kodak, S. A., Belg. Pat. 562,142.

A-169. Naphtho[2,1-*d*]tetrazolo[5,1-*b*]-thiazole*

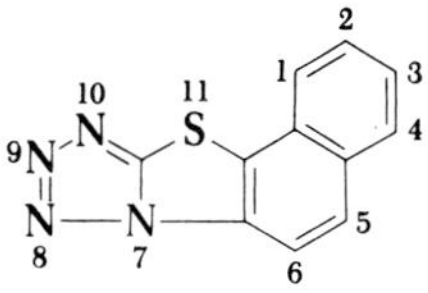

Compound II (m. 114–5°) was obtained[1] by the treatment of I with nitrous acid followed by aqueous sodium azide. The reaction of II with Grignard reagents gave triazenes (III). See Section A-168.

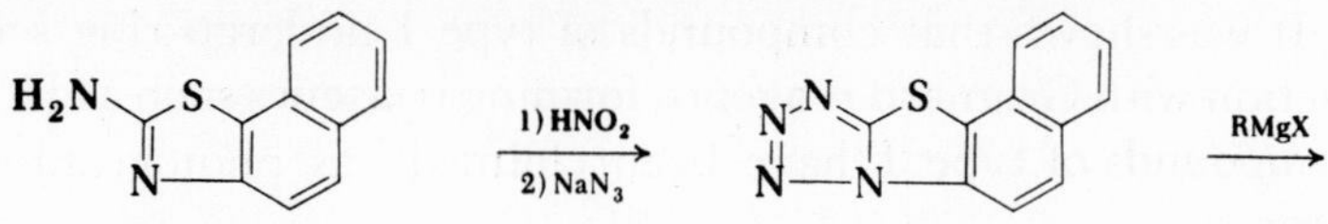

H_2N, S, N (I) — 1) HNO_2; 2) NaN_3 → N, N, S, N, N (II) — RMgX →

RNH—N=N, S, N

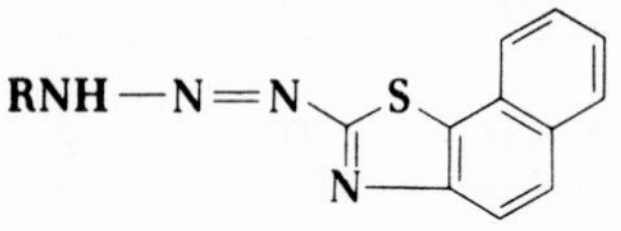

(III)

Reference

1. Pochinok, Zaĭtseva and El'gort, *Ukrain. Khim. Zhur.*, **17,** 509 (1951); *Chem. Abstracts*, **48,** 11392 (1954).

A-170. 1*H*-Pyrazo[2,3]tetrazole

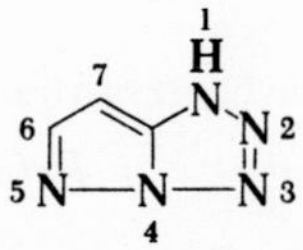

1 H, N, 2 N, 3 N, 4 N, 5 N, 6, 7

Treatment of I with nitrous acid yielded[1] II (m. 135°; *N*-acetyl derivative, m. 75°). An unusual feature of II is the concatenation of *five* nitrogen atoms.

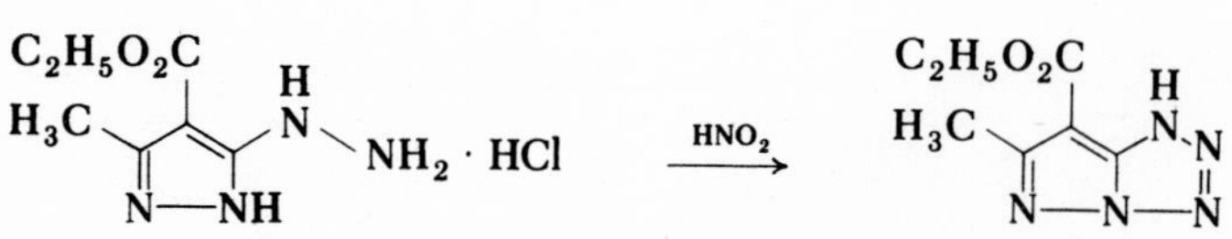

$C_2H_5O_2C$, H_3C, H, N, $NH_2 \cdot HCl$, N—NH (I) — HNO_2 → $C_2H_5O_2C$, H_3C, H, N, N, N—N—N (II)

Reference

1. Beyer, Wolter and Lemke, *Chem. Ber.*, **89,** 2550 (1956).

A-171. 1*H*-Imidazo[1,2]tetrazole

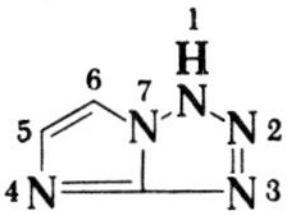

A single example (compound II, m. 163–4°; picrate, m. 122–3°) is known of this ring system. It was prepared[1] by treatment of I with nitrous acid.

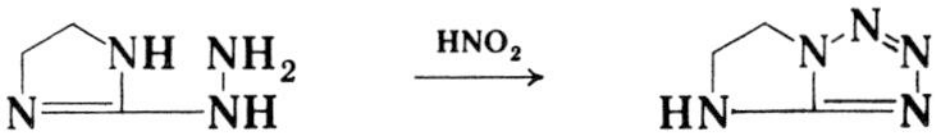

(I) (II)

Reference

1. Finnegan, Henry and Lieber, *J. Org. Chem.*, **18,** 779 (1953).

A-172. 4*H*-Tetrazolo[*a*]benzimidazole*

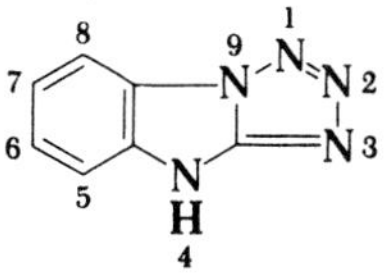

This nucleus has also been named *tetrazolo[5,1-b]benziminazole.*

Treatment of the hydrazine I with nitrous acid is reported[1] to yield II (m. 189° d., darkens upon exposure to light).

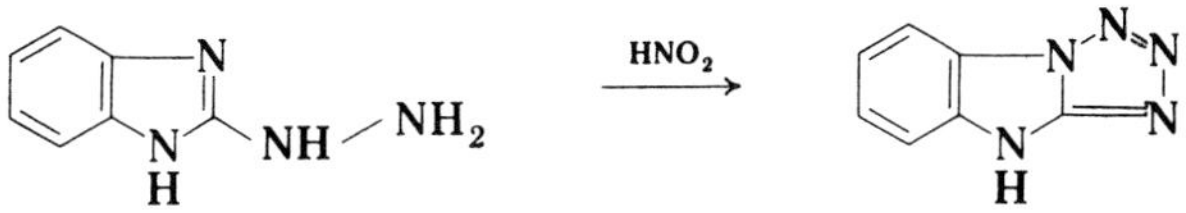

(I) (II)

Reference

1. Bower and Doyle, *J. Chem. Soc.*, **1957,** 727.

A-173. 5*H*-*s*-Triazolo[*b*]-*s*-triazole

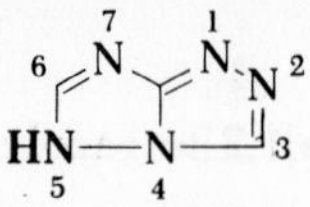

7 1
6 N N 2
N
HN—N—3
5 4

Treatment with benzoyl chloride of a compound identified as I was reported by Hoggarth[1] to yield a product ($C_{22}H_{15}ON_5$, m. 196–8°) presumably II or III, which hydrolyzed to IV (m. 257°), which he named *5:5′-diphenyl-2:3-dihydro-4′:1′:2′-triazolo(4′:3′-2:3)-1:2:4-triazole.*

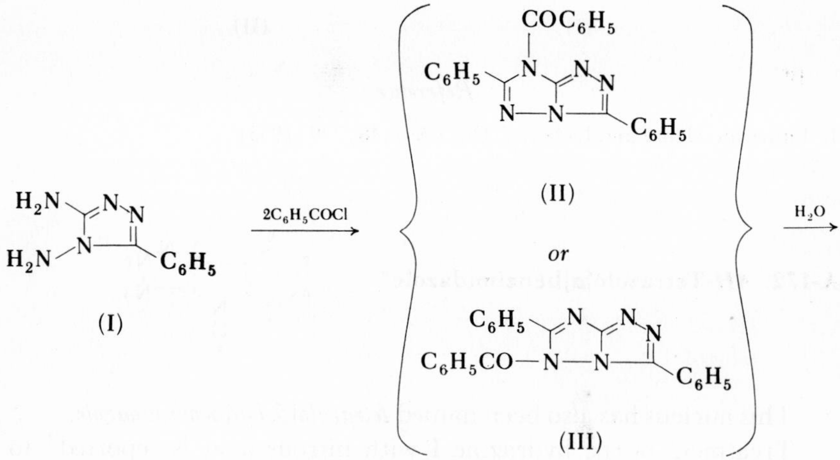

COC_6H_5
C_6H_5 N N N
N—N— C_6H_5

(II)

H_2N N N
H_2N N C_6H_5

(I)

$\xrightarrow{2C_6H_5COCl}$

or

$\xrightarrow{H_2O}$

C_6H_5 N N N
C_6H_5CO—N—N— C_6H_5

(III)

C_6H_5 N N N
HN—N— C_6H_5

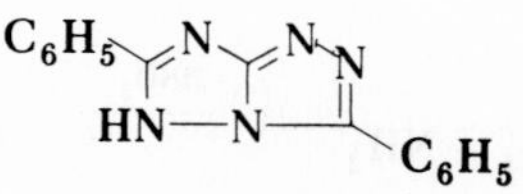

(IV)

Oxidation of V with lead tetraacetate yielded[2] a substance ($C_{15}H_{11}N_5$, m. 268°), presumably either IV or VI. A direct comparison with Hoggarth's IV should disclose the nature of this product.

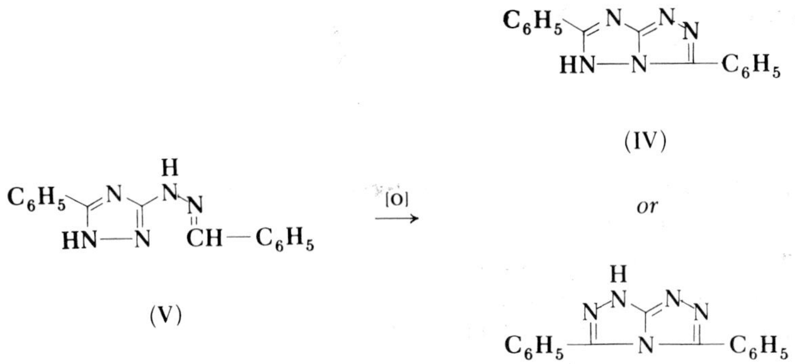

C_6H_5 N N N HN N C_6H_5

(IV)

H
C_6H_5 N N N HN N CH—C_6H_5 [O] →

(V)

or

H N N N N N C_6H_5 N C_6H_5

(VI)

References

1. Hoggarth, *J. Chem. Soc.*, **1950,** 614.
2. Bower and Doyle, *J. Chem. Soc.*, **1957,** 727.

A-174. 1H-*s*-Triazolo[3,4-*c*]-*s*-triazole*

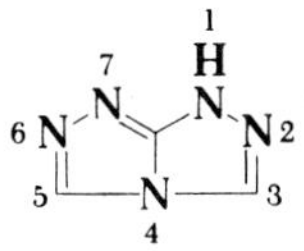

See Section A-173.

A-175. 1*H*,7*H*-Pyrazolo[1,2]pyrazole. R.I. 608

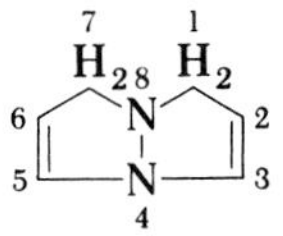

Only derivatives of the perhydro system are known.

The simplest example of this nucleus is the compound I, prepared as shown by Buhle, Moore and Wiselogle[1] during a study of the stereochemistry of certain nitrogen ring systems, and named by them *trimethylenepyrazolidine*. The two rings of this system are presumably non-coplanar, resulting in a V-shaped molecule.

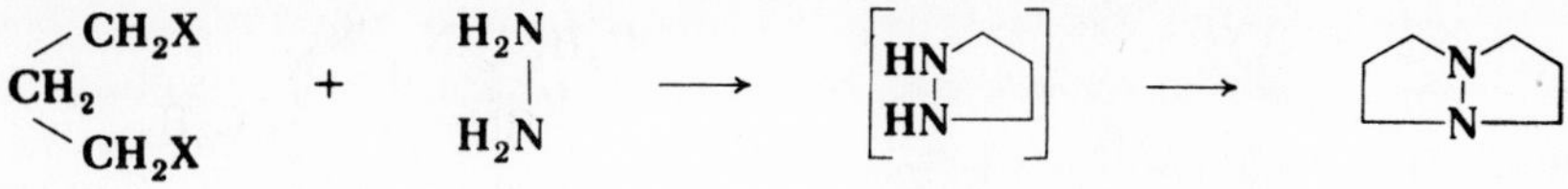

$CH_2(CH_2X)_2$ + $H_2N{-}NH_2$ → [HN–NH ring] →

(I)

In 1930 Wagner-Jauregg[2] reported the preparation of II by the condensation of benzalazine with maleic anhydride. Van Alphen[3] considered and rejected for this product an alternative possibility, structure III, since the product is stable to reducing agents and cannot be acylated (the —NH · NH— linkage of III would be expected to undergo reductive cleavage and acylation). He named compound III *4,8-diphenyl-1,5-diazabicyclo-(0,1,5)-octane-2,3,6,7-tetracarbonic acid anhydride*. Compound II was shown by Kovács, Bruckner and Kandel[4,5] to be a mixture of two stereoisomeric forms, one of which was present in only trace quantities. Esters[2,5,11] corresponding to II, and similar adducts from other azines[3,6,11] have been described. Reactions of II with hydroxylamine or with primary amines replaced the anhydride oxygen atoms by HON= or by RN=, respectively.[11] Benzal- and furfuralazines also condensed[11] with methyl acrylate or acrylonitrile to yield the 1,5-diaryl-2,6-dicarbomethoxy (or dicyano) homologs of I, in which the ester groups could be reduced to hydroxymethyl groups by lithium aluminum hydride without ring scission.

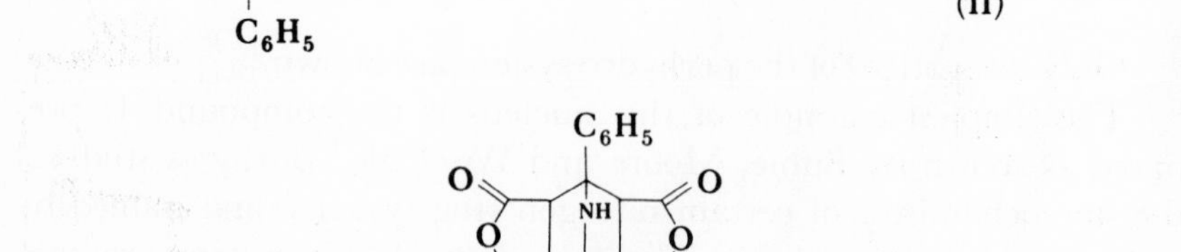

maleic anhydride + $C_6H_5CH{=}N{-}N{=}CHC_6H_5$ + maleic anhydride →

(II)

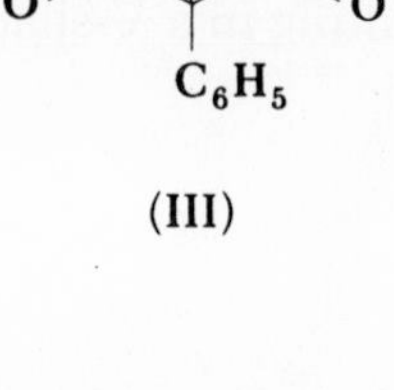

(III)

Freund and Fleischer[7] treated disubstituted malonyl halides with benzal semicarbazone and obtained, through the decomposition of the semicarbazone to yield hydrazine, products (IV) which he named *1,2-dialkylmalonyl-3,5-diketo-4-dialkyl-pyrazolidines*. These products were readily cleaved to V by alkali. Somewhat different results were reported by Dox,[8] who studied the reaction of malonic esters with hydrazine. He found that dialkylmalonic esters invariably reacted with hydrazine to yield pyrazolidiones, whereas monoalkylmalonic esters gave products (VI), which he named *1,3,5,7-tetraketopyrazo[1,2-a]pyrazoles*. Bromination replaced the remaining acidic hydrogens to yield VII. Ruhkopf[9] found that treatment of VIII in acetic acid with bromine yielded IX, presumably through the hydrolysis of one mole of VIII.

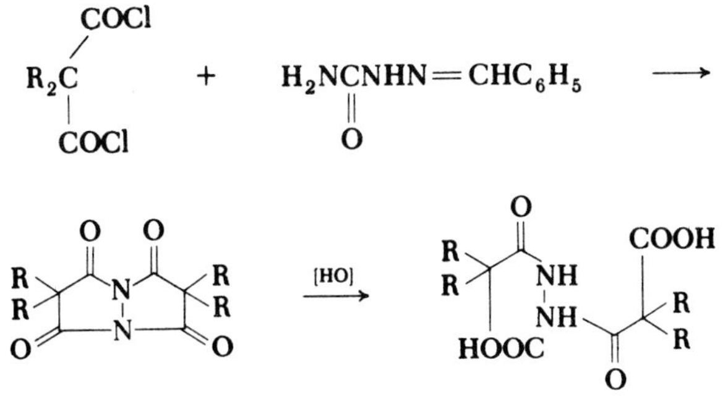

$R_2C(COCl)_2$ + $H_2NC(=O)NHN{=}CHC_6H_5$ ⟶

(IV) —[HO]→ (V)

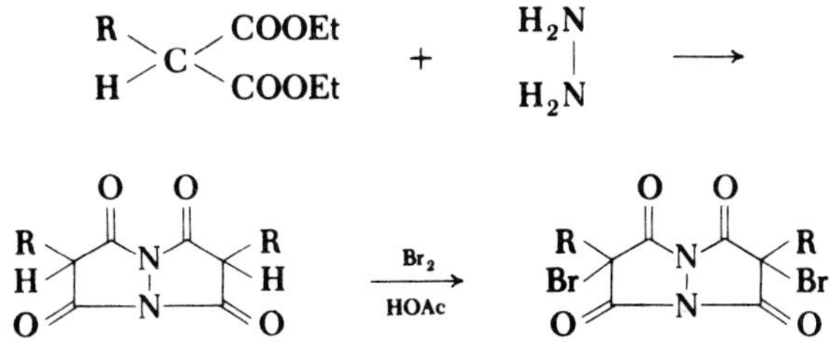

$RHC(COOEt)_2$ + $H_2N{-}NH_2$ ⟶

(VI) —Br_2, HOAc→ (VII)

(VIII) —Br_2, HOAc→ (IX)

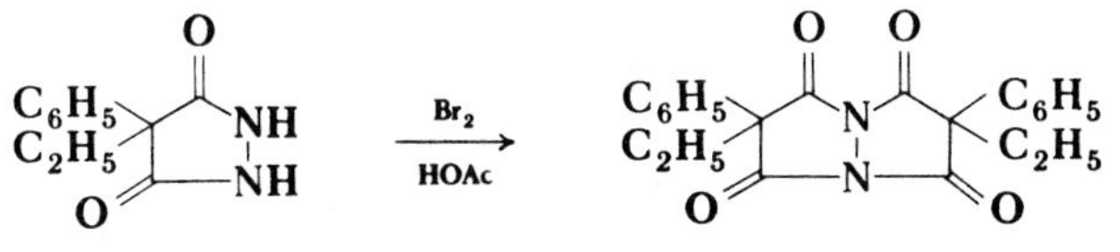

Hepner and Simonberg[10] studied the reaction of malonic ester with hydrazine and found that the initially formed malonhydrazide is converted by alkali into X and that this can be cyclized to *violurazolic acid* (XI) by treatment with sodium nitrite. Reaction of XI with nitric acid gave *dilituratolic acid* (XII), while with sodium hydrosulfite XI gave *thionurazolic acid* (XIII). This underwent acidic cleavage to yield *uramilazole* (XIV), which in turn reacted with cyanic acid to give *pseudo-ureidazolic acid* (XV), which could be dehydrated to *ureidazolic acid* (XVI). Most of these products were yellow solids, insoluble in organic media and decomposed by heat.

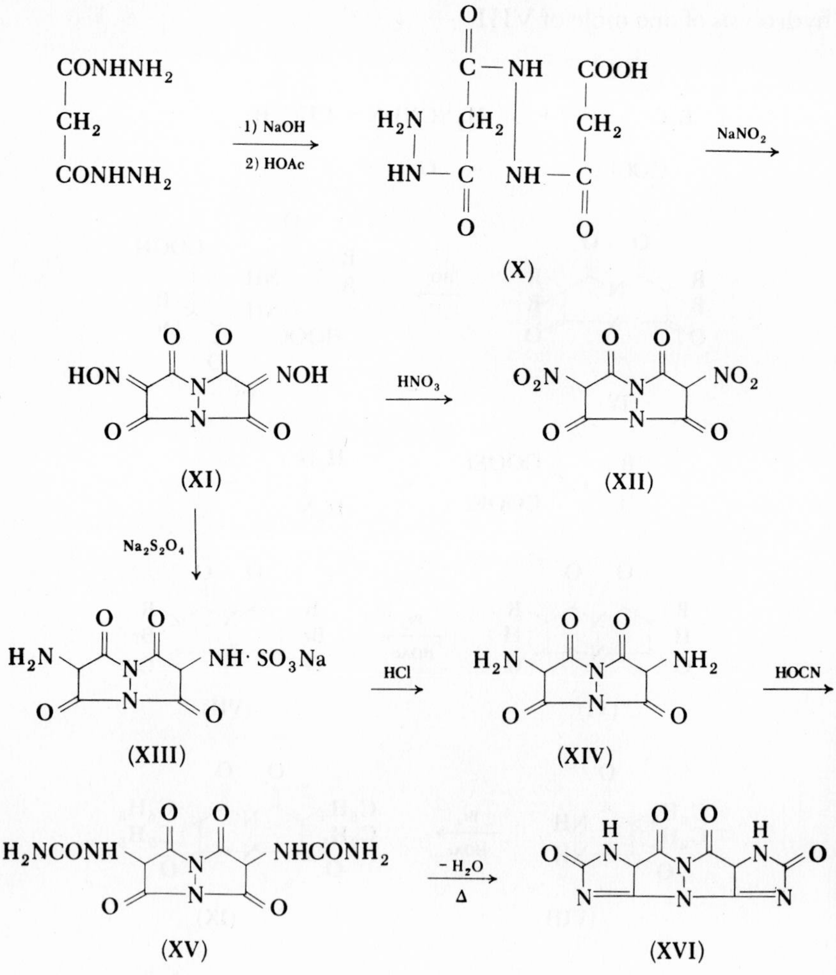

$CH_2(CONHNH_2)_2$ —1) NaOH, 2) HOAc→ (X) —$NaNO_2$→

(XI) —HNO_3→ (XII)

(XI) —$Na_2S_2O_4$→ (XIII) —HCl→ (XIV) —HOCN→

(XV) —$-H_2O$, Δ→ (XVI)

Empirical formula	Structure	Properties and comments	Refs.
$C_6H_2N_4O_6$	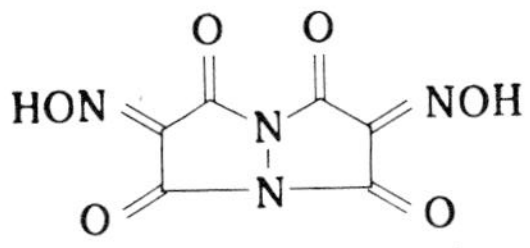	Violurazolic acid. Sodium salt, red-vt., explodes on heating.	10
$C_6H_2N_4O_8$	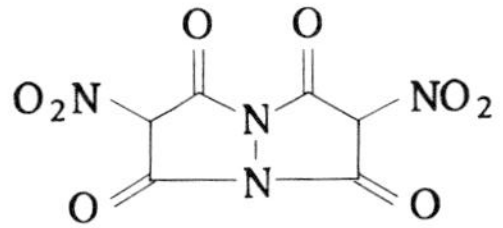	Diliturazolic acid. Sodium salt, yel., d. vig. on heating.	10
$C_6H_6N_4O_4$	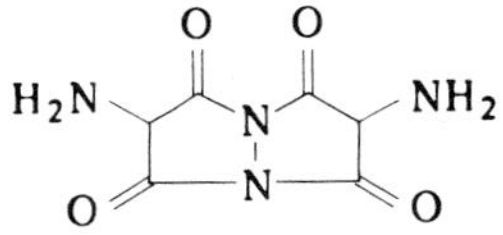	Uramilazole, yel.	10
$C_6H_6N_4O_6$	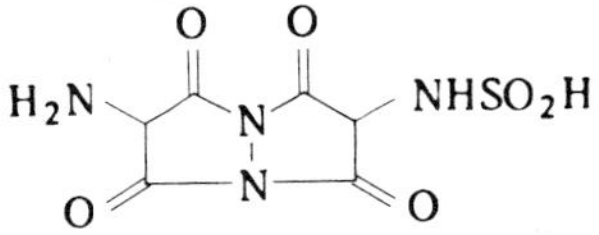	Thionurazolic acid. Sodium salt.	10
$C_6H_{12}N_2$	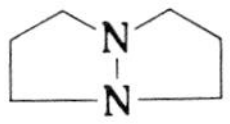	b_{760} 173°; b_{26} 74–5°; m. 1.5–2.5°; $n_D^{20°}$ 1.4895; d_{20}^{20} 1.0000; pK_α 1.0×10^{-6}. Picrate, m. 159.5°. Hydrochloride and methiodide very hygroscopic.	1

(continued)

Derivatives of Perhydropyrazolo[1,2]pyrazole (*continued*)

Empirical formula	Structure	Properties and comments	Refs.
$C_8H_8N_6O_6$	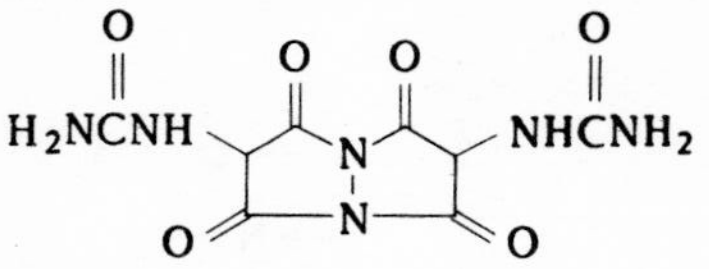	Pseudo-ureidazolic acid.	10
$C_{10}H_{10}Br_2N_2O_4$	2,6-Dibromo-2,6-diethyl-1,3,5,7-tetraoxo-	m. 171–3°.	8
$C_{10}H_{12}N_2O_4$	2,6-Diethyl-1,3,5,7-tetraoxo-	m. 246–7°.	8
$C_{12}H_{14}Br_2N_2O_4$	2,6-Dibromo-2,6-di-*n*-propyl-1,3,5,7-tetraoxo-	m. 138°.	8
$C_{12}H_{16}N_2O_4$	2,6-Di-*n*-propyl-1,3,5,7-tetraoxo-	m. 278°.	8
$C_{14}H_{18}Br_2N_2O_4$	2,6-Dibromo-2,6-di-*sec*-butyl-1,3,5,7-tetraoxo-	m. 111°.	8
$C_{14}H_{20}N_2O_4$	2,6-Di-*sec*-butyl-1,3,5,7-tetraoxo-	m. 207°.	8
	2,2,6,6-Tetraethyl-1,3,5,7-tetraoxo-	m. 202–3°.	7
$C_{18}H_{16}N_2O_{10}$	2,3,6,7-Tetracarboxy-1,5-di(2-furyl)-	m. 219°. Dianhydride, m. 224°.	11
$C_{18}H_{20}N_2$	1,5-Diphenyl-	m. 149–52°.	11
$C_{18}H_{20}N_2O_6$	2,6-Dicarbomethoxy-1,5-di-(2-furyl)-	m. 106°. Dihydrazide, m. 229–30°.	11
$C_{18}H_{24}N_2O_4$	2,2,6,6-Tetra-*n*-propyl-1,3,5,7-tetraoxo-	m. 189°.	7
$C_{20}H_{18}N_4$	2,6-Dicyano-1,5-diphenyl-	m. 223–4°.	11
$C_{20}H_{24}N_2O_2$	2,6-Bis-hydroxymethyl-1,5-diphenyl-	m. 199°.	11
$C_{20}H_{26}N_2O_6$	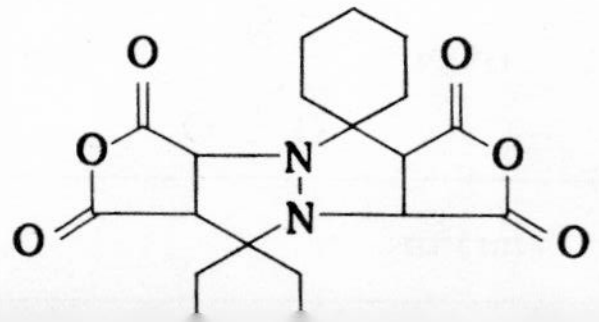	m. 285–7°.	6

$C_{22}H_{14}N_4O_{10}$	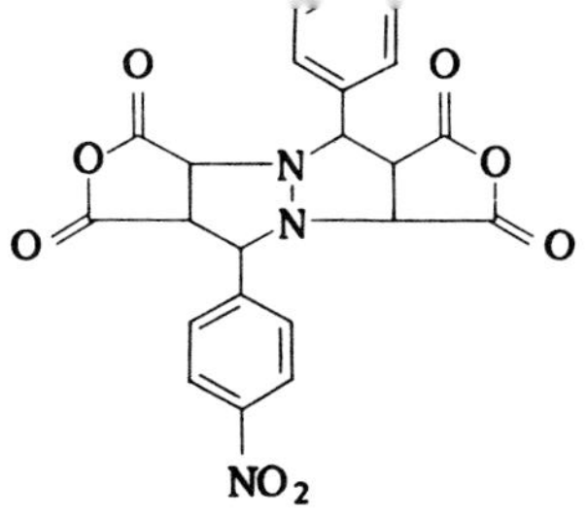	m. 272°.	11
$C_{22}H_{18}Cl_2N_2O_8$	2,3,6,7-Tetracarboxy-1,5-bis-(4-chlorophenyl)-	m. 253°. Dianhydride, m. 284°.	11
$C_{22}H_{18}N_4O_6$	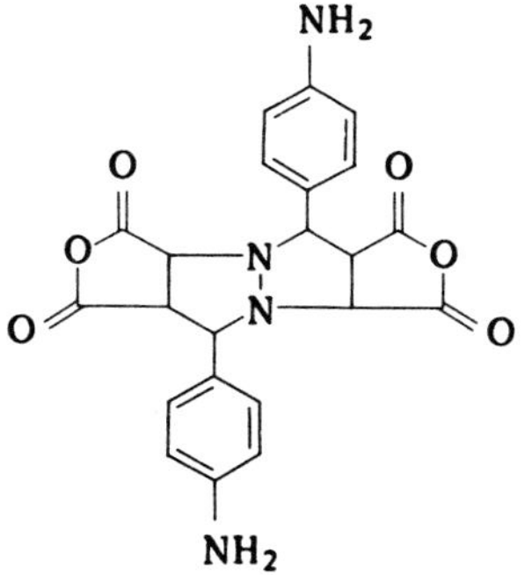	m. >320°.	11
$C_{22}H_{20}N_2O_4$	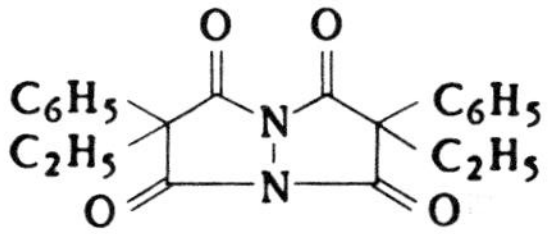	m. 238°.	9

(continued)

Derivatives of Perhydropyrazolo[1,2]pyrazole (*continued*)

Empirical formula	Structure	Properties and comments	Refs.
$C_{22}H_{20}N_2O_8$	2,3,6,7-Tetracarboxy-1,5-diphenyl-	m. 253°. Dianhydride, m. 248–9° (243–4°; 298° d.); stereoisomeric forms: m. 284° and 233°. Tetramethyl ester, m. 232–4°; stereoisomeric forms: m. 220–1° and 180°.	2–5,11
$C_{22}H_{20}N_2O_{10}$	2,3,6,7-Tetracarboxy-1,5-bis-(4-hydroxyphenyl)-	m. 227°.	11
$C_{22}H_{24}N_2O_4$	2,6-Biscarbomethoxy-1,5-diphenyl-	m. 137°. Picrate, m. 207°. Methiodide, m. 202°. Ethobromide, m. 199°. Dihydrazide, m. 217–21° d. Bis-(diethylaminoethylamide), m. 169–71°.	11
$C_{24}H_{22}N_4O_8$	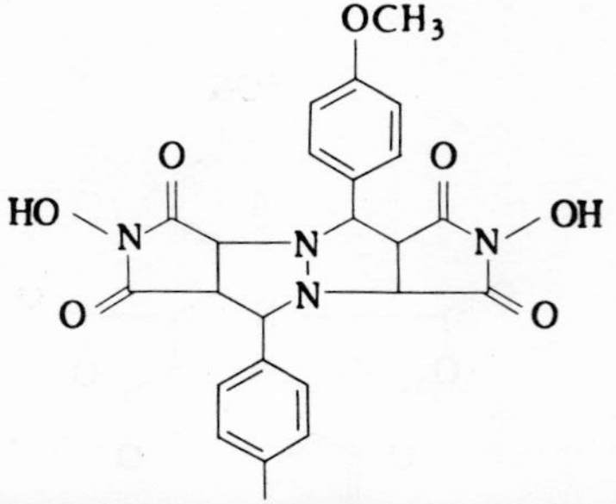	m. 312–4°	11

$C_{24}H_{24}N_2O_{10}$	2,3,6,7-Tetracarboxy-1,5-bis-(4-methoxyphenyl)-	m. 231.5°. Dianhydride, m. 270–1° (d. 265°).	3,11
$C_{26}H_{20}N_2O_{10}$ R = $OCOCH_3$	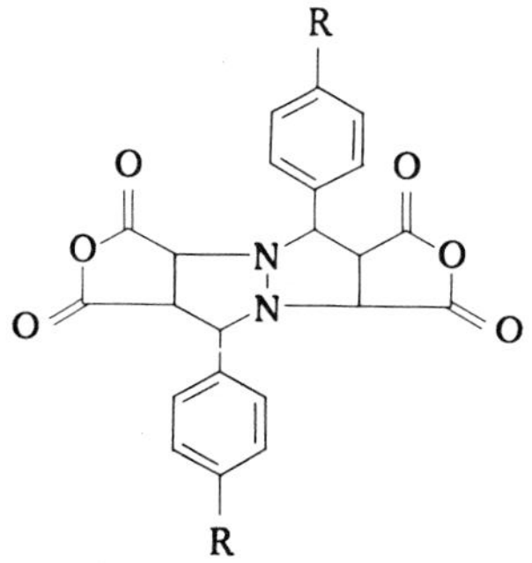	m. 258–60°.	11
$C_{26}H_{26}N_4O_6$ R = $N(CH_3)_2$		m. 281.5–2.5°.	11
$C_{36}H_{48}N_6O_6$ R = OCH_3	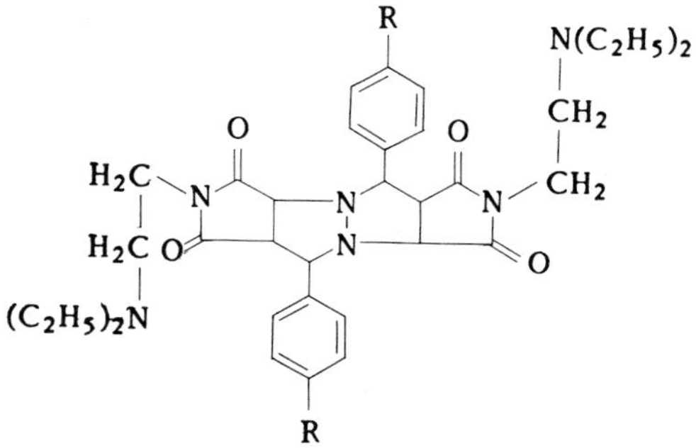	m. 215–6°.	11
$C_{38}H_{54}N_8O_4$ R = $N(CH_3)_2$		m. 246–8°.	11

References

1. Buhle, Moore and Wiselogle, *J. Am. Chem. Soc.*, **65,** 29 (1943).
2. Wagner-Jauregg, *Ber.*, **63,** 3213 (1930).
3. Van Alphen, *Rec. trav. chim.*, **61,** 892 (1942).
4. Kovács, Bruckner and Kandel, *Magyar Kém. Folyóirat*, **56,** 74 (1950); *Chem. Abstracts*, **46,** 8649 (1952).
5. Kovács, Bruckner and Kandel, *Acta. Chim. Hung.*, **1,** 230 (1951); *Chem. Abstracts*, **46,** 2521 (1952).
6. Dutt and Guha, *J. Indian Chem. Soc.*, **27,** 151 (1950); *Chem. Abstracts*, **45,** 1526 (1951).
7. Freund and Fleischer, *Ann.*, **379,** 27 (1911).
8. Dox, *J. Am. Chem. Soc.*, **54,** 3674 (1932).
9. Ruhkopf, *Ber.*, **73,** 820 (1940).
10. Hepner and Simonberg, *Bull. soc. chim. France*, [5]**6,** 1069 (1939).
11. Häring and Wagner-Jauregg, *Helv. Chim. Acta*, **40,** 852 (1957).

A-176. Benzo[*c*]pyrazolo[1,2-*a*]-pyrazole. R.I. 1361

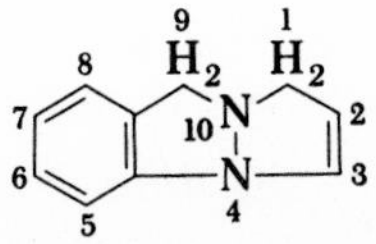

Previously used names for this ring system and its derivatives are: *benzobispyrazole*, *indazolo[1,2-a]pyrazole* and *1(CO)-2-benzoylene-pyrazolone (5)*.

When heated in vacuo, I was found[1] to lose hydrogen chloride, and to rearrange to II (R = H, R′ = CH_3, yellow, m. 268–70°[3]). This same product, and two homologs (II, R = C_2H_5, R′ = CH_3, m. 185° and R = H, R′ = C_6H_5, m. 197–200°) were also prepared[3] by the reaction of III with acylacetic esters in the presence of phosphorus trichloride. Bromination of II (R = H, R′ = CH_3) gave the 2-bromo derivative (II, R = Br, R′ = CH_3, yellow, m. 233°), while alkaline hydrolysis[1-3] of II readily yielded IV. Compounds of type II exhibit a brilliant blue fluorescence in ethanolic or acetic acid solution.

Michaelis suggested[4] that one of the isomeric products obtained from the cyclization of V (R = CH_3, R′ = H) had structure VI (R = CH_3, R′ = H), and another had structure VII (R = CH_3, R′ = H), although he did not indicate which structure corresponded to which product (see Section A-563). Veibel *et. al.*[5-7] studied these

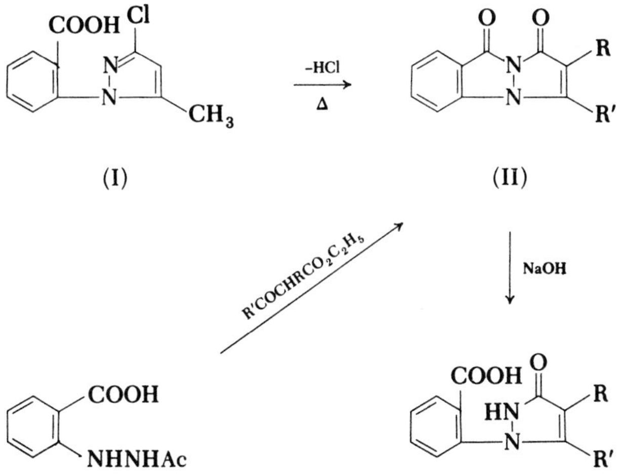

(I) —$-HCl$, Δ→ (II)

(III) —$R'COCHRCO_2C_2H_5$→ (II)

(II) —NaOH→ (IV)

products and concluded that the isomer melting at 135° (*β-pyrazoisocumarazone*) probably had structure VII (R = CH_3, R′ = H), but could not demonstrate conclusively[7] that *α-pyrazoisocumarazone* (m.p. 166–8°) had structure VI (R = CH_3, R′ = H). However, a study[8] of the infrared spectra of these products provided evidence in favor of both structure VI for the α-isomer and VII for the β-isomer.

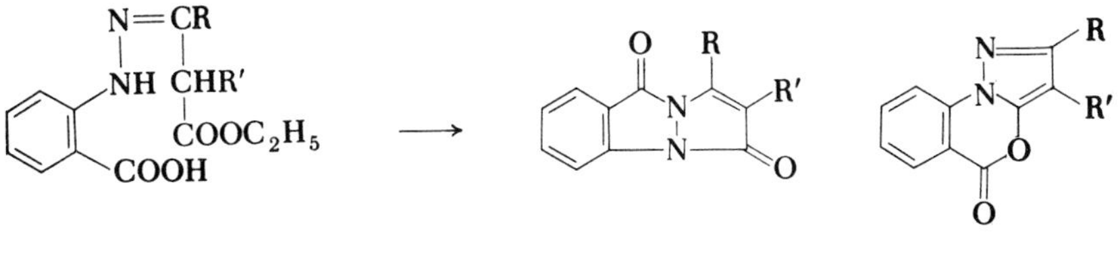

(V) → (VI) (VII)

From V (R = C_6H_5, R′ = H) Michaelis[4] obtained a single product (m. 199°), although Veibel[6] was able to prepare two isomeric products (m. 144–5°, and 201–2°). Similarly, from V (R = CH_3, R′ = C_2H_5) two products (m. 107–8° and 144–5°) were obtained.[6] It seems probable that, in each of these cases, the higher melting product is of type VI, and the lower melting of type VII.

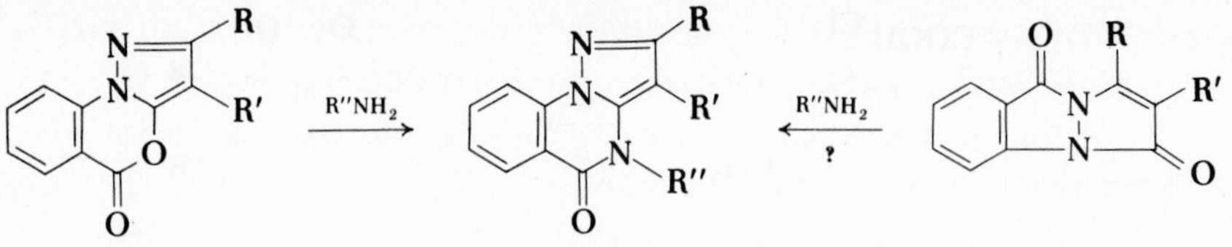

R R O R
N N R'
N R' R''NH2 N R' R''NH2 N
O N ? N O
O R'' O

(VII) (VIII) (VI)

Treatment of VI (R′ = H) with iodine or bromine or phosphorus pentachloride yields 2-halo derivatives (R = CH_3, R′ = Br, m. 187°; R = CH_3, R′ = I, m. 198°; R = C_6H_5, R′ = Br, m. 187°; R = C_6H_5, R′ = Cl, m. 170°). While the reaction of VII with ammonia or primary amines to yield[4] VIII is unambiguous, it seems possible that VI may also be thus converted into VIII (possibly via VII), since Michaelis[4] indicated that his product of m.p. 199° (for which structure VI, R = C_6H_5, R′ = H is proposed) underwent thie reaction. Further work is needed to elucidate the exact nature of these products and reactions.

References

1. Michaelis and Käding, *Ann.*, **373,** 202 (1910).
2. Veibel and Linholt, *Acta Chem. Scand.*, **9,** 970 (1955).
3. Veibel and Lillelund, *XIV Congr. Int. Chem. Handbook*, Zürich, 1955, p. 274. *Tetrahedron*, **1,** 201 (1957).
4. Michaelis, Zeisel, Krug and Leo, *Ann.*, **373,** 129 (1910).
5. Veibel and Arnfeld, *Acta Chem. Scand.*, **2,** 914 (1948).
6. Veibel and Arnfeld, *Acta Chem. Scand.*, **2,** 921 (1948).
7. Veibel, Refn and Friediger, *Acta Chem. Scand.*, **2,** 927 (1948).
8. Mosby, *Chem. and Ind.*, **1956,** 1524.

A-177. 6*H*,12*H*-Indazolo[1,2-*a*]-indazole*

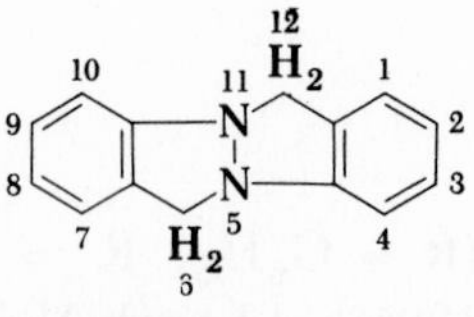

12
10 11 H_2 1
9 N 2
8 N 3
7 5 4
H_2
6

While studying the alkaline reduction products of 2-nitrobenzyl alcohol and 2-nitrobenzaldehyde dimethyl acetal, Freundler[1–5] isolated, together with several other products, a yellow, neutral amide, m. 294–5° and having the empirical formula $C_{14}H_8N_2O_2$. Carré[6–10] heated 2-nitrobenzyl alcohol with aqueous caustic and isolated, *inter alia*, I, which he showed was converted slowly in the cold, but rapidly when heated, into Freundler's compound. This transformation he explained by the hydration of I to II followed by the dehydration of II to Freundler's compound, which he considered to be III. He also prepared Freundler's product by heating II with a phosphorus oxychloride-pentachloride mixture, and Heller[11] likewise obtained the product together with *bisanthranil* (see Section A-564) by heating II with acetic anhydride. Bamberger[12-14] also obtained Freundler's product by photo-irradiating IV or heating it with acetic acid (which gave a purer product m. 299–300°). Part of the reason for Carré's assignment of structure III to Freundler's compound was the evidence that it could be hydrated (reversibly) to the acid V. However, recently the infrared spectra of Freundler's compound and some related materials were

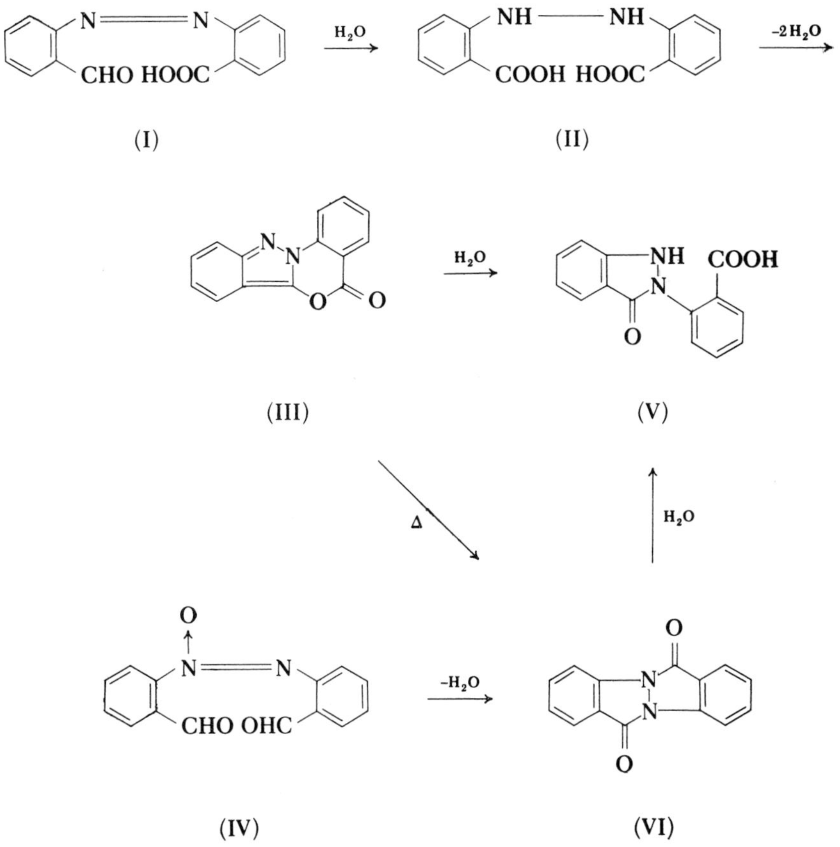

(I) $\xrightarrow{H_2O}$ (II) $\xrightarrow{-2H_2O}$

(III) $\xrightarrow{H_2O}$ (V)

(IV) $\xrightarrow{-H_2O}$ (VI)

(III) $\xrightarrow{\Delta}$ (VI); (VI) $\xrightarrow{H_2O}$ (V) examined,[15] and it was concluded that Freundler's compound has structure VI and Heller's *bisanthranil* has structure III. The thermal isomerization[11] of the latter to the former occurs readily.

Freundler[16-18] found that treatment of VII with phosphorus pentachloride yielded a product [two forms (?), one white, one yellow, *both* m. 241°], which he formulated as VIII but which, in light of the foregoing, is probably IX.

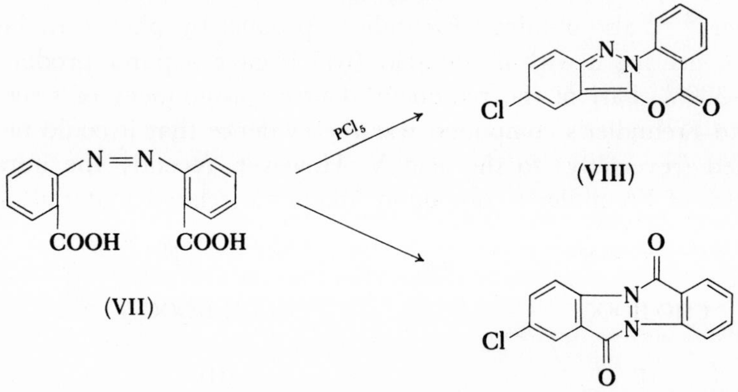

PCl_5

(VII)

(VIII)

(IX)

Similarly, Robinson[19] obtained from X a product (m. 257°) thought to be XI (*Ring Index* No. 3454), but probably actually XII.

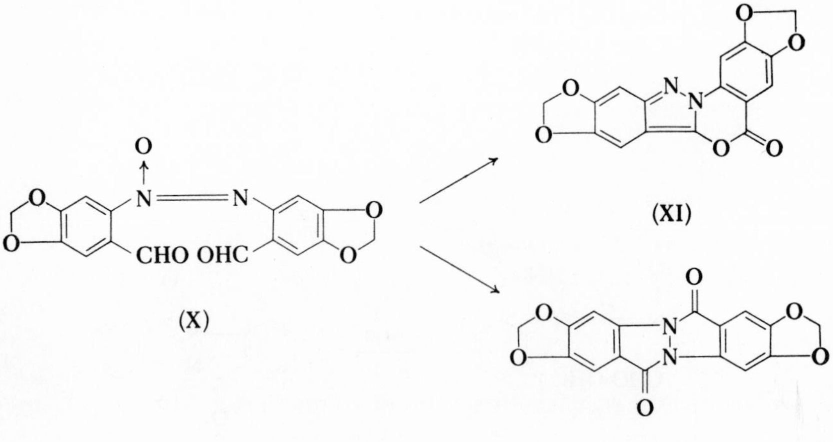

(X)

(XI)

(XII)

Recently, the condensation of azobenzene with carbon monoxide in the presence of nickel carbonyl at 250° was claimed[20] to yield a product (m. 300°), which could be hydrolyzed to V, and which was assigned structure III. Again, it seems probable that this product has structure VI. A methoxy homolog (m. 236°) was similarly obtained from 4-methoxyazobenzene.

References

1. Freundler, *Compt. rend.*, **136,** 370 (1903); *Chem. Zentr.*, **I,** 635 (1903).
2. Freundler, *Compt. rend.*, **138,** 289 (1904); *Chem. Zentr.*, **I,** 722 (1904).
3. Freundler, *Bull. soc. chim. France*, [3]**31,** 449 (1904); *Chem. Zentr.*, **I,** 1497 (1904)
4. Freundler, *Bull. soc. chim. France*, [3]**31,** 876 (1904); *Chem. Zentr.*, **I,** 647 (1904).
5. Freundler, *Compt. rend.*, **138,** 1425 (1904); *Chem. Zentr.*, **II,** 229 (1904).
6. Carré, *Compt. rend.*, **140,** 663 (1905); *Chem. Zentr.*, **I,** 1099 (1905).
7. Carré, *Ann. chim. et phys.*, [8]**6,** 408 (1905); *Chem. Zentr.*, **II,** 1672 (1905).
8. Carré, *Bull. soc. chim. France*, [3] **33,** 1161 (1905); *Chem. Zentr.*, **I,** 32 (1906).
9. Carré, *Compt. rend.*, **143,** 54 (1906); *Chem. Zentr.*, **II,** 611 (1906).
10. Carré, *Bull. soc. chim. France*, [3] **35,** 1275 (1906); *Chem. Zentr.*, **I,** 738 (1907).
11. Heller, *Ber.*, **49,** 523 (1916).
12. Bamberger, *Ber.*, **39,** 4252 (1907).
13. Bamberger and Lublin, *Ber.*, **42,** 1676 (1909).
14. Bamberger, *Ber.*, **44,** 1966 (1911).
15. Mosby, *Chem. and Ind.*, **1957,** 17.
16. Freundler, *Compt. rend.*, **142,** 1153 (1906); *Chem. Zentr.*, **II,** 127 (1906).
17. Freundler, *Bull. soc. chim. France*, [4]**1,** 206 (1907); *Chem. Zentr.*, **I,** 1574 (1907).
18. Freundler, *Bull. soc. chim. France*, [4]**1,** 228 (1907); *Chem. Zentr.*, **I,** 1574 (1907).
19. Robinson, *J. Chem. Soc.*, **111,** 109 (1917).
20. Prichard, U.S. Pat. 2,769,003.

A-178. Indazolo[1,2-*a*]pyrido[4,3-*c*]-pyrazole. R.I. 2264

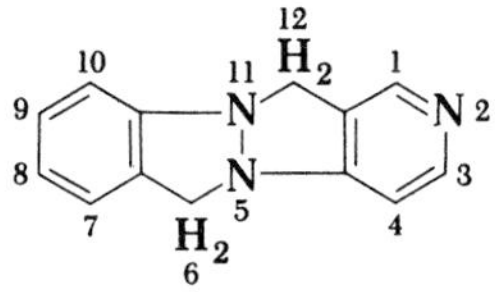

While investigating the reactions of compound I, Michaelis[1] prepared II (light rose crystals, m. 285°; hydrochloride also m. 285°) via the route shown.

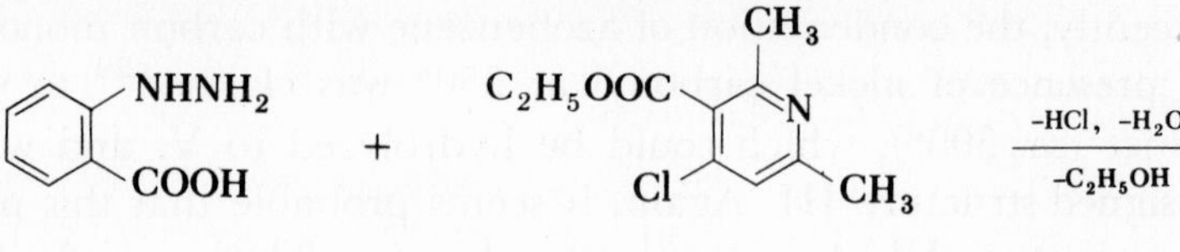

(I)

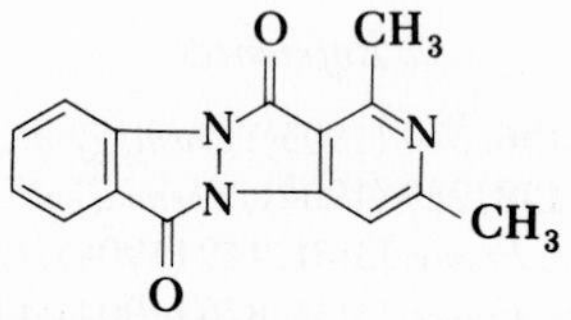

(II)

Reference

1. Michaelis and Reinighaus, *Ann.*, **366,** 324 (1909).

A-179. Imidaz[*c*]imidazo[4′,5′,3,4]-pyrazolo[1,2]pyrazole. R.I. 2225M

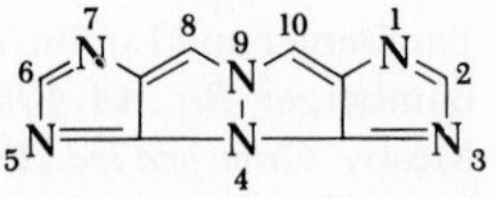

The sole representative of this nucleus, *ureidazolic acid* (I, red crystals), was obtained as shown by Hepner and Simonberg.[1] See Section A-175.

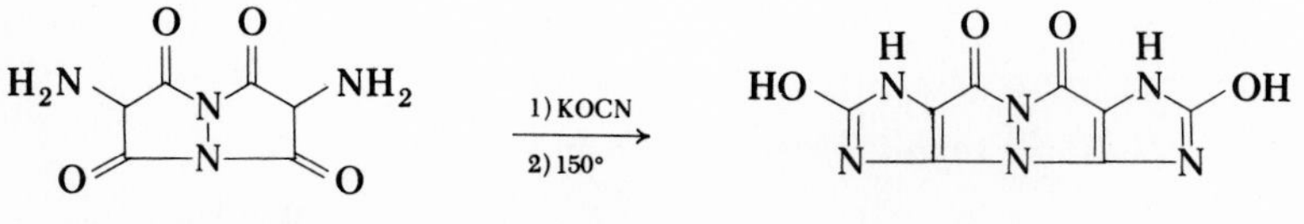

1) KOCN
2) 150°

(I)

Reference

1. Hepner and Simonberg, *Bull. soc. chim. France*, [5]**6,** 1069 (1939).

A-180. *peri*-Dinaphthaleneazotide. R.I. 3463

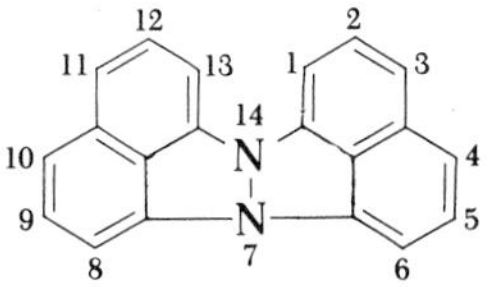

The above name and numbering were accepted by *Chemical Abstracts* and by the *Ring Index*, while *Chemisches Zentralblatt* prefers the name *di(naphthylene-1,8)hydrazine.* Neither name seems desirable.

While investigating the action of sunlight upon solutions of various amines, Malaviya and Dutt [1] found that exposure to sunlight for eighty-seven days of a solution of 1,8-naphthylenediamine in dilute hydrochloric acid produced a brown precipitate. This precipitate was thought to be I, although very little evidence on which to base a structure was available. Further information concerning this nucleus would be highly desirable.

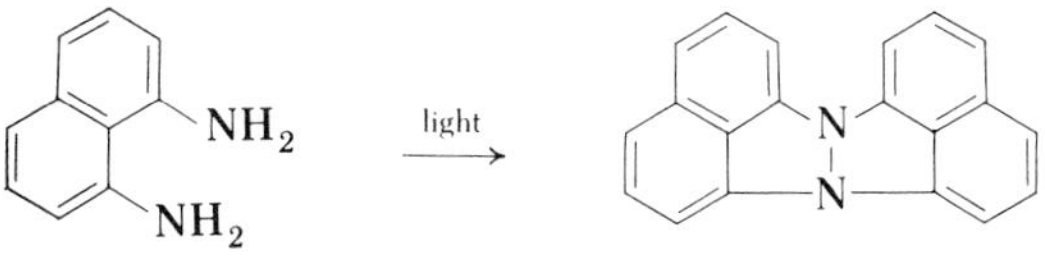

(I)

Reference

1. Malaviya and Dutt, *Proc. Acad. Sci. United Provinces Agra and Oudh, India*, **4,** 319 (1935); *Chem. Abstracts*, **30,** 1057 (1936); *Chem. Zentr.*, **I,** 3487 (1936).

A-181. 1*H*,5*H*-Pyrazolo[1,2-*a*]-*s*-triazole

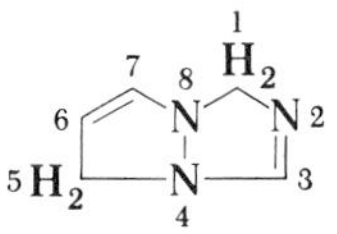

Papini and Checchi heated guanazole (Ia–Ic) with acylacetic esters and obtained [1,2] high-melting (> 360°) products, to which they assigned structure II (R = CH_3 or C_6H_5). However, in view of the evidence favoring structure Ib or Ic for guanazole, and *inter alia*, since 3-amino-1,2,4-triazole reacts with acetoacetic ester to give a 5/6 system (see Section A-580), it seems probable that these products have structure IV. Structure III is also a possibility.

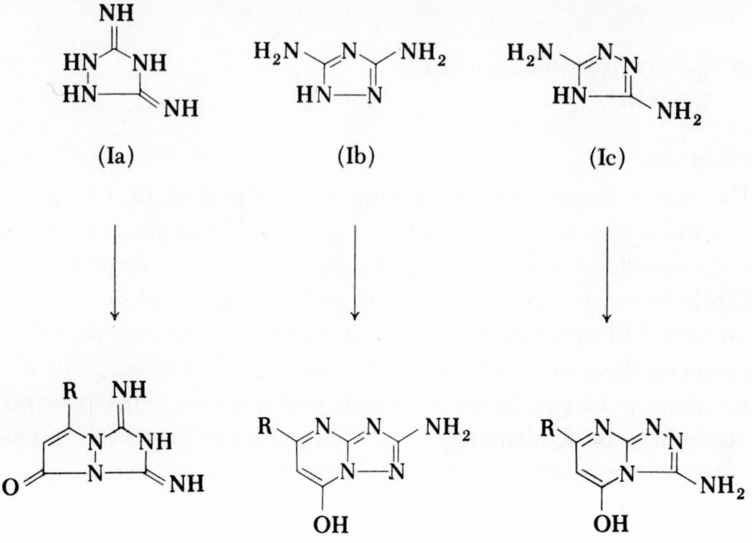

(Ia) (Ib) (Ic)

(II) (III) (IV)

References

1. Papini and Checchi, *Gazz. chim. ital.*, **80,** 100 (1950).
2. Papini and Checchi, *Gazz. chim. ital.*, **82,** 735 (1952).

A-182. 1*H*,7*H*-*s*-Triazolo[*a*]-*s*-triazole.
R.I. 581

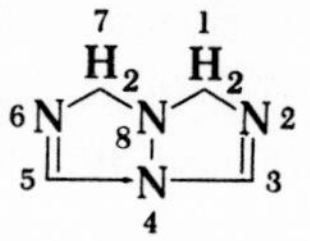

This nucleus has also been named *triazolo[1,2]triazole, 1,2-triazolotriazole, 1,5-triazolotriazole* and *bitriazole*, and the alternative numbering shown in I has been proposed. In addition, certain derivatives of this nucleus have received trivial names indicating their relationship to *urazole* and *guanazole*.

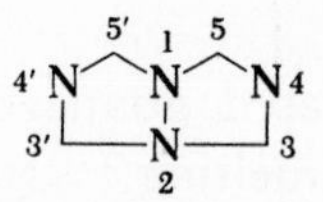

(I)

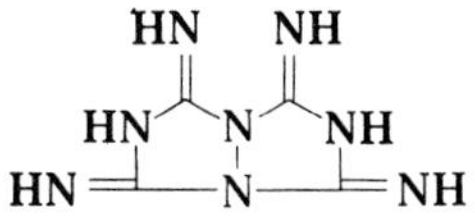

Guanazoguanazole 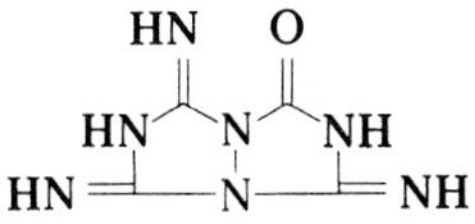　Imidurazoguanazole 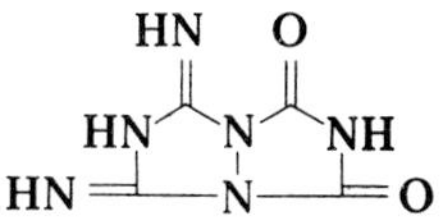　Urazoguanazole

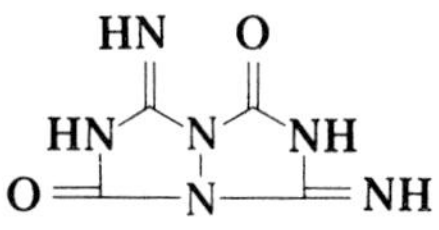

Imidurazoimidurazole 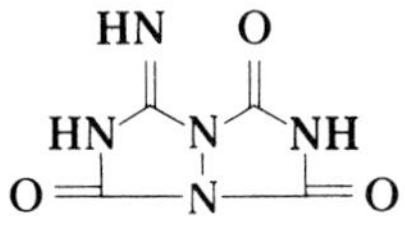　Imidurazourazole 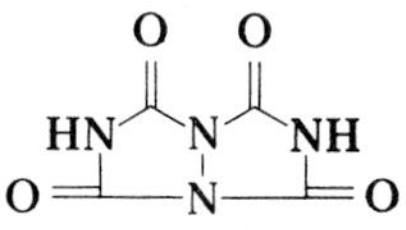　Urazourazole

Pellizzari and Roncagliolo[1] found that guanazole (II) reacted with dicyandiamide (III) to yield a product (which has no m.p.;

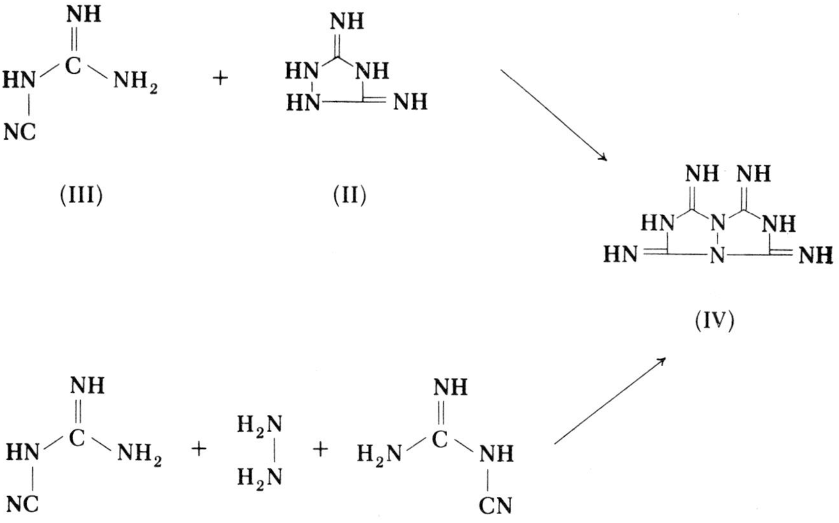

(III)　(II)

(IV)

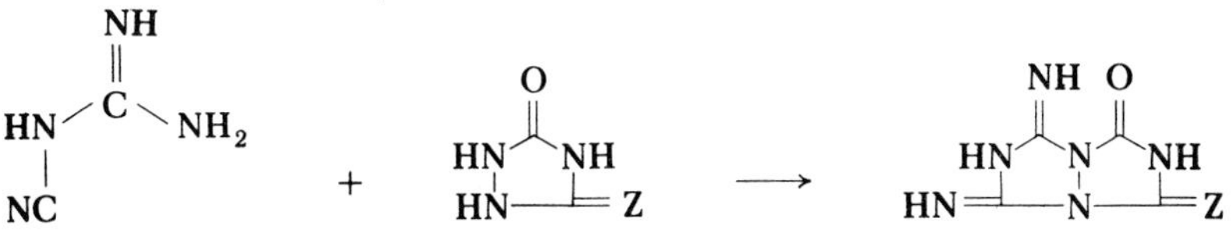

(III)　(Va) (Z=O)
(Vb) (Z=NH)　(VIa) (Z=O)
(VIb) (Z=NH)

picrate, d. ~270°; tribenzoyl deriv., m. 172–5°), to which they assigned structure IV. This same material resulted from the reaction of hydrazine with two moles of dicyandiamide. Similarly, urazole (Va) and imidurazole (Vb) reacted with dicyandiamide to yield, respectively, *urazoguanazole* (VIa) and *imidurazoguanazole* (VIb). This latter product also was formed by the acid hydrolysis of IV. In view of evidence favoring structure IIb or IIc over IIa for guanazole, Kaiser Peters and Wystrach[2] suggested that guanazoguanazole should actually be represented by structure VII (see Section A-655). The alternative structure VIII was eliminated by evidence that oxi-

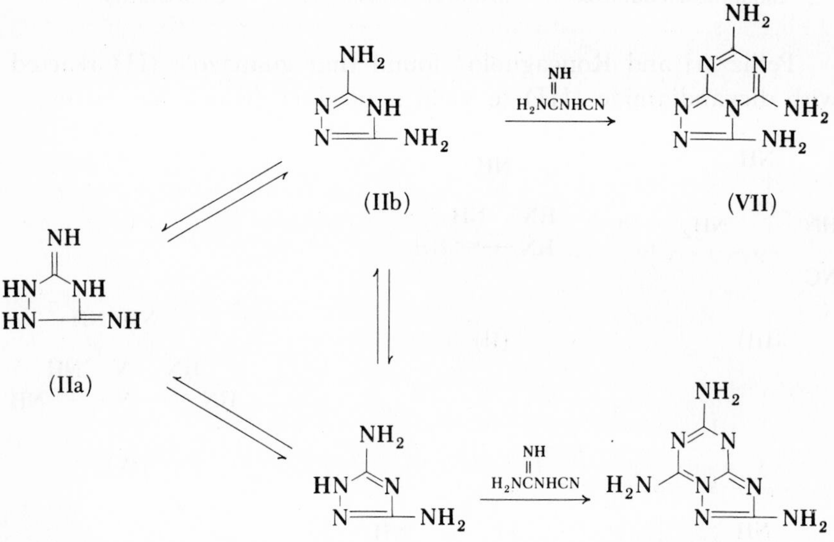

(IIa) ⇌ (IIb) $\xrightarrow{H_2NC(=NH)NHCN}$ (VII)

(IIa) ⇌ (IIc) $\xrightarrow{H_2NC(=NH)NHCN}$ (VIII)

(IIb) ⇌ (IIc)

dation of the product yielded cyanuric acid and nitrogen. By analogy, it is possible that the structure of imidurazoguanazole (VIb) may be represented by IX, but it is evident that no such 6/5 ring system can explain the structure of urazoguanazole (VIa) unless a different reaction mechanism is postulated, in which an NH_2 or NH group instead of the CN group of III is involved in the initial reaction. Also, since VIa is formed from heating both urazole (Vb) with dicyandiamide (III) and guanazole (II) with biuret,[1] unless ring scission and

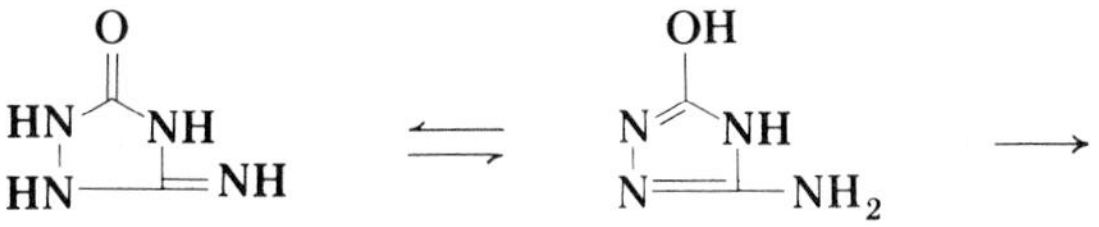

(Vb)

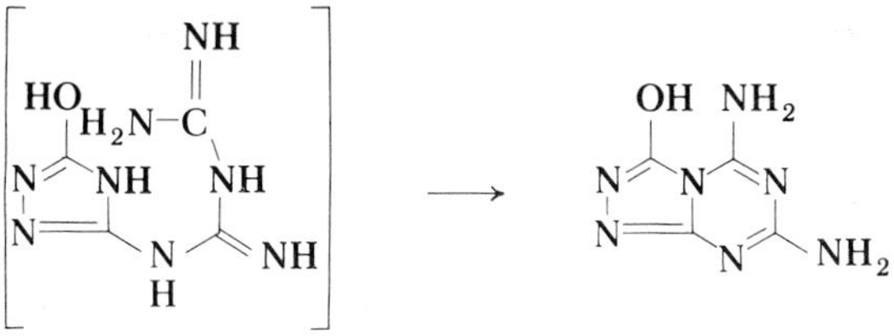

(IX)

recyclization occur during the reaction it is difficult to accomodate a 5/6 structure such as Xa for urazoguanazole. Structures Xb and Xc remain possibilities, however.

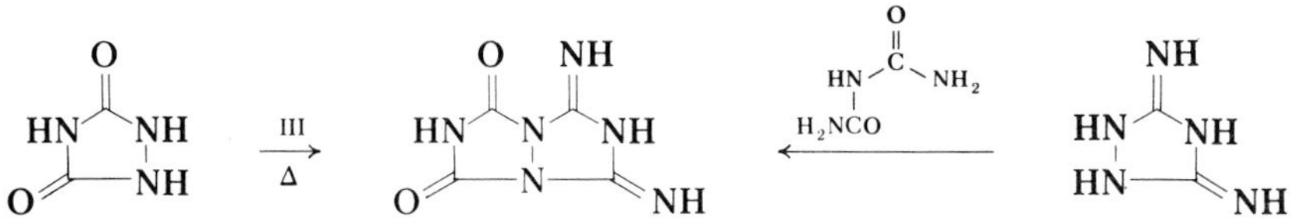

(Va) (VIa) (II)

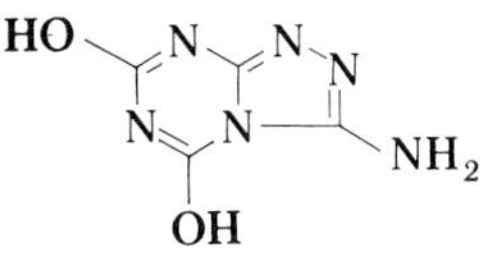

(Xa) 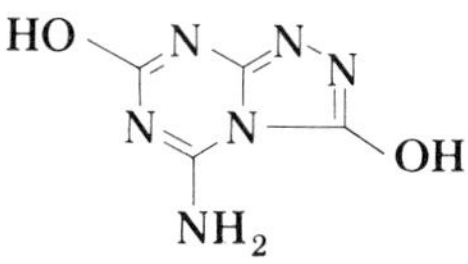 (Xb) 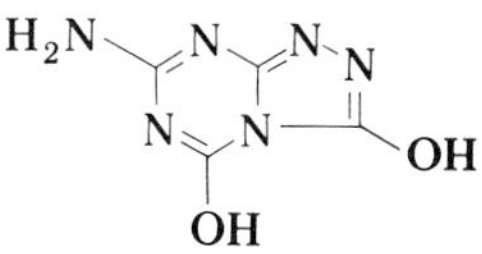 (Xc)

Stollé found[3] that compounds of type XI are decomposed by heat to yield, *inter alia*, products which he considered to have structure XII (R = N=CHC_6H_5, m. 285°; also R = C_6H_5).

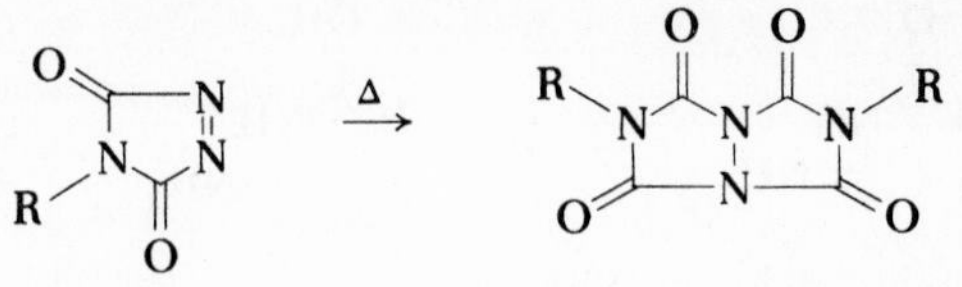

(XI) (XII)

The reactions of phenyl isocyanate, and of isocyanic and isothiocyanic acids with aromatic aldazines was shown by Bailey[4,5] to yield products of structure XIII (Z = O or S). Later it was found that ketazines[6,9] and aliphatic aldazines[7-9] also may be used. However, a number of azines (such as those of acetophenone and benzophenone) failed to react or gave other products.[5,9] Hydrolysis of XIII (where Z = O and R′ = R″ = H) formed hydrazodicarbonamide and RCHO.

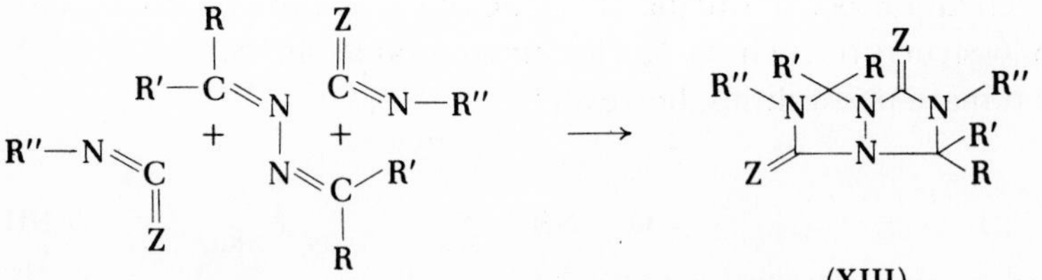

(XIII)

Compounds of Type XIII

R	R′	R″	Z	Properties and comments	Refs.
CH_3	H	H	S	m. 170° d.; diacetyl deriv., m. 115°; two methyl derivs., m. 80–1° and 75–6°.	7,8
C_2H_5	H	H	S	m. 177° d.	7,8
CH_3	CH_3	H	S	m. 180–1° d.	9
CH_3	C_2H_5	H	S	m. 200° d.	9
i-C_3H_7	H	H	S	m. 202–4° d.	7
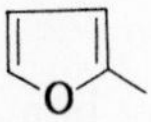	H	H	O	m. 191° d.	5
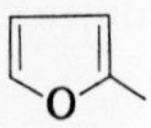	H	H	S	m. 154–6° d.	5

Compounds of Type XIII (*continued*)

R	R′	R″	Z	Properties and comments	Refs.
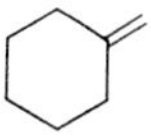		H	O	m. 210°.	6
C_6H_5	H	H	O	m. 234° d. (softens 207–8°); diacetyl deriv., m. 167° d. (softens ~147°).	4
C_6H_5	H	H	S	m. 185–7° (181–7°). Dimethylthio ether, m. 90–2°.	5,7–9
C_3H_7	C_3H_7	H	S	m. 260° d.	9
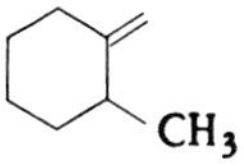 CH_3		H	O	m. 219°.	6
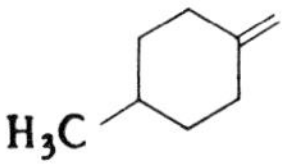 H_3C		H	O	m. 228.5°.	6
$C_6H_5CH{=}CH$	H	H	O	m. 192° d.	5
p-$AcNHC_6H_4$	H	H	S	m. 202–3° d.	9
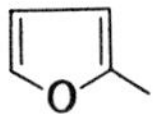 O	H	C_6H_5	O	m. 257° d.	5
m-$NO_2C_6H_4$	H	C_6H_5	O	m. 260° d.	5
C_6H_5	H	C_6H_5	O	m. 263° d.	5
$C_6H_5CH{=}CH$	H	C_6H_5	O	m. 244° d.	5

References

1. Pellizzari and Roncagliolo, *Gazz. chim. ital.*, **31,** I, 477 (1901).
2. Kaiser, Peters and Wystrach, *J. Org. Chem.*, **18,** 1610 (1953).
3. Stollé, *Ber.*, **45,** 273 (1912).
4. Bailey and Moore, *J. Am. Chem. Soc.*, **39,** 279 (1917).
5. Bailey and McPherson, *J. Am. Chem. Soc.*, **39,** 1322 (1917).
6. Dutt and Guha, *Current Sci.*, **18,** 297 (1949); *Chem. Abstracts*, **45,** 614 (1951).
7. Sunner, *Svensk Kem. Tidskr.*, **64,** 121 (1952); *Chem. Abstracts*, **47,** 6411 (1953).
8. Cederquist and Sunner, Swed. Pat. 126,785; *Chem. Abstracts*, **44,** 5396 (1950).
9. Miyatake, *J. Pharm. Soc. Japan*, **73,** 460 (1953); *Chem. Abstracts*, **48,** 5145 (1954).

CHAPTER IV

Fused 5/6 Ring Systems with No Extra Heteroatom

A-183. Pyrrocoline. R.I.814

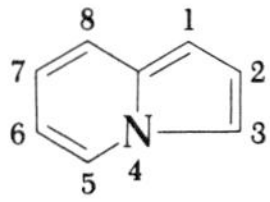

A recent IUPAC conference[1] proposed that the name pyrrocoline be changed to *indolizine*, the title first suggest by Tschitschibabin.[2] Should this proposal be adopted, the names of numerous fused pyrrocoline ring systems will also require amendment. The name *indolizine* (with the numbering shown in I) already has been used extensively by the German and Japanese workers, and care must be exercized to avoid confusion concerning the location of substituents. The names *pyrindole*, *pyrrodine*, *8-pyrrolopyridine* (II) and *pyrrolo[1,2-a]-pyridine* have also been employed.

Perhydropyrrocoline, or *1-azabicyclo[4.3.0]nonane* (III) exists naturally as the alkaloid *δ-coniceïne*, and also has been called *indolizidine* and *piperolidine* (III).

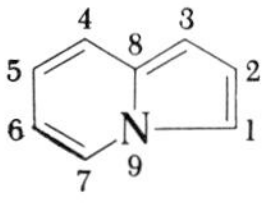

(I) 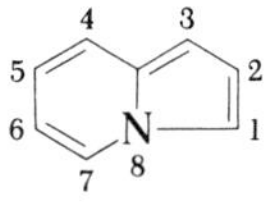 (II) 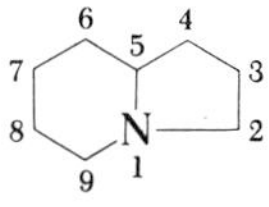 (III)

As has been done in other sections of this book, the pyrrocoline derivatives will be discussed in the order of increasing hydrogenation of the nucleus, and because of their number, the compounds have been divided between a table of aromatic pyrrocolines and a table of hydropyrrocolines.

I. Syntheses

1. *The Tschitschibabin Synthesis.* Perhaps the most useful, and certainly the most widely employed synthesis of substituted pyrrocolines is that devised by Tschitschibabin[2]: the condensation of 2-picoline or its homologs with an α-haloketone or its relatives. This synthesis is analogous to Tschitschibabin's synthesis of imidazo-[1,2-*a*]pyridines (see Section A-271) from 2-aminopyridines and α-haloketones, which, however, appears to proceed with greater facility. The Tschitschibabin reaction has been used chiefly for the preparation of 2-substituted pyrrocolines, but a variety of substituted pyrrocolines have thus been obtained (e.g., references 2–4, 6–8, 12, 14, 25, 26, 49, 59, 66, 69, 71, 75–78, 127–142, etc.).

This synthesis is of little value in the preparation of pyrrocoline itself, as only a 1% yield is obtained[2] from the condensation of 2-picoline with α-bromoacetaldehyde (or α-bromodimethylacetal, or dibromoparaldehyde). However, the yields of 2-alkyl- and, particularly, of 2-arylpyrrocolines are usually very much better, and in several cases exceed 90%. The reaction between the picoline and the haloketone is often exothermic, and the use of a solvent as a moderator is usually desirable. Cyclization of the quaternary salt IV is accomplished by treatment with a base in aqueous or alcoholic solution. The use of sodium bicarbonate for this purpose appears particularly advantageous. Many of the lower alkylpyrrocolines are unstable, and in such cases the comparatively stable quaternary salt IV can be stored[3] and converted in small portions into the pyrrocoline as needed.

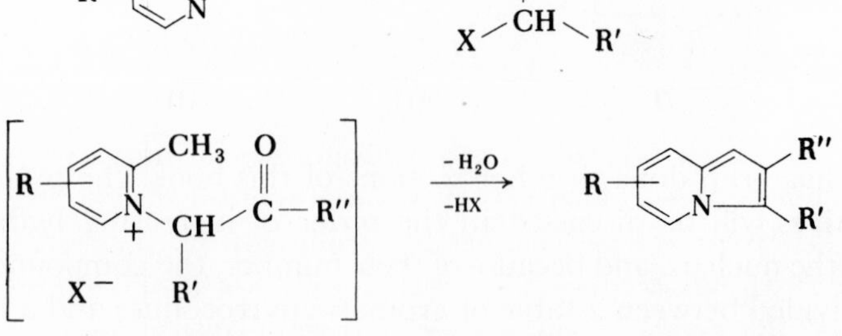

$-H_2O$, $-HX$

(IV) (V)

The reaction of 2-picoline with 3-chloro-2-pentanone was reported[4] to afford only a 1% yield of 3-ethyl-2-methylpyrrocoline, whilst use of the corresponding bromoketone gave a 75% yield. This suggests that the use of iodoketones might, in certain cases, result in improved yields, but no careful study of this effect has been made. As might be expected, steric factors play an important role, and the use of haloketones in which either the halogen[5] or the carbonyl[6] is hindered, or the employment of 6-substituted-2-picolines[2,3,7] sharply reduce the yield of the pyrrocoline.

Borrows, Holland and Kenyon[8] reported little success in efforts to extend the reaction to the use of α-chloroacetylacetone, α-bromobenzoylacetone, ethyl α-chloroacetoacetate or ethyl α-bromobenzoylacetate. Not only were the intermediate picolinium salts (IV, R′ = $COCH_3$, COC_6H_5, or $CO_2C_2H_5$, etc.) usually formed more difficultly in these cases, but, upon attempted cyclization, the acyl (or ester) function invariably was lost despite the use of mild (weakly basic) conditions.

This cleavage of the acyl (or ester) groups was not unexpected, since Kröhnke and his co-workers[9-11] had demonstrated that the nature of the "enol-betaine" resulting from the treatment of quaternary salts such as VI with a base, depends both upon the nature of the salt and the strength of the base. In certain cases, the use of a weak base leads to an enol-betaine of structure VII, while a stronger base causes acyl cleavage and produces VIII. Sometimes

(VII) $\xleftarrow{K_2CO_3}$ (VI) $\xrightarrow[-CH_3COOH]{NaOH}$ (VIII)

the pyridine itself is a sufficiently strong base to induce the formation of enol-betaines. This explains the obtention of picoline hydrohalides as by-products (in varying amounts) in the reactions of picolines with haloketones. However, in most of the Tschitschibabin syntheses, the enol-betaine, which is the intermediate in the conversion of IV into V, is sufficiently stable to permit cyclization.

It is interesting to note that products of types IX and X may be cyclized to XI without loss of an acyl group (see Section A-271), a fact which again points up the greater facility of cyclization in this series.

N–COR, CH_2COR $\xrightarrow{K_2CO_3}$ N, R, COR $\xleftarrow{C_5H_{11}N}$ NH, COR, CH, COR

(IX) (XI) (X)

In contrast to some of the other halodiketones and haloketoesters tried, Borrows and Holland[12] found that ethyl bromopyruvate reacted with 2-picoline to give a 30% yield of pyrrocoline-2-carboxylic acid, decarboxylation of which (v.i.) yields pyrrocoline.

As mentioned earlier, certain pyridines, for reasons other than steric hinderance of the nitrogen atom, resist the reaction with haloketones to form a quaternary salt. Thus 2-pyridylacetone failed[13] to react with ω-bromoacetophenone, while the reaction of quinaldine with either ω-bromoacetophenone or chloroacetone yielded[8] only quinaldine hydrohalides, despite an earlier claim[2] of normal reactivity.

Although 1-substituted pyrrocolines may be prepared by the Tschitschibabin synthesis (e.g. by the reaction[3] of 2-ethylpyridine with haloketones), an attempt[13] to obtain 1-hydroxyethyl-2-phenylpyrrocoline from the reaction of 1-(2-pyridyl)-3-propanol with ω-bromoacetophenone, failed. Treatment of the intermediate quaternary salt with base produced only 2-phenylpyrrocoline, presumably[5] as the result of a retrograde adol condensation at the enol-betaine stage.

It is interesting that, despite the lability of the acyl group in salts of type VI, 2-picoline reacted smoothly with ω-chloroisonitrosoacetophenone, and the resulting quaternary salt could easily be cyclized[14] to 3-nitroso-2-phenylpyrrocoline. By contrast, ω-bromo-ω-nitroacetophenone failed[15] to give a normal quaternary salt with 2-picoline.

A variation of the Tschitschibabin synthesis consists in forming[16] the intermediate quaternary salt by treating 2-picoline and a ketone with iodine. However, the yields appear[8, 16] to be rather low, and the advantages somewhat limited.

2. *The Barrett Synthesis.* The second most extensively utilized pyrrocoline synthesis was discovered by Barrett,[17–20] and despite its very recent origin, a surprisingly large number of pyrrocolines have thus been prepared. As part of an extensive search for compounds with antihistamine activity, a large number of carbinols of type XII were prepared, and dehydrated (e.g. by treatment with sulfuric acid) to olefins of structure XIII. Refluxing either XII or XIII for several hours with acetic anhydride produced XIV in 25–60% yield. When R_4 in XII or XIII is hydrogen, acetylation of the pyrrocoline occurs during the cyclization (so that in XIV, R_4 = $COCH_3$). The reactions are cleaner and slower and the yield of XIV higher when R_2 is alkyl instead of aryl.

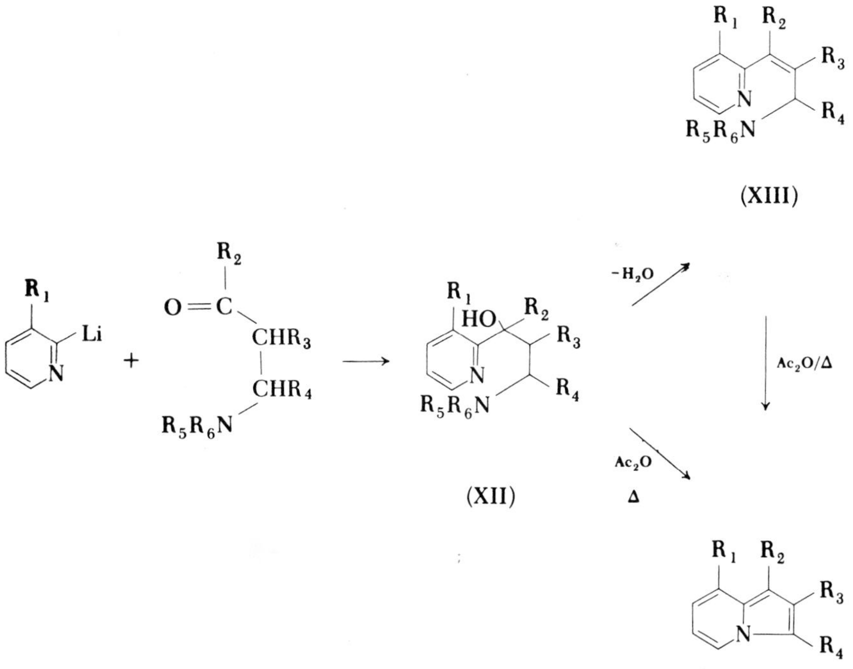

(XIII)

(XII)

(XIV)

The careful study devoted[18] by Barrett and his co-workers to these reactions, and to the by-products produced, has demonstrated their complexity. Cyclization of the carbinols (XII), for example, apparently does not proceed via the olefin XIII, but involves an acetoxy compound. Cyclization of alkenes (XIII) in which R_2 = aryl and R_3 = R = H, was accompanied by the formation of traces of 1,1′-diaryl-3,3′-bipyrrocolyls, while cyclization of carbinols (XII) in which R_4 = H yielded[18] (in addition to XIV) traces of the corresponding dipyrrocolylmethane. This latter by-product was formed as a result of condensation of the pyrrocoline with the formaldehyde liberated during the cyclization of XII (R_4 = H). Cyclization of the *cis* olefins (XIII) occurs in much higher yield than does that of the corresponding *trans* isomers, possibly because of the greater opportunity for side-reactions in the later instance.

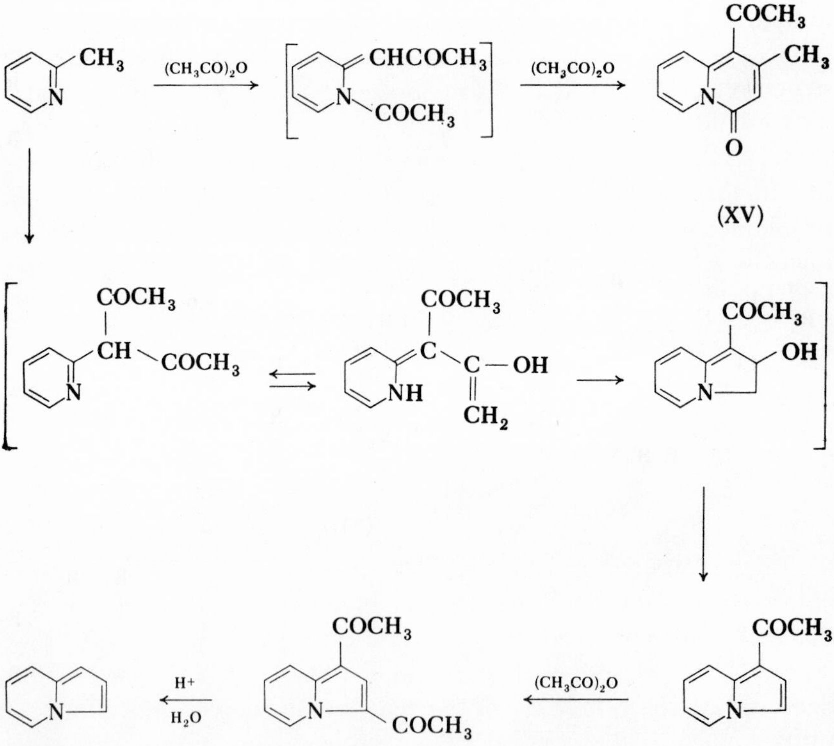

CH_3 $(CH_3CO)_2O$ $CHCOCH_3$ $COCH_3$ $(CH_3CO)_2O$ $COCH_3$ CH_3 O

(XV)

$COCH_3$ CH $COCH_3$ $COCH_3$ C C—OH NH CH_2 $COCH_3$ OH

$COCH_3$ H+ H_2O $COCH_3$ $(CH_3CO)_2O$ $COCH_3$

(XVII) (XVI)

3. *The Scholtz Synthesis*. The reaction of 2-picoline with acetic anhydride was studied by Scholtz,[21] who obtained a product he called *picolide*, and assigned structure XV. However, some years later Tschitschibabin and Stepanow[25] rejected structure XV, and showed that picolide had structure XVI. Acid hydrolysis of picolide yielded[21] a new base (C_8H_7N), to which, despite his erroneous formulation of picolide, Scholtz correctly assigned structure XVII and the name pyrrocoline. This was the first synthesis of pyrrocoline itself, and is still one of the better methods of preparation, affording the base in about 10% over-all yield from 2-picoline. The accuracy of structure XVII was, incidently, confirmed by Diels *et al.*,[27] who reduced pyrrocoline catalytically to the octahydro derivative, and showed the identity of this product with the octahydropyrrocoline previously identified (v.i.) as the alkaloid δ-conicëine.

Scholtz also examined[24] the reaction of 2-picoline with propionic anhydride. Formation of the product in this case, in contrast to that of picolide, required but one mole of anhydride. A different type of structure (XVIII) was therefore proposed for this product. Again, Tschitschibabin and Stepanow[26] showed the correct structure to be XIX. As the methyl group occupies the 3-position of XIX, preventing further acylation, 2-picoline reacts with only one mole of propionic anhydride. Acid hydrolysis of XIX gave 3-methylpyrrocoline, the structure of which was confirmed subsequently by Ochiai and Tsuda.[28]

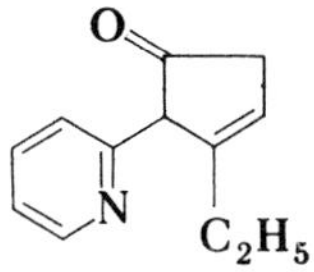

O N C_2H_5

(XVIII)

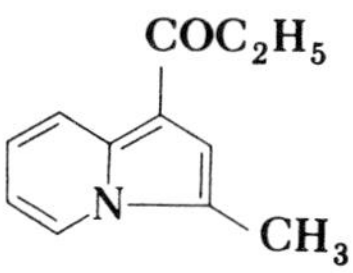

COC_2H_5 N CH_3

(XIX)

In this manner 2,4-lutidine,[21] 6-phenyl-2-picoline[23] and 2-(4-chlorobenzyl)-pyridine[20] have been converted, respectively, into 1,3-diacetyl-7-methylpyrrocoline, 1,3-diacetyl-5-phenylpyrrocoline and 3-acetyl-1-(4-chlorophenyl)-pyrrocoline. These few examples hardly demonstrate the generality of the reaction, however, and efforts to utilize other acid anhydrides[24] or to condense quinaldine with acetic anhydride,[5] were unsuccessful. Nevertheless, within its limitations the method offers the advantages of simplicity and the utilization of readily available reactants.

In a similar reaction, treatment of ethoxymethyl α-picolyl ketone with acetic anhydride was shown[148] recently to yield 1-acetyl-3-ethoxypyrrocoline, and not the expected[105] 2-ethoxymethyl-4*H*-quinolizin-4-one (see Section A-721).

4. *Diels-Alder Syntheses*. In this discussion, the various syntheses are arranged according to the frequency with which they have been used to prepare pyrrocoline derivatives, as well as the generality of the reaction. By these criteria, the next most important pyrrocoline synthesis derives from the very extensive work of Diels and his collaborators[27,29-34] upon the reactions of pyridine and its homologs with acetylenedicarboxylic ester. In ethereal solution pyridine reacts with dimethyl acetylenedicarboxylate to yield[27,29,30] at least three products: a red "labile adduct" (XX), a yellow "stable adduct" (XXI) and the so-called "Kashimoto compound" (XXII). The labile adduct (XX) could be converted readily into the stable adduct (XXI). These products and their anomalies are discussed fully in Section A-721.

The stable adduct (XXI) could be converted[29] by (a) treatment with bromine followed by hydrolysis or (b) oxidation with nitric acid or chromic acid, into trimethyl pyrrocoline-1,2,3-tricarboxylate (XXIII). Saponification and partial decarboxylation afforded a

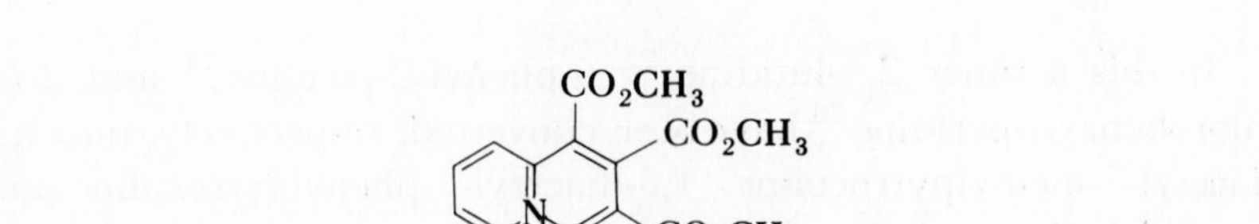

$(CCO_2CH_3)_2$ / $(C_2H_5)_2O$ →

CO_2CH_3 CO_2CH_3 CO_2CH_3 CO_2CH_3 N +

(XX)

CO_2CH_3 CO_2CH_3 CO_2CH_3 CO_2CH_3 N

(XXI)

CO_2CH_3 CO_2CH_3 CO_2CH_3 CO_2^- N +

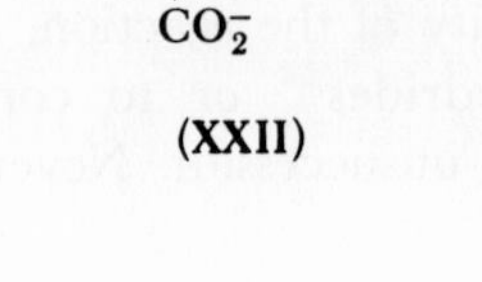

(XXII)

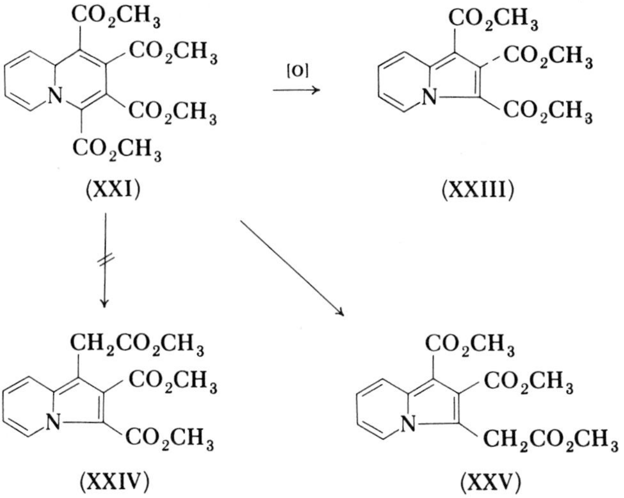

CO_2CH_3 CO_2CH_3 CO_2CH_3 CO_2CH_3
(XXI)

[O] →

CO_2CH_3 CO_2CH_3 CO_2CH_3
(XXIII)

$CH_2CO_2CH_3$ CO_2CH_3 CO_2CH_3
(XXIV)

CO_2CH_3 CO_2CH_3 $CH_2CO_2CH_3$
(XXV)

monocarboxylic acid subsequently identified[12] as pyrrocoline-2-carboxylic acid. Pyrolysis of the calcium salt of this acid produced pyrrocoline, while oxidation of XXIII with peracetic acid gave picolinic acid *N*-oxide, completing the evidence supporting structure XXIII. However, merely heating the stable adduct (XXI) with phenol, or with formic acid induced rearrangement to a tricarboxylic ester at first[31] given structure XXIV, but later changed[33] to XXV, as upon saponification, decarboxylation and hydrogenation of XXI, a mixture of octahydropyrrocoline and its 3-methyl homolog was obtained. 5-Substituted homologs of the foregoing series (XXI, XXIII and XXV) were obtained similarly from 2-picoline[34] and 2-stilbazole.[32]

Quite different results are obtained when pyridine reacts with acetylenedicarboxylic ester in methanol. Diels and Meyer reported[31] the formation of trimethyl pyrrocoline-1,2,3-tricarboxylate (XXIII) when the addition is allowed to occur without cooling. However, when the reaction mixture was kept at 0°, a different product resulted, the so-called "white adduct," which was given structure XXVIII. The formation of both XXIII and XXVIII was postulated[31] to occur via intermediate adducts of types XXVI and XXVII. By treatment with bromine in methanol or acetic acid, the white adduct could be converted into XXIII.

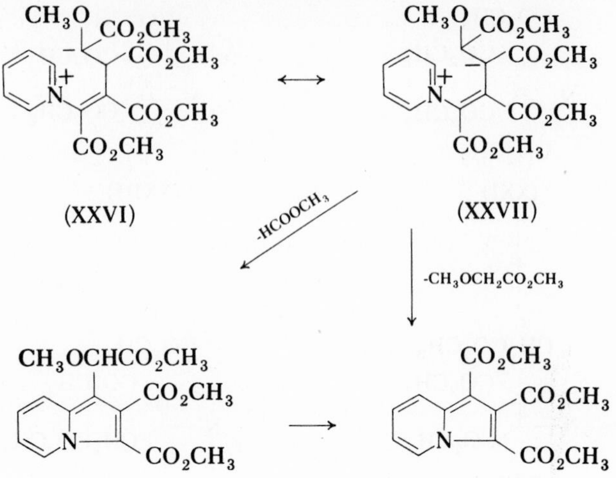

(XXVI) ⟷ (XXVII)

$-HCOOCH_3$

$-CH_3OCH_2CO_2CH_3$

(XXVIII) ⟶ (XXIII)

It is evident, however, that these reactions are understood only imperfectly, as Borrows and Holland's attempt[12] to repeat Diels and Meyer's preparation of XXIII gave only a low yield of XXVIII. Furthermore, the exact nature of the solvent employed may be of less importance than the presence of certain trace impurities, as Wiley and Knabeschuh[35] have shown that in ethereal solution at −78° to −20°, pyridine reacts with acetylenedicarboxylic ester to form XXIII (in 20% yield), *but only if traces of both peroxides and ethanol are present.* Substitution of 3-picoline for pyridine in this reaction gave[35] an adduct, which may be the 6 (or 8)-methyl homolog of XXIII, although it is not certain that this product is actually a pyrrocoline derivative.

A further interesting example of this type of Diels-Alder condensation has been reported.[36] The reaction of 1,2-dimethylimidazole with acetylenedicarboxylic ester yielded an imidazo[1,2-*a*]pyridine derivative (XXIX, see Section A-271), which lost methylamine upon solution in acetic acid, and formed XXX.

5. *Miscellaneous Syntheses.* One of the best methods available for the synthesis of pyrrocoline itself was devised by Boekelheide and Feely,[37] who obtained it in 33% over-all yield from XXXI. Despite the higher yield, this method has the disadvantage, compared to

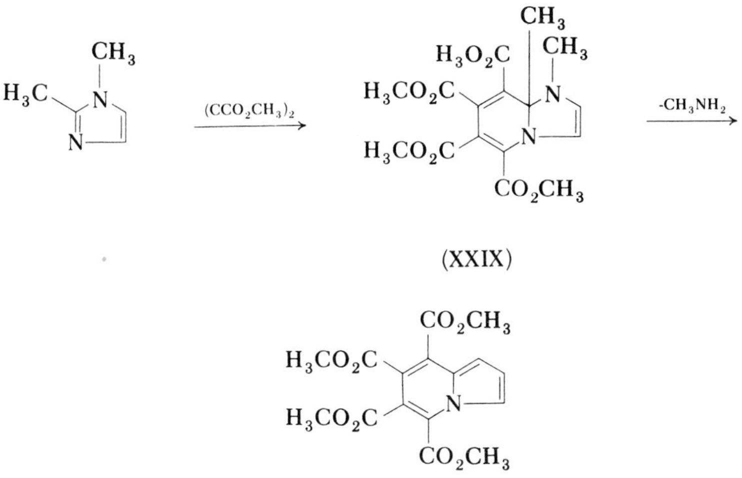

CH_3 H_3C N N $(CCO_2CH_3)_2$ CH_3 H_3O_2C CH_3 H_3CO_2C N H_3CO_2C N CO_2CH_3 $-CH_3NH_2$

(XXIX)

CO_2CH_3 H_3CO_2C H_3CO_2C N CO_2CH_3

(XXX)

Scholtz' synthesis, of commencing with less readily available reactants. This reaction might offer advantages in the synthesis of pyrrocoline homologs, concerning which, however, nothing has been reported.

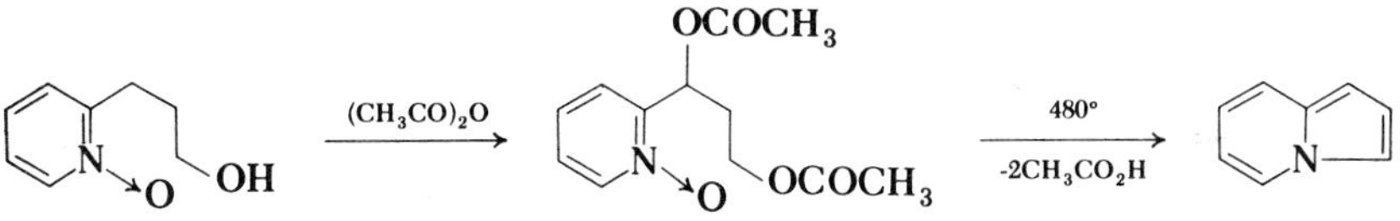

N O OH $(CH_3CO)_2O$ $OCOCH_3$ N O $OCOCH_3$ 480° $-2CH_3CO_2H$ N

(XXXI)

The condensation of 2,4-dimethylpyrrole with acetonylacetone, or with itself, in acetic acid solution (in the presence of zinc acetate) was studied by Plancher,[38,39] who obtained in each case a base of the formula $C_{12}H_{15}N$. Saxton[40] suspected that these products were pyrrocolines and, repeating Plancher's work, isolated the tetramethylpyrrocolines XXXII and XXXIII. While XXXII is produced by refluxing 2,4-dimethylpyrrole with acetonylacetone in acetic acid with zinc acetate for a day, a superior method[40] consists in treating an ethanolic solution of the reactants, at 0°C., with hydrogen chloride for fifteen minutes. The self-condensation of 2,4-

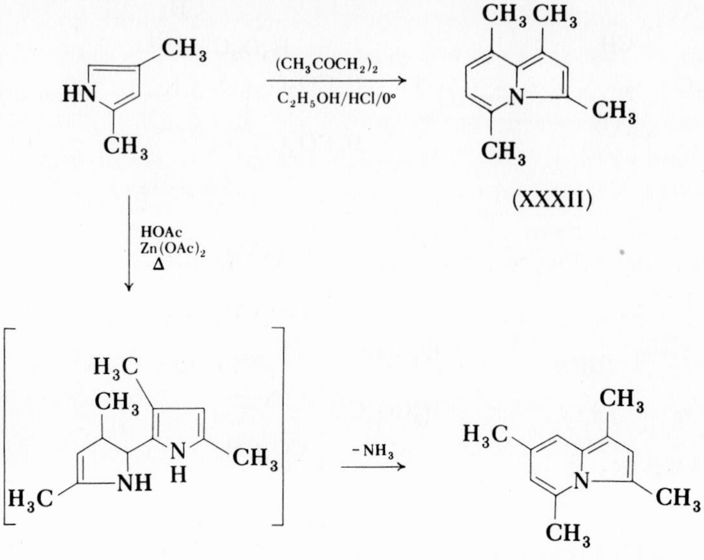

(XXXII)

(XXXIII)

dimethylpyrrole required the older more vigorous conditions and proceeded via a bipyrrolyl adduct. These reactions are of interest because they represent the only examples of the synthesis of an aromatic pyrrocoline (other than XXX) in which the pyridine ring is constructed upon a pentacyclic precursor.

A novel synthesis of the pyrrocoline ring was achieved by Neber and Wörner,[41] who treated collidine with the chloro compound XXXIV and isolated a red-brown substance thought to be either

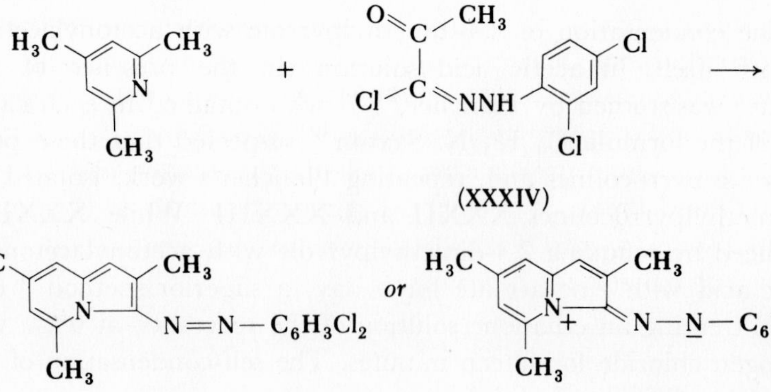

(XXXIV)

(XXXV) *or* (XXXVI)

XXXV or XXXVI. Examination[42] of the ultraviolet and infrared spectra of this and related products confirms the azopyrrocoline structure XXXV. No further study of this potentially interesting synthesis has been reported.

A low yield of XXXVIII was reported[43] to result from the reduction of XXXVII (obtained from the reaction of 2-picoline with chloral). Treatment of XXXVIII with strong aqueous caustic produced pyrrocoline, but the over-all yields do not make the process attractive.

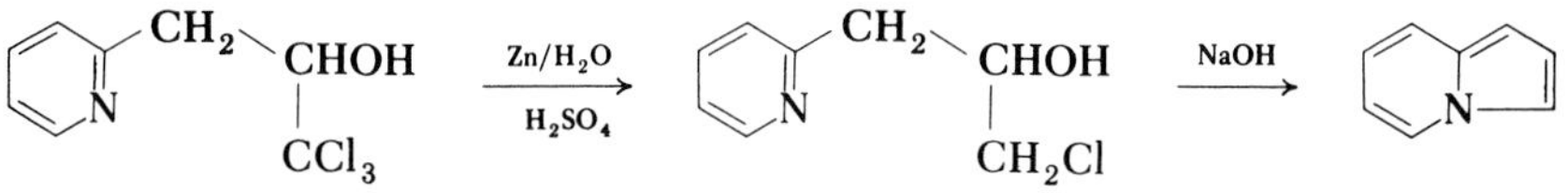

CH_2—CHOH—CCl_3 $\xrightarrow[H_2SO_4]{Zn/H_2O}$ CH_2—CHOH—CH_2Cl $\xrightarrow{NaOH}$

(XXXVII) **(XXXVIII)**

A synthesis of very limited generality was found by Emmert and Groll[44] and by Thayer,[45] who obtained XXXIX by heating 2-picoline with sulfur. Some of compound XL was produced[45] simultaneously and also could be formed[44] by reduction of XXXIX.

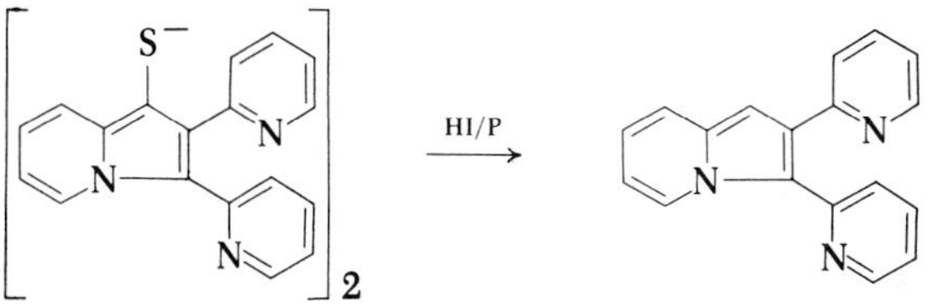

S^- ... $]_2$ $\xrightarrow{HI/P}$

(XXXIX) **(XL)**

A small amount of pyrrocoline was reported[46] formed along with pyrrole, indole and carbazole, when furan and ammonia were passed over alumina at 400°, and pyrrocoline was found[47] among the products of the pyrolytic decomposition of pyridine.

The successful aromatization of a hydropyrrocoline has not been reported, and Prelog and Balenovic report[48] failure to obtain any definite products when octahydropyrrocoline was heated with selenium or with palladium-charcoal.

II. Physical and Chemical Properties

Pyrrocoline and its simple alkyl homologs are liquids or low melting solids, which are steam-volatile and unstable to light and air.

By contrast, the simple aryl pyrrocolines are relatively high-melting, stable crystalline solids. Pyrrocoline and many of its homologs are fluorescent (blue to green) under ultraviolet light; some even under ordinary illumination. Because of this, several homologs have been claimed[71] as optical bleaches. The ultraviolet absorption spectra of numerous pyrrocolines have been recorded[3,5,18,19,35,40,49,50,51,148], and (in most cases) these data are included with the other properties of the various derivatives in the tables which follow. The base strengths of pyrrocoline and ten of its methyl homologs were determined[52] in 60% ethanol, and these data also are included in the table.

Although relatively weakly basic, pyrrocolines readily form salts with mineral acids, and complexes with picric, picrolonic and chloroplatinic acids, and with auric or mercuric chlorides. Some pyrrocolines form normal methiodides, while others undergo nuclear methylation when treated with methyl iodide, and this subject is discussed later. Treatment with nitrous acid converts many pyrrocolines into their green nitroso derivatives, which may serve to characterize the pyrrocoline, as may also the formation of a dipyrrocolylmethane derivative[21-24,43] by reaction of the pyrrocoline in ethanol with an aldehyde.

Most pyrrocolines give the characteristic color reactions of pyrroles and indoles; e.g. they form colored melts with oxalic acid (the Angeli test for indoles) and color a pine splinter in the presence of hydrochloric acid (the Baeyer test for pyrroles, but colors are also given by indoles, phenols, anilines and other substances). Treatment with potassium iodate of a solution of the pyrrocoline in dilute sulfuric acid produces a blue color. Pyrrocolines with a free 1 or 3 position give a positive (blue to violet color) test with Ehrlich's reagent.[3] Pyrrocoline itself yields adducts with chloral[21,43] isatin,[22] quinone[24] and maleic anhydride.[58] The nature of the first two is uncertain, while the last two appear to be 1,3-*bis* adducts. For the condensation product with ethyl acetoacetate, see Section A-228.

For some time it has been known that pyrrocolines could be made to undergo acylation, alkylation, diazonium coupling, nitration, nitrosation and similar characteristic electrophilic aromatic substitution reactions. However, explicit recognition[5,46,53,54] of the aromaticity of pyrrocolines came only recently. By means of molecular orbital calculations Dewar[54] arrived at the figure of 52 kcals./mole for the resonance energy of pyrrocoline, although a somewhat higher figure (62 kcal./mole) was recently suggested.[55] Borrows and Holland[5] considered the ten dipolar resonance forms contributing to the pyrrocoline hybrid and noted that while one such form placed a negative charge at each of the 2,5,6,7,8 and 8*a* positions, two such forms placed the negative charge at the 1 (XLI) and 3 positions (XLII). This is equivalent to the observation[54] that an intact pyridinium ring is present only in the transition states for substitution at the 1 or 3 positions. It was inferred accordingly, that substitution would occur at the 1 and/or 3 positions of pyrrocoline.

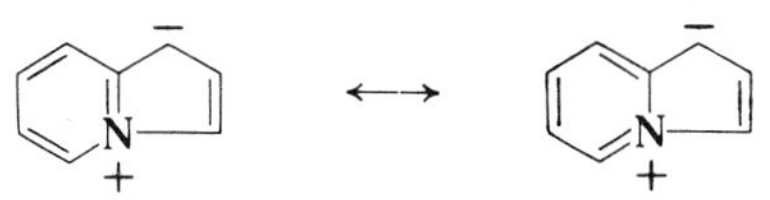

(XLI)

(XLII)

In a more sophisticated approach, using the method of molecular orbitals, Longuet-Higgins and Coulson[53] calculated the mobile bond orders and the π-electron densities (XLIII) of pyrrocoline. They concluded that electrophilic substitution would occur first in position 3, or should this be blocked, in the 1 position. Should both the 1 and 3 positions be occupied, attack would occur at the 5 or 2 positions. As none of the carbon atoms bears an unusually low electron density, nucleophilic attack was not expected to occur with particular facility. Recently, by LCAO treatment using the "frontier electron concept,"[56] the frontier electron densities were calculated[57] for *electrophilic substitution* of pyrrocoline (XLIV). As this method leads to different numerical values at the various atoms depending upon the nature (electrophilic, nucleophilic or radical) of the attack, the values shown in XLIV cannot be compared directly with the π-electron densities shown in XLIII. However, qualitative agreement is evident insofar as the 1 and 3 positions are concerned. In disagree-

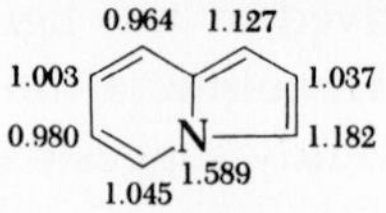

0.964 1.127 1.003 1.037 0.980 N 1.182 1.589 1.045

(XLIII)

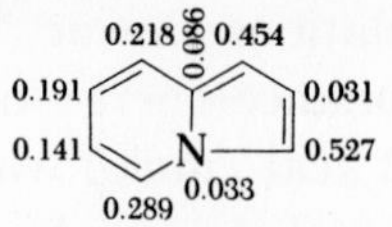

0.218 0.086 0.454 0.191 0.031 0.141 N 0.527 0.033 0.289

(XLIV)

ment with the implications of XLIII (attack at positions 3 > 1 > 5 > 2 > 7 > 6 > 8), the values shown in XLIV indicate preferential electrophilic attach at positions 3 > 1 >> 5 > 8 > 7 > 6 >> 2.

Experimental evidence, insofar as it exists, supports the above predictions. In recent years, systematic studies by the British workers of substitution reactions in the pyrrocoline series, have provided abundent evidence of the great reactivity of the 3 and 1 positions. Except in the case of nitration, position 3 is the site of initial attack. Further evidence of high electron density in the 1 and 3 positions is the preferential decarboxylation[29] of pyrrocoline-1,2,3-tricarboxylic acid to pyrrocoline-2-carboxylic acid. Unfortunately, at the interesting and crucial point of demonstrating the third and subsequent most reactive positions, experimental evidence vanishes. Trimethyl pyrrocoline-1,2,3-tricarboxylate (XXIII) was recovered unchanged from treatment[12] with nitric acid. However, the presence of three negative substituents may have been a contributory factor in this result, and it would be interesting to investigate the behavior of, e.g., 1,2,3-trimethylpyrrocoline. The possible failure of *any* attempt to force substitution in the pyridine ring is adumbrated by evidence[3] that 1,2,3-trimethylpyrrocoline reacts with ethyl iodide to give 1,1,2,3- for 1,2,3,3-tetraalkylpyrrocolinium iodides, and the resistance of the pyridinium nucleus to electrophilic attack is proverbial. Evidently the sole attempt to subject pyrrocoline to nucleophilic substitution (treatment[5] with sodamide) was unsuccessful.

The pharmacological actions (convulsions, motor and respiratory paralysis) of three pyrrocolines have been reported.[121]

III. Substitution Reactions and Products

1. *Alkylpyrrocolines and Alkylation.* The numerous alkylpyrrocolines prepared by syntheses described in Part I are listed in the tables. Others have been obtained by the reduction of various

acylpyrrocolines, for which the reagent of choice appears to be lithium aluminum hydride.[59,60] As is also the case in the reduction of acylindoles with this reagent, complete elimination of the oxygen (i.e., methylene formation) occurs. Under normal conditions, the Clemmensen reduction causes deacylation, while under special conditions 3-acetyl-2-methylpyrrocoline yielded[4] a mixture of 3-ethyl- and 3-(1-hydroxyethyl)-2-methylpyrrocolines. Acylpyrrocolines have also been reduced to alkylpyrrocolines by means of the Wolff-Kishner reaction,[4,59] although cleavage of the acyl group and the production[4] of mixtures appears to be a risk. Hydrogenation using platinum oxide, Raney nickel or copper chromite resulted[4,63] in nuclear attack and the formation of mixtures.

Pyrrocolines having an unsubstituted 1 or 3 position have been condensed with formaldehyde to yield[18,59,60] dipyrrocolylmethanes. The formation of such derivatives with other aldehydes (usually aromatic) was mentioned in Part II. A Mannich base has been prepared[59] from 2,3-dimethylpyrrocoline, and its methiodide (like that of gramine) may be utilized as an alkylating agent. An attempt[4] to ethylate 2-phenyl pyrrocoline, as has been done to pyrrole, with ethanolic sodium ethoxide at 200°, was unsuccessful.

Direct nuclear alkylation was first noted by Scholtz,[22,23] who heated pyrrocoline and its 7-methyl homolog with methyl iodide and obtained, respectively, dimethyl- and trimethylpyrrocoline methiodides. Similarly, 2-methylpyrrocoline afforded[59] first 2,3-dimethyl- and then, 1,2,3-trimethylpyrrocoline. Treatment[3] of XLV with ethyl iodide yielded a mixture of XLVIII and XLIX, while XLVII and XLVIII were formed by the action of methyl iodide upon XLVI. Compound XLIX also was produced by treating L with methyl iodide. Salts of type XLVII (and XLIX) were readily distinguished from those of type XLVIII by means of ultraviolet spectra.[3]

The condensation, in ethanol, of 2-methylpyrrocoline hydriodide with *p*-dimethylaminobenzaldehyde produced[3] a deep blue dye, probably of structure LI (although the 1-isomer cannot be excluded). Recrystallization of 2,3-dimethylpyrrocoline perchlorate from acetone was reported[59] to form some of compound LII. A number of more complex derivatives (e.g. LIII) of this type have been claimed[63–70] for various photographic applications (see tables). Sev-

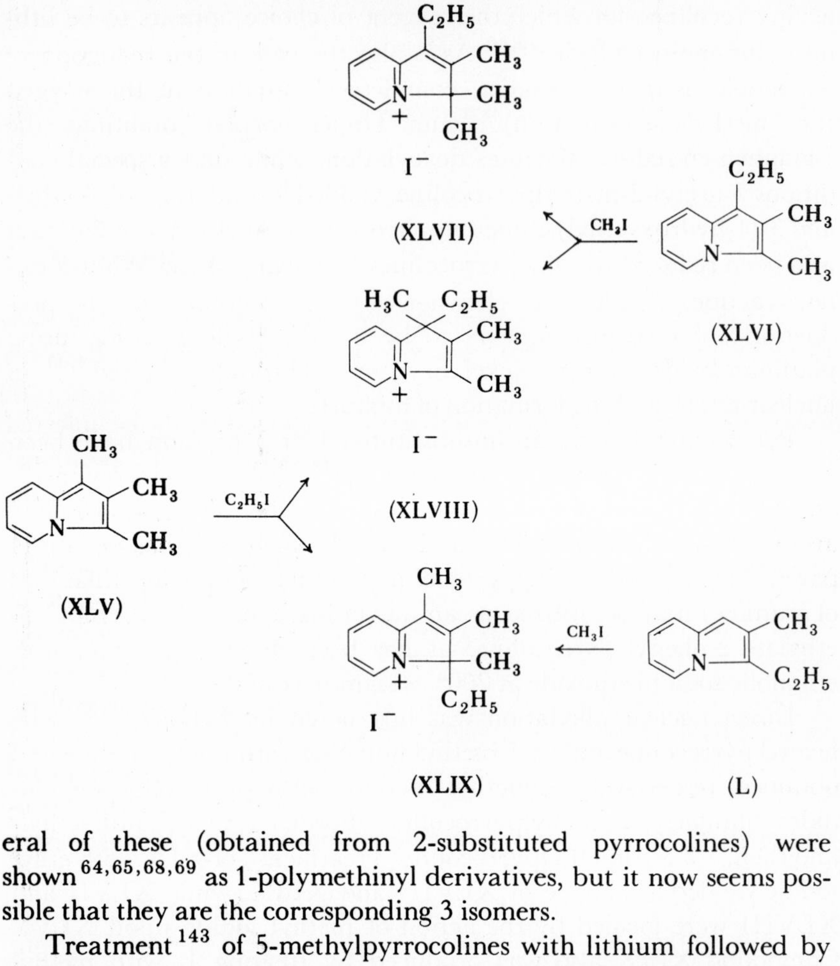

C_2H_5 CH_3 CH_3 CH_3 N + I^-

(XLVII)

CH_3I

C_2H_5 CH_3 CH_3 N

(XLVI)

H_3C C_2H_5 CH_3 CH_3 N + I^-

(XLVIII)

CH_3 CH_3 CH_3 N

C_2H_5I

(XLV)

CH_3 CH_3 CH_3 C_2H_5 N + I^-

(XLIX)

CH_3I

CH_3 C_2H_5 N

(L)

eral of these (obtained from 2-substituted pyrrocolines) were shown[64,65,68,69] as 1-polymethinyl derivatives, but it now seems possible that they are the corresponding 3 isomers.

Treatment[143] of 5-methylpyrrocolines with lithium followed by dialkylamides yielded 5-acylmethylenepyrrocolines, which were dehydrated to pyrrolopyrrocolines (see Section A-69).

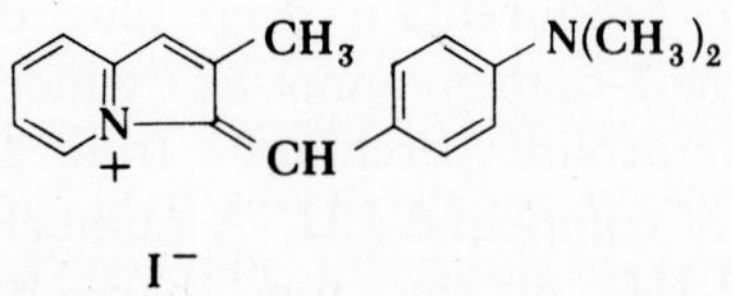

CH_3 $N(CH_3)_2$ CH N + I^-

(LI)

$C(CH_3)_2$ CH_3 CH_3 N + ClO_4^-

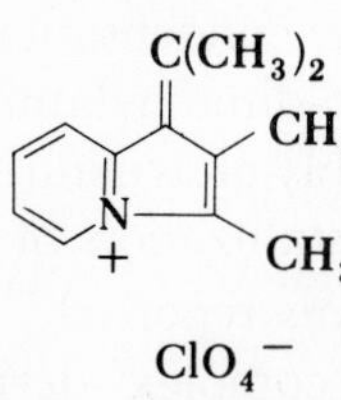

(LII)

$(CH_3O)_2CHCH{=}CHOCH_3$

(LIII)

2. *Carbonyl Derivatives.* Allusion was made earlier to the synthesis of acylpyrrocolines by the Scholtz reaction and by Barrett's synthesis, and to the failure of the Tschitschibabin synthesis to produce these derivatives. From this work, might correctly be inferred the vulnerability of pyrrocolines (with unsubstituted 1 or 3 positions) to direct acylation. Treatment of such pyrrocolines with acid anhydrides and the sodium salt of the acid readily yields[8,15,22,23,25,60] acetyl or benzoyl derivatives, the latter being obtained[8,24,60] also by the action, in the cold, of benzoyl chloride. Indeed, under vigorous conditions, 1,3-diacetylpyrrocolines[8,25] have thus been prepared. Aluminum chloride has been used[8,72] to promote the acetylation of 2-substituted pyrrocolines, but, in the case of 2-phenylpyrrocoline, some 2-(4-acetylphenyl)-pyrrocoline is also formed.

Cleavage of the acyl group is readily effected by mineral acid[8,18,19,21,23,25,26] and, in the case of 3-acetyl-2-phenylpyrrocoline, even by hot 50% acetic acid.[8] Resistance to hydrolysis is greater amongst the diacylpyrrocolines,[8] while derivatives containing also a nuclear nitro[15,22] or nitroso[14] group cannot thus be hydrolyzed. Alcoholic potash was without effect[22] upon 3-acetylpyrrocoline, but the 3-acetyl-2-phenyl compound was hydrolyzed by hot alcoholic sodium ethoxide in a sealed tube.[4] Direct iodination[13] also may cause displacement of an acetyl group, if sodium acetate is not present to neutralize the hydrogen iodide formed.

Most 3-acylpyrrocolines resist the formation (under normal conditions) of carbonyl derivatives such as oximes or phenylhydrazones, although 2,4-dinitrophenylhydrazones can usually be obtained.[8] This behavior parallels that of the 2-acetyl-1-alkylpyrroles. The 1-acylpyrrocolines form carbonyl derivatives normally,[24,59] and with 1,3-diacyl compounds, usually only the acyl group in the 1-position reacts.[8,21,23,25,59] Many aromatic aldehydes will react with the methyl group(s) of acetyl- and diacetylpyrrocolines to yield[8,21,23,24] mono- or dicinnamoyl derivatives, which are useful for the purpose of characterization.

Abnormal products often result from the interaction of acylpyrrocolines and Grignard reagents. The reaction of 3-acetyl-2-methylpyrrocoline with ethylmagnesium bromide originally was reported[25] to yield the 3-ethyl-2-methyl compound, but the product was shown[73] later to be merely 2-methylpyrrocoline, and methyl ethyl ketone was found amongst the reaction products. With an excess of the Grignard reagent some 3-(2-but-2-enyl)-2-methyl- and 3-(2-ethyl-2-butyl)-2-methylpyrrocolines were also isolated.[73] Working with 3-benzoyl-2-phenylpyrrocoline and methyl Grignard reagent, Borrows and Holland[13] isolated 2-phenylpyrrocoline mixed with its 3-benzoyl derivative. They suggested that the initially formed complex (LIV) is decomposed, as shown, by water. In contrast to these results is the work of Scholtz and Fraude,[24] who apparently obtained normal tertiary carbinols from the reaction of picolide (XVI) with one mole of methyl or phenyl Grignard reagents. This suggests that abnormal behavior with Grignard reagents may be confined to the 3-acylpyrrocolines, and that the Grignard complex may *not* be of type LIV, but may involve the ring nitrogen.

R, N, C—R′, O ⇌ (R″MgX / H_2O) R, N, C, OMgX, R′, R″ → (H_2O)

(LIV)

R, N + R′COR″

Esters and acids of the pyrrocoline series are produced via the Diels-Alder synthesis (see Part I-4), and 2-carbethoxypyrrocoline has been made[12] by the Tschitschibabin synthesis. Scholtz and Fraude[24] obtained an unidentified monocarboxylic acid by treating pyrrocoline with phosgene. This is undoubtedly the 3-carboxylic acid, as Holland and Nayler[60] obtained an acid of this orientation from a similar reaction with 2-methylpyrrocoline. The nature of this latter product was demonstrated by treating the acid chloride with dimethyl cadmium to yield the known 3-acetyl-2-methylpyrrocoline. Derivatives of 1- or 3-pyrrocolylacetic acid have been obtained from the Diels-Alder adducts described earlier. The direct carbonation of pyrrocolines, or caustic fusion of the 2-methyl derivative failed[12] to yield carboxylic acids.

Pyrrocolines with unsubstituted 1 or 3 positions are readily formylated by means of the Vilsmaier-Haack technique using phosphorus oxychloride and methylformanilide or dimethylformamide.[59-61] The McFayden-Stevens reduction of 2-methylpyrrocolyl-3-benzenesulfonylcarbohydrazide yielded[60] the 3-formyl-2-methyl compound, and the Reimer-Tiemann reaction also has been utilized[59] successfully.

3. *Halogenation.* Pyrrocoline reacts with bromine or iodine to yield[24] unstable, indefinite products, and similar di- and tetrabromo compounds have been obtained[21] from picolide (XVI). These results have evidently discouraged further experimentation, although 3-acetyl-1-iodo-2-phenylpyrrocoline and 1,3-diiodo-2-phenylpyrrocoline were obtained[13] readily by the direct iodination of 3-acetyl-2-phenylpyrrocoline in the presence and absence, respectively, of sodium acetate.

4. *Nitrosation.* 3-Nitroso-2-phenylpyrrocoline has been synthesized[14] from 2-picoline and ω-*iso*nitrosophenacyl chloride. However, pyrrocolines having an unsubstituted 3 or 1 position readily undergo direct nitrosation, and almost all of the nitroso derivatives were obtained[14,74-78] in this manner.

These derivatives are green to blue in the solid state, but yield yellow to red salts, which have, presumably, an *iso*nitrosopyrrocolinium structure. Careful oxidation with peracetic acid, or treatment with nitric acid converts[14,15] nitrosopyrrocolines into nitro analogs. Both 1- and 3-nitrosopyrrocolines have been condensed with various heterocyclic compounds containing active methyl groups to yield[51] azacyanine dyes, which act as desensitizers to photographic emulsions.

5. *Nitration.* Scholtz claimed[22] that pyrrocoline could not be nitrated because of oxidation, and Borrows, Holland and Kenyon[15]

found this to be true also for 2-substituted pyrrocolines, when the reactions were run for prolonged periods at moderate temperatures. However, by operating at higher temperatures for brief periods, or by nitrating in sulfuric acid at low temperatures, oxidation was minimized and nitropyrrocolines could be obtained.

Among the substitution reactions upon pyrrocolines, nitration is unique in its preference for the 1 position. For example, nitration of 2-methylpyrrocoline in sulfuric acid produced[15] 62% of the 1-nitro isomer and 1.5% of 3-nitro-2-methylpyrrocoline. Under similar conditions 2-phenylpyrrocoline yielded 41% of the 2-(4-nitrophenyl) derivative and a trace of 1-nitro-2-(4-nitrophenyl)pyrrocoline, although by doubling the quantity of nitric acid, the dinitro compound became the sole product and was isolated in a yield of 45%. While nitration of 2-methyl-3-nitropyrrocoline readily yielded the 1,3-dinitro homolog, 2-methyl-1-nitropyrrocoline afforded only a low yield of the dinitro derivative.

Nitration[15] in sulfuric acid of 3-acetyl-2-methylpyrrocoline gave 3-acetyl-2-methyl-1-nitropyrrocoline in 59% yield together with 6% of 2-methyl-1,3-dinitropyrrocoline. Synthesis of the former product by acetylation of 2-methyl-1-nitropyrrocoline confirms the location of the nitro group. A similar nitration of 3-acetyl-2-phenylpyrrocoline yielded all four of the possible products (LVa–LVd) in rather poor yields. As 1-nitro-2-(4-nitrophenyl)pyrrocoline could not be

$COCH_3$ $\xrightarrow[H_2SO_4]{HNO_3}$ R, R′, R″

(LVa) (R=H, R′=NO_2, R″=Ac)
(LVb) (R=R′=NO_2, R″=Ac)
(LVc) (R=H, R′=R″=NO_2)
(LVd) (R=R′=R″=NO_2)

acetylated to form LVb, the structures of these products have not been demonstrated conclusively. The preparation of 3-acetyl-1-nitro- and 1,3-dinitropyrrocolines by the nitration of picolide (1,3-diacetylpyrrocoline) has been reported.[22]

2-Substituted pyrrocolines[14] and their 3-acetyl derivatives[15] having a nitroso group in the 1 or 3 position have been transformed into nitro homologs by careful oxidation with peracetic acid. Concentrated nitric acid converts these nitroso compounds into 1,3-dinitropyrrocolines.

Nitration[12,31] of Diels and Meyer's "white adduct" (XXVIII) led to the formation of LVI. Also, Emmert and Groll showed[44] that nitration of either XXXIX or of XLa gave the 1-nitro compound XLb.

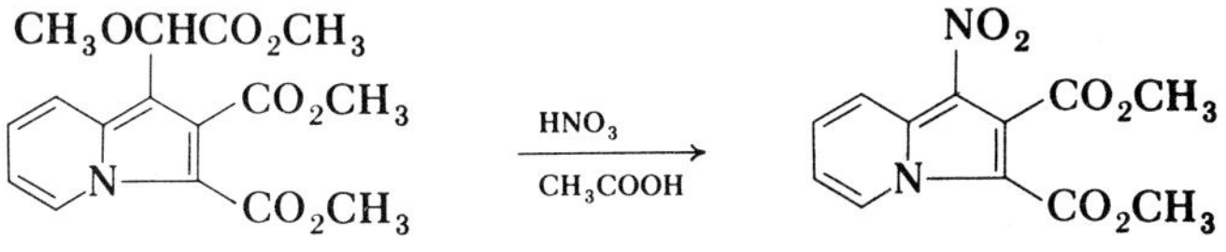

$CH_3OCHCO_2CH_3$ ... $\xrightarrow[CH_3COOH]{HNO_3}$ ... NO_2

(XXVIII) (LVI)

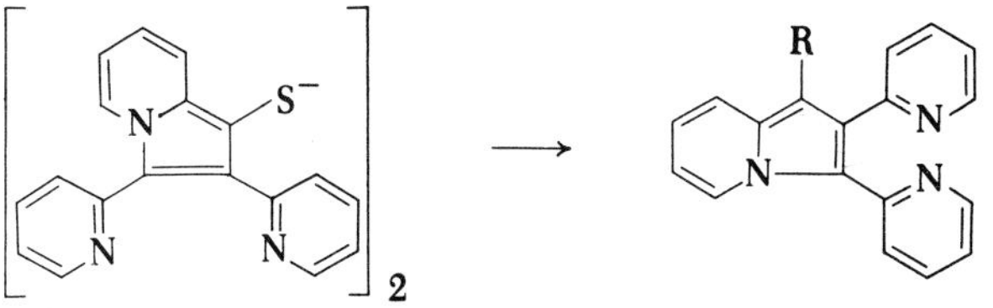

(XXXIX) → (XLa) (R = H)
(XLb) ($R = NO_2$)

6. *Amino- and Azopyrrocolines.* Diazonium coupling occurs without difficulty in the 3 position of pyrrocoline[9,10] and its 2-substituted homologs.[60] Only a few azo derivatives have thus been prepared, however. Blocking the 3 position evidently directs diazonium coupling into the 1 position, as (the sole example of this type) 3-acetyl-2-methyl-1-phenylazopyrrocoline (LVII) has thus been obtained.[74] Despite the ready availability of 1- and 3-nitrosopyrrocolines, their reaction with amines to form azo compounds has not been studied.

Catalytic reduction of LVII afforded the 1-amino compound LVIII, which also could be prepared by reducing 3-acetyl-2-methyl-1-nitrosopyrrocoline.[74] Although evidently unstable to air, this amine was condensed with benzaldehyde and with pyruvic acid or ester to yield products, which probably have structure LIX, although the acetyl group may be involved.

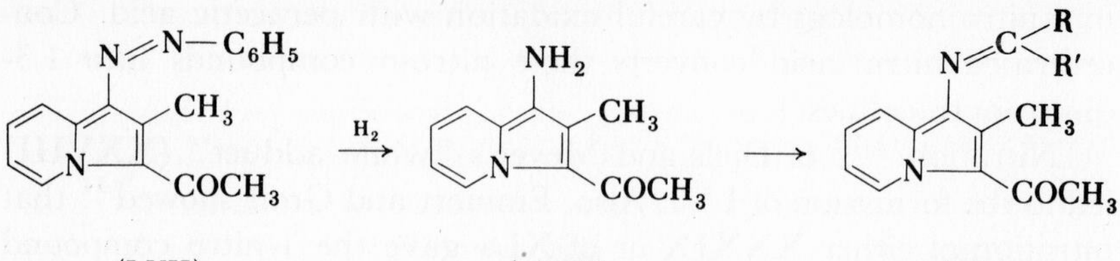

(LVII) $\xrightarrow{H_2}$ (LVIII) $\longrightarrow$ (LIX)

Recently, the Schmidt reaction upon 3-acyl-2-methylpyrrocolines was shown[60] to yield the 3-acylamino derivatives (LX). Treatment of LX with acetic anhydride gave LXII, which could also be obtained by the reductive acetylation of LXI. Acidic hydrolysis of LXII was not successful, while basic hydrolysis gave an unstable, uncharacterizable oil.

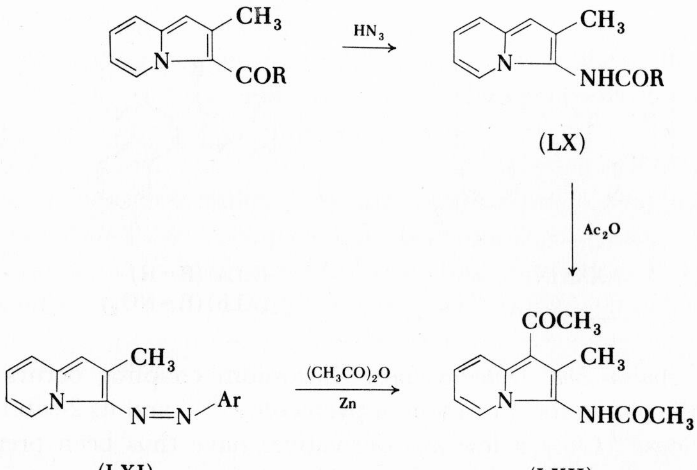

$\xrightarrow{HN_3}$ (LX)

Ac_2O

(LXI) $\xrightarrow[Zn]{(CH_3CO)_2O}$ (LXII)

Catalytic reduction and acetylation of 2,3-dicarbomethoxy-1-nitropyrrocoline yielded[31] an acetamido derivative thought to be LXIII, but which is probably LXIV.

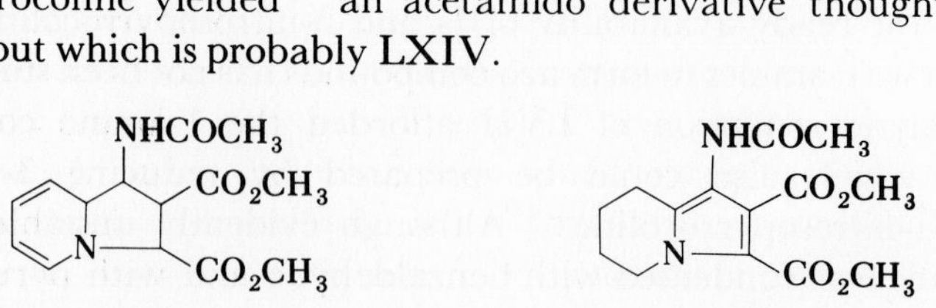

(LXIII) (LXIV)

Several 2-(nitrophenyl)pyrrocolines have been reduced[7] to the aminophenyl analogs.

7. *Oxidation.* While simple alkylpyrrocolines are readily attacked[21,23] by oxidants such as potassium permanganate, chromic acid or even atmospheric oxygen, resistance to oxidation increases through negative substitution, and trimethyl pyrrocoline-1,2,3-tricarboxylate is relatively unaffected by chromic or nitric acids.[12,27]

Oxidation of pyrrocolines with peracetic acid (solutions of hydrogen peroxide in acetic acid) often has been employed[4,8,12-15,31] to establish their structure. The end-product[27] is picolinic acid *N*-oxide or its homologs. The reported[79] oxidation with 3% hydrogen peroxide of 2-methylpyrrocoline to its *N*-oxide, has not been confirmed, and no other pyrrocoline *N*-oxides are known. If obtainable, these derivatives should be of considerable value in orientation studies.

8. *Reduction.* The syntheses and properties of the hydropyrrocolines will be discussed in Part IV, and only the hydrogenation of aromatic pyrrocolines will be considered here.

Treatment of pyrrocoline with sodium and alcohol gave an oily base, which Scholtz considered[21] to be 2-(1-butadienyl)pyrrole. The product gave a red color in the pine splint test, and yielded a colorless melt with oxalic acid. This behavior was later[4] shown to be typical of the 5,6,7,8-tetrahydropyrrocolines. The product evidently was not reduced beyond the dihydro stage by sodium and alcohol, as it might be expected to be if it were the 5,6- or 7,8-dihydro compound. This fact, together with the color reactions, suggest that the product is 5,8-dihydropyrrocoline, but more information is needed.

Pyrrocoline is reported to resist reduction by zinc and acid[21] or hydrogenation over a palladium-charcoal catalyst.[5] By careful hydrogenation of alkylpyrrocolines at low temperatures using a Raney nickel or Adam's catalyst, it appears[4] possible to prepare the 5,6,7,8-tetrahydro compounds, although at higher temperatures, octahydropyrrocolines are formed. Hydrogenation of 3-acetyl-2-methyl (or phenyl)pyrrocolines over Raney nickel or Adams catalyst at room temperature gave the 5,6,7,8-tetrahydro derivatives,[4,62] while at higher temperatures, or in the presence of a copper-chromite catalyst, reduction of the acetyl group and/or complete saturation of the nucleus occurred.[4] Thus it is evident that, while under neutral conditions, hydrogenation occurs preferentially in the pyridine ring regardless of the catalyst used, complete saturation of the nucleus occurs with great facility and, indeed, numerous octahydropyrrocolines[4,27–29,33,37,40,49,62] have been obtained in this manner. By contrast, hydrogenation[149] of pyrrocoline in the presence of strong mineral acid yields 1,2-dihydro-3*H*-pyrrocolinium salts.

An exception to these generalizations concerning preferential hydrogenation of the pyridine ring was reported[31] by Diels and Meyer. Hydrogenation of the "white adduct" (XXVIII) over Adams catalyst, followed by hydrolysis and dehydration yielded an anhydride different from that obtained when the ester was first hydrolyzed and then hydrogenated. The formation of these different anhydrides was explained on the basis of *cis-trans* isomerism resulting from hydrogenation of the pyrrole ring. As this work was done a decade before the hydrogenation studies of Borrows, Holland and Kenyon, there seems to be a good chance that reduction of XXVIII actually gives 5,6,7,8-tetrahydro-derivatives instead of the 1,2,3,8*a*-isomers. The two anhydrides obtained by Diels and Meyer could then have structures such as LXV and LXVI. Further work is needed to

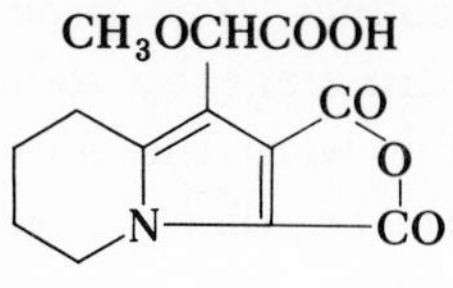

$CH_3OCHCOOH$ … CO, O, CO, N

(LXV)

CH_3O, CH, CO, O, CO, N, COOH

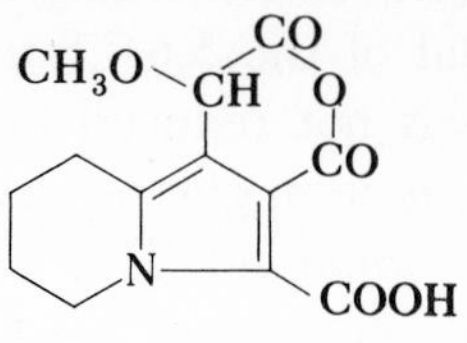

(LXVI)

settle this question, and ultraviolet and infrared spectra should be of assistance.

Further discussion of the hydropyrrocolines follows immediately after the table of pyrrocolines.

Pyrrocolines

Empirical formula	Substituents or structure	Properties and derivatives	Refs.
$C_8H_5I_2N$	1,3-Diiodo-	d. 275°.	24
$C_8H_5N_3O_4$	1,3-Dinitro-	Yel., m. 229°.	22
C_8H_7N	Unsubstituted.	b. 205°; m. 75° (74°); pK_b 11.37; $\lambda_{max}^{C_6H_{12}}$ 237.5, 275.5, 282.5, 294.5, 336*, 346.5, 361 and 381.5 mμ (log ε 4.51, 3.34, 3.45, 3.56, 3.23, 3.29, 3.24 and 2.92). Picrate, m. 101°. Benzylidene deriv., m. 210–2°. *p*-Methylbenzylidene deriv., m. 92°. Piperonylidene deriv., m. 145–50°. Cinnamylidene deriv., m. > 200°. Furfurylidene deriv., m. 148–9°. Chloral deriv., m. 92°. Acetone adduct, m. 244–6°. Acetophenone adduct (2:1), m. 98°. Isatin deriv., m. > 300°.	2,21,22,24,27, 28,29,37,43, 46,47,50,52, 53,57,142
$C_9H_7NO_2$	2-Carboxy-	m. 240–2°. Methyl ester, m. 97–9°.	12,27
	3-Carboxy-	m. 135° d. Acid chloride, m. 81°.	24

Pyrrocolines (*continued*)

Empirical formula	Substituents or structure	Properties and derivatives	Refs.
$C_9H_7N_3O_4$	2-Methyl-1,3-dinitro-	Yel., m. 218–9° d.	15
C_9H_8ClN	2-Methyl-5-chloro-	m. 30–40°.	142
$C_9H_8N_2O$	2-Methyl-3-nitroso-	Dk. grn., m. 106–7°.	14
$C_9H_8N_2O_2$	2-Methyl-1-nitro-	Yel., m. 154.5–5.5°.	15
	2-Methyl-3-nitro-	Yel., m. 103–4° (101–3°).	14,15
C_9H_9N	1-Methyl-	m. 44°; pK_b 10.40; λ_{max} 240, 280, 288, 300, and 360 mμ (ε 33,000, 2,100, 3,200, 4,400 and 2,000).	19,52
	2-Methyl-	$b_{8.8}$ 75–8°, b_{12} 100°; m. 59.5° (57–9°, 68°); pK_b 9.87. HI salt, m. 165–70° d. Perchlorate, m. 95.5–6° (92–3.5°). Picrate, m. 111–2° d. Chloroplatinate, m. > 360°.	2,3,8,15,25,28, 59,73,89,123, 142
	3-Methyl-	b. 230° (224°); pK_b 11.10.	26,28,29,33,52
	5-Methyl-	b_{34} 124°.	143
	7-Methyl-	b. 206–7°; m. 81°. Benzylidene deriv., m. 221–2°. Furfurilidene deriv., m. 160–1°.	23
C_9H_9NO	2-Methyl-N-oxide	Oil, Picrate, m. 165°.	79
$C_{10}H_8N_2O_3$	3 (or 1)-Acetyl-1 (or 3)-nitro-	Yel., m. 196°.	22

$C_{10}H_9NO$	3-Acetyl-	$b_{9.5}$ 148–9°, b_{18} 195°, b_{760} 288° d. Benzylidene deriv., yel., m. 127°.	22,25
	3-Formyl-2-methyl-	m. 56.5–7.5° (56°). Hemiperchlorate, m. 173–5° d. Azine, or., m. 254° d. 2,4-DNPH, blk., m. 267° d.	59,60
	5-Formylmethylene-	—	143
$C_{10}H_9NO_2$	3-Carboxy-2-methyl-	m. 115°. Anhydride, m. 203–4°. Acid chloride, yel., m. 73°. Amide, m. 185–7°. Anilide, m. 142–3°. Hydrazide, m. 171–2°.	60
$C_{10}H_{11}N$	1,2-Dimethyl-	m. 63° (57–8°, 61–2°); pK_b 8.57; λ_{max} 243, 284, 294, 305 and 360 mμ (ε 28,000, 1,800, 2,350, 2,700, and 1,900). HI salt, pale bl. grn., m. 177–9°. Perchlorate, m. 128–9°. Picrate, m. 130–2°. Chloroplatinate, m. indefinitely >214°.	3,19,52,59
	1,3-Dimethyl-	pK_b 10.80. Methiodide, m. 180°.	22,52

(*continued*)

Pyrrocolines (*continued*)

Empirical formula	Substituents or structure	Properties and derivatives	Refs.
	2,3-Dimethyl-	$b_{0.01}$ 74°; m. 39.5–40.5° (37°, 35–6°); pK_b 10.40. Perchlorate, m. 74–5.5°.	3,28,52,59,60
	2,5-Dimethyl-	Oil, b_{14} 116–7°, b. 238–40° (235–8°); m. 8–12°; pK_b 9.04. HI salt, m. 188°.	2,3,52,142
	2,6-Dimethyl-	pK_b 9.39.	52
	2,7-Dimethyl-	m. 78–9°; pK_b 8.74. HI salt, grn., m. 171–2°. Chloroplatinate, d. > 200°.	3,52
	2-Ethyl-	m. 41°. Perchlorate, pale bl., m. 121–3°. Picrate, m. 104.5–5.5°.	59
	6-Ethyl-	b_{18} 124–6°; λ_{max} 225–240, 280, 291 and 332 mμ (ε 5800, 5350, 5480 and 5172). Picrate, brn., m. 152–5° d.	49
$C_{11}H_9NO_2$	1,3-Diformyl-2-methyl-	Pale yel., m. 214–5° (210 °). Monoöxime, m. 196–7°. Monophenylhydrazone, m. 177–9°. Mono-2,4-DNPH, red-brn., d. > 315°.	59,60,61

$C_{11}H_9NO_3$	3-Carboxycarbonyl-2-methyl-	Grn.-yel., m. 151° d. Aniline salt, yel.-brn., m. 149–50° d. Ethyl ester, m. 105–6°.	60
$C_{11}H_9NO_4$	2-Carboxy-3-carboxymethyl-	m. 228–9°.	29
$C_{11}H_{10}N_2O_2$	3-Acetyl-2-methyl-1-nitroso-	Grn.-bl., m. 146–7.5° d.	14,74
$C_{11}H_{10}N_2O_3$	3-Acetyl-2-methyl-1-nitro-	Yel., m. 140.5–1°. 2,4-DNPH, scarlet, m. 276–7° d.	15
$C_{11}H_{11}NO$	3-Acetyl-1-methyl-	$b_{0.2}$ 140–50°; yel., m. 100–1° (98–9°); λ_{max} 227, 266, 370 and 383 mμ (log ε 16,200, 24,500, 15,700 and 14,300).	17,19
	3-Acetyl-2-methyl-	b_7 159–60°, b_{12} 174–5°, b_{16} 179–85°; m. 83°. Dinitrate, grn., m. 115–6°. Benzylidene deriv., m. 102–4°. 2,4-DNPH, deep red, m. 252° d.	8,25,60
	3-Acetyl-7-methyl-	b_{20} 196–7°. Phenylhydrazone, yel., m. 158°.	23
	1-Formyl-2,3-dimethyl-	m. 94–5°. Perchlorate, m. 194–6°. Semicarbazone, yel.-grn., m. 209°.	59

(continued)

Pyrrocolines (*continued*)

Empirical formula	Substituents or structure	Properties and derivatives	Refs.
$C_{11}H_{11}NO_2$	2-Carboxy-6-ethyl-	m. 183–3°; λ_{max} 225–260, 287, 297.5, 331 and 344 mμ (ε 5670, 5172, 5295, 5230 and 5230).	49
$C_{11}H_{12}N_2O$	3-Acetylamino-2-methyl-	m. 148°.	60
	3-Acetyl-1-amino-2-methyl-	m. 172°. HCl salt, m. 254° d. *N*-Acetyl deriv., m. 219°. *N*-Chloroacetyl deriv., m. 223° d. Phenylurea, m. >330°.	74,121,124
	3-Ethyl-2-methyl-1-nitroso-	Dk. grn., m. 110–1°.	14
$C_{11}H_{13}N$	3-Ethyl-2-methyl-	b_9 116–8°, b_{15} 124°; n_D^{18} = 1.5973, n_D^{20} = 1.5968. Picrate, m. 124° d. Chloroplatinate, m. 174° d.	4,25,60,62,73
	1,2,3-Trimethyl-	$b_{0.1}$ 85–7°, b_{13} 135–7°; m. 12–13°; pK_b 9.21. Perchlorate m. 126–8°. Picrate, m. 94–5° d. Chloroplatinate, m. 179° d. Methiodide, m. 197.5° (180–1°).	3,52,59
	1,3,7-Trimethyl-	Methiodide, m. 168°.	23

$C_{11}H_{13}NO$	3-(1-Hydroxyethyl)-2-methyl-	b_{12} 104–7°. Picrate, m. 141.5–2°. *O*-Acetate, b_6 110–1°. Phenylurethane, m. 142–2.5° (137°).	4,62
$C_{12}H_7BrN_2OS$	2-(5-Bromo-2-thienyl)-3-nitroso-	Grn., m. 198–200° d.	75
$C_{12}H_7ClN_2OS$	2-(5-Chloro-2-thienyl)-3-nitroso-	Grn., m. 190–1° d. HCl salt, red. Picrate, m. 195–7° d.	75
$C_{12}H_8BrNS$	2-(5-Bromo-2-thienyl)-	Subl. 199–200° d.	75
$C_{12}H_8ClNS$	2-(5-Chloro-2-thienyl)-	m. 199° d.	75
$C_{12}H_8N_2OS$	3-Nitroso-2-(2-thienyl)-	Deep grn., m. 176–7°. HCl salt, deep red.	75
$C_{12}H_9NS$	2-(2-Thienyl)-	m. 177°.	75
$C_{12}H_{10}N_2O_6$	2,3-Dicarbomethoxy-1-nitro-	Lt. yel., m. 165° (160–1°).	12,31
$C_{12}H_{11}NO_2$	1,3-Diacetyl-	m. 176° (174.5–6.0°). Mono-phenylhydrazone, m. 168°. Mono-semicarbazone, m. 233°. Mono-oxime, m. 244°. Mono-benzylidene deriv., m. 157°; its HCl adduct, m. 125°. Dibenzylidene deriv., m. 208°. Di-*p*-methylbenzylidene deriv., yel., m. 202°. Mono-*p*-methylbenzylidene deriv.,	2,21,22,24,25, 26,148

(*continued*)

Pyrrocolines (*continued*)

Empirical formula	Substituents or structure	Properties and derivatives	Refs.
		yel., m. 152°. Di-*i*-propylbenzylidene deriv., yel., m. 214°. Dianisylidene deriv., yel., m. 212°. Dipiperonylidene deriv., or., m. 141°. Monopiperonylidene deriv., or.-yel., m. 152°. Di-*o*-nitrobenzylidene deriv., yel.-brn., d. 200°, m. 220°. Di-*m*-nitrobenzylidene deriv., yel., m. 212°. Di-*p*-nitrobenzylidene deriv., or.-yel., m. 316°. Mono-*p*-nitrobenzylidene deriv., or., m. 242°. Di-*p*-dimethylaminobenzylidene deriv., or., m. 227°. Dicinnamylidene deriv., or., m. 217°. Difurfurylidene deriv., yel., m. 210°.	
$C_{12}H_{11}NO_4$	[structure: 1,2-dimethylpyrrocoline with 3-CH_2– bearing CO_2CH_3 / CO_2H / H]	m. 200–1° d.	29
$C_{12}H_{12}N_2$	1-Cyanomethyl-2,3-dimethyl-	m. 78–9°.	59

$C_{12}H_{13}NO$	1-Acetyl-2,3-dimethyl-	$b_{0.1}$ 130–40°; m. 81–2°. Oxime, yel., m. 216° d.	60
	3-Acetyl-1,2-dimethyl-	$b_{0.3}$ 140–5°; m. 99–100°; λ_{max} 230, 255, 275, 372, and 384 mμ (ε 20,000, 11,500, 24,000, 13,700 and 12,800).	19
	3-Methyl-1-propionyl-	m. 85–6°. Semicarbazone, yel., m. 201°.	24,26,29
$C_{12}H_{13}NO_2$	1-Ethoxyacetyl-	Pale yel., m. 54–5°.	148
	1-Acetyl-3-ethoxy-	m. 65.5–6.5° (64.5°). 2,4-DNPH, blk., m. 238–9°. Benzylidene deriv., or., m m. 125–6°.	105,148
$C_{12}H_{15}N$	1-Ethyl-2,3-dimethyl-	$b_{0.2}$ 91–2°. Chloroplatinate, m. 177–8°.	60
	1,3,5,7-Tetramethyl-	m. 74–5°. Methiodide, m. 245–8°. Chloroplatinate, m. 213°. Chloroaurate, m. 109°.	38,39,40
	1,3,5,8-Tetramethyl-	m. 135°. Chloroaurate, m. 157° d.	38,40
$C_{12}H_{15}NO$	1-Methoxymethyl-2,3-dimethyl-	$b_{0.05}$ 110°.	59
	3-Ethoxy-1-ethyl-	b_{13} 147.5–152°; λ_{max} 241, 285, 296 and 382 mμ (log ε 4.30, 3.50, 3.50 and 3.17).	148

(*continued*)

Pyrrocolines (*continued*)

Empirical formula	Substituents or structure	Properties and derivatives	Refs.
$C_{13}H_{11}NO_6$	N; COOH, COOH, CH_2—CO_2CH_3	d. ~235–6°.	29
$C_{13}H_{11}NO_7$	1-Carboxymethoxymethyl-2,3-dicarboxy-	m. 100° d.	31
$C_{13}H_{11}NS$	2-(5-Methyl-2-thienyl)-	m. 157°.	75
	7-Methyl-2-(2-thienyl)-	m. 174°.	6
$C_{13}H_{13}NO_2$	1,3-Diacetyl-2-methyl-	m. 123° (122–3°). Phenylhydrazone, m. 210° (208–10°) d. 2,4-DNPH, purple-brn., m. 246° d.	8,25,72
	1,3-Diacetyl-7-methyl-	m. 180°. Oxime, m. 256°. Phenylhydrazone, yel., m. 166°. Dibenzylidene deriv., yel., m. 216°. Difurfurylidene deriv., yel., m. 218°. Di-*p*-methoxybenzylidene deriv., yel., m. 204°.	21,23
$C_{13}H_{13}NO_4$	2-Carboxy-1-ethoxyacetyl-	Lt. yel., m. 175–6° d.	148
$C_{13}H_{14}N_2O_2$	1-Acetyl-3-acetamido-2-methyl-	m. 190°. 2,4-DNPH, purple-blk., m. 265°.	60
$C_{13}H_{15}N$	3-(2-But-2-enyl)-2-methyl-	$b_{3.8}$ 107–8°. Perchlorate, m. 129–30°.	123

$C_{13}H_{15}NO$	3-Acetyl-1-ethyl-2-methyl-	$b_{0.1}$ 140–8°; m. 82°; λ_{max} 231, 256, 275, 370 and 382 mμ (ε 21,900, 12,200, 24,000, 13,900 and 12,800).	19
$C_{13}H_{15}NO_2$	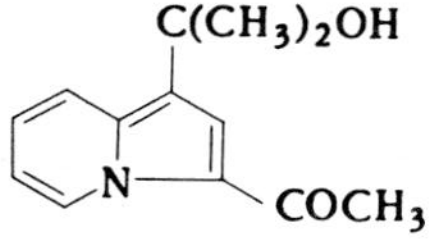 $C(CH_3)_2OH$; $COCH_3$; N (Probable structure)	Yel., m. 169°.	24
$C_{13}H_{16}N$	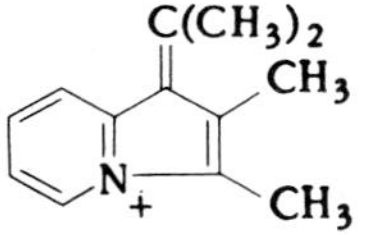 $C(CH_3)_2$; CH_3; CH_3; N^+	Perchlorate, yel., d. 230–3°.	59
$C_{13}H_{17}N$	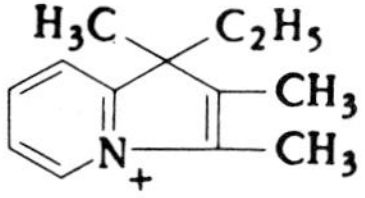 H_3C; C_2H_5; CH_3; CH_3; N^+	Iodide, m. 199–200°.	3
	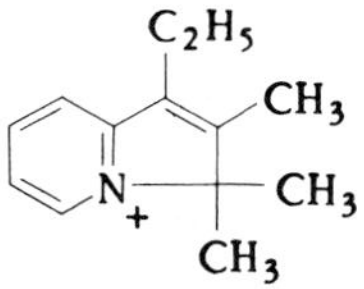 C_2H_5; CH_3; CH_3; CH_3; N^+	Iodide, m. 179°.	3

(continued)

Pyrrocolines (*continued*)

Empirical formula	Substituents or structure	Properties and derivatives	Refs.
	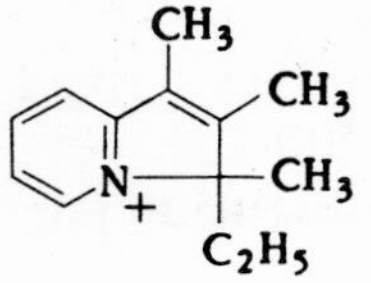	Iodide, m. 167–8°.	3
$C_{13}H_{18}N_2$	1-Dimethylaminomethyl-2,3-dimethyl-	$b_{0.02}$ 85–92°. Picrate, red, m. 137–9°.	59
$C_{14}H_8N_4O_6$	1,3-Dinitro-2-(4-nitrophenyl)-	Yel., m. 232–3° d.	15
$C_{14}H_9Cl_2N$	2-(3,4-Dichlorophenyl)-	m. 177°.	6
$C_{14}H_9I_2N$	1,3-Diiodo-2-phenyl-	HI salt, bronze, m. 203° d.	13
$C_{14}H_9BrN_2O$	2-(4-Bromophenyl)-3-nitroso-	Grn., m. 187–8° d.	75
$C_{14}H_9ClN_2O$	2-(4-Chlorophenyl)-3-nitroso-	Grn., m. 177° d. HCl salt, or.	75
$C_{14}H_9FN_2O$	2-(4-Fluorophenyl)-3-nitroso-	Grn., m. 118°.	76
$C_{14}H_9N_3O_4$	1,3-Dinitro-2-phenyl-	Yel., m. 246–8°.	15
	1-Nitro-2-(4-nitrophenyl)-	Yel., m. 235.5–6° d.	15
	3-Nitro-2-(4-nitrophenyl)-	Yel., m. 211°.	15
$C_{14}H_{10}BrN$	2-(4-Bromophenyl)-	m. 260°.	75
$C_{14}H_{10}ClN$	1-(4-Chlorophenyl)-	m. 73°; λ_{max} 239, 313 and 360 mμ (ε32,000, 15,000 and 6,000).	18
	2-(4-Chlorophenyl)-	m. 248°.	75
$C_{14}H_{10}FN$	2-(4-Fluorophenyl)-	m. 231°.	76
$C_{14}H_{10}IN$	2-(4-Iodophenyl)-	m. 278°.	6

$C_{14}H_{10}ClNOS$	3-Acetyl-1-(2-chloro-5-thienyl)-	Yel., m. 119°; λ_{max} 226, 265, 308 and 361 mμ (ε 20,000, 17,900, 14,300 and 14,700).	17,18
$C_{14}H_{10}N_2O$	3-Nitroso-2-phenyl-	Dk. grn., m. 97.5–8°. HCl salt, brn.-red, m. 115–6°. Picrate, m. 196–7° d.	14
$C_{14}H_{10}N_2O_2$	2-(3-Nitrophenyl)-	Yel., m. 183°.	7
	2-(4-Nitrophenyl)-	Yel., m. 250–1° d.	7,15
$C_{14}H_{11}N$	1-Phenyl-	m. 67–8°; λ_{max} 236, 283*, 305 and 362 mμ (ε 23,000, 8,600, 12,000 and 3,400).	18
	2-Phenyl-	m. 214–5°; $\lambda_{max}^{C_6H_{12}}$ 254.5, 325*, 350, 366 and 384.5 mμ (log ε 4.62, 3.27, 3.45, 3.43 and 3.15). HCl salt, m. 109°. Nitrate, m. 134° d. Picrate, m. 161°.	2,5,8,15,16,50, 142
	5-Phenyl-	m. 123–4°. Benzylidene deriv., m. 230–2°.	23
$C_{14}H_{11}NO$	2-(4-Hydroxyphenyl)-	m. 243°.	137
$C_{14}H_{11}NO_5$	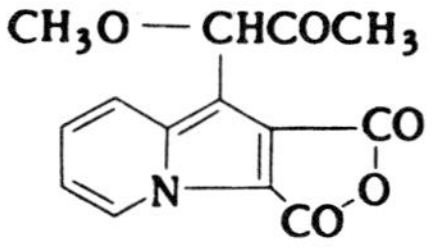 CH_3O — $CHCOCH_3$; N; CO; O; CO	Lt. yel., d. 270°. Grn.-yel. fluoresc. in U.V.	31

(*continued*)

Pyrrocolines (*continued*)

Empirical formula	Substituents or structure	Properties and derivatives	Refs.
$C_{14}H_{11}N_3$	3-Phenylazo-	Red, m. 109°.	24
$C_{14}H_{12}N_2$	2-(3-Aminophenyl)-	m. 173°.	7
	2-(4-Aminophenyl)-	m. 204°.	7
$C_{14}H_{13}NO_6$	1,2,3-Tricarbomethoxy-	m. 152–3° (151–2°, 146–7°).	27,29,31,35
$C_{14}H_{13}NO_7$	1-Carbomethoxymethoxymethyl-2,3-dicarboxy-	d. ~200°.	31
$C_{14}H_{14}N_2O_3$	N=C(COOH)(CH3); CH3; COCH3; N	m. 334°. Methyl ester, yel., m. 120°.	124
$C_{14}H_{15}NO_3$	2-Acetoxymethyl-3-acetyl-1-methyl-	m. 97°; λ_{max} 230, 261, 267 and 378 mμ (ε 19,000, 14,000, 14,000 and 13,000).	19
$C_{14}H_{17}NO$	3-Acetyl-1-*t*-butyl-	Yel., m. 108–9°; λ_{max} 226, 240*, 264, 370 and 380 mμ (ε 17,500, 9,000, 24,000, 16,000, 14,500).	17,19
$C_{14}H_{18}N_2O$	3-Acetyl-1-dimethylaminoethyl-	$b_{0.5}$ 165–75° (170–80°); λ_{max} 225, 262 and 364 mμ (ε 16,000, 19,000 and 11,000). Oxalate ($\cdot H_2O$), m. 100° or (anhydrous) m. 176–7°.	19,144

$C_{14}H_{20}N_2$	1-(1-Dimethylamino-2-propyl)-2-methyl-	Oil; λ_{max} 243, 280, 290, 301 and 350 mμ (ε 29,600, 2,000, 2,700, 3,000 and 2,300). Oxalate, m. 138–40°. Methiodide, m. 177°.	19
$C_{15}H_{11}Cl_2N$	2-(3,4-Dichlorophenyl)-7-methyl-	m. 183°.	6
$C_{15}H_{11}NO$	3-Benzoyl-	Yel., m. 96°.	24
$C_{15}H_{11}Cl_2N_3$	3-(2,4-Dichlorophenylazo)-2-methyl-	Purp.-red, m. 144.8–6.2°.	42
$C_{15}H_{12}ClN$	1-(4-Chlorophenyl)-2-methyl-	m. 77°; λ_{max} 242, 285*, 315 and 360 mμ (ε 25,000, 6,800, 11,000 and 4,500).	18
	1-(4-Chlorophenyl)-3-methyl-	Grn.-yel., m. 91–2°; λ_{max} 243, 277, 320 and 385 mμ (ε 20,000, 4,900, 13,000 and 4,800).	
	2-(4-Chlorophenyl)-5-methyl-	m. 111°.	6
	2-(4-Chlorophenyl)-7-methyl-	m. 287°.	6
$C_{15}H_{12}FN$	2-(4-Fluoro-2-methylphenyl)-	m. 86°.	130
	2-(4-Fluoro-3-methylphenyl)-	m. 174°.	6
	2-(4-Fluorophenyl)-5-methyl-	m. 107°.	6
	2-(4-Fluorophenyl)-7-methyl-	m. 248°.	6
$C_{15}H_{12}BrNO$	2-(3-Bromo-4-methoxyphenyl)-	m. 225°.	6
$C_{15}H_{12}FNO$	2-(3-Fluoro-4-methoxyphenyl)-	m. 197°.	135
	2-(3-Fluoro-6-methoxyphenyl)-	m. 56°.	138
$C_{15}H_{12}ClNS$	2-(3-Chloro-4-methylthiophenyl)-	m. 194°.	133

(continued)

Pyrrocolines (*continued*)

Empirical formula	Substituents or structure	Properties and derivatives	Refs.
$C_{15}H_{12}N_2O$	3-Acetyl-1-(2-pyridyl)-	Yel., m. 112°; λ_{max} 248*, 263, 309 and 260 mμ (ε 14,900, 22,100, 14,900 and 16,800).	17,18
$C_{15}N_{12}N_2O_2$	5-Methyl-2-(3-nitrophenyl)-	m. 125°.	7
	5-Methyl-2-(4-nitrophenyl)-	m. 130°.	7
	7-Methyl-2-(3-nitrophenyl)-	m. 174°.	7
	7-Methyl-2-(4-nitrophenyl)-	m. 219°.	7
$C_{15}H_{13}N$	2-(4-Tolyl)-	m. 222°.	75
	2-Methyl-1-phenyl-	$b_{0.5}$ 140–5°; m. 20–3°; λ_{max} 242, 284, 310 and 347 mμ (ε 24,000, 7,400, 7,800 and 2,900).	2,18,142
	3-Methyl-1-phenyl-	$b_{0.1}$ 180–5°; m. 67–8°; λ_{max} 239, 280*, 312, 355* and 373 mμ (ε 32,000, 6,000, 12,000, 4,100 and 4,500).	17,18
	5-Methyl-2-phenyl-	m. 83–3.5°.	143
	8-Methyl-1-phenyl-	$b_{0.5}$ 155–60°; λ_{max} 235, 303 and 350 mμ (ε 28,000, 8,300 and 3,800).	18
$C_{15}H_{13}NO$	1-(4-Methoxyphenyl)-	m. 72–3°; λ_{max} 240, 277, 305 and 367 mμ (ε 25,600, 10,500, 12,400 and 4,250).	18
	2-(4-Methoxyphenyl)-	m. 205°.	6

$C_{15}H_{13}NO_4$	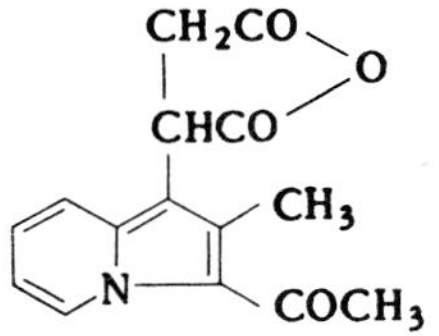 CH_2CO—O—CHCO (1-position); CH_3 (2-position); $COCH_3$ (3-position) [structure]	m. 191–2°.	58
$C_{15}H_{13}NS$	2-(4-Methylthiophenyl)-	m. 255°.	6
$C_{15}H_{13}N_3$	3-(4-Tolylazo)-	Red-brn., m. 98°.	24
	7-Methyl-3-phenylazo-	Red, m. 113–4°.	23
$C_{15}H_{14}N_2$	2-(3-Aminophenyl)-7-methyl-	m. 176°.	7
$C_{15}H_{15}NO_6$	3-Carbomethoxymethyl-1,2-dicarbomethoxy-	m. 75°.	29
	1,2,3-Tricarbomethoxy-5-methyl-	m. 116°.	34
	1,2,3-Tricarbomethoxy-6 (or 8)-methyl-	m. 117–9°; λ_{max} 275 mμ.	35
$C_{15}H_{19}NO$	3-Acetyl-2-ethyl-1-propyl-	$b_{0.5}$ 160–70°; m. 51–2°; λ_{max} 232, 258, 276, 373 and 386 mμ (ε 23,000, 12,800, 23,000, 14,000 and 12,700).	19
$C_{15}H_{20}N_2O$	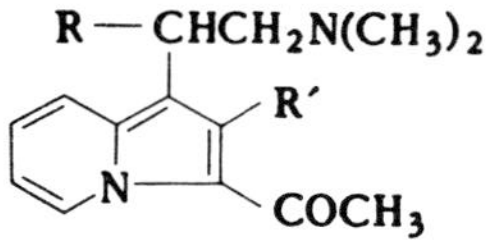 R—$CHCH_2N(CH_3)_2$ (1-position); R′ (2-position); $COCH_3$ (3-position) [structure] (where R = H or CH_3 and R′ = CH_3 or H, respectively).	$b_{0.1}$ 152–8°; λ_{max} 230, 266 and 368 mμ (ε 18,000, 22,000 and 13,600). Oxalate, m. 152–7°.	19,144
$C_{15}H_{21}N$	2-Methyl-3-(3-methyl-3-pentyl)-	$b_{3.8}$ 130°. Perchlorate, m. 114°.	123
$C_{16}H_{11}N_3O_5$	3-Acetyl-1-nitro-2-(4-nitrophenyl)-	Yel., m. 173–5°.	15

(*continued*)

Pyrrocolines (*continued*)

Empirical formula	Substituents or structure	Properties and derivatives	Refs.
$C_{16}H_{12}ClNO$	3-Acetyl-1-(4-chlorophenyl)-	Yel., $b_{0.1}$ 215–35°; m. 175–6° (173–5°); λ_{max} 220, 265, 285 and 369 mμ (ε 18,000, 26,000, 18,000 and 15,000).	17,18,20
$C_{16}H_{12}INO$	3-Acetyl-1-iodo-2-phenyl-	Yel., m. 114–6°.	13
$C_{16}H_{12}N_2$	2-(4-Cyanophenyl)-3-methyl-	m. 181–3°.	66,67,69
$C_{16}H_{12}N_2O_2$	1-Acetyl-3-nitroso-2-phenyl-	HCl salt, red, m. 99°.	14,77
	3-Acetyl-1-nitroso-2-phenyl-	Olive-grn., m. 154–4.5°. Picrate, or., m. 179° d.	14
$C_{16}H_{12}N_2O_3$	3-Acetyl-2-(4-nitrophenyl)-	Yel., m. 190.5–1°.	15
	3-Acetyl-1-nitro-2-phenyl-	Yel., m. 169°. 2,4-DNPH, red, m. 253° d.	15
$C_{16}H_{13}NO$	2-(4-Acetylphenyl)-	m. 240–1° d. 2,4-DNPH, m. ~290° d.	8
	5-Benzoylmethylene-	m. 111–2°.	143
	3-Acetyl-1-phenyl-	$b_{0.2}$ 155–60°; m. 82–3°; λ_{max} 235, 248*, 267, 285 and 370 mμ (ε 14,000, 14,800, 30,000, 17,500, 15,000).	17,18
	3-Acetyl-2-phenyl-	$b_{0.05}$ 162–74°; m. 64.5°; λ_{max}^{EtOH} 233, 264 and 365 mμ (ε 29,000, 24,000 and 15,000). 2,4-DNPH, red, m. 220–1°.	15,81

	3-Benzoyl-2-methyl-	Yel., m. 63°. 2,4-DNPH, blk., m. 288–90°.	60
$C_{16}H_{13}NO_2$	2-(4-Carboxyphenyl)-2-methyl-	—	67,69
$C_{16}H_{13}N_3O_2$	3-(4-Carboxyphenylazo)-2-methyl-	Crimson, m. 249°.	60
$C_{16}H_{14}FN$	2-(4-Fluoro-2-methylphenyl)-5-methyl-	Oil. Picrate, m. 155–6°.	130
	2-(4-Fluoro-2-methylphenyl)-7-methyl-	m. 74°.	130
	2-(4-Fluoro-3-methylphenyl)-7-methyl-	m. 174°.	6
$C_{16}H_{14}ClNO$	2-(3-Chloro-4-ethoxyphenyl)-	m. 218°.	6
$C_{16}H_{14}FNO$	2-(3-Fluoro-4-methoxyphenyl)-7-methyl-	m. 209°.	135
	2-(3-Fluoro-6-methoxyphenyl)-7-methyl-	m. 74°.	138
$C_{16}H_{14}N_2O$	3-Benzamido-2-methyl-	m. 196°.	60
$C_{16}H_{15}N$	2-(2,4-Dimethylphenyl)-	m. 106°.	6
	2-(2,5-Dimethylphenyl)-	m. 69°.	6
	2-(3,4-Dimethylphenyl)-	m. 148°.	6
	3-Benzyl-2-methyl-	m. 93–4°. Chloroplatinate, m. 178–9°.	3,60
	3-Ethyl-2-phenyl-	m. 94°; λ_{max}^{EtOH} 255 mμ (ε 38,000). Picrate, m. 157–8° d.	4,81
	6-Ethyl-2-phenyl-	m. 142–3°.	71
$C_{16}H_{15}NO$	2-(4-Ethoxyphenyl)-	m. 218°.	6
	2-(2-Methoxy-5-methylphenyl)-	m. 86°.	6
	2-(4-Methoxy-3-methylphenyl)-	m. 182°.	6
	2-(4-Methoxyphenyl)-7-methyl-	m. 239°.	6
$C_{16}H_{15}NO_2$	2-(2,4-Dimethoxyphenyl)-	m. 139°.	6
	2-(2,5-Dimethoxyphenyl)-	m. 94°.	6
	2-(3,4-Dimethoxyphenyl)-	m. 179°.	6

(continued)

Pyrrocolines (*continued*)

Empirical formula	Substituents or structure	Properties and derivatives	Refs.
$C_{16}H_{15}NO_3$	5,6,7,8-Tetracarbomethoxy-	m. 138–9°.	36
$C_{16}H_{15}NS$	2-(4-Methylthiophenyl)-7-methyl-	m. 283°.	6
$C_{16}H_{16}N_3$	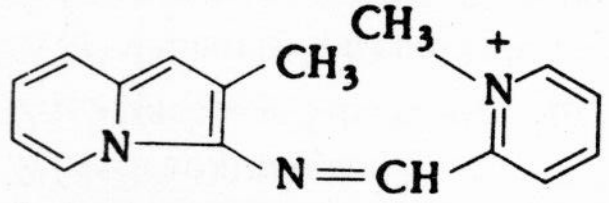 CH_3, CH_3, N^+, N, $N{=}CH$	Iodide, blk., m. 262–3° d. λ_{max} 544 mμ (ε 37,700).	51
$C_{16}H_{17}NO_7$	1-Carbomethoxymethoxymethyl-2,3-dicarbomethoxy-	m. 142–3° (138–9.5°).	12,31
$C_{16}H_{22}N_2O$	3-Acetyl-1-(1-dimethylamino-2-propyl)-2-methyl-	$b_{0.5}$ 160–4°; m. 72°; λ_{max} 230, 276 and 370 mμ (ε 21,000, 22,000 and 13,000). Oxalate, m. 178°. Methiodide, m. 201°.	19,144
	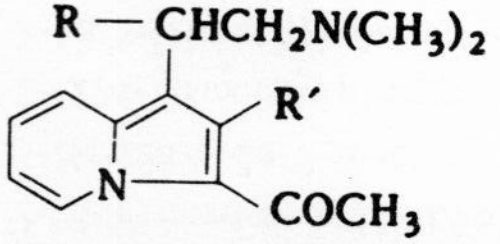 $R - CHCH_2N(CH_3)_2$, R′, N, $COCH_3$ (R = H or C_2H_5 and R′ = C_2H_5 or H, respectively).	$b_{0.2}$ 160–70°; λ_{max} 228, 265 and 368 mμ (ε 19,000, 20,000 and 13,500). Oxalate, m. 152–7°.	19
$C_{17}H_{14}ClNO$	3-Acetyl-2-methyl-1-(4-chlorophenyl)-	m. 155–6°; λ_{max} 225, 245, 273, 363 and 377 mμ (ε 21,200, 15,200, 25,500, 14,500 and 12,200).	17,18
	3-Acetyl-8-methyl-1-(4-chlorophenyl)-	m. 112–3°; λ_{max} 223, 264, and 370 mμ (ε 22,000, 28,000 and 15,200).	17,18

$C_{17}H_{15}NO$	3-Acetyl-1-(2-tolyl)-	m. 65°; λ_{max} 220*, 266, 367 and 385* mμ (ε 12,000, 20,500, 9,600 and 7,500).	17,18
	3-Acetyl-1-(4-tolyl)-	m. 133°; λ_{max} 236*, 269 and 373 mμ (ε 14,500, 30,500 and 14,000).	18
	3-Acetyl-2-methyl-1-phenyl-	Pale yel., m. 127–8°; λ_{max} 225, 258*, 274, 355 and 373 mμ (ε 13,000, 16,000, 23,000, 8,900 and 12,000).	17,18
	3-Acetyl-8-methyl-1-phenyl-	m. 100–1°; λ_{max} 224, 250*, 270 and 365 mμ (ε 14,500, 13,900, 24,200 and 14,500).	17,18
$C_{17}H_{15}NO_2$	3-Acetyl-1-(4-methoxyphenyl)-	Or., m. 122°; λ_{max} 239, 272 and 366 mμ (ε 18,500, 34,500 and 13,700).	17,18
$C_{17}H_{15}Cl_2N_3$	3-(2,4-Dichlorophenylazo)-2,5,7-trimethyl-	Red-brn., d. 180°.	41
$C_{17}H_{15}N_3O$	3-Acetyl-2-methyl-1-phenylazo-	Red, m. 77°.	74
$C_{17}H_{17}N$	2-(2,5-Dimethylphenyl)-7-methyl-	m. 134°.	6
$C_{17}H_{17}NO$	2-(4-Ethoxy-3-methylphenyl)-	m. 200°.	6
	2-(2-Methoxy-3,5-dimethylphenyl)-	m. 136°.	6
	2-(4-Methoxy-2,5-dimethylphenyl)-	m. 124°.	6

(continued)

Pyrrocolines (*continued*)

Empirical formula	Substituents or structure	Properties and derivatives	Refs.
$C_{17}H_{17}NO_8$	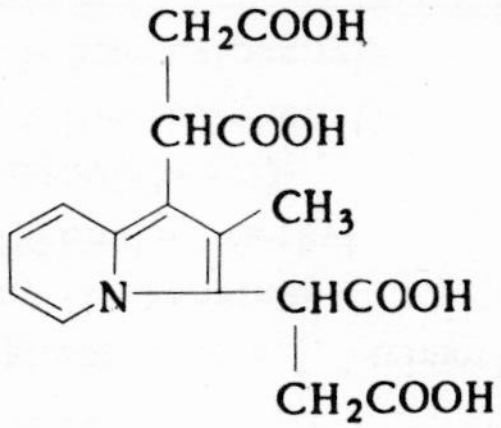 [structure: pyrrocoline with 1-CH(COOH)CH₂COOH, 2-CH_3, 3-CH(COOH)CH₂COOH]	m. 144° d. Tetramethyl ester, m. 126.5–7°.	58
$C_{18}H_{12}FN$	2-(4-Fluoro-1-naphthyl)-	m. 151°.	6
$C_{18}H_{12}ClNS$	2-[5-(4′-Chlorophenyl)-2-thienyl]-	m. 270°.	127
$C_{18}H_{12}N_4O_2$	1-Nitro-2,3-di-(2-pyridyl)-	Grn.-yel., m. 224–5°.	44
$C_{18}H_{13}N$	2-(1-Naphthyl)-	m. 110°.	6
	2-(2-Naphthyl)-	m. 230°.	6
$C_{18}H_{13}N_3$	3-(1-Naphthylazo)-	Brn., m. ~120° d.	24
	2,3-Di-(2-pyridyl)-	Yel., m. 102.5–3° (101–1.5°).	44,45
$C_{18}H_{15}NO_2$	1,3-Diacetyl-2-phenyl-	m. 172.5–3°. 2,4-DNPH, red, m. 254°.	8
	1,3-Diacetyl-5-phenyl-	m. 232–3°. Phenylhydrazone, yel., m. 182°. Dibenzylidene deriv. m. 243°.	23
$C_{18}H_{17}N$	2-(6-Tetralyl)-	m. 155°.	6
$C_{18}H_{17}NO_2$	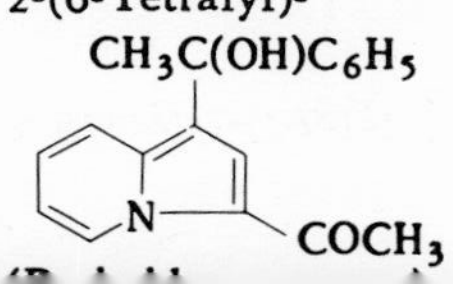 [structure: pyrrocoline with 1-$CH_3C(OH)C_6H_5$, 3-$COCH_3$]	m. 178°.	24

$C_{18}H_{18}N_2O_2$	$NHCH(OH)C_6H_5$; CH_3; $COCH_3$; N	Yel., m. 129–30°.	124
$C_{18}H_{18}N_3O$	N=CH; N^+; CH_3; CH_3; $COCH_3$; N	Iodide, brn.-red, m. 243–5° d.; $\lambda_{max}^{H_2O}$ 478 mμ (ε 18,100).	51
$C_{18}H_{19}N_2$	CH_3; $N(CH_3)_2$; N^+; CH	Iodide, dk. bl.	3
$C_{19}H_{15}N$	7-Methyl-2-(2-naphthyl)-	m. 237°.	6
$C_{19}H_{15}NO$	2-(4-Methoxy-1-naphthyl)-	m. 173°.	6
	2-(6-Methoxy-2-naphthyl)-	m. 210°.	6
$C_{19}H_{15}NS$	2-(6-Methylthio-2-naphthyl)-	m. 276°.	131
	2-[5-(4′-Tolyl)-2-thienyl]-	m. 241°.	127
$C_{19}H_{16}N_2O$	CH_3 H_3C; N; CO; N	Yel., m. 114–5°.	60
$C_{19}H_{18}N_2$	CH_3 H_3C; N; CH_2; N	m. 159–61°.	60
$C_{19}H_{21}NO$	2-(4-Methoxy-2-methyl-5-*i*-propylphenyl)-	m. 98°.	6

(continued)

Pyrrocolines (*continued*)

Empirical formula	Substituents or structure	Properties and derivatives	Refs.
$C_{20}H_{11}NO_4$	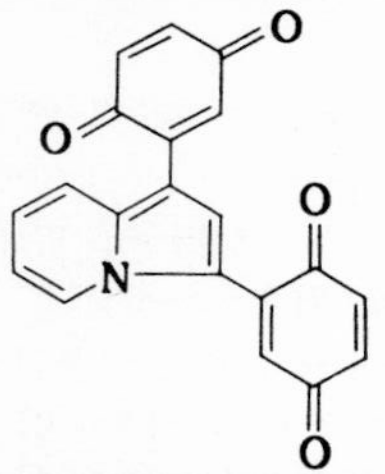	Bl., m. >350°.	24
$C_{20}H_{13}NO$	2-(2-Dibenzofuranyl)-	m. 194–5°.	141
$C_{20}H_{13}NOS$	2-(2-Phenoxathiinyl)-	m. 199–200°.	132
$C_{20}H_{14}ClN$	1-(4-Chlorophenyl)-2-phenyl-	m. 118°; λ_{max} 248, 273, 307 and 357 mμ (ε 38,000, 25,000, 11,600 and 5,100).	18
$C_{20}H_{15}N$	2-(4-Biphenylyl)-	m. 303–4° d. Nitroso deriv., grn.	77
	1,2-Diphenyl-	m. 112°; λ_{max} 250, 264, 305 and 360 mμ (ε 32,000, 24,500, 9,200 and 5,600).	18
	1,3-Diphenyl-	Deep yel., m. 115–6°; λ_{max} 238, 274, 309, 345* and 386* (ε 28,000, 20,000, 19,500, 10,000 and 4,000).	17,18
	2,3-Diphenyl-	m. 94–5°.	66,67,69,71
$C_{20}H_{15}NO$	2-(4-Phenoxyphenyl)-	m. 196°.	6
$C_{20}H_{15}NS$	2-(4-Phenylthiophenyl)-	m. 184°.	6

$C_{20}H_{17}NS$	2-(6-Methylthio-2-naphthyl)-7-methyl-	m. 293°.	131
$C_{20}H_{17}N_3SO_2$	2-(3-Sulfanilamidophenyl)-	m. 186°.	7
	2-(4-Sulfanilamidophenyl)-	m. 310°.	7
$C_{20}H_{18}N_2$	2-[3-(2′,5′-Dimethyl-1-pyrryl)phenyl]-	m. 197°. Picrate, m. 156°.	128
$C_{20}H_{18}N_3$	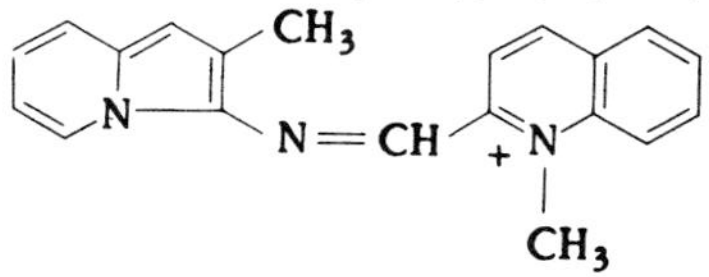	Iodide, dk. grn., m. 252–3° d.; $\lambda_{max}^{H_2O}$ 596 mμ (ε 40,500).	51
$C_{20}H_{18}N_3OS$	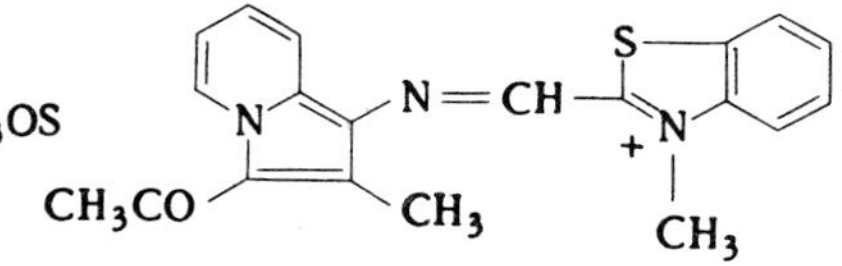	Iodide, m. 246.5–7.5°; λ_{max}^{EtOH} 538 mμ (ε 35,200).	51
$C_{20}H_{19}N_2O$	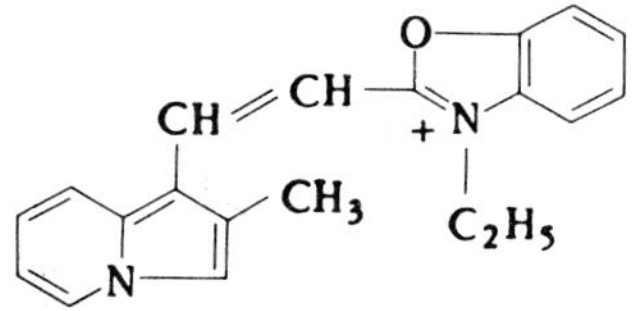 (Or the 3-isomer)	Grn., m. 245–6° d. Or. soln. in CH_3OH.	64,65
$C_{20}H_{20}N_2O$	2-(4-Cyclohexylphenyl)-3-nitroso-	Dk. grn., m. 188°.	78
$C_{20}H_{21}N$	2-(4-Cyclohexylphenyl)-	m. 208°.	78
$C_{21}H_{15}NO$	3-Benzoyl-2-phenyl-	Yel., m. 137–8°. Picrate, brn.-red, m. 121–2°.	8
	2-(2-Dibenzofuranyl)-6-methyl-	m. 187° d.	141
	2-(2-Dibenzofuranyl)-7-methyl-	m. 203° d.	141

(continued)

Pyrrocolines (*continued*)

Empirical formula	Substituents or structure	Properties and derivatives	Refs.
$C_{21}H_{17}N$	2-(4′-Methyl-4-biphenylyl)-	m. 317°.	77
	2-(4-Biphenylyl)-7-methyl-	m. 305–6°.	77
	3-Benzyl-2-phenyl-	m. 100–1°. Picrate, m. 112.5–3.5°.	4
$C_{21}H_{17}NO$	2-(4′-Methoxy-4-biphenylyl)-	m. 310°.	134
$C_{21}H_{17}NS$	7-Methyl-2-(4-phenylthiophenyl)-	m. 191°.	6
$C_{21}H_{18}N_3$	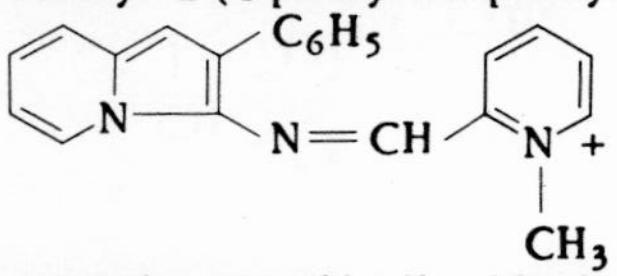	Iodide, grn.-brn., m. 212–3° d.; $\lambda_{max}^{H_2O}$ 548 mμ (ε 27,600).	51
$C_{21}H_{19}N_3SO_2$	7-Methyl-2-(3-sulfanilamidophenyl)-	m. 188°.	7
$C_{21}H_{20}N_2$	2-[3-(2′,5′-Dimethyl-1-pyrryl)-phenyl]-7-methyl-	m. 171°.	128
$C_{21}H_{21}N$	2-(6-*t*-Butyl-2-naphthyl)-	m. 178°.	136
$C_{21}H_{21}N_2O$	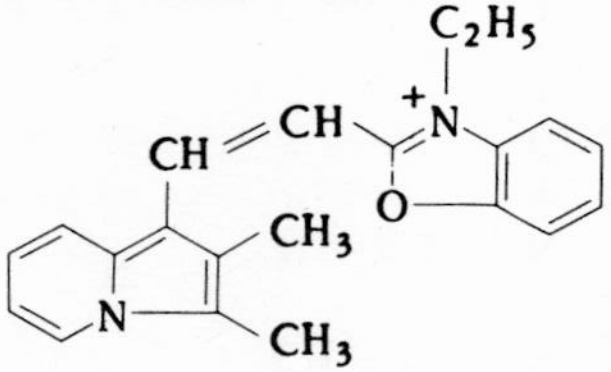	Grn.-red, m. 266–7° d. Or. soln. in CH_3OH.	65
$C_{21}H_{22}N_2$	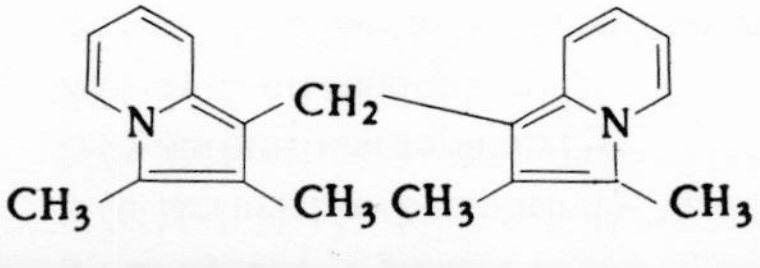	Yel., m. 109–10°.	59

$C_{21}H_{22}N_2O$	2-(4-Cyclohexylphenyl)-6-methyl-3-nitroso-	Dk. grn., m. 190°.	78
	2-(4-Cyclohexylphenyl)-7-methyl-3-nitroso-	Bl.-grn., m. 196°.	78
$C_{21}H_{22}N_3$	CH₃ H₃C CH₃ N N=CH N + CH₃	Iodide, purple, m. 186–9° d.; λ_{max}^{EtOH} 560 mμ (ε 11,500).	51
$C_{21}H_{23}N$	2-(4-Cyclohexyl-phenyl)-6-methyl-	m. 207°.	78
	2-(4-Cyclohexylphenyl)-7-methyl-	m. 226°.	78
$C_{21}H_{23}N_3O_2S$	C₂H₅ O N S CH=CH—CH N C₂H₅ CH₃ O N CH₃	m. 260–2°.	69
$C_{22}H_{15}N$	2-(3-Phenanthryl)-	m. 201°.	6
$C_{22}H_{16}ClNO$	3-Acetyl-1-(4-chlorophenyl)-2-phenyl-	m. 181–2°; λ_{max} 225*, 267 and 371 mμ (ε 20,000, 24,000 and 12,500).	17,18
$C_{22}H_{17}NO$	3-Acetyl-1,2-diphenyl-	m. 175–6°; λ_{max} 247*, 270 and 373 mμ (ε 20,000, 25,000 and 13,000).	17,18
$C_{22}H_{17}NOS$	6-Ethyl-2-(2-phenoxathiinyl)-	m. 155°. Nitroso deriv., grn., m. 245° d.	132
$C_{22}H_{18}N_2$	2-(9-Ethyl-3-carbazolyl)-	m. 198°.	129
$C_{22}H_{19}NO_6$	1,2,3-Tricarbomethoxy-5-styryl-	Yel., m. 147°; grn. fluoresc.	32

(continued)

Pyrrocolines (*continued*)

Empirical formula	Substituents or structure	Properties and derivatives	Refs.
$C_{22}H_{19}N_3SO_3$	2-[3-(4′-Acetamidobenzenesulfonamido)-phenyl]-	Grn., m. 230°.	7
	2-[4-(4′-Acetamidobenzenesulfonamido)-phenyl]-	m. 283°.	7
$C_{22}H_{20}N_3O$		Brn.-red, m. 222–3° d.; $\lambda_{max}^{H_2O}$ 512 mμ (ε 30,700).	51
$C_{22}H_{21}N_2O$	(Or the 3-isomer).	Grn., m. 247–50° d. Bl. soln. in CH_3OH.	64,65
$C_{22}H_{23}N$	2-(6-*t*-Butyl-2-naphthyl)-7-methyl-	m. 175°.	136
$C_{22}H_{23}N_3O_2S$	(Or the 3-isomer).	m. 225°.	69
$C_{22}H_{24}N_2O$	2-(4-Cyclohexylphenyl)-6-ethyl-4-nitroso-	Dk. grn., m. 148°.	78
$C_{22}H_{25}N$	2-(4-Cyclohexylphenyl)-6-ethyl-	m. 159°.	78

$C_{23}H_{16}N_2O_2$	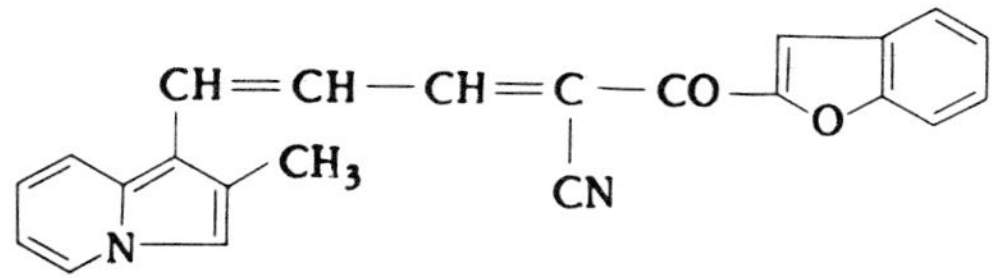 $CH{=}CH{-}CH{=}C(CN){-}CO{-}$, CH_3, N, O (Or the 3-isomer)	m. 189–91° d.	69
$C_{23}H_{20}N_3O$	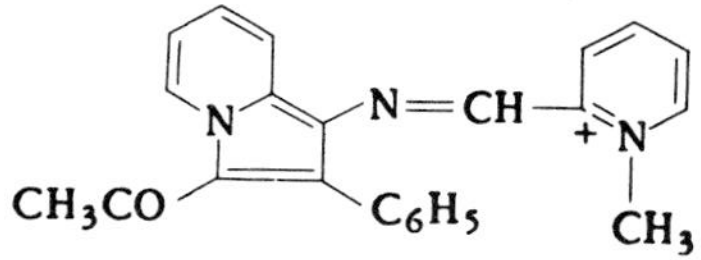 N, $N{=}CH{-}$, ^{+}N, CH_3CO, C_6H_5, CH_3	Iodide, brn., m. 211–2° d.; $\lambda_{max}^{H_2O}$ 476 mμ (ε 20,400).	51
$C_{23}H_{21}NO_6$	3-Carbomethoxymethyl-1,2-dicarbomethoxy-5-styryl-	Yel., m. 157°.	32
$C_{23}H_{21}N_3SO_3$	2-[3-(4′-Acetamidobenzenesulfonamido)-phenyl]-7-methyl-	m. 263°.	7
$C_{23}H_{23}N_2$	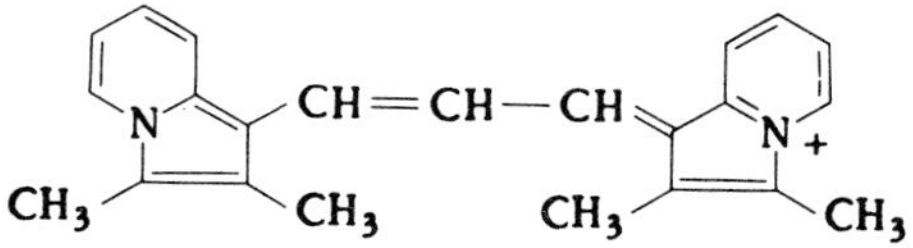 N, $CH{=}CH{-}CH{=}$, N^{+}, CH_3, CH_3, CH_3, CH_3	Bromide, bl.-grn., m. 273–4°.	66
$C_{23}H_{23}N_2S$	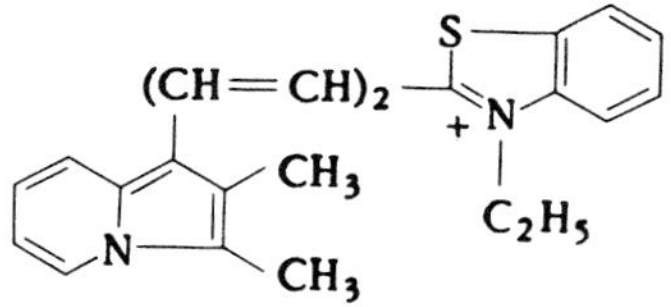 $(CH{=}CH)_2$, S, ^{+}N, C_2H_5, CH_3, CH_3, N	*p*-Toluenesulfonate, grn., m. 272–3° d. Soln. in CH_3OH, bl.	65

(continued)

Pyrrocolines (*continued*)

Empirical formula	Substituents or structure	Properties and derivatives	Refs.
$C_{23}H_{24}N_3O$	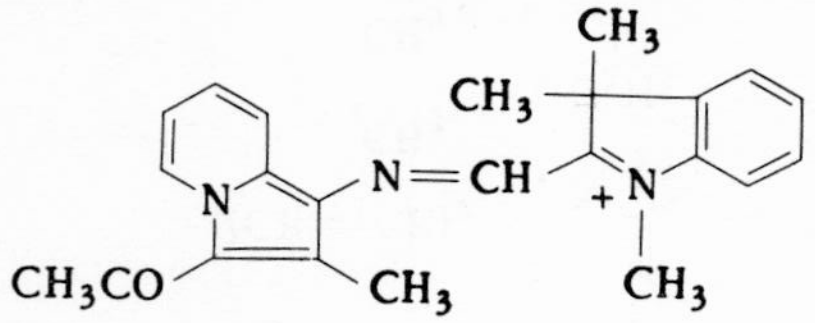 CH_3CO, N, CH_3, N=CH, CH_3, CH_3, +N, CH_3	Iodide, gold-brn., m. 203–5° d.; λ_{max}^{EtOH} 566 mμ (ε 34,200).	51
$C_{23}H_{25}N_3O_2S$	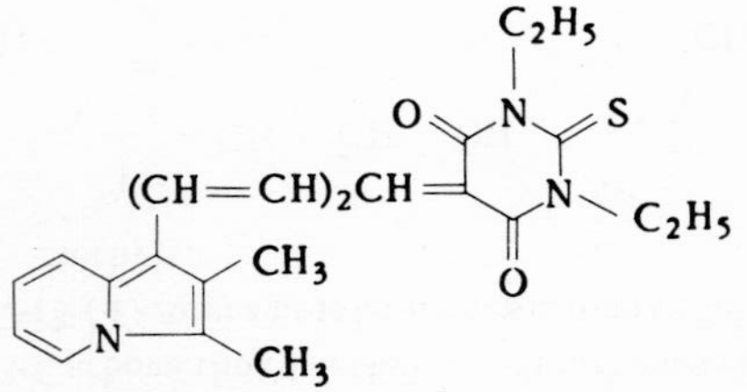 N, CH_3, CH_3, $(CH{=}CH)_2CH{=}$, O, N, C_2H_5, S, N, C_2H_5, O	Dk. grn., m. 229–32°.	69
$C_{24}H_{15}N$	2-(3-Pyrenyl)-	m. 159°.	6
$C_{24}H_{18}N_2O_2$	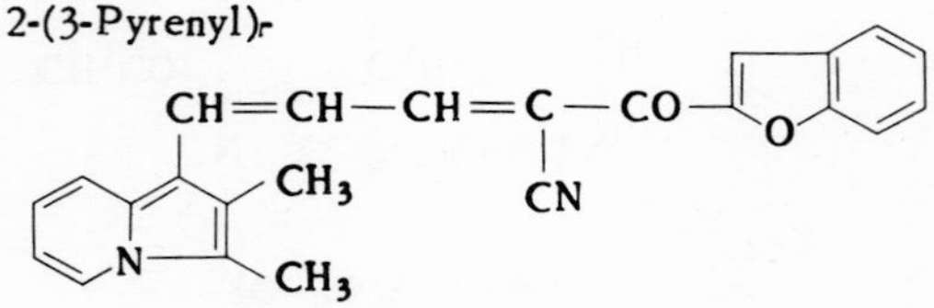 N, CH_3, CH_3, CH=CH—CH=C—CO—, CN, O	Brt. grn., m. 202–3° d.	69
$C_{24}H_{27}N_2$	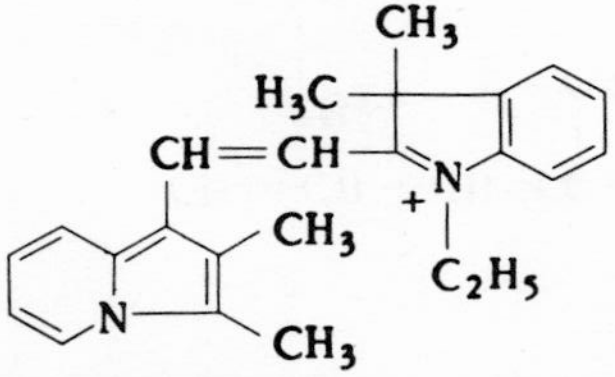 N, CH_3, CH_3, CH=CH—, H_3C, CH_3, +N, C_2H_5		63

$C_{25}H_{20}N_3$	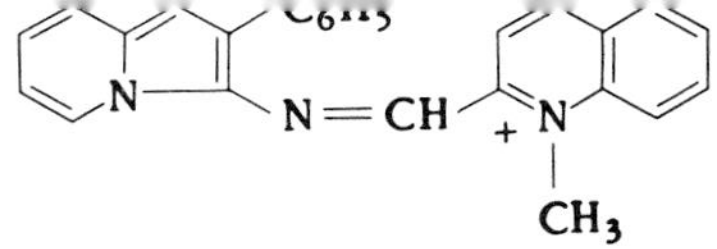	Iodide, red-brn., m. 226–8° d.; $\lambda_{max}^{H_2O}$ 600 mμ (ε 34,000).	51
$C_{25}H_{21}N_2O$	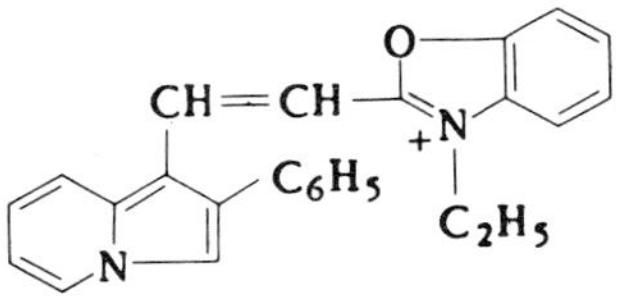 (Or the 3-isomer).	Iodide, red, m. 204–5°.	64,65
$C_{26}H_{21}N_2$	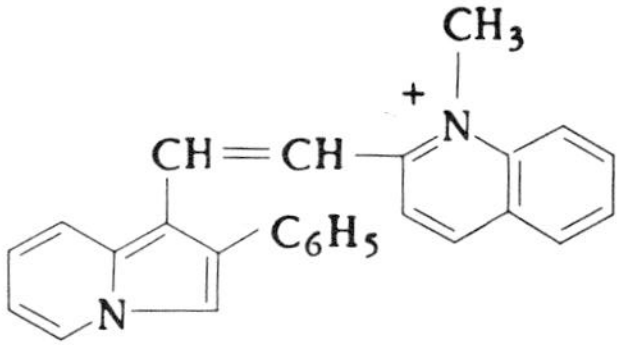 (Or the 3-isomer).	Chloride, m. 251–2°. Iodide, bl.-grn., m. 267–9° d.	65
$C_{26}H_{22}N_2O_2$	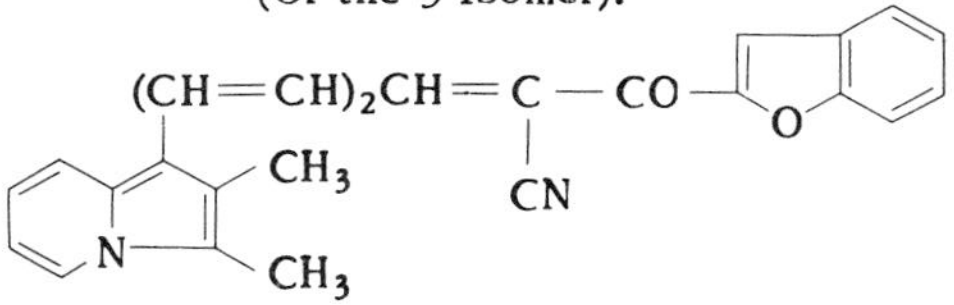	Grn., m. 235–7° d.	69
$C_{26}H_{24}N_3$	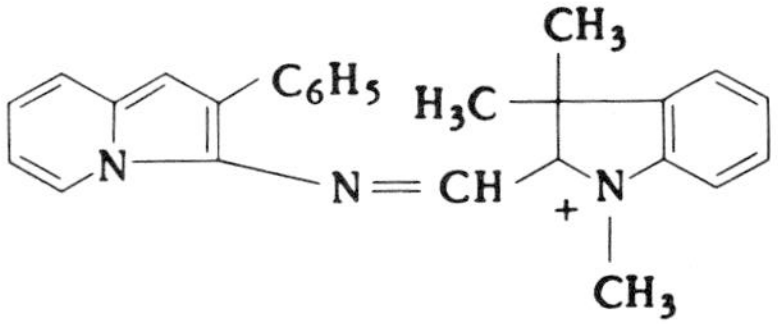	Iodide, purple, m. 249–50°; λ_{max}^{EtOH}, 554 mμ (ε 15,000).	51

(continued)

Pyrrocolines (*continued*)

Empirical formula	Substituents or structure	Properties and derivatives	Refs.
$C_{27}H_{22}N_3O$		Iodide, brn., m. 214–5° d.; $\lambda_{max}^{H_2O}$ 516 mμ (ε 25,100).	51
$C_{27}H_{23}N_2S$	(Or the 3-isomer).	Chloride, grn., m. 85–6°; bl.-red in CH_3OH soln. Iodide, grn., m. 257–9°.	64,65
$C_{27}H_{25}N_3O_2S$	(Or the 3-isomer).	Bl., m. > 330°.	69
$C_{28}H_{18}Cl_2N_2$	1,1′-Di-(4-chlorophenyl)-3,3′-bispyrrocoline	Yel., m. 288–9°; $\lambda_{max}^{dioxane}$ 238, 315 and 375 mμ (ε 35,000, 36,500 and 10,000).	18

$C_{28}H_{18}N_2O_2$	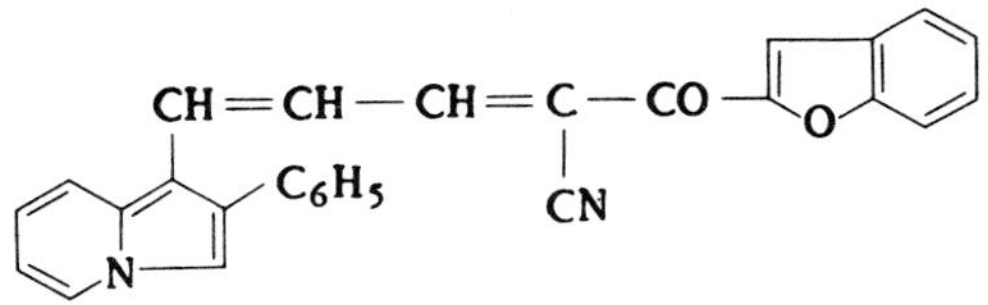 CH=CH—CH=C—CO— ; C_6H_5 ; CN ; N ; O (Or the 3-isomer).	m. 227–30° d.	69
$C_{28}H_{20}N_2$	1,1′-Diphenyl-3,3′-bispyrrocoline	Yel., m. 198–200°; $\lambda_{max}^{dioxane}$ 236, 308 and 358* mμ (ε 37,500, 33,000 and 10,500).	18
$C_{28}H_{21}N$	2-(7-Benzyl-2-fluorenyl)-	m. ~282°; bl. color in H_2SO_4.	140
$C_{28}H_{26}N_3O$	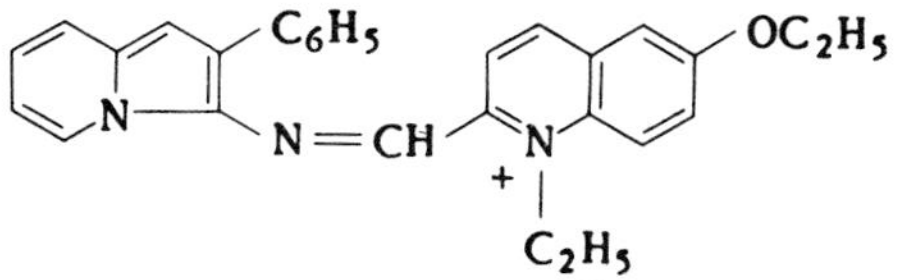 C_6H_5 ; N ; N=CH ; N^+ ; C_2H_5 ; OC_2H_5	Iodide, dk. grn., m. 187° d.; λ_{max}^{EtOH} 606 mμ (ε 60,800).	51
	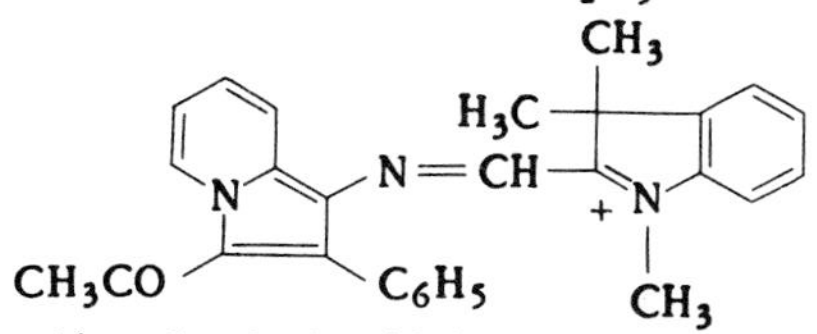 CH_3 ; H_3C ; N ; N=CH ; N^+ ; CH_3CO ; C_6H_5 ; CH_3	Iodide, gold-brn., m. 226–8°; λ_{max}^{EtOH} 560 mμ (ε 26,800).	51
$C_{28}H_{31}N_5O$	3-(6-Hydrocinchonidylazo)-2-methyl-	Or.-red, m. 260–1° d.	125

(continued)

Pyrrocolines (*continued*)

Empirical formula	Substituents or structure	Properties and derivatives	Refs.
$C_{29}H_{20}Cl_2N_2$	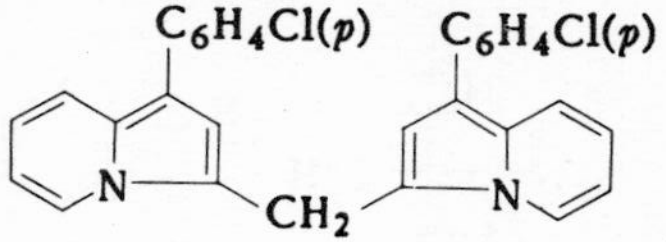 $C_6H_4Cl(p)$ $C_6H_4Cl(p)$ N CH_2 N	Pale yel., m. 255°.	18
$C_{29}H_{22}N_3$	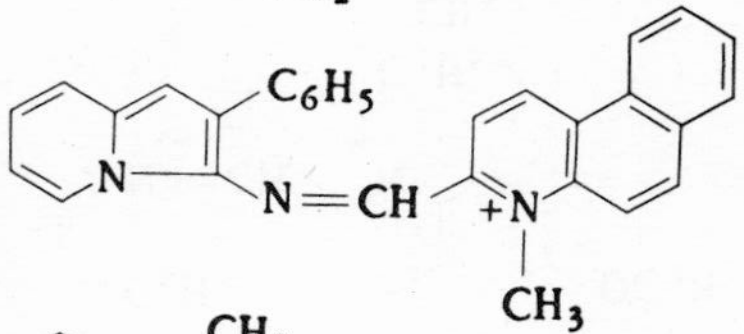 C_6H_5 N N=CH +N CH_3	Iodide, dk. grn., m. 205° d.; λ_{max}^{EtOH} 608 mμ (ε 57,200).	51
$C_{29}H_{23}N_2$	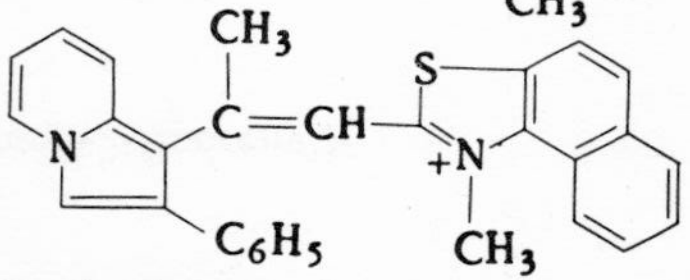 CH_3 N C=CH S +N C_6H_5 CH_3 (Or the 3-isomer).	*p*-Toluenesulfonate, oil.	68,146
$C_{29}H_{23}N_3O_4S$	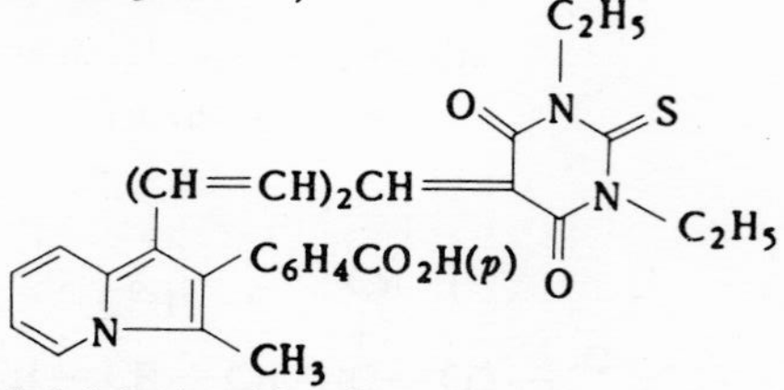 C_2H_5 O N S $(CH{=}CH)_2CH{=}$ N C_2H_5 $C_6H_4CO_2H(p)$ O N CH_3	Dk. gr., m. 242–5° d.	67,69
$C_{29}H_{36}NO_2$	2-(Methyl-6-dehydroabietyl)-	m. 167°. HBr salt, m. 320°.	139

$C_{30}H_{20}N_2O_2$	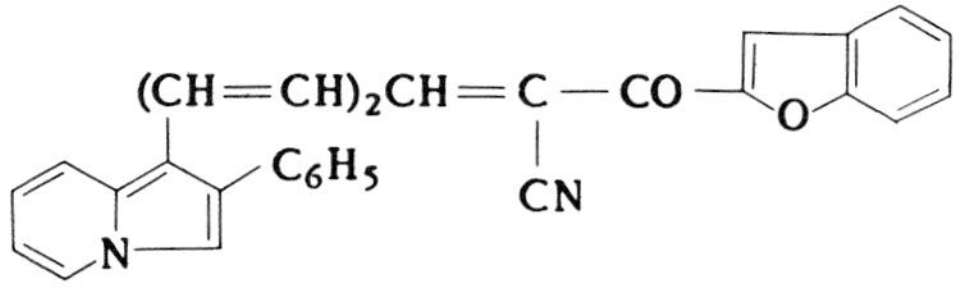 $(CH{=}CH)_2CH{=}C{-}CO{-}$ O; C_6H_5; CN; N (Or the 3-isomer).	Blue, m. > 325°.	69
$C_{30}H_{23}N_4O$	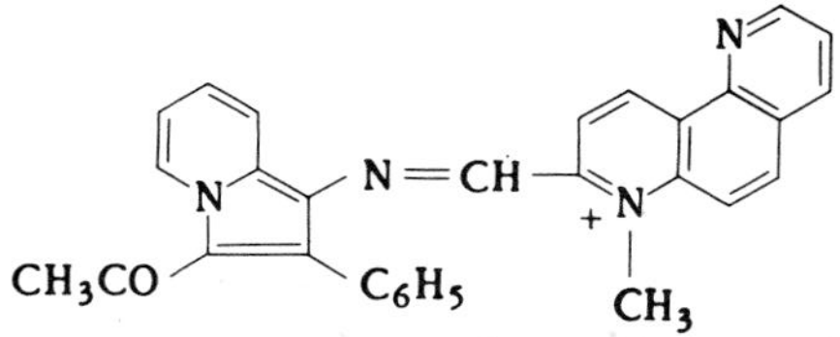 N; N=CH; +N; CH_3CO; C_6H_5; CH_3; N	Iodide, red-brn.; λ_{max}^{EtOH} 610 mμ (ε 61,000).	51
$C_{30}H_{24}N_2O_2$	1,1′-Di-(4-methoxyphenyl)-3,3′-bispyrrocoline	Yel., m. 225°; $\lambda_{max}^{dioxane}$ 245, 266, 304 and 370* mμ (ε 37,000, 31,000, 34,000 and 9,000).	18
$C_{30}H_{28}N_3O_2$	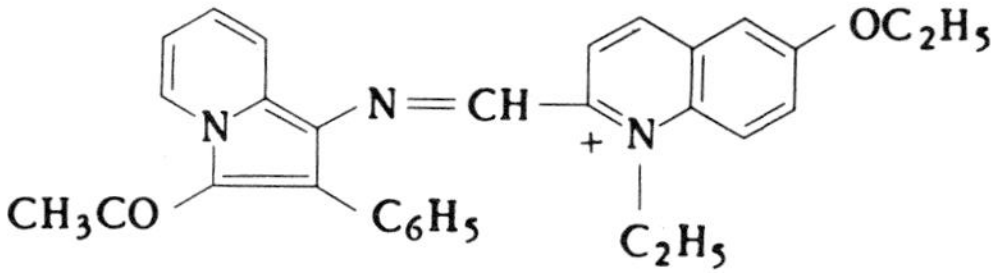 N; N=CH; +N; OC_2H_5; CH_3CO; C_6H_5; C_2H_5	Iodide, gold-brn., m. 211° d.; λ_{max}^{EtOH} 532 mμ (ε 38,400).	51
$C_{31}H_{24}N_3O$	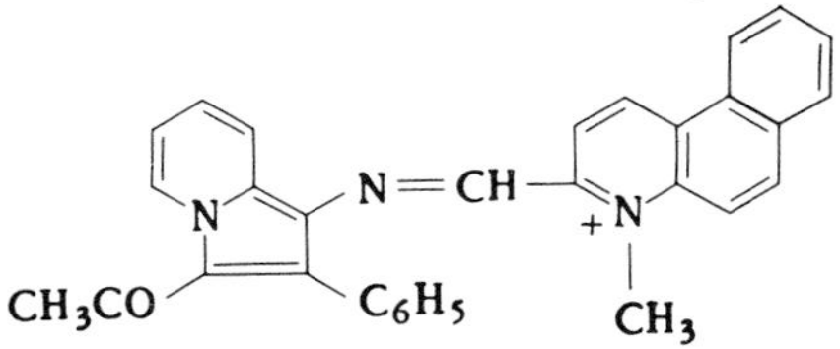 N; N=CH; +N; CH_3CO; C_6H_5; CH_3	Iodide, red-brn., m. 231° d.; λ_{max}^{EtOH} 532 mμ (ε 38,800).	51

(continued)

Pyrrocolines (*continued*)

Empirical formula	Substituents or structure	Properties and derivatives	Refs.
$C_{31}H_{27}N_2$	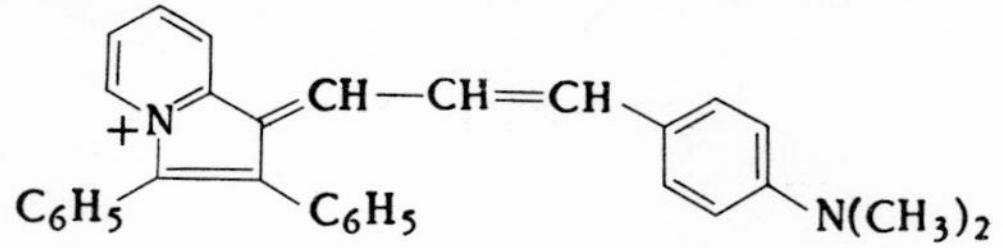 +N, CH—CH=CH, N(CH$_3$)$_2$, C_6H_5, C_6H_5	Perchlorate, grn., m. 253–4° d.	67,69
$C_{35}H_{27}N_2O_4$	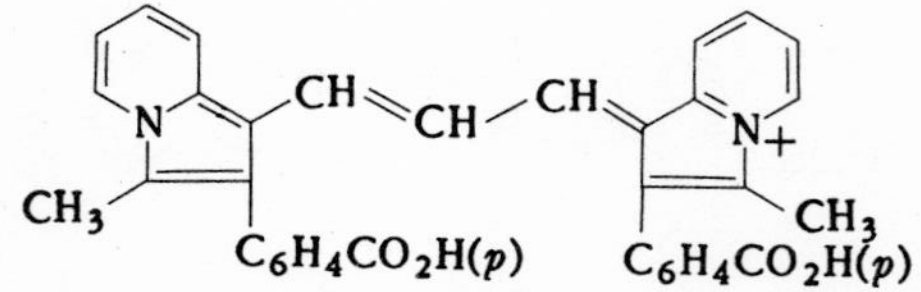 N, CH=CH—CH=, N+, CH_3, $C_6H_4CO_2H(p)$, $C_6H_4CO_2H(p)$, CH_3	Perchlorate, grn., m. 282–4° d.	66
$C_{36}H_{24}N_6S_2$	2,2′,3,3′-Tetra-(2-pyridyl)-1,1′-dithiobispyrrocoline	Yel., m. 201–3° (200–3.5°).	44,45
$C_{36}H_{30}N_4OS$	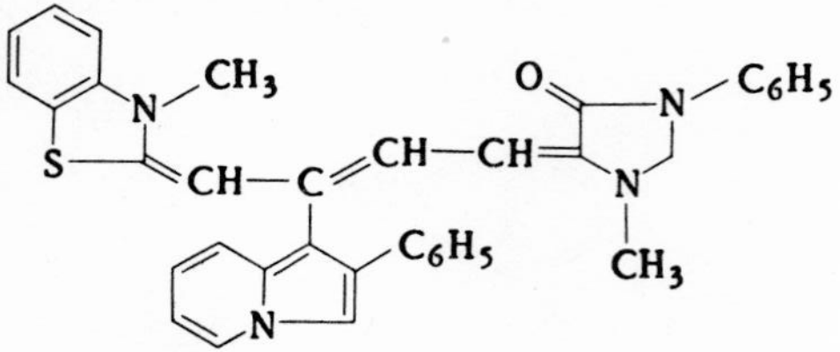 S, N—CH_3, =CH—C=CH—CH=, O, N—C_6H_5, N—CH_3, C_6H_5, N (Or the 3-isomer).	m. 156–9°.	68
$C_{40}H_{51}N_3O_3$	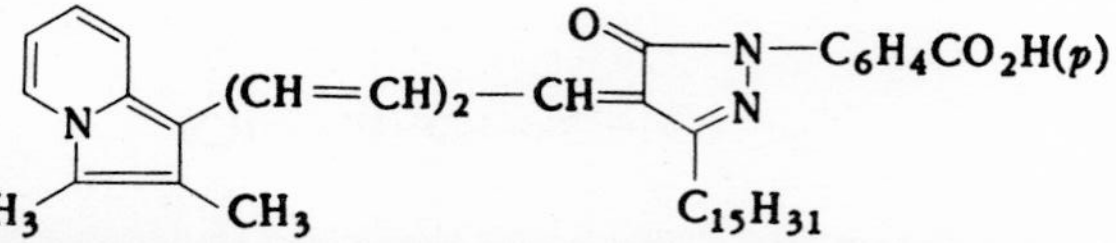 N, (CH=CH)$_2$—CH=, O, N—$C_6H_4CO_2H(p)$, N, $C_{15}H_{31}$, CH_3, CH_3	Dk. bl., m. 192–4°.	69

$C_{41}H_{30}N_2$		Pale yel., m. 250° d.	18
$C_{41}H_{30}N_3S_2$	(Or the 3-isomer)	*p*-Toluenesulfonate, m. 294–5° d.	68, 146
$C_{43}H_{31}N_2$		Bromide, grn., m. 212–4° d.	66

IV. Hydropyrrocolines

Historically, hydropyrrocolines antedate aromatic pyrrocoline derivatives by many years. The first compound having a hydropyrrocoline nucleus was prepared in 1885 by Hofmann,[80] who, however, was ignorant of the exact nature of his product. By heating *N*-bromoconiine with sulfuric acid, he obtained a product (thought to be α-coniceine), which Lellmann[81] later showed to be δ-coniceine, or octahydropyrrocoline. Further discussion of this product is deferred until later, and the hydropyrrocolines are discussed in the order of increasing degrees of hydrogenation.

1. *Di-, Tetra- and Hexahydropyrrocolines.* As mentioned in the previous Part (III-8), reduction of pyrrocoline with sodium and alcohol yielded[21] a product which may be 5,8-dihydropyrrocoline. A number of authentic 5,6,7,8-tetrahydropyrrocolines have been obtained by catalytic hydrogenation. These are discussed in Part III-8, and are listed in the table of hydropyrrocolines.

In 1890, Angeli described[82] the preparation of LXVIII from pyrroylpyruvic ester (LXVII). Condensation of LXVIII with aniline yielded the (presumably 6-) anil.

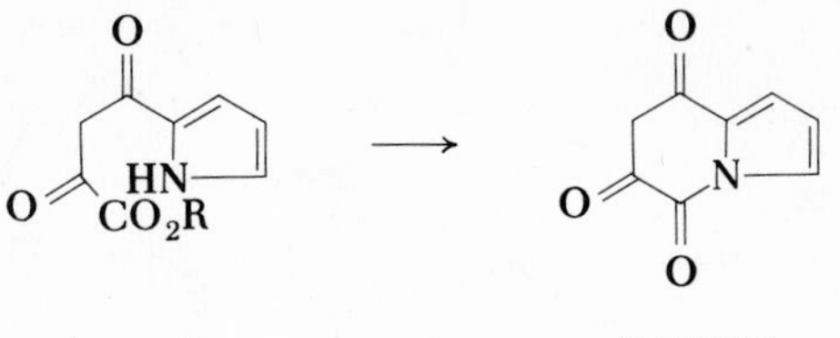

(LXVII) → (LXVIII)

The 5,6,7,8-tetrahydro-8-oxo compound (LXX) was obtained[83] by cyclization of 4-(2-pyrryl)butyronitrile (LXIX) via the ketimine intermediate.

(LXIX) → (LXX)

Cyclization of LXXI (X = Br or Cl) by treatment with caustic and then acid has been reported[84,85] to yield LXXII, which can be hydrogenated[85] over Adam's catalyst to octahydropyrrocoline.

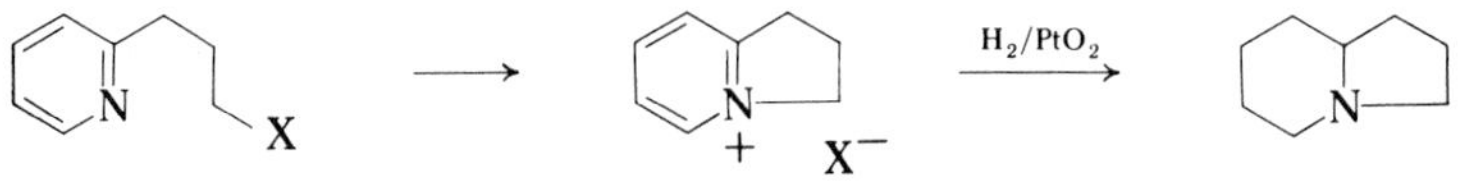

(LXXI) (LXXII)

Clemo and Metcalfe prepared hexahydroalkylpyrrocolines by dehydrating the tertiary carbinols produced by the action of Grignard reagents upon octahydropyrrocolin-1- and 2-ones. Hexahydro compounds could also be obtained by similar dehydration of the alcohols resulting from the reduction of various octahydropyrrocolinones. The exact location of the double bond in these products is uncertain.

The addition[87] of piperidine to divinylketones (LXXIII, R = R′ = C_2H_5 and R = CH_3, R′ = C_3H_7) gave intermediates, which were cyclized by the action of hydrogen chloride to hexahydropyrrocolines of structure LXXIV.

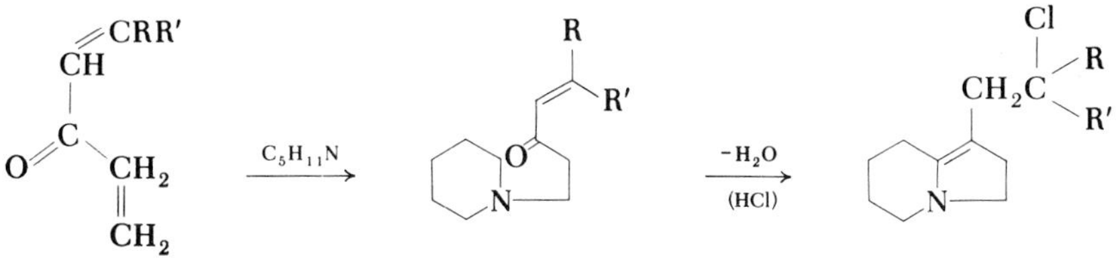

(LXXIII) (LXXIV)

The introduction of unsaturation by the action of mercuric acetate upon various 1-azabicyclic systems was studied in some detail by Leonard and his colleagues. Oxidation in this manner of octahydropyrrocoline (either *dl*- or *l*-) gave[88] hexahydropyrrocoline, probably a mixture of LXXV and LXXVI, which with acids formed salts of structure LXXVII. Treatment of LXXVII with potassium cyanide yielded[89] LXXVIII, which was reconverted into LXXVII

($X = I_3$) by the action of iodine. Grignard reagents react (see also Section A-721) with either LXXVII or LXXVIII to yield[89] LXXIX.

Hg(OAc)$_2$ / HOAc → (LXXV) and/or (LXXVI) —HX→

(LXXVII) ⇌ (KCN / I_2) (LXXVIII) —CH_3MgX→ (LXXIX); (LXXVII) —CH_3MgX→ (LXXIX)

2. *Octahydropyrrocolines; Syntheses.* Reference was made at the beginning of this Part to the work by Hofmann,[80] Lellmann[81,90] and by Löffler *et al.*[91,92] upon the synthesis of the alkaloid δ-conicëine and the demonstration of its identity with octahydropyrrocoline. A number of octahydropyrrocolines were also obtained during studies upon the alkaloid pelletierine.[93-97]

(a) *Via the Dieckmann reaction.* Cyclization of various piperidylacetic and propionic esters by the Dieckmann technique has been utilized to prepare derivatives of 1-, 2-, 7- and 8-oxoöctahydropyrrocolines. Thus products of type LXXXIV,[98] LXXXV,[86,99-101] LXXXVI[102] and LXXXVII[103] were obtained from, respectively, LXXX, LXXXI, LXXXII and LXXXIII. A number of alkyl homologs were obtained similarly.

The 1-, 2- and 7-oxoöctahydropyrrocolines have been reduced to octahydropyrrocolines by the Wolff-Kishner and Clemmensen methods.[86,98-102] Catalytic hydrogenation of the 1-oxo compound gave[104] the secondary alcohol as did[86,99] reduction of some of the 2-oxo derivatives by means of the Clemmensen technique or by sodium-amalgam and alcohol. Reduction of the 8-oxo compound with lithium aluminum hydride gave[103] 8-hydroxyoctahydropyrrocoline. The reaction of LXXXIV and LXXXV with methyl and ethyl Grig-

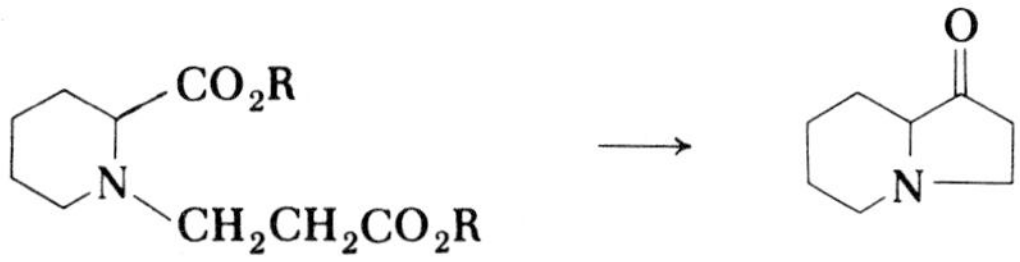

(LXXX) → (LXXXIV)

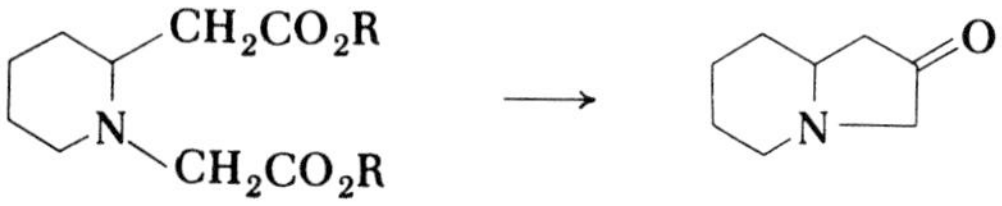

(LXXXI) → (LXXXV)

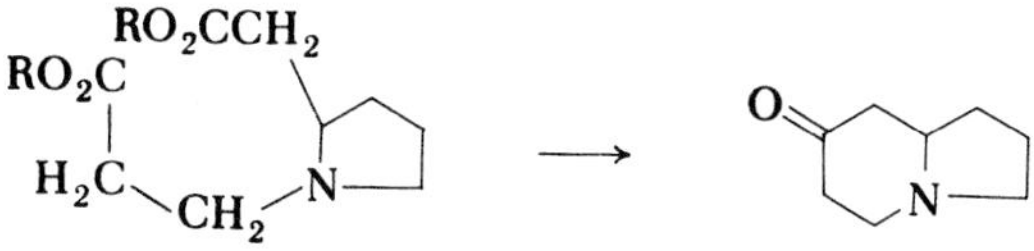

(LXXXII) → (LXXXVI)

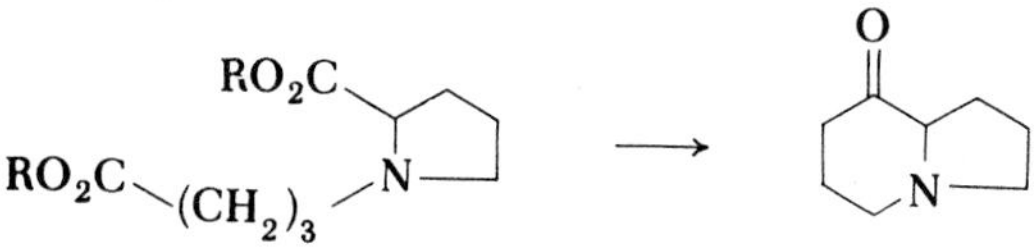

(LXXXIII) → (LXXXVII)

nard reagents, followed by dehydration and hydrogenation was utilized[86,148] to prepare 1-ethyl-, 2-ethyl- and 1-methyloctahydropyrrocolines.

(b) *Via octahydropyrrocolin-3-ones.* Octahydropyrrocolin-3-one has been obtained by (*1*) the thermal dehydration of 2-(2-piperidyl)-propionic acid[91,95] (or its ethyl ester[98]), (*2*) the hydrogenation of 2-(2-pyridyl)acrylic acid over Adams catalyst,[96] or of its ethyl ester over Raney nickel,[106] and (*3*) the reduction with Raney nickel of phenyl 2-(2-piperidyl)thiopropionate.[95] The first and second of these methods have been employed to prepare the 2-hydroxy-,[91] 1-carbethoxy-[107] and 1,2-dicarbethoxyoctahydropyrrocolin-3-ones.[108] The 3-oxo compound has been reduced to octahydropyrrocoline by means of sodium and alcohol,[91,98] by hydrogen with a copper-chromite catalyst[106] and by lithium aluminum hydride.[95,96]

A large excess of lithium aluminum hydride was said[96] to be required, as with only a 20% excess, 2-(2-piperidyl)propionaldehyde (pelletierine) was produced.

(c) *Reductive cyclizations.* Hydrogenation with a platinum catalyst of solutions of 2-(2-pyridyl)propionaldehyde diethyl acetal in acetic or hydrochloric acids yielded,[93,94] depending upon the concentration, octahydropyrrocoline or pelletierine. Reduction of methyl 2-(6-oxo-2-piperidyl)propionate with lithium aluminum hydride yielded[147] pelletierine together with about 15% of octahydropyrrocoline. However, an attempt[97] to make pelletierine by hydrogenating 2-(2-pyridyl)propionaldehyde hydrochloride in ethanol over Adams catalyst, gave solely octahydropyrrocoline, as did a similar reduction[109] of 2-(2-pyridyl)propionitrile. This latter preparation especially, and also the hydrogenation of 2-(3-hydroxypropyl-pyridine over Raney nickel[110] provide convenient laboratory syntheses of octahydropyrrocoline.

CH_2 CH_2 C CH_2 CH_2
CH_2 N OH CO_2R
CO_2R

(LXXXVIII)

H_2
$Cu_2Cr_2O_5$

N

H_2
$Cu_2Cr_2O_5$

$CH_2COCO_2C_2H_5$
N
$CH_2C_6H_5$
O

(LXXXIX)

H_2 $Cu_2Cr_2O_5$

CH_2
CH_2 HN O
CH_2
$CONH_2$

(XC)

The synthesis of 1-azabicyclic systems by the reductive cyclization of oximinodiesters has been elaborated in some detail by Leonard and his associates (see Sections A-64, A-674, A-721, A-878 and A-895). Hydrogenation over a copper-chromite catalyst afforded octahydropyrrocoline in 50–60% yield[111] from LXXXVIII, in unspecified yield[112] from LXXXIX and in 66% yield[113] from XC.

(d) *Miscellaneous syntheses.* An ingenious synthesis of 5-substituted octahydro pyrrocoline-7-ones was devised by Lions and Willison,[114] who condensed various aldehydes with γ-aminobutyraldehyde and acetonedicarboxylic ester. The intermediate dicarbethoxy compounds XCI are rather unstable, but, upon hydrolysis, readily yield XCII. In the case of aliphatic aldehydes (R = H, CH_3 or $CH(CH_3)CH_2CH_3$) the yield of XCI is 88–95%, and 40–63% of XCII; however, when R = C_6H_5, the yield of XCII drops to 16%.

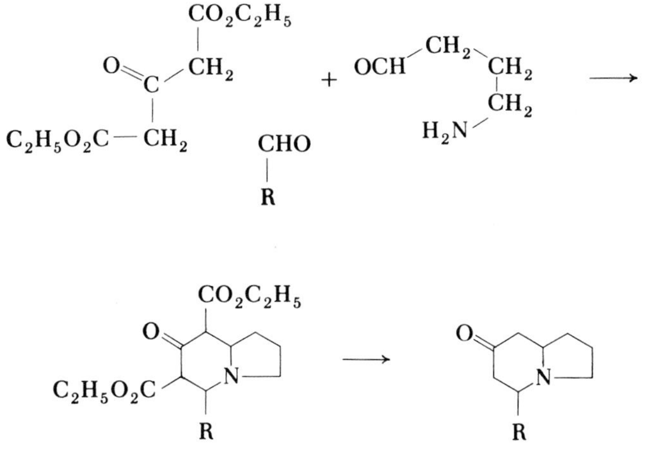

$CO_2C_2H_5$, CH_2, O=C, $C_2H_5O_2C—CH_2$, CHO, R, +, OCH, CH_2, CH_2, CH_2, H_2N ⟶

$CO_2C_2H_5$, O, $C_2H_5O_2C$, N, R ⟶ O, N, R

(XCI) (XCII)

A somewhat similar synthesis was reported[105] by Galinovsky *et al.* The reaction of pelletierine in buffered solutions with acetonedicarboxylic acid or with benzoylacetic acid yielded XCIII (R = CH_3 or C_6H_5, respectively).

NH, CHO + $RCOCH_2COOH$ ⟶ N, CH_2, CO, R

(XCIII)

In a preliminary report,[115] Witkop and Cohen described the oxidation of XCIV to XCV. As this is the only recorded example of an octahydropyrrocoline-5-one, the reaction is of interest, but the details have not yet been published.

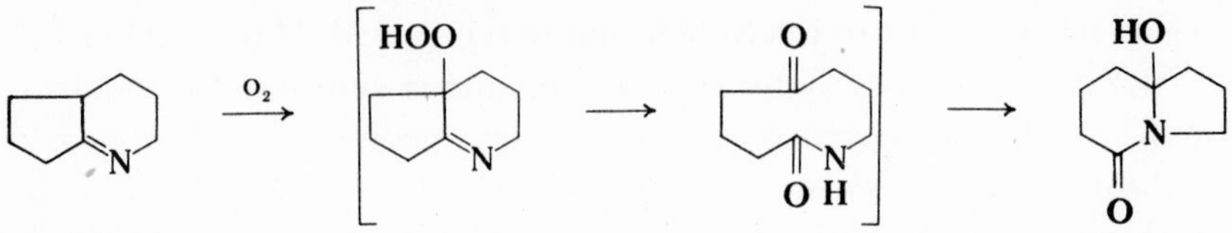

(XCIV) (XCV)

Dehydrohalogenation of 2-(3-halopropyl)piperidines has been utilized to prepare octahydropyrrocoline[92] (and its 6-ethyl homolog[116]), as has[92] the dehydration of 2-(3-hydroxypropyl)piperidine. As mentioned earlier (Part IV-1), catalytic reduction of 1,2-trimethylenepyridinium bromide (LXXII) yielded[85] octahydropyrrocoline. Also previously mentioned was the synthesis by Hofmann[80] and Lellmann,[81] who dehydrohalogenated *N*-bromoconiine (XCVII). This type of cyclodehydrohalogenation has become known as the Löffler-Freytag reaction.

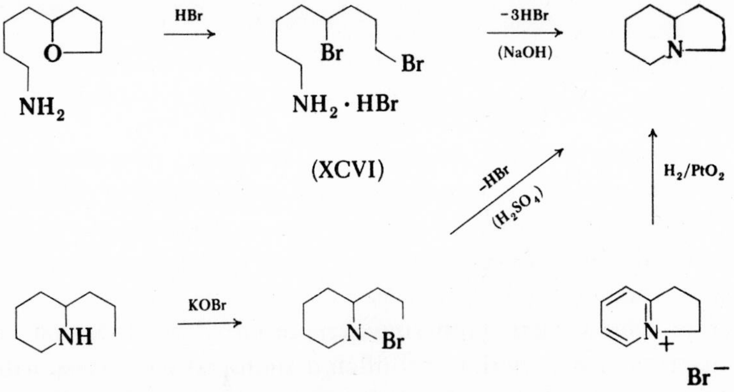

(XCVI)

(XCVII) (LXXII)

Octahydropyrrocoline has also been obtained[117] by the cyclodehydrohalogenation of XCVI. This synthesis is of a type which has been used to prepare a number of 1-azabicyclic systems (see Sections A-64, A-674, A-721, A-895, B-20 and B-84).

Many octahydropyrrocolines have been obtained by the catalytic hydrogenation of pyrrocolines. This was discussed in detail in Part III-8.

The Clemmensen reduction of XCVIII was shown[120] to yield not XCIX, but the rearranged product, 3-methyloctahydropyrrocoline (C).

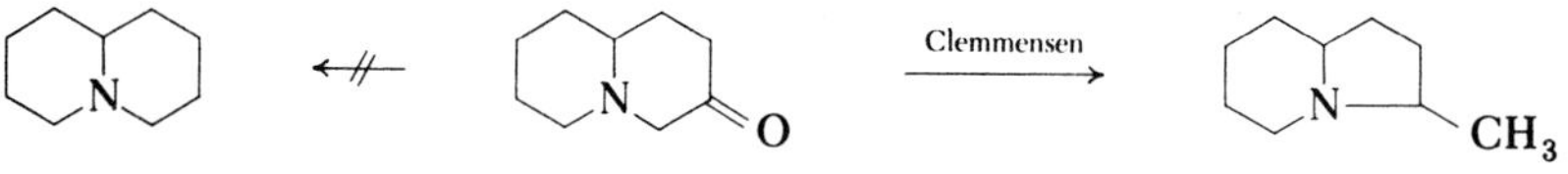

Clemmensen

(XCIX) (XCVIII) (C)

Treatment[118] of CI with thionyl chloride yielded a quaternary salt of structure CII, which was called *1,5-endoethyleneoctahydropyridocolinium chloride*, or *1-azoniatricyclo*[$5.3.2.0^{1,6}$]*dodecane chloride*.

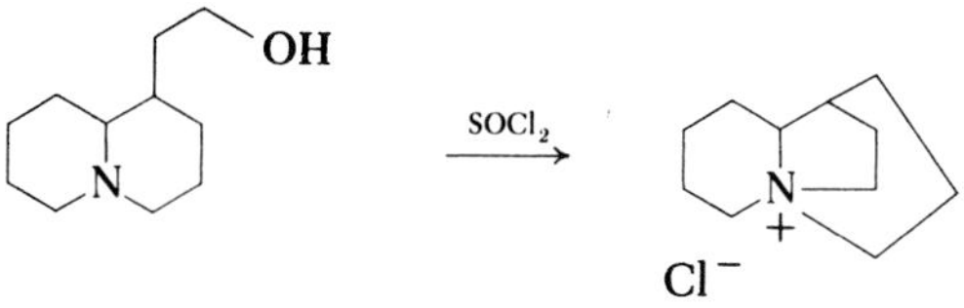

$SOCl_2$

(CI) (CII)

3. *Octahydropyrrocolines; Properties and Reactions.* Octahydropyrrocolines form readily the customary salts and complexes characteristic of amines. Application of the von Braun degradation to octahydropyrrocolines seems, generally, to result in scission of the five-membered ring, although in the case of the 2-methyl homolog, some cleavage of the six-membered ring was reported.[33] Although this degradation has been of value[27,28,33] in demonstrating various structures, the related Emde and Hofmann degradations do not appear to have been investigated. Electrolytic reduction of 1- and 8-oxooctahydropyrrocolines has been reported[103] to cause cleavage of the bridgehead bond, with the formation, in 49 and 73% yield, respectively, of 4- and 5-hydroxazacyclononanes.

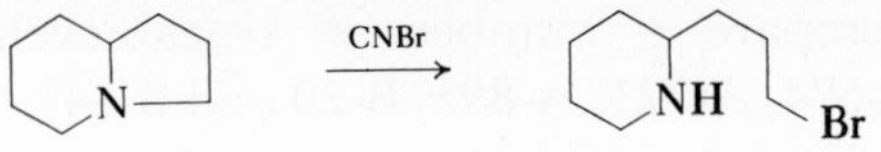

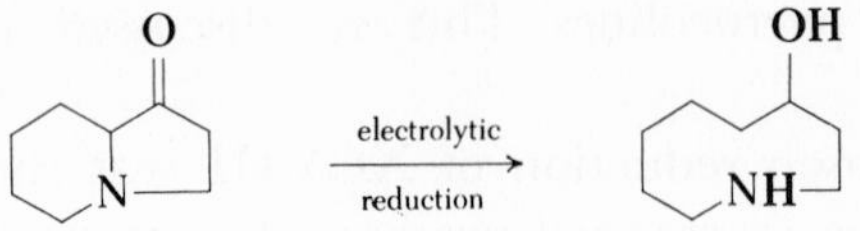

The Clemmensen reduction product from octahydropyrrocolin-1-one yielded[98] two isomeric picrates; m. 226° and m. 135°. The former is identical with octahydropyrrocoline picrate prepared in other ways, whilst the nature of the latter has not been demonstrated. Clemo and Ramage[98] suggested that the two picrates were stereoisomers of the *cis-trans* decalin type. Several objections to this hypothesis may be offered, and, in view of the frequency with which rearrangements are encountered in the Clemmensen reduction of α-aminoketones, it seems reasonable to expect the lower melting picrate to be that of a structural isomer, possibly the yet undescribed *1-azabicyclo[5.2.0]nonane*.

Recently, Leonard and Middleton[119] succeeded in resolving octahydropyrrocoline via the dibenzoyl-D-tartrate salt. The product so obtained possessed an optical rotation identical with that of δ-conicëine prepared by Lellmann from (+)-coniine. Insomuch as this last alkaloid has been related to D(+)-pipecolinic acid, laevorotatory octahydropyrrocoline may be assigned the D configuration.

While octahydropyrrocoline itself exists as single racemate, its monosubstitution products (except in position 8*a*) exist as pairs of racemates. In several cases (e.g. the 2-hydroxy-,[86] 5-methyl-,[114] 5-phenyl-[114] and 6-ethyloctahydropyrrocolines[100] and the 5-methyl-7-oxo homolog[114]) these pairs have been separated by means of their picrates, while separation of the two racemates of 3-methyloctahydropyrrocoline was achieved[120] by chromatography.

Hydropyrrocolines

Empirical formula	Substituents or structure	Properties and derivatives	Refs.
$C_8H_5NO_3$	5,6,7,8-Tetrahydro-5,6,8-trioxo-	Yel., d. ~250°. Anil, or.-yel., m. 218°.	82
C_8H_9N	5,8(?)-Dihydro-	b_{754} 198–9°; d_4^{20} 1.0211. $HgCl_2$ complex, *d*. >90°. Benzylidene deriv., m. 118–20°. Furfurylidene deriv., m. 132°.	21
C_8H_9NO	5,6,7,8-Tetrahydro-8-oxo-	m. 34°. Semicarbazone, m. 193°. Piperonylidene deriv., m. 136°.	83
$C_8H_{10}N$	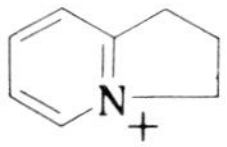	Bromide, m. 178–80° (176–9°). Iodide, m. 113–6° (112–4°). *p*-Toluenesulfonate, m. 120–2°. Picrate, m. 109–11°.	84,149
$C_8H_{13}N$	1,2,3,5,6,7- and/or 2,3,5,6,7,8-Hexahydro-	b_{18} 68–9°; n_D^{20} 1.5090. Salts: see $C_8H_{14}N$.	88
$C_8H_{13}NO$	Octahydro-1-oxo-	b_3 85°, b_{18} 93°; n_D^{20} 1.4812. Picrate, m. 175–6°.	98,103
	Octahydro-2-oxo-	b_1 64°, b_{11} 76–7°. Picrate, m. 187° d.	86
	Octahydro-3-oxo-	b_1 93–4°, $b_{1.2}$ 84–6°, b_{12} 126–7° (130–40°), b_{18} 135°, b_{20} 146–9°, b_{28} 152–4°, b_{760} 263–4°; n_D^{25} 1.4993; d_4^{15} 1.0715. HBr salt, m. 164–5°.	91,95,96,98,106
	Octahydro-7-oxo-	b_{18} 104–5°. Picrate, m. 198–200°.	114
	Octahydro-8-oxo-	$b_{5.5}$ 79–80°; n_D^{20} 1.4893. Picrate, m. 144.5–5.5°.	103
$C_8H_{13}NO_2$	Octahydro-2-hydroxy-3-oxo-	b_{18} 183–4°, b_{760} 304–5°; m. 129–30°. Aurichloride, m. 89–90°. Platinichloride, m. 92–4°.	91
	Octahydro-8*a*-hydroxy-5-oxo	—	115
$C_8H_{14}N$	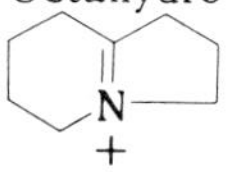	Perchlorate, m. 218–9°. Triiodide (I_3^-), brn.-purple, m. 90–1°.	88,89

(continued)

Hydropyrrocolines (*continued*)

Empirical formula	Substituents or structure	Properties and derivatives	Refs.
$C_8H_{15}N$	Octahydro-	b_{11} 45°, b_{12} 53°, b_{15} 55° (60°), b_{18} 66–7°, b_{20} 50–1° (60–3°), b_{22} 60–2°, b_{32} 71–2°, b_{43} 75°, b_{760} 161°; n_D^{20} 1.4711 (1.4700), n_D^{21} 1.4702, n_D^{25} 1.4682; $d_4^{10.5}$ 0.9074, d_4^{15} 0.9040 (0.9012). HCl salt, m. 186°. HBr salt, m. 196°. Picrate, m. 231–2° (215°, 223–6°, 225°, 226°, 228°, 230°, 232°; 233–4°). Picrolonate, m. 208.5–9° (207–8°). Platinichloride, m. 215° (213°, 218°). Aurichloride, m. 207° (~196°, 193°, 188–92°). $HgCl_2$ complex, m. 235–8° (237°, 232–5°). Methiodide, m. 280–3° d.	27,28,37,85,86, 91–94,96,97, 98,106, 110–114,117, 147
$C_8H_{15}NO$	Octahydro-1-hydroxy-	Oil. Picrate, m. 176–8°. Diphenylacetate ($\cdot 3H_2O$), m. 64–6°.	104,122
	Octahydro-2-hydroxy-	Two forms: b_{11} 90° and b_{14} 95°; picrates, m. 133° and 175°. Picrolonate, m. 174°.	86
	Octahydro-8-hydroxy-	$b_{0.3}$ 100° (bath temp.); n_D^{20} 1.5000. Picrate, m. 175–6°.	103
$C_9H_{14}N_2$	8*a*-Cyano-octahydro-	b_{14} 98°; $n_D^{28.5°}$ 1.4790.	89
$C_9H_{15}N$	2,3,5,6,7,8 (or 3,5,6,7,8,8*a*)-Hexahydro-1-methyl-	b_{11} 80°. Picrolonate, m. 183°.	86
$C_9H_{15}NO$	Octahydro-3-methyl-2-oxo-	b_1 67–9°, $b_{3.9}$ 75–6°; n_D^{20} 1.4782. Picrate, m. 162° (158–60°). Picrolonate, m. 187–9° d.	99,120
	Octahydro-3-methyl-7-oxo-	b_1 72–5°. Picrate, m. 204°. Picrolonate, m. 203°.	102
	Octahydro-5-methyl-7-oxo-	b_{20} 119°. Picrate, two forms: m. 188°, and 194° d.	114

$C_9H_{17}N$	Octahydro-1-methyl-	b_{11} 62°. Picrate, m. 191° d. Picrolonate, m. 198° d.	86
	Octahydro-2-methyl-	b_{26} 71.2° (72°), b_{760} 172°; n_D^{26} 1.4668; $d_4^{10.5}$ 0.8837. HBr salt, m. 164°. Picrate, m. 161–2°. Aurichloride, m. 106°. Methiodide, m. 227°.	28,33,121
	Octahydro-3-methyl-	b_1 27° (32–5°), b_{40} 81°, b_{760} 173°, b_{764} 168–9°. Picrate, two forms: m. 195–7° (191°, 193°) and m. 215–6° d. Picrolonate (m. 309–11°, 311–2°) two forms: m. 216–8° (208°) and 166–8°. Chloroaurate, m. 145–6°. $HgCl_2$ complex, m. 221°. Methiodide, m. 311–2°.	28,33,99,102, 120
	Octahydro-5-methyl-	b_5 79°. Picrate, two forms: m. 196° d. and 235°.	114
	Octahydro-8*a*-methyl-	b_{18} 68°; n_D^{28} 1.4753. HI salt, m. 256.5–7.5°. Picrate, m. 274° d.	89
$C_9H_{17}NO$	Octahydro-1-hydroxy-1-methyl-	b_1 72–3°. Picrate, m. 142°. Picrolonate, m. 207°.	86
	Octahydro-2-hydroxy-3-methyl-	b_{16} 100–105°. Picrate, m. 159°. Picrolonate, or.-yel., m. 181°.	99
	Octahydro-5-hydroxymethyl-	b_{16} 109–14°. HCl salt, subl. 204–15°/14 mm.	145
$C_{10}H_{13}NO_5$	1,2-Dicarboxyoctahydro-3-oxo-	m. 17°; pK_a 4.1 and 5.7 (in 50% CH_3OH). Diethyl ester, $b_{0.001}$ 120°.	108
$C_{10}H_{17}N$	1-Ethyl-2,3,5,6,7,8 (or 3,5,6,7,8,8*a*)-hexahydro-	b_1 74–5°. Picrolonate, m. 185°.	86
	2-Ethyl-3,5,6,7,8,8*a*-hexahydro-	b_1 50°, b_{11} 73–4°. Picrolonate, m. 191°.	86
$C_{10}H_{17}NO$	3-Ethyloctahydro-2-oxo-	b_{12} 120–5°. Picrate, m. 165°.	101
	5-Ethyloctahydro-2-oxo-	b_{12} 118–23°. Picrate, m. 158°.	101
	6-Ethyloctahydro-2-oxo-	b_1 53–5°, b_{15} 120–5°. Picrate, m. 143°. Picrolonate, m. 150–1°.	100
	Octahydro-1,7-dimethyl-2-oxo-	b_3 80°. Picrate, m. 175°.	100

(continued)

Hydropyrrocolines (*continued*)

Empirical formula	Substituents or structure	Properties and derivatives	Refs.
$C_{10}H_{17}NO_2$	5-Carbomethoxyoctahydro-	b_{14} 125–6°. HCl salt, m. 117–20°.	145
$C_{10}H_{19}N$	1-Ethyloctahydro-	b_{11} 64°; $n_D^{24°}$ 1.4729. Picrate, m. 146–7° (134°). Picrolonate, m. 184.5–5.5° (176°).	86,148
	2-Ethyloctahydro-	b_1 41°. Picrate, m. 149°. Picrolonate, m. 161°. Methiodide, m. 232°.	86
	3-Ethyloctahydro-	b_{12} 140–50°. Picrolonate, m. 140°.	101
	5-Ethyloctahydro-	b_{12} 140–50°. Picrate, m. 175°.	101
	6-Ethyloctahydro-	b_{12} 100–5°, b_{15} 77–8°. b_{18} 80–5°. Picrate, m. 178° (176°) also (?) 118–9°. Picrolonate, m. 185° (182–3°). Methiodide, m. 222–3°.	4,49,100,116
	Octahydro-2,3-dimethyl-	b_{23} 81–2°, b. 190–1°; n_D 1.4704; $d_4^{10.5}$ 0.8849. HBr salt, d. 268°. Picrate, m. 177°. Platinichloride, d. 215°. Methiodide, m. 207°.	28,121
	Octahydro-1,7-dimethyl-	b_{15} 150°. Picrate, m. 116°.	100
$C_{10}H_{19}NO$	1-Ethyloctahydro-1-hydroxy-	b_1 85–7°, $b_{0.9}$ 80–2°; $n_D^{23.5°}$ 1.4887.	86,148
	2-Ethyloctahydro-2-hydroxy-	b_1 82°. Picrolonate, grn.-yel., m. 198°.	86
$C_{11}H_{15}NO$	3-Acetyl-5,6,7,8-tetrahydro-2-methyl-	m. 74.0–4.5°. Benzylidene deriv., m. 126–7°. 2,4-Dinitrophenylhydrazone, deep red, m. 209–10°.	4
$C_{11}H_{17}NO_3$	2-Carbethoxyoctahydro-1-oxo-	b_1 103°.	86
	1-Carbethoxyoctahydro-3-oxo-	b_1 148–50°.	107
	6(or 8)-Carbethoxyoctahydro-7-oxo-	b_1 131.5°; m. 60°. Picrate, m. 137°.	114
$C_{11}H_{19}NO$	3-Acetonyloctahydro-	b_{12} 115–25°. Picrate, m. 136–7°. Picrolonate, m. 161–2°. Oxime, m. 130°.	96

$C_{11}H_{20}N$	N+	Chloride, v. hygroscopic. Picrate, d. 253–7°.	118
$C_{11}H_{21}N$	Octahydro-5-*i*-propyl-	b_{23} 99–101°. Picrolonate, m. 197° d.	114
	3-Ethyloctahydro-2-methyl-	b_6 68–70°, b_{11} 79–86°, b_{12} 83–5°; n_D^{20} 1.4686. HBr salt, m. 236.5–7°, HI salt, m. 249–51° (248°). Perchlorate, m. 221.5–3° (220–1°). Picrate, m. 156–7°. **Methiodides (two), m. 197–8° and** 229.0–9.5°.	4,62
$C_{11}H_{21}NO$	Octahydro-3-(1-hydroxyethyl)-2-methyl-	b_6 102–3°, b_{11} 106–10°. Picrate, m. 133–4°. HI salt, m. 187°. Methiodide, m. 169°. Phenylurethane, m. 136–7°. Acetyl deriv., b_6 110–1°. Picrate, m. 122–3°.	4,62
$C_{12}H_{15}N_2O_4$	1-Amino-2,3-dicarbomethoxy-5,6,7,8 (or 1,2,3,8*a*)-tetrahydro-	m. 105°. *N*-Acetyl deriv., m. 167°.	31
$C_{12}H_{23}N$	Octahydro-1,3,5,8-tetramethyl-	b_8 86–7°. Picrate, m. 172–7°.	40
$C_{13}H_{15}NO_7$	$CH_3OCHCOOH$; COOH; COOH; N	m. 130°. Trimethyl ester, m. 103–5°. 1,2-Anhydride, m. 154–5°. Originally assigned the 1,2,3,8*a*-tetrahydro structure.	31
$C_{14}H_{14}NO_5$	$CH_3OCHCOOCH_3$; CO; O; CO; N	m. 260°. Originally[31] assigned the 1,2,3,8*a*-tetrahydro structure.	31

(continued)

Hydropyrrocolines (*continued*)

Empirical formula	Substituents or structure	Properties and derivatives	Refs.
$C_{14}H_{15}N$	5,6,7,8-Tetrahydro-2-phenyl-	m. 76.5–7.5°. Picrate, red, m. 111.5–2.5°.	4
$C_{14}H_{19}N$	Octahydro-5-phenyl-	b_{20} 155°. Picrates (two) m. 174° and 193°.	114
$C_{14}H_{21}NO_5$	6,8-Dicarbethoxyoctahydro-7-oxo-	Oil.	114
$C_{14}H_{24}ClN$	1-(2-Chloro-2-hexyl)-2,3,5,6,7,8-hexahydro-	HCl salt, m. 115–6°.	87
	1-(3-Chloro-3-hexyl)-2,3,5,6,7,8-hexahydro-	HCl salt, m. 163°.	87
$C_{14}H_{27}N_2O_2$	[structure: CH_3; N^+; $CH_2CH_2OCON(CH_3)_2$]	Iodide, m. 150–1.5°.	126
$C_{15}H_{16}NO_7$	[structure: $COCO_2CH_3$; CO_2CH_3; N; CO_2CH_3]	m. 162–4°. Originally[31] assigned the 1,2,3,8*a*-tetrahydro structure.	31
$C_{15}H_{23}NO_5$	6,8-Dicarbethoxyoctahydro-5-methyl-7-oxo-	m. 102°. Picrate, m. 150°.	114
$C_{15}H_{29}N$	Octahydro-2-methyl-3-(3-methyl-3-pentyl)-	$b_{3.8}$ 105°. HCl salt, m. 197–8°. Perchlorate, m. 158–9°. Picrate, m. 138–9°.	123
$C_{16}H_{17}NO$	3-Acetyl-5,6,7,8-tetrahydro-2-phenyl-	m. 81–2°; λ_{max}^{EtOH} 303 mμ (ε 16,700). 2,4-Dinitrophenylhydrazone, red, m. 228–9°.	4,81
$C_{16}H_{19}N$	3-Ethyl-5,6,7,8-tetrahydro-2-phenyl-	b_{12} 198–204°; m. 100–1°; λ_{max}^{EtOH} 278 mμ (ε 7700). Chloroplatinate, m. 115–20°.	4,81

$C_{16}H_{22}NO$	Octahydro-3-phenacyl-	$b_{0.1}$ 115–25°. Picrate, m. 165°. Picrolonate, m. 164–5°.	96
$C_{16}H_{23}N$	3-Ethyloctahydro-2-phenyl-	b_{11} 156–7°; n_D^{20} 1.5345 (1.5348, 1.5350). HCl salt (two forms), m. 199–200° and 231–2°.	4
$C_{16}H_{29}N$	2-Cyclohexyl-3-ethyloctahydro-	b_{12} 156–8°; n_D^{20} 1.4988. HCl salt, m. 219–20°. HBr salt, m. 211–2°. Methiodide, m. 201–2°.	4
$C_{17}H_{27}NO_5$	6,8-Dicarbethoxyoctahydro-5-*i*-propyl-7-oxo-	Picrate, m. 135°.	114
$C_{19}H_{32}N_2O$	CH_2COCH_2	$b_{0.1}$ 155–60°. Dipicrate, m. 184–5° d. Dipicrolonate, m. 210–2° d.	96
$C_{20}H_{25}NO_5$	6,8-Dicarbethoxyoctahydro-7-oxo-5-phenyl-	—	114

References

1. IUPAC, "Tentative Rules for Organic Nomenclature," *Comptes rendus de la dix-huitième conférence*, Zürich, July 20–28, 1955.
2. Tschitschibabin, *Ber.*, **60,** 1607 (1927).
3. Holland and Nayler, *J. Chem. Soc.*, **1955,** 1657.
4. Borrows, Holland and Kenyon, *J. Chem. Soc.*, **1946,** 1083.
5. Borrows and Holland, *Chem. Rev.*, **42,** 611 (1948).
6. Buu-Hoï, Jacquignon, Xuong and Lavit, *J. Org. Chem.*, **19,** 1370 (1954).
7. Buu-Hoï and Khôi, *Compt. rend.*, **230,** 967 (1950).
8. Borrows, Holland and Kenyon, *J. Chem. Soc.*, **1946,** 1069.
9. Kröhnke, *Ber.*, **66,** 604 and 1386 (1933); **68,** 1177 (1935).
10. Kröhnke and Fasold, *Ber.*, **67,** 656 (1934).
11. Kröhnke and Timmler, *Ber.*, **69,** 614 (1936).
12. Borrows and Holland, *J. Chem. Soc.*, **1947,** 672.
13. Borrows and Holland, *J. Chem. Soc.*, **1947,** 670.
14. Borrows, Holland and Kenyon, *J. Chem. Soc.*, **1946,** 1075.
15. Borrows, Holland and Kenyon, *J. Chem. Soc.*, **1946,** 1077.
16. King and McWhirter, *J. Am. Chem. Soc.*, **68,** 717 (1946).
17. Barrett, Brit. Pat. 765,874; *Chem. Abstracts*, **51,** 14829 (1957).
18. Barrett, *J. Chem. Soc.*, **1958,** 325.
19. Barrett and Chambers, *J. Chem. Soc.*, **1958,** 338.
20. Adamson, Barrett, Billinghurst and Jones, *J. Chem. Soc.*, **1957,** 2315.
21. Scholtz, *Ber.*, **45,** 734 (1912).
22. Scholtz, *Ber.*, **45,** 1718 (1912).
23. Scholtz, *Arch. Pharm.*, **251,** 666 (1913); *Chem. Zentr.*, **I,** 1284 (1914); *Chem. Abstracts*, **8,** 2698 (1914).
24. Scholtz and Fraude, *Ber.*, **46,** 1069 (1913).
25. Tschitschibabin and Stepanow, *Ber.*, **62,** 1068 (1929).
26. Tschitschibabin and Stepanow, *Ber.*, **63,** 470 (1930).
27. Diels, Alder, Kashimoto, Friedrichsen, Eckhardt and Klare, *Ann.*, **498,** 16 (1932).
28. Ochiai and Tsuda, *Ber.*, **67,** 1011 (1934).
29. Diels, Alder, Friedrichsen, Klare, Winkler and Schrum, *Ann.*, **505,** 103 (1933).
30. Diels, Alder, Friedrichsen, Petersen, Brodersen and Kech, *Ann.*, **510,** 87 (1934).
31. Diels and Meyer, *Ann.*, **513,** 129 (1934).
32. Diels and Möller, *Ann.*, **516,** 45 (1935).
33. Diels and Schrum, *Ann.*, **530,** 68 (1937).
34. Diels and Pistor, *Ann.*, **530,** 87 (1937).
35. Wiley and Knabeschuh, *J. Org. Chem.*, **18,** 836 (1953).
36. Diels, Alder, Winkler and Petersen, *Ann.*, **498,** 1 (1932).
37. Boekelheide and Feely, *J. Org. Chem.*, **22,** 589 (1957).
38. Plancher, *Ber.*, **35,** 2606 (1902); *Atti reale accad. Lincei*, [5]**11,** II, 210 (1902); *Chem. Zentr.*, **II,** 1472 (1902).
39. Plancher and Ciusa, *Atti reale accad. Lincei*, [5]**15,** II, 453 (1906); *Chem. Zentr.*, **II,** 1847 (1906).

40. Saxton, *J. Chem. Soc.*, **1951,** 3239.
41. Neber and Wörner, *Ann.*, **526,** 173 (1936).
42. Mosby, unpublished observations.
43. Brand and Reuter, *Ber.*, **72,** 1668 (1939).
44. Emmert and Groll, *Chem. Ber.*, **86,** 205 (1953).
45. Thayer, U. S. Pat. 2,496,319.
46. Wilson, *J. Chem. Soc.*, **1945,** 63.
47. Krumholtz, *Selecta chim.*, No. 8, 3 (1949); *Chem. Abstracts*, **44,** 3992 (1950).
48. Prelog and Balenovic, *Ber.*, **74,** 1508 (1941).
49. Clemo, Fox and Raper, *J. Chem. Soc.*, **1953,** 4173.
50. Bower, *J. Chem. Soc.*, **1957,** 4510.
51. Holliman and Schickerling, *J. Chem. Soc.*, **1951,** 914.
52. Miller and Brown, American Chemical Society, 130th National Meeting, Atlantic City, N. J., Sept. 16–21, 1956; *Abstracts*, p. 49-O.
53. Longuet-Higgins and Coulson, *Trans. Faraday Soc.*, **43,** 87 (1947).
54. Dewar, *The Electronic Theory of Organic Chemistry*, Oxford University Press, London, 1949, pp. 36, 161 and 191.
55. Matteson, "University of Illinois, Organic Seminar Reports," 1st Semester, 1955–6, p. 11.
56. Fukui, Yonezawa and Shingu, *J. Chem. Phys.*, **20,** 722 (1952).
57. Fukui, Yonezawa, Nagata and Shingu, *J. Chem. Phys.*, **22,** 1433 (1954).
58. Kondo and Hamamoto, *J. Pharm. Soc. Japan*, **56,** 7 (1936); *Chem. Zentr.*, **I,** 4158 (1936); *Chem. Abstracts*, **30,** 3431 (1936).
59. Rossiter and Saxton, *J. Chem. Soc.*, **1953,** 3654.
60. Holland and Naylor, *J. Chem. Soc.*, **1955,** 1504.
61. Holland and Naylor, *Chem. and Ind.*, **1954,** 224.
62. Ochiai and Kobayashi, *J. Pharm. Soc. Japan*, **56,** 376 (1936); *Chem. Zentr.*, **II,** 1938 (1936); *Chem. Abstracts*, **30,** 6364 (1936).
63. Widmer and Carroll, U. S. Pat. 2,405,106.
64. Brooker and Sprague, U. S. Pat. 2,409,612.
65. Sprague and Brooker, U. S. Pat. 2,511,222.
66. Sprague, U. S. Pat. 2,571,775.
67. Sprague, U. S. Pat. 2,622,082.
68. Heseltine and Brooker, U. S. Pat. 2,666,761; Brit. Pat. 756,226.
69. Sprague, U. S. Pat. 2,706,193.
70. Carroll and Jones, U. S. Pat. 2,688,545.
71. Craig, U. S. Pat. 2,785,133.
72. Ochiai, *J. Pharm. Soc. Japan*, **60,** 164 (1940); *Chem. Abstracts*, **34,** 5449 (1940).
73. Kondo and Osawa, *J. Pharm. Soc. Japan*, **56,** 73 (1936); *Chem. Zentr.*, **II,** 2910 (1936).
74. Kondo and Nishizawa, *J. Pharm. Soc. Japan*, **56,** 1 (1936); *Chem. Zentr.*, **I,** 4158 (1936); *Chem. Abstracts*, **30,** 3431 (1936).
75. Buu-Hoï and Hóan, *Rec. trav. chim.*, **68,** 441 (1949).
76. Buu-Hoï, Hóan and Jacquignon, *Rev. trav. chim.*, **68,** 781 (1949).
77. Buu-Hoï, Hóan and Royer, *Bull. soc. chim. France*, **1950,** 489.

78. Buu-Hoï, Binh, Loc, Xuong and Jacquignon, *J. Chem. Soc.*, **1957**, 3126.
79. Ochiai, Ito and Maruyama, *J. Pharm. Soc. Japan*, **59**, 705 (1939); *Chem. Abstracts*, **34**, 1988 (1940).
80. Hofmann, *Ber.*, **18**, 5 and 109 (1885).
81. Lellmann, *Ann.*, **259**, 193 (1890).
82. Angeli, *Ber.*, **23**, 1793 (1890).
83. Clemo and Ramage, *J. Chem. Soc.*, **1931**, 49.
84. Bavley, U. S. Pat. 2,418,748.
85. Winterfeld and Müller, *Arch. Pharm.*, **284**, 269 (1951); *Chem. Abstracts*, **47**, 4345 (1953).
86. Clemo and Metcalfe, *J. Chem. Soc.*, **1937**, 1518.
87. Nazarov and Khomenko, *Bull. acad. sci. U.R.S.S., classe sci. chim.*, 226 (1942); *Chem. Abstracts*, **39**, 1621 (1945).
88. Leonard, Middleton, Thomas and Choudhury, *J. Org. Chem.*, **21**, 344 (1956).
89. Leonard and Hay, *J. Am. Chem. Soc.*, **78**, 1984 (1956).
90. Lellmann, *Ber.*, **23**, 2141 (1890).
91. Löffler and Kaim, *Ber.*, **42**, 94 (1909).
92. Löffler, Kaim and Flugel, *Ber.*, **42**, 3420 (1909).
93. Beets and Wibaut, *Rec. trav. chim.*, **60**, 905 (1941).
94. Beets, *Rec. trav. chim.*, **62**, 553 (1943).
95. King, Hofmann and McMillan, *J. Org. Chem.*, **16**, 1100 (1951).
96. Galinovsky, Vogl and Weiser, *Monatsh.*, **83**, 114 (1952); *Chem. Abstracts*, **46**, 11198 (1952).
97. Miller, *J. Am. Chem. Soc.*, **75**, 4849 (1953).
98. Clemo and Ramage, *J. Chem. Soc.*, **1932**, 2969.
99. Clemo, Morgan and Raper, *J. Chem. Soc.*, **1935**, 1743.
100. Clemo, Fletcher, Fulton and Raper, *J. Chem. Soc.*, **1950**, 1140.
101. Prasad and Raper, *J. Chem. Soc.*, **1956**, 217.
102. Clemo, Metcalfe and Raper, *J. Chem. Soc.*, **1935**, 1429.
103. Leonard, Swann and Figueras, *J. Am. Chem. Soc.*, **74**, 4620 (1952).
104. Sternbach and Kaiser, *J. Am. Chem. Soc.*, **74**, 2215 (1952).
105. Winterfeld and Schneider, *Ann.*, **581**, 66 (1953).
106. Tullock and McElvain, *J. Am. Chem. Soc.*, **61**, 961 (1939).
107. Clemo, Morgan and Raper, *J. Chem. Soc.*, **1937**, 965.
108. Edwards, Chaput, Clarke and Singh, *Can. J. Chem.*, **32**, 785 (1954).
109. Boekelheide, Linn, O'Grady and Lamborg, *J. Am. Chem. Soc.*, **75**, 3243 (1953).
110. Boekelheide and Rothchild, *J. Am. Chem. Soc.*, **70**, 864 (1948).
111. Leonard and Goode, *J. Am. Chem. Soc.*, **72**, 5404 (1950).
112. Leonard and Boyer, *J. Am. Chem. Soc.*, **72**, 2980 (1950).
113. Tsuda and Saeki, *J. Org. Chem.*, **23**, 91 (1958).
114. Lions and Willison, *J. Proc. Roy. Soc., N.S. Wales*, **73**, 240 (1940); *Chem. Abstracts*, **34**, 5841 (1940).
115. Witkop and Cohen, *XIV Congress I.U.P.A.C.*, Zürich, 1955, *Handbook*, p. 134.
116. Prelog and Metzler, *Helv. Chim. Acta*, **29**, 1163 (1946).
117. Arh-Lipovac and Seiwerth, *Monatsh.*, **84**, 992 (1953); *Chem. Abstracts*, **48**, 10750 (1954).

118. Clemo and Rudinger, *J. Chem. Soc.*, **1951,** 2714.
119. Leonard and Middleton, *J. Am. Chem. Soc.*, **74,** 5776 (1952).
120. Leonard and Pines, *J. Am. Chem. Soc.*, **72,** 4931 (1950).
121. Hirosawa, *Japan. J. Med. Sci. IV, Pharmacol.*, **11,** No. 2/3; *Proc. Japan Pharmacol. Soc.*, **12,** 218 (1938); *Chem. Abstracts*, **34,** 7425 (1940).
122. Sternbach and Kaiser, *J. Am. Chem. Soc.*, **74,** 2219 (1952).
123. Kondo and Kokeguchi, *J. Pharm. Soc. Japan*, **57,** 573 (1937); *Chem. Abstracts*, **31,** 6230 (1937); *Chem. Zentr.*, **II,** 3747 (1937).
124. Ochiai, Wada, Nishizawa and Suzuki, *J. Pharm. Soc. Japan*, **58,** 627 (1938); *Chem. Zentr.*, **II,** 3395 (1938); *Chem. Abstracts*, **32,** 8412 (1938).
125. Ochiai, Hamana and Nogachi, *J. Pharm. Soc. Japan*, **66,** 48 (1946); *Chem. Abstracts*, **45,** 6648 (1951).
126. Kaplan and Noller, *J. Am. Chem. Soc.*, **71,** 3259 (1949).
127. Buu-Hoï and Hóan, *Rec. trav. chim.*, **69,** 1455 (1950).
128. Buu-Hoï and Khôi, *Bull. soc. chim. France*, **1950,** 753.
129. Buu-Hoï and Royer, *J. Org. Chem.*, **15,** 123 (1950).
130. Buu-Hoï and Xuong, *J. Chem. Soc.*, **1953,** 386.
131. Buu-Hoï, Hóan and Lavit, *J. Chem. Soc.*, **1953,** 485.
132. Lescot, Buu-Hoï and Xuong, *J. Chem. Soc.*, **1956,** 2408.
133. Vo-Thi and Hóan, *Compt. rend.*, **237,** 1016 (1953).
134. Buu-Hoï, Xuong and Van Thang, *Rec. trav. chim.*, **72,** 774 (1953).
135. Buu-Hoï, Xuong and Lavit, *J. Org. Chem.*, **18,** 910 (1953).
136. Buu-Hoï, Le Bihan and Leroux, *J. Org. Chem.*, **18,** 582 (1953).
137. Buu-Hoï, Xuong and Lavit, *J. Chem. Soc.*, **1954,** 1034.
138. Buu-Hoï, Lavit and Xuong, *J. Org. Chem.*, **19,** 1617 (1954).
139. Thoi and Belloc, *Industrie plastiques mod.* (Paris), **6,** No. 3, 90–2; No. 4, 39, 41, 43; No. 5, 47, 49 (1954); *Chem. Abstracts*, **49,** 14697 (1955).
140. Buu-Hoï, Royer and Bisagni, *Rec. trav. chim.*, **74,** 24 (1955).
141. Buu-Hoï, Saint-Ruf, Loc and Xuong, *J. Chem. Soc.*, **1957,** 2593.
142. Tschitschibabin, Ger. Pat. 464,481; *Frdl.*, **16,** 2652 (1931).
143. Boekelheide and Windgassen, *J. Am. Chem. Soc.*, **80,** 2020 (1958).
144. Barrett, Brit. Pat. 783,627; *Chem. Abstracts*, **52,** 7361 (1958).
145. Seiwerth and Djokić, *Croat. Chem. Acta*, **29,** 403 (1957).
146. Heseltine and Brooker, U.S. Pat. 2,719,151.
147. Segre and Viterbo, *Experientia*, **14,** 54 (1956).
148. Leonard, Conrow and Fulmer, *J. Org. Chem.*, **22,** 1445 (1957).
149. Lowe and King, *J. Org. Chem.*, **24,** 1200 (1959).

A-184. 7*H*-Cyclopenta[*a*]indolizine*

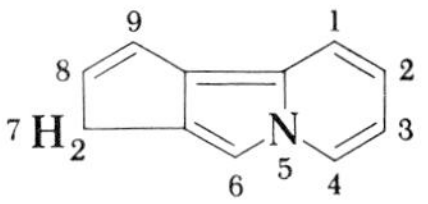

Treatment of carbinols of structure I with acetic anhydride produced[1] indolizines (II, R = H, m. 109–10°, λ_{max} 230, 256, 275, 371

and 383 mμ (ϵ 21,500, 12,200, 25,700, 13,600 and 12,200); R = $CH_2N(CH_3)_2$, oil). See Sections A-183, A-188 and A-190.

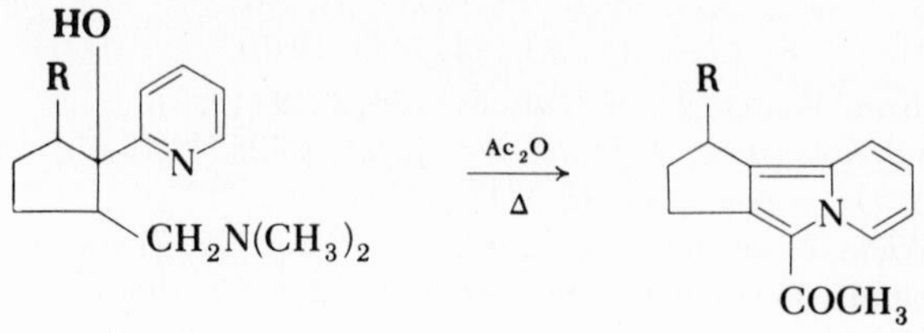

HO R $CH_2N(CH_3)_2$ N $\xrightarrow[\Delta]{Ac_2O}$ R N $COCH_3$

(I) (II)

Reference

1. Barrett and Chambers, *J. Chem. Soc.*, **1958,** 338.

A-185. Cyclopenta[*h,i*]pyrrocoline

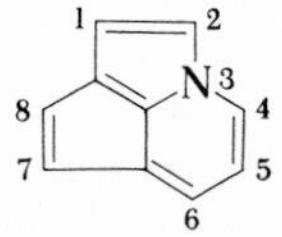

The saturated system was named *1-azatricyclo[6.2.1.0^{5,11}]hendecane* (I).

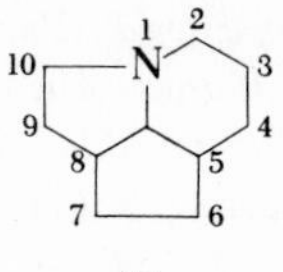

(I)

Catalytic reduction of the oximino ester II yielded III ($b_{0.2}$ 45°; n_D^{20} 1.4982; $d_{4°}^{20°}$ 0.9657; picrate, m. 242–3° d. and picrolonate, m. 183–4°), which tentatively was assigned the *trans-cis* configuration shown.

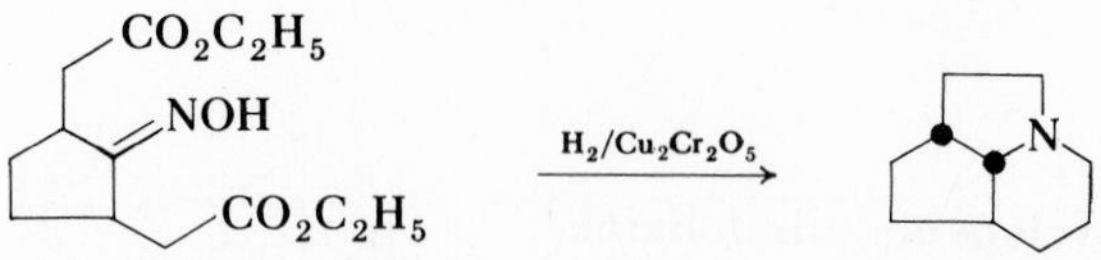

$CO_2C_2H_5$ NOH $CO_2C_2H_5$ $\xrightarrow{H_2/Cu_2Cr_2O_5}$ N

(II) (III)

Reference

1. Leonard and Middleton, *J. Am. Chem. Soc.*, **74,** 5114 (1952).

A-186. Furo[3,4-*b*]pyrrocoline.
R.I. 1408

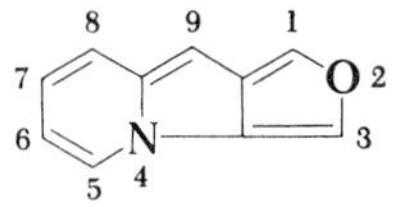

See pyrrocoline (Section A-183).

A-187. 1*H*-Dipyrrolo[1,2-*a*, 2′,3′-*d*]-pyridine

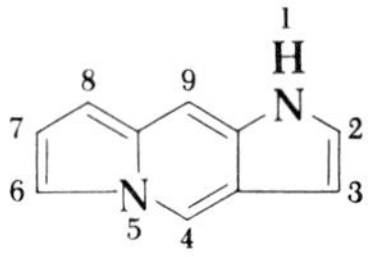

Treatment of dipyrrylmethanes such as I with sodium or other alkaline condensing agents yielded strongly fluorescent products shown[1] to have structure II (R = R′ = C_2H_5, m. 204°; R = CH_3,

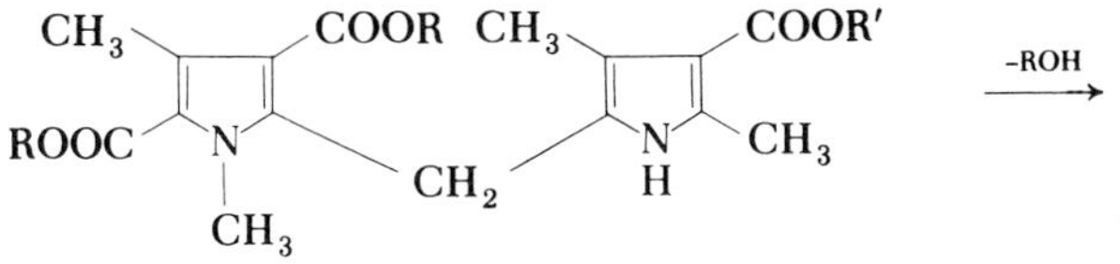

(I)

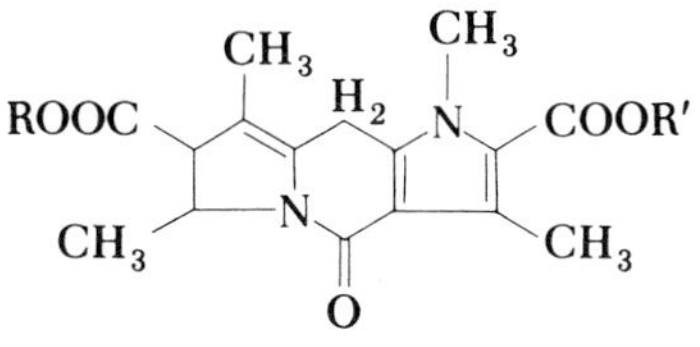

(II)

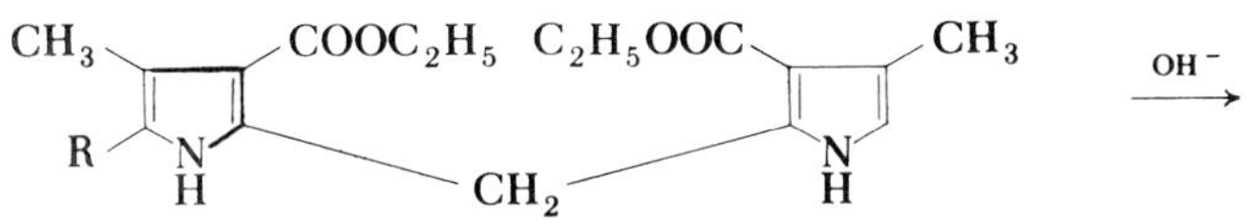

(III)

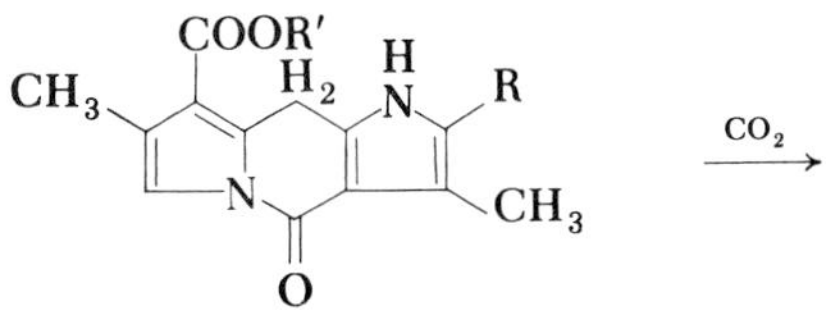

(IV)

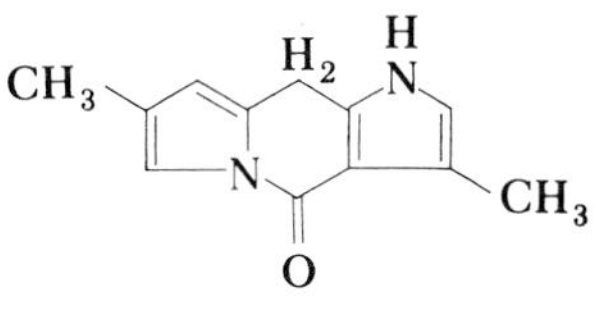

(V)

R′ = C_2H_5, m. 210–1°; R = C_2H_5, R′ = CH_3, m. 194°). Similarly, caustic hydrolysis converted III into IV (R = $COOC_2H_5$, R′ = C_2H_5, orange, darkens at 235°, d. 245°; R = R′ = H, dark yellow), which (when R = R′ = H) could be decarboxylated to V.

References

1. Corwin and Ellingson, *J. Am. Chem. Soc.*, **66,** 1146 (1944).
2. Corwin and Buc, *J. Am. Chem. Soc.*, **66,** 1151 (1944).

A-188. Benzo[*a*]indolizine*

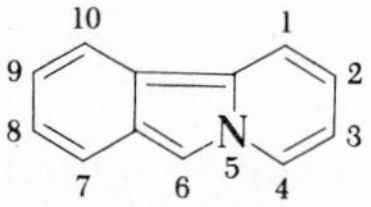

Tetrahydro derivatives of structure II [R = H, yellow, m. 117°, λ_{max} 230, 276 and 370 mμ (ϵ 19,000, 21,000 and 13,000); R = $CH_2N(CH_3)_2$, m. 70–1°, λ_{max} 230, 275, 370 and 382 mμ (ϵ 19,000, 20,000, 11,500 and 10,400)], were obtained[1,2] by treatment of I, with acetic anhydride. Hydrolysis of II (R = H) yielded III [m. 59–60°, λ_{max} 244, 250, 287, 296, 308 and 360 mμ (ϵ 29,000, 30,000, 2,300, 3,000, 4,200 and 2,100)]. See Sections A-183, A-184 and A-190.

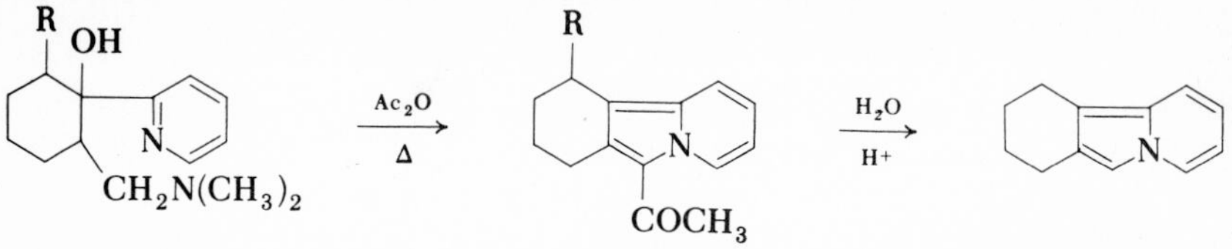

(I) $\xrightarrow[\Delta]{Ac_2O}$ (II) $\xrightarrow[H^+]{H_2O}$ (III)

References

1. Barrett and Chambers, *J. Chem. Soc.*, **1958,** 338.
2. Barrett, Brit. Pat. 765,874; *Chem. Abstracts*, **51,** 14829 (1957).

A-189. 1*H*-Pyrano[4,3-*a*]pyrrocoline. R.I. 1635

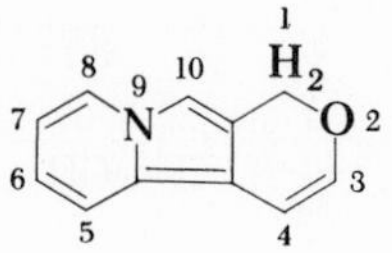

See pyrrocoline (Section A-183).

A-190. 7*H*-Cyclohepta[*a*]indolizine*

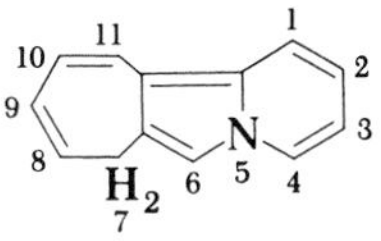

Treatment of I with acetic anhydride yielded[1] II [R = H, non-basic oil, λ_{max} 232, 268, 276 and 374 mμ (ϵ 16,000, 13,000, 14,000 and 7,000); R = $CH_2N(CH_3)_2$, oil; oxalate, m. 210°, λ_{max} 230, 272 and 366 mμ (ϵ 27,000, 21,000 and 11,500); methiodide, m. 242–4°, λ_{max} 232, 262 and 366 mμ (ϵ 31,000, 21,000 and 11,000); R = CH_2OCOCH_3, m. 112°, λ_{max} 231, 274, 368 and 383* mμ (ϵ 26,000, 23,000, 13,000 and 11,600)]. Hydrolysis of II (R = $CH_2N(CH_3)_2$) yielded III [R = $CH_2N(CH_3)_2$, m. 82–3°, λ_{max} 243, 283, 292, 303 and 306 mμ (ϵ 31,000, 2,000, 2,500, 2,800 and 2,300); oxalate m. 175–8° d.; methiodide, m. 175–8° d.]. See Sections A-183, A-184 and A-188.

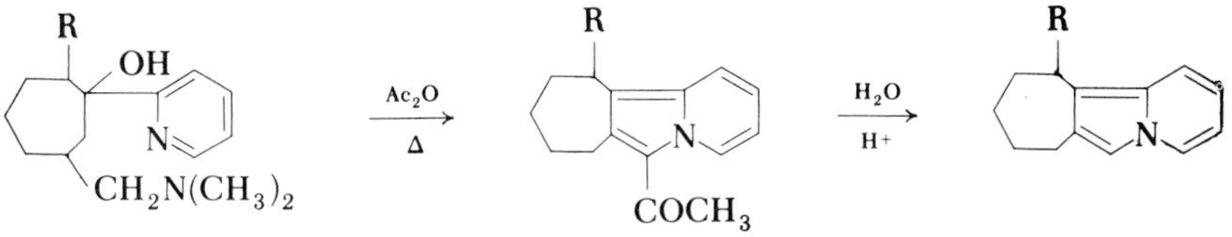

(I) (II) (III)

Reference

1. Barrett and Chambers, *J. Chem. Soc.*, **1958,** 338.

A-191. Benzo[*b*]pyrrocoline.
R.I. 1647

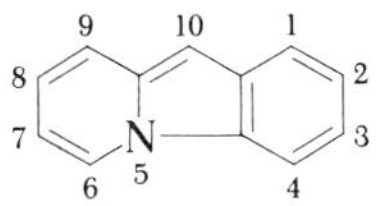

The names and numbering *2:3-benzopyrrocoline* (I) and, for the perhydrogenated system, *11-azaperhydrofluorene* (II) have also been used.

(I) (II)

The prototype of this ring system (III) was obtained[1,2] in 40% yield by the passage of 2-benzylpyridine over heated copper turnings. A more indirect synthesis, from α-picoline and 2-bromocyclo-

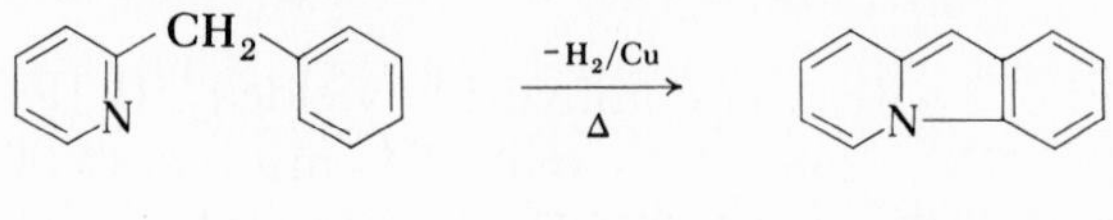

CH_2 $-H_2/Cu$, Δ

(III)

hexanone, also has been achieved.[3] Efforts to obtain III directly from IV by heating with sulfur gave[3] only α-picoline. However, acetylation of IV protected the nucleus, and V could be dehydrogenated to VI, which was hydrolyzed to III. The synthesis of V from VII also was reported.[10]

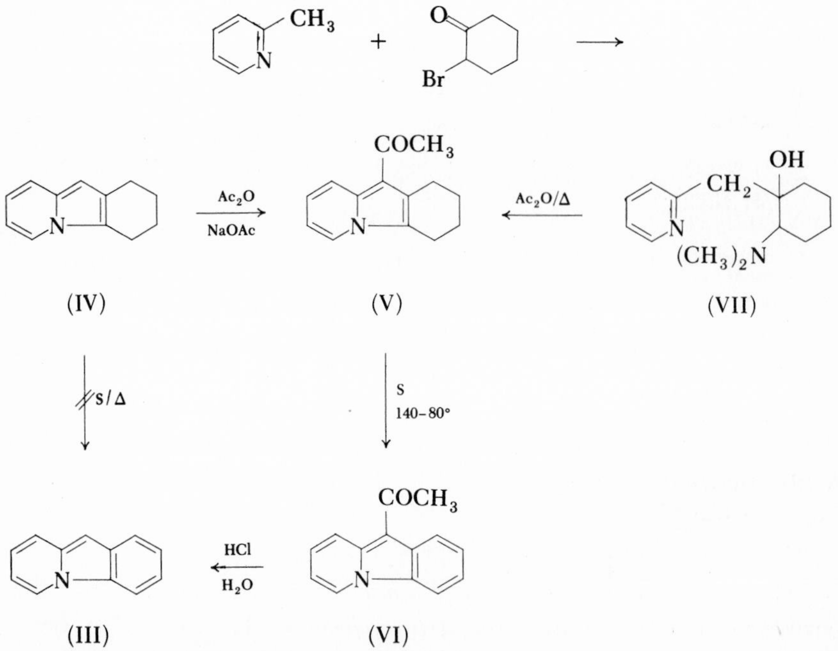

CH_3 + O, Br →

Ac_2O / NaOAc; $COCH_3$; Ac_2O/Δ; OH, CH_2, $(CH_3)_2N$

(IV) (V) (VII)

S/Δ; S 140–80°

HCl / H_2O; $COCH_3$

(III) (VI)

Apparently only a single substitution reaction upon III has been reported. Treatment of III with nitrous acid afforded[1] a nitroso derivative, and the nitroso group was said to be in the 2-position. However, consideration of the reactive positions in pyrrocoline (see

Section A-183), and of the resonance structures possible in III, leads to the conclusion that the product may be the 10-nitroso compound.

Several alkyl homologs (VIII) of III were obtained by Robinson and Saxton[4,5] from the reaction of 1,4-dicarbonyl compounds (or their derivatives) with 3-substituted indoles. Thus skatole reacted with succinaldehyde dioxime to give 10-methylbenzo[*b*]pyrrocoline, and with acetonylacetone to give the 6,9,10-trimethyl homolog. In the condensation of skatole with levulinic acid, a side-reaction produced[4] IX.

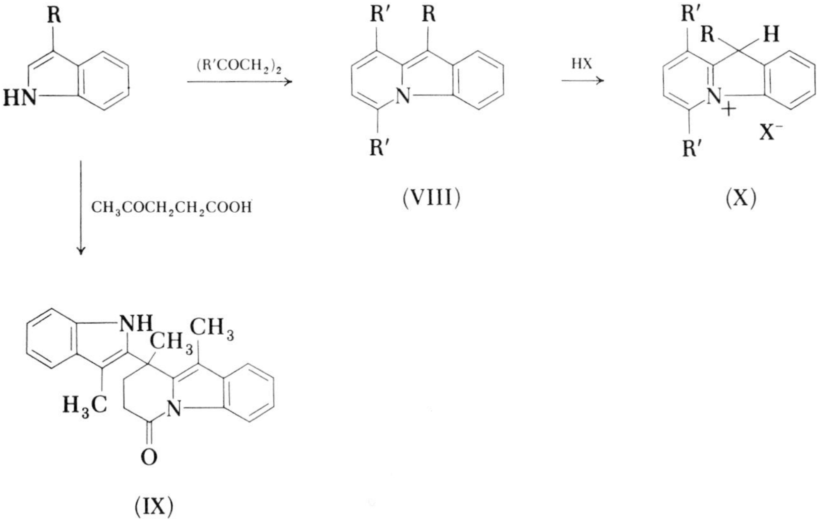

R, HN —$(R'COCH_2)_2$→ R′ R, N, R′ (VIII) —HX→ R′, R, H, N+, R′, X^- (X)

↓ $CH_3COCH_2CH_2COOH$

NH, CH_3, CH_3, H_3C, N, O (IX)

The proposal[5] that salts of benzo[*b*]pyrrocolines have structure X seems well-grounded, as it has been shown[5] that treatment of XI with ethyl iodide and of XII with methyl iodide leads to the same quaternary salt XIII. Further, the ultraviolet absorption spectra of solutions of XI and XII in dilute acid closely resemble that of XIII.

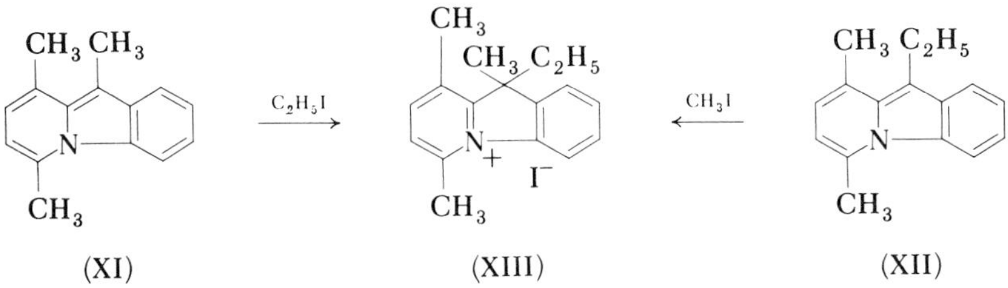

CH_3 CH_3, N, CH_3 (XI) —C_2H_5I→ CH_3, CH_3 C_2H_5, N+, I^-, CH_3 (XIII) ←CH_3I— CH_3 C_2H_5, N, CH_3 (XII)

Condensation of quaternary salts such as XIV with *p*-dimethylaminobenzaldehyde or with *p*-nitrosodimethylaniline produced[5] red dyes such as XV. Alkaline oxidation of the quaternary salt XVI, with an unblocked 6-position, gave[5] the pyridone XVII.

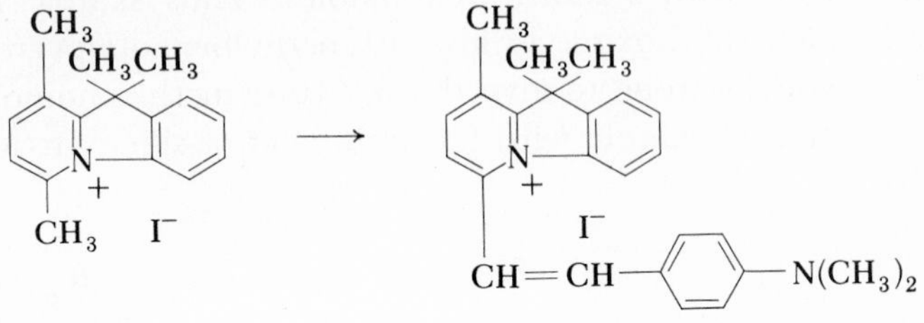

(XIV) (XV)

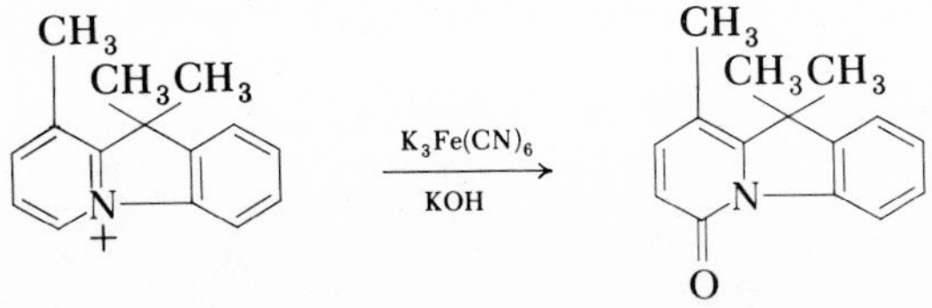

$K_3Fe(CN)_6$, KOH

(XVI) (XVII)

The reaction of chloranil with acetoacetic ester[6,7] or acetylacetone[8] and one to two molecular equivalents[8] of pyridine produced violet quinones of structure XVIII. Further reaction of XVIII with pyridine and the acyl compound gave benzobisindolizines (see Sections A-226/7). Reductive acetylation of XVIII (R = $COCH_3$) gave the yellow acetyldichlorohydroquinone diacetate.

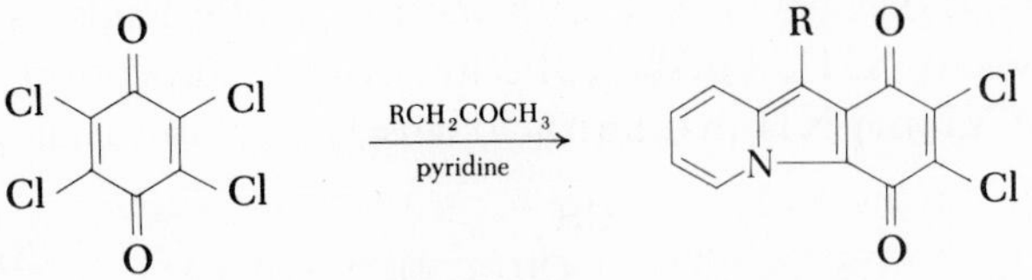

RCH_2COCH_3, pyridine

(XVIII)

From the reaction of indole Grignard reagent with γ-valerolactone, Katritzky and Robinson[9] prepared XIX (R = CH_3), which they cyclized in sulfuric acid to XX. In basic solution XX showed an intense green fluorescence, soon fading in air, probably attributable to the anion XXI. Considerable difficulty was encountered in obtaining XX, and efforts to cyclize other products of type XIX were completely unsuccessful.

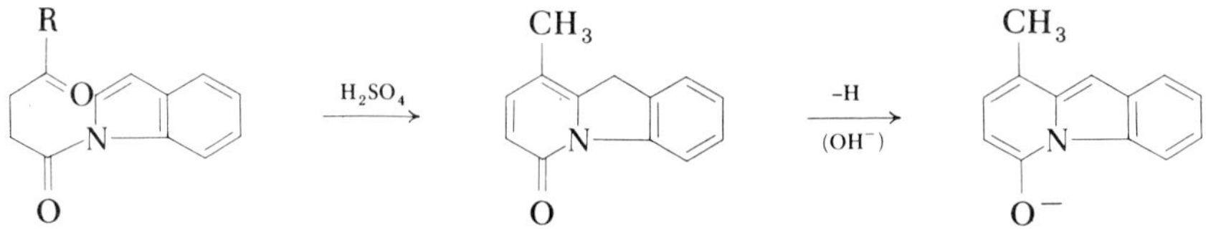

(XIX) $\xrightarrow{H_2SO_4}$ (XX) $\xrightarrow[(OH^-)]{-H}$ (XXI)

The syntheses of the 1,2,3,4-tetrahydro compound (IV)[3] and of its 10-acetyl derivative (V)[3,10] were mentioned earlier. The preparation[10] of V from VII is similar to conversion[11] of XXII into XXIII.

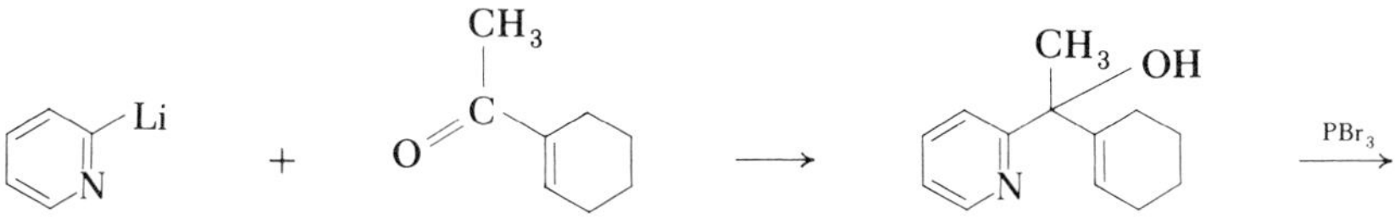

$\longrightarrow$ (XXII) $\xrightarrow{PBr_3}$

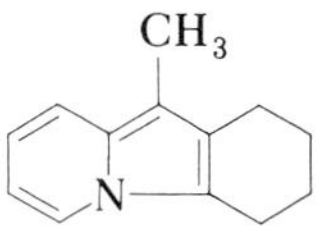

(XXIII)

In addition to compound XX, several hexa- and octahydrobenzo[*b*]pyrrocolines[12,13] also were prepared to serve as model compounds for studies upon the structure of strychnine. Compound XXV (prepared[12] from XXIV) underwent[13] alkaline hydrolysis to yield a substance having either structure XXVI or XXVII, which reacted with dinitrophenylhydrazine to yield XXVIII. Treatment of the hydrolysis product with sulfuric acid gave XXIX (R = H), while methanolic hydrogen chloride yielded the corresponding ester XXIX (R = CH_3). Catalytic hydrogenation of XXIX (R = H or CH_3) yielded XXX (R = H or CH_3). The esters XXIX and XXX (R = CH_3) were also obtained by treatment of the acids with diazomethane. The position of the double bond in the pyrrole ring of XXIX is probably[13] that shown, but the $\Delta^{4a,10a}$ isomer is also a possible structure.

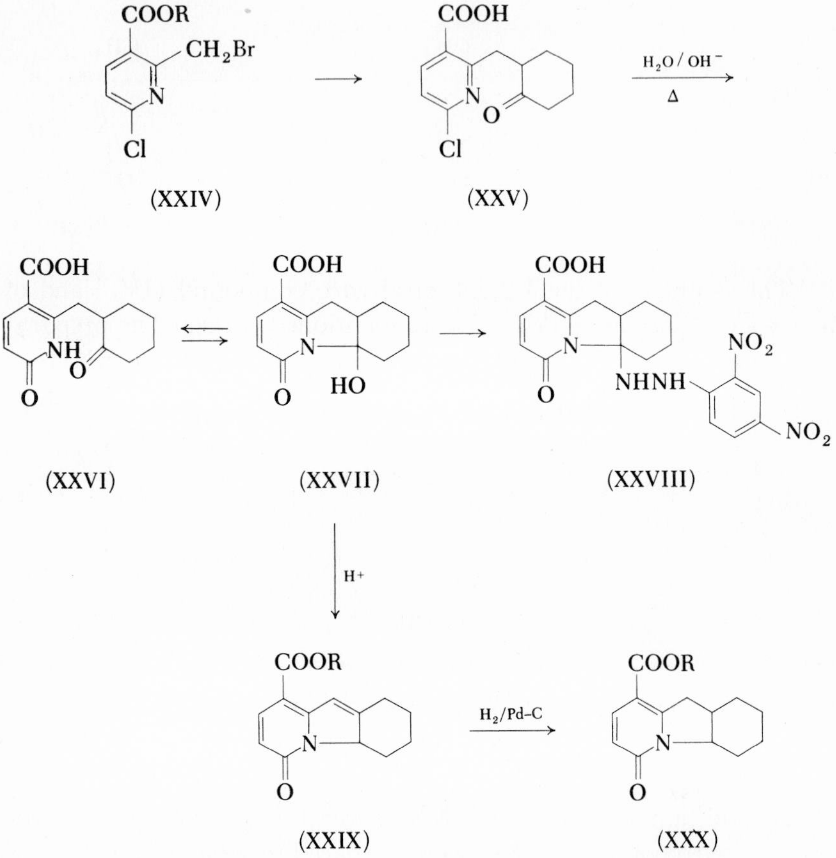

(XXIV) (XXV)

(XXVI) (XXVII) (XXVIII)

(XXIX) (XXX)

Reduction of III with sodium and ethanol yielded a tetrahydro derivative, which Braun and Nelles believed[1] to be XXXI. Further reduction of XXXI by means of tin and acid yielded XXXII.

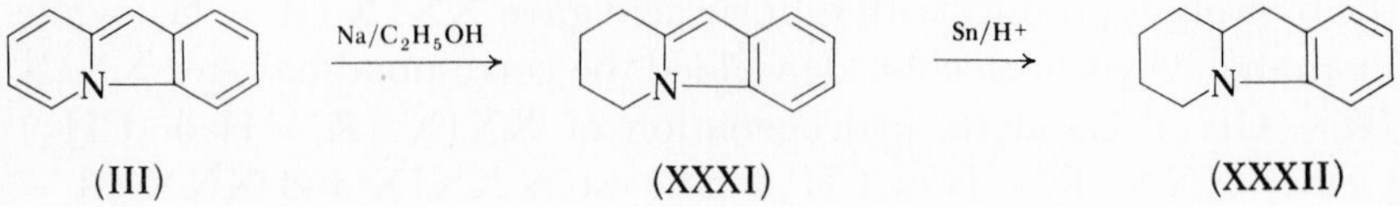

(III) (XXXI) (XXXII)

Hydrogenation of XI over a Raney Nickel or palladium-on-strontium carbonate catalyst gave[5] the tetrahydro compound (XXXIII), whereas the use of Adams catalyst produced the perhydro compound (XXXIV). Reduction[11] of XXIII over platinum oxide likewise yielded the perhydro compound.

CH_3 CH_3 N CH_3 ← H_2 / Pd or Ni — CH_3 CH_3 N CH_3 → H_2 / PtO_2 — CH_3 CH_3 N CH_3

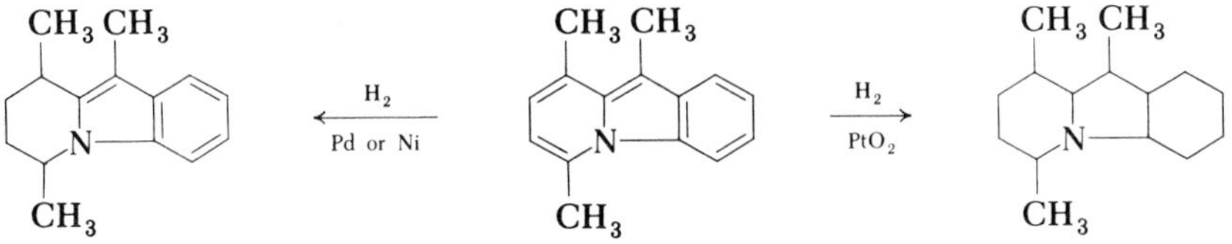

(XXXIII) (XI) (XXXIV)

Hydrogenolysis of XXXVI (obtained in three steps from XXXV) yielded[14] the perhydro compound XXXVII.

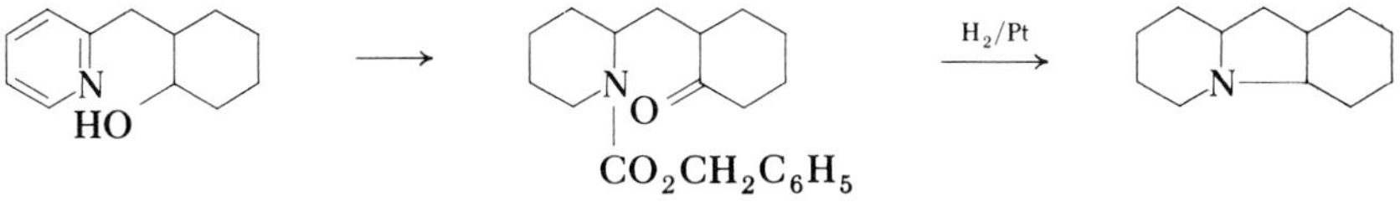

N HO → N O $CO_2CH_2C_6H_5$ → H_2/Pt — N

(XXXV) (XXXVI) (XXXVII)

Benzo[*b*]pyrrocolines

Empirical formula	Substituents or structure	Properties	Refs.
$C_{12}H_8N_2O$	10(or 2)-Nitroso-	Gr., m. 221–3°. Methiodide, m. 190°.	1
$C_{12}H_9N$	Unsubstituted	b_3 110–174°, m. 175–6° (173.5–4.0°). HCl salt, m. 132°. Picrate, m. 138°. Methiodide, m. 231°.	1,3
$C_{12}H_{13}N$	1,2,3,4-Tetrahydro-	b_3 108–13°; m. 52°.	3
	6,7,8,9-Tetrahydro-	$b_{0.3}$ 152–4°. Methiodide, m. 127°. Dinitroso deriv.	1
$C_{12}H_{15}N$	6,7,8,9,9*a*,10-Hexahydro-	$b_{0.25}$ 118–22°; m. 26°. HCl salt, m. 150°. Picrate, m. 132°. Methiodide, m. 140°.	1
$C_{12}H_{21}N$	Perhydro-	b_{10} 98–102°; b_{12} 110–20°. Picrate, m. 209°. Picrolonate, m. 197.5°.	3,14
$C_{13}H_{11}N$	10-Methyl-	Gold, m. 67–8°.	5
$C_{13}H_{11}NO$	6,10-Dihydro-9-methyl-6-oxo-	m. 154.0–5.5°. Perchlorate, m. 275° d.	9
$C_{13}H_{13}NO_3$	9-Carboxy-1,2,3,4,4*a*,6-hexahydro-6-oxo-	Yel., m. 190–1° (202–7°?), λ_{max}^{EtOH} 278, 286, 328, 338 and 348 mμ (ε 17,900, 16,800, 9,400, 10,700 and 7,700). Methyl ester, yel. oil, λ_{max}^{EtOH} 225, 277, 288, 325, 338 and 352 mμ.	13
$C_{13}H_{15}N$	1,2,3,4-Tetrahydro-10-methyl-	m. 41–3°.	11
$C_{13}H_{15}NO_3$	9-Carboxy-1,2,3,4,4*a*,6,10,10*a*-octahydro-6-oxo-	m. 253–4°, λ_{max}^{EtOH} 263 and 302 mμ (ε 14,700 and 5,900). Methyl ester, yel. oil, λ_{max}^{EtOH} 267 and 300 mμ.	13
$C_{13}H_{15}NO_4$	9-Carboxy-1,2,3,4,4*a*,6,10,10*a*-octahydro-4*a*-hydroxy-	m. 237–8°, λ_{max}^{EtOH} 262 and 303 mμ (ε 14,800 and 6,000).	13
$C_{13}H_{23}N$	Perhydro-10-methyl-	b_{13} 121–8°. HCl salt, m. 178–80°.	11
$C_{14}H_7Cl_2NO_3$	10-Acetyl-2,3-dichloro-1,4-dihydro-1,4-dioxo-	Vt., m. 246–8°.	8
$C_{14}H_{11}NO$	10-Acetyl-	b_3 140–80°; m. 133.5–4.0°.	3

$C_{14}H_{13}N$	9,10-Dimethyl-	Yel., m. 86–7°. Perchlorate, m. 173–6°. Methiodide, m. 252° d.	5
$C_{14}H_{15}NO$	10-Acetyl-1,2,3,4-tetrahydro-	Yel., m. 154° (151.5–2.0°); λ_{max} 237, 274, 283, 364 and 380* mμ (ε 26,000, 4,400, 4,000, 14,000 and 11,000).	3,10
$C_{15}H_9Cl_2NO_4$	10-Carbethoxy-2,3-dichloro-1,4-dihydro-1,4-dioxo-	Vt., m. 165°.	6,7
$C_{15}H_{15}N$	10-Ethyl-9-methyl-	Gold, m. 71–3°. Perchlorate, m. 166–8°. Methiodide, m. 219–21°.	5
	6,9,10-Trimethyl-	Yel., m. 134°. Perchlorate, m. 196–7°. Methiodide, m. 239–41°. Ethiodide, m. 247–9° d.	4,5
$C_{15}H_{15}NO$	6,10-Dihydro-9,10,10-trimethyl-6-oxo-	Oil. Perchlorate, m. 202–4°.	5
$C_{15}H_{19}N$	6,7,8,9-Tetrahydro-6,9,10-trimethyl-	$b_{0.08}$ 120°, m. 76–80°.	4
$C_{15}H_{27}N$	Perhydro-6,9,10-trimethyl-	$b_{0.65}$ 116°. Picrate, m. 161–6°.	4
$C_{16}H_{17}N$	10-Ethyl-6,9-dimethyl-	Gold, m. 74°. Perchlorate, d. 205–15°. Methiodide, m. 247–9° d.	4,5
$C_{18}H_{14}Cl_2NO_5$	1,4-Diacetoxy-10-acetyl-2,3-dichloro-	Yel., m. 244°.	8
$C_{18}H_{20}N_2O$	10-(2-Acetamidoethyl)-6,9-dimethyl-	Yel., grn. fluoresc., m. 190–1°. Perchlorate, m. 202°.	4
$C_{19}H_{19}N_5O_7$	[structure: COOH, N, O, NH — NH, O_2N, NO_2]	Yel., m. 182–3°, λ_{max}^{EtOH} 265 and 340 mμ (ε 23,200 and 19,600).	13

(continued)

Benzo[*b*]pyrrocolines (*continued*)

Empirical formula	Substituents or structure	Properties	Refs.
$C_{23}H_{22}N_2O$		m. 220°.	4
$C_{24}H_{26}N_3$		Iodide, grn.-blk., d. 215–6°.	5
$C_{25}H_{27}N_2$		Iodide, red, d. 209–10°.	5

References

1. Braun and Nelles, *Ber.*, **70,** 1767 (1937).
2. Delfs, (I.G. Farbenindustrie, A.G.), *P.B. Report No.* 52013, frame 314.
3. Arata, Ohashi and Uwai, *J. Pharm. Soc. Japan*, **75,** 265 (1955); *Chem. Abstracts*, **49,** 10278 (1955).
4. Robinson and Saxton, *J. Chem. Soc.*, **1950,** 3136.
5. Robinson and Saxton, *J. Chem. Soc.*, **1952,** 976.
6. Tilak and Venkiteswaran, *J. Sci. Ind. Research* (India), **15B,** 561 (1956).
7. Tilak and Venkiteswaran, *Chem. and Ind.*, **1956,** R33.
8. Islam and Selim, *J. Org. Chem.*, **22,** 1641 (1957).
9. Katritzky and Robinson, *J. Chem. Soc.*, **1955,** 2481.
10. Barrett and Chambers, *J. Chem. Soc.*, **1958,** 338.
11. Heer and Hoffmann, *Helv. Chim. Acta*, **39,** 1820 (1956).
12. Ramirez and Paul, *J. Org. Chem.*, **19,** 183 (1954).
13. Ramirez and Paul, *J. Am. Chem. Soc.*, **77,** 3337 (1955).
14. Prelog, Frenkiel and Szpilfogel, *Helv. Chim. Acta*, **29,** 484 (1946).

A-192. Pyrrolo[*a*]quinoline.
R.I. 1661

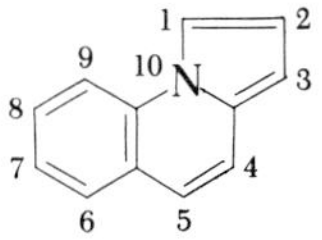

Although Tschitschibabin reported[1,11] the probable preparation of "non-crystalline" products of type I, he did not give any details, and efforts[2] to repeat this work gave only quinaldine hydrohalide salts.

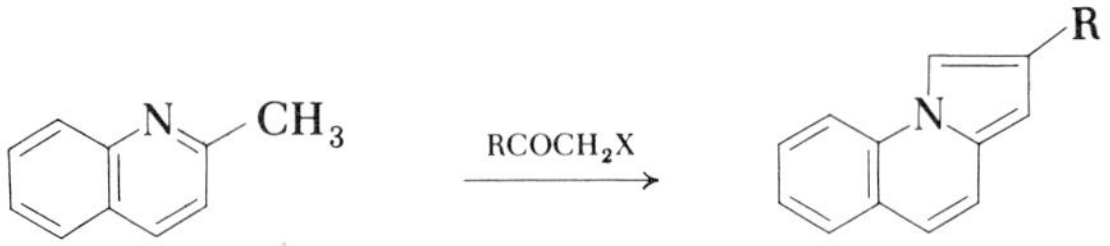

$\xrightarrow{RCOCH_2X}$

(I)

However, the prototype of this nucleus (IV) was obtained[3] in 85% yield from III by treatment with hydrogen bromide followed by caustic. The reduction of II to III was peculiar in that sodium borohydride does not normally reduce ester functions. On the other hand, lithium aluminum hydride, which would be expected to convert II into III, produced instead an unstable amphoteric hydroxy compound thought[3] to be 2- or 3-hydroxypyrrolo[*a*]quinoline

(V). Efforts to prepare[3] 5-hydroxy-1-methylpyrrolo[*a*]quinoline by the cyclization of 1-(2-carbomethoxyphenyl)-2,5-dimethylpyrrole, failed.

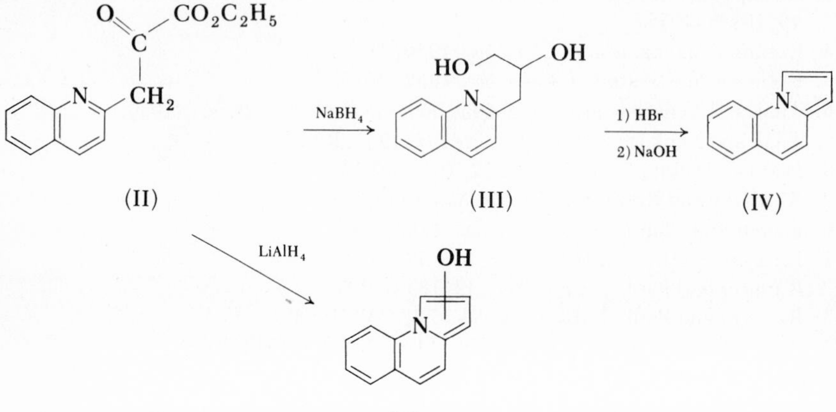

O C $CO_2C_2H_5$ CH_2 N (II) $NaBH_4$ → HO OH N (III) 1) HBr 2) NaOH → N (IV)

$LiAlH_4$ → OH N (V)

The condensation of quinoline with dimethyl acetylenedicarboxylate yielded[4] a "labile yellow" (VI) and a "stable red" (VII) adduct (see Section A-729). Oxidation of each adduct with nitric or chromic acid produced VIII, which was saponified and partially decarboxylated to, presumably, the 1,2- or 2,3-dicarboxy compound.

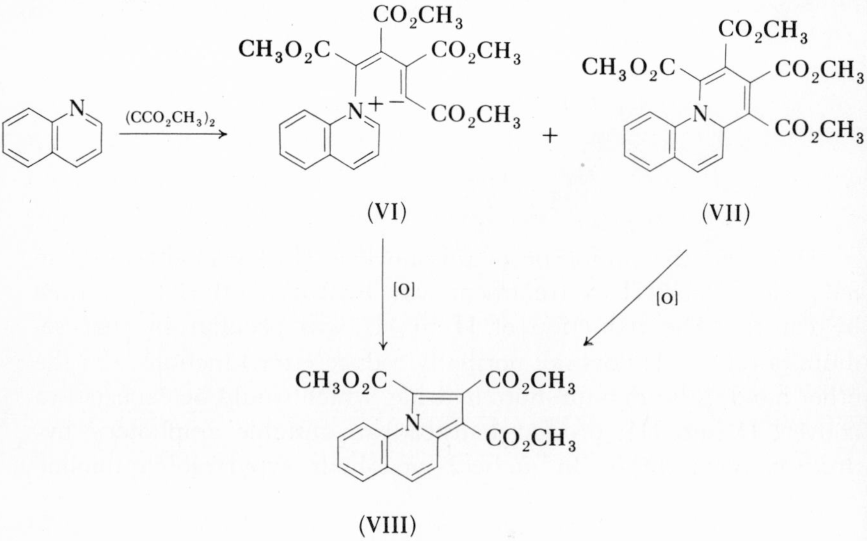

N $(CCO_2CH_3)_2$ → CO_2CH_3 CH_3O_2C CO_2CH_3 N^+ $^-$ CO_2CH_3 (VI) + CO_2CH_3 CH_3O_2C CO_2CH_3 N CO_2CH_3 (VII)

[O] [O]

CH_3O_2C CO_2CH_3 N CO_2CH_3 (VIII)

Among the products resulting when quinalidine was heated with sulfur, was a yellow substance ($C_{30}H_{19}N_3$) assigned[5] (by analogy with the product similarly obtained from α-picoline—see Section A-183) structure IX.

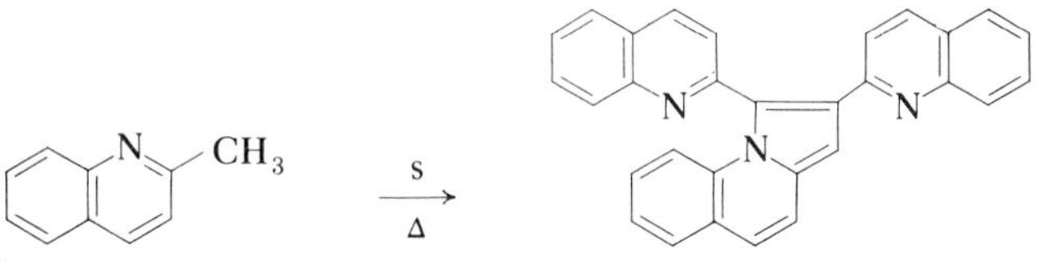

(IX)

Heating X in pyridine solution with acetic anhydride or benzoyl chloride produced[6] deep blue products of structure XI. These products are reminiscent of the red acyl derivatives formed by 3-nitrosoimidazo[1,2-*a*]pyridin-2(3*H*)-one (see Section A-271).

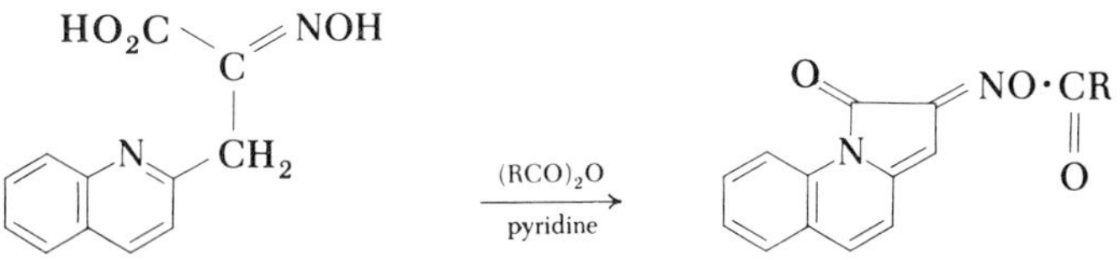

(X) (XI)

In the rearrangement of alkaline solutions of chloralquinaldine (XII) into 2-quinolylacrylic acid (XVI), intermediates of structures XII–XV have been postulated.[7] These intermediates have not, of course, actually been isolated.

The first synthesis of a pyrrolo[*a*]quinoline derivative was conducted by Koenigs,[8] who prepared the lactam XVIII by heating XVII. A Clemmensen reduction of XVIII yielded[9] the hexahydro compound XIX.

Two syntheses of the perhydro compound (XX) have been reported, and different properties were recorded for the product obtained by each method. High pressure by hydrogenation of II over a copper chromite catalyst gave[10] a well-characterized product without evidence of the presence of more than one stereoisomeric form. Without reference to this earlier work, the hydrogenation of IV was reported[3] to yield two stereoisomeric modifications of XX (characterized as picrates). The melting point of one of these is virtually

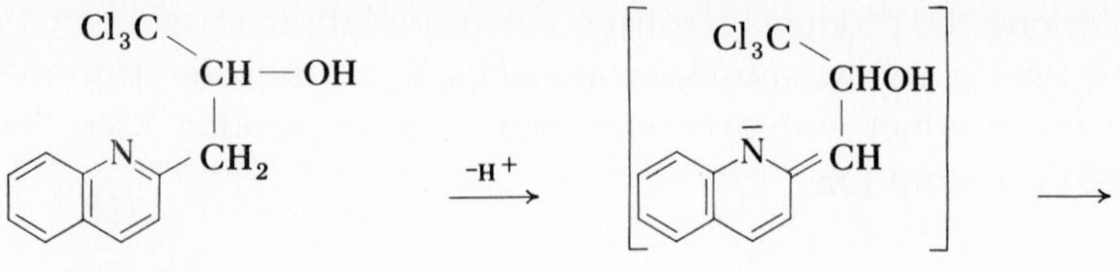

(XII)

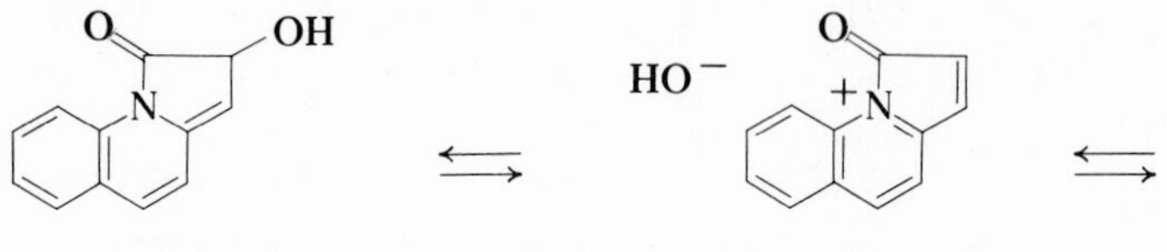

(XIII) (XIV)

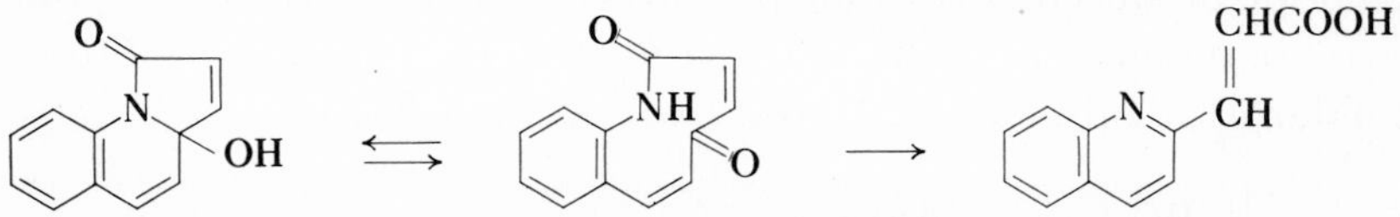

(XV) (XVI)

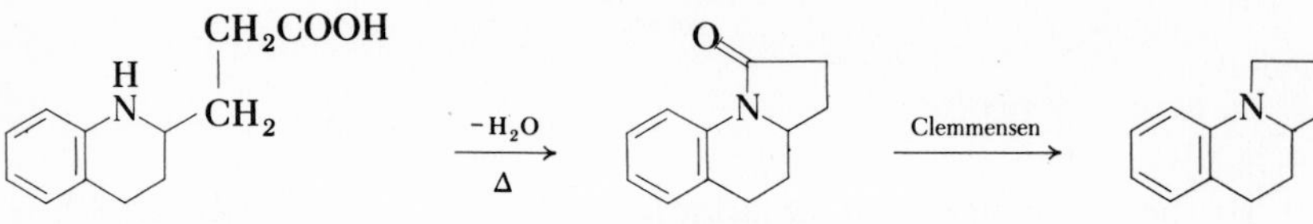

(XVII) (XVIII) (XIX)

identical with that of the picrate[9] of XIX, although the microanalyses reported,[3] while not good, would seem to exclude this structure.

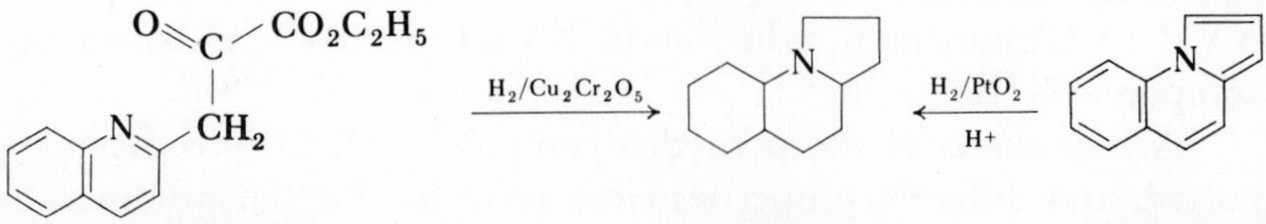

(II) (XX) (IV)

It is possible that the three picrates reported represent three of the four possible racemates of structure XX.

Pyrrolo[*a*]quinolines

Empirical formula	Substituents or structure	Properties	Refs.
$C_{12}H_9N$	Unsubstituted	m. 108–9°, light bl. fluoresc. Deep bl. Ehrlich test.	3
$C_{12}H_9NO$	1 (or 2)-Hydroxy-	Unstable, yel., m. 95–7° (or 66–8° as dihydrate). Perchlorate, red, m. 145–6°. Picrate, m. 141–2°. *O*-Acetyl deriv., m. 110–1°.	3
$C_{12}H_{13}NO$	1,2,3,3*a*,4,5-Hexahydro-1-oxo-	m. 115–6°.	8,9
$C_{12}H_{15}N$	1,2,3,3*a*,4,5-Hexahydro-	Oil. Picrate, m. 146° d.	9
$C_{12}H_{21}N$	Dodecahydro-	Product from II: b_1 65–6°; n_D^{20} 1.5000, d_4^{20} 0.962. Picrate, m. 184.5°. Picrolonate, m. 215–6°.	10
		Product from IV: oil, giving two picrates, m. 146–7° and 169–70°.	3
$C_{14}H_9NO_4$	1,2 (or 2,3)-Dicarboxy-	d. 259°.	4
$C_{14}H_{10}N_2O_3$	O N $NOCOCH_3$	Bl.-blk., m. 185–6°.	6
$C_{18}H_{15}NO_6$	1,2,3-Tricarbomethoxy-	m. 129°.	4
$C_{19}H_{12}N_2O_3$	O N $NOCOC_6H_5$	Deep bl., m. and turns red at 172°, then resolidifies and does not remelt below 260°.	6
$C_{30}H_{19}N_3$	1,2-Di-(2-quinolyl)-	Yel., m. 197–8°. HCl salt red. Methiodide, red, m. 219–20°.	5

References

1. Tschitschibabin, *Ber.*, **60,** 1607 (1927).
2. Borrows, Holland and Kenyon, *J. Chem. Soc.*, **1946,** 1069.
3. Roberts, Gates and Boekelheide, *J. Org. Chem.*, **20,** 1442 (1955).
4. Diels, Alder, Friedrichsen, Petersen, Brodersen and Kech, *Ann.*, **510,** 87 (1934).
5. Skidmore and Tidd, *Chem. and Ind.*, **1954,** 1295.
6. Borsche and Manteuffel, *Ann.*, **526,** 22 (1936).
7. Dauben and Vaughan, *J. Am. Chem. Soc.*, **75,** 4651 (1953).
8. Koenigs, *Ber.*, **33,** 218 (1900).
9. Kondo and Watanabe, *J. Pharm. Soc. Japan*, **54,** 905 (1934); *Chem. Abstracts*, **31,** 104 (1937).
10. Leonard and Boyer, *J. Am. Chem. Soc.*, **72,** 2980 (1950).
11. Tschitschibabin, Ger. Pat. 464,481; *Frdl.*, **16,** 2652 (1931).

A-193. Pyrido[2,3-*e*]pyrrocoline

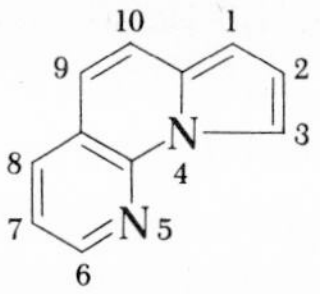

Ochiai and Miyaki hydrogenated I over platinum oxide or Raney nickel and obtained a tetrahydro compound thought to be II. The reaction of this with chloroacetone followed by base gave an impure resinous product assigned structure III on the basis of color reactions. Further evidence obviously is necessary to establish structure III.

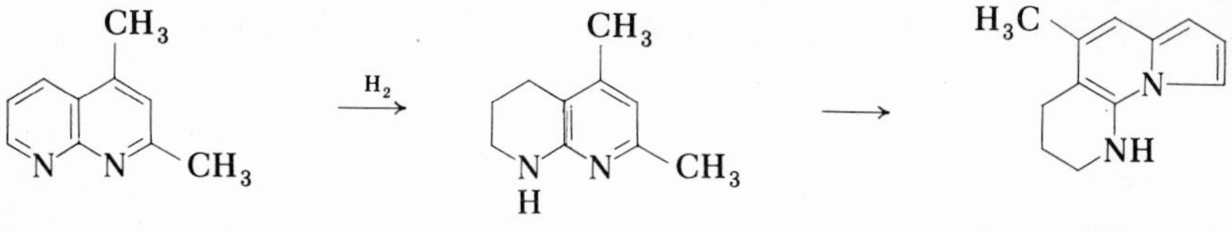

(I) (II) (III)

Reference

1. Ochiai and Miyaki, *Ber.*, **74,** 1115 (1941).

A-194. Benzo[*f*]pyrrocoline. R.I. 1641

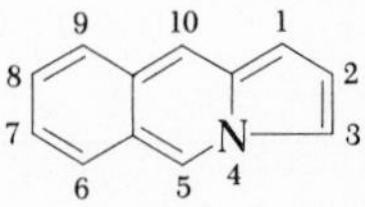

The names *2,3-pyrrolisoquinoline* and *benzo-6,7-pyrrocoline* are also encountered.

In 1884, Ciamician and Dennstedt[1] heated pyrrole with phthalic anhydride in acetic acid at 180°, and obtained a product ($C_{12}H_7NO_2$) known as *pyrrolene-phthalide*. Structures I,[2] II[2] and III[3] were proposed for this product. Structure II was used by Oddo initially,[4] though he later[5] favored structure III, as did Ciamician[3] and Fischer.[8] Thus structure III was accepted (without strong evidence) until very recently, when Cornforth and Firth[11] examined the

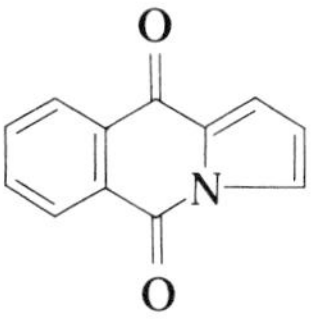

(I) 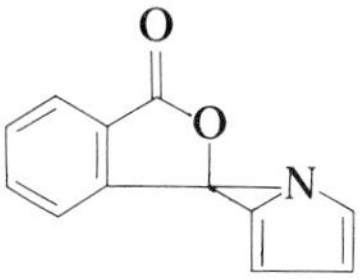 (II) 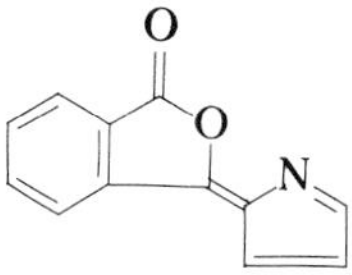 (III)

spectra of this product and several of its alkyl homologs. The ultraviolet spectra resembly those of many anthraquinones, while the infrared spectra are consistent only with structure I.

Most simple pyrroles react in this manner with phthalic anhydride, and the resulting stable, crystalline, yellow derivatives offer a convenient means of characterizing[7,8] pyrroles. Under the rather strenuous conditions of the reaction, pyrroles having carbonyl,[8] carbethoxy[8] or methyl[7] groups in the 5 position may lose these substituents. Where they are shown at all, the structures of these derivatives are usually depicted[13] as being of type III. They must now be changed to I, and even the name pyrrolene-phthalide is now unsuitable. These products are tabulated as substituted benzo[*f*]pyrrocoline-5,10-diones.

Anderlini[12] prepared a mononitro and a dibromo derivative of I, in which the substituents were shown (by oxidation to phthalic acid) to be in the pyrrole ring. Also, bromination of *kryptopyrrolene-phthalide* yielded[8] 1-bromomethyl-2-ethyl-3-methylbenzo[*f*]pyrrocoline-5,10-dione, in which the halogen could be replaced by reaction with methanol or aniline. The lactam bond of I is readily cleaved by alkalies, and treatment of I with hydriodic acid in acetic acid causes scission of phthalic acid and regeneration of the pyrrole. The reaction of pyrroles with substituted phthalic anhydrides does not appear to have been described, but would seem worthy of investigation.

The preparation of the orange phenyl derivative IV from 3-methylisoquinoline was recently claimed,[14,15] but no details were offered. Condensation of IV with *p*-dimethylaminobenzaldehyde[14,15] or *p*-dimethylaminocinnamaldehyde[15] yielded quaternary methine dyes such as V (dull red, m. 142–4° d.).

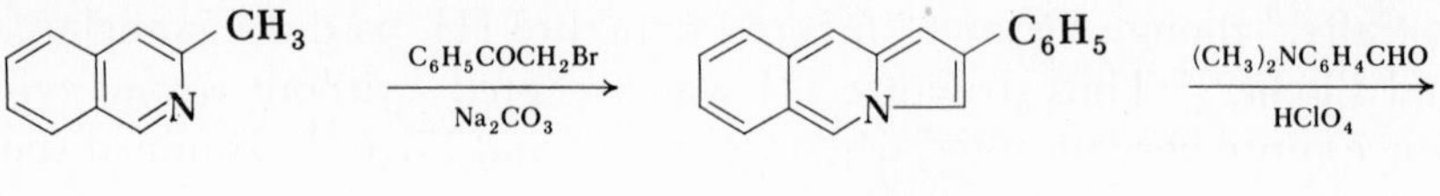

$C_6H_5COCH_2Br$, Na_2CO_3 → (IV) → $(CH_3)_2NC_6H_4CHO$, $HClO_4$ → (V)

(IV)

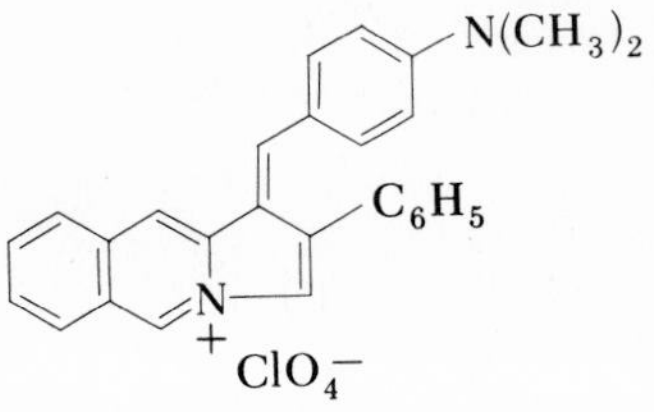

(V)

The Dieckmann cyclization of the diester VI, followed by hydrolysis and decarboxylation of the intermediate ketoester, yielded[16] the ketone VII (yellow-brown, m. 85–6°). Reduction of VII by the Wolff-Kishner technique afforded the hexahydro compound VIII ($b_{0.06}$ 87–92°, n_D^{20} 1.5582; picrate, m. 186.5–8.0°), which was also a major product from the electrolytic reduction of VII.

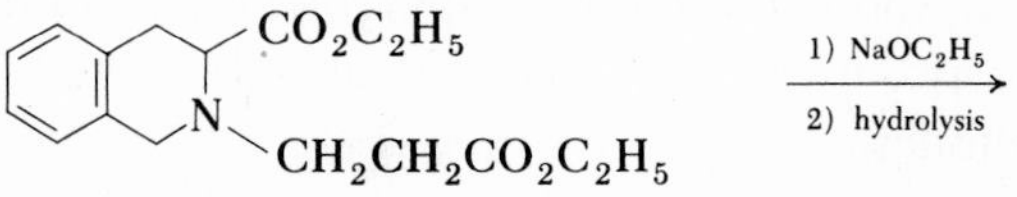

1) $NaOC_2H_5$ 2) hydrolysis

(VI)

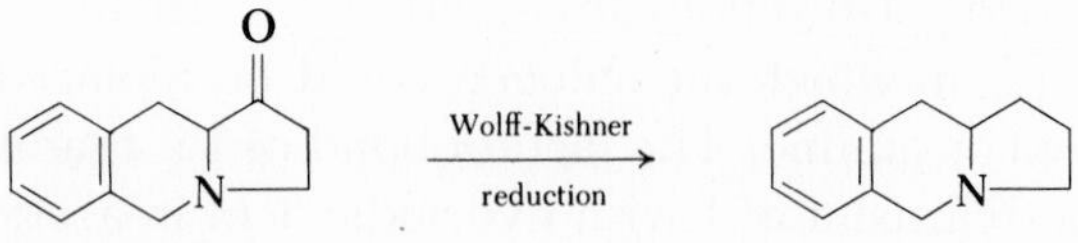

Wolff-Kishner reduction

(VII) (VIII)

Benzo[*f*]pyrrocoline-5,10-diones

Empirical formula	Substituents	Properties	Refs.
$C_{12}H_5Br_2NO_2$	*x*,*x*-Dibromo-	Yel., m. 199°.	12
$C_{12}H_6N_2O_4$	*x*-Nitro-	—	12
$C_{12}H_7NO_2$	Unsubstituted	Yel., m. 240–1°.	1
$C_{13}H_9NO_2$	1 (or 2)-Methyl-	Yel., m. 169–70° (157°).	2,11
	2 (or 1)-Methyl-	Yel., m. 223°.	2,11
	3-Methyl-	Yel., m. 173–4° (215°?)	2,11
$C_{14}H_{11}NO_2$	3-Ethyl-	Yel., m. 114°.	11
	1,3-Dimethyl-	Yel., m. 181–3° (170°?); λ_{max}^{EtOH} 237, 267, 318 and 378 mμ. (log ε 4.42, 4.28, 3.71 and 3.67).	6,11
$C_{15}H_{13}NO_2$	1,2,3-Trimethyl-	Yel., m. 205°.	7,6
$C_{16}H_{13}NO_3$	2-Acetyl-1,3-dimethyl-	Yel., m. 183°.	7
$C_{16}H_{14}BrNO_2$	1-Bromomethyl-2-ethyl-3-methyl-	Yel., m. 192°.	8
$C_{16}H_{15}NO_2$	1-Ethyl-2,3-dimethyl-	Yel., m. 140°.	7
	2-Ethyl-1,3-dimethyl-	Yel., m. 169°.	7,8
$C_{17}H_{15}NO_4$	1-(2-Carboxyethyl)-2,3-dimethyl-	Yel., m. 225–6°.	7,10
$C_{17}H_{17}NO_3$	2-Ethyl-1-methoxymethyl-3-methyl-	Yel., m. 157°.	8
$C_{18}H_{17}NO_3$	3-Ethyl-1-methyl-2-propionyl-	Yel., m. 105°.	9
$C_{18}H_{17}NO_4$	2-(2-Carboxyethyl)-3-ethyl-1-methyl-	Yel., m. 133°.	9
$C_{22}H_{20}N_2O_2$	1-Anilinomethyl-2-ethyl-3-methyl-	m. 170°.	8

References

1. Ciamician and Dennstedt, *Ber.*, **17,** 2944 (1884).
2. Dennstedt and Zimmermann, *Ber.*, **19,** 2200 (1886).
3. Ciamician, *Ber.*, **37,** 4200 (1904).
4. Oddo and Mingoia, *Gazz. chim. ital.*, **55,** 235 (1925); *Chem. Zentr.*, **II,** 1428 (1925).
5. Oddo, *Gazz. chim. ital.*, **55,** 242 (1925); *Chem. Zentr.*, **II,** 1429 (1925).
6. Fischer and Hahn, *Z. physiol. Chem.*, **82,** 254 (1913); *Chem. Zentr.*, **II,** 159 (1913).

7. Fischer and Krollpfeiffer, *Z. physiol. Chem.*, **82**, 266 (1913); *Chem. Zentr.*, **I**, 815 (1913); *Chem. Abstracts*, **7**, 1362 (1913).
8. Fischer and Orth, *Ann.*, **502**, 237 (1933).
9. Fischer and Klarer, *Ann.*, **447**, 48 (1926).
10. Fischer and Treibs, *Ber.*, **60**, 377 (1927).
11. Cornforth and Firth, *J. Chem. Soc.*, **1958**, 1091.
12. Anderlini, *Ber.*, **21**, 2869 (1888).
13. Fischer and Orth, *Die Chemie des Pyrrols*, Akademische Verlagsgesellschaft, Leipzig, 1934, Vol. I, p. 72.
14. Sprague, U. S. Pat. 2,622,082.
15. Sprague, U. S. Pat. 2,706,193.
16. Leonard, Swann and Fuller, *J. Am. Chem. Soc.*, **76**, 3193 (1954).

A-195. Benzo[*g*]pyrrocoline.
R.I. 1659

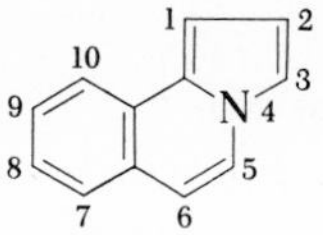

The names *pyrrolo[a]isoquinoline* and *7,8-benzopyrrocoline* as well as the numbering shown in I, have been used.

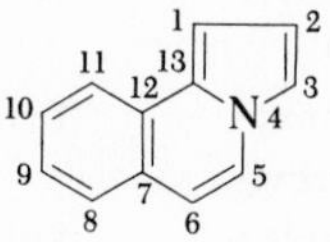

(I)

The prototype of this ring system and some of its homologs have been prepared[1] by catalytic dehydrogenation (with palladium-charcoal) of the 2,3,5,6-tetrahydro or 5,6-dihydro compounds (v.i.). An interesting synthesis of 3-substituted benzo[*g*]pyrrocolines was found by Boekelheide and Godfrey,[1] who obtained III from the reaction of Reissert compounds such as II with acrylonitrile in the presence of phenyl lithium. Complete cleavage of the amide group and formation of IV resulted when III was heated with 100% phosphoric acid, while hot concentrated hydrochloric acid converted III into V. However, V could be cyclized to IV by the action of hot 100% phosphoric acid. Reduction of III (R = C_6H_5) with lithium aluminum hydride yielded VI. A somewhat different reaction occurred between II (R = C_6H_5) and either ethyl acrylate or 2-vinylpyridine, and products of structure VII were obtained.[1] Heating VII (R′ = $COOC_2H_5$) produced the deep red 2-benzoyl-3-hydroxy derivative (VIII), while treatment of VII (R′ = 2-pyridyl) with sulfuric acid gave IX.

CN O C N R CH_2=CHCN C_6H_5Li $CONH_2$ N R 100% H_3PO_4 Δ N R

(II) (III) (IV)

R′CH=CH_2 LiAlH_4 HCl 100% H_3PO_4

R′ CH C C_6H_5 CH_2 O N CH_2NH_2 N C_6H_5 CH_2 CH_2 C R N O

(VII) (VI) (V)

(R′=$COOC_2H_5$)/Δ (R′=2-Pyridyl) H_2SO_4

COC_6H_5 N OH N N C_6H_5

(VIII) (IX)

The Tschitschibabin pyrrocoline synthesis was extended by Sprague[2] to the preparation of X from 1-methylisoquinoline. Condensation of X with *p*-dimethylaminobenzaldehyde or *p*-dimethylaminocinnamaldehyde in the presence of perchloric acid yielded dark blue or green methine dyes (e.g., XI).

CH_3 ... N $\xrightarrow[Na_2CO_3]{C_6H_5COCH_2Br}$ ... N ... C_6H_5 $\xrightarrow[HClO_4]{p\text{-}(CH_3)_2NC_6H_4CHO}$

(X)

$(CH_3)_2N$ — — CH= ... C_6H_5 ... N^+ ClO_4^-

(XI)

From the reaction of isoquinoline with dimethyl acetylenedicarboxylate in ethereal solution at ordinary temperatures Diels and Harms[3] isolated two "labile adducts" (see Section A-725), one of which, upon bromination and treatment with base, yielded a tricarbomethoxy compound assigned structure XII. However, working at −78°, Wiley and Knabeschuh[4] apparently obtained compound XII directly. The reaction appears complex, and there is evidence[4] that the presence of traces of both peroxides and alcohol is mandatory.

N $\xrightarrow[(C_2H_5)_2O]{(CCO_2CH_3)_2}$ "labile adduct" $\xrightarrow[K_2CO_3]{Br_2}$ CH_3O_2C ... CO_2CH_3 ... N ... CO_2CH_3

$\xrightarrow[(C_2H_5)_2O/-78°]{(CCO_2CH_3)_2}$

(XII)

Various tetra- and hexahydrobenzo[*g*]pyrrocolines have been prepared in connection with studies upon *emetine*[5-8] and the *Erythrina* alkaloids.[9,10] Child and Pyman[5] prepared compound XV (together with XIV) by treating XIII with phosphorus oxychloride. A more convenient and general synthesis was developed by Sugasawa,[6] who cyclized 1-phenylethylbutyrolactams (XVI) and obtained XV and its 8,9-methylenedioxy analog. Structure XV is representative of the salts of these compounds, whereas the bases have the $\Delta^{10b,1}$ structure XVII. Several compounds of type XVII have thus been prepared.[1,7,9,10]

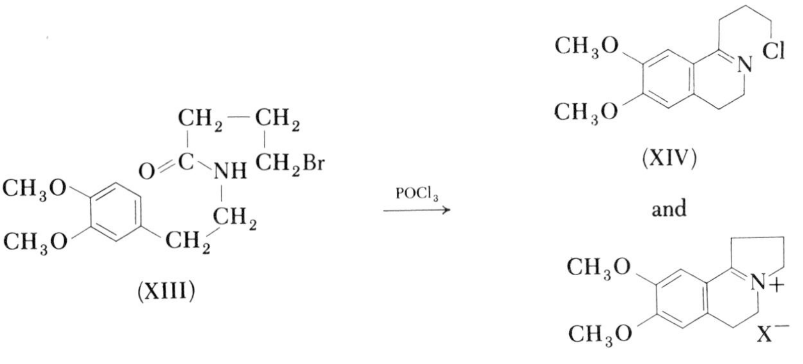

(XIII) $\xrightarrow{POCl_3}$ (XIV) and (XV)

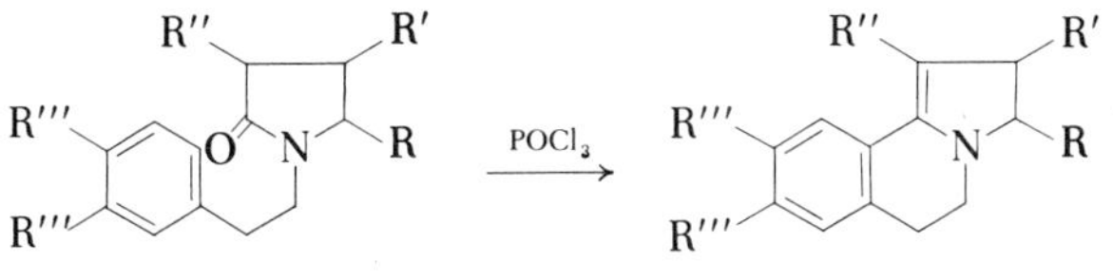

(XVI) $\xrightarrow{POCl_3}$ (XVII)

Catalytic hydrogenation of XVII yielded[6,7] XIX, which could also be obtained by reduction of salts of type XVIII with tin and acid[5] or sodium borohydride.[1] The reaction[9,10] of XVIII (R = R′ = H, R″ = H or allyl, R‴ = OCH_3) with allyl magnesium

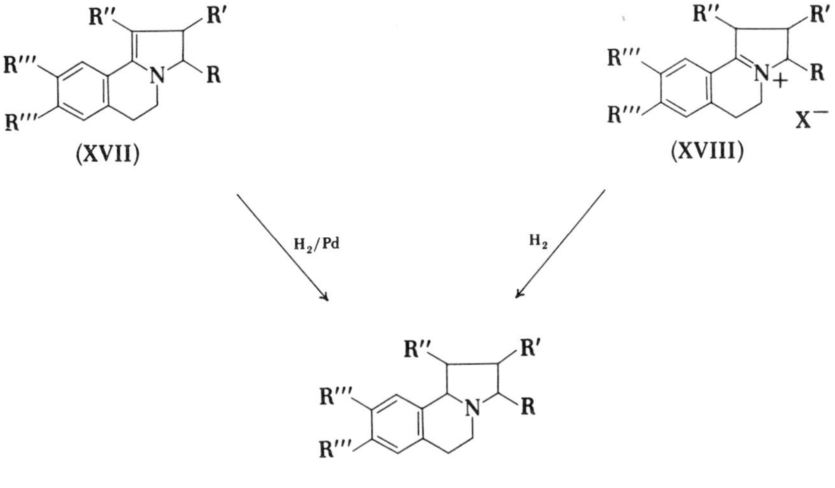

(XVII) $\xrightarrow{H_2/Pd}$ (XIX) $\xleftarrow{H_2}$ (XVIII)

bromide afforded good yields of XX (R = H or allyl). Oxidation of the diallyl compound XX (R = allyl) yielded a mixture of XXI and (mostly) XXII.

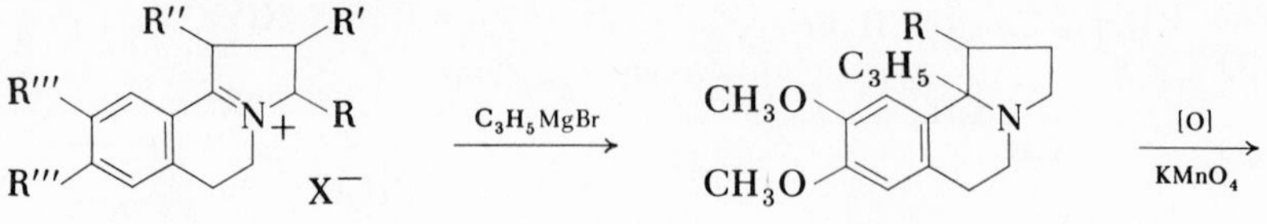

(XVIII) $\xrightarrow{C_3H_5MgBr}$ (XX) $\xrightarrow[KMnO_4]{[O]}$

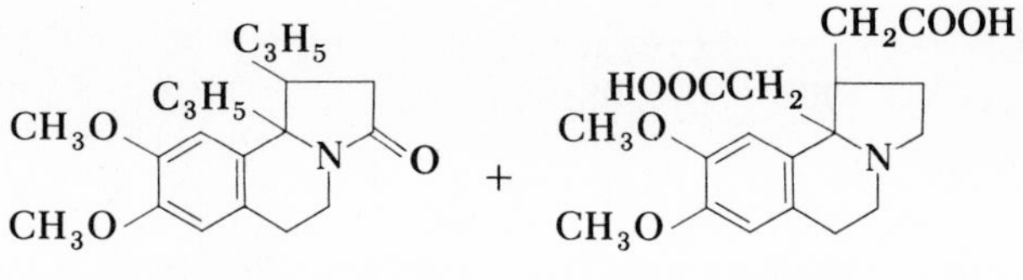

(XXI) + (XXII)

In a synthesis similar to that employed by Sugasawa, Hahn and Stiehl[11] obtained XXIII by condensing 2-(3,4-dihydroxyphenyl)-ethylamine with α-ketoglutaric acid. Methylation and reduction of XXIII yielded[12] XXIV.

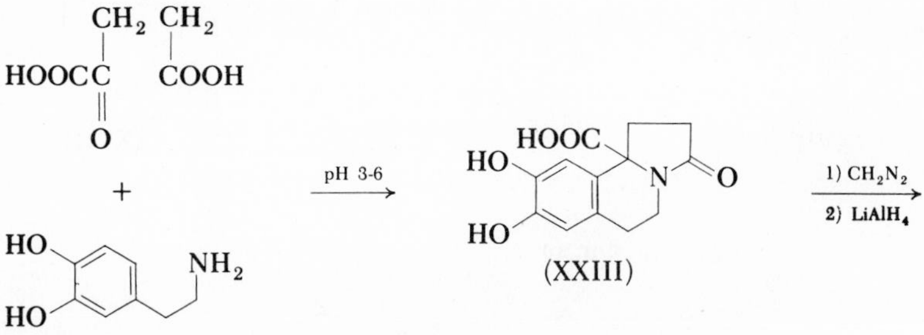

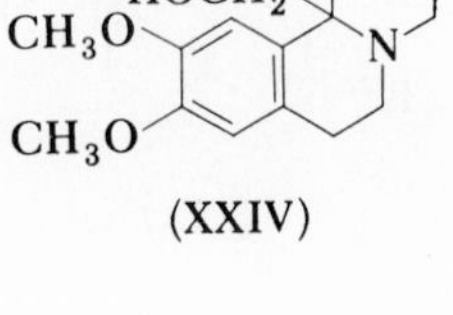

$\xrightarrow{pH\ 3\text{-}6}$ (XXIII) $\xrightarrow[2)\ LiAlH_4]{1)\ CH_2N_2}$

(XXIV)

The action of polyphosphoric acid upon heteroauxin β-phenylethylamide (XXV) has been studied by Thesing and his co-workers,[13,14] who obtained compound XXVII, and postulated an intermediate (not isolated) of type XXVI. However, recently he indicated[15] the product to have structure XXVIII, but as no details were given, futher information must be awaited.

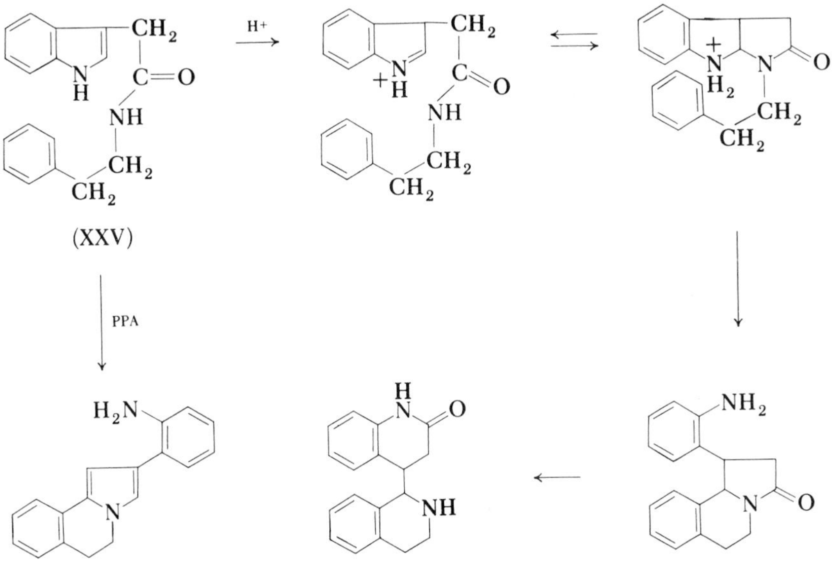

CH_2 C=O NH CH_2 CH_2 N H $\xrightarrow{H^+}$ CH_2 C=O NH CH_2 CH_2 $\overset{+}{N}$H $\rightleftarrows$ $\overset{+}{N}H_2$ N O CH_2 CH_2

(XXV)

PPA

H_2N N H N O NH NH_2 N O

(XXVIII) (XXVII) (XXVI)

The perhydro derivative (XXX) was obtained in 66% yield by Leonard and Boyer,[16] who hydrogenated the ester XXIX over a copper-chromite catalyst.

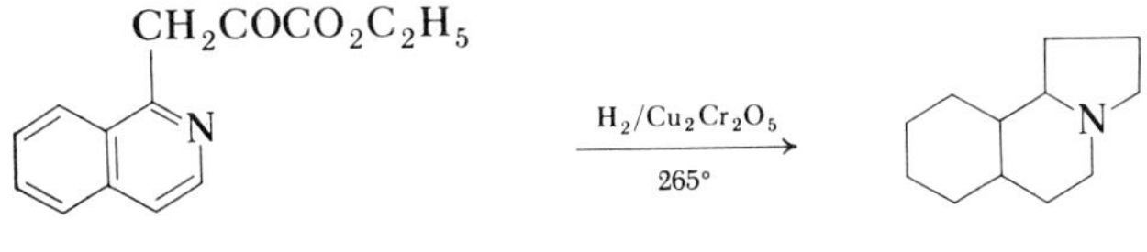

$CH_2COCO_2C_2H_5$ N $\xrightarrow[265°]{H_2/Cu_2Cr_2O_5}$ N

(XXIX) (XXX)

Benzo[*g*]pyrrocolines

Empirical formula	Substituents or structure	Properties	Refs.
$C_{12}H_9N$	Unsubstituted	m. 83.5–4.0°.	1
$C_{12}H_{13}N$	2,3,5,6-Tetrahydro-	Oil, b_3 125–9°.	1
$C_{12}H_{21}N$	Perhydro-	b_1 75–6°, n_D^{20} 1.4960, d_4^{20} 0.950. Picrate, m. 212–4°. Picrolonate, m. 209–10°.	16
$C_{13}H_{11}N$	3-Methyl-	m. 129–30°.	1
$C_{13}H_{13}NO_5$	10*b*-Carboxy-1,2,3,5,6,10*b*-hexahydro-8,9-dihydroxy-3-oxo-	Yel.-brn., darkens at 215°, d. 255–60°.	11
$C_{13}H_{15}N$	2,3,5,6-Tetrahydro-3-methyl-	$b_{0.6}$ 85°, n_D^{25} 1.5942°.	1
$C_{13}H_{15}NO_2$	1,2,3,5,6,10*b*-Hexahydro-8,9-methylenedioxy-	m. 75.5°. HCl salt, d. 234°. *R.I.* 2279M.	6
$C_{14}H_{12}N_2O$	2-Carboxamido-3-methyl-	Yel., m. 189–90°.	1
$C_{14}H_{17}NO_2$	2,3,5,6-Tetrahydro-8,9-dimethoxy-	HBr salt, m. 201–3°. HCl salt, m. 204–5°. Picrate, m. 201.2° (d. 193–4°).	5,6,10
$C_{14}H_{19}NO_2$	1,2,3,5,6,10*b*-Hexahydro-8,9-dimethoxy-	m. 88–9° (87–8°).	
$C_{15}H_{19}NO_2$	2,3,5,6-Tetrahydro-8,9-dimethoxy-3-methyl-	$b_{0.02}$ 120–30°. Picrate, m. 154–5°.	7
$C_{15}H_{21}NO_2$	1,2,3,5,6,10*b*-Hexahydro-8,9-dimethoxy-3-methyl-	$b_{0.02}$ 110–20°. HCl salt, m. 246–8° d. Picrate, m. 173–5°.	7
$C_{15}H_{22}NO_3$	1,2,3,5,6,10*b*-Hexahydro-10*b*-hydroxymethyl-8,9-dimethoxy-	Oil. Picrate, m. 201–2°.	12
$C_{16}H_{21}NO_2$	2,3,5,6-Tetrahydro-8,9-dimethoxy-2,3-dimethyl-	$b_{0.01}$ 135–45°. Picrate, m. 171–3°.	7
$C_{16}H_{23}NO_2$	1,2,3,5,6,10*b*-Hexahydro-8,9-dimethoxy-2,3-dimethyl-	$b_{0.02}$ 150–5°. HCl salt, m. 213–6° d. Picrate, m. 163–4°.	7

$C_{17}H_{21}NO_2$	1-Allyl-2,3,5,6-tetrahydro-8,9-dimethoxy-	Picrolonate, m. 71°.	9,10
$C_{17}H_{23}NO_2$	1-Allyl-1,2,3,5,6,10*b*-hexahydro-8,9-dimethoxy-	Oil. Picrate, m. 158°.	10
	10*b*-Allyl-1,2,3,5,6,10*b*-hexahydro-8,9-dimethoxy-	Oil. Picrate, m. 134–6°.	10
$C_{18}H_{13}N$	2-Phenyl-	Lt. tan.	2
	3-Phenyl-	m. 98.5–9.0°.	1
$C_{18}H_{15}N$	5,6-Dihydro-3-phenyl-	m. 107.5–8.5°.	1
$C_{18}H_{15}NO_6$	1,2,3-Tricarbomethoxy-	m. 150–1°, bl. fluoresc., λ_{max}^{EtOH} 240, 269, 337 and 354 mμ.	3,4
$C_{18}H_{23}NO_6$	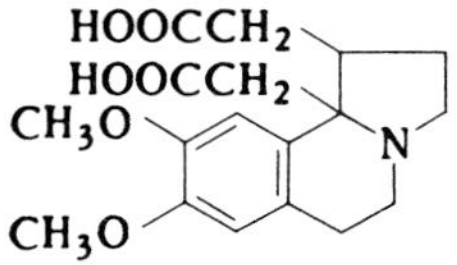	Dimethyl ester, m. 123°.	10
$C_{19}H_{13}NO_2$	2-Benzoyl-3-hydroxy-	Deep red, m. 117–8°.	1
$C_{19}H_{14}N_2O$	2-Carboxamido-3-phenyl-	Or.-red, m. 168–9°.	1
$C_{19}H_{16}N_2$	2-Aminomethyl-3-phenyl-	Lt. yel., m. 127–8°.	1
$C_{20}H_{25}NO_3$	1,10*b*-Diallyl-1,2,3,5,6,10*b*-hexahydro- , 8,9-dimethoxy-3-oxo-	m. 109–10°.	10
$C_{20}H_{27}NO_2$	1,10*b*-Diallyl-1,2,3,5,6,10*b*-hexahydro-8,9-dimethoxy-	Oil. Picrate, m. 139–40°.	9,10
$C_{23}H_{16}N_2$	3-Phenyl-2-(2-pyridyl)-	m. 156–7°. Picrate, m. 251–2°.	1

(*continued*)

Benzo[*g*]pyrrocolines (*continued*)

Empirical formula	Substituents or structure	Properties	Refs.
$C_{27}H_{23}N_2$	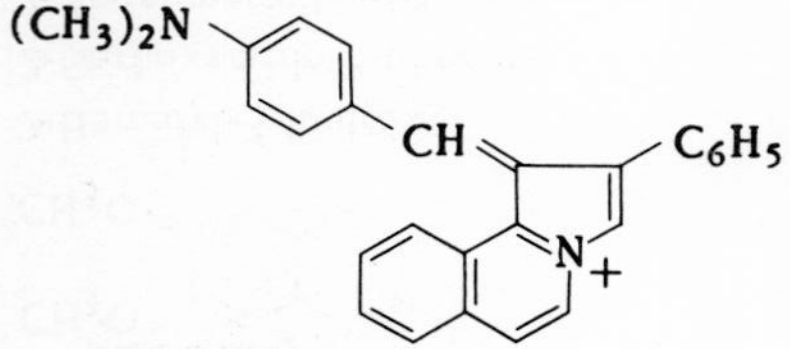 $(CH_3)_2N$, CH, C_6H_5, N^+	Perchlorate, dk. bl., m. 145–7° d.	2
$C_{29}H_{25}N_2$	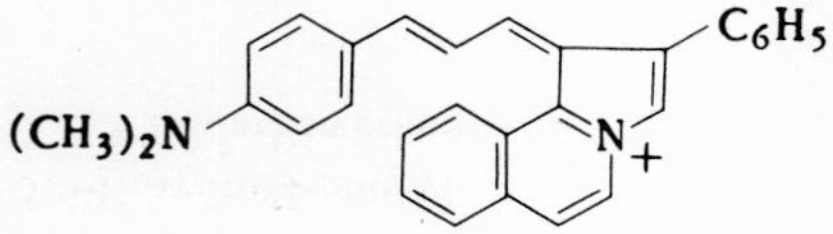 $(CH_3)_2N$, C_6H_5, N^+	Perchlorate, grn., m. 225–8° d.	2

References

1. Boekelheide and Godfrey, *J. Am. Chem. Soc.*, **75,** 3679 (1953).
2. Sprague, U. S. Pats. 2,622,082 and 2,706,193.
3. Diels and Harms, *Ann.*, **525,** 73 (1936).
4. Wiley and Knabeschuh, *J. Org. Chem.*, **18,** 836 (1953).
5. Child and Pyman, *J. Chem. Soc.*, **1931,** 36.
6. Sugasawa, Sakurai and Sugimoto, *Proc. Imp. Acad.* (Tokyo), **15,** 82 (1939); *Chem. Abstracts*, **33,** 6318 (1939).
7. Pailer and Brandstetter, *Monatsh.*, **83,** 523 (1952); *Chem. Abstracts*, **47,** 2187 (1953).
8. Openshaw in Schofield, Editor, *Recent Work on Naturally Occurring Nitrogen Heterocyclic Compounds*, Special Publication No. 3, The Chemical Society, London, 1955, p. 28.
9. Manson and Wiesner, *Chem. and Ind.*, **1953,** 641.
10. Wiesner, Valenta, Manson and Stonner, *J. Am. Chem. Soc.*, **77,** 675 (1955).
11. Hahn and Stiehl, *Ber.*, **69,** 2627 (1936).
12. Little, Smith, Taylor and Thomas, *J. Chem. Soc.*, **1954,** 2636.
13. Thesing, Ramlock, Willersinn and Funk, *Angew. Chem.*, **68,** 387 (1956).
14. Thesing and Funk, *Chem. Ber.*, **89,** 2498 (1956).
15. Thesing, *Angew. Chem.*, **69,** 727 (1957).
16. Leonard and Boyer, *J. Am. Chem. Soc.*, **72,** 2980 (1950).

A-196. [1,3]Dioxolo[*g*]pyrrolo[*a*]-isoquinoline. R.I. 2279M

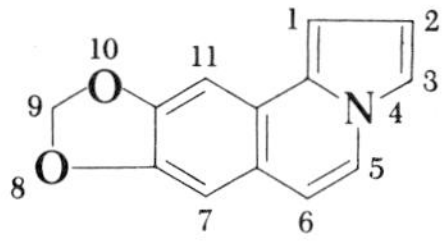

See under benzo[*g*]pyrrocoline (Section A-195).

A-197. 4*H*-Pyrrolo[3,2,1-*ij*]quinoline. R.I. 1663

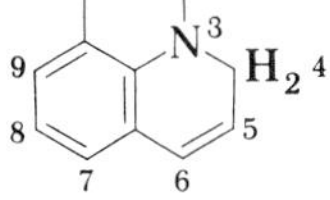

The names (and numbering) *4H-benzo[hi]pyrrocoline*, 2-peri-*pyrroloquinoline* (I) and *liline* (II) also have been used, while the dihydro compounds have been called *liloline* (III) and *1,7-* or *1,8-trimethyleneindole* (IV). The tetrahydro derivatives are known as *lilolidines* (V), and the perhydro system was called *1-azatricyclo-*[*7.2.1.0*^{5,12}]*dodecane* (VI) or *hexahydrolilolidine.*

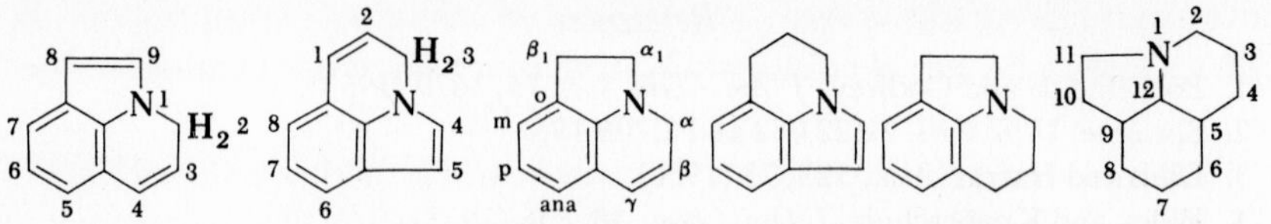

(I) (II) (III) (IV) (V) (VI)

Only hydrogenated derivatives of this nucleus appear to be known. The first reported example was compound VIII, obtained by Bamberger and Sternitzki,[1] who condensed 2-methylindoline with malonic ester and treated the resulting acylindoline (VII) with hot hydrochloric acid. Nitrosation of, and diazonium coupling into VIII occur at the 5-position, and metallic salts of VIII may be obtained.

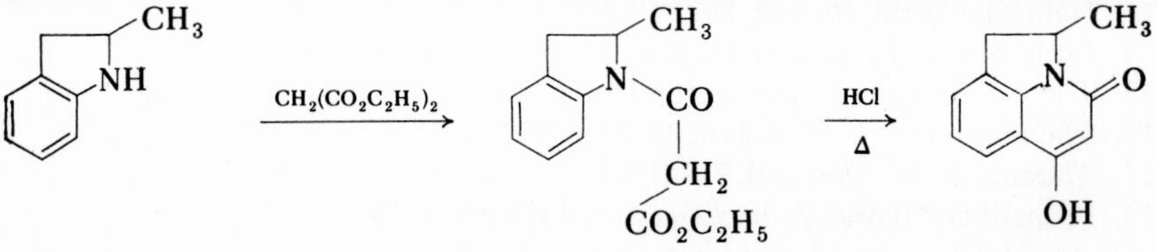

$CH_2(CO_2C_2H_5)_2$ → (VII) $\xrightarrow[\Delta]{HCl}$ (VIII)

Acetoacetic and related esters[2,3] also have been condensed with indolines to yield products of type IX. Reduction of IX with lithium

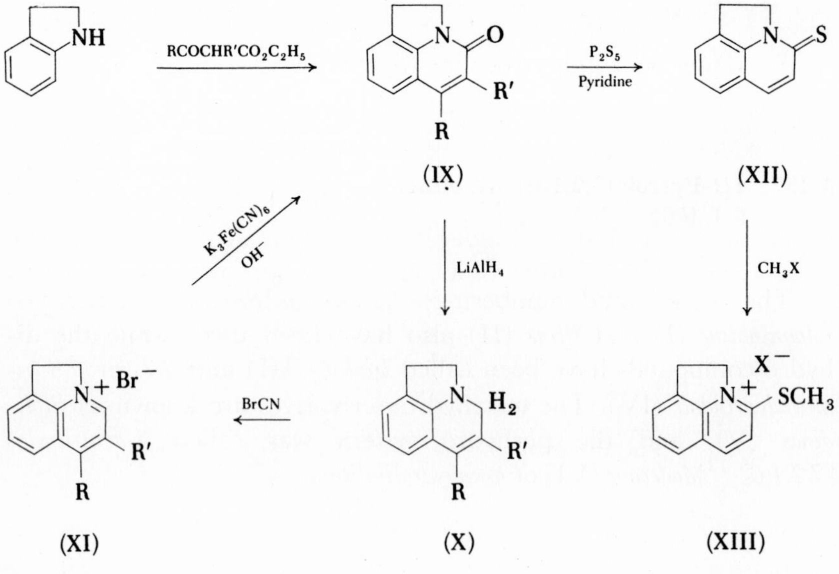

$RCOCHR'CO_2C_2H_5$ → (IX) $\xrightarrow[\text{Pyridine}]{P_2S_5}$ (XII)

(IX) $\xrightarrow{LiAlH_4}$ (X); (X) $\xrightarrow{BrCN}$ (XI); (XI) $\xrightarrow[OH^-]{K_3Fe(CN)_6}$ (IX); (XII) $\xrightarrow{CH_3X}$ (XIII)

(XI) (X) (XIII)

aluminum hydride gave[2] the unstable dihydro compounds X, which could be converted into XI by reaction with cyanogen bromide. Alkaline oxidation of XI produced IX.

Compound IX (R = R′ = H) was transformed, by the action of phosphorus pentasulfide, into the thio homolog (XII), treatment of which with methyl *p*-toluenesulfonate yielded[3] XIII. Treatment of indoline, in the presence of zinc chloride and an oxidant such as ferric chloride or *o*-nitrophenol, with paraldehyde or methyl vinyl ketone yielded, respectively, XIV[4] and XV.[5] Compounds XIII–XV were utilized[3] in the preparation of a number of cyanine dyes.

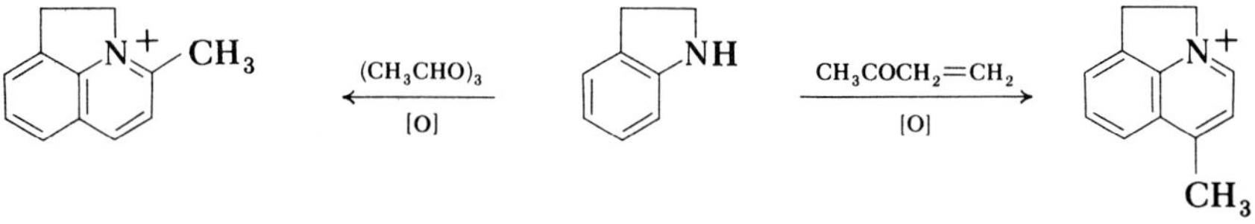

$(CH_3CHO)_3$, [O] ← → $CH_3COCH_2{=}CH_2$, [O]

(XIV) (XV)

An interesting synthesis of this ring system was discovered[6] during an attempt to obtain XVII from the von Braun reaction upon XVI. Instead of XVII, a product was obtained having properties compatible with structure XVIII.

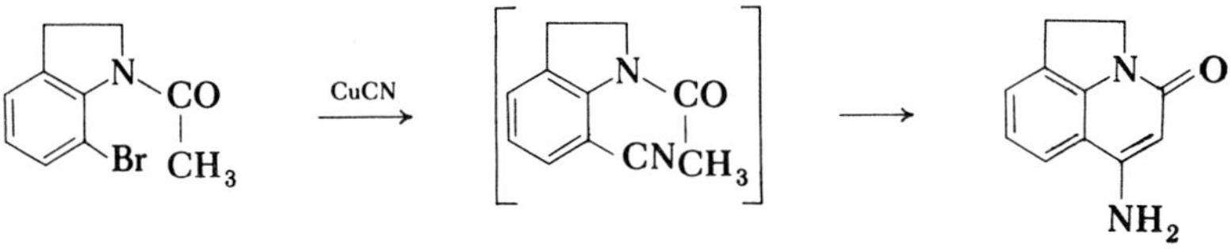

CuCN →

(XVI) (XVII) (XVIII)

5,6-Dihydro-4*H*-pyrrolo[3,2,1-*ij*]quinolines (XX) were prepared[7] by means of the Fischer indole synthesis from hydrazones of type XIX (where R = COOH or C_6H_5, although the reaction failed

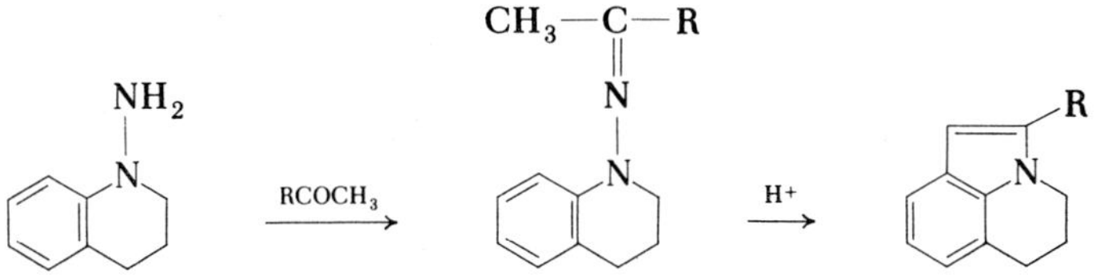

$RCOCH_3$ → H^+ →

(XIX) (XX)

when R = CH_3). The unsubstituted 5,6-dihydro compound was obtained by decarboxylating XX (R = COOH), Unlike X, compounds of type XX are quite stable.

The reaction of 2,3-dimethylindole with acrylonitrile yielded[8] XXI (R = CN), but unlike cyanoethylcarbazole (see Section A-213), it could not be cyclized by heating with aluminum chloride. The corresponding acid (XXI, R = COOH), however, readily afforded XXII, the yellow color (red in strongly acidic solutions) and properties of which probably reflect a substantial contribution to the resonance hybrid by forms such as XXIII.

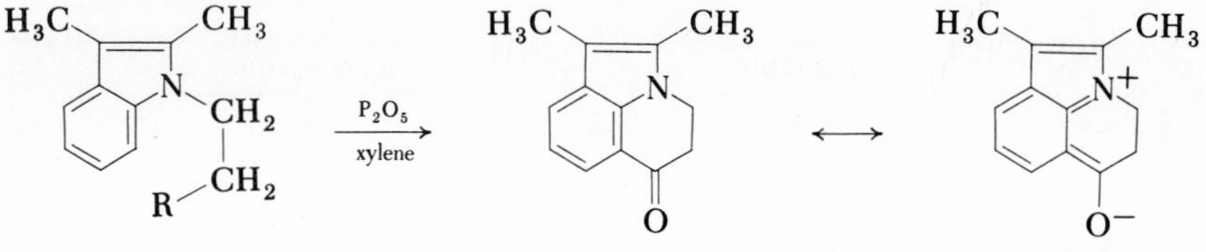

P_2O_5, xylene

(XXI) (XXII) (XXIII)

Lilolidines (XXIV) have been prepared[9] (in about 40% yield) in a manner analogous to the synthesis of julolidines (see Section A-732), by condensing indolines with trimethylene chlorobromide. Other routes to the lilolidines include reduction of XX with zinc or tin and acid, and hydrogenation[2] of XI over Adams catalyst.

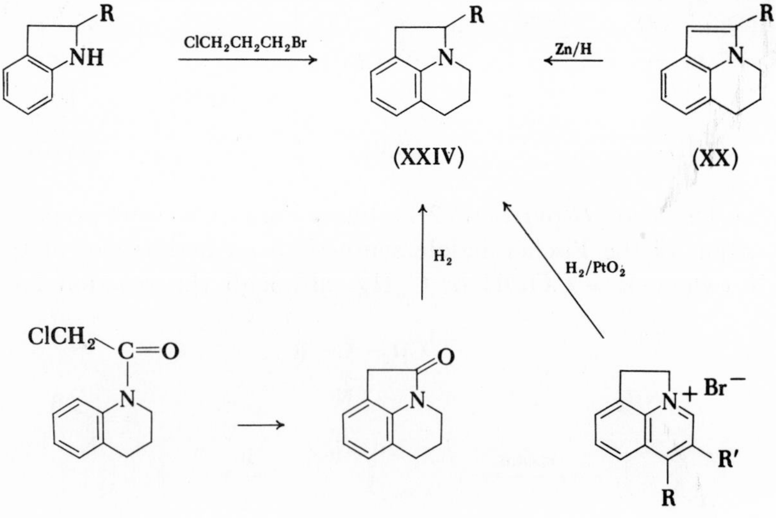

$ClCH_2CH_2CH_2Br$ Zn/H

(XXIV) (XX)

H_2 H_2/PtO_2

(XXV) (XXVI) (XI)

Treatment with sodium and alcohol of the methochloride of XXIV (R = H) was reported merely to reform XXIV (R = H), but the 2-methyl homolog XXIV (R = CH_3) under these conditions gave a product thought[9] to be 1,2-dimethyl-7-propylindoline. Diazonium coupling occurs in the 8-position of XXIV (R = H), and reduction of the resulting azo compounds yielded[10] aminolilolidine. Sugimoto[11] applied Stoll's oxindole synthesis to XXV and obtained XXVI, electrolytic reduction of which gave a mixture of lilolidine and 2-hydroxylilolidine (XXIV, R = OH).

Cyclization of 1-cyanoethylindoline afforded[22,23] only 8–13% yields of 6-oxolilolidine (XXVII), but an 87% yield (61% conversion) could be obtained[22] by heating β-(1-indolinyl-)propionic acid with polyphosphoric acid. The 2-methyl homolog of XXVII was similarly obtained.[21] As is the case with related systems such as 7-oxojulolidine (see Section A-732) and 1-methyl-1,2,3,4-tetrahydro-4-quinolone, XXVII is feebly basic and does not form a picrate or hydrochloride. The condensation of XXVII with diazomethane or with nitromethane failed,[23] although a low yield of the cyanhydrin of XXVII could be obtained. The Beckmann rearrangement of the oxime of XXVII failed, but the reaction of the ketone with hydrazoic acid[23] produced a diazepinoindole derivative (see Section A-690). Reduction of XXVII with sodium borohydride

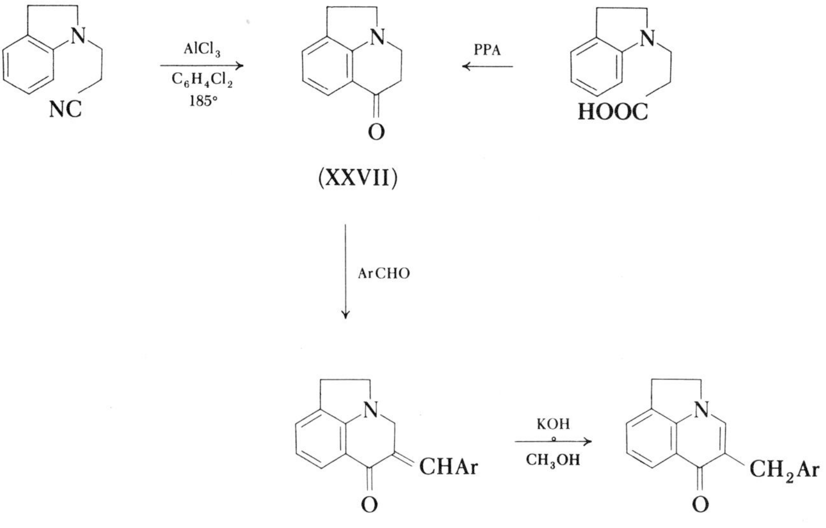

NC — $AlCl_3$, $C_6H_4Cl_2$, 185° → (XXVII) ← PPA — HOOC

(XXVII) — ArCHO → (XXVIII) CHAr — KOH, CH_3OH → (XXIX) CH_2Ar

gave[22] the normal carbinol, whereas the use[23] of lithium aluminum hydride resulted in complete deoxygenation and formation of lilolidine. An attempt[22] to prepare liloline (III) by heating the *p*-toluenesulfonylhydrazone of XXVII in ethylene glycol with sodium glycolate led only to 6-(2-hydroxyethoxy)lilolidine. The condensation of XXVII with aromatic aldehydes produced[22] red products of type XXVIII, which were readily isomerized to yellow 6-oxolilolines of structure XXIX.

While studying the preparation of dioxindoles from the reaction of aromatic amines with mesoxalic ester, Martinet[12–18] obtained XXX. Hydrolysis and decarboxylation of XXX in the absence of oxygen led to XXXI, while in the presence of air, XXXII was obtained. The 4-methyl and 4,8-dimethyl homologs of these compounds were similarly prepared. Treatment of XXXIII with sulfuric acid was reported[19] to provide an alternative synthesis of XXXII. Condensation of XXXII with indoxyl, phenylglycine or with isatin anilide yielded[18] brownish-violet (yellow vats) indirubine dyes of type XXXIV, which could be sulfonated to provide direct dyes.

$CO(CO_2CH_3)_2$

(XXX) (XXXI)

[O]

H_2SO_4, Δ

(XXXIII) (XXXII) (XXXIV)

The perhydro derivative (XXXVI) of this nucleus was recently obtained[20] by the reductive cyclization of the oxime XXXV. The product tentatively was assigned the *trans-cis* (racemate) configuration shown.

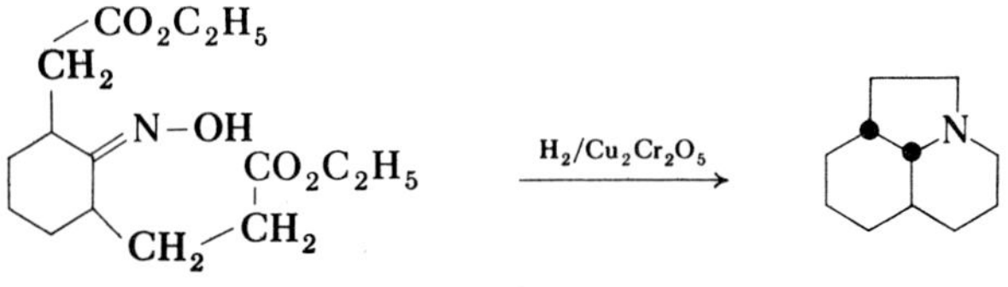

$CO_2C_2H_5$
CH_2
N−OH
$CO_2C_2H_5$
CH_2
CH_2

$\xrightarrow{H_2/Cu_2Cr_2O_5}$

N

(XXXV) (XXXVI)

4H-Pyrrolo[3,2,1-*ij*]quinolines

Empirical formula	Substituents or structure	Properties	Refs.
$C_{11}H_9NO$	1,2-Dihydro-4-oxo-	b_1 190–200°. m. 157–8°.	3
$C_{11}H_9NO_2$	1,2,5,6-Tetrahydro-1,2-dioxo-	Red, m. 197° (195°). Phenylhydrazone, m. 150°. Cu salt, red, d. 155°. Pb salt, red, d. 158°. K salt, yel.	12,13,16,17,19
$C_{11}H_9NS$	1,2-Dihydro-4-thio-	Yel., m. 177–8°.	3
$C_{11}H_{10}N_2O$	6-Amino-1,2-dihydro-4-oxo-	Yel., m. 324–6°.	6
$C_{11}H_{11}N$	5,6-Dihydro-	m. 86.5–8°. Picrate, m. 138–9°.	7
$C_{11}H_{11}NO$	1,2,5,6-Tetrahydro-2-oxo-	m. 91–2°. Chloroaurate, m. 167°.	11
	1,2,5,6-Tetrahydro-6-oxo-	Yel., m. 58–9° (55–6°) grn. fluoresc., λ_{max}^{EtOH} 236, 256, 376 mμ (ε 20,000, 8,200, 4,200). Oxime, yel., m. 152–4°. 4-Nitrophenylhydrazone, red, m. 245°. 2,4-Dinitrophenylhydrazone, m. > 270° d. *p*-Toluenesulfonylhydrazone, yel., m. 217°. Cyanhydrin, yel., m. 110–2°.	22,23
$C_{11}H_{11}NO_2$	1,2,5,6-Tetrahydro-1-hydroxy-2-oxo-	m. 160° (157°).	12,14,15,17
$C_{11}H_{13}N$	1,2,5,6-Tetrahydro-	b_4 110–2°; b_{12} 140°; b_{15} 156°. HCl salt, d. 216°. Picrate, m. 167.5–8.5° (168–70°).	7,9,11,23,24
$C_{11}H_{13}NO$	1,2,5,6-Tetrahydro-2-hydroxy-	b_4 182–3°. Picrate, m. 172–3°.	11
	1,2,5,6-Tetrahydro-6-hydroxy-	m. 54.0–4.5°, λ_{max} 251 and 304 mμ (ε 7400 and 2400).	22
$C_{11}H_{14}N_2$	8-Amino-1,2,5,6-tetrahydro-	Bisulfate, m. 244–5°.	10
$C_{11}H_{19}N$	Decahydro-	$b_{0.8}$ 56°; n_D^{20} 1.4988; d_4^{20} 0.9606. Picrate, m. 168–70°. Picrolonate, m. 205–6° d.	20
$C_{12}H_9NO_3$	6-Carboxy-1,2-dihydro-4-oxo-	m. > 320°.	3
$C_{12}H_{11}NO$	1,2-Dihydro-6-methyl-4-oxo-	m. 174.5–5.5°.	2

$C_{12}H_{11}NO_2$	2-Carboxy-5,6-dihydro-	m. 210–2° d.	7
	1,2,5,6-Tetrahydro-8-methyl-1,2-dioxo-	Red, m. 185°. Phenylhydrazone, m. 177°. Cu salt, red, d. 160°.	13,17
	1,2-Dihydro-6-hydroxy-2-methyl-4-oxo-	m. 298°. HCl salt, m. 298°. Nitroso deriv., red, m. 151–2°.	1
$C_{12}H_{12}N$	(structure: N⁺, CH₃)	Iodide, m. 254–5°.	4
	(structure: N⁺, CH₃)	Iodide, yel., m. 192–4° d.	5
$C_{12}H_{12}NS$	(structure: N⁺, SCH₃)	*p*-Toluenesulfonate, m. 187–8°.	3
$C_{12}H_{13}NO$	1,2,5,6-Tetrahydro-2-methyl-6-oxo-	$b_{0.9}$ 130–4°; m. 64°.	21
$C_{12}H_{13}NO_2$	1,2,5,6-Tetrahydro-1-hydroxy-8-methyl-2-oxo-	m. 193°.	14,15,17
$C_{12}H_{15}N$	1,2,5,6-Tetrahydro-2-methyl-	b_{15} 165–7°. Picrate, m. 140°. Methiodide, m. 202°.	9
$C_{12}H_{16}N_2$	6-Aminomethyl-1,2,5,6-tetrahydro-	Yel. oil, $b_{0.005}$ 130°.	23

(*continued*)

4H-Pyrrolo[3,2,1-*ij*]quinolines (*continued*)

Empirical formula	Substituents or structure	Properties	Refs.
$C_{13}H_{13}NO$	5,6-Dihydro-1,2-dimethyl-6-oxo-	Yel., m. 98–9°. Phenylhydrazone, m. 165–6°.	8
	1,2-Dihydro-5,6-dimethyl-4-oxo-	m. 151.5–3.5°.	2
$C_{13}H_{13}NO_2$	1,2,5,6-Tetrahydro-4,8-dimethyl-1,2-dioxo-	Dk. red, m. 165°. Phenylhydrazone, m. 141°.	13,17
$C_{13}H_{13}NO_4$	1-Carbomethoxy-1,2,5,6-tetrahydro-1-hydroxy-2-oxo-	m. 188°.	12,14,15,17
$C_{13}H_{14}N$	[structure: 1,2-dihydro-4H-pyrrolo[3,2,1-ij]quinolinium with N^+, CH_3, CH_3]	Bromide, m. 280–5° d.	2
$C_{13}H_{15}N$	1,2-Dihydro-5,6-dimethyl-	Unstable. Methiodide, m. 170–1.5°. Methyl argenticyanide, m. 149–51°.	2
$C_{13}H_{15}NO_2$	1,2,5,6-Tetrahydro-1-hydroxy-4,8-dimethyl-2-oxo-	Unstable oil.	15
$C_{13}H_{17}NO_2$	1,2,5,6-Tetrahydro-6-(2-hydroxy-ethoxy)-	Oil, λ_{max} 252 and 307 mμ (ε 7100 and 2700).	22
$C_{14}H_{15}NO$	6-Ethyl-1,2-dihydro-5-methyl-4-oxo-	m. 85.0–5.7°.	2
$C_{14}H_{15}NO_4$	1-Carbethoxy-1,2,5,6-tetrahydro-1-hydroxy-2-oxo-	m. 174°. Acetate, m. 95°.	12,13,14,17

$C_{14}H_{16}N$	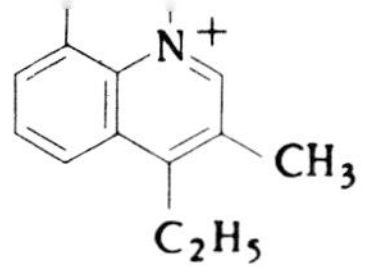	Bromide, m. 234–6°.	2
$C_{14}H_{17}N$	6-Ethyl-1,2-dihydro-5-methyl-	Unstable. Methiodide, m. 167–8°. Methylargenticyanide, m. 138–40°.	2
$C_{14}H_{19}N$	6-Ethyl-1,2,5,6-tetrahydro-5-methyl-	b_5 150°.	2
$C_{15}H_{17}NO_4$	1-Carbethoxy-1,2,5,6-tetrahydro-1-hydroxy-8-methyl-2-oxo-	m. 162°.	13,14,17
$C_{16}H_{13}NO_2$	5-Furfural-1,2,5,6-tetrahydro-6-oxo-	Red, m. 148–9°, λ_{max}^{EtOH} 252 and 340 mμ (ε 17,500 and 20,000).	22
	5-Furfuryl-1,2-dihydro-6(6*H*)-oxo-	Pale yel., m. 177–8°, λ_{max}^{EtOH} 245, 335 and 350 mμ (ε 27,000, 14,200 and 14,800).	22
$C_{16}H_{19}NO_4$	1-Carbethoxy-1,2,5,6-tetrahydro-1-hydroxy-4,8-dimethyl-2-oxo-	m. 108°.	13,14
$C_{17}H_{15}N$	5,6-Dihydro-2-phenyl-	m. 133–4°.	7
$C_{18}H_{15}NO$	5-Benzyl-1,2-dihydro-6(6*H*)-oxo-	Or.-yel., m. 171–2°, λ_{max}^{EtOH} 248,336 and 352 mμ (ε 32,000, 14,600 and 15,400).	22
$C_{19}H_{14}N_2O_2$	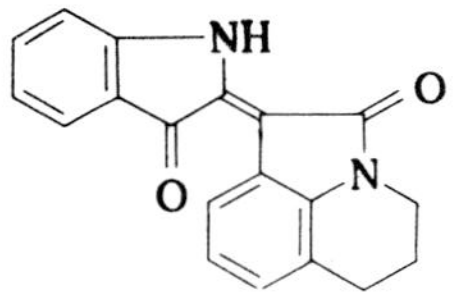	Brn.-vt., m. 252°.	18

(continued)

4H-Pyrrolo[3,2,1-*ij*]quinolines (*continued*)

Empirical formula	Substituents or structure	Properties	Refs.
$C_{20}H_{16}N_2O_2$	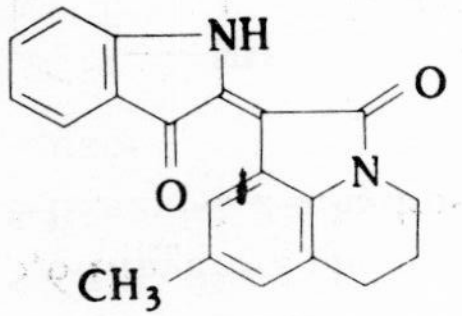	Brn.-vt., m. ~265°.	18
$C_{21}H_{18}N_2O_2$	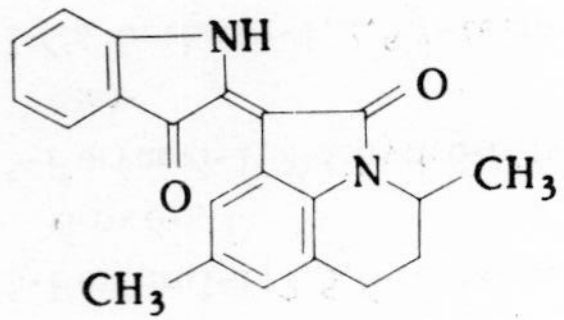	Brn.-vt., m. 204–5°.	18
$C_{21}H_{19}N_2S$	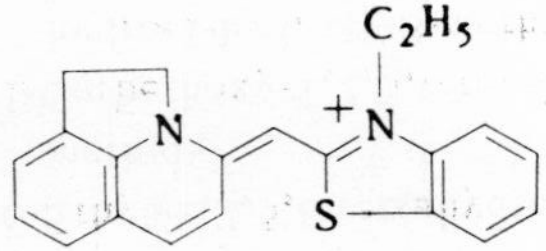	Iodide, or., m. 322–4° d.	3
$C_{21}H_{21}N_2$	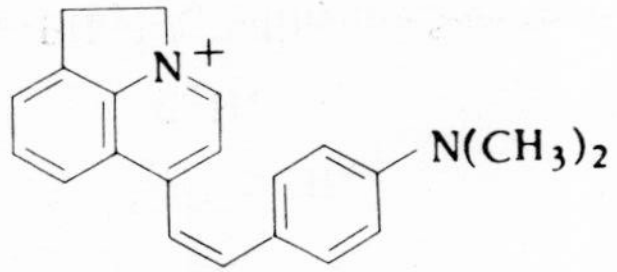	Iodide, m. 256–7°.	3

$C_{23}H_{19}N_2$	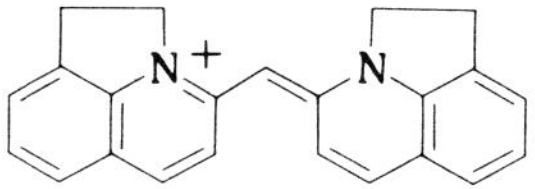	Iodide, brn., m. > 350°.	3
$C_{23}H_{21}N_2$	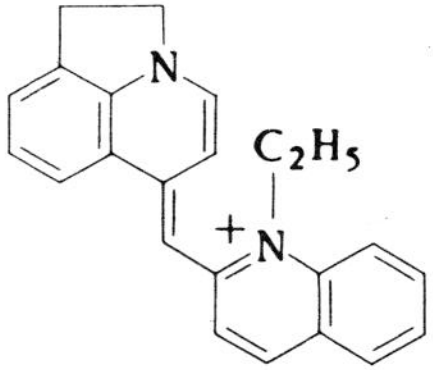	Iodide, m. 251–2° d.	3
$C_{23}H_{21}N_2S$	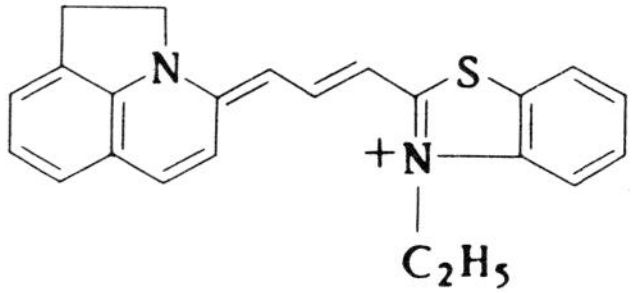	Iodide, dk. grn., m. 292–3° d.	3
	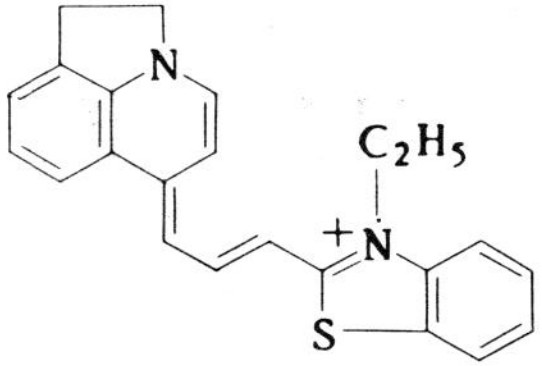	Iodide, m. 252–3° d.	3

(*continued*)

4H-Pyrrolo[3,2,1-*ij*]quinolines (*continued*)

Empirical formula	Substituents or structure	Properties	Refs.
$C_{24}H_{23}N_2S$	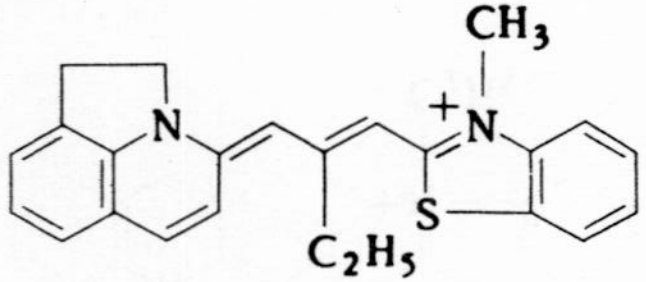 CH_3, N, ^+N, S, C_2H_5	Iodide, purple, m. 272–3 ° d.	3
$C_{25}H_{22}N_2$	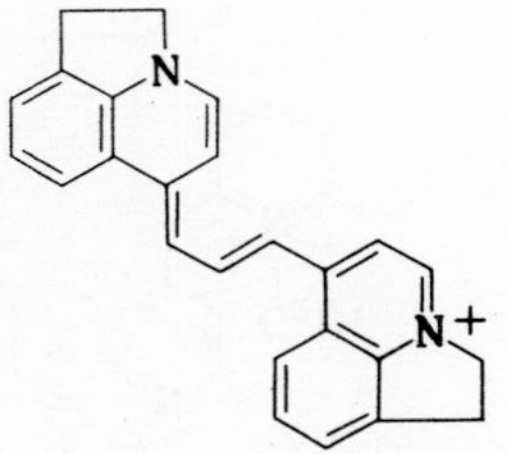 N, N^+	Iodide, m. 275–7° d.	3

References

1. Bamberger and Sternitzki, *Ber.*, **26,** 1291 (1893).
2. Boekelheide and Gall, *J. Org. Chem.*, **19,** 504 (1954).
3. Brooker and Heseltine, U. S. Pat. 2,646,430. Brit. Pat. 713,255.
4. Heseltine, U. S. Pats. 2,578,303 and 2,646,433.
5. Heseltine and Brooker, U. S. Pats. 2,578,304 and 2,636,035.
6. Gall, Astill and Boekelheide, *J. Org. Chem.*, **20,** 1538 (1955).
7. Barger and Dyer, *J. Am. Chem. Soc.*, **60,** 2414 (1938).
8. Almond and Mann, *J. Chem. Soc.*, **1952,** 1870.
9. Braun, Heider and Wyczatkowska, *Ber.*, **51,** 1215 (1918).
10. Raasch, U. S. Pat. 2,707,681.
11. Sugimoto, *J. Pharm. Soc. Japan*, **64,** No. 7A, 4 (1944); *Chem. Abstracts*, **46,** 114 (1952).
12. Guyot and Martinet, *Compt. rend.*, **156,** 1625 (1913); *Chem. Zentr.*, **II,** 362 (1913); *Chem. Abstracts*, **7,** 3112 (1913).
13. Martinet, *Compt. rend.*, **166,** 998 (1918); *Chem. Zentr.*, **II,** 538 (1918); *Chem. Abstracts*, **12,** 2538 (1918).
14. Martinet, *Ann. chim.*, [9] **11,** 85 (1918); *Chem. Abstracts*, **13,** 1581 (1919); *Chem. Zentr.*, **III,** 568 (1919).
15. Martinet, *Ann. chim.*, [9] **11,** 15 (1919); *Chem. Zentr.*, **III,** 193 (1919).
16. Martinet, *Compt. rend.*, **168,** 689 (1919); *Chem. Abstracts*, **13,** 1463 (1919); *Chem. Zentr.*, **III,** 263 (1919).
17. Martinet, *Rev. gén. mat. col.*, **23,** 53 (1919); *Chem. Zentr.*, **III,** 710 (1919).
18. Martinet, *Compt. rend.*, **169,** 183 (1919); *Chem. Zentr.*, **III,** 879 (1919); *Chem. Abstracts*, **13,** 3182 (1919).
19. Deutsche Gold und Silber-Scheideanstalt, vorm. Roessler, Austr. Pat. 125,211; *Chem. Zentr.*, **II,** 778 (1932).
20. Leonard and Middleton, *J. Am. Chem. Soc.*, **74,** 5114 (1952).
21. I.G. Farbenindustrie, A.G., Fr. Pat. 806,715; *Chem. Zentr.*, **I,** 3229 (1937).
22. Rapoport and Tretter, *J. Org. Chem.*, **23,** 248 (1958).
23. Astill and Boekelheide, *J. Org. Chem.*, **23,** 316 (1958).
24. Quilico, Cardani and Piozzi, *Gazz. chim. ital.*, **85,** 3 (1955); *Chem. Abstracts*, **50,** 7822 (1956).

A-198. 4*H*-Pyrrolo[3,2,1-*ij*][1,6]-naphthyridine*

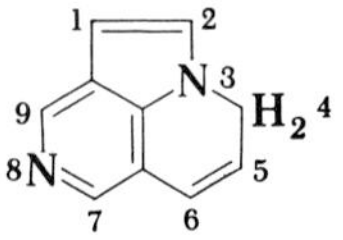

The name 4H-*pyrido*[*3,4,5*-hi]*indolizine* has been used.

Hydrogenation of I over a copper-chromite catalyst yielded[1] II (b_{12} 145–50°; flavianate salt, yellow, m. 267° d.). See Sections A-64, A-70 and A-183.

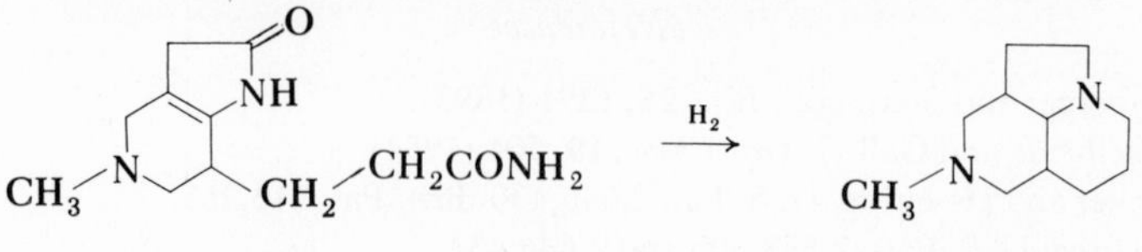

(I) $\xrightarrow{H_2}$ (II)

Reference

1. Tsuda and Saeki, *J. Org. Chem.*, **23,** 91 (1958).

A-199. 6*H*-Benzo[*i*]pyrrocoline

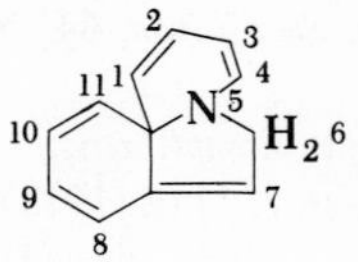

and

A-200. 2*H*,8*H*-Benzo[*i*]pyrano[3,4-*g*]-pyrrocoline

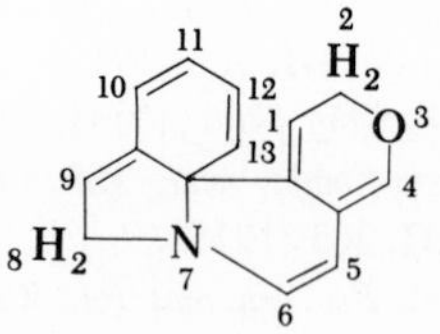

and

A-201. 6*H*-Indolo[7*a*,1-*a*]isoquinoline

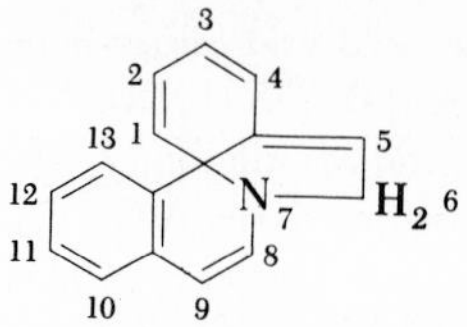

Derivatives of these three nuclei were obtained during studies upon the erythrina alkaloids.[1-8]

References

1. Marion, in Manske and Holmes, *The Alkaloids*, Academic Press, New York, Vol. 2, 1952, p. 499
2. Boekelheide and Prelog, in Cook, *Progress in Organic Chemistry*, Academic Press, New York, Vol. 3, 1955, p. 218.
3. Prelog, McKusick, Merchant, Julia and Wilhelm, *Helv. Chim. Acta*, **39,** 498 (1956).
4. Mondon, *Angew. Chem.*, **68,** 578 (1956).
5. Belleau, *J. Am. Chem. Soc.*, **75,** 5765 (1953).

6. Godfrey, Tarbell and Boekelheide, *J. Am. Chem. Soc.*, **77,** 3342 (1955).
7. Belleau, *Can. J. Chem.*, **35,** 651 (1957).
8. Belleau, *Can. J. Chem.*, **35,** 663 (1957).

A-202. Benzo[*e*]pyrrolo[4,3,2-*hi*]-pyrrocoline

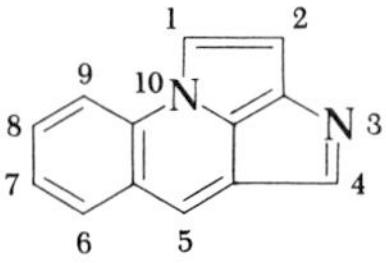

1 2 9 10 N N 3 8 7 4 6 5

One of the products formed[1] from the reaction of I with diethyl malonate was the ester II. When this was heated in refluxing diphenyl ether, the product (m. 295–6° d.) formed was not the expected dichlordihydroxybiquinolyl, but was believed to have structure III. When heated with caustic, III decomposed to ethanol, *m*-chloraniline, carbon dioxide and an acid thought to be 2-acetyl-7-chloro-4-hydroxyquinoline-3-carboxylic acid.

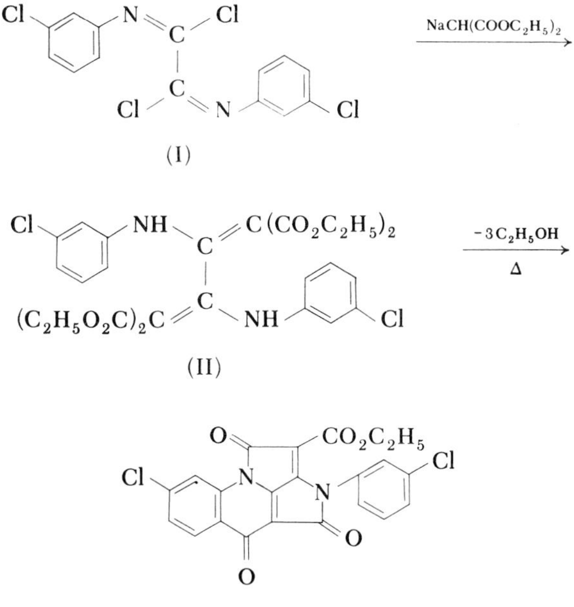

Cl N C Cl C Cl N Cl

$\xrightarrow{NaCH(COOC_2H_5)_2}$

(I)

Cl NH C $C(CO_2C_2H_5)_2$ C $(C_2H_5O_2C)_2C$ NH Cl

$\xrightarrow[\Delta]{-3C_2H_5OH}$

(II)

O $CO_2C_2H_5$ Cl Cl N N O O

(III)

Reference

1. Price and Velzen, *J. Org. Chem.*, **12,** 386 (1947).

A-203. Dibenzo[*a,e*]pyrrocoline.
R.I. 2429

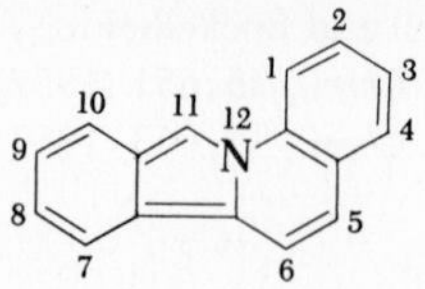

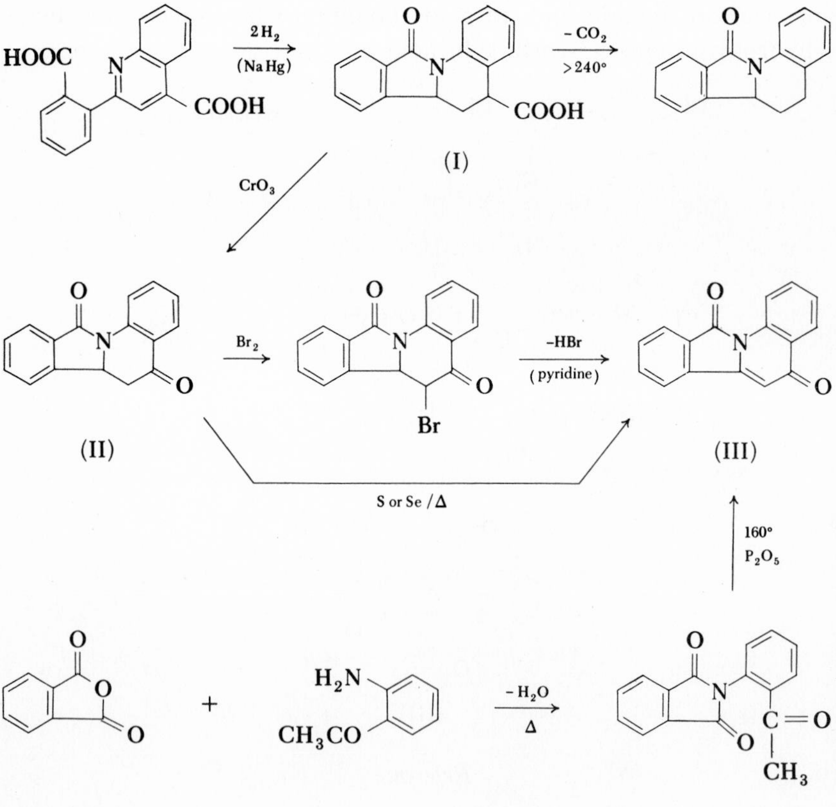

Alkaline hydrolysis of *Höchst Yellow R* (see Section A-210) afforded, together with benzoic and anthranilic acids, a yellow substance assigned[1] structure III. However, synthesis[2] of III via two different routes clearly demonstrated it to be different from the yellow hydrolysis product, which was shown to have another structure (see Section A-209). The lactam bond of III was cleaved by alcoholic caustic, but the resulting amino acid could be dehydrated to reform III. Compound III failed[2] to yield a phenylhydrazone, but, when heated with phosphorus pentasulfide, formed the 5-thio analog. Bromination of III produced[2] the 6-bromo derivative.

Nitration[2] of II was accompanied by oxidation, and the product was the 6-nitro derivative of III, while I yielded a nitro derivative of unknown orientation, but which, when oxidized with chromic acid, yielded a mixture of nitro derivatives of both I and III. Bromination of I gave[2] a monobromo derivative (IV), in which the bromine atom was shown to be in positions 1–4, since it could be oxidized to V, which was converted into VI. Further bromination of VI in acetic acid yielded VII.

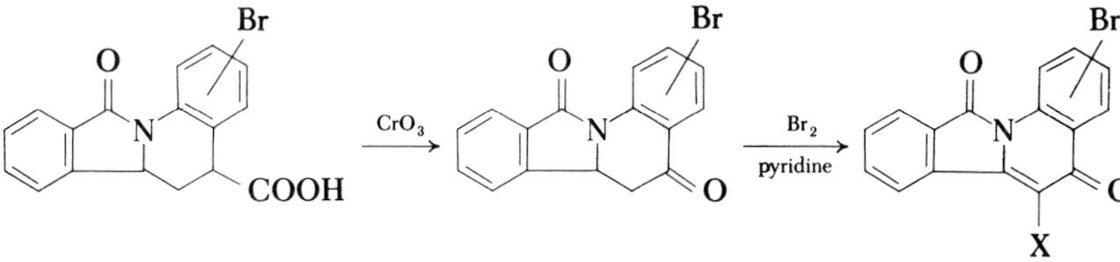

(IV) $\xrightarrow{CrO_3}$ (V) $\xrightarrow[\text{pyridine}]{Br_2}$ (VI) X=H; (VII) X=Br

The Diels-Alder addition of 2,3-dimethylbutadiene with ethyl quinolyl-2-acrylate followed by aromatization of the adduct, gave[3] VIII, catalytic hydrogenation of which produced IX. Electrolytic reduction of IX afforded[3,4] the tetrahydro derivative (X).

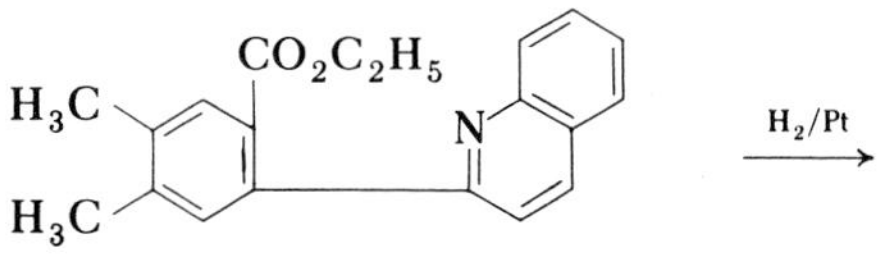

(VIII) $\xrightarrow{H_2/Pt}$

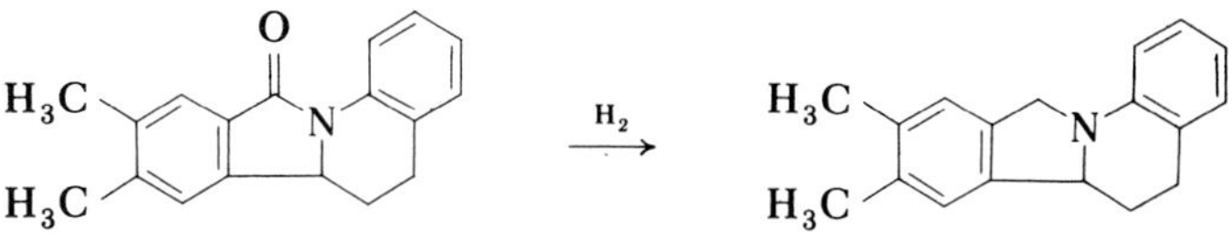

(IX) $\xrightarrow{H_2}$ (X)

Dibenzo[*a, e*]pyrrocolines

Empirical formula	Substituents	Properties and derivatives	Refs.
$C_{16}H_7Br_2NO_2$	*x*,6-Dibromo-5,11-dihydro-5,11-dioxo-	m. 272°.	2
$C_{16}H_8BrNO_2$	6-Bromo-5,11-dihydro-5,11-dioxo-	Yel., m. 233°.	2
	x-Bromo-5,11-dihydro-5,11-dioxo-	Yel., m. 261°.	2
$C_{16}H_8N_2O_4$	5,11-Dihydro-6-nitro-5,11-dioxo-	Yel., m. 253°.	2
	5,11-Dihydro-*x*-nitro-5,11-dioxo-	Yel., m. 309–10°.	2
$C_{16}H_9NOS$	5,11-Dihydro-11-oxo-5-thiono-	Vt.-blk., m. 253–4°. Phenylhydrazone, m. 224–5°.	2
$C_{16}H_9NO_2$	5,11-Dihydro-5,11-dioxo-	m. 267°.	2
$C_{16}H_{10}BrNO_2$	6-Bromo-5,6,6*a*,11-tetrahydro-5,11-dioxo-	Yel., m. 257°.	2
	x-Bromo-5,6,6*a*,11-tetrahydro-5,11-dioxo-	Yel., m. 202°. Phenylhydrazone, m. 247–8°; benzylidene deriv., m. 231–2°.	2
$C_{16}H_{10}N_2O_4$	5,6,6*a*,11-Tetrahydro-*x*-nitro-5,11-dioxo-	Phenylhydrazone, m. 264°.	2
$C_{16}H_{11}NO_2$	5,6,6*a*,11-Tetrahydro-5,11-dioxo-	m. 168°. Phenylhydrazone, m. 222°; benzylidene deriv., m. 228°; *o*-nitrobenzylidene deriv., m. 262°; *o*-acetamidobenzylidene deriv., m. 283°.	2
$C_{16}H_{13}NO$	5,6,6*a*,11-Tetrahydro-11-oxo	m. 140°.	2
$C_{17}H_{12}BrNO_3$	*x*-Bromo-5-carboxy-5,6,6*a*,11-tetrahydro-11-oxo-	m. 257°.	2
$C_{17}H_{12}N_2O_5$	5-Carboxy-5,6,6*a*,11-tetrahydro-*x*-nitro-11-oxo-	Yel., m. 260° d.	2
$C_{17}H_{13}NO_3$	5-Carboxy-5,6,6*a*,11-tetrahydro-11-oxo-	m. 239°. Ethyl ester, m. 175°.	2

Dibenzo[*a,e*]pyrrocolines (*continued*)

Empirical formula	Substituents	Properties and derivatives	Refs.
$C_{18}H_{17}NO$	5,6,6*a*,11-Tetrahydro-8,9-dimethyl-11-oxo-	m. 197–8°.	3
$C_{18}H_{19}N$	5,6,6*a*,11-Tetrahydro-8,9-dimethyl-	Yel., m. 140–2° (129–31° d.)	3,4

References

1. Hope, Kersey, and Richter, *J. Chem. Soc.*, **1933,** 1000.
2. de Diesbach, Rey-Bellet, and Kiang, *Helv. Chim. Acta*, **26,** 1869 (1943).
3. Sugasawa and Kodama, *J. Pharm. Soc. Japan*, **62,** 367 (1942); *Chem. Abstracts*, **45,** 5168 (1951).
4. Sugasawa and Kodama, *J. Pharm. Soc. Japan*, **63,** 96 (1943); *Chem. Abstracts*, **45,** 5168 (1951).

A-204. Dibenzo[*a,f*]pyrrocoline. R.I. 2424

and

A-205. [1,3]Dioxolo[*f*]isoquinolo-[3,2-a]isoindole. R.I. 2949

and

A-206. [1,3]Dioxolo[*e*]isoquinolo-[3,2-*a*]isoindole. R.I. 2950

and

A-207. [1,3]Dioxolo[*h*]isoindolo-[2,1-*b*]isoquinoline. R.I. 2951

The names *dibenzo-1'.2':2.3;1''.2'':5.6-indolizine* (numbered as shown in I) and *isoindolo[2,1-b]isoquinoline* have been applied to the first of these nuclei, while the others have been named, respectively,

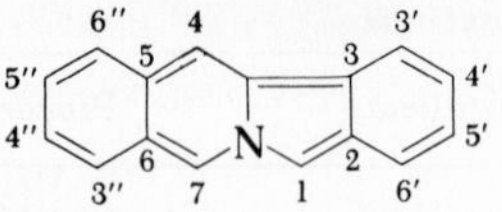

6'' 4 3'
5 3
5'' 4'
4'' N 5'
6 2
3'' 7 1 6'

(I)

4',5'-methylenedioxy[dibenzo-1',2',2,3 ; 1'',2'',5,6-indolizine], *5',6'-methylenedioxy[dibenzo-1',2',2,3; 1'',2'',5,6-indolizine]* and *3'',4''-methylenedioxy-[dibenzo-1',2',2,3: 1'',2'',5,6-indolizine]*.

The last three of the above nuclei are grouped here along with the first because of their fundamental similarity. They are represented only by certain degradation and rearrangement products of the alkaloids *berberine*[1,2] and *isocyptopine*,[3,4] and, therefore, will not be considered further here.

Ephraim[5] found that treatment of II with alcoholic ammonia gave a lactam having either structure III or (more probably) IV, and that dehydration of this lactam produced a yellow substance thought to be V. No other information concerning V has been reported.

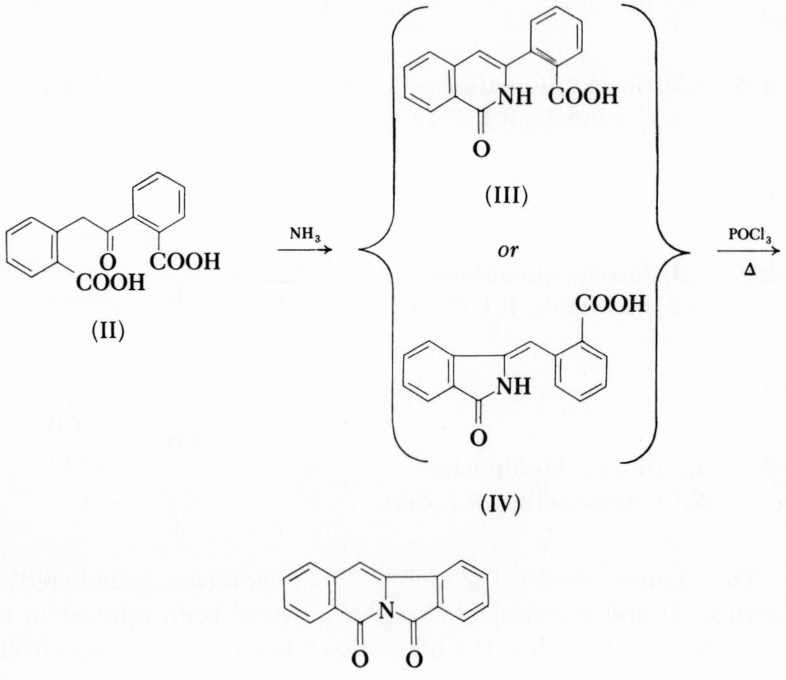

O COOH
COOH

(II)

$\xrightarrow{NH_3}$

NH COOH
O

(III)

or

COOH
NH
O

(IV)

$\xrightarrow[\Delta]{POCl_3}$

N
O O

(V)

In a similar reaction, Kodama[6] subjected VI to a Leuckart reaction with formamidine, and obtained VII. Electrolytic reduction of VII gave VIII, which was converted into IX (HCl salt, m. 194–5°) by treatment with formalin and hydrochloric acid.

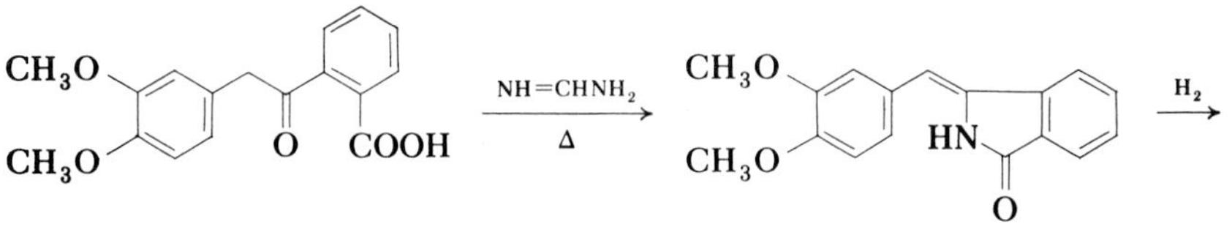

CH_3O CH_3O O COOH — $NH{=}CHNH_2$, Δ → CH_3O CH_3O HN O — H_2 →

(VI) (VII)

CH_3O CH_3O HN — HCHO, HCl → CH_3O CH_3O N

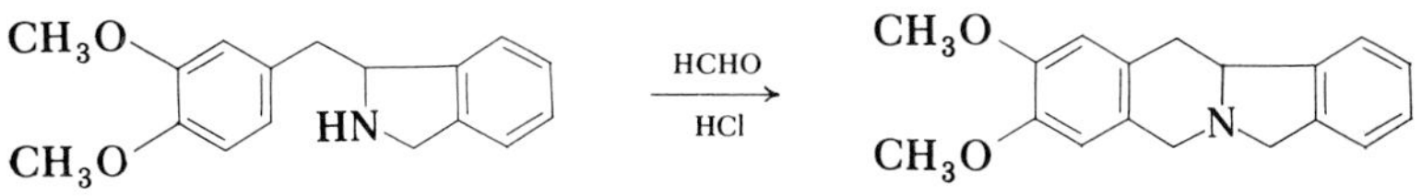

(VIII) (IX)

Compound XI (m. 109–10°; methobromide, two forms, m. 122–4° and 242.0–2.5°) was isolated[7] in 41% yield as the major product of the reaction of X in ether solution with phenyl lithium.

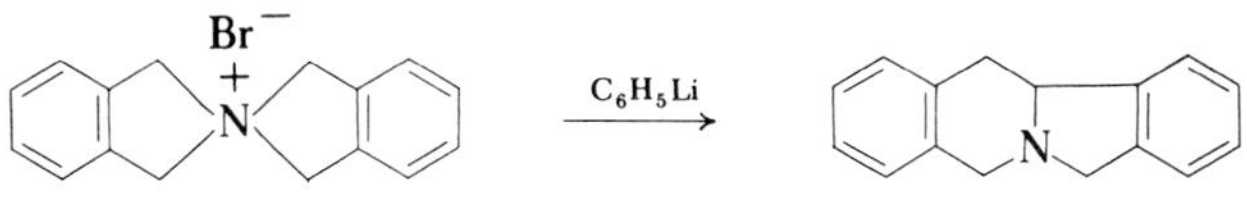

Br^- $\overset{+}{N}$ — C_6H_5Li → N

(X) (XI)

A similar treatment of the methobromide of XI produced[7] XII, while the Hofmann degradation gave XIII.

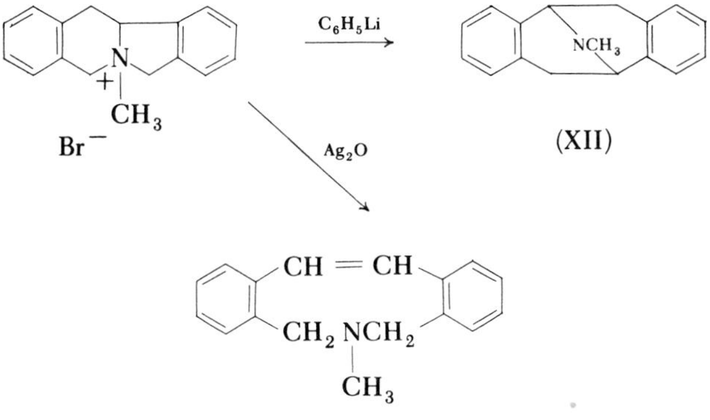

$\overset{+}{N}$ CH_3 Br^- — C_6H_5Li → NCH_3

(XII)

Ag_2O ↘

$CH = CH$

$CH_2\,NCH_2$

CH_3

(XIII)

References

1. Freund and Lachmann, *Ann.*, **397,** 70 (1913).
2. Perkin, *J. Chem. Soc.*, **113,** 722 (1918).
3. Perkin, *J. Chem. Soc.*, **109,** 815 (1916).
4. Perkin, *J. Chem. Soc.*, **115,** 713 (1919).
5. Ephraim, *Ber.*, **24,** 2820 (1891).
6. Kodama, *J. Pharm. Soc. Japan*, **63,** 54 (1943); *Chem. Abstracts*, **45,** 5169 (1951).
7. Wittig, Tenhaeff, Schoch and Koenig, *Ann.*, **572,** 1 (1951).

A-208. Dibenzo[*a,g*]pyrrocoline

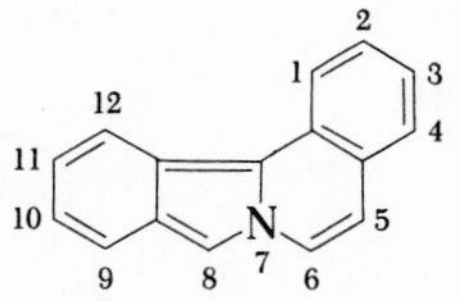

Cyclodehydration of I yielded[1] II (not described), which was reduced by means of a zinc-cadmium amalgam and acetic acid to III (m. 112°). Efforts to dehydrogenate III failed.

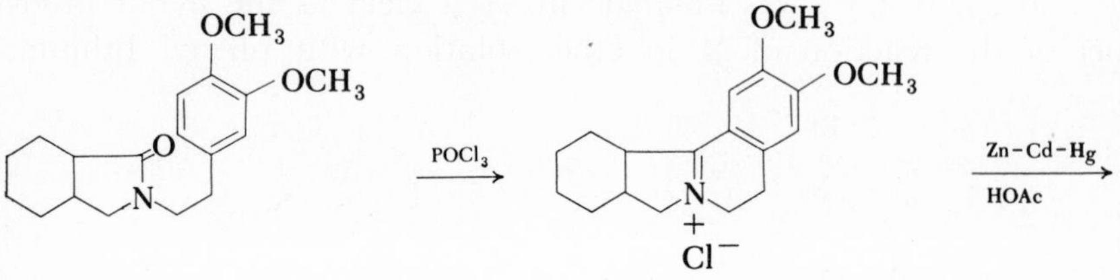

$\xrightarrow{POCl_3}$ $\xrightarrow[HOAc]{Zn-Cd-Hg}$

(I) (II) 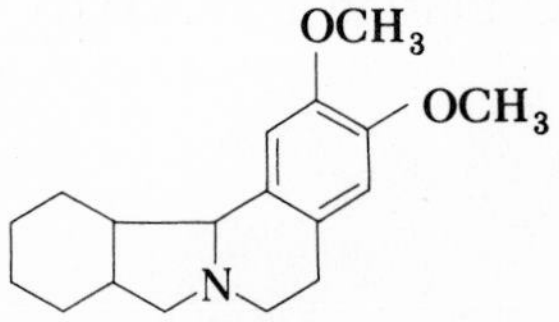 (III)

Reference

1. Sugasawa and Ohki, *J. pharm. soc. Japan*, **64,** 190 (1944); *Chem. Abstracts*, **45,** 5169 (1951).

A-209. Dibenzo[*b,f*]pyrrocoline

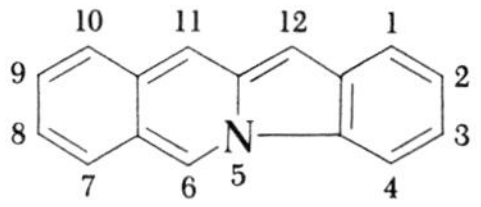

Treatment of I with chloranil produced[1,2] the unstable quaternary salt II, which was methylated to yield III (X = Cl^-, m. 215–20°; X = I^-, d. 248–9°). When heated, III lost methyl chloride and formed IV (m. 147–7°).

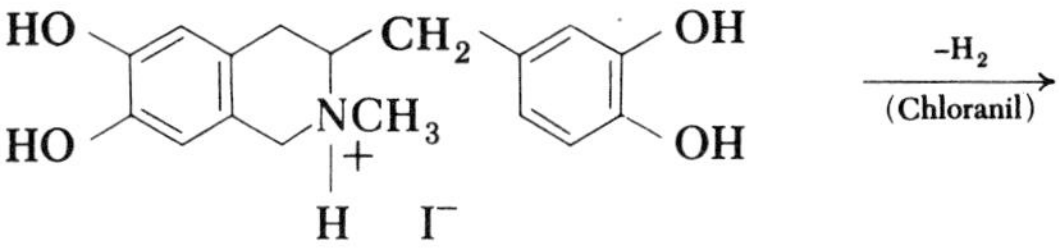

$-H_2$ (Chloranil)

(I)

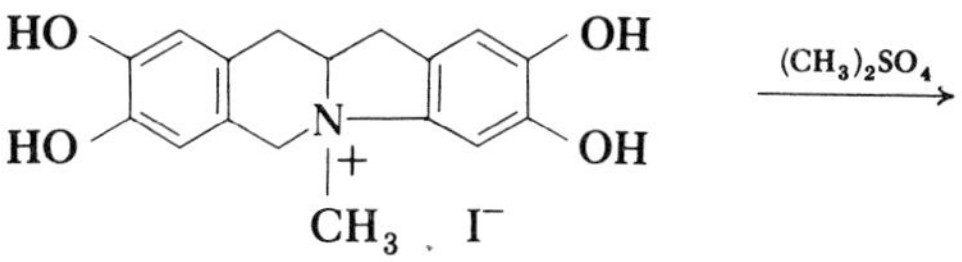

$(CH_3)_2SO_4$

(II)

$-CH_3Cl$, Δ

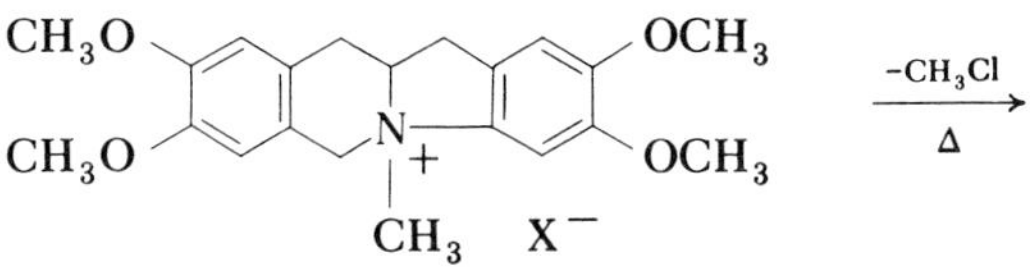

(III)

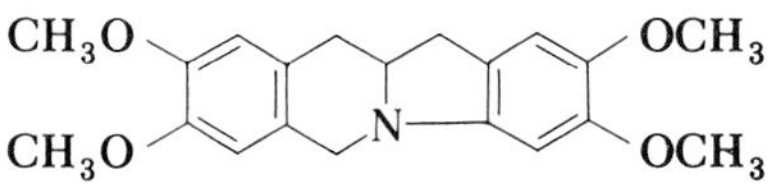

(IV)

When heated with acetic anhydride, II underwent[1,2] simultaneous acetylation, demethylation and dehydrogenation to yield a product (m. 198–200°) giving a positive test with Ehrlich's reagent, and therefore formulated as the indole derivative V. Similar treatment of IV gave VI (m. 193–4°).

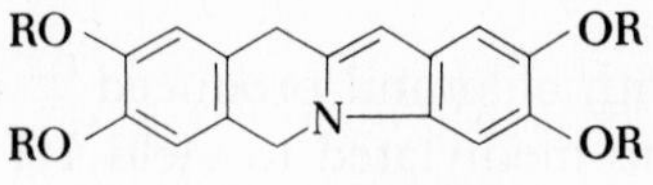

(V) R = $COCH_3$
(VI) R = CH_3

Amongst the products resulting[3,4] from alkaline hydrolysis of the dye Höchst Yellow R (VII, see Section A-210) was a yellow lactam (VIII, m. 235° (232°); phenylhydrazone, m. 227°). The identity of this product was demonstrated[5,6] by its synthesis from indoxyl and phthalaldehydic acid.

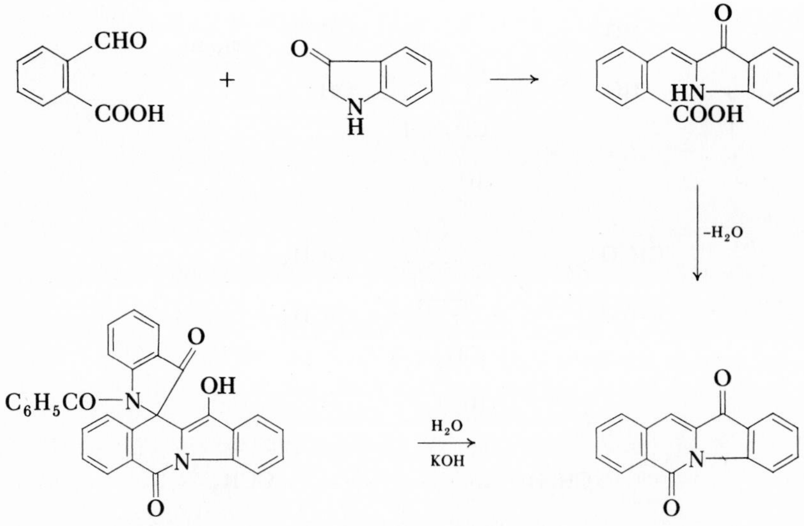

$-H_2O$

H_2O, KOH

(VII) (VIII)

Heating Dessoulavy's compound (IX, see Section A-210) with aniline produced a substance (m. > 300°) at first thought[7] to have the formula $C_{27}H_{21}N_3O$, but later[8] amended to $C_{28}H_{21}N_3O$. This substance was assigned structure X, and was thought to be converted into XI (m. > 300°) by the action of nitrous acid, but more evidence for these structures would be welcome.

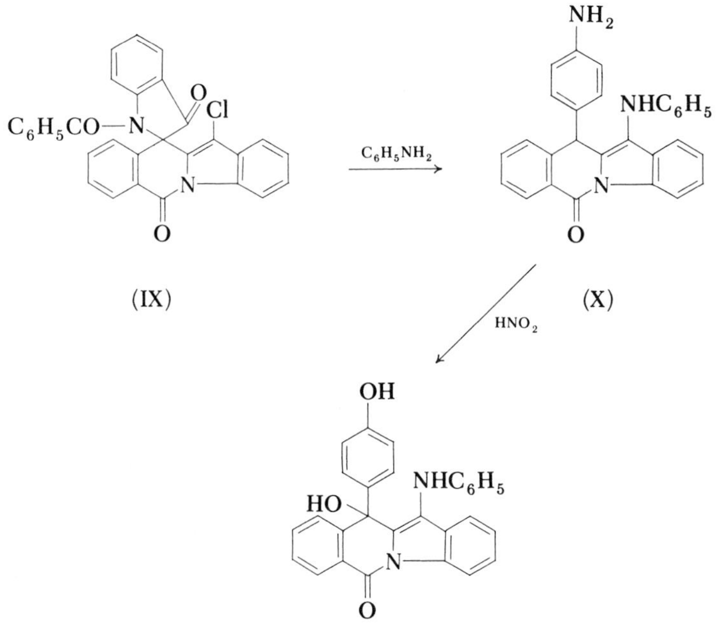

(IX) (X) (XI)

References

1. Sugasawa and Kodama, *Ber.*, **74,** 1237 (1941).
2. Sugasawa Kodama and Akatuka, *Proc. Imp. Acad.* (Tokyo), **17,** 102 (1941); *Chem. Abstracts*, **35,** 5896 (1941).
3. Hope, Kersey and Richter, *J. Chem. Soc.*, **1933,** 1000.
4. de Diesbach, Rey-Bellet and Kiang, *Helv. Chim. Acta*, **26,** 1869 (1943).
5. de Diesbach, Hepner and Siegwart, *Helv. Chim. Acta*, **31,** 724 (1948).
6. de Diesbach, Capponi and Farquet, *Helv. Chim. Acta*, **32,** 1214 (1949).
7. de Diesbach, Jacobi and Taddei, *Helv. Chim. Acta*, **23,** 469 (1940).
8. de Diesbach and Frossard, *Helv. Chim. Acta*, **37,** 701 (1954).

A-210. Spiro[dibenzo[*b,f*]pyrrocoline-11(6*H*)-2′-indoline]

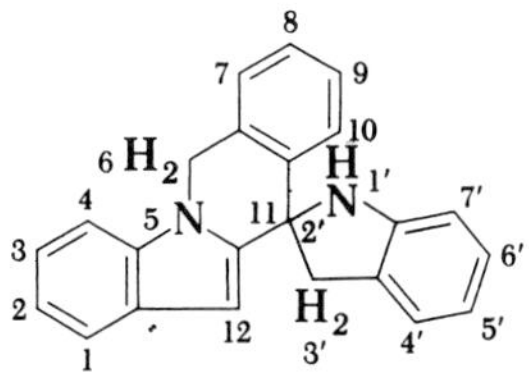

Interest in this nucleus derives from its presence in two products: *Dessoulavy's compound* (I) and *Höchst Yellow R* (II), obtained

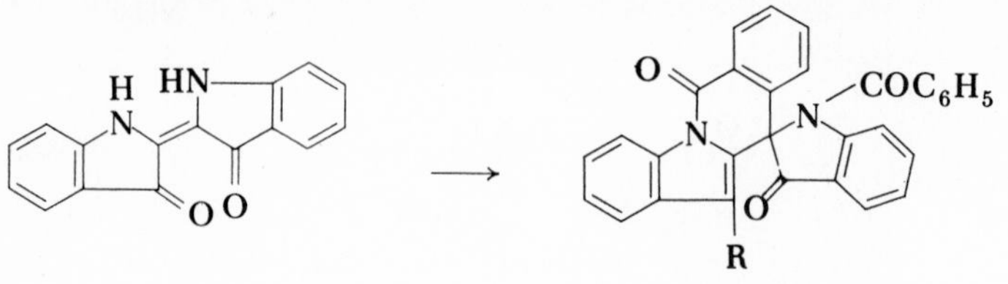

(I) R=Cl
(II) R=OH

from the reaction of indigo with benzoyl chloride. A complete chart of the products of these reactants and of their inter-relationships is shown in Section A-259.

From the reaction of indigo with benzoyl chloride at 180°, Schwartz[1] isolated a crude brown product, which he believed to be *N,N'*-dibenzoylindigo. This latter product (dark violet, m. 257°), however, was prepared in pure state by Posner[2] by treating indigo with benzoyl chloride in pyridine, and it is obviously quite different. Schwartz's product was shown[3] to be a crude form of the colorless base ($C_{30}H_{17}ClN_2O_3$, m. 243°) prepared[2,4,5] by Dessoulavy[4] by refluxing indigo with an excess of benzoyl chloride. This substance, which has become known as Dessoulavy's compound (I), is also obtained[6] by heating *N,N'*-dibenzoylindigo with benzoyl chloride.

The treatment of I with ammonia in methanol at 0° was reported[6] to product a yellow substance, $C_{30}H_{20}N_4O_2$ (m. 247°), possibly having structure III. Repetition[7] of this experiment, however, gave quite different results. None of the product thought to be III was formed, and in its place was obtained a complex mixture of products assigned[7] structures IV (orange, m. 231°), V (orange, m. 257–8°), VI (see Section A-74) and VII, together with a yellow substance ($C_{46}H_{26}N_4O_7$, m. 293°) of unknown structure.

Heating Dessoulavy's compound (I) with aniline affords a "grey substance" (m. >300°) once[8] thought to have the empirical formula $C_{27}H_{21}N_3O$. However, upon repetition[7] of the experiment, the formula was modified to $C_{28}H_{21}N_3O$ and structure VIII was suggested. Treatment of this product with nitrous acid gave another "grey substance" (m. >300°) thought[7] to be IX. No substantial evidence for these structures was presented. The reaction of I with *p*-toluidine appears to take a different course, and is mentioned later.

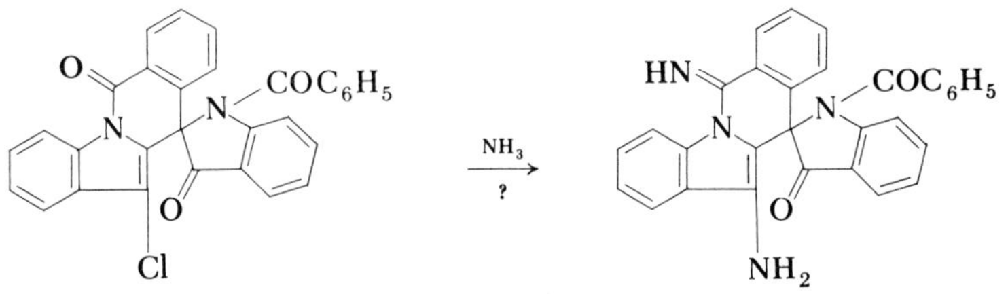
COC$_6$H$_5$
HN
NH$_3$
?
Cl
NH$_2$

(I) (III)

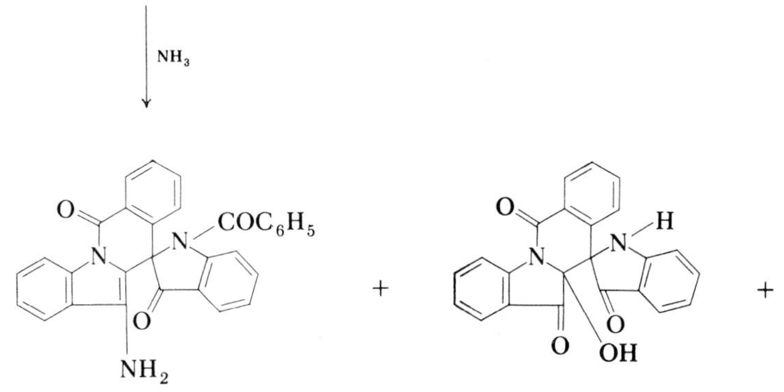
NH$_3$
COC$_6$H$_5$
NH$_2$
H
OH
+

(IV) (V)

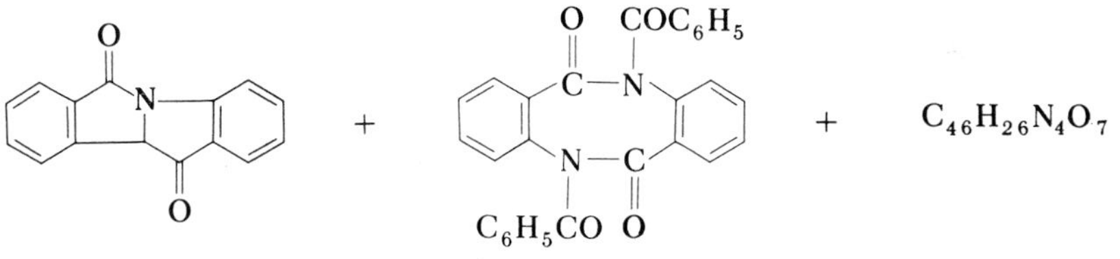
COC$_6$H$_5$
C$_6$H$_5$CO
+
C$_{46}$H$_{26}$N$_4$O$_7$

(VI) (VII)

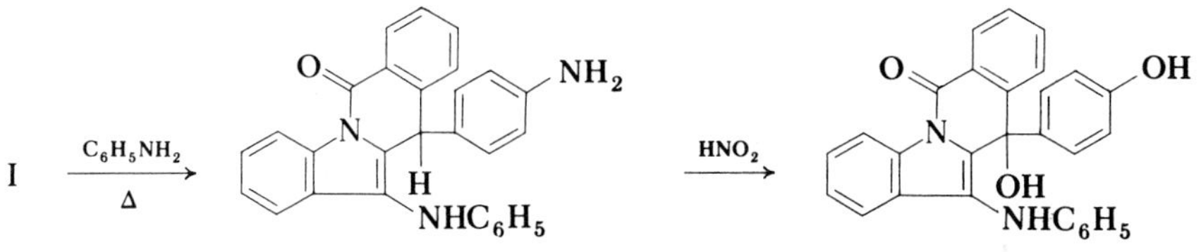
I
C$_6$H$_5$NH$_2$
Δ
NH$_2$
NHC$_6$H$_5$
HNO$_2$
OH
NHC$_6$H$_5$

(VIII) (IX)

When I was heated for a week with anhydrous pyridine, 80% was recovered unchanged, together with a small amount of the dyes Ciba Yellow 3G (see Section A-259) and Höchst Yellow R (II), while in 50% aqueous pyridine, the latter dye was the major product. Compound II is more conveniently obtained[6] from I by the action of sulfuric acid at 25°; at higher temperatures Höchst Yellow U (see Section A-260) results.[5,9] Höchst Yellow R [a pale yellow, nonvattable solid, m. 359° (357°)] is also obtained by heating indigo with either benzoyl chloride or with benzoic anhydride and zinc chloride.[10,11] In view of the conversion of I into II, it is curious that the reverse reaction has, apparently, not been attempted.

Before the accuracy of structure II had been demonstrated,[12] structures X and XI were proposed,[13,14] at different times, as the

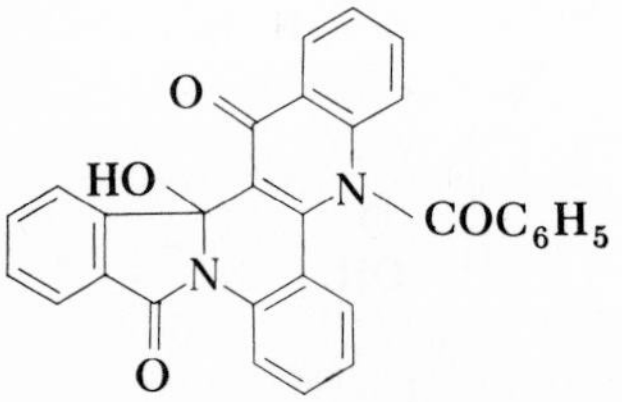

(X)

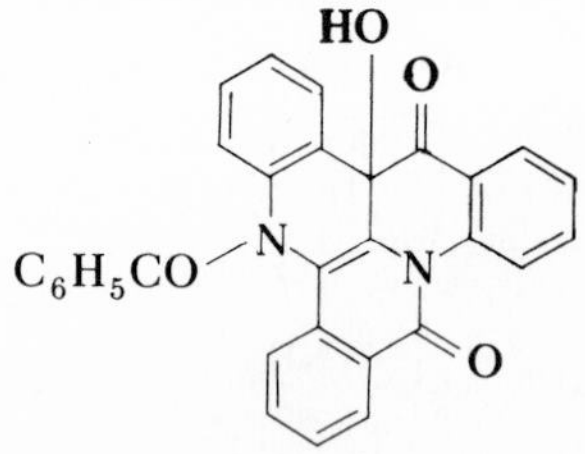

(XI)

structure of Höchst Yellow R. Hydrolysis with hot aqueous caustic produced benzoic and anthranilic acids and a lactam thought to be XII, which induced Hope, Kersey and Richter to suggest[13] structure X. However, an independent synthesis[15] of XII (see Section A-203) showed it was not the lactam obtained from the dye, and further work[16] resulted in the synthesis of XIII (see Section A-209) and demonstration of its identity with the lactam. Fusion of Höchst Yellow R with caustic yielded[14] a lactone thought to be XIV, which led to the proposal of structure XI for the dye. Condensation of XIII with *p*-toluidine yielded[12] a mixture of XV and XVI, which also resulted when Dessoulavy's compound (I) was heated with *p*-toluidine.

While no homologs of Dessoulavy's compound appear to have been reported, several derivatives of Höchst Yellow R have been prepared. Condensation[10] of indigo with zinc chloride and *p*-toluic anhydride or *p*-methoxybenzoic anhydride or *o*-chlorobenzoic an-

Höchst Yellow R

NaOH Δ

10% KOH Δ

(XII) (II) (XIV)

(XIII) (XV) (XVI)

hydride yielded pale yellow homologs of II, melting, respectively, at 330°, 320° and above 340°. Similarly, dibromoindigo reacted with benzoic anhydride and *p*-toluic anhydride to yield yellow homologs of II melting at 340° and above 330°, respectively. All of these products are non-vattable.

References

1. Schwartz, *J. prakt. Chem.*, **91,** 382 (1863).
2. Posner, *Ber.*, **59,** 1799 (1926).
3. Hope and Richter, *J. Chem. Soc.*, **1932,** 2783.
4. Dessoulavy, *Inaugural Dissertation*, Neuchâtel, 1909.
5. Farbwerke vorm. Meister Lucius & Brüning, Ger. Pats. 247,154 and 254,567; *Frdl.*, **10,** 403 and 1335 (1913).
6. Posner, Zimmermann and Kautz, *Ber.*, **62,** 2150 (1929).
7. de Diesbach and Frossard, *Helv. Chim. Acta*, **37,** 701 (1954).
8. de Diesbach, Jacobi and Taddei, *Helv. Chim. Acta*, **23,** 469 (1940).
9. Farbwerke vorm. Meister Lucius & Brüning, Ger. Pat. 270,943; *Frdl.*, **11,** 298 (1915).
10. Farbwerke vorm. Meister Lucius & Brüning, Ger. Pat. 250,744; *Frdl.*, **11,** 297 (1915).
11. Farbwerke vorm. Meister Lucius & Brüning, Ger. Pat. 279,196; *Frdl.*, **12,** 268 (1916).

12. de Diesbach, Capponi and Farquet, *Helv. Chim. Acta*, **32,** 1214 (1949).
13. Hope, Kersey and Richter, *J. Chem. Soc.*, **1933,** 1000.
14. de Diesbach, de Bie and Rubli, *Helv. Chim. Acta*, **17,** 113 (1934).
15. de Diesbach, Rey-Bellet and Kiang, *Helv. Chim. Acta*, **26,** 1869 (1943).
16. de Diesbach, Heppner and Siegwart, *Helv. Chim. Acta*, **31,** 724 (1948).

A-211. Dibenzo[*b*,*g*]pyrrocoline. R.I. 2427

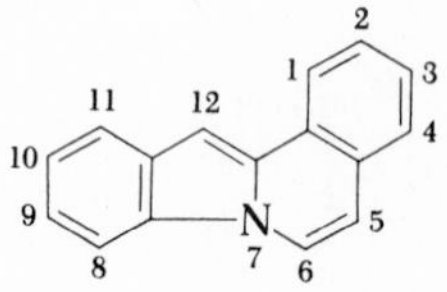

The name *2′,1′:1,2-2″,1″:5,6-dibenzoindolizine* has been used, as has the numbering shown in I.

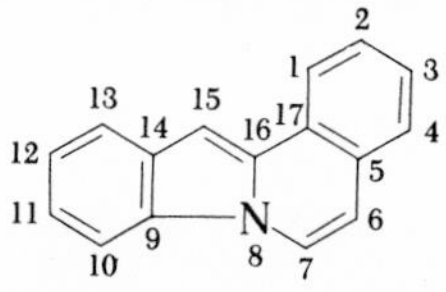

(I)

The prototype of this ring system (II) was obtained[1] in 40% yield by passage of 1-benzylisoquinoline over heated copper turnings. Compound II is a non-basic, yellowish green solid (m. 238°). A product with very similar properties, and believed to be identical with II, was obtained[1] from a similar dehydrogenation of 1-(2-methylbenzyl)-isoquinoline.

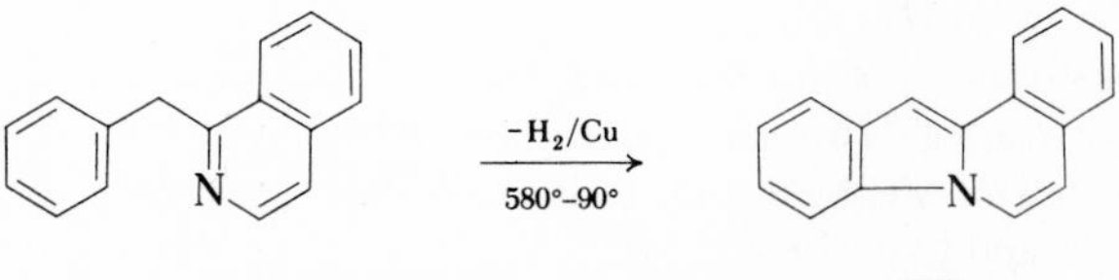

$-H_2/Cu$, 580°–90°

(II)

Treatment of III (R = R′ = H[2] or R = H, R′ = OCH_3[3]) with aluminum chloride yielded the oxindoles IV, which were cyclized by the action of phosphorus oxychloride to salts of structure V. As is the case with related systems (e.g., see Sections A-721, A-725, etc.), the bases corresponding to these salts have the structure exemplified by VIII. This synthesis failed in the case of the tetramethoxy compound III (R = R′ = OCH_3), and an alternative route was found[3] to convert it into VII via the dihydroisoquinolinium salt VI.

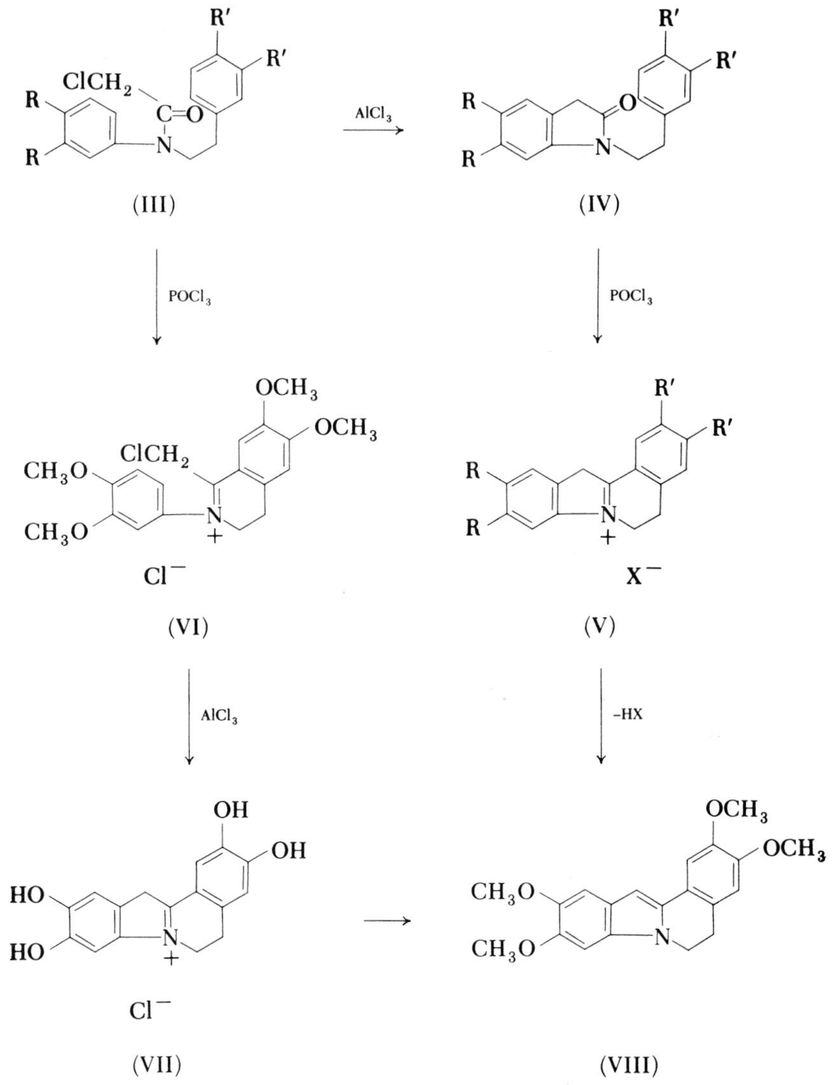

Harley-Mason[4] oxidized tetrahydropapaveroline (IX) with potassium ferricyanide, and readily obtained X, which is of interest for the facility (merely exposure to air for two days) with which it is oxidized. Acetylation of the crude oxidation product gave XI, the

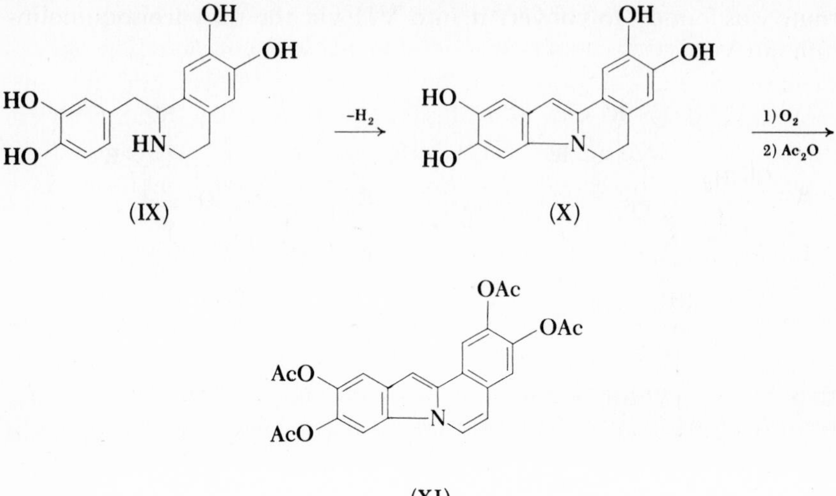

(IX) $\xrightarrow{-H_2}$ (X) $\xrightarrow[2)\ Ac_2O]{1)\ O_2}$ (XI)

only other (besides II) completely aromatic dibenzo[*b*,*g*]pyrrocoline reported.

Some twenty years earlier, laudanosoline (XII) had similarly been oxidized to dehydrolaundanosoline (XIII) by Robinson and

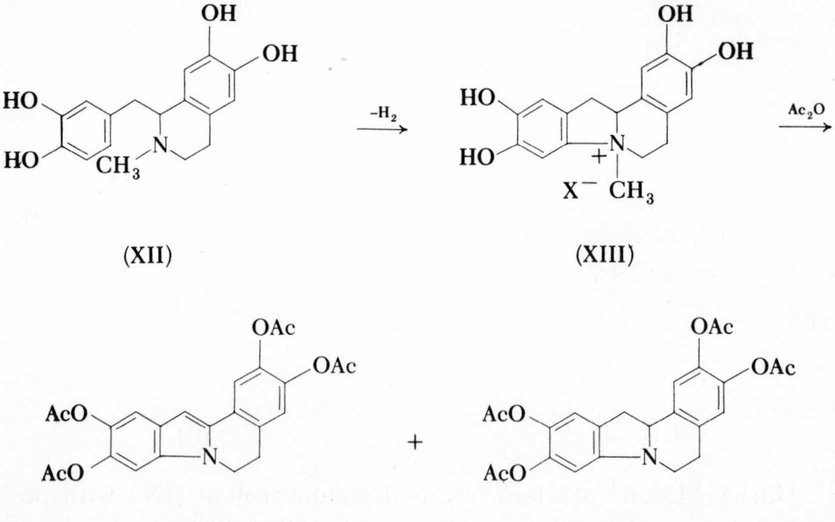

(XII) $\xrightarrow{-H_2}$ (XIII) $\xrightarrow{Ac_2O}$ (XIV) + (XV)

Sugasawa[5] and independently by Schöpf and Thierfelder.[6] This dehydrocyclization occurs with considerable facility, and a variety of oxidants such as potassium ferricyanide, chloranil, or even atmospheric oxygen (with or without a platinum black catalyst) are effective. Methylation of XIII followed by pyrolysis was demonstrated[1] to yield the tetramethoxytetrahydro compound, but as a result of rapid air-oxidation, VIII is the product actually isolated. Similarly, heating XIII with acetic anhydride in pyridine yielded[1] a mixture of XIV and XV.

The facility with which XII could be oxidized to XIII led to the conclusion[6] that such products might be susceptible to biosynthesis. The recent isolation[7-8] of two such alkaloids, XVI and XVII, from the bark of a Queensland tree [*Crypocaria bowiei* (Hook.)] vindicates this prediction.

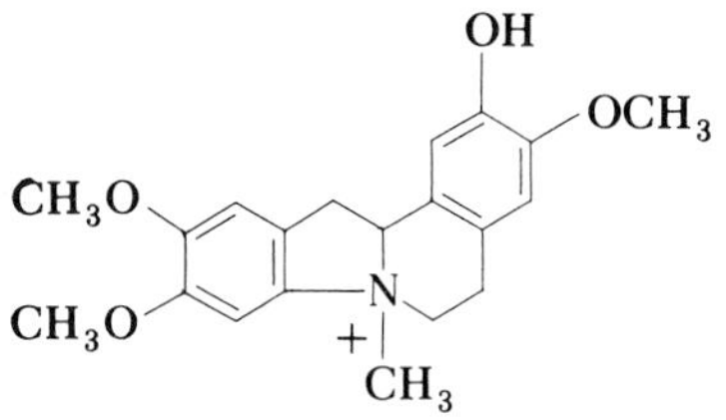

(XVI) 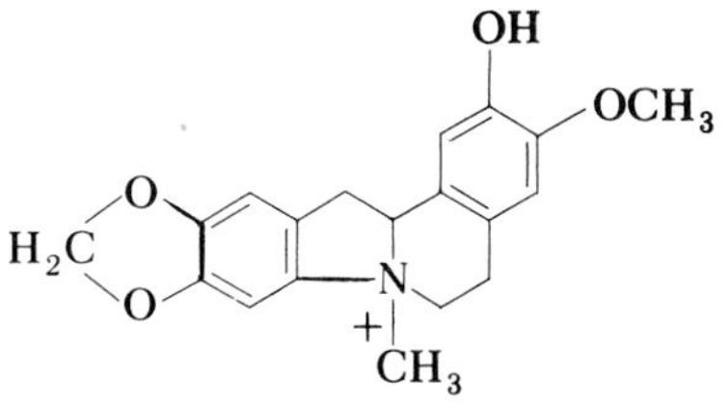 (XVII)

The 5,6-dihydrodibenzo[*b*,*g*]pyrrocolines (e.g., VIII, XI or XIV) are relatively non-basic and do not form methiodides; however, as indole derivatives, they do give a strongly positive Ehrlich test. By contrast, tetrahydro compounds such as XV are basic, form methiodides and give a positive Ehrlich test only when heated.

For a period, the Erythrina alkaloids were thought[9-11] to contain a dibenzo[*b*,*g*]pyrrocoline skeleton, although another structure (see Sections A-199–201) is now accepted. In an effort to verify the structure of hexahydroapoerysodine, XVIII was cyclized[12] to XIX and reduced to XX, which was thought[13] to possess the *cis*-configuration shown.

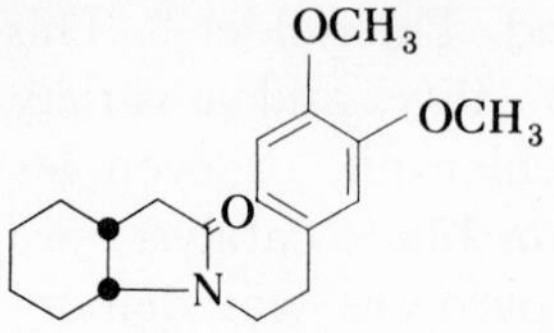

(XVIII) 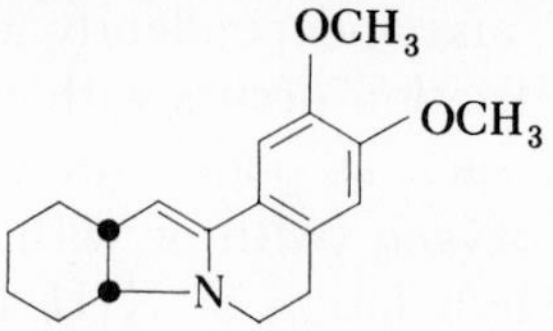 → (XIX) $\xrightarrow{H_2/Pt}$ (XX)

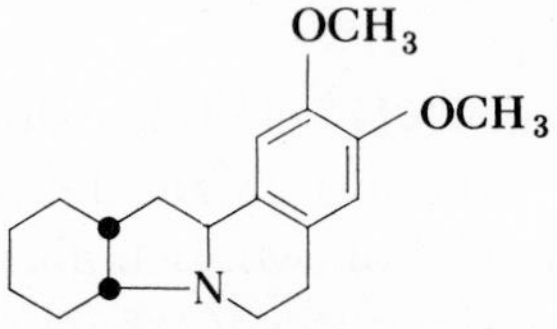

Dibenzo[*b*,*g*]pyrrocolines

Empirical formula	Substituents or structure	Properties	Refs.
$C_{16}H_{11}N$	Unsubstituted	m. 238°.	1
$C_{16}H_{13}N$	5,6-Dihydro-	m. 200–1°. Bl. fluoresc. in H_2SO_4 solution.	2
$C_{16}H_{13}NO_4$	5,6-Dihydro-2,3,9,10-tetrahydroxy-	Pale yellow, m. 253–5°.	4
$C_{16}H_{14}NO_4$	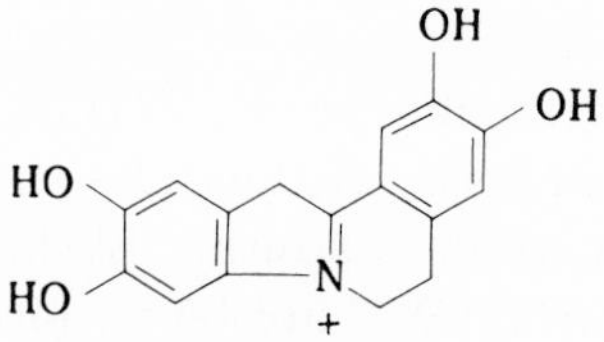	Chloride.	3
$C_{16}H_{15}N$	5,6,12,12*a*-Tetrahydro-	$b_{0.6}$ 170–5°. HCl salt, m. 155–7°. Picrate, m. 139–40°. Chloroplatinate, m. 180°. Methiodide, m. 217°.	1
$C_{17}H_{18}NO_4$	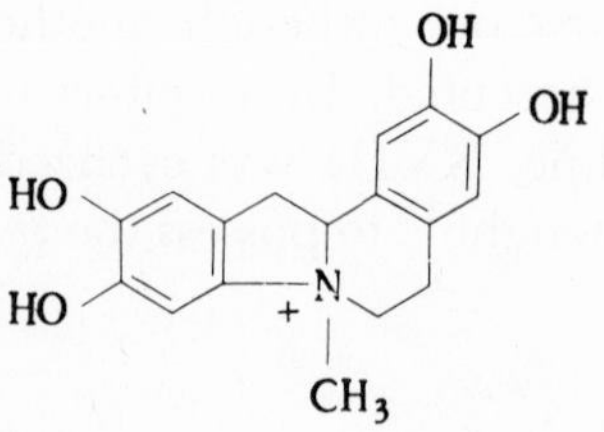	Chloride ($\cdot H_2O$), m. 303–5°. Bromide ($\cdot H_2O$), m. 262° d. "Phenol betaine" ($C_{17}H_{17}NO_4$) m. 257°; monohydrate, m. 275–6°.	5,6

Dibenzo[b,g]pyrrocolines (*continued*)

Empirical formula	Substituents or structure	Properties	Refs.
$C_{18}H_{17}NO_2$	5,6-Dihydro-2,3-dimethoxy-	Pale yel., m. 147°.	3
$C_{18}H_{21}NO_2$	Hexahydro-2,3-dimethoxy-(Exact structure unknown)	Red, m. 176° d.	12
$C_{18}H_{23}NO_2$	5,6,7*a*,8,9,10,11,11*a*-Octahydro-2,3-dimethoxy-	m. 113-5°. Picrolonate, m. 174-6°.	12
$C_{18}H_{25}NO_2$	5,6,7*a*,8,9,10,11,11*a*,12,12*a*-Decahydro-2,3-dimethoxy-	Oil. Picrate, m. 158.5-9.5°.	12
$C_{20}H_{21}NO_4$	5,6-Dihydro-2,3,9,10-tetramethoxy-	m. 201-3° (199-200°, 199°), λ_{max}^{EtOH} 335, 350 mμ.	3,5, 6
$C_{21}H_{26}NO_4$	OCH_3, OCH_3, CH_3O, CH_3O, $\overset{+}{N}$, CH_3	Iodide (·5H_2O), m. 242-3°. Chloride, m. 225° d. Methosulfate (·2.5 H_2O), m. 228° (222-6°).	5,6
$C_{24}H_{19}NO_8$	2,3,9,10-Tetraacetoxy-	Yel., m. 269-70°. Strong bl.-grn. fluoresc. in solns.	4
$C_{24}H_{21}NO_8$	2,3,9,10-Tetraacetoxy-5,6-dihydro-	m. 214-5°.	5
$C_{24}H_{23}NO_8$	2,3,9,10-Tetraacetoxy-5,6,12,12*a*-tetrahydro-	m. 148°. HBr salt, m. 170-2°. Picrolonate, m. 207° d.	5,6
$C_{34}H_{31}NO_8$	2,3,9,10-Tetrabenzoxy-5,6,12,12*a*-tetrahydro-	m. 222-5°.	6

References

1. Braun and Nelles, *Ber.*, **70,** 1767 (1937).
2. Mathew and Menon, *Proc. Indian Acad. Sci.*, **29A,** 361 (1949); *Chem. Abstracts*, **44,** 3998 (1950).
3. Sugasawa and Mizukami, *Pharm. Bull.* (Japan), **3,** 42 (1955); *Chem. Abstracts*, **50,** 13913 (1956).
4. Harley-Mason, *J. Chem. Soc.*, **1953,** 1465.
5. Robinson and Sugasawa, *J. Chem. Soc.*, **1932,** 789.
6. Schöpf and Thierfelder, *Ann.*, **497,** 22 (1932).

7. Ewing, Hughes, Ritchie and Taylor, *Nature*, **169**, 618 (1952); *Australian J. Chem.*, **6**, 75 (1953); *Chem. Abstracts*, **47**, 12400 (1953).
8. Hughes, Ritchie and Taylor, *Australian J. Chem.*, **6**, 315 (1953); *Chem. Abstracts*, **48**, 6446 (1954).
9. Folkers, Koniuszy and Shavel, *J. Am. Chem. Soc.*, **64**, 2146 (1942).
10. Prelog, Wiesner, Khorana and Kenner, *Helv. Chim. Acta*, **32**, 453 (1949).
11. Folkers, Koniuszy and Shavel, *J. Am. Chem. Soc.*, **73**, 589 (1951).
12. Wiesner, Clarke and Kairys, *Can. J. Research*, **28B**, 234 (1950).
13. Clair, Clarke, Edmiston and Wiesner, *Can. J. Research*, **28B**, 745 (1950).

A-212. 6*H*-Benzo[*hi*]cyclopenta[*b*]-pyrrocoline

The reaction of I with paraldehyde or with methyl vinyl ketone in the presence of oxidants such as ferric chloride or *o*-nitrophenol, yielded,[1,2,3] respectively, II and III. The latter was used[3] to make the cyanine dyes IV (m. 215–7° d.), V (m. 215–7° d.) and VI (m. 194–6° d.).

$(CH_3CHO)_3$; $CH_2{=}CHCOCH_3$

(II) (I)

(III) (IV)

(V) R = $-C_6H_4-N(CH_3)_2$

(VI) R = (1-C_6H_5-2,5-dimethylpyrrol-3-yl)

References

1. Heseltine, U. S. Pats. 2,578,303 and 2,646,433.
2. Heseltine and Brooker, U. S. Pats. 2,578,304 and 2,636,035.
3. Brooker and Heseltine, U. S. Pat. 2,646,430. Brit. Pat. 713,255.

A-213. 4*H*-Pyrido[3,2,1-*jk*]carbazole.
R.I. 2440

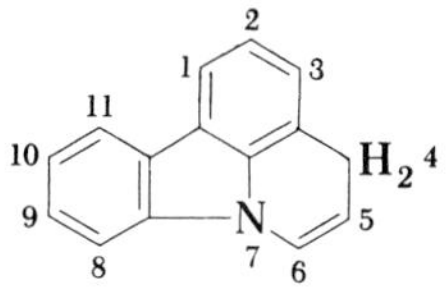

The names (and numbering) *1-peri-pyridocarbazole* (I) and *dibenzo[b,hi]pyrrocoline* have been used by *Chemical Abstracts*, while for the parent nucleus and its hydro and oxo derivatives, one encounters *1,8-o-phenylenequinoline*, *1,9-trimethylenecarbazole*, *9:8-carbazoleanhydropropionic acid* and *1,9-malonylcarbazole*.

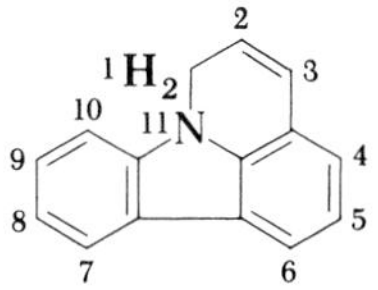

(I)

Clemo and Perkin[1] treated a mixture of II and cyclohexanone with zinc and acid, and subjected the resulting hydrazone (III) to the Fischer indole synthesis, thereby obtaining IV.

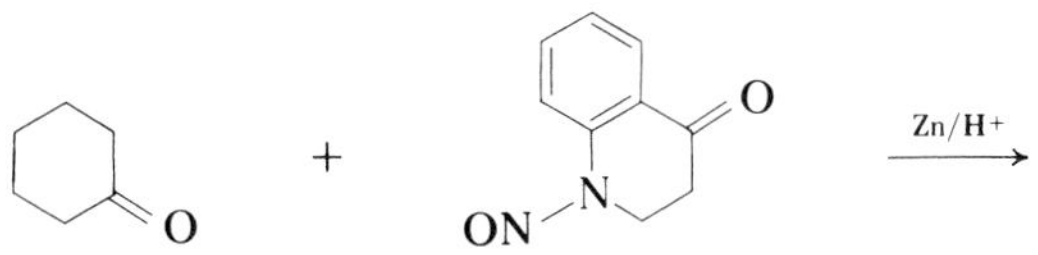

Zn/H+

(II)

H+

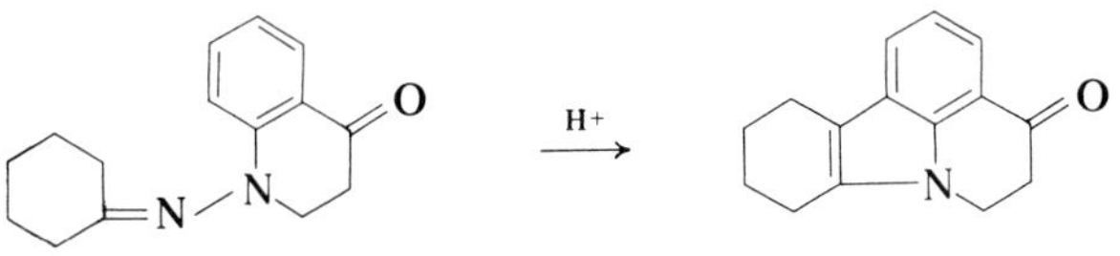

(III)

(IV)

Cyclization of V in a salt melt afforded[2] the 5,6-dihydro-4-oxo-compound (VI), in which the carbonyl group reacted with anilines or cyanacetic ester to yield, respectively, the 4-anils and compound VII. With aromatic aldehydes, VI gave 5-arylidene-4-oxo derivatives.

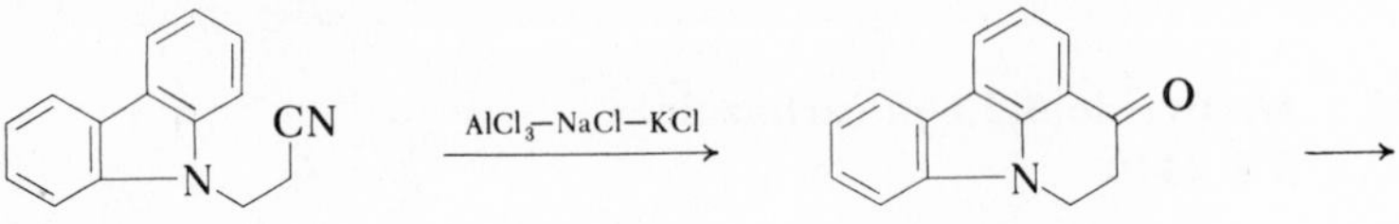

$AlCl_3$–NaCl–KCl

(V) (VI)

$CO_2C_2H_5$ CN

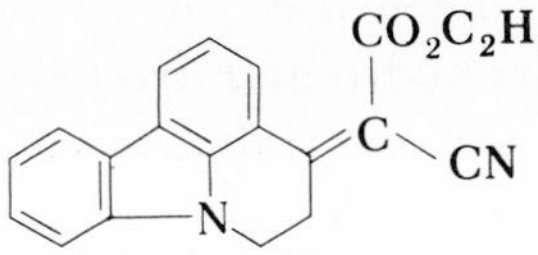

(VII)

Dehydration of VIII, by solution in sulfuric acid for 24 hours at room temperature, was reported[3] to afford a quantitative yield of IX. Refluxing carbazole with ethylmalonic ester produced[4] X in 76% yield, and a Clemmensen reduction of the 4-oxo group yielded XI. Thus convenient, efficient routes to both 4- and 5-alkyl-6-oxo derivatives are available.

Subjection of XII (R = H) to the Fischer indole synthesis yielded[5] XIII, which could be dehydrogenated to XIV by the action of chloranil in refluxing xylene,[8] or reduced electrolytically to XV. Dehydrogenation of XV with palladium charcoal gave XVI. During their extensive studies upon alkaloids of the Strychnos species, Robinson and his co-workers[5-7] prepared a number of products of structure XVII (R = C_2H_5, CH_2CH_2COOH, $CH_2CH_2NH_2$, etc.). The initially formed products of the Fischer indole reaction were usually hydrogenated (without isolation) to XVII for more convenient separation. Several products derived from XVII were prepared[9] during an investigation of the Strychnos alkaloid *vomicine*.

An early German patent[10] claimed the preparation of a product, thought to be either XVIII or XIX, by the reaction of potassium carbazole with epichlorhydrin. More recent work[11] favors structure XVIII. Nitration of XVIII yielded the 2-nitro derivative, and

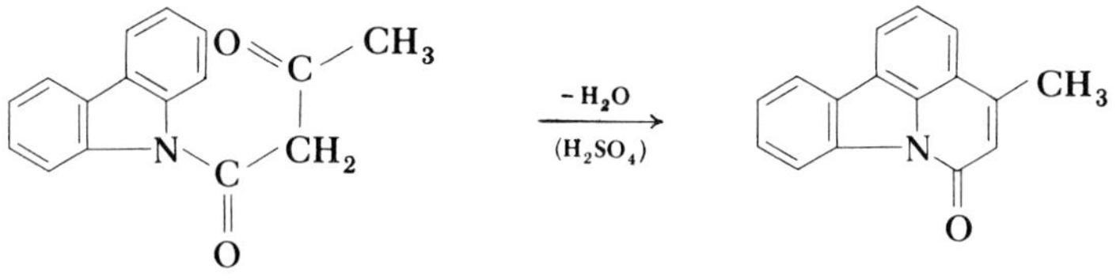

O, CH_3, N, C, CH_2, C, O — $-H_2O$ (H_2SO_4) → N, CH_3, O

(VIII) (IX)

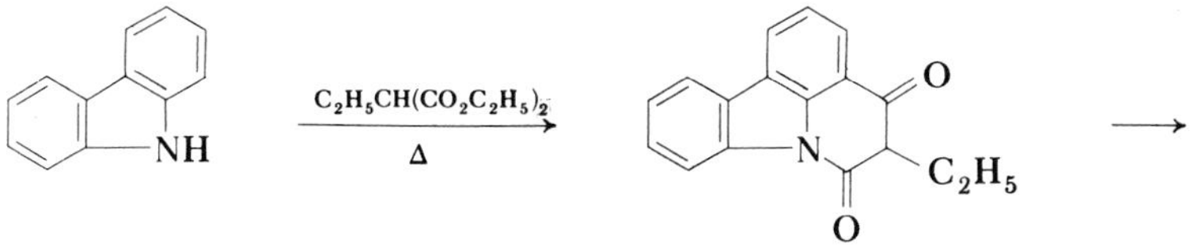

NH — $C_2H_5CH(CO_2C_2H_5)_2$, Δ → N, O, C_2H_5, O →

(X)

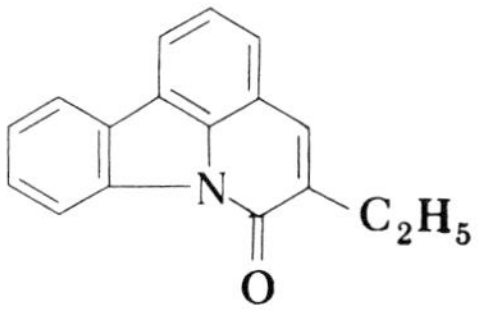

N, C_2H_5, O

(XI)

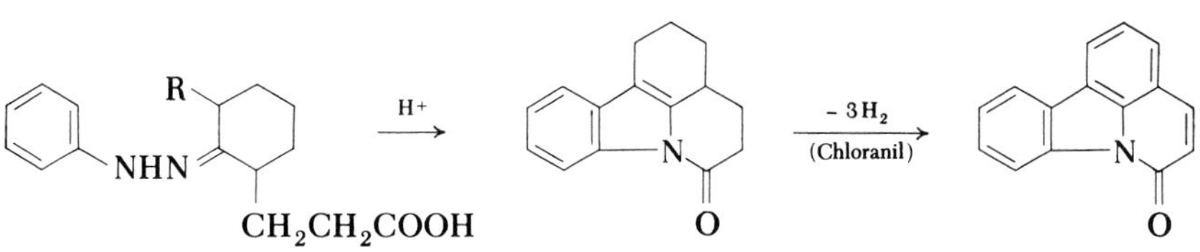

R, NHN, CH_2CH_2COOH — H^+ → N, O — $-3H_2$ (Chloranil) → N, O

(XII) (XIII) (XIV)

(XII) — 1) H^+ 2) H_2 → (XVII); (XIII) — $3H_2$ → (XV)

R, N, O — N — $-H_2$/Pd–C → N

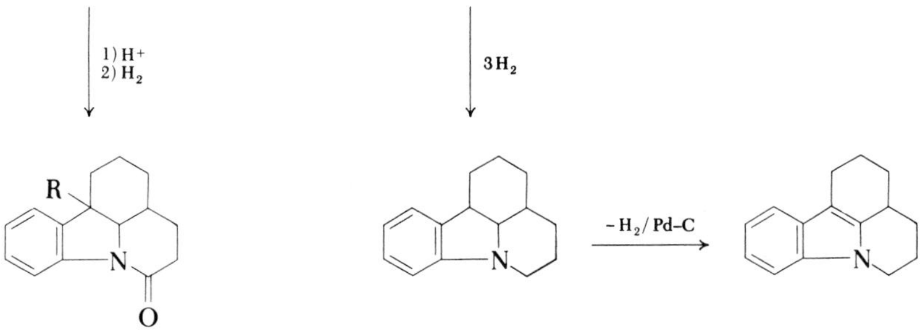

(XVII) (XV) (XVI)

the 10-nitro isomer was obtained[11] from potassium 3-nitrocarbazole and epichlorhydrin. Bromination of the 10-nitro derivative of XVIII afforded the 2-bromo-10-nitro homolog of XVIII, as was shown by its synthesis from the known[12] 3-bromo-6-nitrocarbazole. Compound XVIII could, presumably, undergo oxidation to 5,6-dihydropyrido[3,2,1-*jk*]carbazole-5(4*H*)-one, thus making conveniently available all three of the 4-, 5- and 6-oxo-5,6-dihydro derivatives.

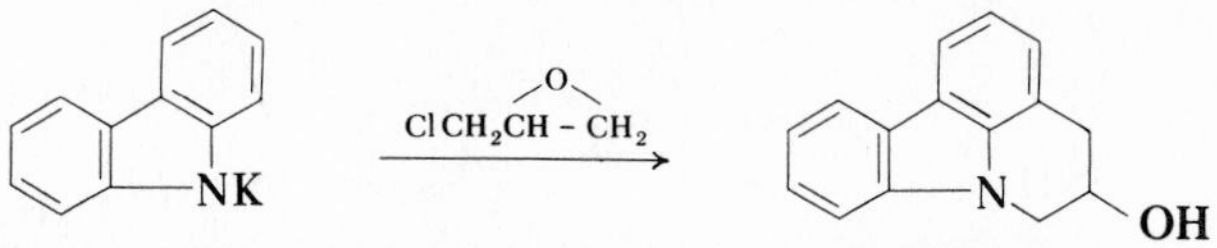

NK $\xrightarrow{ClCH_2\overset{O}{CH-CH_2}}$ N OH

(XVIII)

N $CH_2\overset{O}{CH-CH_2}$

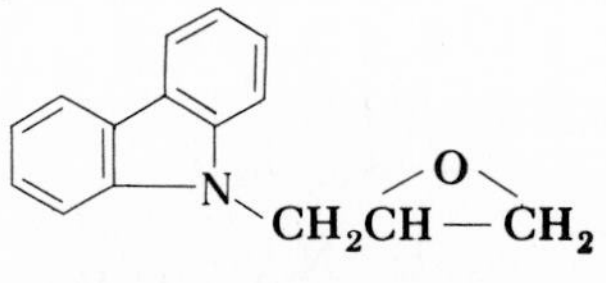

(XIX)

In the presence of zinc chloride and an oxidant such as ferric chloride or *o*-nitrophenol, carbazole condenses with paraldehyde or methyl vinyl ketone to form low yields of respectively, XX[13,14] or XXI.[13,15] Several cyanine dyes derived from XXI have been patented[16] as photographic sensitizers.

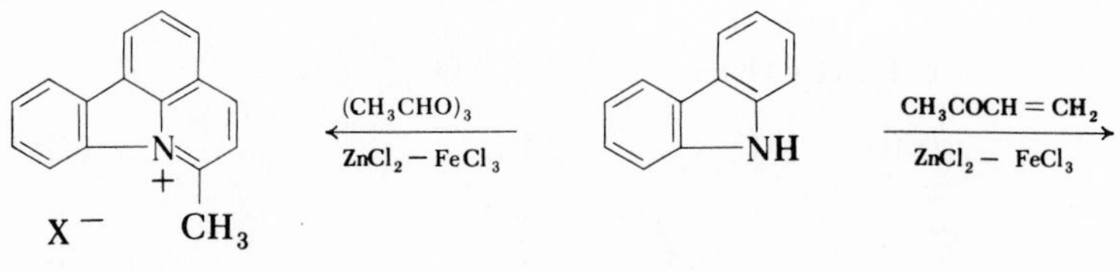

X^- $\overset{+}{N}$ CH_3 $\xleftarrow[ZnCl_2-FeCl_3]{(CH_3CHO)_3}$ NH $\xrightarrow[ZnCl_2-FeCl_3]{CH_3COCH=CH_2}$

(XX)

CH_3 $\overset{+}{N}$ X^-

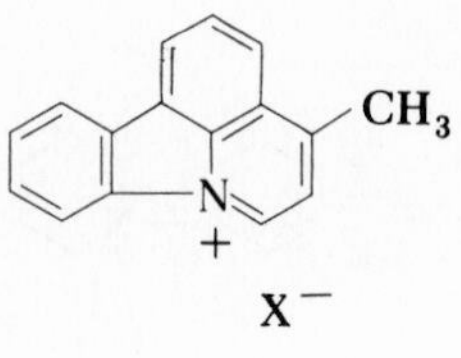

(XXI)

Pyrido[3,2,1-*jk*]carbazoles

Empirical formula	Substituents or structure	Properties	Refs.
$C_{15}H_9NO$	6-Oxo-6*H*-	m. 135–6°.	8
$C_{15}H_{11}NO$	5,6-Dihydro-4-oxo-4*H*-	m. 98–9°. Benzylidene deriv., *cis*-isomer, m. 148°; *trans*-isomer, m. 215°. *p*-Diethylaminobenzylidene deriv., *cis*-isomer, m. 144°; *trans*-isomer, m. 182°. *p*-Phenetide, m. 147°. 2,4-DNPH, or., m. 298°.	2,17
$C_{15}H_{11}BrN_2O_3$	2-Bromo-5,6-dihydro-5-hydroxy-10-nitro-4*H*-	Yel., m. 342°.	11
$C_{15}H_{12}N_2O_3$	5,6-Dihydro-5-hydroxy-2-nitro-4*H*-	Yel., m. 152–3°; vt. soln. in H_2SO_4.	
	5,6-Dihydro-5-hydroxy-10-nitro-4*H*-	m. 285° d.; cherry red soln. in H_2SO_4.	11
$C_{15}H_{13}NO$	5,6-Dihydro-5-hydroxy-4*H*-	m. 112°.	10,11
$C_{15}H_{15}NO$	5,6,8,9,10,11-Hexahydro-4-oxo-4*H*-	Brn., m. 135–6°; grn. fluoresc. in H_2SO_4. Phenylhydrazone, m. 191°.	1
	1,2,3,3*a*,4,5-Hexahydro-6-oxo-6*H*-	m. 126°.	5
$C_{15}H_{17}N$	1,2,3,3*a*,5,6-Hexahydro-4*H*-	m. 87–8°.	5
$C_{15}H_{19}N$	1,2,3,3*a*,5,6,11*b*,11*c*-Octahydro-4*H*-	m. 81–2°.	5
$C_{16}H_{11}NO$	4-Methyl-6-oxo-6*H*-	m. 156–7°.	3
$C_{16}H_{12}N$	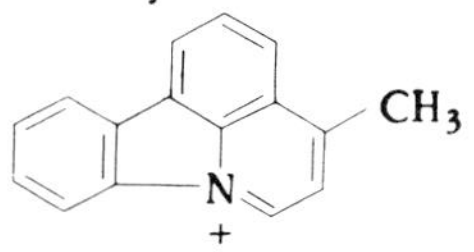 CH_3 N^+	Iodide, yel.	13,15,16

(*continued*)

Pyrido[3,2,1-*jk*]carbazoles (*continued*)

Empirical formula	Substituents or structure	Properties	Refs.
$C_{16}H_{12}N$ (*cont.*)	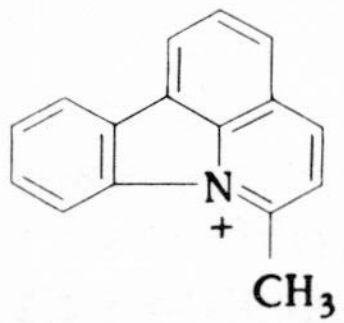	Iodide.	13,14,16
$C_{16}H_{15}NO_3$	2-Carboxy-1,2,3,3*a*,4,5-hexahydro-6-oxo-6*H*-	m. 270–1°.	7
$C_{16}H_{16}N$	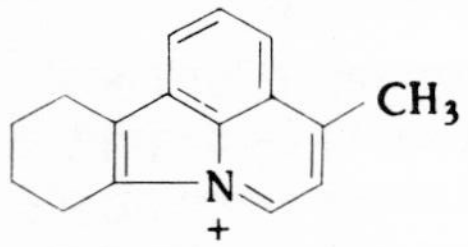	Iodide, yel., m. 268–70°.	13,15,16
$C_{17}H_{13}NO$	5-Ethyl-6-oxo-6*H*-	m. 128–9°.	4
$C_{17}H_{13}NO_2$	5-Ethyl-5,6-dihydro-4,6-dioxo-4*H*-	m. 257–8°.	4
$C_{17}H_{20}NO$	11*b*-Ethyl-1,2,3,3*a*,4,5,11*b*,11*c*-octahydro-6-oxo-6*H*-	m. 106.8–7.5°.	6
$C_{17}H_{21}N_2O$	11*b*-(2-Aminoethyl)-1,2,3,3*a*,4,5,11*b*,11*c*-octahydro-6-oxo-6*H*-	Grn. oil, $b_{0.2}$ 220°. Hydrogen *d*-tartrate, m. 201–3°.	7
$C_{17}H_{22}N$	11*b*-Ethyl-1,2,3,3*a*,5,6,11*b*,11*c*-octahydro-4*H*-	b_{16} 189°, m. 51.2°.	6
$C_{18}H_{20}NO_3$	11*b*-(2-Carboxyethyl)-1,2,3,3*a*,4,5,11*b*,11*c*-octahydro-6-oxo-6*H*-	Two isomers, m. 232° and m. 271° (269–70°).	5,7
$C_{19}H_{20}NO_5$	2-Carboxy-11*b*-(2-carboxyethyl)-1,2,3,3*a*,4,5,11*b*,11*c*-octahydro-6-oxo-6*H*	m. 257–8°.	7

$C_{20}H_{16}N_2O_2$	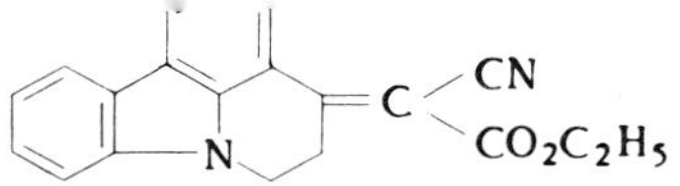 N; C; CN; $CO_2C_2H_5$	m. 161–2°.	3
$C_{20}H_{28}N_2O$	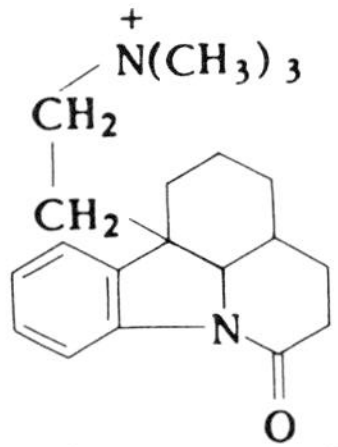 $\overset{+}{N}(CH_3)_3$; CH_2; CH_2; N; O	*d*-Bromocamphorsulfonate, m. 265°.	7
$C_{21}H_{13}NO_2$	5,6-Dihydro-4,6-dioxo-5-phenyl-4*H*-	m. 207–8°.	4
$C_{21}H_{23}NO_3$	Desazadesoxyvomicine	m. 186°.	9
$C_{21}H_{27}NO_3$	Tetrahydrodesazadesoxyvomicine	Two isomers, m. 182° and m. 246°.	9
$C_{23}H_{20}N_2O_3$	3-*sec*.-Butylidene-11*b*-(2-dimethylaminoethyl)-1,2,3,5,11*b*,11*c*-hexahydro-1,8-dihydroxy-6-oxo-6*H*-	m. 220°, $[\alpha]_D^{20°}$ 99°. Methiodide, m. 294°. Acetate, m. 137–8°.	9
	11*b*-(2-Dimethylaminoethyl)-1,2,3,4,11*b*,11*c*-hexahydro-1,8-dihydroxy-3-(1-methylpropenyl)-6-oxo-6*H*-	m. 206°, $[\alpha]_D^{20°}$ 34° ($CHCl_3$). Methiodide, m. 280° d.	9
$C_{23}H_{34}N_2O_3$	3-*sec*.-Butyl-11*b*-(2-dimethylaminoethyl)-1,2,3,3*a*,4,5,11*b*,11*c*-octahydro-1,8-dihydroxy-6-oxo-6*H*-	Two isomers, m. 150–1° and 212–4°. Two methiodides, m. 265° and m. 260° d.	9
$C_{25}H_{21}N_2$	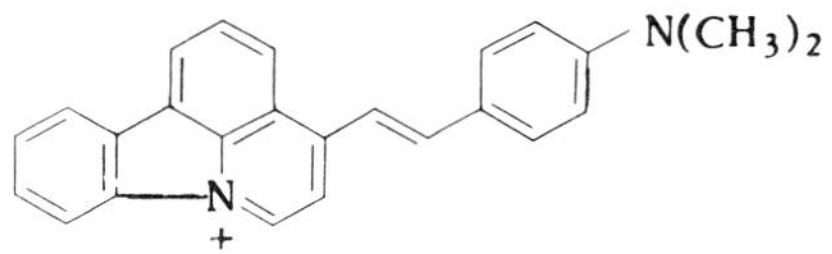 $N(CH_3)_2$; $\overset{+}{N}$	Perchlorate, m. 257–9° d.	16

(*continued*)

Pyrido[3,2,1-*jk*]carbazoles (*continued*)

Empirical formula	Substituents or structure	Properties	Refs.
$C_{25}H_{25}N_2$	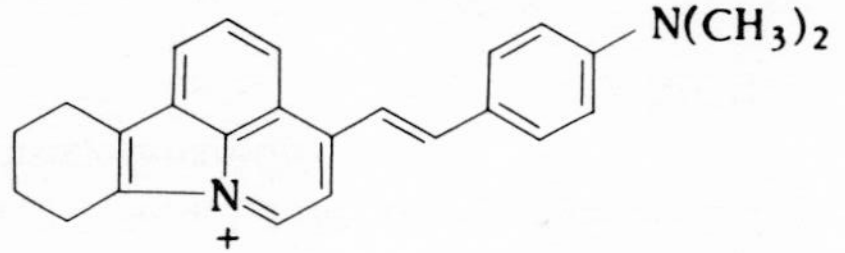	Iodide, m. 256–7°.	16
$C_{27}H_{21}N_2$	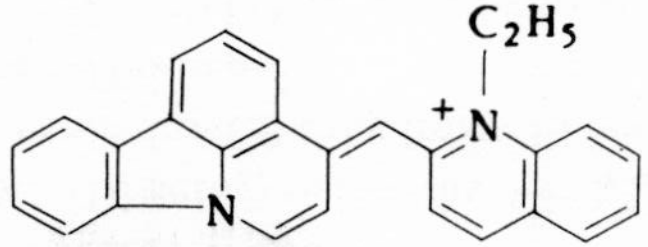	Perchlorate, m. 295–6°.	16
$C_{27}H_{21}N_2X$	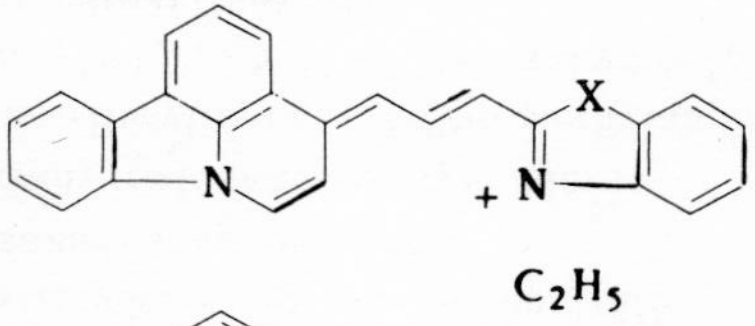	Iodides, X = O, m. 215–7° d; X = S, m. 193–5° d.	16
$C_{27}H_{25}N_2O$	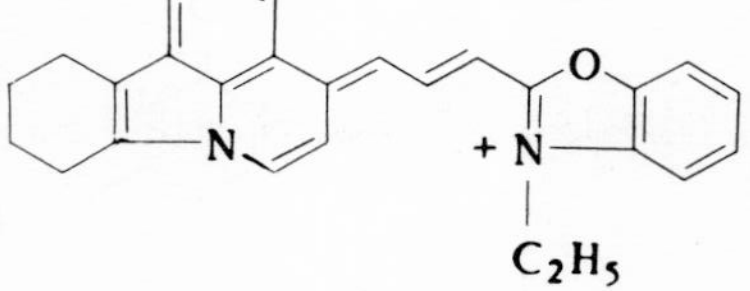	Perchlorate, m. 215–7° d.	16
$C_{33}H_{21}N_2$	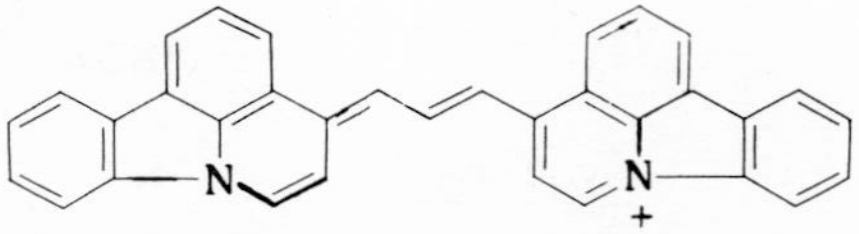	Iodide, m. 259–60° d.	16

References

1. Clemo and Perkin, *J. Chem. Soc.*, **125,** 1608 (1924).
2. I. G. Farbenindustrie, A. G., Fr. Pat. 806,715; *Chem. Zentr.*, **I,** 3229 (1937).
3. Perekalin and Lerner, *Zhur. Obshcheĭ Khim.*, **21,** 1995 (1951); *Chem. Abstracts*, **46,** 8115 (1952).
4. Baumgarten and Riedel, *Ber.*, **75,** 984 (1942).
5. Openshaw and Robinson, *J. Chem. Soc.*, **1937,** 941.
6. Holmes, Openshaw and Robinson, *J. Chem. Soc.*, **1946,** 910.
7. Openshaw and Robinson, *J. Chem. Soc.*, **1946,** 912.
8. Prelog, Szpilfogel and Battegay, *Helv. Chim. Acta*, **30,** 366 (1947).
9. Huisgen, Wieland and Eder, *Ann.*, **561,** 193 (1949).
10. Farbwerke vorm. Meister, Lucius & Brüning, Ger. Pat. 284,291; *Frdl.*, **12,** 152 (1917).
11. Deresser and Eichler, *I. G. Farbinindustrie, A.G., 39 Wissenschaftlicher Austausch der Gruppe IX*, Mainkur, June 21–2, 1938; *P. B. Report No.* 70338, frame 10457ff.
12. Mazzura and Leonardi, *Gazz. chim. ital.*, **22,** II, 574 (1892).
13. Heseltine and Brooker, U. S. Pat. 2,578,304.
14. Heseltine, U. S. Pats. 2,646,433 and 2,578,303.
15. Heseltine and Brooker, U. S. Pat. 2,636,035.
16. Brooker and Heseltine, U. S. Pat. 2,646,430. Brit. Pat. 713,255.
17. Fujii, *Yakugaku Zasshi*, **77,** 1065 (1957); *Chem. Abstracts*, **52,** 5417 (1958).

A-214. 1*H*-Indolo[3,2,1-*de*][1,5]-naphthyridine. R.I. 2421

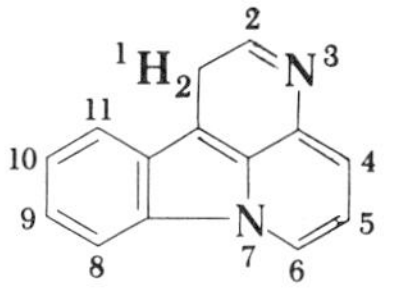

The trivial name *canthine* has been proposed.

Price *et al.*[1,2] have isolated three alkaloids from the leaves and wood of the Australian rain-forest tree (*Pentaceras australis*, Hook.) and have shown them to possess structures I-III.

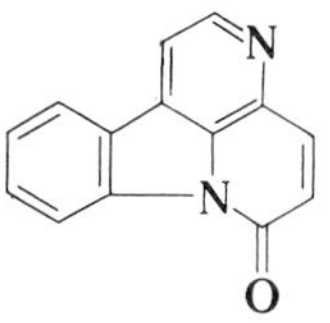

(I) 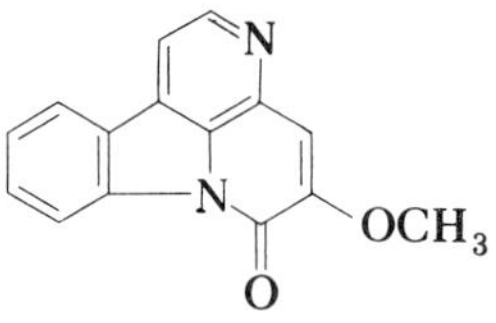 (II) 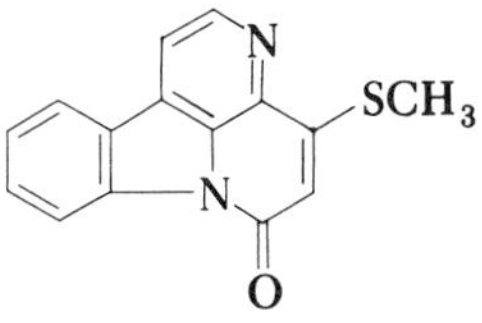 (III)

The condensation of tryptamine (IV) with succinic acid[3] or with α-ketoglutaric acid[4] yields products assigned, respectively, structures V (m. 172°) and VI (d. 149°; hydrochloride, d. 285°). Reduction of VI yielded[6] VII (m. 172–3° d.). When heated, VIII gave[6] a product (m. 194°) thought to be IX.

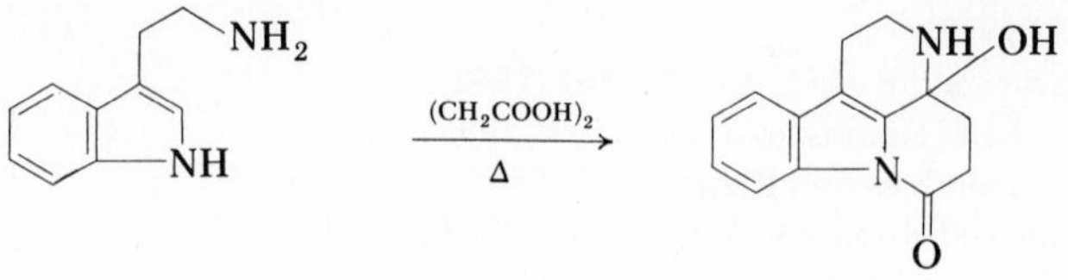

NH_2 NH $(CH_2COOH)_2$ Δ NH OH N O

(IV) (V)

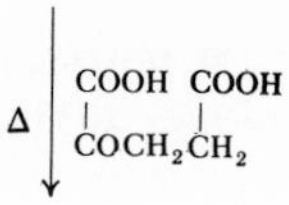

Δ COOH COOH COCH$_2$CH$_2$

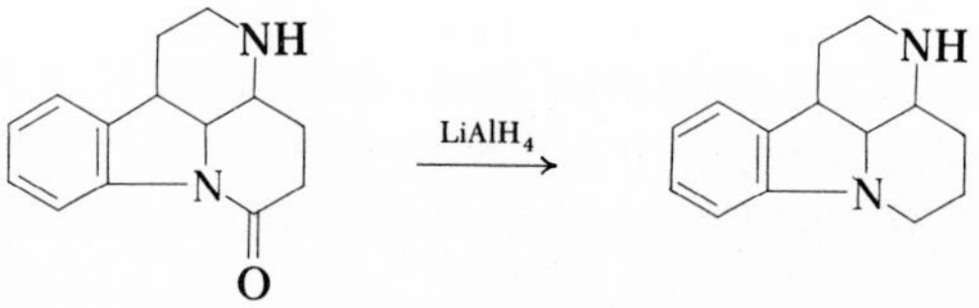

NH N O LiAlH$_4$ NH N

(VI) (VII)

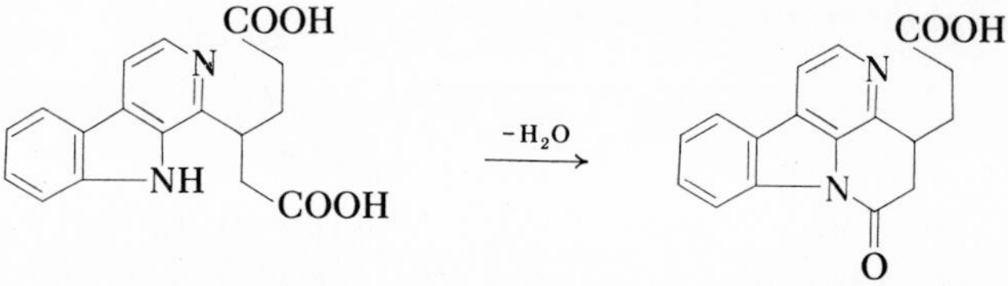

COOH N NH COOH $-H_2O$ COOH N N O

(VIII) (IX)

References

1. Haynes, Nelson and Price, *Australian J. Sci. Res.*, **5A**, 387 (1952); *Chem. Abstracts*, **47**, 3858 (1953).
2. Nelson and Price, *Australian J. Sci. Res.*, **5A**, 563 and 768 (1952); *Chem. Abstracts*, **47**, 6956 and 9983 (1953).
3. Marion and Manske, *Can. J. Res.*, **16B**, 432 (1938).
4. Hahn and Hausel, *Ber.*, **71**, 2163 (1938).
5. Saxton, *Quart. Rev.*, **10**, 108 (1956).
6. Wieland and Neeb, *Ann.*, **600**, 161 (1956).

A-215. 4*H*-Benzo[*hi*]pyrido[4,3-*b*]-pyrrocoline

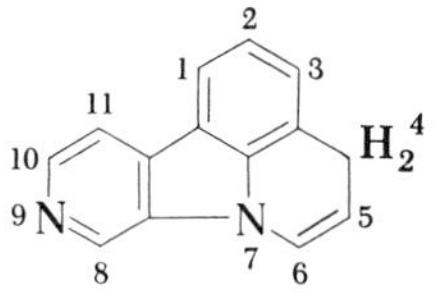

Structure I, originally proposed[1] for the alkaloid *folicanthine*, has been replaced by other, quite different, structures. See Section A-429.

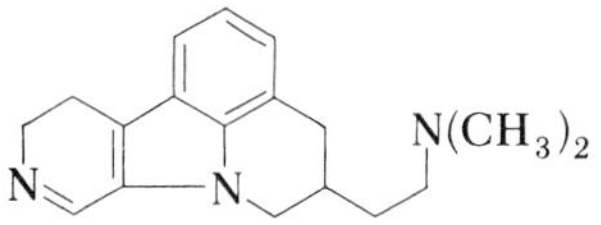

(I)

Reference

1. Eiter and Svierak, *Monatsh.*, **82,** 186 (1951); *Chem. Abstracts*, **45,** 7577 (1951).

A-216. Dibenzo[*e,g*]pyrrocoline

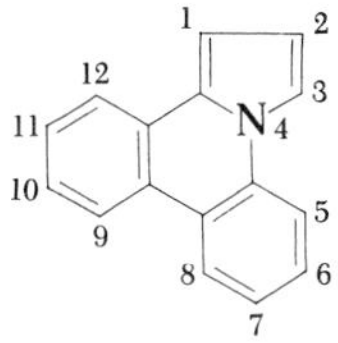

The name *pyrrolo[1,2-f]phenanthridine* has been used, and the 1,2,3,12b-tetrahydro compounds have been called *5,6-* or *9,10-trimethylenephenanthridines*.

The "labile adduct" I was obtained,[1] together with II, from the condensation of phenanthridine with acetylene dicarboxylic ester. Boiling quinoline converted I into the "stable adduct" III (see Section A-735), which could be oxidized to II (m. 224°).

By heating with sodium acetate a substance considered to have structure IV, a product (sesquihydrate, m. 251–3° d.) assigned structure V was obtained.[2] Electrolytic reduction yielded VI (d. 165–6°; HCl salt, d. 250–1°; methiodide, d. 234°). Compound VI was reoxidized to V when heated with potassium iodide (iodine).

Reductive cyclization of VII afforded[3] a 40% yield of VIII ($b_{0.5}$ 114°, n_D^{20} 1.5310; d_4^{20} 1.014; picrate, m. 176–7°; picrolonate, m. 204–5°).

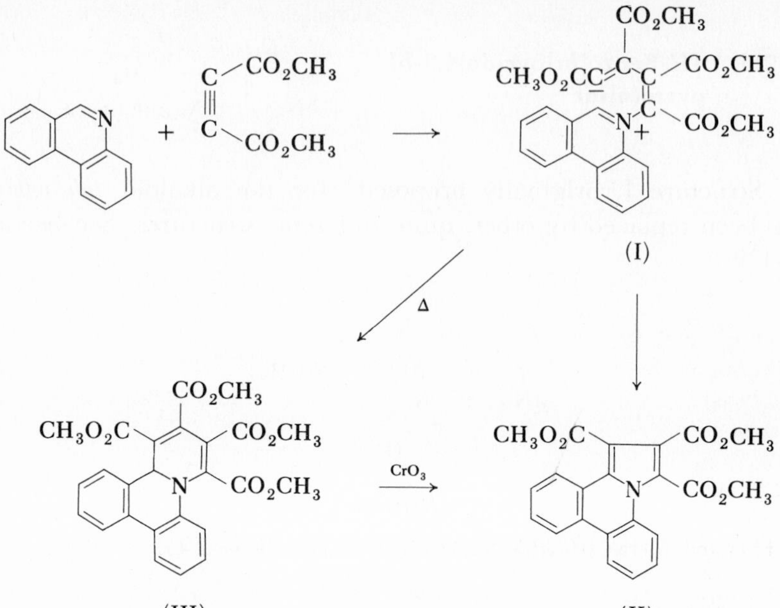

N + $C(CO_2CH_3)\equiv C(CO_2CH_3)$ ⟶ CO_2CH_3, CH_3O_2CC, CO_2CH_3, CO_2CH_3, N^+

(I)

Δ

CO_2CH_3, CH_3O_2C, CO_2CH_3, CO_2CH_3, N

CrO_3

CH_3O_2C, CO_2CH_3, CO_2CH_3, N

(III)

(II)

CH_3O, CH_3O, N, Br, OCH_3, OCH_3

1) NaOAc/Δ
2) KI

CH_3O, CH_3O, N^+, I^-, OCH_3, OCH_3

(IV)

(V)

I_2 H_2

CH_3O, CH_3O, N, OCH_3, OCH_3

(VI)

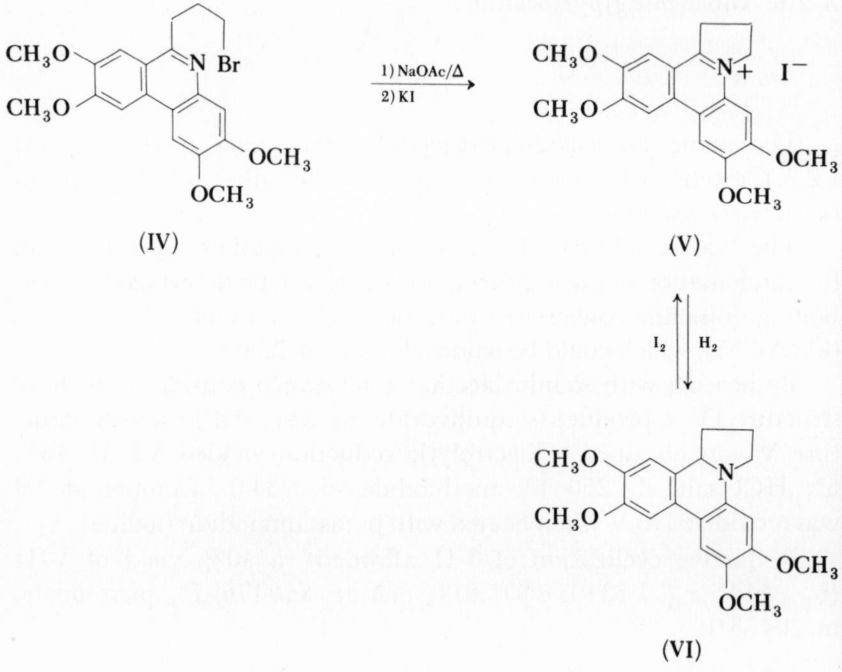

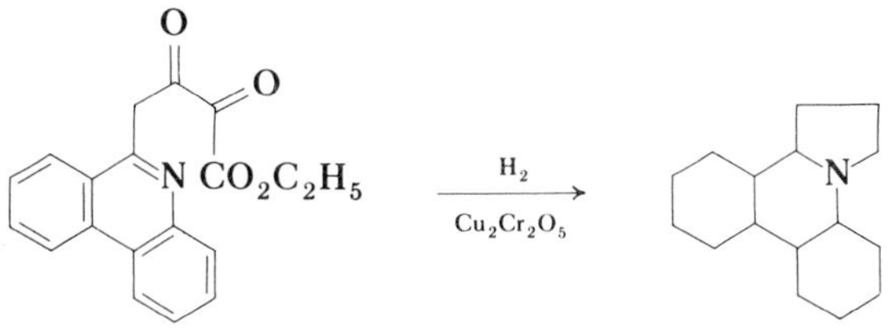

(VII) $\xrightarrow[Cu_2Cr_2O_5]{H_2}$ (VIII)

References

1. Diels and Theile, *J. prakt. Chem.*, **156,** 195 (1940).
2. Sugasawa and Ohki, *J. Pharm. Soc. Japan*, **62,** 398 (1942); *Chem. Abstracts*, **45,** 5168 (1951).
3. Leonard and Boyer, *J. Am. Chem. Soc.*, **72,** 2980 (1950).

A-217. 3*H*-Pyrrolo[*de*]acridine. R.I. 2437

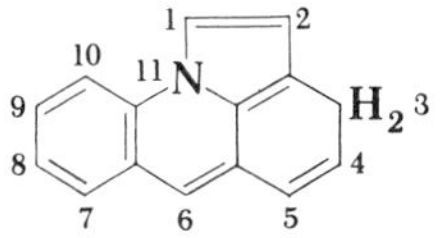

Treatment of I in pyridine with acetic anhydride or with benzoyl chloride gave,[1] respectively, IIa (R = CH_3, violet, m. 180°) and IIb (R = C_6H_5, blue-violet, m. 168–9°).

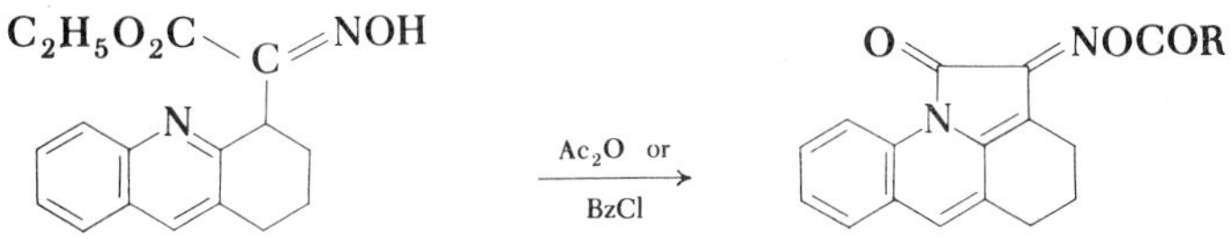

(I) $\xrightarrow[BzCl]{Ac_2O\ or}$ (IIa) R = CH_3; (IIb) R = C_6H_5

Reference

1. Borsche and Manteuffel, *Ann.*, **534,** 56 (1938).

A-218. 7*H*-Pyrrolo[*de*]phenanthridine

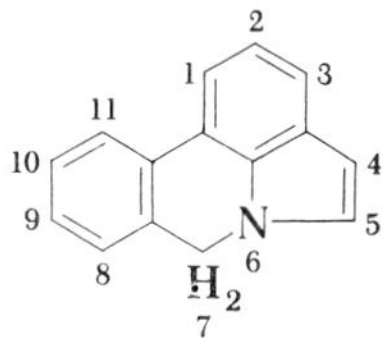

and

A-219. 7*H*-[1,3]Dioxolo[*j*]pyrrolo[*de*]-phenanthridine

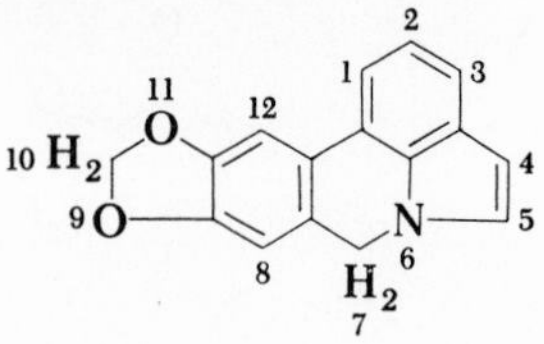

Derivatives of these nuclei have been studied in connection with investigations upon the Amaryllidaceae alkaloids.[1-4]

References

1. Cook and Loudon, in Manske and Holmes, *The Alkaloids*, Academic Press, New York, Vol. 2, 1952, p. 331.
2. Warnhoff and Wildman, *J. Am. Chem. Soc.*, **79,** 2192 (1957).
3. Renz, Stauffacher and Seebeck, *Helv. Chim. Acta*, **38,** 1209 (1955).
4. Takagi, Taylor, Uyeo and Yajiima, *J. Chem. Soc.*, **1955,** 4003.

A-220. Pyrrocolo[1,2-*b*]quinoline

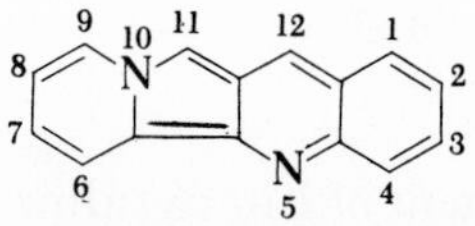

Treatment of two stereoisomeric indole alkaloid derivatives of structure I with ozone and base yielded[1] two isomers of compound II (*a*, sinters at 145°, m. 228°, $[\alpha]_D$ 42°; *b*, m. 218–21°, $[\alpha]_D$ 12°). See Section A-239.

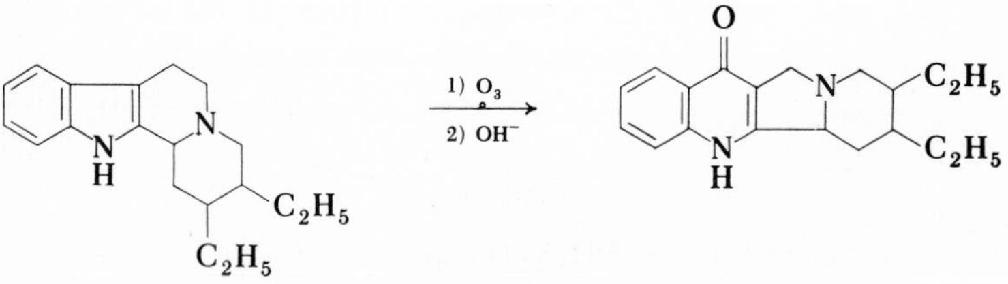

1) O_3 2) OH^-

(I) (II)

Reference

1. Janot, Goutarel, Le Hir, Tsatsas and Prelog, *Helv. Chim. Acta*, **38,** 1073 (1955).

A-221. Naphtho[1,2-*b*]pyrrocoline. R.I. 2428

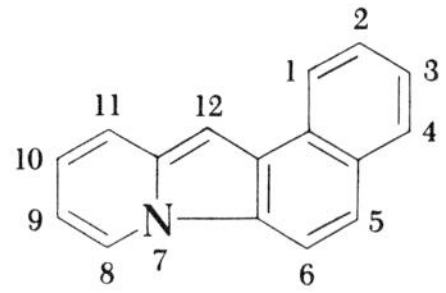

Passage of I over very hot copper turnings gave[1] II (yellowish-brown, m. 220–1°; hydrochloride, m. 85°; picrate, m. 128°), the only example of this nucleus.

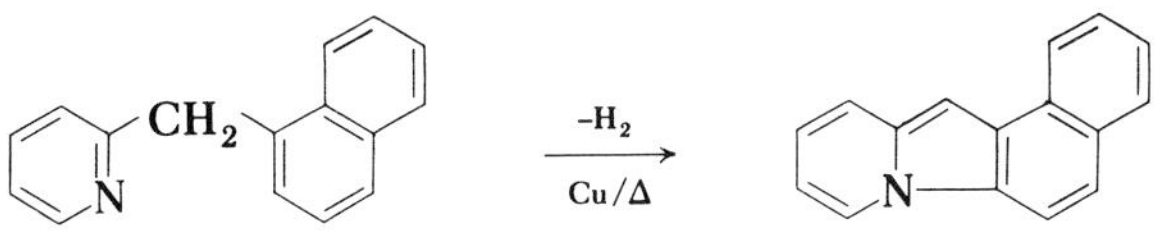

(I) $\xrightarrow[\text{Cu}/\Delta]{-H_2}$ (II)

Reference

1. Braun and Nelles, *Ber.*, **70,** 1767 (1937).

A-222. Naphtho[2,3-*b*]indolizine

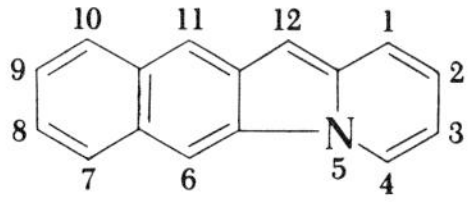

This nucleus is also called *naphtho[2,3-b]pyrrocoline.*

Suryanarayana and Tilak[1-3] described the condensation of 2,3-dichlor-1,4-naphthoquinone (I) with pyridine and acetoacetic esters or anilides, and assigned the dipolar structure II (R = OC_2H_5 or NHC_6H_5, etc.) to the products so obtained. Almost simultaneously, Pratt *et al.*[4] studied this reaction, and gave the correct structure, III, to the products.

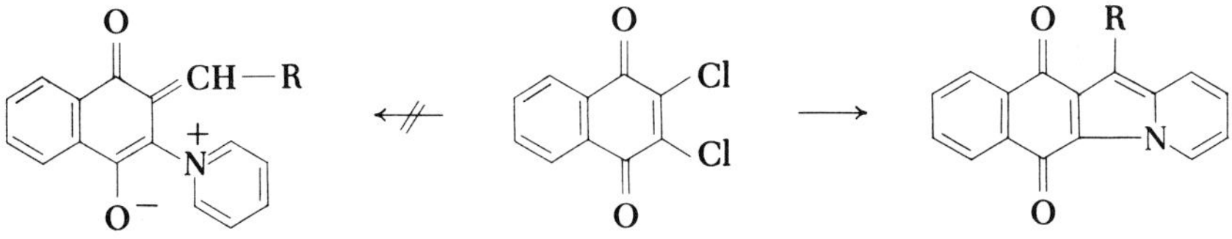

(II) ↚ (I) → (III)

Various other active hydrogen compounds such as acetylacetone, cyanoacetic ester, nitroethane, etc., also may be condensed[3,5,6] with I and pyridine to obtain III (R = CH_3CO, CN, CH_3, etc.). In addition to the anilide (III, R = $CONHC_6H_5$), during the condensation of I with acetoacetanilide (and its homologs) some of the acetyl compound (III, R = $COCH_3$) is usually also obtained.[3] A small yield of the parent compound III (R = H) was obtained[5] from I and α-picoline, but it is more conveniently prepared[3] by decarboxylation of III (R = COOH). The acetyl compound V (R = CH_3) was obtained[2] from the reaction of IV with pyridine, and V (R = CH_3 or C_6H_5) was prepared[6] from I and VI.

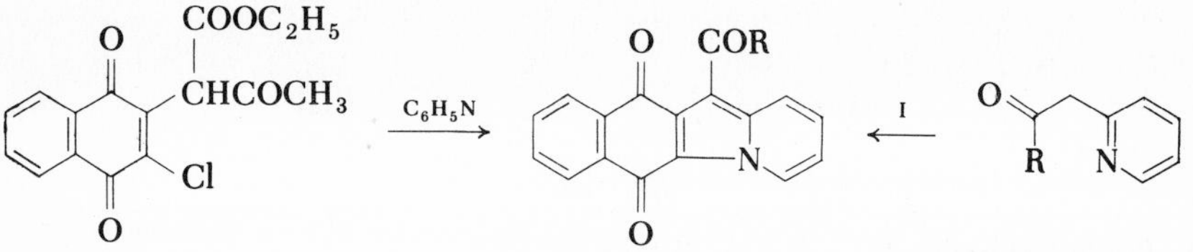

(IV) (V) (VI)

The amide was obtained[6] by hydration of the nitrile, and it and several anilides also were prepared[3,4,9,10] via the acid chloride. Several of these compounds, including anthraquinone derivatives, were claimed of interest as vat dyes, but very little information concerning their properties was reported.[7-10] Products with a nitro group in the 10 (or 7) position[8] or with alkyl groups in the 1,2 or 3 positions[9] have been mentioned briefly.

Reductive acetylation of III (R = CN or C_6H_5) yields[6] the corresponding hydroquinone diacetate. The quinone system of III is sufficiently stable to withstand oxidation of substituents (e.g., where R = $COCH_3$) to the carboxylic acid (III, R = COOH). Treatment

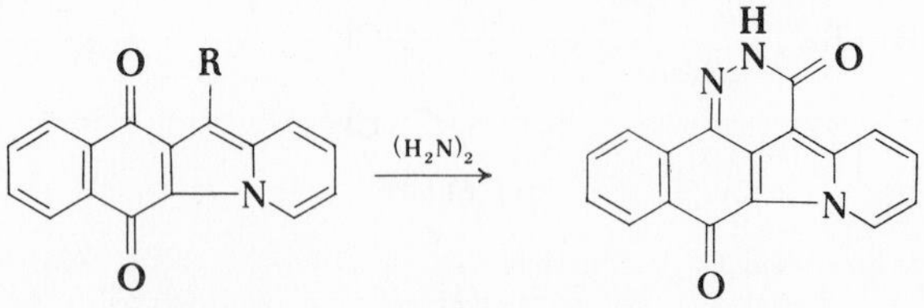

III
(R = $COOC_2H_5$)

(VII)

of the ester (III, R = $COOC_2H_5$) with hydrazine involved also the carbonyl group in the 11 position, and yielded[3] VII (yellow, m. > 300°).

The condensation of VIII with acetoacetic ester and pyridine gave[11] IX (violet needles, m. 262° d.), which showed no substantivity for cellulose or cellulose acetate.

(VIII) → (IX)

Naphtho[2,3-*b*]indolizine-6,11-diones

12-Substituent	Properties	Refs.
None	Or., m. 239.5° (240°).	5
CH_3	Red, m. 245.5–6.0°.	6
COOH	Maroon, m. 313.5–4.5° (m. 307–8° d.).	2,3,4,6
$CONH_2$	Dimorphic, maroon, m. 302–3°; or., m. 313.5–4.5°.	4,6
CN	Or., m. 307.5–8.5°. Hydroquinone diacetate, yel., m. 268–9°.	6
$COCH_3$	Red, m. 205–6° (203–5, 204–5°).	2,3,6
$COOCH_3$	Yel., m. 190–1° d.	4
$COOC_2H_5$	Or., m. 157–8° (154–5°). Oxime, or., m. 205–7°. 2,4-DNPH, yel., m. 261° d.	1,2,3,4,6
C_6H_5	Red, m. 244.5–5.5°. Hydroquinone diacetate, red, m. 229–31°.	6
COC_6H_5	Maroon, m. 256.0–7.5° (or or.-red, m. 259° ?)	5,6
$CONHC_6H_5$	Vt., m. 255–7°.	2,3
$CO-C_6H_4-CO$	Red, m. > 360°.	2

References

1. Suryanarayana, *Bombay Technologist*, **3,** 83 (1952-3); *Chem. Abstracts*, **48,** 5501 (1954).
2. Suryanarayana and Tilak, *Current Science* (India), **22,** 171 (1953); *Chem. Abstracts*, **48,** 14212 (1954).

3. Suryanarayana and Tilak, *Proc. Indian Acad. Sci.*, **39A,** 185 (1954); *Chem. Abstracts*, **49,** 12411 (1955).
4. Pratt, Luckenbaugh and Erickson, *J. Org. Chem.*, **19,** 176 (1954).
5. Acharya, Suryanarayana and Tilak, *J. Sci. Ind. Research* (India), **14B,** 394 (1955); *Chem. Abstracts*, **50,** 12971 (1956).
6. Pratt, Rice and Luckenbaugh, *J. Am. Chem. Soc.*, **79,** 1212 (1957).
7. Schmidt-Nickels and Lugg, U. S. Pat. 2,772,274.
8. Schmidt-Nickels and Lugg, U. S. Pat. 2,772,275.
9. Schmidt-Nickels and Randall, U. S. Pat. 2,772,272.
10. Randall and Schmidt-Nickels, U. S. Pat. 2,773,873.
11. Tilak and Rao, *Chem. and Ind.*, **1957,** 1320.

A-223. Pyrrocolo[5,6-*b*]quinoxaline.
R.I. 2409

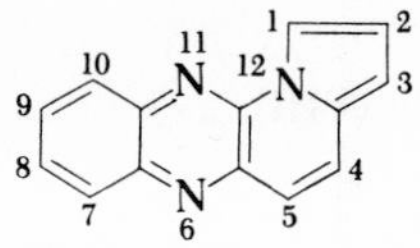

A yellowish-red crystalline product (solutions show a green fluorescence), which darkens at 250° without melting, was obtained[1] from the condensation of I with *o*-phenylenediamine. It was thought to have structure II.

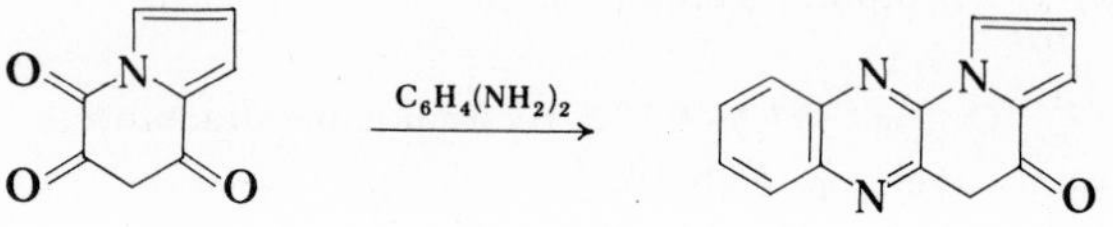

$C_6H_4(NH_2)_2$

(I) (II)

Reference

1. Angeli, *Ber.*, **23,** 2154 (1890).

A-224. 1*H*-Naphtho[1,2,3-*hi*]pyrrocoline.
R.I. 2438

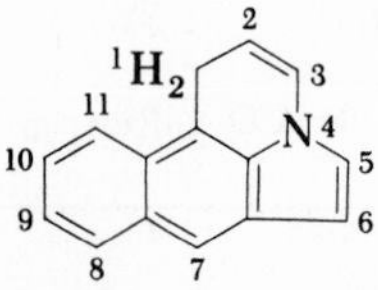

Compound II (violet-brown, m. 183°), which was called *1,7-trimethylene-5,6-benzoisatin,* was obtained[1] by heating I in sulfuric acid.

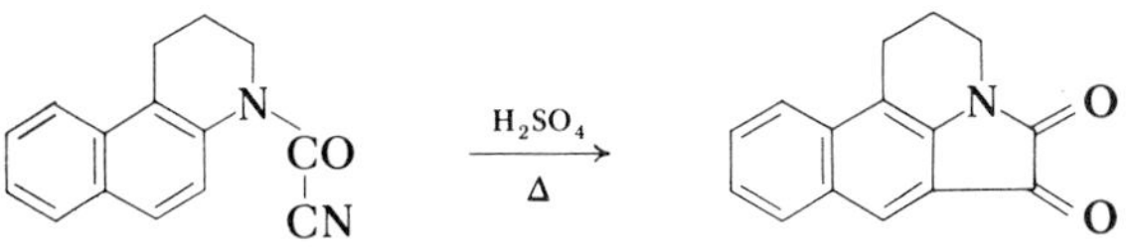

(I) $\xrightarrow[\Delta]{H_2SO_4}$ (II)

Reference

1. Deutsche Gold und Silber-Scheideanstalt, vorm. Roessler, Austrian Pat. 125,211 (1928); *Chem. Zentr.*, **II**, 778 (1932).

A-225. Isoindolo[7,1,2-*hij*]quinoline*

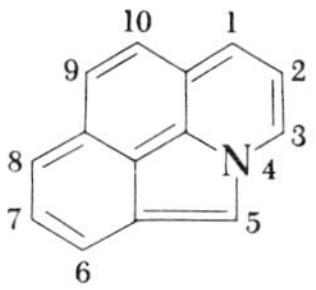

Among the products resulting from the selenium dehydrogenation of the alkaloid *annotinine* was found[1] a yellow oil (reddish-black trinitrobenzoate, m. 175°; black picrate), which was considered, tentatively, to be the 9-methyl homolog of this nucleus.

Reference

1. Bankiewicz, Henderson, Stonner, Valenta and Wiesner, *Chem. and Ind.*, **1954,** 1068.

A-226. Benzo[1,2-*b*, 4,5-*b'*]bisindolizine

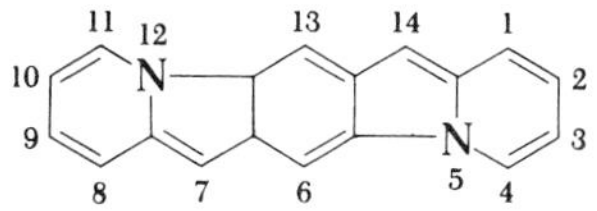

and

A-227. Benzo[1,2-*b*, 5,4-*b'*]bisindolizine

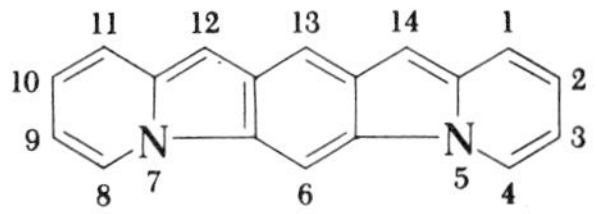

Condensation of benzoquinone with pyridine and acetylacetone gave, in low yield, a high-melting, green product, which, upon the basis of an incomplete analysis, was thought[1] to have structure I. Islam and Raphael reinvestigated[2] this product and proposed for it structure II. They also claimed the same product was formed when benzoquinone was replaced by chloranil. However, Tilak and his co-workers[3,4] showed by chromatography that, while the product obtained from benzoquinone was homogeneous and had structure II, the crude green product obtained from chloranil was actually a mixture of II and III. The identity of II was demonstrated by an independent synthesis from IV.

COCH$_3$ HO OH COCH$_3$ (I)

pyridine acetylacetone

O CH$_3$OC O COCH$_3$ O COCH$_3$ N N N N O CH$_3$OC O

Cl Cl Cl Cl O

(III) (II)

C$_6$H$_5$OK

C$_6$H$_5$N

O Cl OC$_6$H$_5$ C$_6$H$_5$O Cl O

Ac$_2$CH$_2$ NaOC$_2$H$_5$

O Cl CHAc$_2$ Ac$_2$CH Cl O

(IV) (V)

Certain other active hydrogen compounds such as acetoacetic ester, acetoacetanilides, dibenzoylmethane, etc., have been used[3-5] in this reaction with chloranil and pyridine. In each case, a mixture of VI and VII results. The ester VI (R = $COOC_2H_5$) also was synthesized from the reaction of IV with acetoacetic ester followed by pyridine. It is interesting, however, that an attempted similar synthesis of VII (R = $COOC_2H_5$) from 2,6-dichlorobenzoquinone gave a *mixture* of VI and VII (R = $COOC_2H_5$).

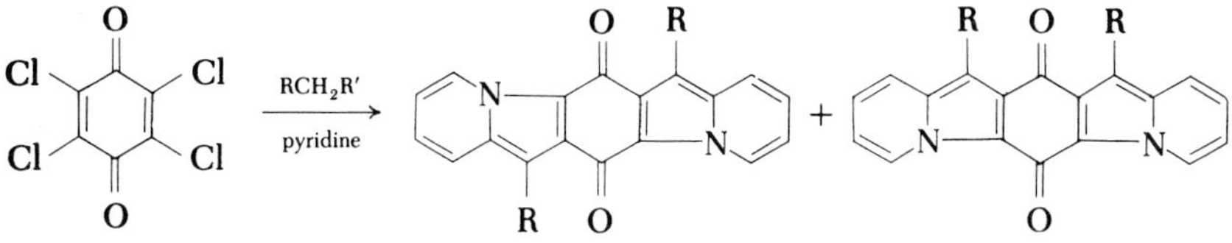

RCH_2R' / pyridine

(VI) (VII)

Hydrolysis of the esters VI and VII (R = $COOC_2H_5$) afforded the corresponding acids, which were decarboxylated when heated with copper and quinoline. The acids also were converted into acid chlorides and thence to anilides, which were claimed[5] of interest as vat dyes. Grey vat dyes assigned structure VI, but presumably mix-

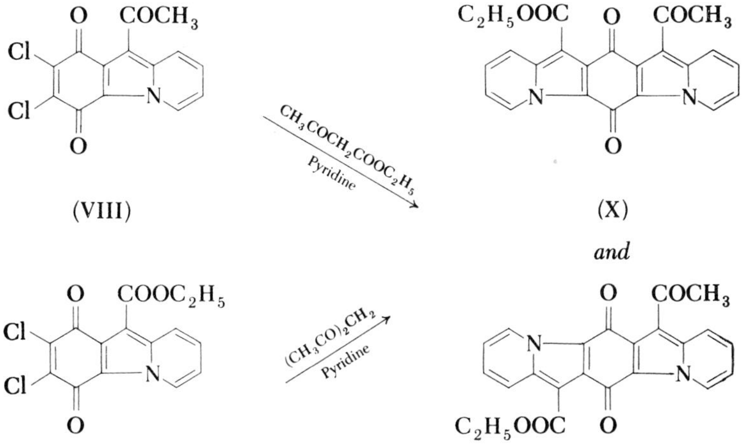

(VIII) —$CH_3COCH_2COOC_2H_5$ / Pyridine→ (X)

and

(IX) —$(CH_3CO)_2CH_2$ / Pyridine→ (XI)

tures of VI and VII, were claimed[6] to be obtained from various acetoacetanilides.

Reaction of VIII (see Section A-191) with acetoacetic ester and pyridine (or of IX with acetylacetone and pyridine) yielded[7] a mixture of X (green, m. 316°; olive-green solution in sulfuric acid) and XI (green, m. 214°; blue color in sulfuric acid), although the reaction of VIII with acetylacetone and pyridine was said[7] to yield III without mention of II.

Reductive acetylation of III gave[7] XII (brown, m. >300°), while heating with zinc dust in either phosphoric acid or a sodium chloride-zinc chloride melt yielded[7] XIII (violet, m. >360°).

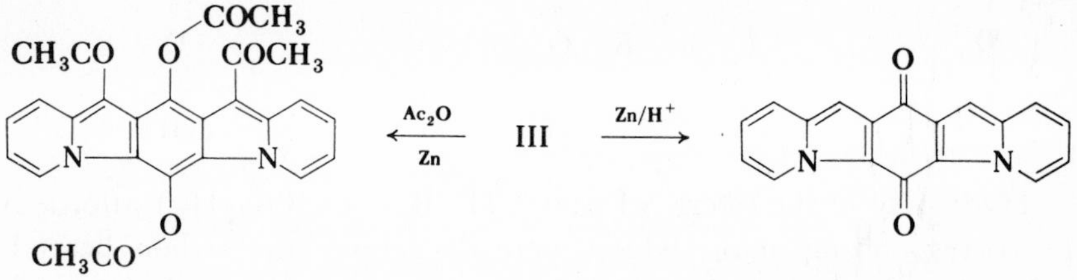

CH_3CO O $COCH_3$ $COCH_3$ O CH_3CO N N $\xleftarrow[Zn]{Ac_2O}$ III $\xrightarrow{Zn/H^+}$ O O N N

(XII) (XIII)

Condensation of pyrrocoline with acetoacetic ester yielded a product, which may be a derivative of benzo[1,2-*b*, 5,4-*b*′]bisindolizine (see Sections A-183 and A-228).

Products of Structure VI

R	Properties	Refs.
H	Red-brn., m. >360°.	4,5
$COCH_3$	Red-brn., d. >370°. Vt. soln. in H_2SO_4. λ_{max} 345, 362 and 478 mμ. (log ε 4.25, 4.35 and 4.28).	4,5
COOH	Brn., d. >250°, gives red alkaline and blue H_2SO_4 solns.	4,5
$COOC_2H_5$	Scarlet, m. 281–2°.	4,5
COC_6H_5	Red, m. 310°.	4,5
$CONHC_6H_5$	Grn. (dk. brn.?), m. >360°. Vt.-bl. H_2SO_4 soln. Dyes vt. from bl. vat.	4,5

Products of Structure VII

R	Properties	Refs.
H	Vt., m. >360°.	4,5
$COCH_3$	Grn., m. 362–3° (364°). Olive-grn. soln. in H_2SO_4. λ_{max} 340,368 and 592 mμ (log ε 4.44, 4.19 and 3.98). Dioxime, dk. red, m. >320° d.	2,4,5,7
COOH	Dk. brn., d. >250°; gives blue alkaline and grn. H_2SO_4 solns.	4,5
$COOC_2H_5$	Vt., m. 220–1°.	4,5
COC_6H_5	Vt., m. 328–9° (327–8°).	4,5
$CONHC_6H_5$	Vt., m. >360°. Dk. grn. soln. in H_2SO_4. Dyes olive-grn. from vt. vat.	4,5

References

1. Ionescu, *Bull. soc. chim. France*, **41,** 1094 (1927).
2. Islam and Raphael, *Chem. and Ind.*, **1955,** 1635.
3. Tilak and Venkiteswaran, *Chem. and Ind.*, **1956,** R33.
4. Acharya, Tilak and Venkiteswaran, *J. Sci. Ind. Research* (India), **14B,** 250 (1955); *Chem. Abstracts*, **50,** 15531 (1956).
5. Tilak and Venkiteswaran, *J. Sci. Ind. Research* (India), **15B,** 561 (1956); *Chem. Abstracts*, **51,** 8746 (1957).
6. Schmidt-Nickels and Lugg, U. S. Pat. 2,772,273.
7. Islam and Selim, *J. Org. Chem.*, **22,** 1641 (1957).

A-228. *7H*, *14H*-Benzo[1,2-*a*, 5,4-*a*′]-dipyrrocoline. R.I. 2967

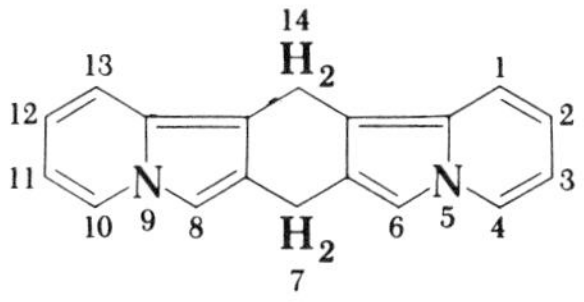

The name *benzodipyrindole* has also been used.

A product (yellowish-green, m. 140°) assigned[1] structure II was obtained from the reaction of pyrrocoline (I) with acetoacetic ester. However, in view of the reactivity of the 3-position of pyrrocoline (see Section A-183), structure III (see Section A-227) must also be considered.

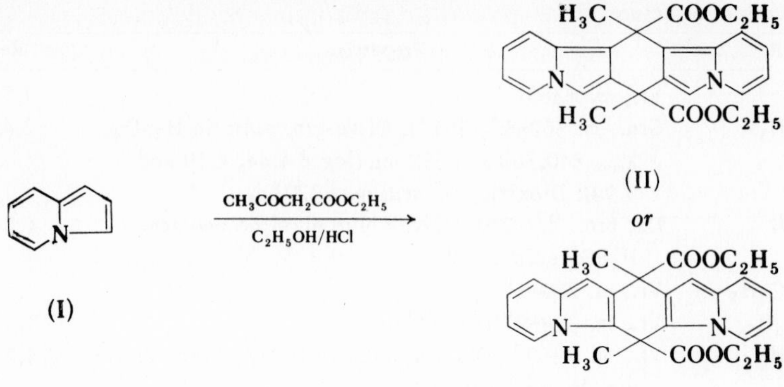

$$\text{(I)} \xrightarrow[C_2H_5OH/HCl]{CH_3COCH_2COOC_2H_5} \text{(II)} \text{ or } \text{(III)}$$

H_3C, $COOC_2H_5$, N, N, H_3C, $COOC_2H_5$

(I)

(II)

or

(III)

Reference

1. Scholtz and Fraude, *Ber.*, **46**, 1069 (1913).

A-229. Benzo[*b*]thianaphtheno[3,2-*g*]-pyrrocoline. R.I. 2971

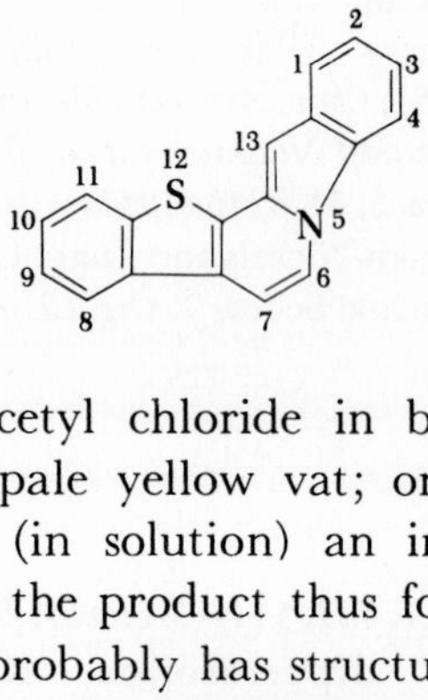

The condensation of I with phenylacetyl chloride in boiling xylene yielded[1,2] a red crystalline dye (pale yellow vat; orange-brown solution in sulfuric acid) having (in solution) an intense orange-yellow fluorescence. By analogy to the product thus formed from indigo (see Section A-232), this dye probably has structure II. Heating II with 24% oleum gave an orange sulfonic acid, which dyes wool and silk deep orange.

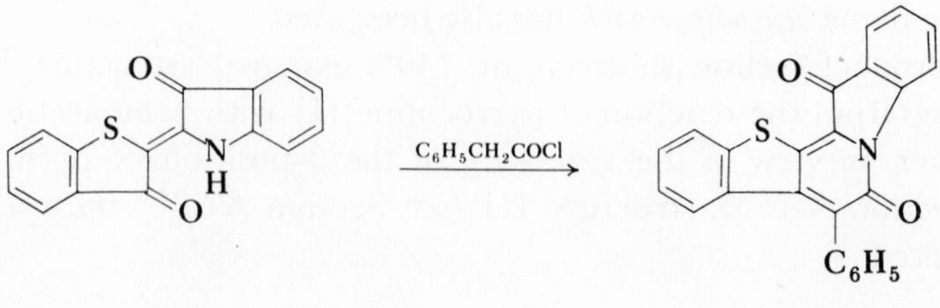

$$\text{(I)} \xrightarrow{C_6H_5CH_2COCl} \text{(II)}$$

(I)

(II)

The bordeaux-red crystalline tribromo homolog of II (solutions show a yellow fluorescence; sulfuric acid solution; olive-green) was obtained[1] similarly from tribromo-I.

References

1. Ciba, Ger. Pat. 263,470; *Frdl.*, **11,** 295 (1915).
2. Engi, *Z. angew. Chem.*, **27,** 144 (1914).

A-230. 1*H*-Thianaphtheno[2,3-*d*]quino-[1,8-*ab*]pyrrole

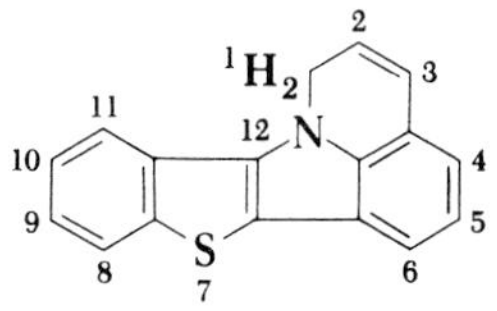

The name *4,6-trimethylenethionaphthindole* was given to the 2,3-dihydro compound.

Condensation of thioindoxyl (I) with 1-amino-1,2,3,4-tetrahydroquinoline (II) afforded[1] a 63% yield of III (m. 139°; picrate, m. 149°). Efforts[1] to obtain V by the cyclization of IV were unsuccessful. See Sections A-251/2.

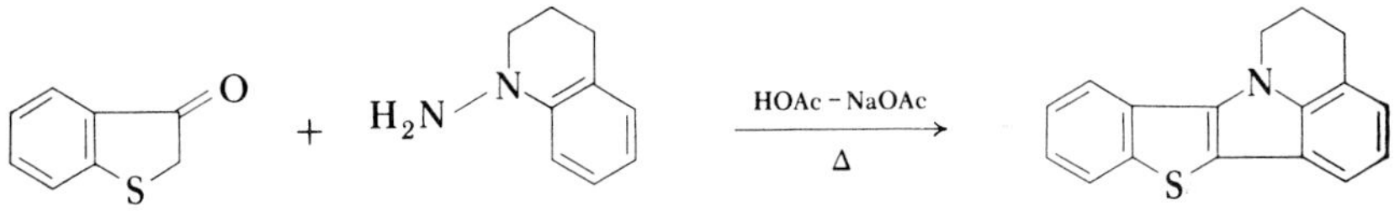

HOAc - NaOAc, Δ

(I) (II) (III)

- HCl

(IV) (V)

Reference

1. Dalgliesh and Mann, *J. Chem. Soc.*, **1947,** 653.

A-231. 8*H*-Diindolo[1,2-*a*, 3′,2′-*c*]pyridine

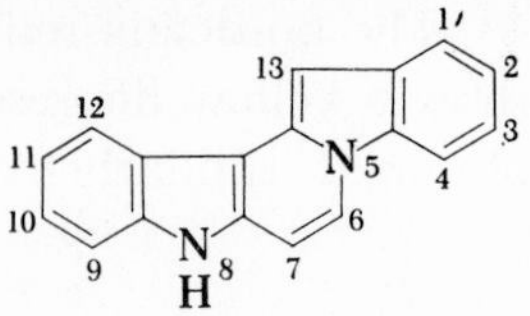

When heated with malonic ester, indirubin (I) gives a product, presumably II, analogous to that (see Section A-232) obtained under these conditions from indigo. Posner[1] describes II as forming dark red scales and a yielding dark red *N*-benzoyl derivative.

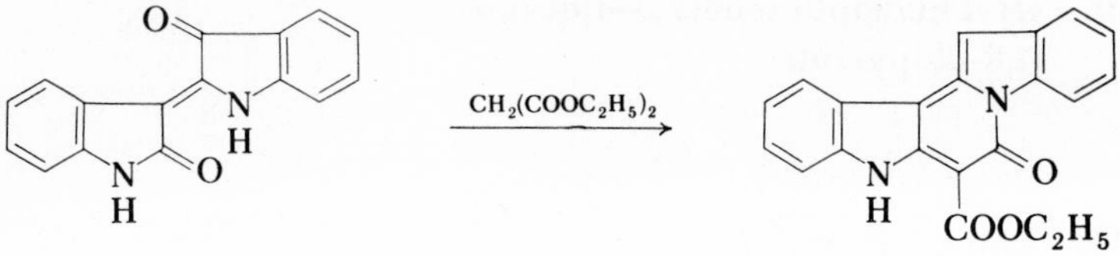

$CH_2(COOC_2H_5)_2$

(I) (II)

Reference

1. Posner, *Ber.*, **59,** 1799 (1926).

A-232. 12*H*-Diindolo[1,2-*a*, 2′,3′-*c*]-pyridine. R.I. 2968

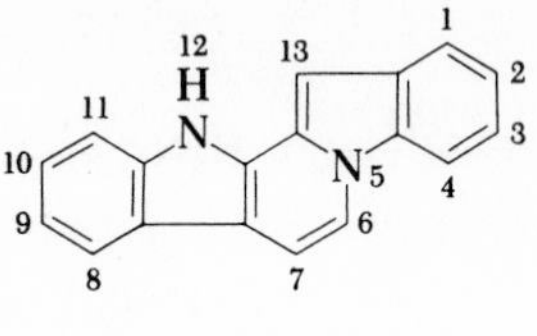

Posner and his associates[1–4] found that solutions of indigo (I) in solvents such as nitrobenzene, when refluxed with diethyl malonate or with ethyl phenylacetate, yielded violet crystalline vat dyes of structure II (IIa,[1,2,4] red-violet, m. 296–7°, λ_{max} 550 mμ; IIb,[3,4] violet, m. >320°, λ_{max} 555 mμ). Compound IIa was reported[1,2] to dissolve in sulfuric acid with a brownish-red color, to give an emerald green solution in alcoholic caustic, and to give a red acetyl derivative (m. 182°), an orange benzoyl derivative (m. 240°) and a red nitroso derivative (d. 267–70°). Compound IIb gave[3] a red benzoyl derivative (m. 307° d.).

Reduction and benzoylation of IIa and IIb yielded colorless benzoyloxyhydro derivatives[2,3] (d. >190° and m. 235°, respectively)

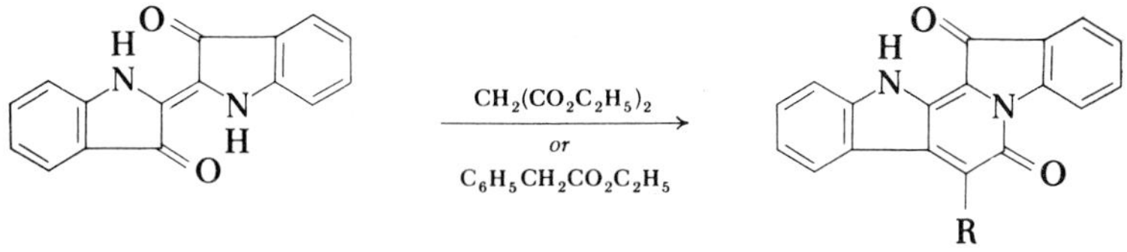

$CH_2(CO_2C_2H_5)_2$ *or* $C_6H_5CH_2CO_2C_2H_5$

(I)

(IIa) $R=CO_2C_2H_5$
(IIb) $R=C_6H_5$

of uncertain structure. Benzoylation of the nitroso derivative of IIa gave, apparently, a benzoyloxydihydronitroso compound (d. ~245–50°). Compound IIa was stated[5] to form green metal complexes with salts of sodium, silver, zinc, magnesium, copper, iron, cobalt and nickel. Condensation of IIa or IIb with a second molecule of malonic ester or phenylacetyl chloride gave hexacyclic products (see Section A-257).

Oxidation of tryptophane (IIIa) or tryptamine (IIIb) in aqueous acetic acid solution with potassium iodate, yielded a vattable, red, fluorescent (greenish-orange in solution) pigment (λ_{max} in chloroform 290, 338, 515 and 555 mμ) called *tryptochrome*,[6,7] which was assigned, provisionally, structure IV. Further evidence for this structure is needed.

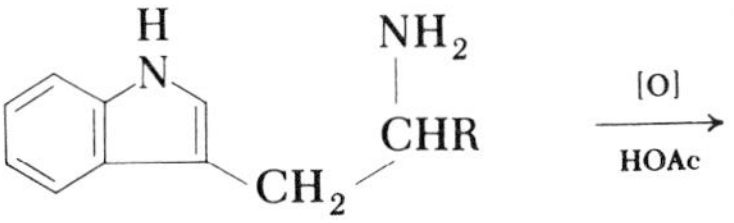

[O] / HOAc

(IIIa) R=COOH
(IIIb) R=H

(IV)

References

1. Posner, Ger. Pat. 281,998; *Frdl.*, **12,** 269 (1917).
2. Posner and Pyl, *Ber.*, **56,** 31 (1923).
3. Posner and Kemper, *Ber.*, **57,** 1311 (1924).
4. Posner, *Ber.*, **59,** 1799 (1926).
5. Kuhn and Machemer, *Ber.*, **61,** 118 (1928).
6. Fearon, *Nature*, **162,** 338 (1948).
7. Fearon and Boggust, *Biochem. J.*, **46,** 62 (1950).

A-233. 9*H*-Pyrido[1,2,3-*lm*]pyrrolo-[2,3-*d*]carbazole

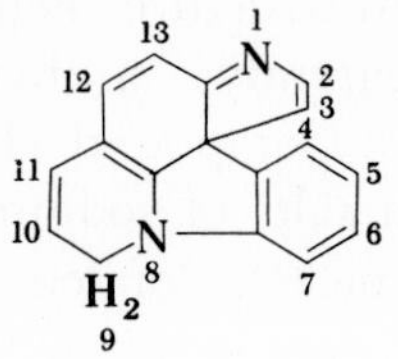

Derivatives of this nucleus have been obtained by degrading strychnine[1,2] and have been utilized in its synthesis.[3]

References

1. Holmes in Manske and Holmes, *The Alkaloids*, Academic Press, New York, Vol. 2, 1952, p. 513.
2. Edward and Robinson, *Tetrahedron*, **1,** 28 (1957).
3. Woodward, Cava, Ollis, Hunger, Daeniker and Schenker, *J. Am. Chem. Soc.*, **76,** 4749 (1954).

A-234. Indolo[3,2-*c*]pyrrolo[3,2,1-*ij*]-quinoline

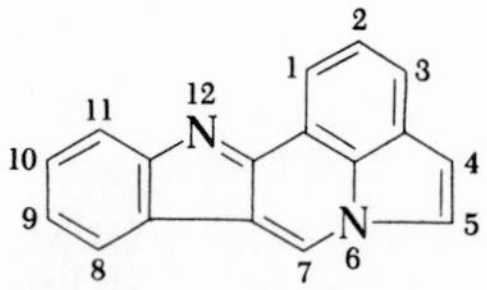

The name *ψ-indolo[2′:3′-1,2]liline* has been used.

The ψ-indole II (yellow, m. 258° in an evacuated, sealed capillary) was obtained[1] in about 50% yield from the Fischer indole reaction upon I. Studies of the infrared spectra revealed that salt formation occurred to give normal indoles of type III (hydrochloride, m. 363–5°; methiodide, m. 362–3° d.).

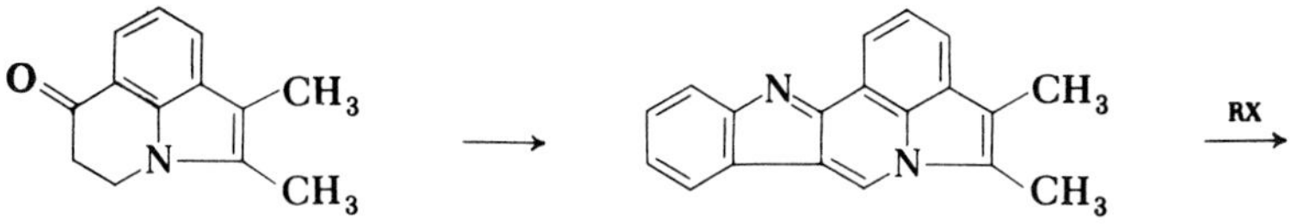

(I) (II) 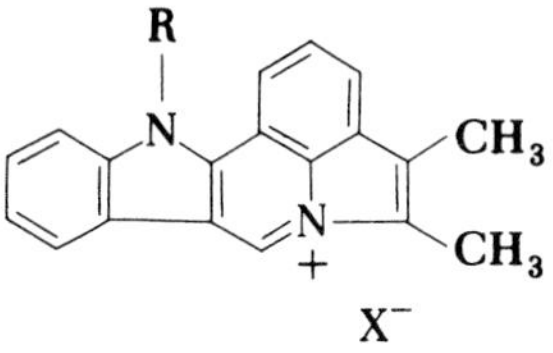 (III)

Reference

1. Almond and Mann, *J. Chem. Soc.*, **1952,** 1870.

A-235. 2*H*-Dipyrrolo[3,2,1-*de*, 2′,3′,4′-*kl*]-acridine*

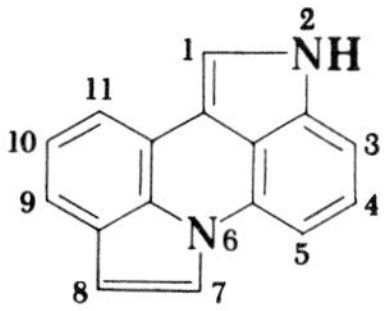

Structure I was once proposed[1] for *calycanine* (a degradation product of the alkaloid *calycanthine*), now known[2,3] to have structure II.

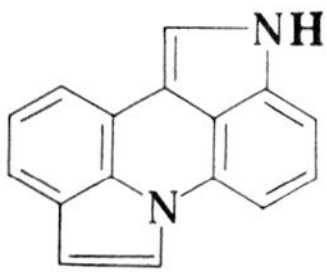

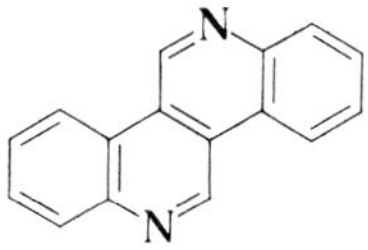

(I) (II)

References

1. Barger, Madinaveitia and Strueli, *J. Chem. Soc.*, **1939,** 510.
2. Robinson and Teuber, *Chem. and Ind.*, **1954,** 783.
3. Saxton, *Quart. Rev.*, **10,** 108 (1956).

A-236. 8*H*-Indolo[3,2,1-*de*]acridine.
R.I. 3069

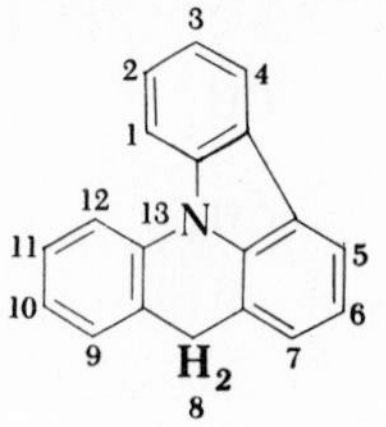

The 8-oxo derivative was called *carbazoleacridone*.

Cyclization of the acid (or acid chloride) I by treatment with aluminum chloride yielded[1] the ketone II, for which a melting point of 190° was first reported. Repetition[2] of this synthesis gave the same product, but the melting point was said to be 180–1°. Compound II was also obtained[3,4] by heating diphenylamine with 2-iodobenzoic acid, and the melting point of the product so obtained was 181.9°.

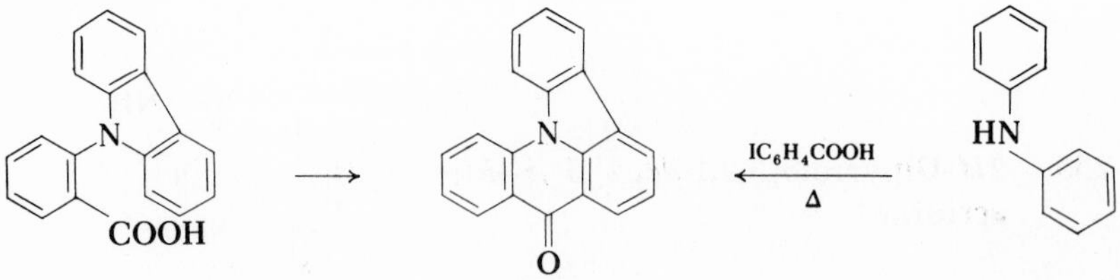

(I) (II)

Reduction[5] of III in the presence of cyclohexanone gave IV, which was cleaved at the lactam bond by caustic to the corresponding amino acid, and cyclization of this with sulfuric acid yielded V.

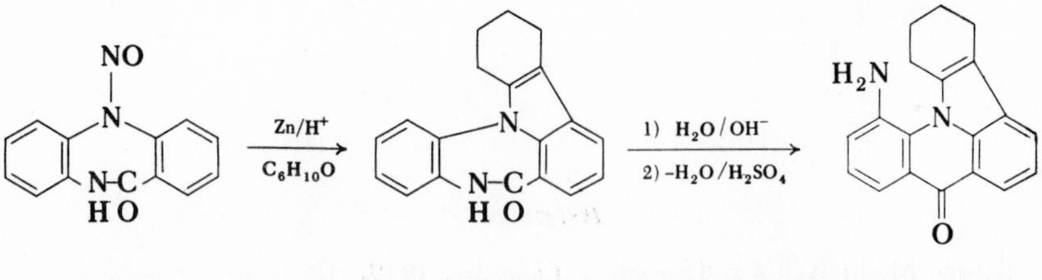

(III) (VI) (V)

Although Hayashi could not prepare[3] a phenylhydrazone of II, it was possible to obtain[2] an oxime. Reduction of II with sodium and ethanol yielded[1] the parent desoxy compound. Nitration[3] of II gave an 83% yield of a product thought to be the 6-nitro derivative, which was reduced to the amine and converted into the corresponding nitrile, carboxylic acid, etc. Efforts to resolve some of these derivatives, which contain an "asymmetric" nitrogen atom, were unsuccessful.

8*H*-Indolo[3,2,1-*de*]acridines

Empirical formula	Substituents	Properties and derivatives	Refs.
$C_{19}H_{10}N_2O_3$	6-Nitro-8-oxo-	Yel., m. 304–5°.	3
$C_{19}H_{11}NO$	8-Oxo-	m. 180–1° (181.9°, 190°). Oxime, m. 175–6°.	1,2,3
$C_{19}H_{12}N_2O$	6-Amino-8-oxo-	Red-or., m. 279–80°. HCl salt, m. 270–8°; picrate, m. 163–4.5°; acetyl deriv., m. 225–6°; benzoyl deriv., m. 286–8°; benzonesulfonyl deriv., m. 224.5–6°; salicylidine deriv., m. 251–2° d.; diazonium chloride, d. ~230°; *d*-α-bromocamphorsulfonate, m. 252–4°; *l*-tartrate, m. 171–2° d.; helicin cpd., two isomers, m. 239–9° and d. 223.5–5°; *d*-hydroxymethylenecamphor deriv., m. 176.5–8°; *d*-methylenecamphor deriv., two isomers, m. 186–7° and m. 235–6°.	3,4
$C_{19}H_{13}N$	Unsubstituted	m. 158–60°	1
$C_{19}H_{16}N_2O$	12-Amino-1,2,3,4-tetrahydro-8-oxo-	m. 168°.	5
$C_{20}H_{10}N_2O$	6-Cyano-8-oxo	Yel., m. 248–9°	3
$C_{20}H_{11}NO_3$	6-Carboxy-8-oxo-	Yel., m. 288–90°. Brucine salt, m. 269–70°. Cinchonine salt, m. 220–2°. Strychnine salt, m. 180–4°.	3
$C_{20}H_{14}N_2O$	6-Methylamino-8-oxo-	Red-or., m. 193.5–5°	3

References

1. Eckert, Seidel and Endler, *J. prakt. Chem.*, **104,** 85 (1922).
2. Gilman, Stuckwisch and Kendall, *J. Am. Chem. Soc.*, **63,** 1758 (1941).

3. Hayashi, *Bull. Inst. Phys. Chem. Research* (Tokyo), **9,** 970 (1930); *Sci. Papers Inst. Phys. Chem. Research* (Tokyo), **15,** 278 (1930); *Chem. Abstracts*, **25,** 2998 (1931); *Chem. Zentr.*, **I,** 1758 (1931).
4. Hayashi, *Sci. Papers Inst. Phys. Chem. Research* (Tokyo), **16,** 200 (1931); *Chem. Abstracts*, **26,** 127 (1932).
5. Linnell and Perkin, *J. Chem. Soc.*, **125,** 2451 (1924).

A-237. 13*H*-Indolo[3,2,1-*de*]phenanthridine. R.I. 3068

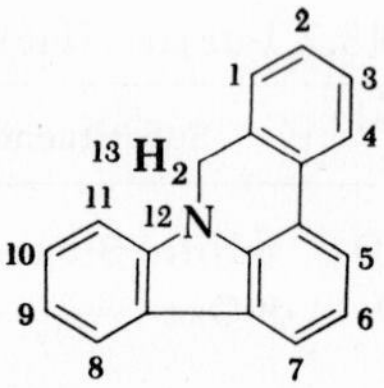

The name *phenanthridindocoline*, with the numbering shown in I, has also been used.

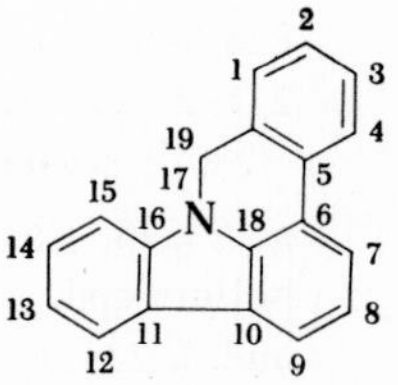

(I)

When heated with acetic anhydride, II undergoes rearrangement to a yellow product (b_{16} ~300°, m. 225°) thought[1] to be III. The assignment of this structure was confirmed[2] by the synthesis of III from IV.

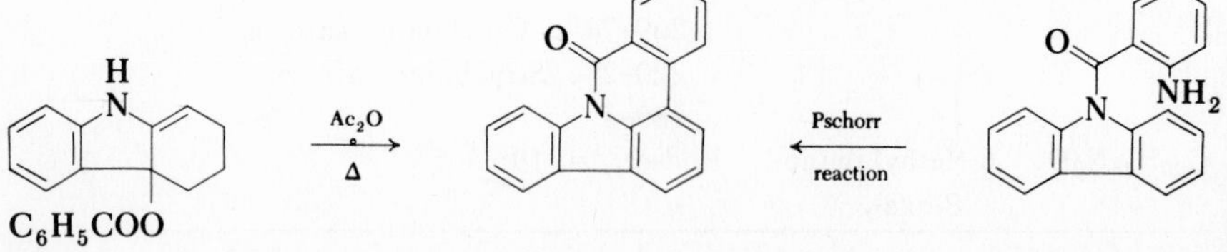

(II) (III) (IV)

References

1. Plant and Tomlinson, *J. Chem. Soc.*, **1931,** 3324.
2. Plant and Tomlinson, *J. Chem. Soc.*, **1933,** 2188.

A-238. 9*H*-Indolo[3,2,1-*de*]1-azaphenanthrene. R.I. 3066M

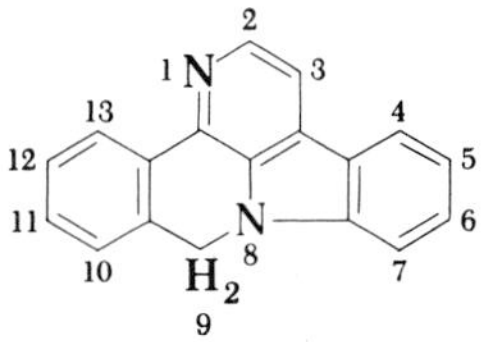

This nucleus has been called *benzcanthine*.

Fusion of tryptamine (I) with phthalic anhydride yielded a product (m. 227°) thought to be II, which was also obtained when the alkaloid *calycanthine* was heated with phthalic anhydride.

$C_6H_4(CO)_2O$

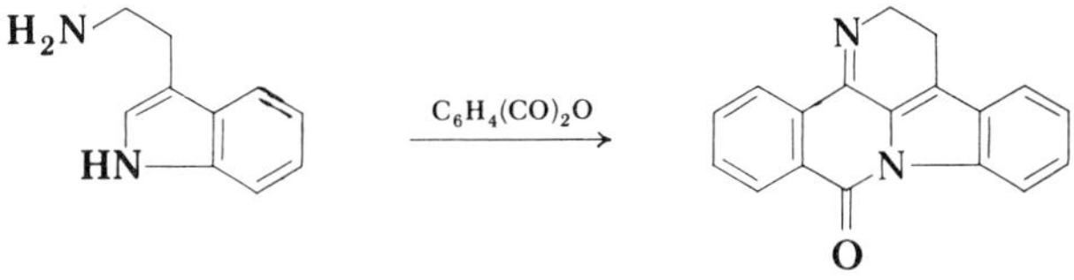

(I) (II)

Reference

1. Marion and Manske, *Can. J. Res.*, **16B,** 432 (1938); *Chem. Abstracts*, **33,** 3798 (1939).

A-239. Benzo[*f*]quino[2,3-*a*]-pyrrocoline*

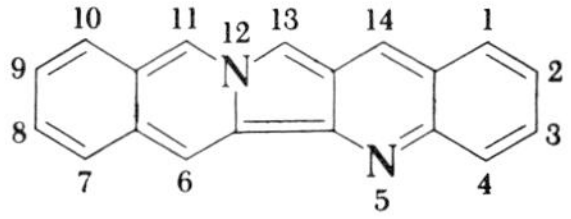

Oxidation of a series of tetrahydroharman alkaloids (I) with ozone yielded intermediates (II), which rearranged to III when treated with base.[1,2]

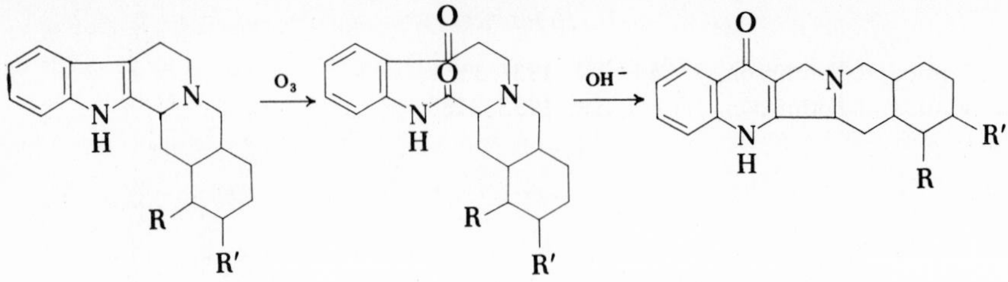

(I) (II) (III)

References

1. Witkop and Goodwin, *J. Am. Chem. Soc.*, **75,** 3371 (1953).
2. Witkop, *Bull. soc. chim. France*, **1954,** 423.

A-240. Benzo[*e*]naphtho[2,3-*b*]-indolizine

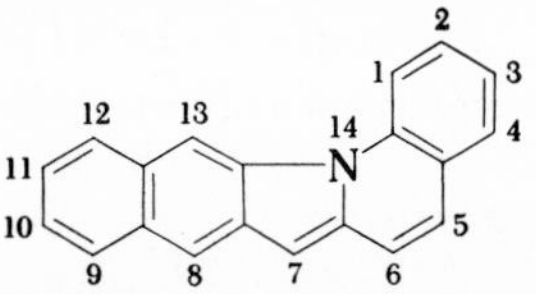

The name *benzo[e]naphtho[2,3-b]pyrrocoline* has been used.

The reaction of 2,3-dichloro-1,4-naphthoquinone with quinoline and acetoacetic esters was reported[1] to yield I (R = CH_3, orange, m. 244–5°; R = C_2H_5, yellow, m. 238–9°). Reductive acetylation of I (R = C_2H_5) yielded II (yellow, m. 239.5–40.5°; benzene solutions show a green fluorescence).

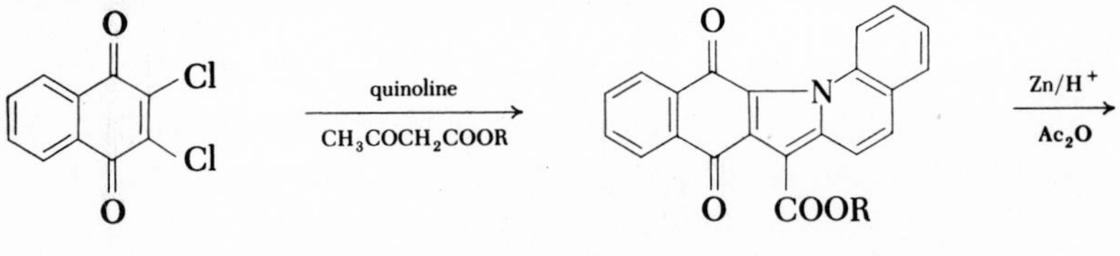

quinoline, CH_3COCH_2COOR → (I) COOR → Zn/H^+, Ac_2O →

(I)

OAc, OAc $COOC_2H_5$

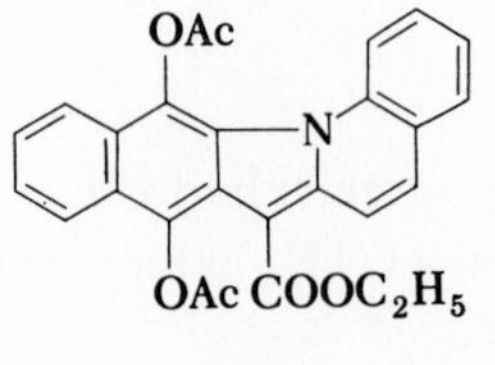

(II)

The condensation of III with dichloronaphthoquinone yielded[2] IV (R = $COCH_3$, orange-red, m. 278.5–9°). The acetyl compound was degraded (via the phenacyl pyridinium iodide) to the acid IV (R = COOH, purple-brown, m. 310.5–1.5°) and thence to IV (R = H, red-brown, m. 240.5–1.5°). See Sections A-222 and A-241.

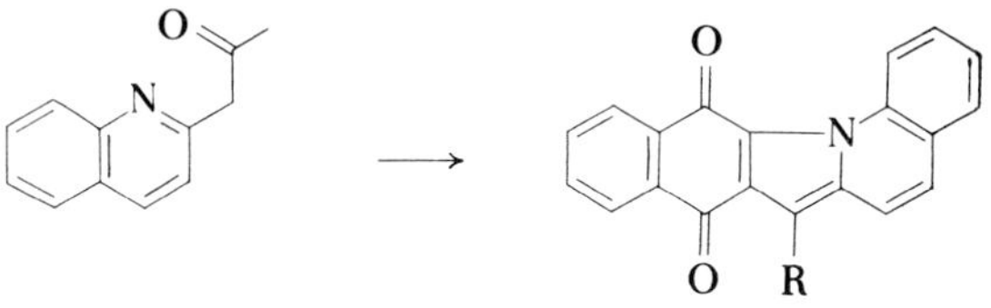

(III) (IV)

References

1. Pratt, Luckenbaugh and Erickson, *J. Org. Chem.*, **19,** 176 (1954).
2. Pratt, Rice and Luckenbaugh, *J. Am. Chem. Soc.*, **79,** 1212 (1957).

A-241. Benzo[*f*]naphtho[2,3-*b*]-indolizine*

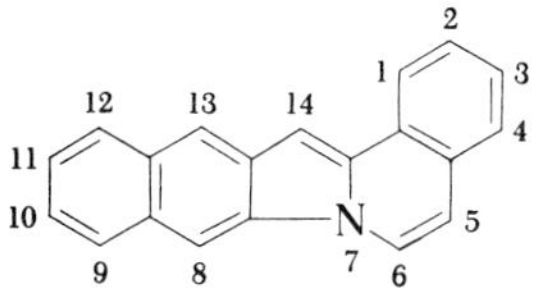

The condensation[1] of 2,3-dichloro-1,4-naphthoquinone and isoquinoline with various active methylene compounds such as acetoacetic esters, benzylacetone, nitromethane, etc. affords products of type I in quite good yield. Reductive acetylation of some of these quinones gave the corresponding hydroquinone diacetates. See Sections A-222 and A-240.

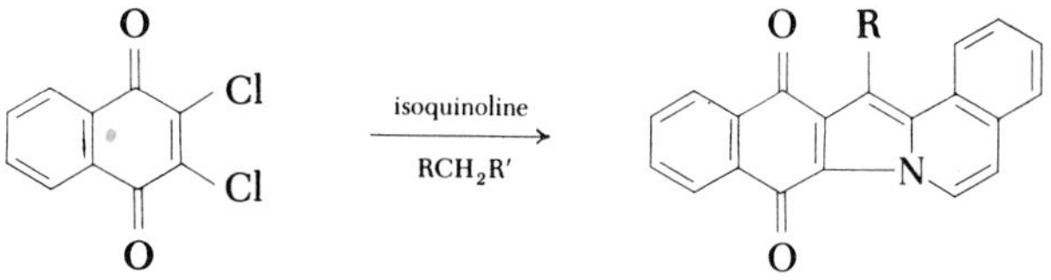

isoquinoline

RCH_2R'

(I)

Products of Type I

R	Properties
H	Red, m. 296–7°.
CH_3	Red, m. 292.5–3.5°. Hydroquinone diacetate, yel., m. 265.0–6.5°.
CN	Yel., m. 350.0–0.5°.
$COCH_3$	Or., m. 281–2°.
C_2H_5	Red, m. 240.0–0.5°.
$COOCH_3$	m. 246.5–7.5°.
$COOC_2H_5$	m. 240.5–1.5°.
C_6H_5	Or.-red, m. 314.5–5.5°. Hydroquinone diacetate, m. 256.0–7.5°.
C_6H_5CO	Or., m. 307.5–8.5°.

Reference

1. Pratt, Rice and Luckenbaugh, *J. Am. Chem. Soc.*, **79**, 1212 (1957).

A-242. Benzo[*b*]naphtho[1,2-*g*]-pyrrocoline*

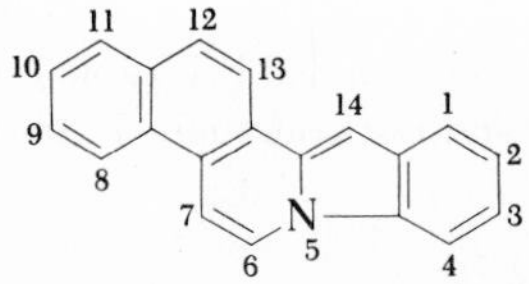

When compound I[1] was heated briefly with an excess of phenylacetyl chloride in xylene, red crystals of a dye (orange-yellow vat, red-brown to cherry-red color in sulfuric acid and a blue color in 24% oleum) separated.[2] The product was assigned structure II.

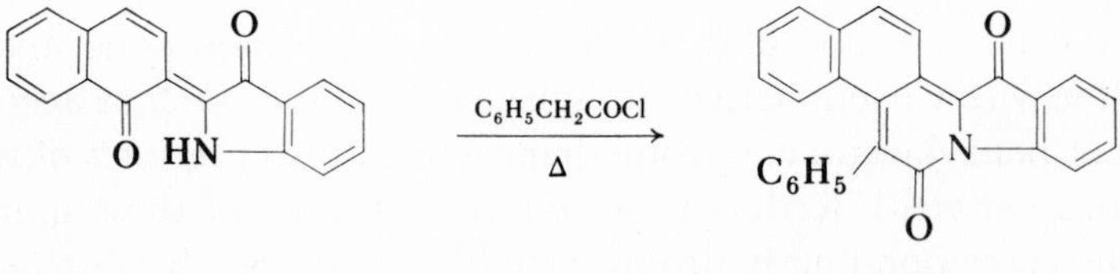

$C_6H_5CH_2COCl$, Δ

(I) (II)

References

1. Bezdzik and Friedlaender, *Monatsh.*, **29**, 375 (1908).
2. Engi, *Z. Angew. Chem.*, **27**, 144 (1914).

A-243. Indolo[3,2,1-*de*]pyrido[3,2,1-*ij*]-[1,5]naphthyridine*

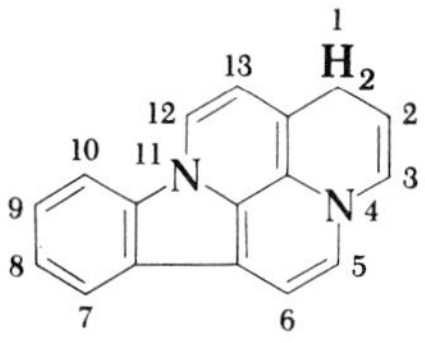

Treatment of I with hydrogen bromide yielded[1] a product (X = Br, m. >300°; X = picrate, m. 188–9°) thought to be either II or III. Acidic solutions of the compound show a blue-violet fluorescence. Reduction with sodium borohydride yielded a base (m. 109–11°; picrate, m. 215–6°d.; methiodide, m. 281°d.), presumably either IV or V.

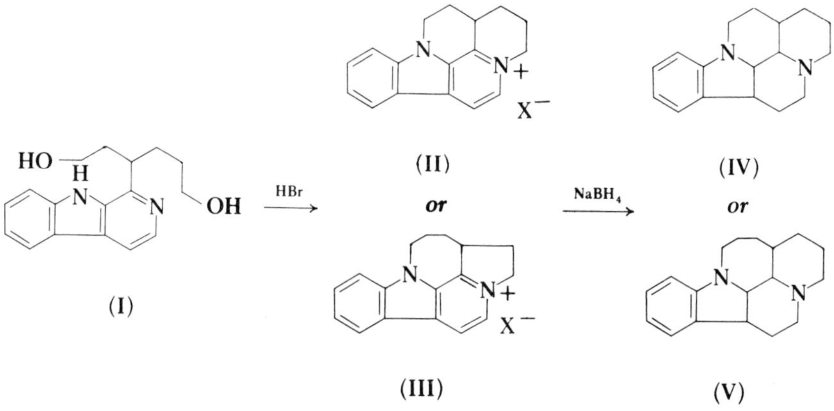

(I) —HBr→ (II) or (III) —$NaBH_4$→ (IV) or (V)

Reference

1. Wieland and Neeb, *Ann.*, **600,** 161 (1956).

A-244. 7*H*-Pyrrolo[3,2,1-*ij*]quinolo-[3,2-*c*]quinoline

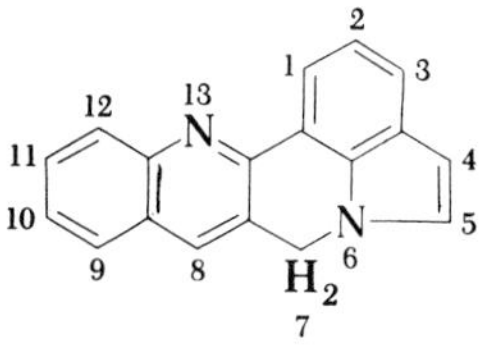

The name *quinolino(2′:3′–1:2)liline* has been used.

Subjection of I to the Pfitzinger synthesis yielded[1] II (R = COOH, deep red, m. 261–2°), which, in view of its deep color, probably possesses a zwitterionic structure. Thermal decarboxylation of this acid yielded II (R = H, yellow, m. 208°; hydrochloride, red, m. 302–4°). Oxidation of II (R = H) with potassium permanganate yielded III (pale yellow, m. 251–2°; hydrochloride, orange, m. 251°).

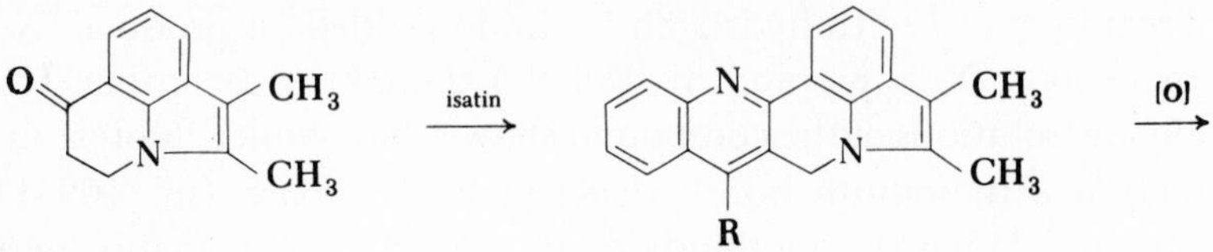

(I) —isatin→ (II) —[O]→

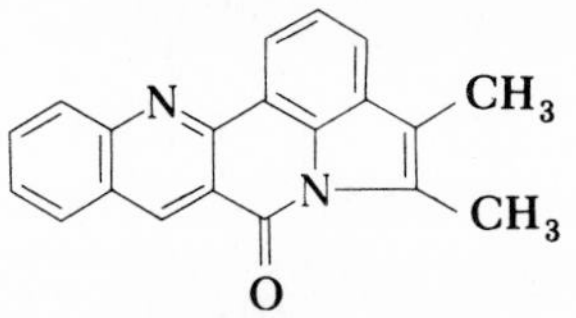

(III)

Reference

1. Almond and Mann, *J. Chem. Soc.*, **1952,** 1870.

A-245. 3*H*-Benzo[*h*]pyrrocolo[1,2,3-*de*]-cinnoline*

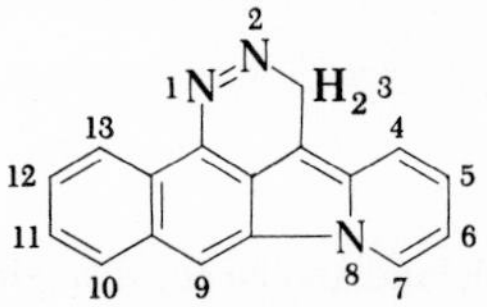

See Section A-222.

A-246. Phenanthro[9,10-*f*]indolizine*

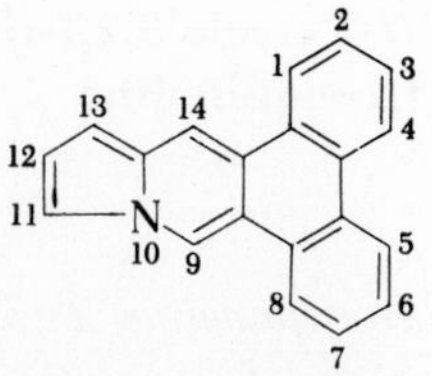

The name *phenanthro(9:10:6′7′)indolizine* has been used.

It has been suggested[1] that the alkaloid *tylophorine* is the 2,3,6,7-tetramethoxy compound.

Reference

1. Govindachari, Lakshmikantham, Nagarajan and Pai, *Chem. and Ind.*, **1957,** 1484.

A-247. 2*a*,8*b*-Diaza-3*H*-azuleno-[1,8,7-*aml*]fluorene*

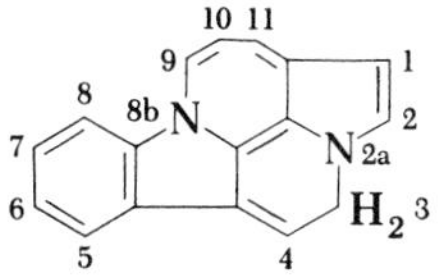

See Section A-243.

A-248. 13*H*-Phenanthro[1′,2′-4,5]-cyclopenta[1,2-*b*]pyrrocoline

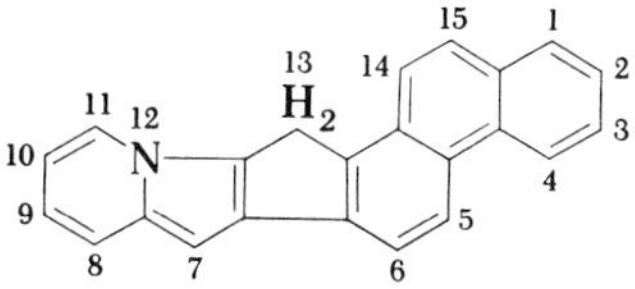

and

A-249. 15*H*-Naphth[2′,1′-1,2]indeno-[5,4-*b*]pyrrocoline

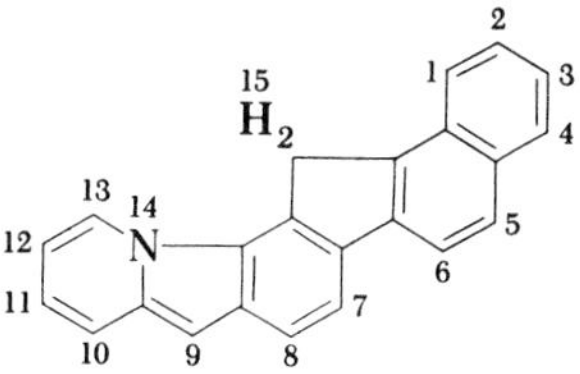

and

A-250. 15*H*-Naphth[2′,1′-1,2]indeno-[5,6-*b*]pyrrocoline

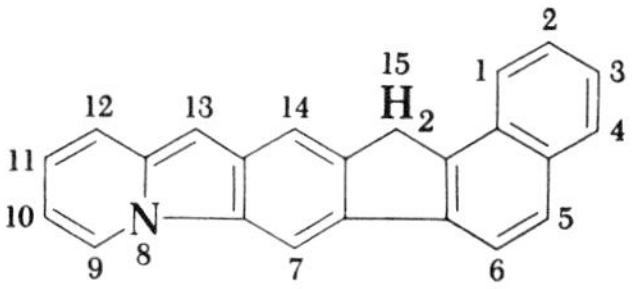

Derivatives of these nuclei have been discussed[1-7] in connection with structural studies upon the steroidal alkaloids.

References

1. McKenna, *Quart. Rev.*, **7,** 231 (1953).
2. Prelog and Jeger, in Manske and Holmes, *The Alkaloids*, Academic Press, New York, 1953, Vol. 3, p. 248.

3. Wintersteiner, Moore and Iselin, *J. Am. Chem. Soc.*, **76**, 5609 (1954).
4. Wintersteiner and Moore, *J. Am. Chem. Soc.*, **78**, 6193 (1956).
5. Heer and Hoffmann, *Helv. Chim. Acta*, **39**, 1820 (1956).
6. Sato and Latham, *J. Am. Chem. Soc.*, **78**, 3146 (1956).
7. Morgan and Barltrop, *Quart. Rev.*, **12**, 34 (1958).

A-251. 1*H*-Benzo[6,7]thianaphtheno-[3,2-*b*]pyrid[3,2,1-*hi*]indole

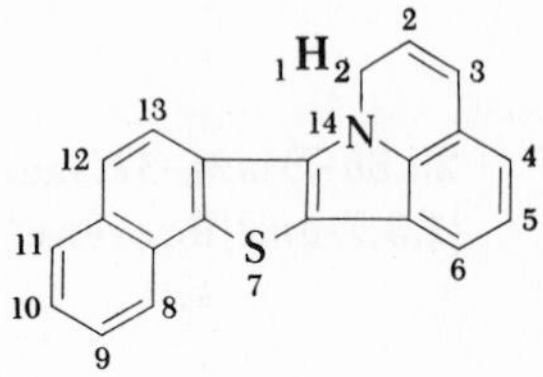

Condensation of I with II, and subjection of the resulting hydrazone to the Fischer indole synthesis, yielded[1] III (m. 237°; dipicrate, chocolate-colored, m. 184°), which was named *4,6-trimethylene-11,12-benzthionaphthindole*. See Sections A-230 and A-252.

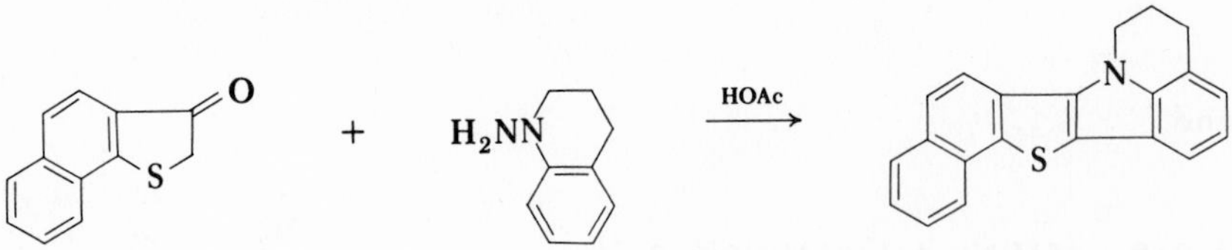

HOAc

(I) (II) (III)

Reference

1. Dalgliesh and Mann, *J. Chem. Soc.*, **1947**, 653.

A-252. 1*H*-Benzo[5,6]thianaphtheno-[3,2-*b*]pyrid[3,2,1-*hi*]indole

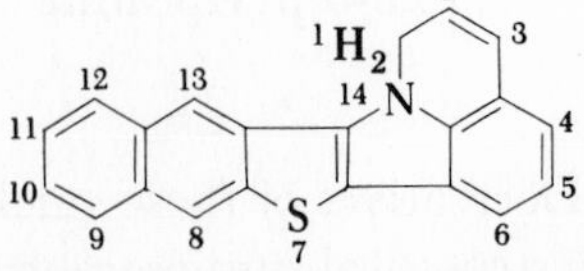

The 2,3-dihydro derivative (III) was named *4,6-trimethylene-10,11-benzthionaphthindole*. Compound III (m. 195–7°) was prepared[1] by the Fischer indole synthesis using the hydrazone obtained from the condensation of I and II. See Sections A-230 and A-251.

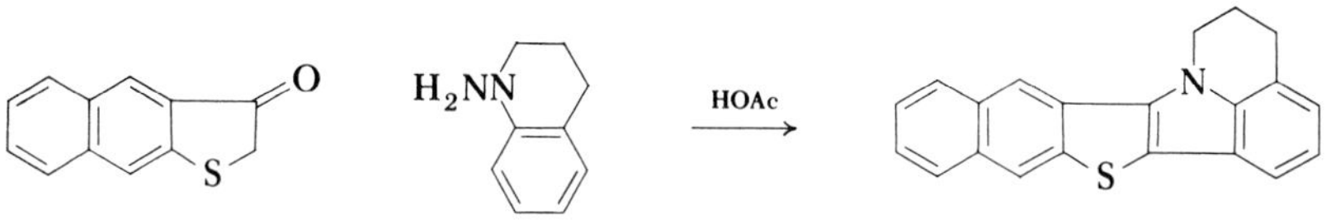

(I) (II) (III)

HOAc

Reference

1. Dalgliesh and Mann, *J. Chem. Soc.*, **1947,** 653.

A-253. Dibenzo[*a,e*]quino[2,3-*g*]-pyrroçoline. R.I. 3508

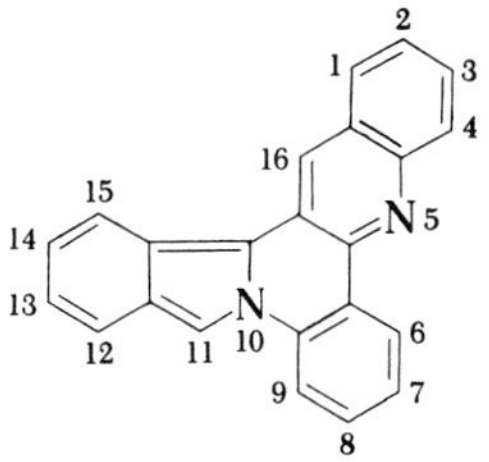

Structure I, once proposed[1] for the vat dye Höchst Yellow R (see Section A-210), is now known to be incorrect, and no other examples of this nucleus have been reported.

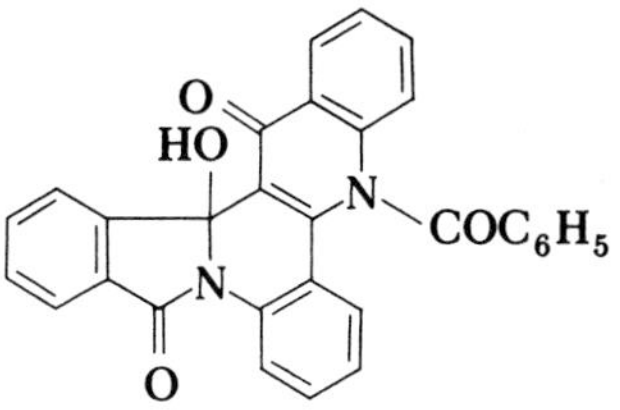

(I)

Reference

1. Hope, Kersey and Richter, *J. Chem. Soc.*, **1933,** 1000.

A-254. 15*H*-Isoquino[2,3,4-*no*]quindolin

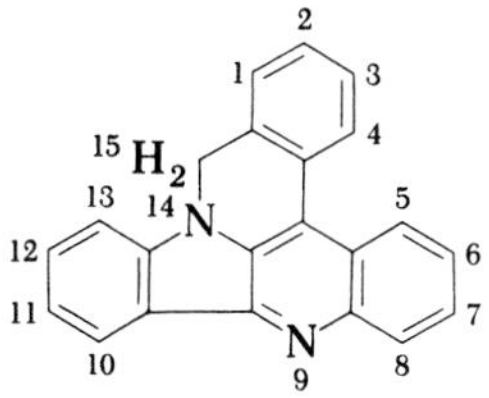

and

A-255. 11*H*-Indolo[3,2-*c*]isoindolo-[2,1-*a*]quinoline

When Dessoulavy's compound (I, see Section A-210) was heated with aniline, amongst the products formed[1] were two bases: $C_{22}H_{12}N_2O$ (A) and $C_{22}H_{14}N_2O$ (B). Because of the structure then accepted for Dessoulavy's compound, base A was assigned structure II, while B was thought to be its dihydro derivative. Homologous products resulted when aniline was replaced by *p*-toluidine, *p*-chloraniline or 2,4-xylidine, but not with *o*- or *m*-toluidines or 1- or 2-naphthylamines.

However, it was later found[2] that the same compound ($C_{23}H_{14}N_2O$) obtainable from I and *p*-toluidine could also be prepared by heating III with *p*-toluidine and boric acid, and it was assigned structure VI. Compound III was thought to form the anil (IV), which rearranged to V and lost hydrogen to give VI. It therefore seems[2] probable that the various products obtained from amines and I are of structures V and VI and they are so listed in the table.

The lactam bond of V, but not VI, is cleaved by ethanolic sodium ethoxide, providing a convenient method for the separa-

15*H*-Isoquino[2,3,4-*no*]quindolin-15-ones

Empirical formula	Substituents	Properties	Refs.
$C_{22}H_{11}ClN_2O$	6-Chloro-	Yel., m. 293°.	1,2
$C_{22}H_{12}N_2O$	Unsubstituted	Yel., m. 241–5°.	1
$C_{22}H_{13}ClN_2O$	6-Chloro-4*b*,9-dihydro-	Yel., m. 362–5°.	2
$C_{22}H_{14}N_2O$	4*b*,9-Dihydro-	—	1
$C_{23}H_{14}N_2O$	6-Methyl-	Yel., m. 264°.	1,2
	8-Methyl-	Yel., m. 203–4°.	2
$C_{23}H_{16}N_2O$	4*b*,9-Dihydro-6-methyl-	Yel., m. 263°.	1,2
$C_{24}H_{16}N_2O$	6,8-Dimethyl-	Yel., m. 278°.	1

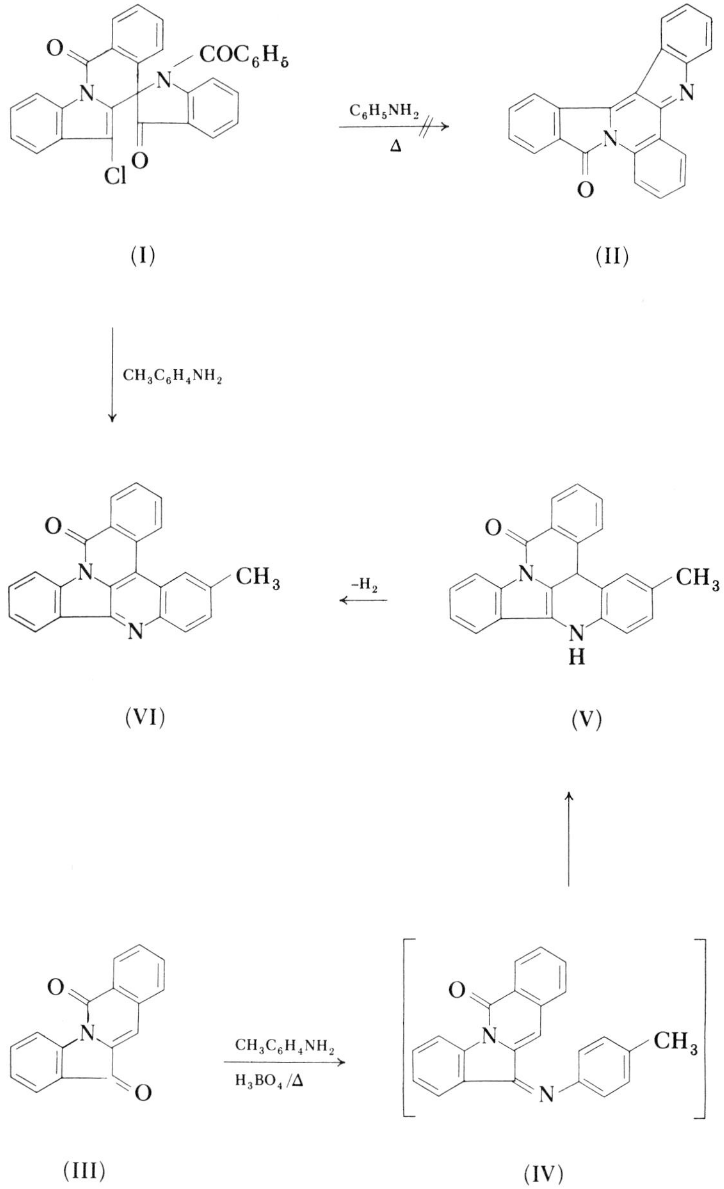

$C_6H_5NH_2$, Δ

(I) (II)

$CH_3C_6H_4NH_2$

$-H_2$

(VI) (V)

$CH_3C_6H_4NH_2$, H_3BO_4/Δ

(III) (IV)

tion of mixtures of the two. The acid thus obtained from V may again be cyclodehydrated.

References

1. de Diesbach, Jacobi, and Taddei, *Helv. Chim. Acta*, **23**, 469 (1940).
2. de Diesbach, Capponi, and Farquet, *Helv. Chim. Acta*, **32**, 1214 (1949).

A-256. 6*H*-Benzo[*a*]benzo[7,8]-pyrrocolino[2,3-*h*]quinolizine

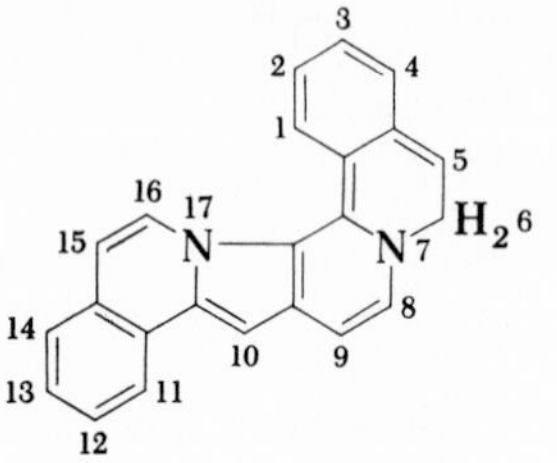

Rubremetine and other derivatives of the *Ipecac* alkaloids are thought[1,2] to contain this nucleus.

References

1. Janot, in Manske and Holmes, *The Alkaloids*, Academic Press, New York, 1953, Vol. 3, p. 363.
2. Openshaw and Battersby, in Schofield, *Recent Work on Naturally Occurring Nitrogen Heterocyclic Compounds*, Special Publication No. 3, The Chemical Society, London, 1955, pp. 28 and 36.

A-257. Diindolo[3,2,1-*de*, 3′,2′,1′-*ij*][1,5]-naphthyridine. R.I. 3471

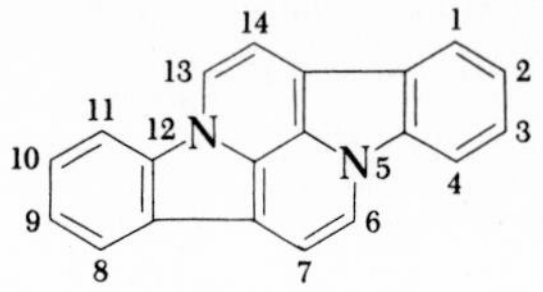

By heating indigo (I) with an excess of phenylacetyl chloride, either alone or in nitrobenzene solution, Engi[1,2] obtained the pigment *Ciba Lake Red B* (*Color Index No.* 1149). Structure III was proposed for this red pigment, and was supported by evidence[6] that the same product could be obtained by treating II (see Section A-232) with a second mole of phenylacetyl chloride. Ciba Lake Red B is a non-vattable, bright red, crystalline pigment, solutions of which, in organic solvents, exhibit an intense orange-yellow fluorescence ($\lambda_{max}^{CHCl_3}$ 290, 370, 515 and 552 mμ [8]). It may be sulfonated to yield a carmine-red dye for wool and silk. Bromination of III yields[3,4] red to violet pigments, depending upon the extent of bromi-

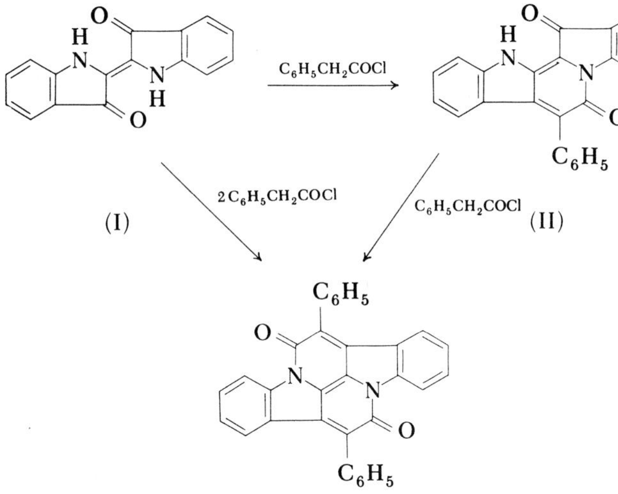

$C_6H_5CH_2COCl$

$2\,C_6H_5CH_2COCl$ (I) $C_6H_5CH_2COCl$ (II)

(III)

nation, and red to violet compounds of type III have been obtained[1-3] from 7,7′-dimethylindigo, 5,5′-dibromindigo and from tetra- and hexabromindigos.

Heating IV with phenylacetyl chloride,[5] or II with malonic ester and copper powder[6] yielded brick red (greenish fluorescence in solution), non-vattable crystals of V (m. > 320°).

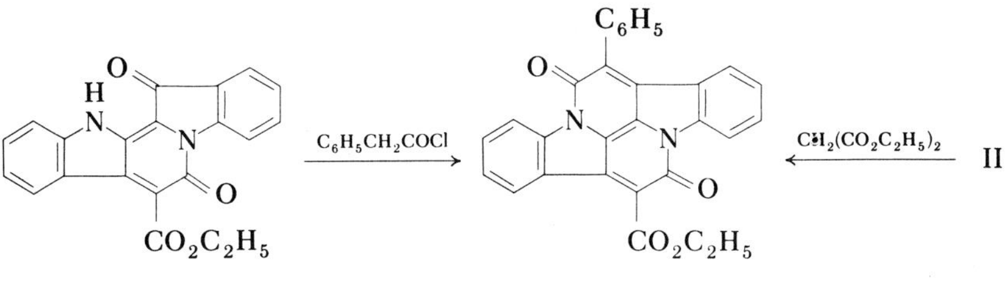

$C_6H_5CH_2COCl$ $CH_2(CO_2C_2H_5)_2$ II

(IV) (V)

In the formation of the pigment *tryptochrome* (see Section A-232) by the oxidation of tryptophane in aqueous acetic acid with potassium iodate, a fluorescent, violet, iodinated precursor (*iodoprotryptochrome*, d. ~300°, λ_{max}^{EtOH} 254, 293, 340, 420, 515 and 550 mμ) was observed.[8] This precursor was converted into tryptochrome by further oxidation with iodate. Structure VI was assigned provisionally to *iodoprotryptochrome*, largely because of the similarity between its absorption spectrum and that of compound III.

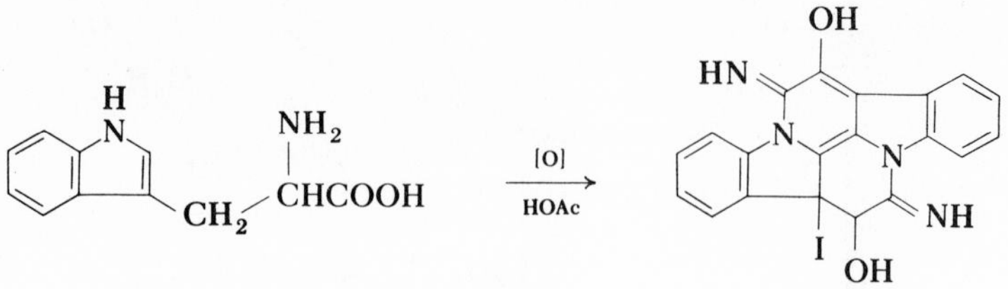

(VI)

References

1. Engi, *Z. angew. Chem.*, **27,** 144 (1915).
2. Engi, Ger. Pat. 260,243; *Frdl.*, **11,** 293 (1915). U. S. Pat. 1,043,682.
3. Ciba, Ger. Pat. 254,684; *Frdl.*, **11,** 290 (1915).
4. Ciba, Ger. Pat. 254,622; *Frdl.*, **11,** 291 (1915).
5. Posner and Pyl, *Ber.*, **56,** 31 (1923).
6. Posner and Kemper, *Ber.*, **57,** 1311 (1924).
7. Posner, *Ber.*, **59,** 1799 (1926).
8. Fearon and Boggust, *Biochem. J.*, **46,** 62 (1950).

A-258. *7H,11H*-Benzo[*ij*]carbazolo-[1,9,8-*cdef*]quinolizine

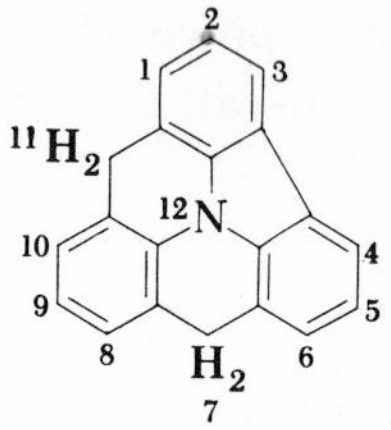

The diketone III (light yellow m. 228–30°; monoxime, m. 262–4°) was obtained[1] in 80 and 60% yields, respectively, by cyclization of the acid chlorides I and II.

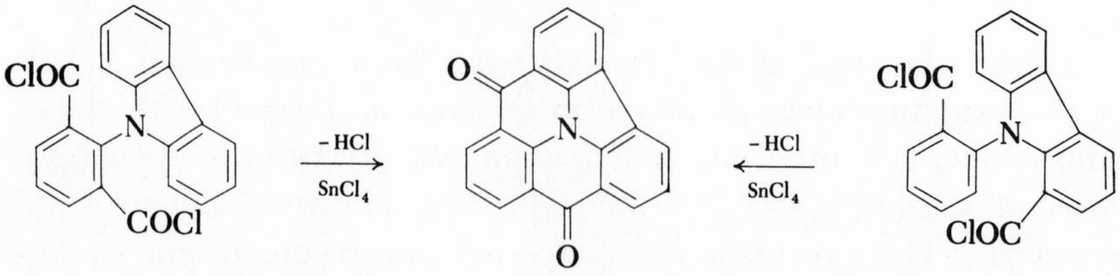

(I) (III) (II)

Reference

1. Gilman and Stuckwisch, *J. Am. Chem. Soc.*, **65,** 1729 (1943).

A-259. [1]Benzazepo[2,3,4-*hi*]dibenzo-[*b,f*]pyrrocoline

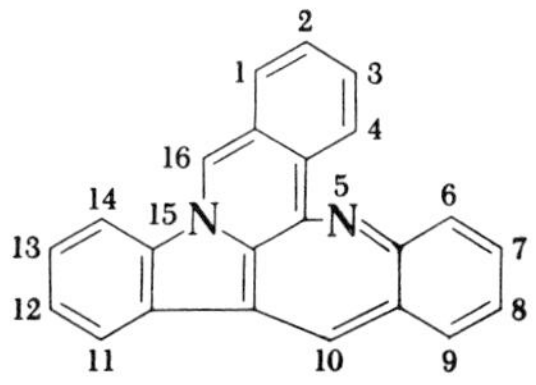

Depending upon the conditions, indigo reacts with benzotrichloride, benzoyl chloride or benzoic anhydride to yield several different products. Because of the interest in some of these products as dyestuffs, and because of the complex rearrangements encountered, a considerable amount of study has been devoted to this area. Although certain questions still remain unanswered, the structures of the major products are now quite firmly established. In the present section, only *Ciba Yellow 3G* and its derivatives will be discussed. *Höchst Yellow U* is considered in Section A-260, while *Höchst Yellow R* and *Dessoulavy's compound* are included in Section A-210.

When indigo is heated in nitrobenzene at 150–60° for a few hours with copper powder and either benzoyl chloride or benzotrichloride, the blue color of the mixture changes slowly to reddish-brown, and the resulting greenish-yellow product[1,2,3,19] has become known as *Ciba Yellow 3G* or *Indigo Yellow 3G* (*Color Index No.* 1195). Structures I-V were proposed in turn for the product until structure VI, proposed by deDiesbach,[4] was shown[4,5] to be correct.

Structure I, proposed by Engi,[2] was based upon an incorrect empirical formula for the dye, which was correctly shown to be $C_{23}H_{12}N_2O_3$ by Posner and Hofmeister,[6] who proposed structure II. However, by dilute alkaline hydrolysis and methylation of the hydrolysis products, Ciba Yellow 3G was shown[7] to contain a lactam group, and this excludes structure II. Therefore, Hope and Richter[7] proposed structure III.

Fusion of Ciba Yellow 3G with sodium hydroxide gave[8] benzoic and phthalic acids and two basic products: $C_{15}H_{10}N_2O_2$ and $C_{15}H_{10}N_2$, the latter of which was thought to be indolo[3,2-*c*]quinoline (XII, v.i.). This previously known[9] but ill-described compound

N,N′-Dibenzoylindigo
$C_{30}H_{18}N_2O_4$
m. 257°

C_6H_5COCl, pyridine

Indigo
$C_{16}H_{10}N_2O_2$
m. 390°

C_6H_5COCl or $(C_6H_5CO)_2O/ZnCl_2$

Höchst Yellow R
$C_{30}H_{18}N_2O_4$
m. 359°

Cu with $C_6H_5CCl_3$ or C_6H_5COCl in $C_6H_5NO_2$

C_6H_5COCl, Δ

C_6H_5COCl (reflux)

H_2SO_4 (25°)

H_2SO_4 (100°)

Ciba Yellow 3G
$C_{23}H_{12}N_2O_2$
m. 280°

$-C_6H_5COCl$, Δ

Dessoulavy's Compound
$C_{30}H_{17}ClN_2O_3$
m. 243°

Höchst Yellow U
$C_{23}H_{12}N_2O_2$
m. 287°

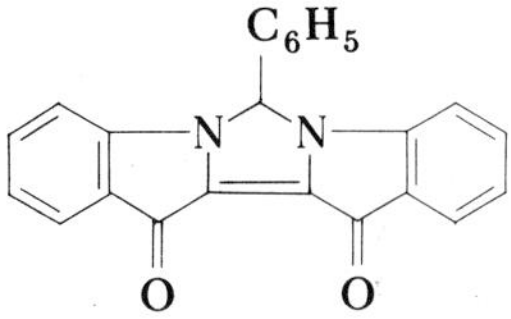

(I) 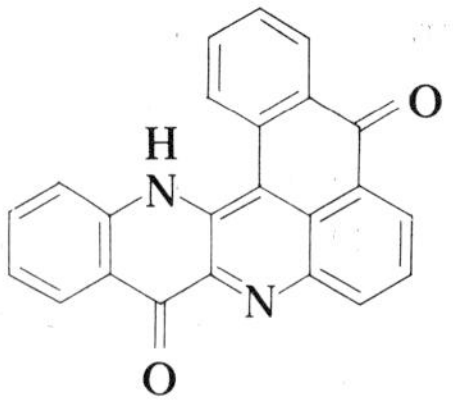 (II) 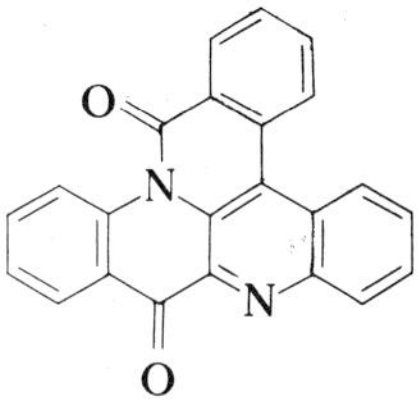 (III)

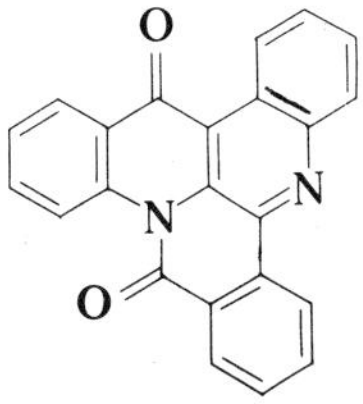

(IV) 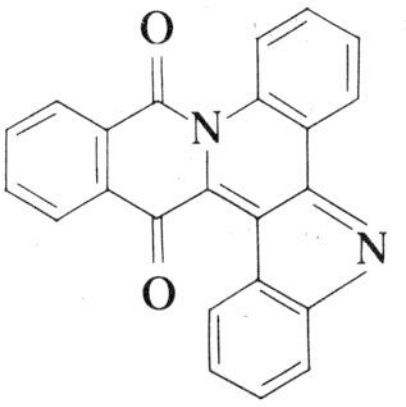 (V) 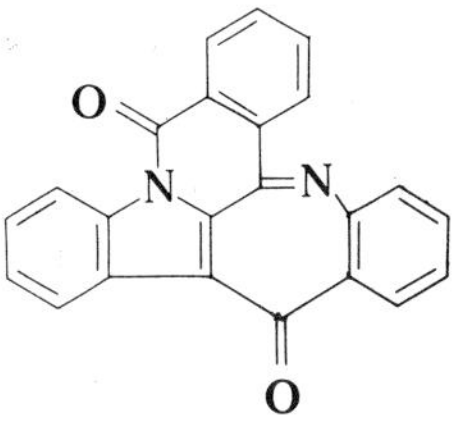 (VI)

was later demonstrated[5] to be, indeed, the product formed. To account for the formation of this cleavage product, which could not be formed from III, deDiesbach, deBie and Rubli suggested[8] structure IV.

Compounds II and IV (See Section A-771) were prepared independently[10, 11] and were shown to be different from Ciba Yellow 3G. Structure V also was considered,[5] but could not be substantiated. However, it was known[7, 12] that Dessoulavy's compound (VII, see Section A-210) could be converted by heat, with loss of the elements of benzoyl chloride, into Ciba Yellow 3G. This, and other considerations, lead deDiesbach, Capponi and Farquet[4] to propose structure VI.

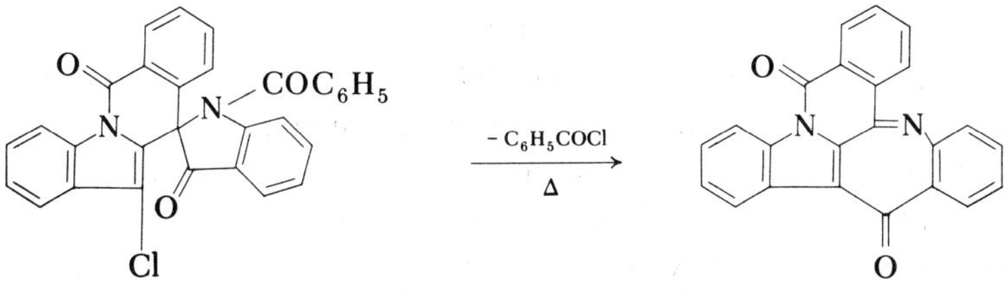

(VII) $\xrightarrow[\Delta]{-\,C_6H_5COCl}$ (VI)

With structure VI in mind, the baffling reactions of Ciba Yellow 3G become more reasonable. Mild alkaline hydrolysis[7] opens the lactam ring, and methylation followed by decarboxylation led to a product formulated as VIII. The structure of VIII was proven[5] by its conversion, upon reaction with hydrazine, into IX, which, after deamination, proved identical with an otherwise obtained sample of X. Formation of the indoloquinoline XII during the caustic fusion of VI was postulated[4,13] to occur via XI, resulting from the cleavage of phthalic anhydride from Ciba Yellow 3G. Alkaline oxidation[5] of the dye gave a dibasic acid formulated as XIII, since upon treatment with hydrazine, it lost anthranilic acid and formed XIV, the structure of which was demonstrated by an independent synthesis.

The preparation of Ciba Yellow 3G was studied in some detail by deDiesbach and Dobbleman[14] in an effort to establish the mechanism of the reaction. A mixture of Höchst Yellow R and Dessoulavy's compound resulted when indigo and benzoyl chloride were heated in nitrobenzene without copper powder. When heated in trichlorobenzene, a mixture of indigo, benzoyl chloride and copper powder yielded only Höchst Yellow R, while addition of sodium nitrite to this reaction again produced Ciba Yellow 3G. The need for the presence of nitrobenzene (or another oxidant) was therefore established, and the best conditions found (36% yield) for the preparation of the dye consist in bubbling air into a mixture of indigo, copper powder and benzoyl chloride in nitrobenzene at 160°. It was shown that benzoic anhydride is formed during the reaction, while the copper is converted into cuprous chloride.

Ciba Yellow 3G forms greenish-yellow crystals (bordeaux or violet-red vat) and is reported (variously) to melt at 288°, 280–3°, 278–81°, 277–9°, 275–6°, 275° or 270–2°. Its solution in sulfuric acid is yellowish-brown, while that in nitrobenzene is yellow, and it dyes[3] cotton and wool greenish-yellow. Reductive benzoylation of VI gave[6] XV (orange-yellow, m. 274°).

Chlorination of Ciba Yellow 3G gave a yellow dye containing about 15% chlorine, and bromination in nitrobenzene at 170–175° gave (predominantly) a dibromo derivative known as *Ciba Yellow G* (*Color Index No.* 1196). These halogenated derivatives[15,16,19] dye cotton and wool slightly redder shades of yellow than Ciba Yellow 3G. Reduction of Ciba Yellow G with sodium hydrosulfite in aqueous alcohol gave[2,16] a bromine-containing yellow dye (bordeaux vat)

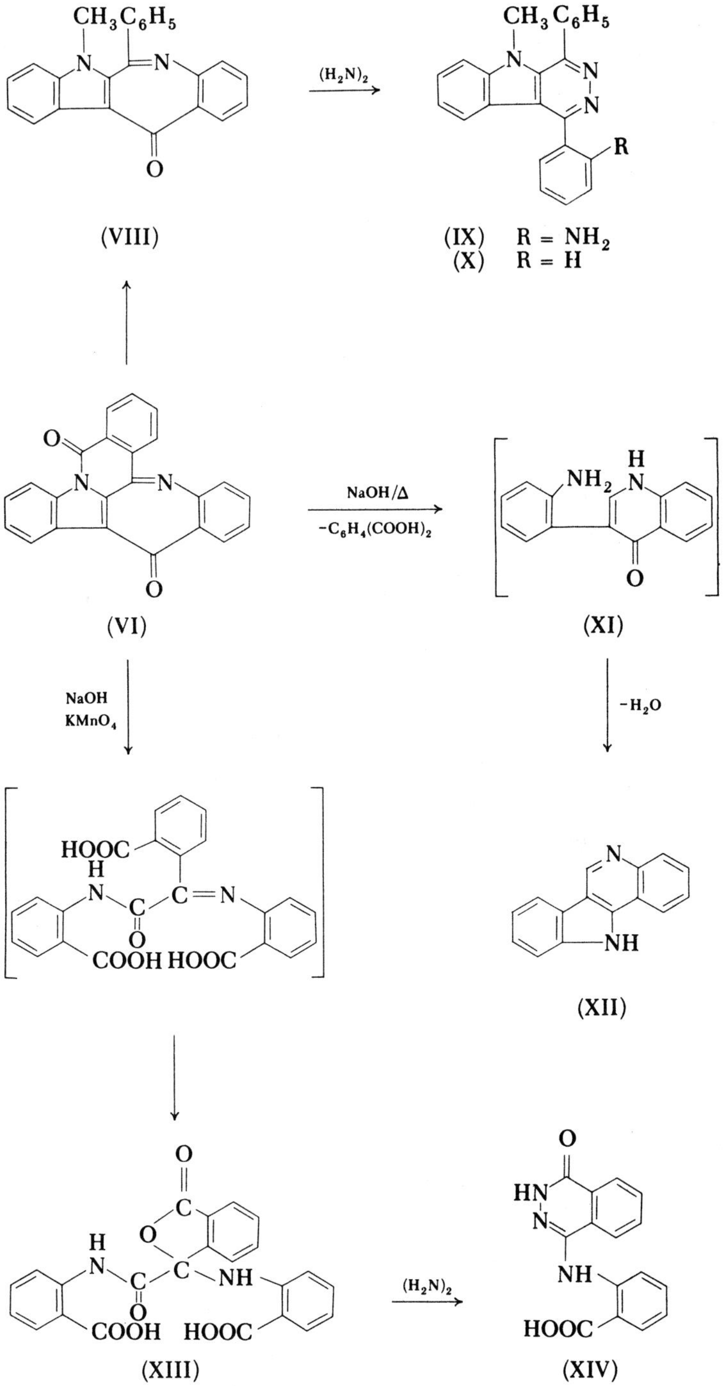

(VIII)
$(H_2N)_2$
(IX) R = NH_2
(X) R = H
(VI)
NaOH/Δ
$-C_6H_4(COOH)_2$
(XI)
NaOH
$KMnO_4$
$-H_2O$
(XII)
(XIII)
$(H_2N)_2$
(XIV)

known as *Ciba Yellow 5R (Color Index No.* 1197), the exact structure of which is unknown.

Substitution of *m*-chlorobenzoyl chloride for benzoyl chloride in the preparation of Ciba Yellow 3G gave[7] a yellow dye (m. 306°), probably the 2-chloro derivative of VI. The use of dibromindigo in place of indigo gave a greenish-yellow dye (m. >320°) probably of structure XVI (R = Br).

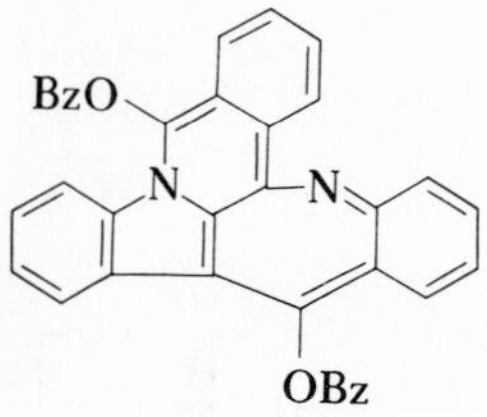

(XV)

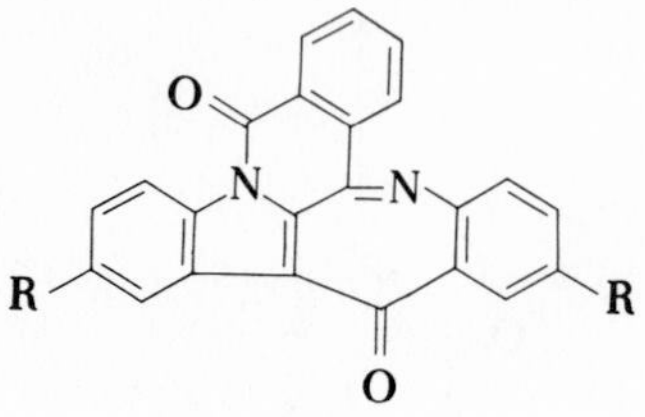

(XVI)

Similar treatment of 5,5-dimethyl indigo gave[17] a dimethyl homolog, probably XVI (R = CH_3). Treatment of this dye, or of Ciba Yellow 3G with 20% oleum yielded[18] sulfonated derivatives.

References

1. Engi and Fröhlich, Ger. Pat. 259,145; *Frdl.*, **11,** 292 (1915). U. S. Pat. 994,988. Fr. Pat. 434,828, Brit. Pat. 29,368 (1910).
2. Engi, *Z. Angew. Chem.*, **27,** 144 (1914).
3. Engi and Fröhlich, U. S. Pat. 1,026,574. Ger. Pat. Aplns. G 32,682/3; *Frdl.*, **10,** 400,402 (1913).
4. de Diesbach, Capponi and Farquet, *Helv. Chim. Acta*, **32,** 1214 (1949).
5. Staunton and Topham, *J. Chem. Soc.*, **1953,** 1889.
6. Posner and Hofmeister, *Ber.*, **59,** 1827 (1926).
7. Hope and Richter, *J. Chem. Soc.*, **1932,** 2783.
8. de Diesbach, deBie and Rubli, *Helv. Chim. Acta*, **17,** 113 (1934).
9. Clemo and Perkin, *J. Chem. Soc.*, **125,** 1608 (1924).
10. de Diesbach and Klement, *Helv. Chim. Acta*, **24,** 158 (1941).
11. de Diesbach and Miserez, *Helv. Chim. Acta*, **31,** 673 (1948).
12. Farbwerke vorm. Meister Lucius & Brüning, Ger. Pats. 247,154 and 254,734; *Frdl.*, **10,** 403 and 1334 (1913).
13. de Diesbach and Moser, *Helv. Chim. Acta*, **20,** 132 (1937).
14. de Diesbach and Dobbleman, *Helv. Chim. Acta*, **19,** 1213 (1936).
15. Ciba, Ger. Pat. 246,837; *Frdl.*, **10,** 400 (1913). Fr. Pat. 437,181. Brit. Pat. 8,900 (1911). U. S. Pat. 997,766.

16. Engi, Ger. Pat. 257,973; *Frdl.*, **11,** 289 (1915) Brit. Pat. 9,940 (1912). U. S. Pat. 1,074,850.
17. Farbwerke vorm. Meister Lucius & Brüning, Ger. Pat. 266,875; *Frdl.*, **11,** 298 (1915).
18. Farbwerke vorm. Meister, Lucius & Brüning, Ger. Pat. 267,384; *Frdl.*, **11,** 299 (1915).
19. Wuth, *Chem. Ztg.*, **35,** 667 (1911).
20. Engi, *Chem. Ztg.*, **38,** 199 (1914).

A-260. [1]Benzazepo[4,3,2-*hi*]dibenzo-[*b,f*]pyrrocoline*

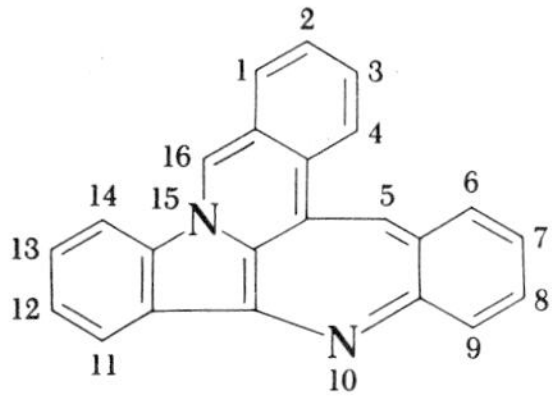

A vat dye, *Höchst Yellow U*, and its homologs are the only examples of this nucleus. Höchst Yellow U (III) is formed when either Dessoulavy's compound (I), or Höchst Yellow R (II) is heated with sulfuric acid or with zinc chloride in nitrobenzene.[1,2,3] Compounds I and II are two of the products resulting from the reaction of indigo with benzoyl chloride under various conditions. A complete diagram of these products and their interrelationships is shown in Section A-259.

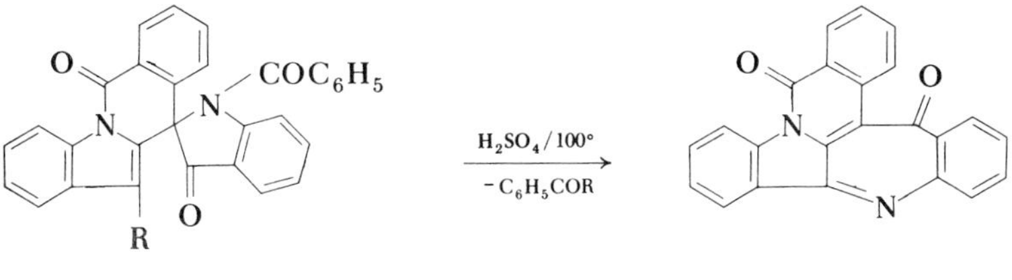

$$\xrightarrow[-\ C_6H_5COR]{H_2SO_4/100°}$$

(I) R = Cl
(II) R = OH

(III)

Two other structures (IV and V) were proposed for Höchst Yellow U before it was shown by deDiesbach, Capponi and Farquet[4] to have structure III. Because of certain similarities between Höchst Yellows U and R, structure IV was proposed[5] for the former dye upon the basis of the (erroneous) structure then accepted

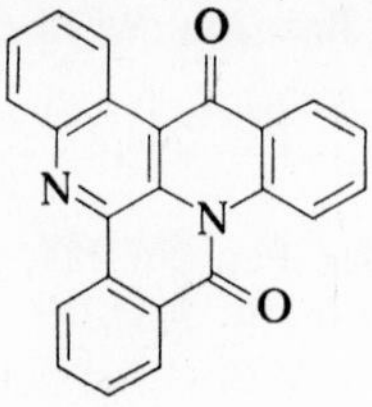

(IV) 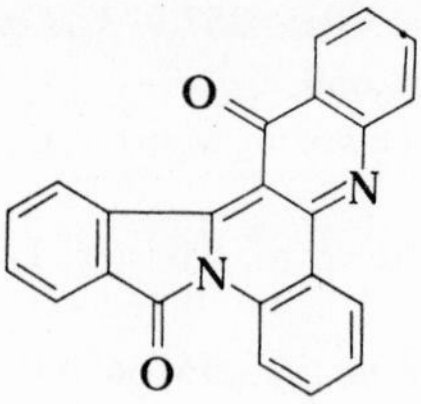 (V)

for Höchst Yellow R. Structure V was suggested[6] to account for the properties (incompatible with structure IV) of two carboxylic acids obtained by subjecting Höchst Yellow U to alkaline hydrolysis.

The pyridone ring of Höchst Yellow U is opened by treatment with aqueous caustic to yield[6] a carboxylic acid (VI), which, when heated, does not revert to the lactam (III), but lactonizes to form VII. A different lactone (VIII) is formed,[5] together with anthranilic acid, when III is fused with caustic.

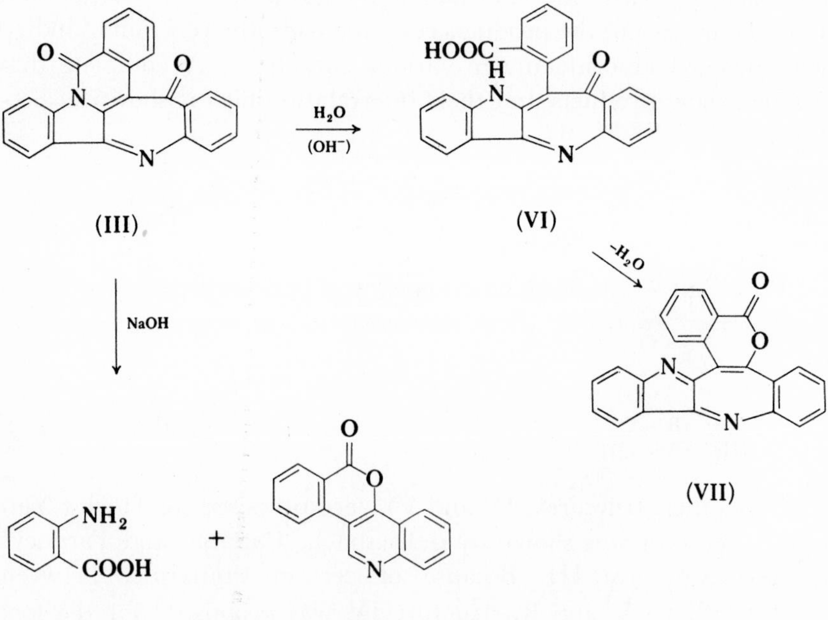

(III) $\xrightarrow[(OH^-)]{H_2O}$ (VI) $\xrightarrow{-H_2O}$ (VII)

(III) $\xrightarrow{NaOH}$ anthranilic acid (NH_2, COOH) + (VIII)

Höchst Yellow U is a yellow to orange-yellow crystalline solid, m. 287° (285°, 280°), which dyes cotton yellow from an orange-yellow vat. It is no longer of commercial interest.

Sulfonation of III yields a yellow wool dye. Substitution of dibromoindigo for indigo in the preparation of Höchst Yellow U leads[3] to a yellow dibromo homolog, presumably the 7,12-dibromo compound. A brown dye (blue-violet vat), probably the 3-methoxy homolog of III, is obtained similarly from indigo and 4-methoxybenzoyl chloride.

References

1. Farbwerke vorm. Meister Lucius & Brüning, Ger. Pats. 247,154, 254,567 and 254,734; *Frdl.*, **10,** 403, 1335 and 1334 (1913).
2. Farbwerke vorm. Meister Lucius & Brüning, Ger. Pat. 270,943; *Frdl.*, **11,** 298 (1915).
3. Posner, Zimmerman and Kautz, *Ber.*, **62,** 2150 (1929).
4. de Diesbach, Capponi and Farquet, *Helv. Chim. Acta*, **32,** 1214 (1949).
5. de Diesbach, de Bie and Rubli, *Helv. Chim. Acta*, **17,** 113 (1934).
6. Hope and Anderson, *J. Chem. Soc.*, **1936,** 1474.

A-261. Phenanthro[9′,10′,1′, 3,4,5]indolo-[1,2-*a*]quinoline*

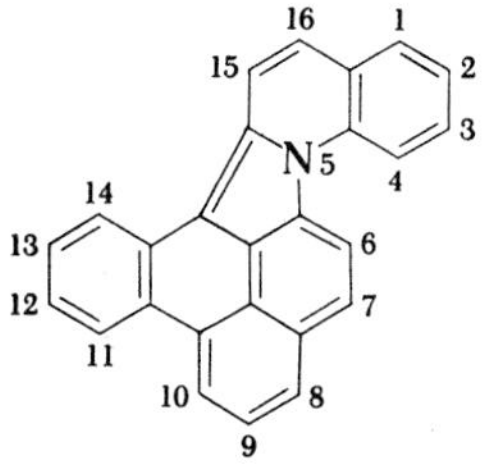

When a mixture of quinaldic acid and benzanthrone was heated at 180° for two hours, there was isolated,[1] in very small yield, a

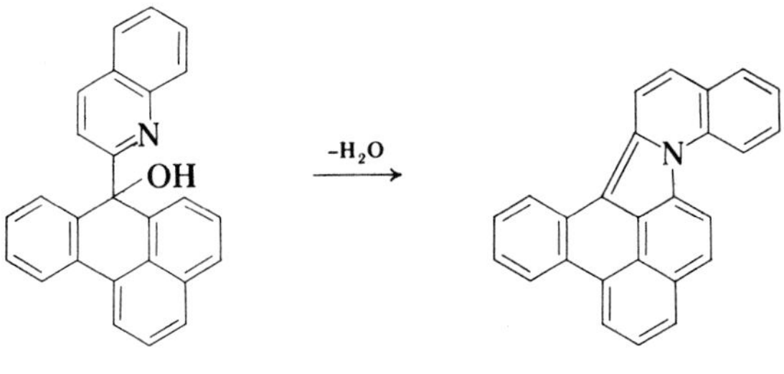

(I) $\xrightarrow{-H_2O}$ (II)

yellow product (m. 228–9°) thought to have structure II, possibly formed via the intermediate I. The ultraviolet spectrum of II was recorded.[1]

Reference

1. Bradley and Nursten, *J. Chem. Soc.*, **1955,** 4027.

A-262. Triindolo[1,2-*a*, 2′,3′-*c*, 3″,2″-*e*]-pyridine. R.I. 3686

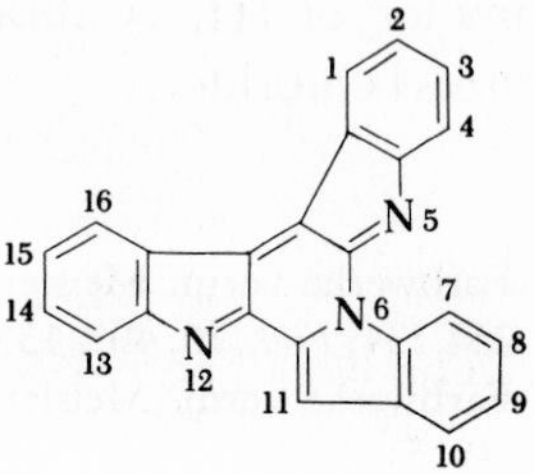

This nucleus was proposed[1] as the structure of indole trimer ("triindole"), which is now known to be a linear polymer. For another erroneous formulation of triindole see Section A-444.

References

1. Oddo and Crippa, *Atti reale accad. naz. Lincei*, [5] **33, I,** 31 (1924); *Chem. Zentr.*, **I,** 2364 (1924); *Gazz. chim ital*, **54,** 341 (1924).
2. Schmitz-Dumont and ter Horst, *Ann.*, **538,** 261 (1939).

A-262A. Indolo[3,2,1-*de*]naphth-[3,2,1-*kl*]acridine*

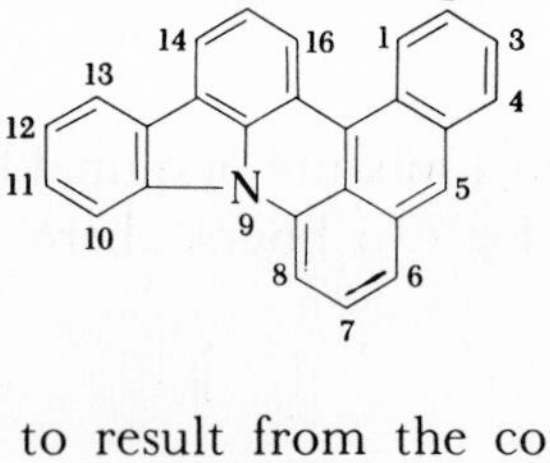

The red product I was reported[1] to result from the condensation of octahydrocarbazole with 1-chloroanthraquinone.

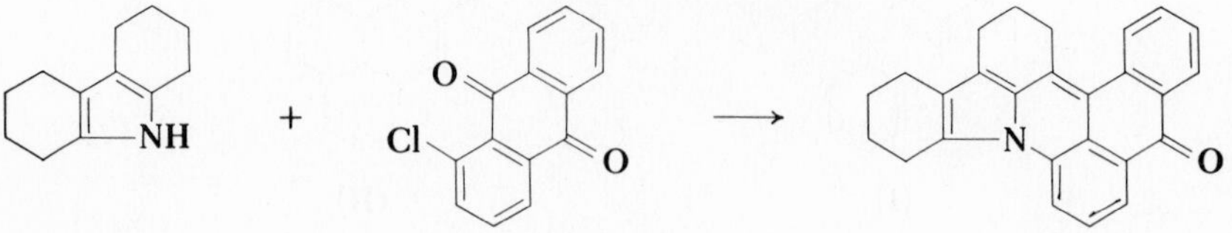

(I)

Reference

1. Eckert, *I. G. Farbenindustrie, A. G., 30 Wissenschaftlicher Austausch der Gruppe IX*, Leverkusen, Feb. 6, 1934; *PB Report No.* 25632, frame 170.

263. Bisbenz[4,5]indolo-[3,2,1-*de*, 3′,2′,1′-*ij*][1,5]-naphthyridine*

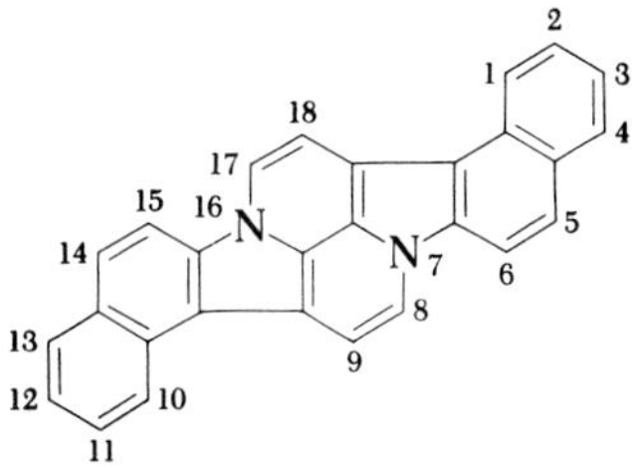

The treatment of β-naphthindigo (Ciba Green, I) with phenylacetyl chloride was reported by Engi[1] to yield a red pigment. No further description of the product was given, but it seems probable that it has structure II by analogy with the product formed similarly from indigo (see Section A-257).

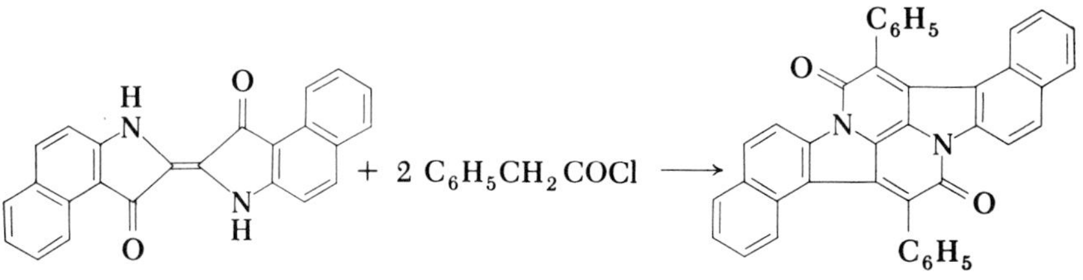

$+ 2\ C_6H_5CH_2COCl \longrightarrow$

(I) (II)

Reference

1. Engi, *Z. Angew. Chem.*, **27,** 144 (1914).

A-264. 5*H*-Anthr[2,1,9-*mna*]indolo-[1,2,3-*fg*]acridine*

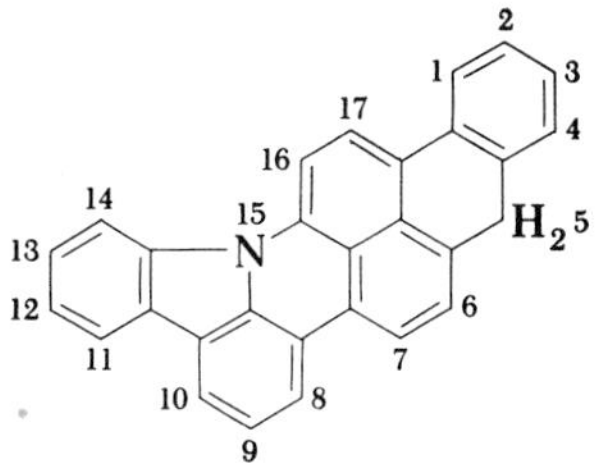

The condensation of carbazole and certain of its 3,6-disubstituted derivatives (I) with 3-bromobenzanthrone (II) in an Ullmann reaction yielded[1,2] intermediates of structure III, which could be cyclized[2] by fusion with caustic to yield IV (R = H, blue-black, m. 173–5°; R = NO_2, black-brown, m. 298°; R = NH_2, black, m. >360°; R = NHC_3H_7, black, m. >360°; R = Cl, m. 360°; R = Br, m. 240°).

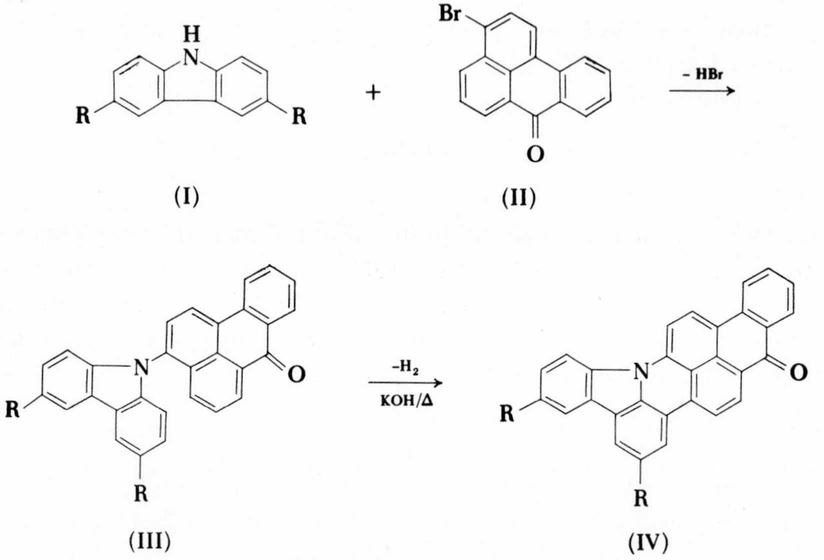

H N R R + Br O − HBr

(I) (II)

N R R O $-H_2$ KOH/Δ N R R O

(III) (IV)

References

1. Müller and Wilke, Ger. Pat. 468,896; *Frdl.*, **16,** 1454 (1931).
2. Murata, Harada and Kuwata, *Bull. Fac. Eng. Hiroshima Univ.*, **4,** 275 (1955); *Chem. Abstracts*, **51,** 8067 (1957).

A-265. Tetrabenzo[*b,b',f,f'*]benzo-[1,2,3-*hi*, 4,5,6-*h'i'*]-bisindolizine*

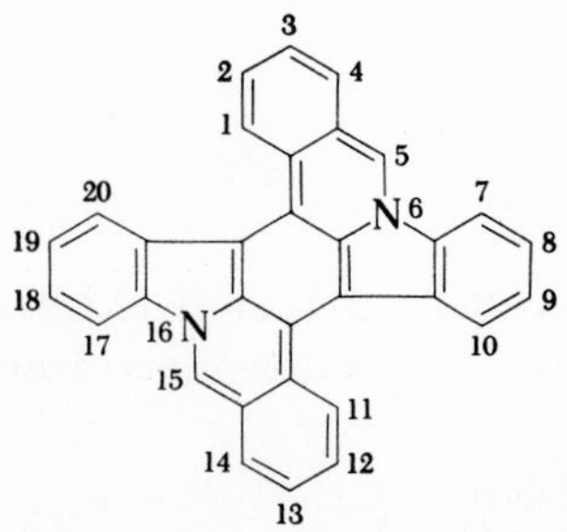

1 2 3 4 5 N6 7 8 9 10 11 12 13 14 15 16N 17 18 19 20

Heating[1] the dye Ciba Yellow 3G (I, see Section A-259) with aqueous caustic and sodium hydrosulfite in an autoclave at 220°

transformed it into anthranilic acid and a yellow substance $C_{32}H_{16}N_2O_2$ (m. 353°). This same product was obtained when II (see Section A-209) was heated with boric acid, zinc chloride or phosphorus pentoxide, and was thought to have structure III. This last synthesis is peculiar in that the two molecules of II provide only half of the hydrogen needed for the elimination of two molecules of water during the formation of III.

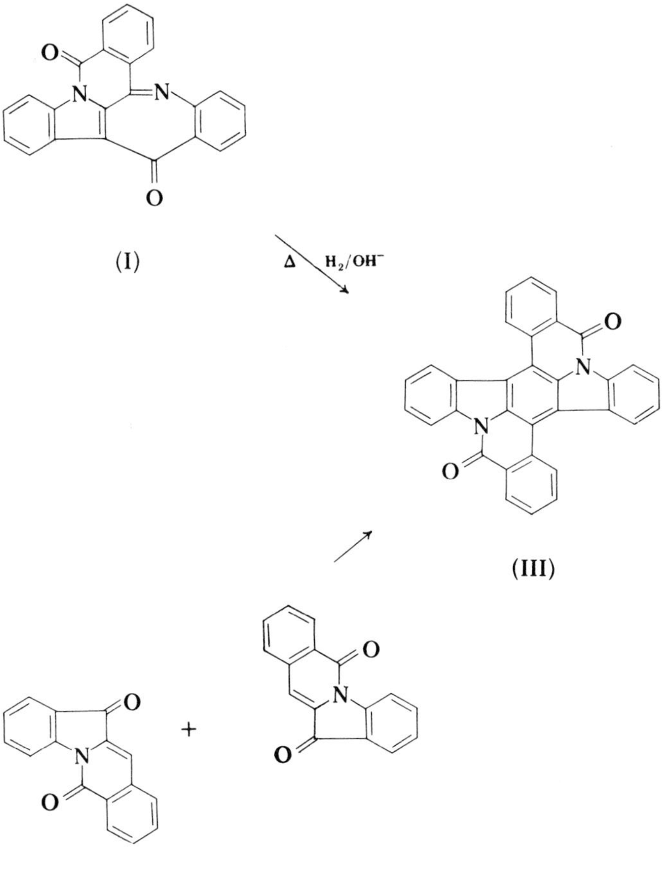

(I)

Δ H_2/OH^-

(III)

+

(II)

Reference

1. de Diesbach, Capponi and Farquet, *Helv. Chim. Acta*, **32,** 1214 (1949).

transformed it into an [illegible] yellow [illegible] C[illegible]H[illegible]N[illegible]O[illegible] (m.p. 183°). This same product was obtained when II [illegible] was heated with [illegible] pentoxide [illegible] was thought to have structure III. This last synthesis is peculiar in that the two molecules of II provide only half of the hydrogen needed for the elimination of two molecules of water during the formation of III.

II

III

References

1. de Diesbach, Capponi and Farquet, *Helv. Chim. Acta* 32, 1214 (1949).

CHAPTER V

Fused 5/6 Ring Systems with One Extra Heteroatom

A-266. 5*H*-Oxazolo[3,2-*a*]pyridine

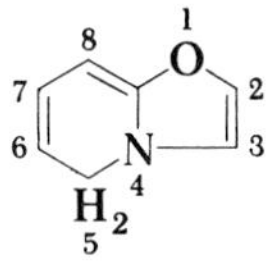

The reaction of α-pyridone with α-bromoacrylic acid[1] has been shown[2] to yield, via I, the acid II (m. 122–3°).

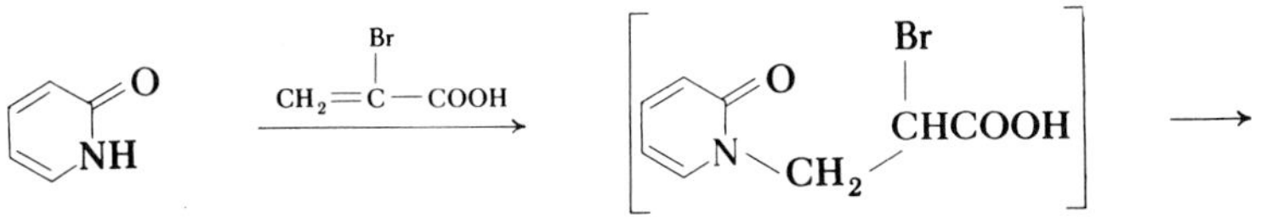

$$CH_2{=}C(Br){-}COOH$$

(I)

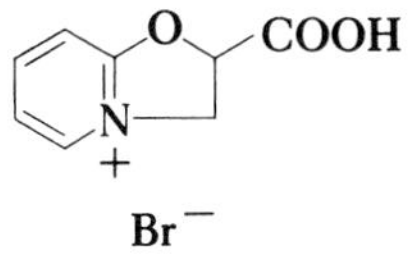

(II)

Treatment of III with hot acetic or propionic anhydrides yielded[6] the mesoionic compounds IV (R = CH_3, m. 170–1°; R = C_2H_5, m. 145–7°).

Condensation of V with ethanolamine yielded[7] VI (b_{12} 118°, n_D^{20} 1.4885).

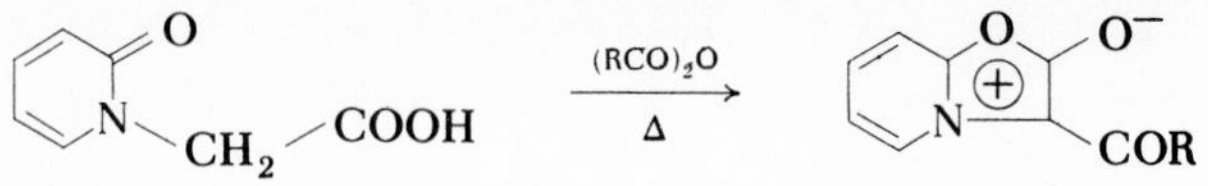

(III) (IV)

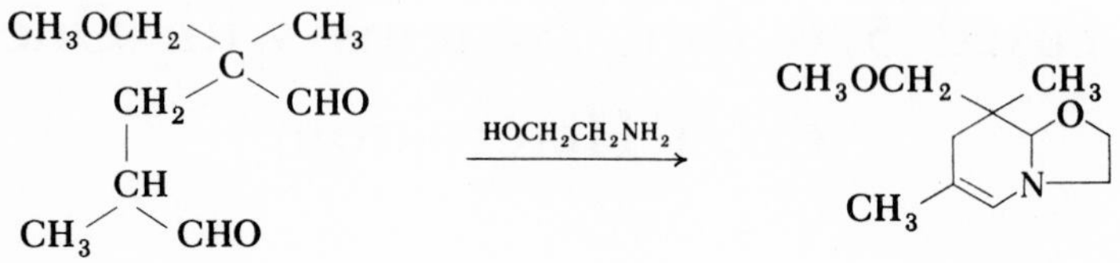

(V) (VI)

This nucleus has also been shown to be contained in the structures of the alkaloids *atisine* and *garryine* and their congeners.[3-5]

References

1. Adams and Jones, *J. Am. Chem. Soc.*, **71,** 3826 (1949).
2. Adams and Pachter, *J. Am. Chem. Soc.*, **74,** 4906 (1952).
3. Wiesner and Edwards, *Experientia*, **11,** 255 (1955).
4. Valenta and Wiesner, *Chem. and Ind.*, **1956,** 354.
5. Djerassi, Smith, Lippman, Figdor and Herran, *J. Am. Chem. Soc.*, **77,** 4801 (1955).
6. Lawson and Miles, *Chem. and Ind.*, **1958,** 461.
7. Abbott and Graham, Brit. Pat. 742,053; *Chem. Abstracts*, **50,** 16877 (1956).

A-267. 5*H*-Pyrido[2,1-*b*]thiazole

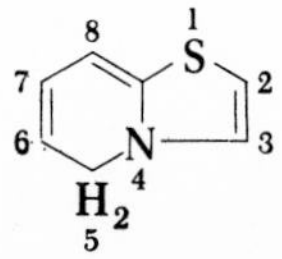

The saturated nucleus has been called *4-thia-1-azabicyclo*[*3.2.0*]-*nonane*.

From the reaction of thiazolines[2,3] (I) or thiazolidines[1] (II) with ketenes, a number[1-3] of compounds of type III have been prepared: (a) R = R_1 = H, R_2 = CH_3, R_3 = $COOCH_3$, m. 99–102°;[1] (b) R = CH_3, R_1 = R_2 = R_3 = H, not isolated;[2] (c) R = R_1 = CH_3, R_2 = R_3 = H, oil;[2] (d) R = CH_3, R_1 = C_6H_5, R_2 = R_3 = H, m. 136–7°;[2] (e) R = R_2 = CH_3, R_1 = H, R_3 = $COOCH_3$, m. 75–

95°;[2] (f) R = R_2 = CH_3, R_1 = C_6H_5, R_3 = $COOCH_3$, m. 154°;[1,2] (g) R = C_6H_5, R_1 = R_2 = R_3 = H, m. 191–2°;[3] (h) R = C_6H_5, R_1 = CH_3, R_2 = R_3 = H, m. 160.5–1.0°;[2] (i) R = C_6H_5, R_1 = $C_6H_5CH{=}CH{-}$, R_2 = R_3 = H, a glass;[2] (j) R = C_6H_5, R_1 = R_2 = CH_3, R_3 = $COOCH_3$, m. 215°.[2]

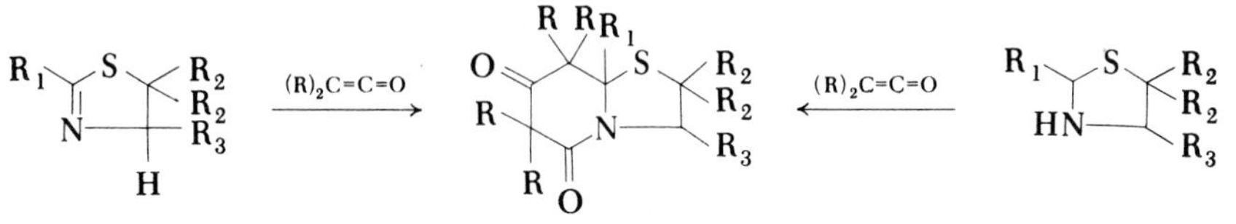

$(R)_2C{=}C{=}O$ $(R)_2C{=}C{=}O$

(I) (III) (II)

The reaction of 2-methylthiazoline with ketene yielded[4] IV, with V (m. 104–5°; λ_{max} 325 mμ, ϵ = 54,000) as a by-product, whereas with diketene, VI (m. 92°; λ_{max} 320 mμ, ϵ = 14,500) was produced.[5]

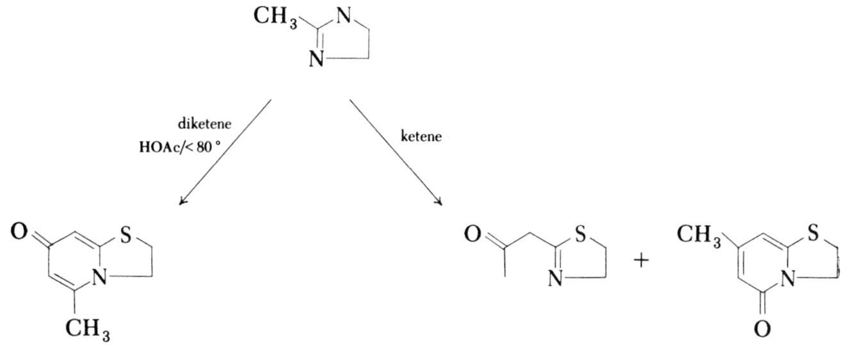

diketene HOAc/< 80° ketene

(VI) (IV) (V)

In a similar reaction, phthalimidoacetyl chloride reacted with thiazolines to yield the desired β-lactams VII (R_1 = phthalimido), and by-products thought[6,7] to have structure VIII [(a), R_1 = phthalimido, R_2 = R_3 = H, m. 253–4°; (b), R_1 = phthalimido, R_2 = CH_3, R_3 = $COOCH_3$, m. 264–6°].

The reaction of IX with L-cysteine or DL-penicillamine yielded[8] X (R = H, m. 212.5–4.0°, sulfone, m. 203°, R = CH_3, m. 157.0–8.5°, sulfone, m. 224–31°d.). Efforts to prepare the Δ^6 analog of X were unsuccessful.

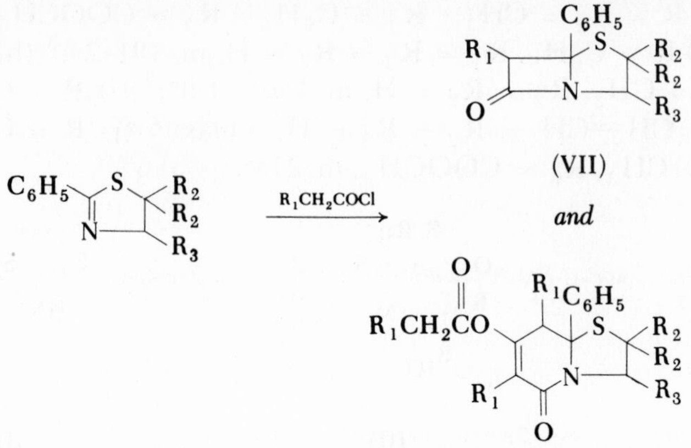

C_6H_5, S, R_1, N, O, R_2, R_2, R_3

(VII)

C_6H_5, S, N, R_2, R_2, R_3 —R_1CH_2COCl→

and

O, R_1CH_2CO, R_1, C_6H_5, S, N, R_1, O, R_2, R_2, R_3

(VIII)

CHO, $COOCH_3$ + HS, R, R, H_2N, COOH → S, R, R, N, O, COOH

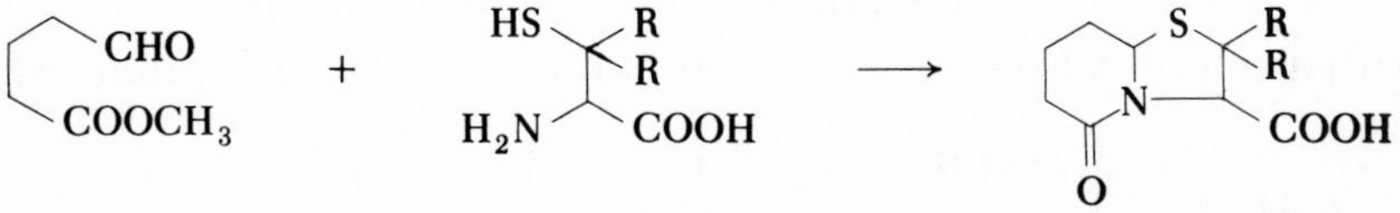

(IX)

(X)

Koenigs and Geisler[9] heated XI with acetic anhydride, and obtained a yellow product, which they considered to be XII. By an alternative synthesis of XII, Tschitschibabin and Woroshtzow[10] ex-

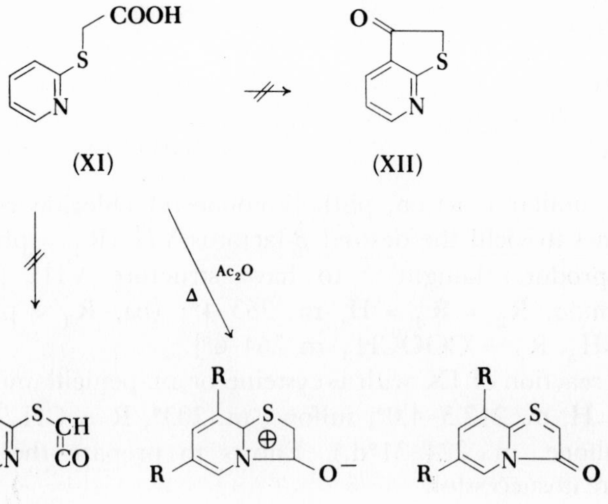

COOH, S, N

O, S, N

(XI)

(XII)

Ac_2O

Δ

S, CH, N, CO

R, S, ⊕, R, N, O^-

R, S, R, N, O

(XIII)

(XIV)

(XV)

cluded this structure, and they proposed XIII. However, Duffin and Kendall[11] have recently suggested a more reasonable formulation of this product as a resonance hybrid of XIV and its seven dipolar forms (R = H, yellow, m. 180°; R = Br,[10] yellow, m. 222–4°). Structure XV has also been favored.[12] See Section A-269.

References

1. Cook and Heilbron, "Thiazolidines," in Clarke *et al.*, *The Chemistry of Penicillin*, Princeton University Press, Princeton, N. J., 1949, p. 921.
2. Ballard, Melstrom and Smith, "The Chemistry of β-Lactams," in Clarke, *et al.*, *The Chemistry of Penicillin*, Princeton University Press, Princeton, N. J., 1949, p. 973.
3. Panizzi, *Gazz. chim. ital.*, **78,** 207 (1948); *Chem. Abstracts*, **42,** 7294 (1948).
4. Kuhn, Quadbeck and Röhm, *Chem. Ber.*, **86,** 468 (1953).
5. Kuhn and Drawert, *Ann.*, **590,** 55 (1954).
6. Sheehan and Ryan, *J. Am. Chem. Soc.*, **73,** 4367 (1951).
7. Sheehan, Hill and Buhle, *J. Am. Chem. Soc.*, **73,** 4373 (1951).
8. Todd and Teich, *J. Am. Chem. Soc.*, **75,** 1895 (1953).
9. Koenigs and Geisler, *Ber.*, **57,** 2076 (1924).
10. Tschitschibabin and Woroshtzow, *Ber.*, **66,** 364 (1933).
11. Duffin and Kendall, *J. Chem. Soc.*, **1951,** 734.
12. Baker and Ollis, *Quart. Rev.*, **11,** 15 (1957).

A-268. 1*H*-Pyrido[2,1-*b*]benzothiazole

De Smet and Schwarz treated I with trimethylene bromide and obtained[1] II (m. 250°), which was used in the synthesis of cyanine dyes.[2,3]

$BrCH_2CH_2CH_2Br$, Δ

(I) (II)

Van Dormael and Nys[4] obtained IV (m. 294–5°, strong blue fluorescence) from the reaction of III with ethyl orthoformate.

The reaction of benzothiazole with ketenes yields[5] V (R = CH_3, m. 81–3°; R = C_6H_5, m. 163.0–4.5°).

(III) (IV)

(V)

References

1. Schwarz and De Smet, Brit. Pat. 587,434; *Chem. Abstracts*, **42,** 619 (1948).
2. De Smet and Schwarz, *Natuurw. Tijdschr.*, **21,** 271 (1940); *Chem. Abstracts*, **34,** 3603 (1940).
3. Schwarz and De Smet, Brit. Pat. 615,205; *Chem. Abstracts*, **43,** 8293 (1949).
4. Van Dormael and Nys, *Chim. & ind.* (*Paris*), **63,** No. 3 bis, 483 (1950); *Chem. Abstracts*, **47,** 57 (1953).
5. Ballard, Melstrom and Smith, "The Chemistry of β-Lactams," in Clarke *et al.*, *The Chemistry of Penicillin*, Princeton University Press, Princeton, N. J., 1949, p. 973.

A-269. 5*H*-Thiazolo[3,2-*a*]quinoline*

For some reason *Chemical Abstracts* have failed to include this ring system in their indices, although the references have been abstracted.

Duffin and Kendall[1] found that acids such as I were dehydrated to yellow products by heating in acetic or propionic anhydride. Similar products resulted when substituents were present upon the methylene carbon atom of the thioacetic acid group, or in positions 3 to 7 (but not 8) of the quinoline nucleus. Esters or amides of I, the

4-quinolyl isomer of I or β-(2-quinolylthio)-propionic acid did not yield anhydro compounds. These facts are compatible with the assignment to the yellow products of a pentacyclic structure involving the ring nitrogen atom. Therefore, it was thought that the products were best represented by a resonance hybrid of the meso ionic structure II and its seven dipolar forms. Knott[2] suggests that the yellow

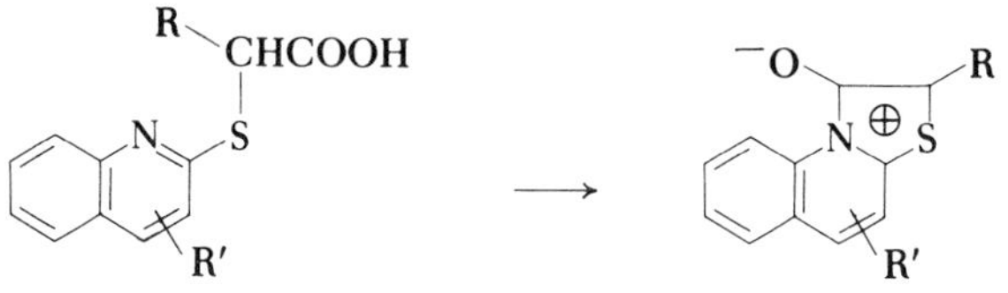

(I) (II)

color of these compounds may be explained by involvement of the *d*-orbital electrons and expansion of the sulfur octet giving a resonance hybrid of structures III–IV. Spectroscopic studies[3] on II (R = H, R′ = 5-CH_3) seem to indicate that structure V makes an important contribution to the hybrid (see also Baker and Ollis[5]).

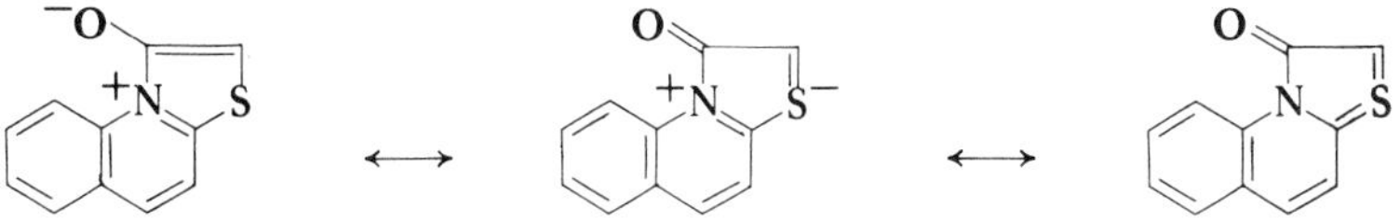

(III) (IV) (V)

The compounds of type II decompose when heated above their melting points and are hydrolyzed to I by hot 50% sulfuric acid. However, they show different degrees of hydrolytic stability; those in which R′ = H and R = CH_3 or C_2H_5, are cleaved by hot water, whereas II in which R′ = 5-CH_3 and R = H, is stable to hot concentrated hydrochloric acid.

A number of dyes of this class (such as VI), useful for sensitizing photographic emulsions, have been patented.[4]

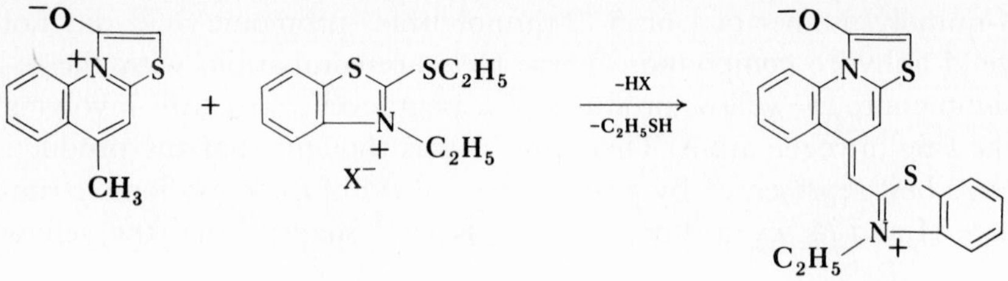

$$\xrightarrow[-C_2H_5SH]{-HX}$$

(VI)

TABLE I. Derivatives of II

R	R′	Properties	Refs.
H	H	Yel., m. 194°.	1
CH_3	H	Or., m. 135–6°	1
H	5-CH_3	Yel., m. 227°. λ_{max} (in MeOH) 250, 292, 325 and 445 mμ with log ε 4.14, 3.81, 3.62 and 4.02, respectively.	1,3
H	4,5-$(CH_3)_2$	Yel., m. 223°.	1
C_2H_5	H	Or., m. 139°.	1

TABLE II. Derivatives of [structure: CH–R]

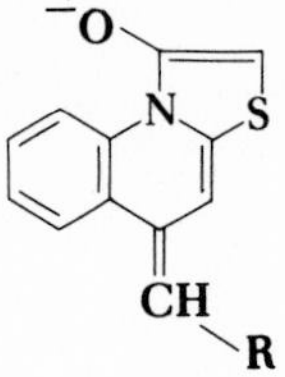

R	Properties	Refs.
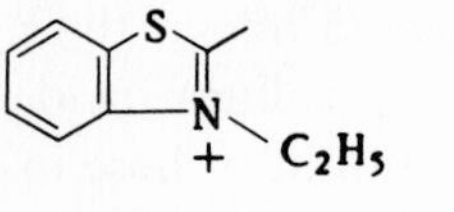 3-ethylbenzothiazolium-2-yl (N^+–C_2H_5)	Dk. with rose reflex, m. 225–6° d.	4
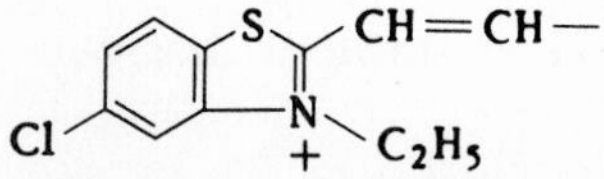 5-Cl-3-ethylbenzothiazolium-2-yl–CH=CH– (N^+–C_2H_5)	Dk., m. 237–8° d.	4
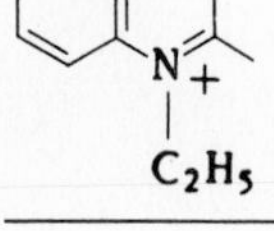 1-ethylquinolinium-2-yl (N^+–C_2H_5)	Dk., m. 174–7° d.	4

TABLE II (*continued*)

R	Properties	Refs.
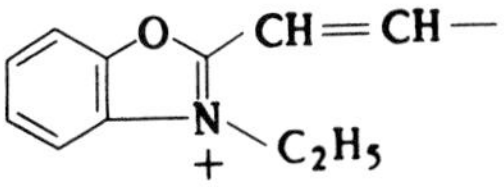 O, CH=CH—, $\overset{+}{N}$, C_2H_5	Grn., m. 238–40° d.	4
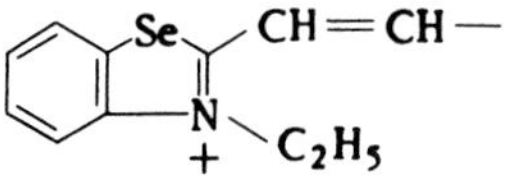 Se, CH=CH—, $\overset{+}{N}$, C_2H_5	Dk., m. 180–2° d.	4
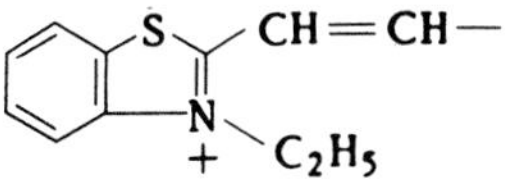 S, CH=CH—, $\overset{+}{N}$, C_2H_5	Dk. grn., m. 244–5° d.	4
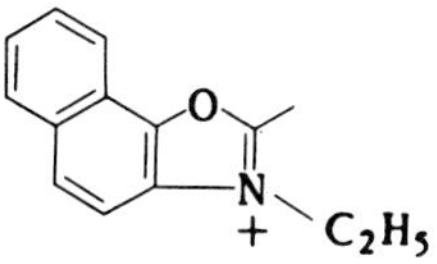 O, $\overset{+}{N}$, C_2H_5	Dk. brn., m. 276–7° d.	4
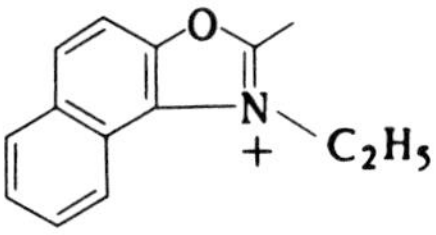 O, $\overset{+}{N}$, C_2H_5	Dk. grn., m. 261–2°.	4
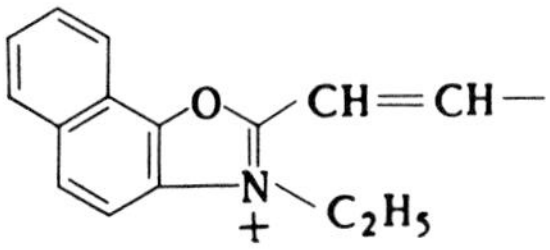 O, CH=CH—, $\overset{+}{N}$, C_2H_5	Dk., m. 205–7° d.	4
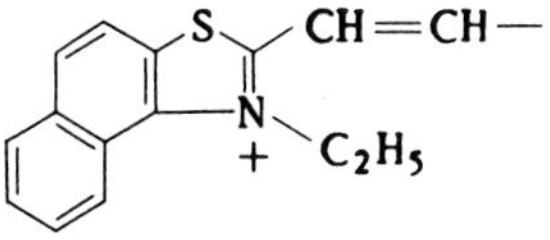 S, CH=CH—, $\overset{+}{N}$, C_2H_5	Dk., m. 209–10° d.	4
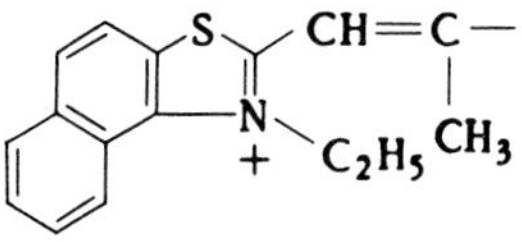 S, CH=C(CH_3)—, $\overset{+}{N}$, C_2H_5	Dk., m. 192–4° d.	4
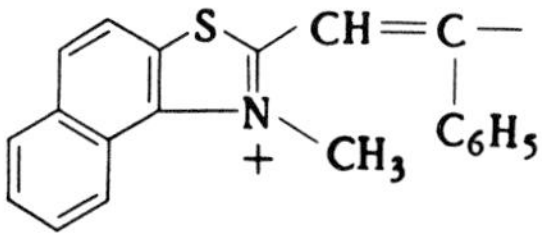 S, CH=C(C_6H_5)—, $\overset{+}{N}$, CH_3	Dk., m. 223–4°.	4

References

1. Duffin and Kendall, *J. Chem. Soc.*, **1951,** 734.
2. Knott, *J. Chem. Soc.*, **1955,** 916.
3. Knott, *J. Chem. Soc.*, **1955,** 937.
4. Brooker and Van Lare, U. S. Pat. 2,748,115.
5. Baker and Ollis, *Quart. Rev.*, **11,** 15 (1957).

A-270. 8*H*-Naphtho[2,1-*d*]pyrido-[2,1-*b*]thiazole

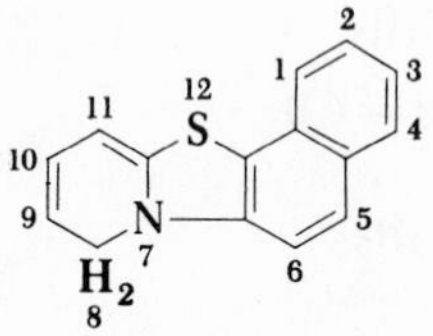

The reaction of I with trimethylene bromide yielded[1] II (m. ~200°), which was used[2,3] in the preparation of cyanine dyes. See Section A-84.

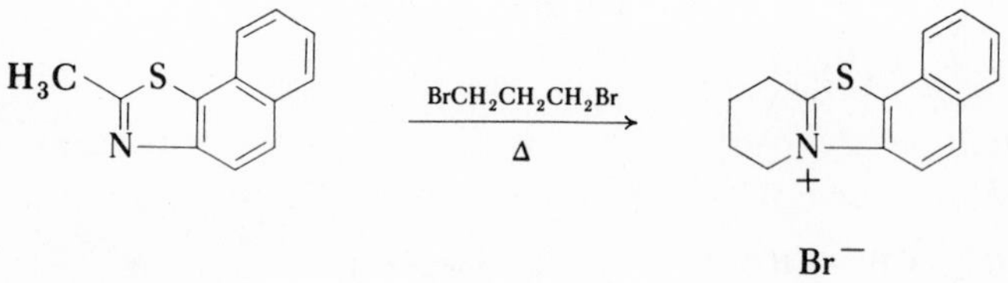

$$\xrightarrow[\Delta]{BrCH_2CH_2CH_2Br}$$

(I) (II)

References

1. Schwarz and De Smet, Brit. Pat. 587,434; *Chem. Abstracts*, **42,** 619 (1948).
2. De Smet and Schwarz, *Natuurw. Tijdschr.*, **21,** 271 (1940); *Chem. Abstracts*, **34,** 3603 (1940).
3. Schwarz and De Smet, Brit. Pat. 615,205; *Chem. Abstracts*, **43,** 8293 (1949).

A-271. Imidazo[1,2-*a*]pyridine. R.I. 765

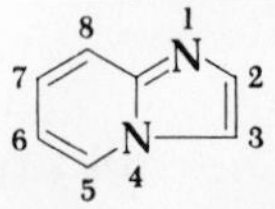

Although comparatively new, this nucleus has accumulated many alternative names: *1,4-imidazopyridine* (used by *Chemical Abstracts* from 1917 to 1936), *pyrimidazole*, *pyridino(1′:2′-1:2)glyoxaline*, *3a-azaindole*, 9-

azaindolenine, *1,3a-diazaindene* and *3,7a-diazaindene*. A numbering system (I) slightly different from that above was suggested by Tschitschi-

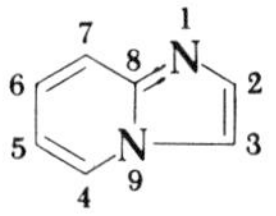

(I)

babin, and is still encountered in some of the Russian papers. A concise review of this ring system has recently appeared.[8]

The earliest-reported examples of this nucleus were 2(3*H*)-oxo derivatives, but these compounds and their history will be discussed later (v.i.), as will the 3(2*H*)-oxo compounds and the 2- and 3-amino compounds and their derivatives.

I. Imidazo[1,2-a]pyridines

In 1925, Tschitschibabin[1] prepared III by treating 2-aminopyridine with bromoacetaldehyde in a sealed tube at 150–200°. However, these drastic conditions are not necessary, and high yields of III are obtained[2] by reacting II with chloro- or bromoacetaldehyde and sodium bicarbonate in aqueous-alcoholic solution. Compound III has also been obtained[3] (in 79% yield) by oxidizing the 2,3-dihydro derivative[4] with alkaline potassium ferricyanide. Pure III is a colorless liquid with an odor similar to that of other cyclic nitrogen bases, and it turns dark upon exposure to light and air. The ultraviolet spectra of III and certain of its simple derivatives have been discussed[5] and compared[3] with those of related polyazaindenes.

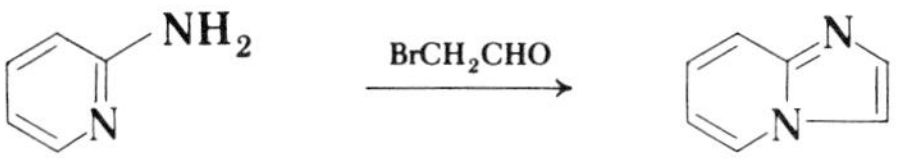

$BrCH_2CHO$

(II) (III)

Imidazo[1,2-*a*]pyridine might reasonably be expected to behave as an aromatic system like pyrrocoline and similar heterocyclic nuclei. Resonance forms of types IIIa and (especially) IIIb probably make the major contributions to the resonance hybrid, with lesser contributions from forms not involving an intact pyridinium ring.

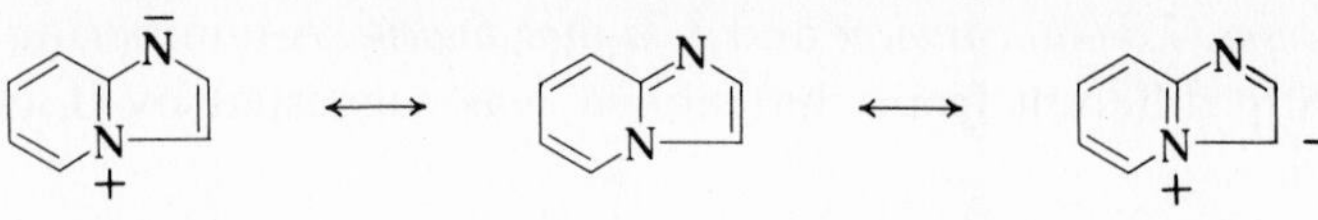

(IIIa) ⟷ (III) ⟷ (IIIb)

Electrophilic attack might be predicted, therefore, to occur first in the 3-position. Such limited experimental data as are available, support this hypothesis. Although no evidence is available concerning III itself, the 2-alkyl, 2-acyl and 2-aryl derivatives readily give 3-substituted products (see Table I, pp. 470–479).

The reaction of II with chloroacetone yielded[1] a methyl homolog of III, which Tschitschibabin[6] decided was the 2-methyl isomer. The reaction of II with an α-halocarbonyl compound could, a priori, lead either to 2- or 3-substituted imidazo[1,2-*a*]pyridines via intermediates, respectively, of type IV or V. Considerable evidence was available[6] that the ring nitrogen of II was the site of attack by alkyl, benzyl and phenacyl halides, although acyl halides react only with the amino group. Therefore, the numerous compounds prepared by the reaction of II with α-haloaldehydes, α-haloketones, etc., were generally accorded the 2-substituted structure.

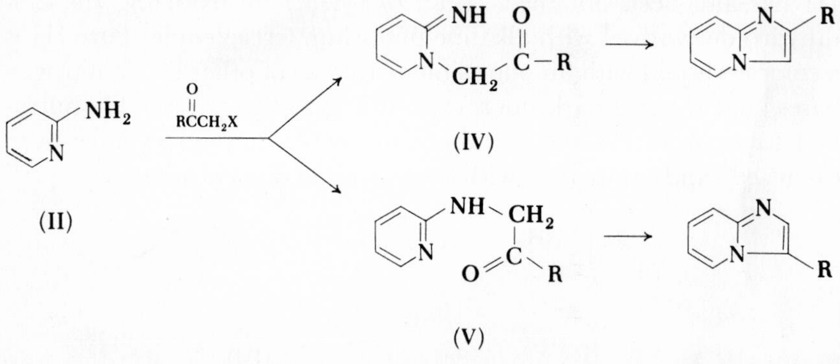

(II) —$RCOCH_2X$→ (IV) → 2-R; (V) → 3-R

However, Campbell and McCall[5] offered evidence that an intermediate of type V was formed to the extent of 30% (no evidence upon the nature of the other 70%) in the reaction of II with 2-chlorocyclohexanone. Also, since Djerassi and Pettit[7] treated the lithium derivative of II with phenacyl bromide and obtained the same phenylimidazo[1,2-*a*]pyridine formed from II and phenacyl bromide, they argued that the product must be the 3-phenyl isomer formed via V (R = C_6H_5).

The structure of these products, however, was demonstrated conclusively by Kröhnke, Kickhöfen and Thoma.[9] They prepared 2-phenylimidazo[1,2-*a*]pyridine both from VI and from 2-acetaminopyridine. In repeating the reaction of the lithium derivative of II

(VI)

with phenacyl bromide, they found that water formed during cyclization of the intermediate V (R = C_6H_5) reacted with the lithium derivative liberating II, which gave rise to the 2-phenylimidazo[1,2-*a*]pyridine obtained by Djerassi and Pettit. The 2-phenyl compound was also obtained[10] from the reaction of II with dypnone.

(II)

There is thus little doubt that products of this general reaction are 2-substituted imidazo[1,2-*a*]pyridines. A slight modification of this synthesis was introduced by Takahashi and Shibasaki,[11] who replaced the customary α-halocarbonyl compound by ethyl-1,2-dichlorethyl ether.

A careful study[13,14] of the reactions of VII (obtained by treating 2-acylaminopyridines with α-haloketones) revealed that products of structure VIII are formed in dilute hydrobromic acid, whereas in

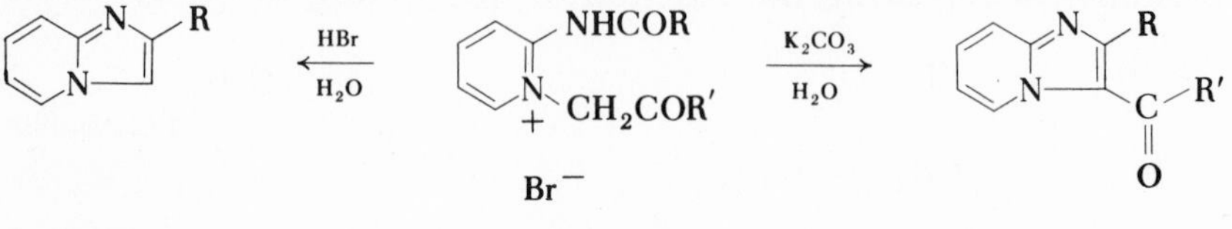

(VIII) (VII) (IX)

dilute potassium carbonate solution, IX is produced. The position of the acyl group in IX was demonstrated[14] by preparing XII both from X and from XI.

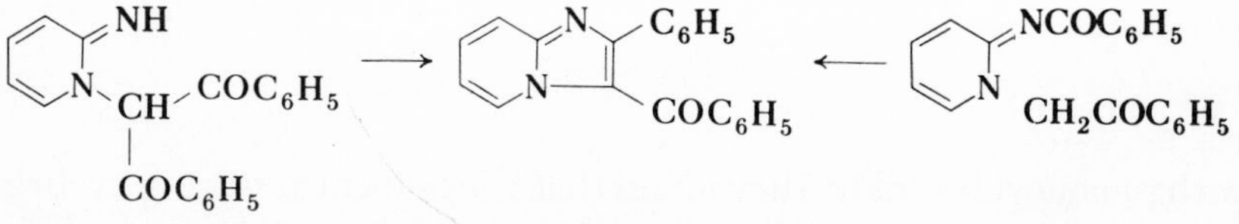

(X) (XII) (XI)

A very similar synthesis of 3-arylimidazo[1,2-*a*]pyridines (XIV) also was found by Kröhnke and Kickhöfen.[15] The intermediate 1-benzylacylimino-2-pyridones (XIII) are more difficult to cyclize than the 1-phenacyl analogs (VII) and more vigorous conditions must be employed.

The great majority of the compounds listed in Table I were prepared by the reaction of α-halocarbonyl compounds with 2-aminopyridines. Yields are generally very good, and it is probable that improvements could often be effected if the reaction conditions chosen were less vigorous. Thus a quantitative yield of 2-phenylimidazo-[1,2-*a*]pyridine was easily obtained[16,17] by treating an alcoholic solution of II with phenacyl bromide in the presence of sodium bicarbonate. The failure of 2,6-diaminopyridine to undergo the Tschitschibabin reaction has been reported.[40]

Nitrosation of the 2-phenyl compound was shown[18] to occur in the 3-position, and the nitroso group was readily displaced by bromine, giving the same 3-bromo-2-phenyl compound obtained by

NHCOR

N

NCOR

N

CH_2

R'

NH_2

N

(II)

(XIII)

$(RCO)_2O/RCOOK$

NH

N

CH_2

R'

$(RCO)_2O$

RCOOK

N

R

N

R'

(XIV)

direct bromination of 2-phenylimidazo[1,2-*a*]pyridine. Removal of the bromine from the 3-position was easily accomplished by treatment with zinc and acid. This lability of substituents in the 3-position also occurs in the case of related systems, e.g., pyrrocoline.

Considerable study was devoted by Russian workers to the reactions of α- and α'-aminonicotines with α-halocarbonyl compounds. The reaction of α-aminonicotine (XV) with bromopyruvic ester gave[19] a product, which is undoubtedly XVI, and nitration of this yielded a derivative which must be XVII, since upon oxidation,

CH_3N

NH_2

N

$BrCH_2COCO_2C_2H_5$

CH_3N

N

$COOC_2H_5$

N

HNO_3

(XV)

(XVI)

CH_3N

N

$COOC_2H_5$

N

NO_2

(XVII)

or treatment with alcoholic caustic, it underwent scission to reform XV. The 2-methyl analog of XVI behaved similarly.[20]

Imidazo[1,2-*a*]pyridines react with variable ease, depending upon the substituents, with haloketones (especially phenacyl bromide) to give quaternary salts[6,14] (e.g., XVIII). When heated with alcoholic caustic, XVIII decomposes[14] to a 1-methylimidazo[1,2-*a*]pyridinium salt and benzoic acid, while treatment of XVIII with *p*-nitrosodimethylaniline and sodium cyanide gives rise[14] to products of type XIX. Strong aqueous caustic converts XVIII into colored "enol-betaines" having contributions to the resonance hybrid by structures such as XXa–XXc. In the preparation of enol-betaines from salts of

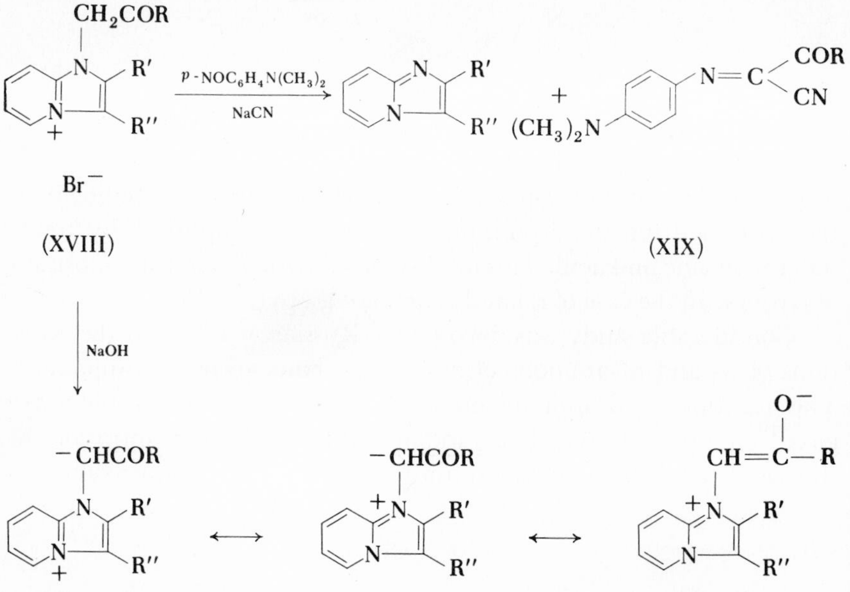

(XVIII) (XIX)

(XXa) (XXb) (XXc)

structure XXI, a further reaction occurs[14] and colored products are formed by loss of water. It is difficult to draw a satisfactory structure for these compounds, although forms XXIIa–XXIId, *inter alia*, are probably contributors to the resonance hybrid.

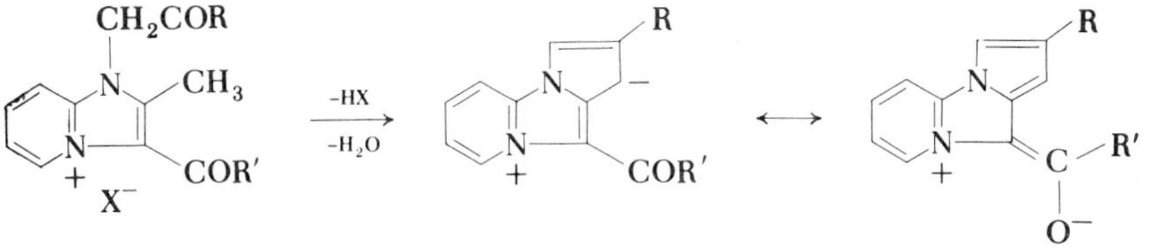

(XXI) (XXIIa) (XXIIb)

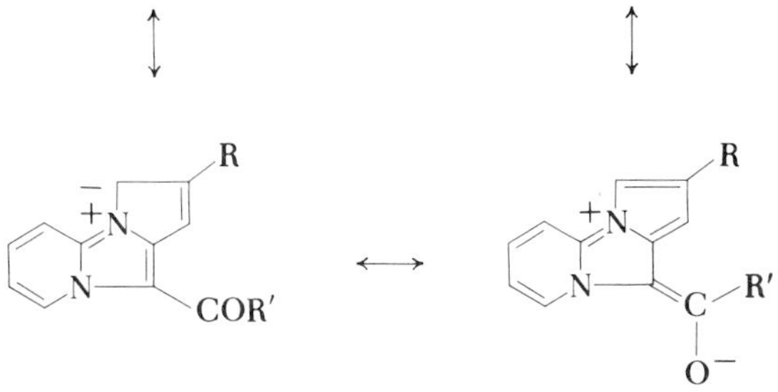

(XXIIc) (XXIId)

Hydroxyethylaminopyridines (XXIII, obtained by treating 2-chloropyridines with ethanolamine[4] or 2-aminopyridines with ethylene chlorohydrin[21]) were cyclized, either thermally,[21] or by treatment with thionyl chloride and alkali,[4,22] to 2,3-dihydroimidazo-[1,2-*a*]pyridines (XXIV).

(XXIII) (XXIV)

The only synthesis of an imidazo[1,2-*a*]pyridine which commences with an imidazole derivative and constructs the pyridine ring, was reported by Diels and Alder.[23] Condensation of 1,2-dimethylimidazole with methyl acetylenedicarboxylate gave XXV, which yielded XXVI when treated with bromine. Hot acetic acid decomposed XXV to XXVIII, possibly via XXVII.

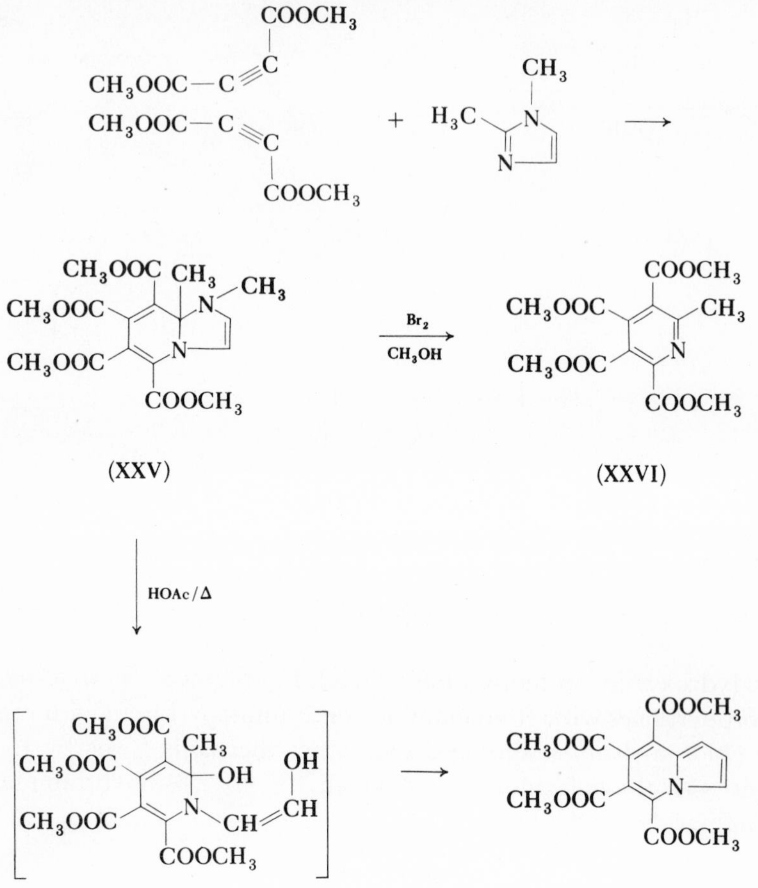

$COOCH_3$
$CH_3OOC—C≡C$
$CH_3OOC—C≡C$
$COOCH_3$
+ H_3C CH_3 N N →

CH_3OOC CH_3 CH_3
CH_3OOC N
CH_3OOC N
$COOCH_3$

Br_2 / CH_3OH →

$COOCH_3$
CH_3OOC CH_3
CH_3OOC N
$COOCH_3$

(XXV) (XXVI)

HOAc/Δ ↓

CH_3OOC CH_3
CH_3OOC OH OH
CH_3OOC N CH=CH
$COOCH_3$

→

$COOCH_3$
CH_3OOC
CH_3OOC N
$COOCH_3$

(XXVII) (XXVIII)

Hydrogenation of 2-methylimidazo[1,2-*a*]pyridine in acetic acid over a platinum catalyst afforded[24] a monobasic product containing no >NH group, thought to be the 5,6,7,8-tetrahydro-2-methyl compound. However, reduction[12] of XXIX (prepared from II and α-bromoacrylic acid) in ethanol over Adams catalyst gave the hexahydro compound XXX. Ultraviolet spectra, apparently determined in neither case, should indicate clearly the structure of these products.

CH_3 $\xrightarrow[\text{HOAc}]{H_2/Pt}$ CH_3

H COOH $\xrightarrow[C_2H_5OH]{H_2/PtO}$ H COOH

Br^- Br^-

(XXIX) (XXX)

Several imidazo[1,2-*a*]pyridines have been examined for physiological activity.[4,22,25-27] Pyrrolidyl derivatives related to XXVI have been reported to stimulate respiration[27] and to have powerful anesthetic activity.[26] Various simple imidazo[1,2-*a*]pyridines have been claimed[28] of value as optical bleaches for textile fibers.

TABLE I. Imidazo[1,2-*a*]pyridines

Empirical formula	Substituents or structure	Properties and comments	Refs.
$C_7H_5N_3O_2$	6-Nitro-	Yel., m. 225°.	11
$C_7H_6N_2$	Unsubstituted	b_{27} 153–5°, b_3 114–5°. HBr salt, m. 186.4–7.0°. Picrate, 205° (199–200° d.). Methiodide, m. 207°.	1–3
$C_7H_6BrN_3O_2$	8-Bromo-2,3-dihydro-6-nitro-	Or.-yel., m. 222° d.	4
$C_7H_7N_3$	2-Amino-	m. 73–83°. Picrate, m. 200° d. Acetyl deriv., m. 230°.	29
	3-Amino-	Acetyl deriv., m. 199°. Benzoyl deriv., m. 170°. HCl salt of benzoyl deriv., m. 295–6°. Picrate of benzoyl deriv., m. 264°. $C_6H_5SO_2$ deriv., m. 212°. Bis-($C_6H_5SO_2$) deriv., m. 165°.	29
	6-Amino-	Benzoyl deriv., m. 193–5°.	11
$C_7H_7N_3O_2$	2,3-Dihydro-6-nitro-	Or.-yel., m. 258° d. HCl salt, m. >280°. Methiodide, m. 246–7°.	4,22
$C_7H_8N_2$	2,3-Dihydro-	b_{20} 140–50°, m. 36–8°, or as monohydrate, 64–5°. Picrate, m. 213°. Methiodide, yel., m. 169–70°.	3,4,21, 22
$C_8H_6Br_2N_2$	6,8-Dibromo-2-methyl-	m. 144–5°. HBr salt, m. >300°.	5
$C_8H_7BrN_2$	6-Bromo-2-methyl-	m. 102–3°. HBr salt, m. 210–20°. Picrate, m. 226–8°.	5,30
$C_8H_7IN_2$	6-Iodo-2-methyl-	Yel., m. 151–2°.	11
$C_8H_7N_3O_2$	2-Methyl-6-nitro-	Yel., m. 197–9° (161°?) d. HBr salt, m. >300°. Picrate, m. 181–4° d.	5,30

$C_8H_8N_2$	2-Methyl-	b_{760} 262–3°, $b_{6.5}$ 117–9°, b_{15} 134–6°; m. 45–6°; d_0^0 1.1263, $d_0^{23.5}$ 1.1105. HBr salt, m. 197–8° (195°). Perchlorate, m. 157°. Picrate, m. 198–200°. Styphnate, d. 238°. Methiodide, m. 190–2°. $HgCl_2$ complex, m. 166.5°. Chloroplatinate, red, d. 225–6°.	1,5,6,11, 14,24, 31
	8-Methyl-	b_{12} 112–7°.	32,33
$C_8H_8N_2O_2$	2-Carboxy-2,3-dihydro-	m. 261–2° d. HBr salt, m. 203–4°.	12
$C_8H_9N_3$	3-Methylamino-	Benzyl iodide salt, yel., m. 156°.	29
	6-Amino-2-methyl-	m. 77°. Acetyl deriv., m. 181°.	30
$C_8H_9N_3O_2$	2,3-Dihydro-3-methyl-6-nitro-	Or.-yel., m. 185°.	4
$C_8H_{12}N_2$	5,6,7,8-Tetrahydro-2-methyl- (Probable structure)	b_5 107–10°. Picrate, m. 162°. Chloroaurate, m. 142–3°. Chloroplatinate, d. 204–6°. Methiodide, m. 140–2°. *N*-Methyl-chloroplatinate, d. 211–2°.	24
$C_8H_{12}N_2O_2$	2-Carboxy-2,3,5,6,7,8-hexahydro-	HBr salt, m. 183–5°.	12
$C_9H_8N_2O$	3-Acetyl-	m. 98–9°.	14
$C_9H_8N_2O_2$	3-Carboxy-2-methyl-	d. 185°.	31
$C_9H_{10}N_2$	2,8-Dimethyl-	m. 42–5°. HBr salt, m. 248–50°. Picrate, m. 192–4°.	5
$C_9H_{11}ClN_3O_2$	1-(2-Chloroethyl)-2,3-dihydro-6-nitro-	Chloride monohydrate, m. 82–4°.	22
$C_9H_{11}BrN_2$	1-(2-Bromoethyl)-2,3-dihydro-	Bromide, m. 186–9°.	22
$C_9H_{12}N_3O_3$	2,3-Dihydro-1-(2-hydroxyethyl)-6-nitro-	Chloride, m. 204–5°.	22
$C_{10}H_{10}N_2O$	3-Acetyl-2-methyl-	m. 111°. Methiodide, m. 241.2°.	14
$C_{10}H_{10}N_2O_2$	2-Carbethoxy-	HBr salt, m. 155–7°. Picrate, m. 162–3°.	2

(*continued*)

TABLE I. Imidazo[1,2-*a*]pyridines (*continued*)

Empirical formula	Substituents or structure	Properties and comments	Refs.
$C_{10}H_{12}N_4S$	Imidazo[1,2-a]pyridin-3-yl–$NH\overset{S}{\overset{\Vert}{C}}NHC_2H_5$	m. 206°.	72
$C_{11}H_7BrN_2S$	2-(5-Bromo-2-thienyl)-	Subl. 140°; m. 144°.	34
$C_{11}H_{10}N_2O_3$	2-Acetoxy-3-acetyl-	m. 198°.	35,36
$C_{11}H_{11}IN_2O_2$	3-Carbethoxy-6-iodo-2-methyl-	Yel., m. 134–5°.	11
$C_{11}H_{11}N_3O_4$	3-Carbethoxy-2-methyl-6-nitro-	Lt. yel., m. 150–1°.	37
$C_{11}H_{12}N_2O_2$	3-Carbethoxy-2-methyl-	Lt. yel., m. 64–5°.	37
$C_{11}H_{13}N_3O$	3-(*N*-Methylpropionamido)-	Benzyl iodide, m. 135°.	29
$C_{12}H_9BrN_2S$	2-(5-Bromo-2-thienyl)-7-methyl-	m. 158°.	34
$C_{12}H_9ClN_2S$	2-(5-Chloro-2-thienyl)-7-methyl-	m. 128°.	34
$C_{12}H_{10}N_2S$	7-Methyl-2-(2-thienyl)-	m. 129°. Picrate, d. ~189°. Nitroso deriv., or.	34
$C_{12}H_{15}N_3$	6-(1-Methyl-2-pyrrolidyl)-	b_4 160°. Picrate, m. 204–5°.	19,25
	8-(1-Methyl-2-pyrrolidyl)-	b_5 159°, m. 44–7°. HCl salt, d. 257°. Picrate, m. 240°.	19
$C_{13}H_8Cl_2N_2$	2-(3,4-Dichlorophenyl)-	m. 172°.	38
$C_{13}H_9BrN_2$	2-(4-Bromophenyl)-	m. 218°.	34
	3-Bromo-2-phenyl-	m. 89.5–90.5°. HBr salt, m. 252°. Nitrate, m. 129–30°.	18
$C_{13}H_9ClN_2$	2-(4-Chlorophenyl)-	Subl. 170°, m. 208°.	34
$C_{13}H_9FN_2$	2-(4-Fluorophenyl)-	m. 165–6°.	39
$C_{13}H_9IN_2$	2-(4-Iodophenyl)-	m. 227° (*in vac.*).	40
$C_{13}H_9N_3O$	3-Nitroso-2-phenyl-	Dimorphic. Lt. grn., m. 164°.	18

$C_{13}H_9N_3O_2$	2-(3-Nitrophenyl)-	Yel., m. 205°.	40,41
	2-(4-Nitrophenyl)-	Yel., m. 263–4° (261°).	41,42
$C_{13}H_{10}N_2$	2-Phenyl-	m. 135–6° (135.5°, 137.5°, 140°). HBr salt, m. 123° (122–3°, 129°), then resolidifies and remelts at 164–5°. Perchlorate, m. 168°. Sulfate, m. 190°. Oxalate, d. 195°. Picrate, m. 236–8°. Methiodide, m. 220–1° (214°). Complex (2:1) with phloroglucinol, m. 163–5°. 1-Nonyl perchlorate, m. 98–100°.	3,5,7,9, 10,14, 16–18, 21,25, 26,31, 40,44–46
	3-Phenyl-	b_8 198–200°, m. 97–8°. HBr salt, m. 195°. Picrate, m. 237–8° (236°).	9,26,47
$C_{13}H_{10}N_2O$	2-(3-Hydroxyphenyl)-	$b_{0.05}$ 245–50°, m. 266° (*in vac.*).	40
	3-Hydroxy-2-phenyl-	m. 81.5–2.0°.	40
$C_{13}H_{10}N_2O_2$	2-(3,4-Dihydroxy-phenyl)-	m. 255°. HCl salt, m. >285°. Picrate, m. 137° d.	48
$C_{13}H_{11}N_3$	2-(3-Aminophenyl)-	m. 185°. Acetyl deriv., m. 88–92°.	40,41
	2-(4-Aminophenyl)-	m. 216°. HCl salt, m. >300°. Acetyl deriv., m. 248°.	41–43
$C_{13}H_{14}N_2O_2$	2-(*dl*-Pilopyl)-	HCl salt, oily. Picrate, m. 167–8°.	49
$C_{13}H_{14}N_4O_4$	2-Carboxy-8-(1-methyl-2-pyrrolidyl)-3-nitro-	m. 96–7°.	19
$C_{13}H_{16}N_3O_2$	2-Methyl-8-(1-methyl-2-pyrrolidyl)-3-nitro-	m. 121°.	20
$C_{13}H_{16}N_4O$	2-Carboxamido-6-(1-methyl-2-pyrrolidyl)-	—	25
	2-Carboxamido-8-(1-methyl-2-pyrrolidyl)-	m. 225°. HCl salt, m. 244–5°.	19
$C_{13}H_{17}N_3$	2-Methyl-6-(1-methyl-2-pyrrolidyl)-	m. 70–1°. Picrate, m. 211°.	50
	2-Methyl-8-(1-methyl-2-pyrrolidyl)-	b_7 162–3°, b_{12} 178–81°; m. 86–7°. Picrate, m. 219–20°.	20,50

(*continued*)

TABLE I. Imidazo[1,2-*a*]pyridines (*continued*)

Empirical formula	Substituents or structure	Properties and comments	Refs.
$C_{14}H_9N_3$	2-(3-Cyanophenyl)-	m. 167° (vac.).	40
$C_{14}H_{10}N_2O$	3-Benzoyl-	m. 105°. Picrate, m. 224–6°. Oxime, m. 175°.	14
$C_{14}H_{10}N_2O_2$	2-Benzoxy-	m. 130°.	51,52
	2-(3-Carboxyphenyl)-	m. >350°.	40
	2-Carboxy-3-phenyl-	m. 201–2°. HBr salt, m. 246° d. HCl salt, m. 246° d. HCl salt, m. 225–7°. Picrate, m. 205–7°.	25,47
$C_{14}H_{10}Cl_2N_4$	3-(2,4-Dichlorphenylazo)-2-methyl-	Golden-yel., m. 149–50°.	2
$C_{14}H_{11}N_3$	3-Benzylideneamino-	m. 114°.	29
$C_{14}H_{11}N_3O_2$	2-Methyl-3-(4-nitrophenyl)-	m. 162–3°, strong yel. fluoresc. in U.V. HBr salt, m. 316–7°. Picrate, m. 250–2°. Methiodide, m. 246–8°.	15
$C_{14}H_{11}BrN_2$	2-(4-Bromophenyl)-7-methyl-	m. 210°.	34
$C_{14}H_{11}ClN_2$	2-(4-Chlorophenyl)-7-methyl-	Subl. 175°; m. 188°.	34
$C_{14}H_{11}FN_2$	2-(6-Fluoro-3-tolyl)-	m. 143°.	38
$C_{14}H_{11}ClN_2S$	2-(3-Chloro-4-methylthiophenyl)-	m. 179°.	53
$C_{14}H_{12}N_2$	2-Methyl-3-phenyl-	Oil. Picrate, m. 189–90°.	15
	8-Methyl-2-phenyl-	m. 108–10°. Picrate sinters at 210°, m. 240–1° d.	5
$C_{14}H_{12}N_2O$	2-(4-Methoxyphenyl)-	m. 139°.	38
$C_{14}H_{13}N_3$	3-Benzylamino-	m. 100°. Picrate, m. 184°.	29
$C_{14}H_{13}N_3O_2S$	3-*N*-Methylbenzenesulfonamido)-	Benzyl iodide, m. 201°.	29
$C_{14}H_{16}N_2O_2$	2-(*d*-Homopilopyl)-	HCl salt, m. 164–5.5°. Picrate, m. 178–80°.	49

	2-(*d*-Homoisopilopyl)-	HCl salt, m. 228–8.5°.	49
$C_{15}H_{12}N_2O$	3-Benzoyl-2-methyl-	m. 88°. HBr salt, m. 265°. Perchlorate, m. 259–61° d. Methiodide, m. 250–1°. Oxime, m. 222° d.	14
$C_{15}H_{13}N_3O_2$	2-Ethyl-3-(4-nitrophenyl)-	Pale yel., m. 158–9°. Strong yel. fluoresc. in U.V. HBr salt, m. 283°. Methiodide, m. 207–8°.	15
$C_{15}H_{13}BrN_2O$	2-(3-Bromo-4-methoxyphenyl)-	m. 160°.	38
$C_{15}H_{14}N_2$	7-Methyl-2-(*p*-tolyl)-	m. 166°.	34
	2-(3,4-Dimethylphenyl)-	m. 120°.	38
$C_{15}H_{14}N_2O$	2-(4-Ethoxyphenyl)-	m. 148°.	38
	2-(4-Methoxyphenyl)-7-methyl-	m. 160°.	38
	2-(4-Methoxyphenyl)-8-methyl-	m. 122°.	38
$C_{15}H_{14}N_2O_2$	2-(2,5-Dimethoxyphenyl)-	m. 117°.	38
$C_{15}H_{14}N_2S$	2-(4-Methylthiophenyl)-	m. 177°.	38
$C_{15}H_{18}N_4O_4$	2-Carbethoxy-8-(1-methyl-2-pyrrolidyl)-3-nitro-	m. 111–2°.	19
$C_{15}H_{19}N_3O_2$	2-Carbethoxy-6-(1-methyl-2-pyrrolidyl)-	b_6 235–7°, m. 154°. Picrate, d. 225°.	19,25
	2-Carbethoxy-8-(1-methyl-2-pyrrolidyl)-	b_6 233–4°, m. 96–7°. HBr salt, d. 220–2°. Picrate, m. 177–8°.	19
$C_{16}H_{15}N_3O$	3-Acetamido-2-benzyl-	m. 73–88°, resolidifies and remelts at 164°.	29
$C_{16}H_{15}ClN_2O$	2-(3-Chloro-4-ethoxyphenyl)-7-methyl-	m. 171°.	38
	2-(3-Chloro-4-ethoxyphenyl)-8-methyl-	m. 115°.	38
$C_{16}H_{16}N_2$	2-(2,5-Dimethylphenyl)-7-methyl-	m. 133°.	38
$C_{16}H_{16}N_2O$	2-(2-Methoxy-5-methylphenyl)-7-methyl-	m. 119°.	38
	2-(4-Ethoxyphenyl)-7-methyl-	m. 142°.	38
	2-(4-Ethoxyphenyl)-8-methyl-	m. 122°.	38

(*continued*)

TABLE I. Imidazo[1,2-*a*]pyridines (*continued*)

Empirical formula	Substituents or structure	Properties and comments	Refs.
$C_{16}H_{16}N_2O_2$	2-(2,4-Dimethoxyphenyl)-7-methyl-	m. 152°.	38
	2-(3,4-Dimethoxyphenyl)-8-methyl-	m. 167°.	38
$C_{16}H_{17}N_4O_7S$	2,3-Dihydro-1-[2-(4-methyl-3-nitrobenzene-sulfonoxy)-ethyl]-6-nitro-	Quaternary 4-methyl-3-nitrobenzene-sulfonate salt, monohydrate, m. 152-4°.	22
$C_{16}H_{20}N_4$	[CH_2– N N+]$_2$	Bromide, dihydrate, m. 318-20°.	22
$C_{16}H_{21}N_3O_2$	3-Carbethoxy-2-methyl-8-(1-methyl-2-pyrrolidyl)-	b_5 185-95°, m. 83-4°. Picrate, m. 198°. Di-HCl salt ("Ciperin").	20,27
$C_{17}H_{12}N_2$	2-(2-Naphthyl)-	m. 160°.	38
$C_{17}H_{19}N_4O_6S$	$CH_2CH_2OSO_2$–(C6H4)–$NHCOCH_3$; N; N+; O_2N	Chloride, dihydrate, m. 129-30°.	22
$C_{17}H_{20}N_2O_8$	5,6,7,8-Tetracarbomethoxy-1,8*a*-dihydro-1,8*a*-dimethyl-	Red, m. 163° d.	23
$C_{17}H_{22}N_4$	[CH_2– N N+]$_2$=CH_2	Bromide, dihydrate, m. 156-7°.	22

$C_{18}H_{14}N_2O$	2-(4-Methoxy-1-naphthyl)-	m. 131°.	38
	2-(6-Methoxy-2-naphthyl)-	m. 152°.	38
$C_{18}H_{14}N_2S$	2-(5-*p*-Tolyl-2-thienyl)-	m. 209°.	54
	2-(6-Methylthio-2-naphthyl)-	m. 189°.	55
$C_{18}H_{19}N_3$	6-(1-Methyl-2-pyrrolidyl)-2-phenyl-	—	25
	8-(1-Methyl-2-pyrrolidyl)-2-phenyl-	Yel. oil. Di-HBr salt, m. 272–4°. Picrate, m. 209.5–11°.	26,47,56
	8-(1-Methyl-2-pyrrolidyl)-3-phenyl-	b_5 213°, m. 94–5°. Picrate, m. 240°.	26,47
$C_{18}H_{20}N_2O$	2-(4-Methoxy-2-methyl-5-*i*-propylphenyl)-	m. 113°.	38
$C_{19}H_{12}N_2OS$	2-(2-Phenoxathiinyl)-	m. 185°.	57
$C_{19}H_{13}N_3O_2$	3-(4-Nitrophenyl)-2-phenyl-	Yel., m. 179–81°. Strong yel. fluoresc. in U.V. HBr salt, m. 290–2°. Methiodide, 209–10°.	15
$C_{19}H_{14}N_2$	2,3-Diphenyl-	m. 151.5–3°. HCl salt d. 151°.	17,21
	2-(4-Biphenylyl)-	Yel., m. 215–6°.	58
$C_{19}H_{16}N_4O_2S$	2-(3-Sulfanilamidophenyl)-	m. 210°. *N′*-Acetyl deriv. m. 250°.	41
	2-(4-Sulfanilamidophenyl)-	m. 252°. *N′*-Acetyl deriv., m. 265°.	41
$C_{19}H_{17}N_3$	2-[4-(2′,5′-Dimethyl-1-pyrryl)-phenyl]-	m. 126°. Picrate, m. 185°.	59
$C_{19}H_{19}N_3O_2$	2-Carboxy-8-(1-methyl-2-pyrrolidyl)-3-phenyl-	m. 216–7°. Di-HBr salt, m. 284° d.	47
$C_{19}H_{25}N_3O_2$	2-(*d*-Homoisopilopyl)-8-(1-methyl-2-pyrrolidyl)-	Nitrate, m. 123–5°.	49
	2-(*dl*-Homoisopilopyl)-8-(1-methyl-2-pyrrolidyl)-	HCl salt, oily. Nitrate, m. 132–3°.	49
	2-(*d*-Homopilopyl)-6-(1-methyl-2-pyrrolidyl)-	Picrate, m. 99–103°.	49
	2-(*d*-Homopilopyl)-8-(1-methyl-2-pyrrolidyl)-	HCl and HNO_3 salts, oily. Picrate, m. 93–7°.	49
$C_{20}H_{14}N_2O$	3-Benzoyl-2-phenyl-	m. 132°. HBr salt, m. 241°. Methiodide, m. ~236°.	14
$C_{20}H_{14}N_2O_2$	2-(2-Methoxy-3-dibenzofuranyl)-	HBr salt, yel., m. 310°.	60

(continued)

TABLE I. Imidazo[1,2-*a*]pyridines (*continued*)

Empirical formula	Substituents or structure	Properties and comments	Refs.
$C_{20}H_{15}N_3O_2$	2-Benzyl-3-(4-nitrophenyl)-	m. 218–9°.	15
$C_{20}H_{16}N_2$	2-(4′-Methyl-4-biphenylyl)-	m. 241°.	58
	2-(4-Biphenylyl)-7-methyl-	Yel., d. >210°, m. 217°.	58
	2-(4-Biphenylyl)-8-methyl-	m. 199°.	38
$C_{20}H_{16}N_2O$	2-(4′-Methoxy-4-biphenylyl)-	m. 200°.	61
$C_{21}H_{14}N_2O_3$	2-Benzoxy-3-benzoyl-	m. 171–3°.	51,52
$C_{21}H_{16}N_2$	2-(2-Fluorenyl)-7-methyl-	m. 229°.	38
$C_{21}H_{16}N_2O$	[structure: imidazo[1,2-a]pyridinium, N-substituent CH=C(C$_6$H$_5$)O$^-$, 2-C$_6$H$_5$]	Or., m. 158°. HBr salt.	6,14
$C_{21}H_{18}N_2$	2-[4-(2-phenylethyl)-phenyl]-	m. 139°.	38
$C_{21}H_{19}N_3$	3-Dibenzylamino-	Picrate, m. 154°.	29
$C_{22}H_{16}N_2O_2$	[structure: imidazo[1,2-a]pyridinium, N-substituent CH=C(O$^-$)—C$_6$H$_5$, 3-COC$_6$H$_5$]	Red, m. 108–10° d. HBr salt, m. 255–6°. HClO$_4$ salt, m. 200–1°.	14

$C_{22}H_{17}N_3O_3$	$CH=C(O^-)-C_6H_5$; N; CH_3; N^+; NO_2	Or., m. 143–5°.	15
$C_{23}H_{19}N_2O_2$	$CH_2COC_6H_5$; N; CH_3; COC_6H_5; N^+	Bromide, m. 262°.	14
$C_{25}H_{28}N_4O_8S_2$	$CH_2CH_2OSO_2C_6H_4NHCOCH_3$; N; N^+; $^-OSO_2C_6H_4NHCOCH_3$	Monohydrate, m. 178–80°.	22
$C_{27}H_{20}N_2$	2-(7-Benzyl-2-fluorenyl)-	d. ~191°. Red color with H_2SO_4.	62
$C_{28}H_{20}N_2O_2$	$CH=C(O^-)-C_6H_5$; N; C_6H_5; COC_6H_5; N^+	Yel., m. 145°. HBr salt, m. 223–4°.	14
$C_{28}H_{35}N_2O_2$	2-(Carbomethoxy-6-dehydroabietyl)-	m. 206°. HBr salt, m. 232° d.	63

II. Imidazo[1,2-a]pyridin-2(3H)-ones

These derivatives are sufficiently numerous to merit special consideration. The first example of the imidazo[1,2-*a*]pyridine ring system was of this group, since, as was noted by Tschitschibabin,[51] the product obtained by Sucharda[64] from the condensation of chloroacetic acid with α-aminonicotinic acid, undoubtedly has structure XXXI. Sucharda, however, was unaware of the correct structure of his product.

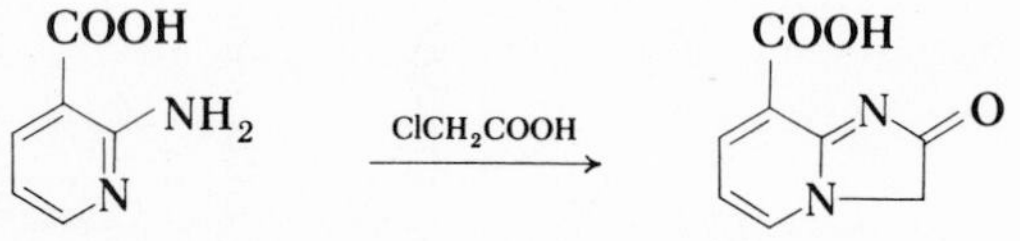

COOH
NH_2
N
$ClCH_2COOH$
COOH
N
O
N

(XXXI)

In 1924 Reindel described[52] his efforts to make a pyridine analog of indigo by oxidizing the condensation product of 2-aminopyridine (II) and chloroacetic acid. This product could have one of structures XXXIII, XXXV or XXXVI. Reindel believed the product to have structure XXXV, while Finger and Kraft[65] preferred structure XXXVI. However, it was shown conclusively by Tschitschibabin[51] that the final product obtained from the reaction of

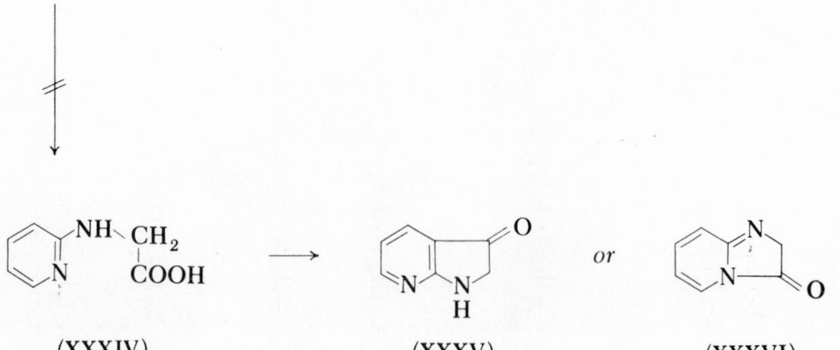

NH_2
N
NH
N
CH_2COOH
N
O
N

(II) (XXXII) (XXXIII)

NH CH_2
N
COOH
O
N
N
H
or
N
N
O

(XXXIV) (XXXV) (XXXVI)

II with haloacetic acids, halides or esters has, in each case, structure XXXIII. This was accomplished by showing that decarboxylation of the intermediate glycine yielded 1-methyl-2-pyridonimine instead of 2-methylaminopyridine. Thus the glycine must have structure XXXII rather than XXXIV. Also, it was shown[66] that the reaction of 2-(4-aminobenzenesulfonamido)-pyridine ("Sulfapyridine") with chloroacetic ester yields XXXIII.

Compound XXXIII is amphoteric, giving water-soluble salts with either mineral acids or with strong bases. Benzoylation of XXXIII under Schotten-Baumann conditions gave[51,52] the alkali-soluble compound XXXVII, while heating XXXIII with benzoyl chloride in pyridine gave XXXVIII. Each, upon further treatment, gave XXXIX. Similarly, heating XXXIII with acetic anhydride yielded[35] a diacetyl derivative (analogous to XXXIX) which

N O COC$_6$H$_5$ (XXXVII) N OCOC$_6$H$_5$ (XXXVIII) N OCOC$_6$H$_5$ COC$_6$H$_5$ (XXXIX)

was readily hydrolyzed to a monoacetyl compound similar to XXXVII.

Nitrosation of XXXIII occurs[35,51] in the 3-position, and the resulting yellow nitroso derivative yields red acetyl and benzoyl derivatives, which might have structure XL, XLI or XLII. Examination[2] of the infrared spectrum of the acetyl derivative shows it to have structure XL (R = CH_3).

N O C—R O N O (XL) N OCR NO (XLI) N O COR NO (XLII)

Bromination of XXXIII occurs in the 3-position to give[67] a mono- and a dibromo derivative, the latter also obtainable by brominating 3-nitrosoimidazo[1,2-*a*]pyridin-2(3*H*)-one. Replacement of the two bromine atoms in the 3-position by aniline has been accomplished,[67] but efforts[67-69] to hydrolyze any of these derivatives to imidazo[1,2-*a*]pyridin-2,3-dione, or to obtain the dione from II and ethyloxalyl chloride[67] were uniformly unsuccessful.

Aromatic aldehydes[69,70] (but not acetaldehyde or phenylacetaldehyde) condense with XXXVIII to yield products of type XLIII, which (where Ar = C_6H_5 or *o*-C_6H_4OH) disproportionate to XLIV (which forms a dibenzoyl derivative under Schotten-Baumann conditions). While the exocyclic double bond in XLIII does not add bromine, it may be hydrogenated over a platinum catalyst.[69] Derivatives of structure XLIII (in which Ar represents a *p*-dialkylaminophenyl group) form deeply colored salts probably having structure XLV. With acenaphthoquinone or with isatins, XXXIII forms red, vattable 1:1 or 2:1 derivatives of type XLVI (R = OH or an imidazo[1,2-*a*]pyrid-2(3*H*)-on-3-yl group).

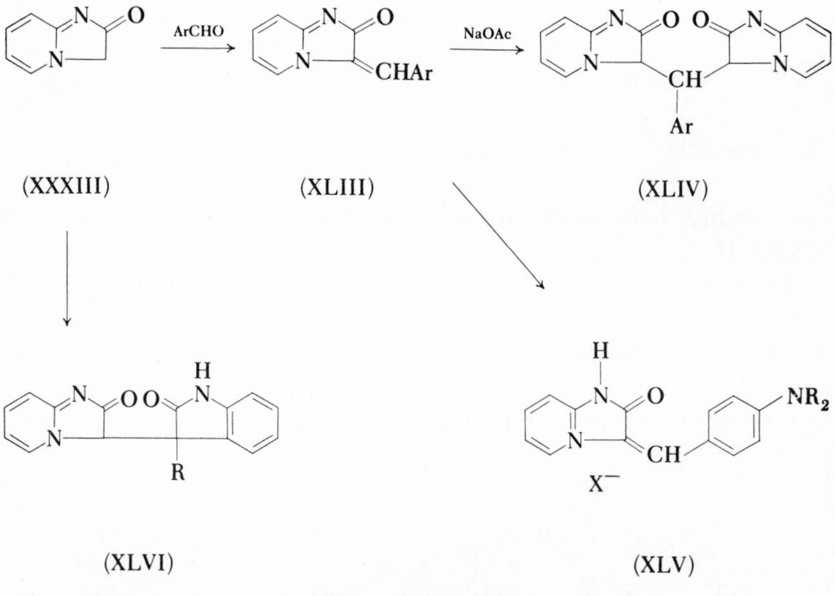

ArCHO NaOAc

(XXXIII) (XLIII) (XLIV)

(XLVI) (XLV)

The magenta compound XLVII results from the condensation of *p*-nitrosodimethylaniline with 2-acetoacetylaminopyridine,[71] or with XXXIII[67] or with the 3-benzal, 3-acetyl or 3,3-dibromo derivatives[36] of XXXIII. The facile displacement of these groups and the previously mentioned replacement of the 3-nitroso group by halogen, recall the lability of substituents in the 3-position of

VIII and of pyrrocoline (see Section A-183). Blue-black salts of structure XLVIII are formed[36] from XLVII with acids or alkyl halides. Colored azo dyes are obtained[2] by coupling diazonium compounds into the 3-position of XXXIII.

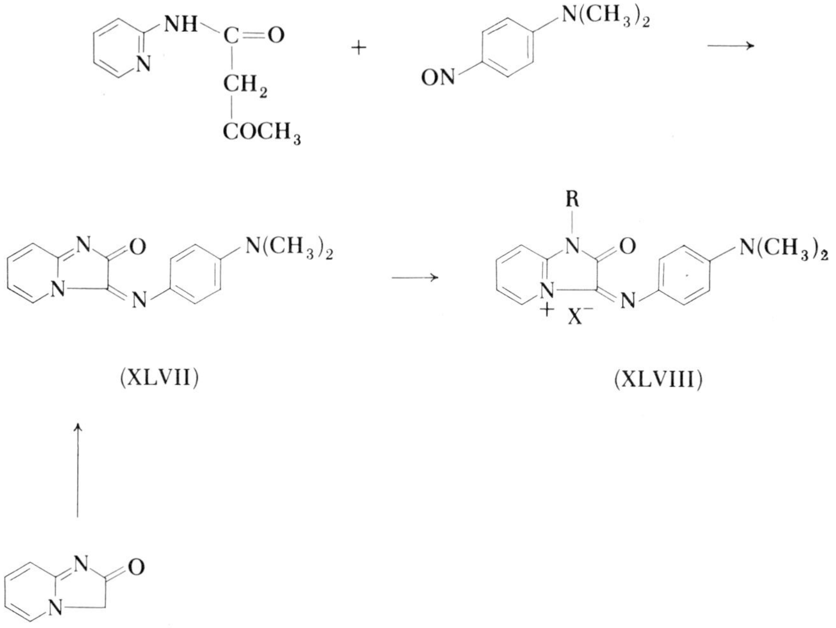

(XLVII)

(XLVIII)

(XXXIII)

Numerous methine dyes derived from XXXIII have been prepared[73-77] and patented[74,75,77] as photographic sensitizing agents. The simplest of these is XLIX, an amphoteric, brick-red high melting solid prepared by condensing XXXIII with ethyl isoformanilide[77] or ethyl orthoformate.[76] A typical merocyanine dye is L.[77] The abnormally polar nature of dimethinecyanine dyes of this class (e.g., LI) was noted[73] by Knott, who compared the spectra and properties of various representatives with their isomers[78] derived from imidazo[1,2-*a*]pyrid-3(2*H*)-one (v.i.).

It has long been known[51,64] that oxidation of XXXIII results in the formation of a vattable red dye. Under the illusion that the product obtained from II and chloroacetic acid had structure

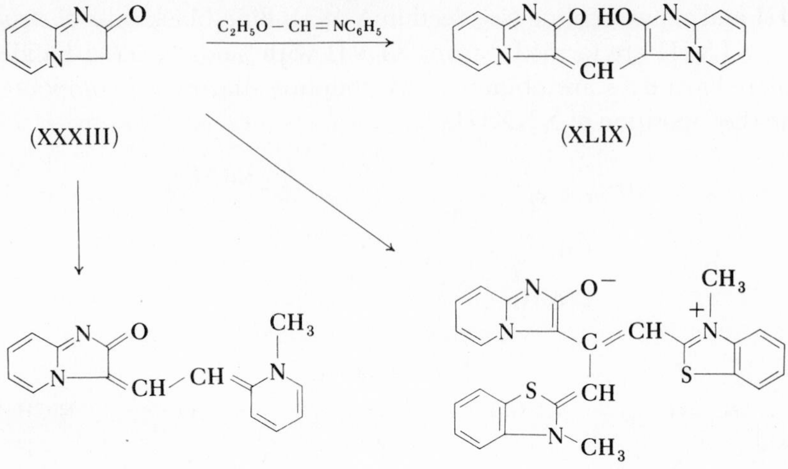

N O
N
$C_2H_5O-CH=NC_6H_5$
N O HO N
N CH N

(XXXIII)

(XLIX)

N O
N CH CH N
CH_3

N O^-
N C CH N
CH_3
S
S CH
N CH_3

(LI)

(L)

XXXV, Reindel[52,79] formulated the red oxidation product as LII. Finger and Kraft,[65] struck by the similarity between Reindel's dye and "glyoxaline red" (LIII, described some time previously by Ruhemann[80]), proposed structure LIV. Tschitschibabin suggested[51] structure LV, while Reindel and Rauch[68] considered and rejected the possibility that the dye had structure LVII, produced via LVI by a series of transformations similar to those encountered in the conversion[81] of diketohydrindene into iso-ethinediphthalide.

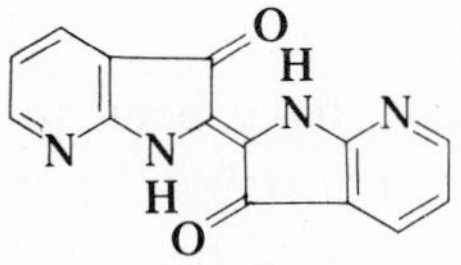

O H
N N
N N
H O

HN O
C_6H_5 N N C_6H_5
O NH

O N
N N
N O

(LII)

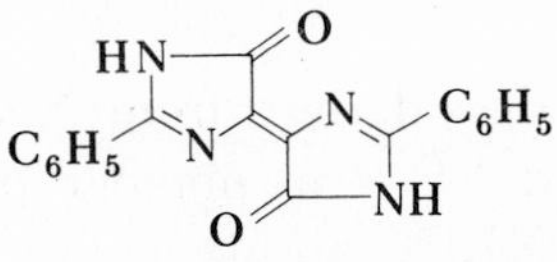

(LIII)

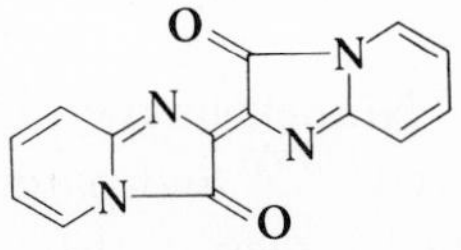

(LIV)

N OH
N
N
HO N

NH O N
N N
C
HOOC

→

N N
N N
COOH

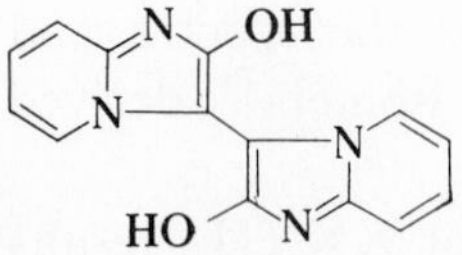

(LV)

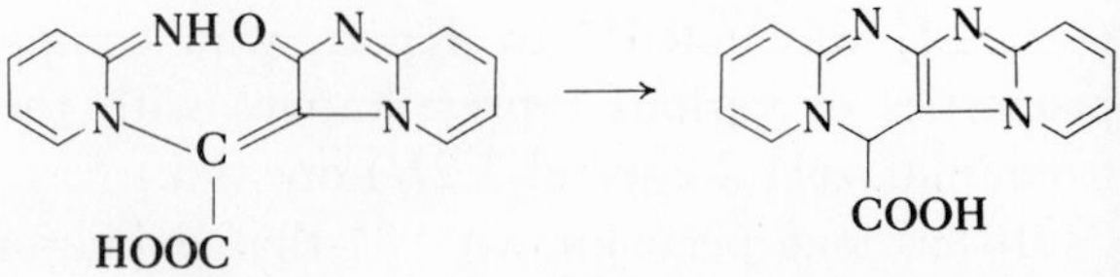

(LVI)

(LVII)

Structure LVIII, proposed by Reindel,[68] is probably most nearly correct. It is evident that heteropolar forms such as LVIIIa may make a substantial contribution to the resonance hybrid. The color of the structurally similar indigo molecule has been explained[82] partially on the basis of such a tetrapolar structure (LIX). The incursion of resonance forms of type LVIIIa would be favored by the presence of two aromatic pyridinium rings lacking in the analogous resonance form of indigo. That structures such as LVIIIa are large contributors to the resonance hybrid might be inferred from the discovery by Knott of the abnormally polar nature of

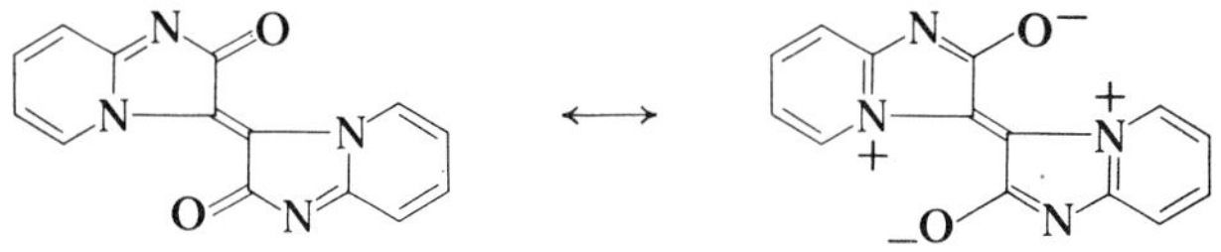

(LVIII) (LVIIIa)

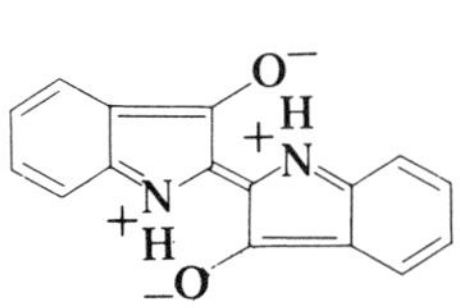

(LIX)

the dimethinemerocyanine dyes derived from XXXIII (v.s.). Finally, if we accept structure LVIII for the red dye, structure LV must represent its "leuco derivative."

TABLE II. Imidazo[1,2-*a*]pyridin-2(3*H*)-ones

Empirical formula	Substituents or structure	Properties and comments	Refs.
$C_7H_4Br_2N_2O$	3,3-Dibromo-	Yel., d. 135°. HBr_3 complex, d. 150–2°.	36,67,68
	6,8-Dibromo-	HBr salt. Chloroplatinate.	51
$C_7H_5BrN_2O$	3-Bromo-	HBr salt.	67
	6-Bromo-	HBr salt, m. 243°.	87
$C_7H_5IN_2O$	6-Iodo-	HBr salt, lt. yel., m. 254°.	87
$C_7H_5N_3O_2$	3-Nitroso-	Yel., m. 229° (darkens at 230°, m. 270° d.). Acetyl deriv., or.-red, m. 204–4.5°. Benzoyl deriv., brn.-red, m. 242–4° (180°).	2,35,51
$C_7H_6N_2O$	Unsubstituted	m. 243° (127°). HCl salt, m. 244–5°. HBr and HI salts. Picrate, m. 207–8°. Methiodide, m. 168–70°. *N*-Methylperchlorate, m. 174–5°. Forms Na^+ and K^+ "enolate" salts.	21,29,36,40, 51,52,65, 66,73,83
$C_7H_7N_3O$	5-Amino-	HCl salt, m. 207–8°. Picrate, m. 198–9°.	2
	6-Amino-	HCl salt.	83
$C_8H_5N_3O_4$	8-Carboxy-3-nitroso-	m. 250–60°.	64
$C_8H_6N_2O_3$	8-Carboxy-	Yel., m. 220°. HCl salt, m. 284° d. Sulfate·$4H_2O$, yel., m. 225° d.	64
$C_8H_8N_2O$	3-Methyl-	HBr salt.	21
	5-Methyl-	HCl salt.	83
	8-Methyl-	HCl salt, m. 266° (265°). Chloroplatinate, red. HBr salt.	35,51,84

$C_9H_8N_2O_2$	3-Acetyl-	m. 300–1° d.	35
$C_9H_8N_3O_4$	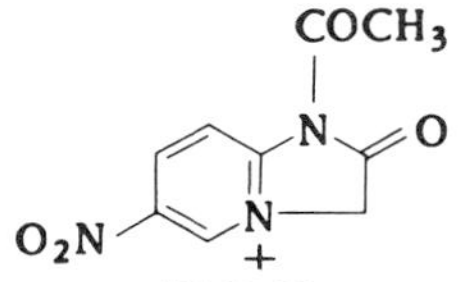	Acetate. (Structure correct?)	83
$C_{10}H_{11}N_2O_2$	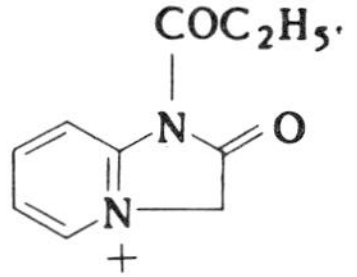	Propionate. (Structure correct?)	83
$C_{12}H_{12}N_2O_2$	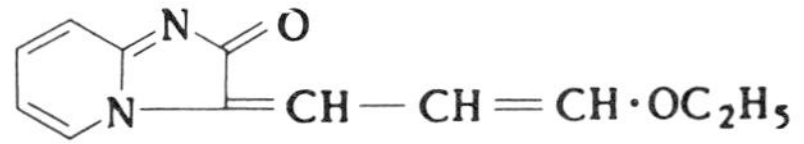	HBr salt, brn. oil.	76
$C_{13}H_{10}N_2O$	3-Phenyl-	m. ~246–8° d.	88
$C_{13}H_{11}N_3O_2S_2$	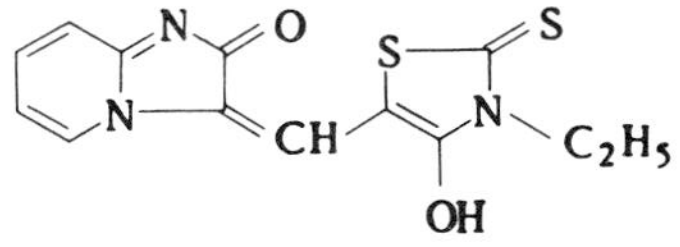	Grey, m. 300°.	73
$C_{13}H_{11}N_3O_3S$	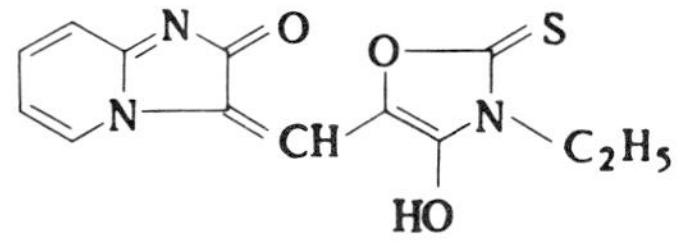	Or., m. 292°.	73
$C_{14}H_8ClIN_2O$	3-(4-Chlorobenzylidene)-6-iodo-	Brn., m. 179°.	87
$C_{14}H_8IN_3O_3$	6-Iodo-3-(4-nitrobenzylidene)-	Brn.-red, m. 224°.	87

(continued)

TABLE II. Imidazo[1,2-*a*]pyridin-2(3*H*)-ones (*continued*)

Empirical formula	Substituents or structure	Properties and comments	Refs.
$C_{14}H_8N_4O_2$	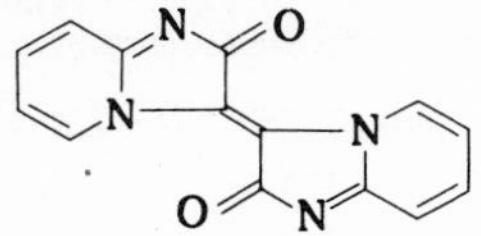 [structure]	Red (gives yellow vat), λ_{max} 480–540 mμ. Benzoyl deriv. of "leuco," m. 225–32°.	21,51,52,65, 68,79
$C_{14}H_9N_3O_3$	3-(2-Nitrobenzylidene)-	Or.-yel., m. 214°. HCl salt, m. 239° d.	69
	3-(3-Nitrobenzylidene)-	Sulfate, m. 236° d.	69
$C_{14}H_{10}N_2O$	3-Benzylidene-	Or.-yel., m. 233°. HCl salt, m. 253° d. Br_2 complex, yel., m. 171–3°.	36,69
$C_{14}H_{10}N_2O_2$	3-Benzoyl-	Sinters at 275°, m. 293° d.	51,52
	3-(2-Hydroxybenzylidene)-	HBr salt, yel., m. 220–5°. HCl salt, m. 245° d.	69,70
	3-(4-Hydroxybenzylidene)-	Yel., m. 278° d. Sulfate, m. 237° d.	69
$C_{14}H_{10}N_4O_3$	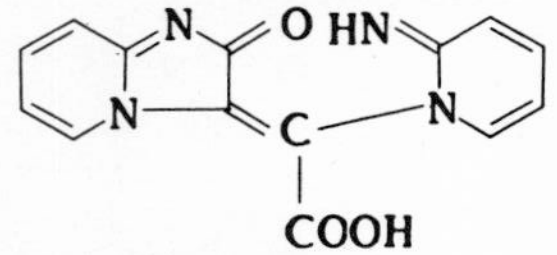 [structure: O, HN, N, C, COOH]	m. 176° d.	68
$C_{14}H_{12}N_2O$	3-Benzyl-	HCl salt, m. 216° d. Picrate, m. 189° d.	69
$C_{14}H_{15}N_3OS$	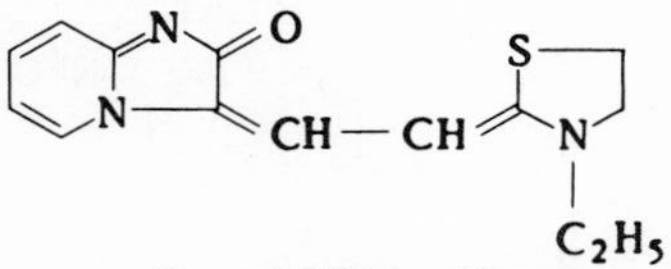 [structure: O, CH—CH, S, N, C_2H_5]	HBr salt, or., m. 236°; λ_{max} 479 mμ (MeOH).	73–75
$C_{14}H_{10}N_4O_2$	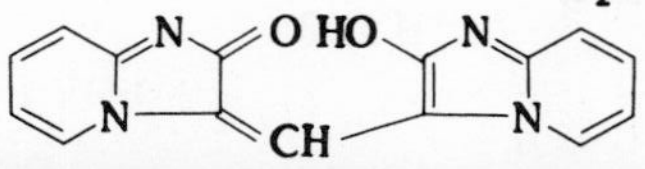 [structure: O HO, CH, N]	Brick-red, m. 300°; λ_{max} 507 mμ (EtOH). HBr salt, red, m. 245–7°, λ_{max} 490 mμ (log ε 4.63). HCl salt·$2H_2O$, or.	73,76,78

$C_{15}H_{11}N_3OS$	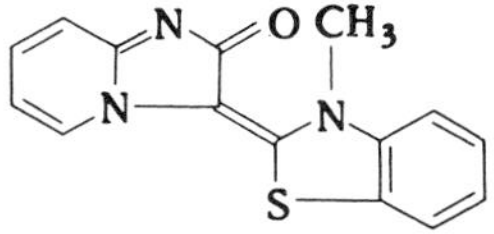	HBr salt, yel., m. 225–9°, λ_{max} 425 mμ (log ε 4.70).	76
$C_{15}H_{11}N_3O_3$	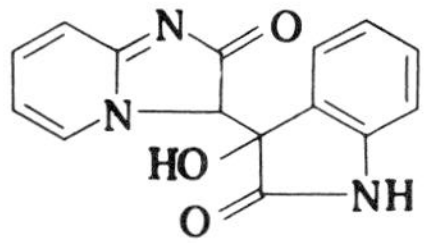	Red, m. 170°. HCl salt, m. 230°.	69
$C_{15}H_{12}N_2O_3$	3-(4-Hydroxy-3-methoxybenzylidene)-	HBr salt, or.-yel., d. ~260°.	70
$C_{15}H_{13}N_3O$	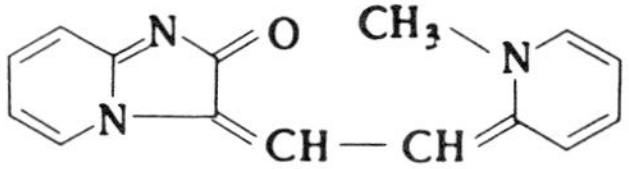	Purple, m. 261° (245°), λ_{max} 464 mμ (H_2O) or 525 mμ (MeOH). HBr salt, purple, m. 268°.	73–75
$C_{15}H_{14}N_4O$	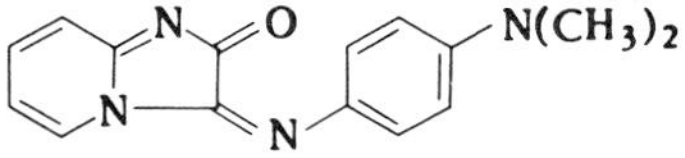	Magenta, m. 248°. Forms 1:1 complex with *p*-R-C_6H_4-NH_2, where R = OCH_3 (m. 145°) or R = $(CH_3)_2N$ (m. 186°). HCl salt, bl.-blk., m. 210–1° d. Methiodide, bl., m. 236–7°, λ_{max} 593 mμ *N*-Methyl perchlorate, m. 230°.	36,67,71
$C_{16}H_8N_4O_6$	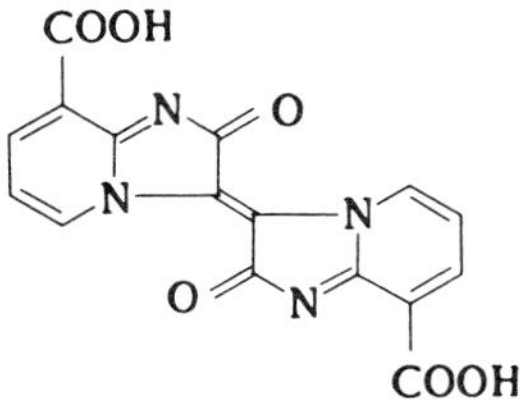	Red, m. 259–60°.	51,64

(*continued*)

TABLE II. Imidazo[1,2-*a*]pyridin-2(3*H*)-ones (*continued*)

Empirical formula	Substituents or structure	Properties and comments	Refs.
$C_{16}H_{12}IN_3O_2$	3-(4-Acetamidobenzylidene)-6-iodo-	Red-brn., m. 175°.	87
$C_{16}H_{14}N_2O_3$	2-(3,4-Dimethoxybenzylidene)-	HBr salt, or.-yel., m. 242°.	70
$C_{16}H_{14}BrN_3O$	6-Bromo-3-(4-dimethylaminobenzylidene)-	Brt. grn., m. 258°.	87
$C_{16}H_{14}IN_3O$	3-(4-Dimethylaminobenzylidene)-6-iodo-	Brt. grn., m. 292°.	87
$C_{16}H_{15}N_3O$	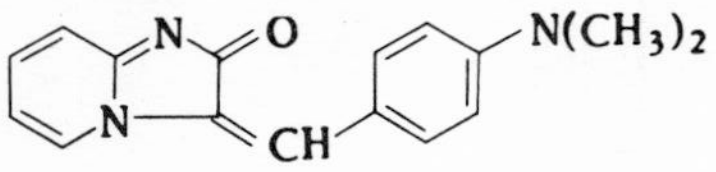 N, O, N, CH, $N(CH_3)_2$	Brick-red, m. 275° d., λ_{max} 480 mμ (pyridine), 495 mμ (EtOH), and 511 mμ (pyridine-H_2O). HBr salt, red, m. 264–5° (260° d.), λ_{max} 514 mμ (log ε 4.5) or 520 mμ. (H_2O). HCl salt, bl.-vt., m. 256° d.	36,69,70,78
	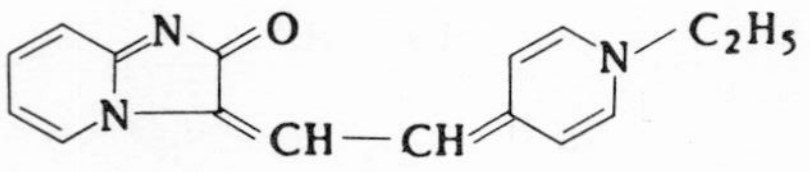 N, O, N, CH—CH, N, C_2H_5	Dihydrate, red. Anhydr., grn., m. 250°, λ_{max} 542 mμ (MeOH). HI salt, purple, m. 267°.	73–75
	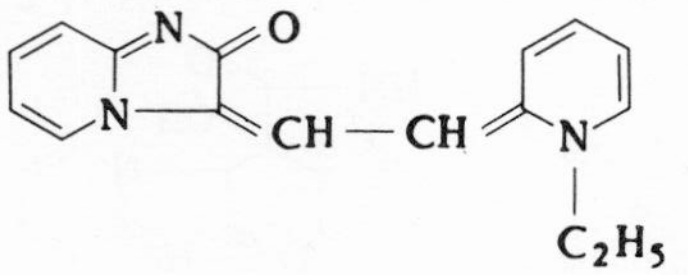 N, O, N, CH—CH, N, C_2H_5	λ_{max} 536 (EtOH) or 570 mμ (pyridine).	78
$C_{17}H_{11}BrN_4O_2$	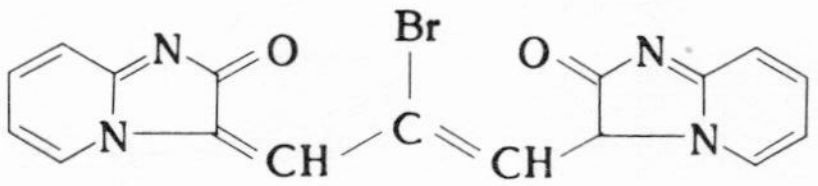 N, O, N, CH, Br, C, CH, O, N, N	*N*-Methyl *p*-toluenesulfonate, bronze, m. 300°, λ_{max} 587 mμ (H_2O) or 600 mμ (MeOH).	74,75

$C_{17}H_{11}ClN_4O_2$	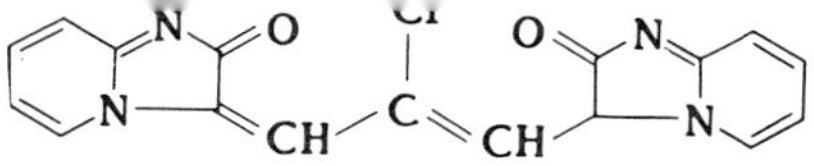 Purple, m. 300°, λ_{max} 592 mμ (H_2O) or 602 mμ (MeOH). *N*-Methyl *p*-toluenesulfonate, steel-grey, m. 300°, λ_{max} 590 mμ (H_2O) or 600 mμ (MeOH).	74,75
$C_{17}H_{12}N_4O_2$	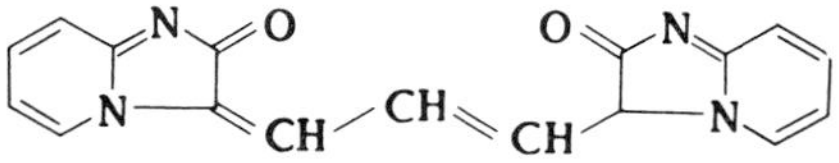 Purple, m. 284°, λ_{max} 600 mμ (MeOH) (617 mμ H_2O?). *N*-Methyl *p*-toluenesulfonate, grn., λ_{max} 585 mμ (MeOH) or 595 mμ (MeOH) or 595 mμ (H_2O). Bismethiodide, grn., m. 300°.	74-76
$C_{17}H_{13}BrN_2O$	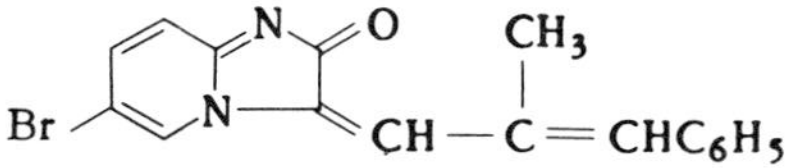 Brn., m. 184°.	87
$C_{18}H_{14}N_4O_2$	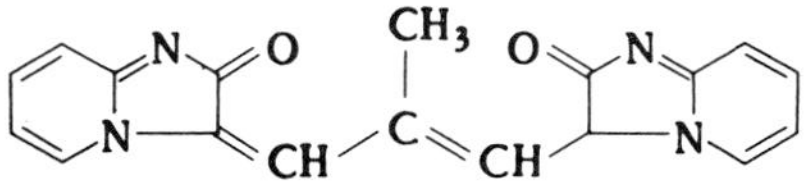 Brn., m. 235°, λ_{max} 600 mμ (MeOH).	75
$C_{18}H_{15}N_3OSe$	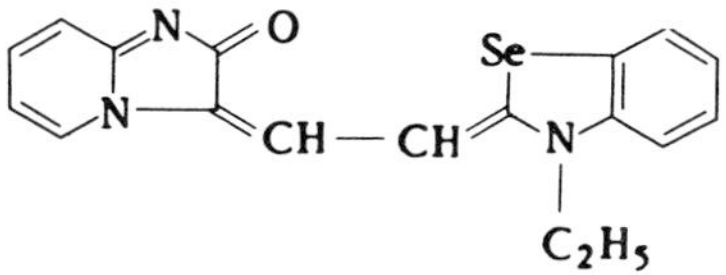 m. 294-6°, λ_{max} 542 mμ (log ε 5.14).	76
$C_{18}H_{15}N_3OS$	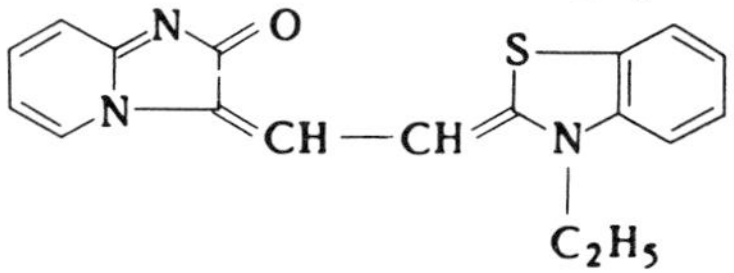 Red or grn., m. 271°, λ_{max} 532 mμ (MeOH) or 538 mμ (EtOH) or 548 mμ (pyridine). HBr salt, red (vt.), m. 310-5° (309°), λ_{max} 532 mμ (log ε 5.15).	73-76,78

(*continued*)

TABLE II. Imidazo[1,2-*a*]pyridin-2(3*H*)-ones (*continued*)

Empirical formula	Substituents or structure	Properties and comments	Refs.
$C_{18}H_{15}N_3O_2$	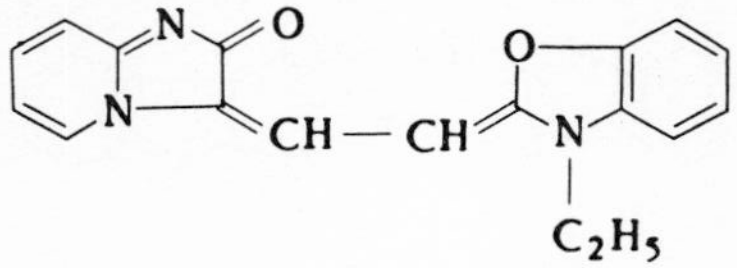	Or., m. 269° λ_{max} 597 mμ (pyridine) or 598 mμ (EtOH). HBr salt, red, m. 202°, λ_{max} 502 mμ (MeOH).	73–75,78
$C_{18}H_{16}BrN_3O$	6-Bromo-3-(4-dimethylaminocinnamylidene)-	Brt. grn., m. 238°.	87
$C_{18}H_{16}IN_3O$	3-(4-Dimethylaminocinnamylidene)-6-iodo-	Red-purple, m. 186°.	87
$C_{18}H_{17}N_3O$	3-(4-Dimethylaminocinnamylidene)-	Brt. grn., m. 226°.	87
$C_{18}H_{19}N_3O$	3-(4-Diethylaminobenzylidene)-	HBr salt, red, m. 230° d., λ_{max} 590 mμ.	70
$C_{18}H_{20}N_4O$	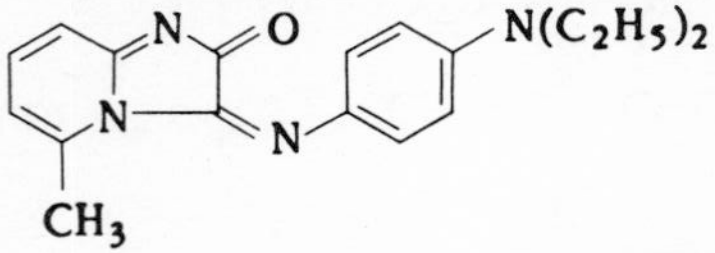	λ_{max} 560 mμ.	36
	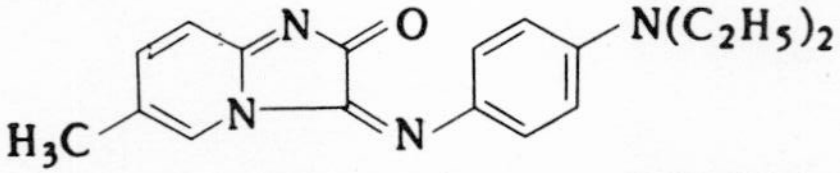	λ_{max} 564 mμ.	36
	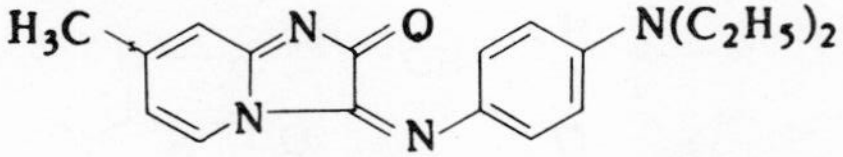	λ_{max} 554 mμ.	36
	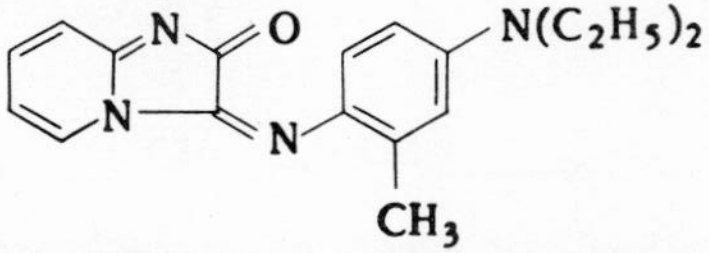	m. 203°.	36

$C_{19}H_{14}N_4O_2$	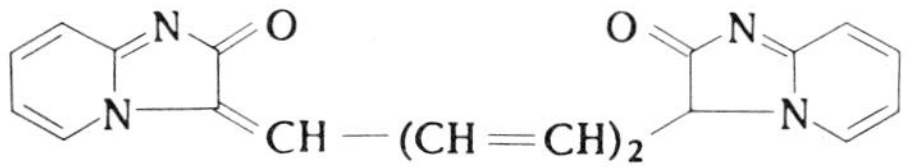 N, O, N, CH — (CH=CH)$_2$, O, N, N	Grn., λ_{max} 590 mμ. HCl salt, grn., m. 218° d. *N*-Methyl *p*-toluenesulfonate, grn., m. 269°, λ_{max} 658 mμ (H_2O) or 685 mμ (MeOH). Bismethiodide, brt.-grn.	74,75
$C_{19}H_{16}N_4O$	3,3-Bis-anilino-	m. 167–8°.	67
$C_{19}H_{17}N_3OS$	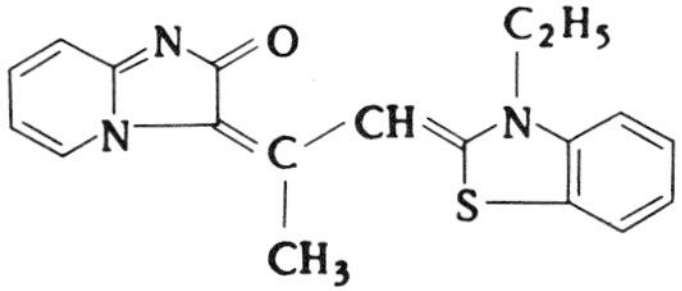 N, O, N, C, CH, CH_3, C_2H_5, N, S	Vt., m. 231–4°, λ_{max} 495.7 mμ (log ε 4.57) and 529.5 mμ (log ε 4.82). HBr salt, dk. vt., m. 278–9°, same λ_{max} as base.	76
$C_{19}H_{17}N_3OS_2$	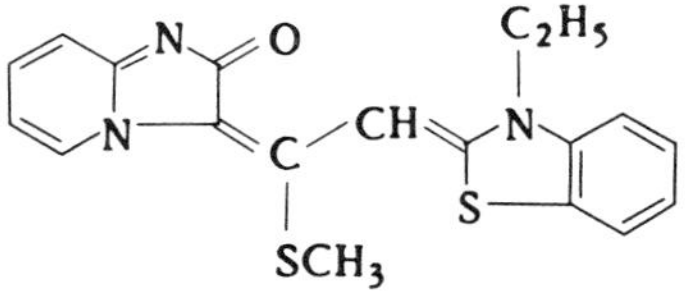 N, O, N, C, CH, SCH_3, C_2H_5, N, S	HBr salt, bl., m. 169–72°, λ_{max} 537 mμ (log ε 4.52).	76
$C_{20}H_{16}N_4O_2$	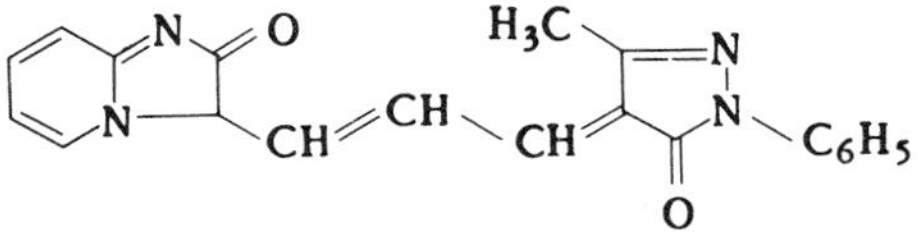 N, O, N, CH=CH, CH, H_3C, N, N, C_6H_5, O	m. 174–7°, λ_{max} 528 mμ (log ε 3.46).	76

(*continued*)

TABLE II. Imidazo[1,2-*a*]pyridin-2(3*H*)-ones (*continued*)

Empirical formula	Substituents or structure	Properties and comments	Refs.
$C_{20}H_{17}N_3O$		Purple, m. 268° d., λ_{max} 543 mμ (aq. MeOH), 562 mμ (MeOH) or 569 mμ (EtOH) or 557 and 595 mμ (pyridine). HBr salt, gold, m. >300°. HI salt, gold, m. 300°.	73,74,78
$C_{20}H_{17}N_3O_2$		Grn., m. 300°. *N*-Methyl *p*-toluenesulfonate, dk. brassy, m. 300°, λ_{max} 585 mμ (H_2O) or 600 mμ (EtOH).	74,75
$C_{21}H_{16}N_4O_2$		m. 207°. Dibenzoyl deriv., m. 204°.	69
$C_{21}H_{16}N_4O_3$		m. 216° d.	69

$C_{22}H_{13}Br_2N_5O_3$	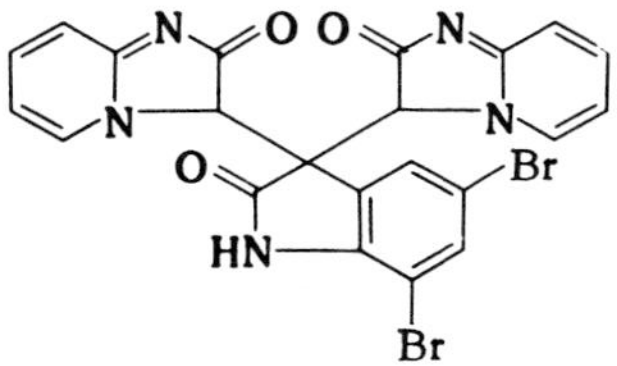	m. 294° d.	69
$C_{22}H_{14}BrN_5O_3$	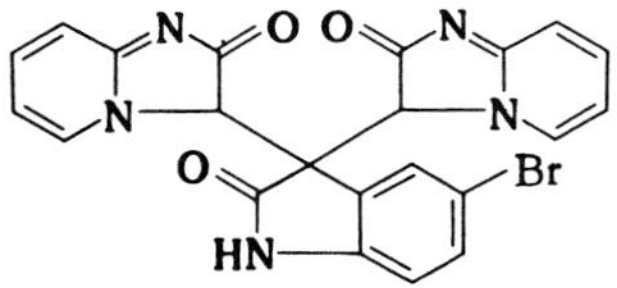	m. 287° d.	69
$C_{22}H_{15}N_5O_3$	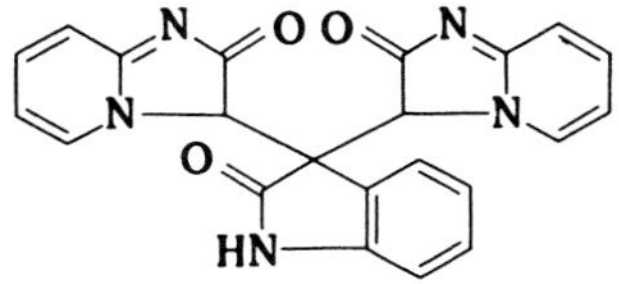	m. 249° d.	69
$C_{23}H_{16}N_4O$	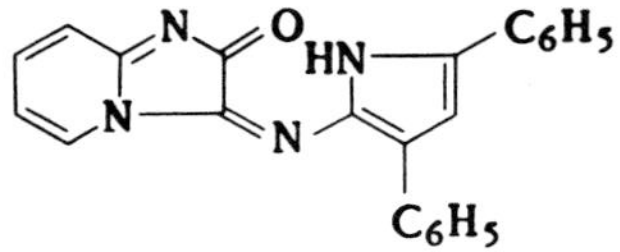	m. 260°, λ_{max} ~596 mμ.	71

(continued)

TABLE II. Imidazo[1,2-*a*]pyridin-2(3*H*)-ones (*continued*)

Empirical formula	Substituents or structure	Properties and comments	Refs.
$C_{23}H_{19}N_3OS$	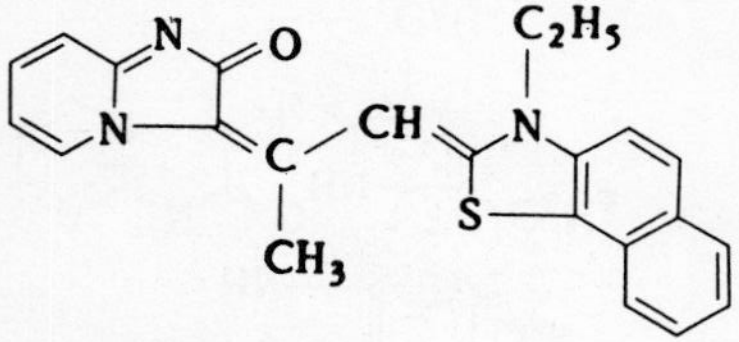 [structure: N, O, C, CH, CH$_3$, C$_2$H$_5$, N, S]	HBr salt, bl., m. 203–5°, λ_{max} 548 mμ (log ε 5.10).	76
$C_{25}H_{43}N_2O$	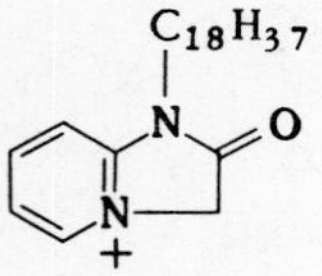 [structure: C$_{18}$H$_{37}$, N, O, N$^+$]	Chloride. (Structure correct?)	83
$C_{26}H_{18}N_4O_4$	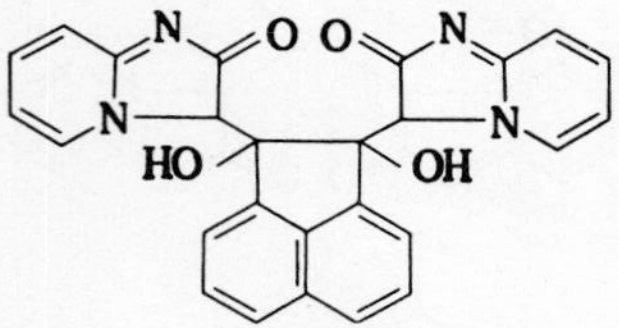 [structure: N, O, O, N, N, N, HO, OH]	m. 280°. (Structure correct?)	69
$C_{26}H_{20}N_4OS_2$	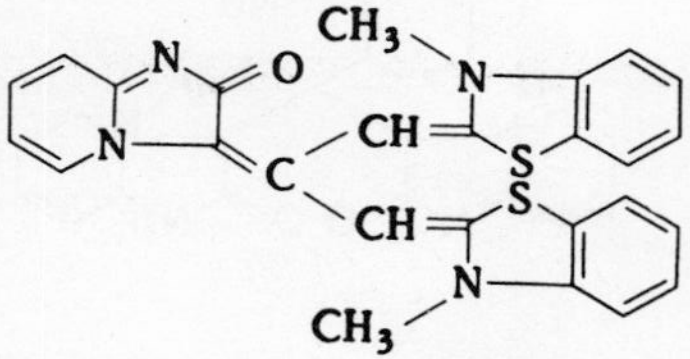 [structure: N, O, N, C, CH, CH, CH$_3$, N, S, S, N, CH$_3$]	m. 242–4° d.	77

$C_{27}H_{22}N_4OS_2$	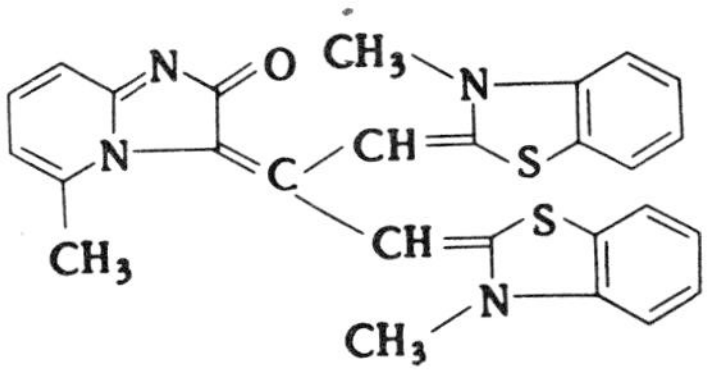 [structure]	Dk. grn., m. 239–41° d.	77
	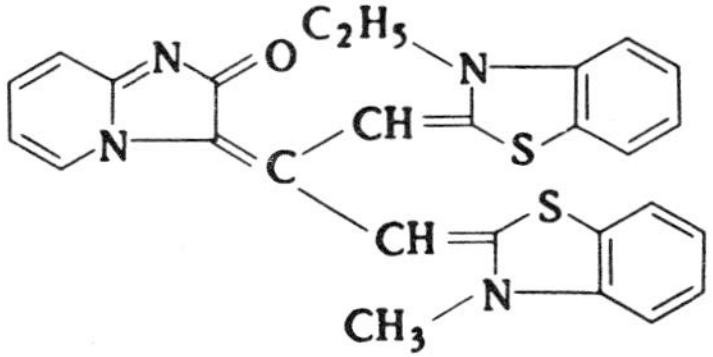 [structure]	HI salt, m. 229–31°; λ_{max} 584 mμ (log ε 4.97), inflexion at 555 mμ (log ε 4.50).	76
$C_{30}H_{26}N_4O_2S$	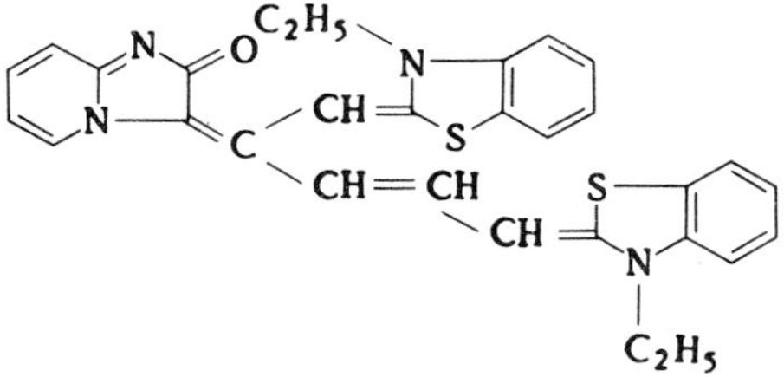 [structure]	Grn., m. 214–5° d.	77
$C_{43}H_{76}N_2O_4$	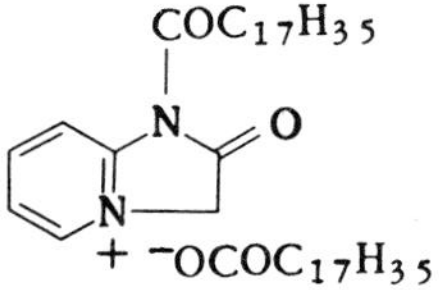 [structure]	Structure correct?	83

III. *Imidazo[1,2-a]pyridin-3(2H)-ones*

Comparatively few compounds of this type have been described. Dehydration of *N*-(2-pyridyl)-glycine yielded[78] LX, which proved to be unstable in water or alcohol. By working under anhydrous conditions, however, a group of merocyanine dyes derived from LX was obtained.[78] For example, with ethyl orthoformate, LX formed LXI, which, in contrast to the red XLIX, is green, a fact probably related[78] to the non-coplanarity of XLIX. In general, these dyes are more polar and more deeply colored than their isomers derived from XXXIII.

H N CH_2 N COOH $\xrightarrow[\Delta]{PCl_3}$ N N O $\xrightarrow{HC(OC_2H_5)_3}$ N CH N N O O N

(LX) (LXI)

Heating II with benzil was reported[86] to yield an unstable product thought to be LXII, which readily absorbed water and decomposed to LXIII.

NH_2 N $\xrightarrow{(C_6H_5CO)_2}$ [N OH C_6H_5 N C_6H_5 OH] $\rightarrow$

(II)

[N C_6H_5 C_6H_5 N O] $\xrightarrow{H_2O}$ NH C_6H_5 C_6H_5 N COOH

(LXII) (LXIII)

The reaction of 2-aminopyridine with ω-bromo-ω-nitroacetophenone was claimed[40] to yield the 2-phenyl homolog, but this synthesis could not be duplicated,[88] and the analogous reaction in the pyrrocoline series (see Section A-183) also failed.

TABLE III. Imidazo[1,2-*a*]pyridin-3(2*H*)-ones

Empirical formula	Structure	Properties	Refs.
$C_7H_6N_2O$	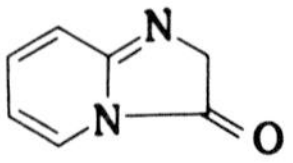 N, N, O	HCl salt, m. ~ 190° d.	78
$C_{13}H_{10}N_2O$	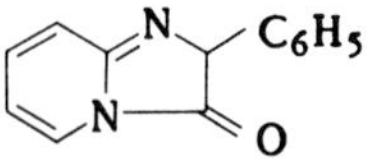 N, C_6H_5, N, O	m. 81.5–2°.	40
$C_{13}H_{11}N_3O_2S_2$	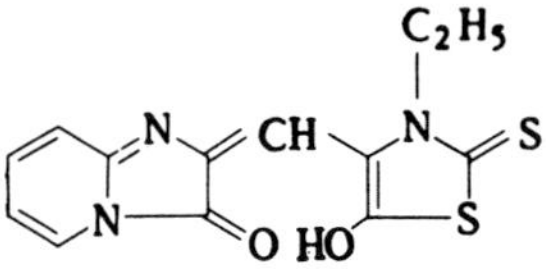 C_2H_5, N, CH, N, S, N, O HO, S	Grn., m. indefinitely.	78
$C_{15}H_{10}N_4O_2$	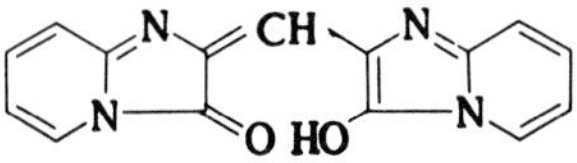 N, CH, N, N, O HO, N	Grn., d. 240°, λ_{max} 560, 606 mμ (EtOH).	78
$C_{15}H_{13}N_3O$	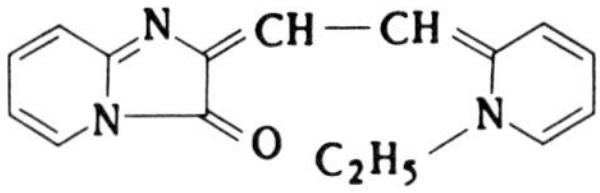 N, CH—CH, N, O, C_2H_5, N	Grn.-brn., m. 124–5°, λ_{max} 592 mμ (pyridine), 562 mμ (EtOH) and 536 mμ (aq. pyridine).	78
$C_{16}H_{12}N_4O_2$	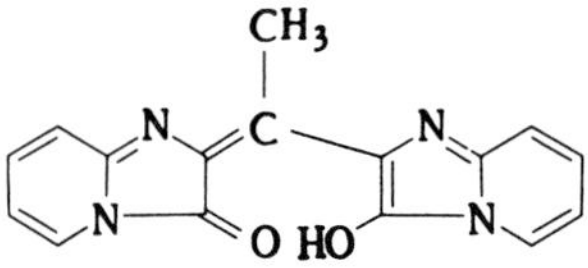 CH_3, N, C, N, N, O HO, N	Bronze-grn., m. indefinitely.	78
$C_{16}H_{13}N_3OS$	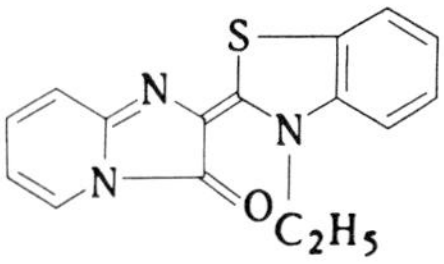 S, N, N, N, O, C_2H_5	Or., m. 256°.	78
$C_{16}H_{15}N_3O$	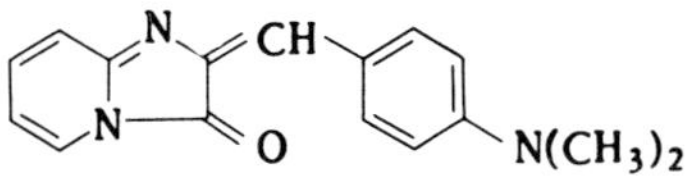 N, CH, N, O, $N(CH_3)_2$	Purple, m. 199°, λ_{max} 520, 560 mμ (pyridine), 520, 562 mμ (EtOH), 532, 565 mμ (aq. pyridine).	78
$C_{17}H_{13}N_3O$	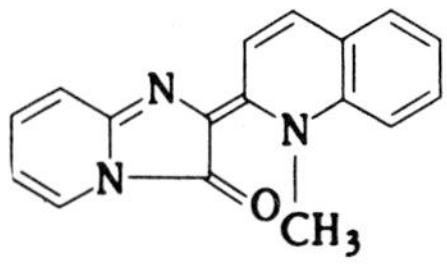 N, N, N, O, CH_3	Olive-grn., m. 190°.	78

(*continued*)

TABLE III. Imidazo[1,2-*a*]pyridin-3(2*H*)-ones (*continued*)

Empirical formula	Structure	Properties	Refs.
$C_{18}H_{15}N_3OS$	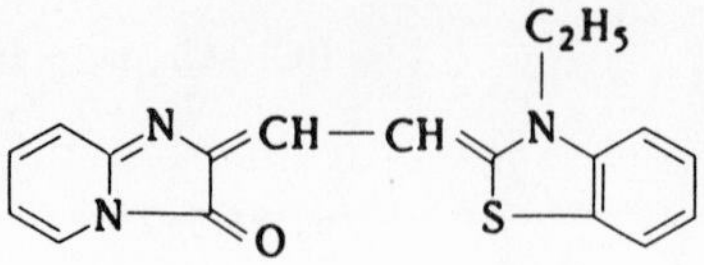 [structure: imidazo[1,2-a]pyridin-3(2H)-one =CH—CH= 3-ethylbenzothiazoline (C_2H_5 on N, S)]	Grn., m. 260°, λ_{max} 563, 605 mμ (pyridine), 555, 593 mμ (EtOH) and 555, 590 mμ (aq. pyridine). Ethiodide, grn., m. 247°.	78
$C_{18}H_{15}N_3O_2$	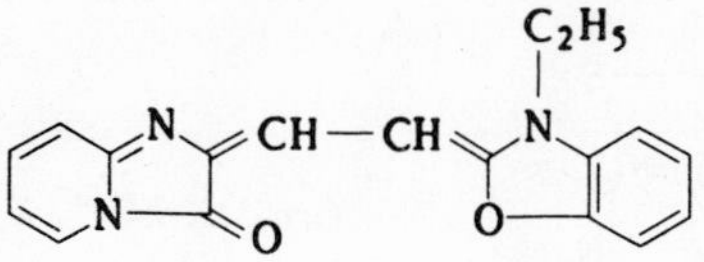 [structure: imidazo[1,2-a]pyridin-3(2H)-one =CH—CH= 3-ethylbenzoxazoline (C_2H_5 on N, O)]	Brn.-grn., m. 237–8°, λ_{max} 538, 575 mμ (pyridine), 522, 558 mμ (EtOH) and 522, 550 mμ (aq. pyridine). HCl salt, magenta, m. 259–62°.	78
$C_{19}H_{14}N_2O$	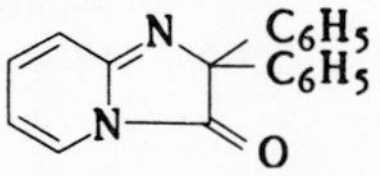 [structure: 2,2-di(C_6H_5)imidazo[1,2-a]pyridin-3(2H)-one]	Unstable. Lactam bond cleaved by water.	86
$C_{20}H_{17}N_3O$	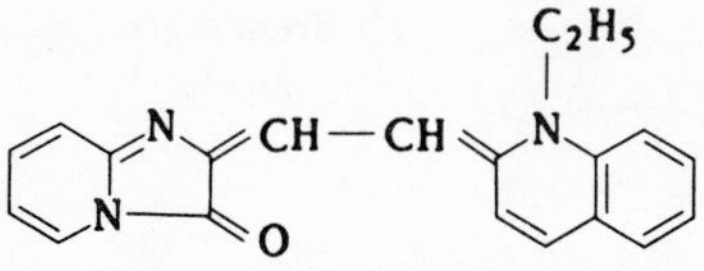 [structure: imidazo[1,2-a]pyridin-3(2H)-one =CH—CH= 1-ethyl-2(1H)-quinolylidene (C_2H_5 on N)]	Grn., m. 197°, λ_{max} 578, 620 mμ (pyridine), 600 mμ (EtOH), and 594 mμ (aq. pyridine).	78

IV. 2- and 3-Aminoimidazo[1,2-a]pyridines

These derivatives are of recent origin. Although the reaction of II with chloroacetamide gave[40] only XXXIII, heating LXIV (obtained from 2-(4-toluenesulfonamido)-pyridine and chloroacetamide) with acetic anhydride produced[29] LXV (in 75% yield), from which the free amine was obtained by alkaline hydrolysis. Apparently no other 2-aminoimidazopyridines have been described.

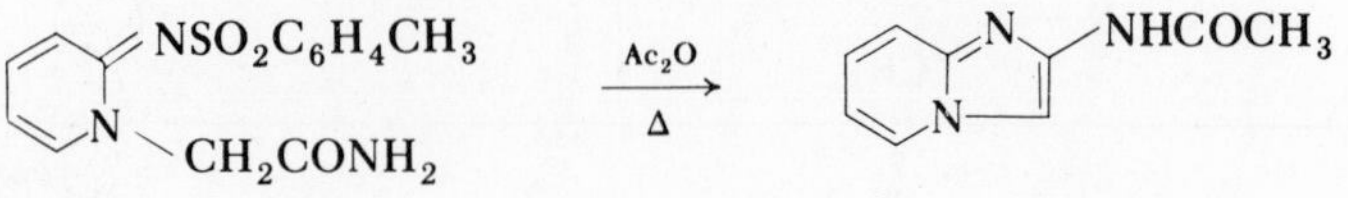

$$\text{(LXIV)}\ \ 1\text{-}(CH_2CONH_2)\text{-}2(1H)\text{-pyridinylidene}=NSO_2C_6H_4CH_3 \xrightarrow[\Delta]{Ac_2O} \text{(LXV)}\ \ 2\text{-}NHCOCH_3\text{-imidazo[1,2-a]pyridine}$$

(LXIV) (LXV)

When 2-pyridylaminoacetonitrile (LXVI) is treated with benzenesulfonyl chloride, a mixture of the 3-mono- and di-benzenesulfonamidoimidazo[1,2-*a*]pyridines results,[29] while heating LXVI with acetic anhydride or benzoyl chloride yields LXVII (R = CH_3 or C_6H_5, respectively). Even heating LXVI with benzaldehyde at 100° is sufficient to effect cyclization to LXIX. Reduction with lithium aluminum hydride of the 3-benzamido derivative (LXVII, R = C_6H_5) or catalytic reduction of LXIX afforded the 3-benzylamino compound (LXVIII), also found amongst the products obtained by treating LXVI with benzyl chloride.[29] Instead of the expected thiohydantoin, Knott[28] obtained 3-(ethylthiocarbamylamino)-imidazopyridine from the reaction of LXVI with ethyl isothiocyanate.

$NHSO_2C_6H_5$ + $N(SO_2C_6H_5)_2$

$C_6H_5SO_2Cl$

NH–CH_2–CN

(LXVI)

C_6H_5CHO

NHCOR

$C_6H_5CH_2Cl$

N=CHC_6H_5

(LXVII)

(LXIX)

$LiAlH_4$

H_2/Pd-C CH_3OH

$NHCH_2C_6H_5$

(LXVIII)

An interesting group of mesoionic compounds (LXXI) was obtained[29] by heating LXX (R″ = CN or CH=NOH) with acetic anhydride, etc. These products show a green fluorescence in chloroform solution under ultraviolet light, but none in dilute aqueous acid solution.

(LXX) → (LXXI)

Products of type LXXI are listed in Table IV, while the other 2- and 3-amino compounds are to be found in Table I.

TABLE IV. Mesoionic Imidazo[1,2-*a*]pyridines of Structure LXXI

Empirical formula	R	R′	Properties	Refs.
$C_{11}H_{13}N_3O$	CH_3CO-	Ethyl-	Trihydrate, m. 92°. Anhydr., yel., m. 163°d. HI salt, m. 248°.	29
$C_{14}H_{12}N_4O$	CH_3CO-	2-Pyridyl-	m. 210–2°.	29
$C_{14}H_{13}N_3OS$	CH_3CO-	2-Thienylmethyl-	Dihydrate, m. 93°. Anhydr., yel., m. 185–6°d. Picrate, m. 149–50°.	29
$C_{15}H_{13}N_3O$	CH_3CO-	Phenyl-	Yel., m. 193°.	29
$C_{16}H_{15}N_3O$	CH_3CO-	Benzyl-	Yel., m. 201°d. Picrate, m. 147°. Tosylate, m. 186°. Methiodide, m. 194°. Ethiodide, m. 185°. Allyl reineckate, m. 158–60°. Propyl tosylate, m. 147.5°. Tetrahydro deriv. m. 274–5°.	29
$C_{17}H_{17}N_3O$	C_2H_5CO-	Benzyl-	m. 135–6°. Methiodide, m. 135°.	29
$C_{19}H_{21}N_3O$	CH_3CO-	2,4,6-Trimethylbenzyl-	Yel., m. 210°.	29
$C_{20}H_{17}N_3O_2S$	$C_6H_5SO_2$-	Benzyl-	Grn., m. 208°.	29
$C_{21}H_{17}N_3O$	C_6H_5CO-	Benzyl-	Yel., m. 188°.	29

References

1. Tschitschibabin, *Ber.*, **58,** 1704 (1925).
2. Mosby, unpublished observations.
3. Bower, *J. Chem. Soc.*, **1957,** 4511.
4. Bremer, *Ann.*, **521,** 286 (1935).
5. Campbell and McCall, *J. Chem. Soc.*, **1951,** 2411.
6. Tschitschibabin, *Ber.*, **59,** 2048 (1926). *J. Russ. Phys. Chem. Soc.*, **58,** 1159 (1926).
7. Djerassi and Pettit, *J. Am. Chem. Soc.*, **76,** 4470 (1954).
8. Kickhöfen, *Arch. Pharm.*, **288,** 473 (1955).
9. Kröhnke, Kickhöfen and Thoma, *Chem. Ber.*, **88,** 1117 (1955).
10. Schmid and Bangler, *Ber.*, **59,** 1360 (1926).
11. Takahashi and Shibasaki, *J. Pharm. Soc. Japan*, **69,** 496 (1949); *Chem. Abstracts*, **44,** 4474 (1950).
12. Adams and Pachter, *J. Am. Chem. Soc.*, **74,** 5491 (1952).
13. Schilling, Dissertation, Berlin, 1942. Mentioned in "FIAT Review of German Science," Preparative Organic Chemistry, **I,** 329 (1948).
14. Schilling, Kröhnke and Kickhöfen, *Chem. Ber.*, **88,** 1093 (1955).
15. Kröhnke and Kickhöfen, *Chem. Ber.*, **88,** 1103 (1955).
16. Matveev, *Bull. acad. sci. U.S.S.R., Classe sci. math. nat., sér. chim.*, **1936,** 533; *Chem. Zentr.*, **I,** 1125 (1938); *Chem. Abstracts*, **31,** 6654 (1937); *Brit. Chem. Abstracts*, **AII,** 263 (1937).
17. Kaye, Parris and Burlant, *J. Am. Chem. Soc.*, **75,** 746 (1953).
18. Matveev, *Bull. acad. sci. U.S.S.R., Classe sci. math. nat., sér. chim.*, **1936,** 1005; *Chem. Zentr.*, **I,** 603 (1938); *Chem. Abstracts*, **31,** 5364 (1937).
19. Gol'dfarb and Kondakova, *J. Gen. Chem.* (U.S.S.R.), **10,** 1055 (1940); *Chem. Abstracts*, **35,** 4020 (1941).
20. Kondakova and Gol'dfarb, *Izvest. Akad. Nauk S.S.S.R. Otdel. Khim. Nauk*, **1946,** 523; *Chem. Abstracts*, **42,** 6364 (1948).
21. Tschitschibabin, Ger. Pat. 451,733; *Frdl.*, **15,** 335 (1928).
22. Copp and Timmis, *J. Chem. Soc.*, **1955,** 2021.
23. Diels, Alder, Winckler and Peterson, *Ann.*, **498,** 1 (1932).
24. Kondo and Mitsugi, *J. Pharm. Soc. Japan*, **57,** 397 (1937); *Chem. Zentr.*, **II,** 991 (1937); *Chem. Abstracts*, **33,** 2139 (1939).
25. Konson, *Farmakol. i Toksikol.*, **9,** No. 2, 3 (1946); *Chem. Abstracts*, **41,** 3220 (1947).
26. Mednikyan, *Farmakol. i Toksikol.*, **9,** No. 1, 26 (1946); *Chem. Abstracts*, **41,** 1333 (1947).
27. Aluf and Raspopova, *Farmakol. i Toksikol.*, **8,** No. 1, 26 (1945); *Chem. Abstracts*, **40,** 5843 (1946).
28. Craig, U. S. Pat. 2,785,133.
29. Bristow, Charlton, Peak and Short, *J. Chem. Soc.*, **1954,** 616.
30. Takahashi, Senda and Yatsuka, *J. Pharm. Soc. Japan*, **64,** No. 8A, 26 (1944); *Chem. Abstracts*, **46,** 111 (1952).
31. Adams and Pachter, *J. Am. Chem. Soc.*, **76,** 1845 (1954).
32. Räth, *Ber.*, **58,** 346 (1925).
33. Tschitschibabin, *Ber.*, **58,** 1707 (1925).

34. Buu-Hoi and Hoan, *Rec. trav. chim.*, **68,** 441 (1949).
35. Reindel and Rauch, *Ber.*, **58,** 393 (1925).
36. Allen and Van Allen, *J. Org. Chem.*, **13,** 599 (1948).
37. Takahashi and Yajima, *J. Pharm. Soc. Japan*, **67,** 181 (1947); *Chem. Abstracts*, **45,** 9530 (1951).
38. Buu-Hoï, Jacquignon, Xuong and Lavit, *J. Org. Chem.*, **19,** 1370 (1954).
39. Buu-Hoï, Hoán and Jacquignon, *Rec. trav. chim.*, **68,** 781 (1949).
40. Schmid and Gründig, *Monatsh.*, **84,** 491 (1953).
41. Buu-Hoï and Khôi, *Compt. rend.*, **230,** 967 (1950).
42. Matsukawa and Ban, *J. Pharm. Soc. Japan*, **71,** 760 (1951); *Chem. Abstracts*, **46,** 8094 (1952).
43. Matsukawa and Ban, *J. Pharm. Soc. Japan*, **72,** 884 (1952); *Chem. Abstracts*, **47,** 6411 (1953).
44. Verkade and Van Leeuwen, *Rec. trav. chim.*, **70,** 142 (1951).
45. Palazzo and Marogna, *Atti reale accad. Lincei*, [5]**21,** II, 512 (1912). *Gazz. chim ital*, **43,** I, 44 (1913).
46. Allen and Wilson, U. S. Pat. 2,299,782.
47. Gol'dfarb and Kondakova, *J. Appl. Chem.* (U.S.S.R.), **15,** 151 (1942); *Chem. Abstracts*, **37,** 2380 (1943).
48. Tschitschibabin and Plaschenkowa, *Ber.*, **64,** 2842 (1931).
49. Preobrazhenskii and Kuleshova, *J. Gen. Chem.* (U.S.S.R.), **15,** 237 (1945); *Chem. Abstracts*, **40,** 2147 (1946).
50. Gol'dfarb and Katrenko, *Compt. rend. acad. sci. U.S.S.R.*, **27,** 673 (1940); *Chem. Abstracts*, **35,** 2149 (1941).
51. Tschitschibabin, *Ber.*, **57,** 2092 (1924).
52. Reindel, *Ber.*, **57,** 1381 (1924).
53. Vo-Thi and Hoán, *Compt. rend.*, **237,** 1016 (1953).
54. Buu-Hoï, Hoán, *Rec. trav. chim.*, **69,** 1455 (1950).
55. Buu-Hoï, Hoán and Lavit, *J. Chem. Soc.*, **1953,** 485.
56. Gol'dfarb and Andrijchuk, *Compt. rend. acad. sci. U.S.S.R.*, **15,** 473 (1937); *Chem. Abstracts*, **32,** 176 (1938); *Chem. Zentr.*, **I,** 3205 (1938).
57. Lescot, Buu-Hoï and Xuong, *J. Chem. Soc.*, **1956,** 2408.
58. Buu-Hoï, Hoán and Royer, *Bull. soc. chim. France*, **1950,** 489.
59. Buu-Hoï and Khôi, *Bull. soc. chim. France*, **1950,** 753.
60. Routier, Buu-Hoï and Royer, *J. Chem. Soc.*, **1956,** 4276.
61. Buu-Hoï, Xuong and Thang, *Rec. trav. chim.*, **72,** 774 (1953).
62. Buu-Hoï, Royer and Bisagni, *Rec. trav. chim.*, **74,** 24 (1955).
63. Thoi and Belloc, *Industrie plastiques mod.* (Paris), 6, No. 3, 90–2; No. 4, 39, 41, 43; No. 5, 47, 49 (1954); *Chem. Abstracts*, **49,** 14694 (1955).
64. Sucharda, *Roczniki Chem.*, **3,** 236 (1923); *Chem. Abstracts*, **19,** 72 (1925); *Chem. Zentr.*, **II,** 659 (1924).
65. Finger and Kraft, *Ber.*, **57,** 1950 (1924).
66. Magidson and Elina, *J. Gen. Chem.* (U.S.S.R.), **16,** 1933 (1946); *Chem. Abstracts*, **41,** 6219 (1947).
67. Reindel and Rosendahl, *Ber.*, **59,** 1064 (1926).
68. Reindel and Rauch, *Ber.*, **59,** 2921 (1926).

69. Reindel and Putzer-Reybegg, *Ber.*, **59,** 2926 (1926).
70. Schwartz, U. S. Pat. 2,481,953.
71. Allen, Van Allen and Wilson, *J. Am. Chem. Soc.*, **66,** 1805 (1944).
72. Knott, *J. Chem. Soc.*, **1956,** 1644.
73. Knott, *J. Chem. Soc.*, **1951,** 3033.
74. Knott, U. S. Pat. 2,514,649.
75. Knott, Brit. Pat. 656,607.
76. van Dormael, *Bull. soc. chim. Belges*, **58,** 167 (1949); *Chem. Abstracts*, **45,** 4153 (1951).
77. Brooker and White, U. S. Pat. 2,739,964.
78. Knott, *J. Chem. Soc.*, **1956,** 1360.
79. Reindel, Ger. Pat. 414,146; *Frdl.*, **15,** 455 (1928).
80. Ruhemann and Singleton, *J. Chem. Soc.*, **77,** 804 (1900).
81. Gabriel and Leupold, *Ber.*, **31,** 1159 and 1272 (1898).
82. Kuhn, *Naturwiss.*, **20,** 618 (1932).
83. Harriman, U. S. Pat. 2,421,693.
84. Hach and Protiva, *Collection Czechoslov. Chem. Communs.*, **18,** 684 (1953); *Chem. Listy*, **47,** 729 (1953).
85. Gol'dfarb and Andrijchuk, Russ. Pat. 51,041; *Chem. Abstracts*, **33,** 4604 (1939).
86. Sokov, *J. Gen. Chem.* (U.S.S.R.), **10,** 1457 (1940); *Chem. Abstracts*, **35,** 2510 (1941); *Brit. Chem. Abstracts*, **AII,** 331 (1941).
87. Takahashi and Satake, *J. Pharm. Soc. Japan*, **75,** 20 (1955); *Chem. Abstracts*, **50,** 1004 (1956).
88. Mosby and Boyle, *J. Org. Chem.*, **24,** 374 (1959).

A-272. 1*H*-Cyclopent[4,5]imidazo-[1,2-*a*]pyridine*

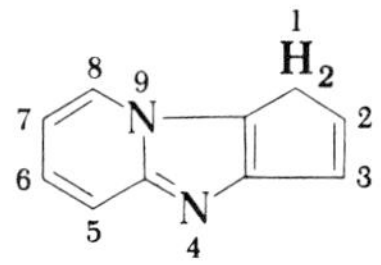

The reaction of 2-bromocyclopentanone with 2-aminopyridine yields a solid product, $b_{2.5}$ 145°. This product was first[1] thought by Reitmann to have structure I, but he later[2] favored the more reasonable structure II.

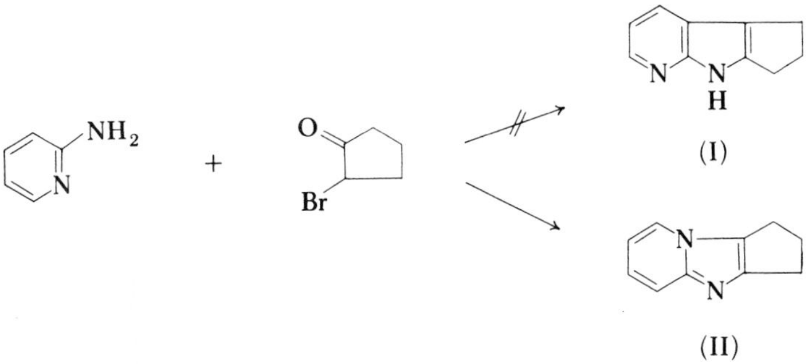

(I)

(II)

References

1. Reitmann, Ger. Pat. 547,985; *Frdl.*, **18,** 2782 (1933); *Chem. Abstracts*, **26,** 3514 (1932); Brit. Pat. 360,027; *Brit. Chem. Abstracts*, **B-III,** 252 (1932).
2. Reitmann, U. S. Pat. 2,057,978.

A-273. 3*H*-Imidazo[1,2-*a*]triazolo[*c*]-pyridine. R.I.1320M

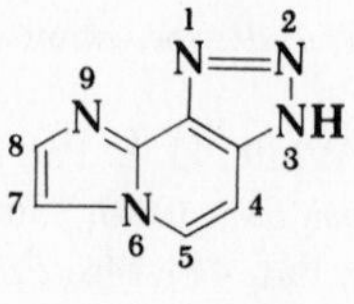

This nucleus has also been called *6,7-pyrimidazolo-13,14-triazole* and numbered as shown in I.

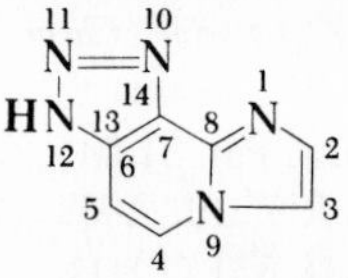

(I)

The only reported representative of this nucleus is the 3-*n*-butyl-7,8-dihydro-derivative II (m. 75°; ethiodide, m. 176°), prepared by Bremer[1] from 4-chloro-3-nitro-pyridine.

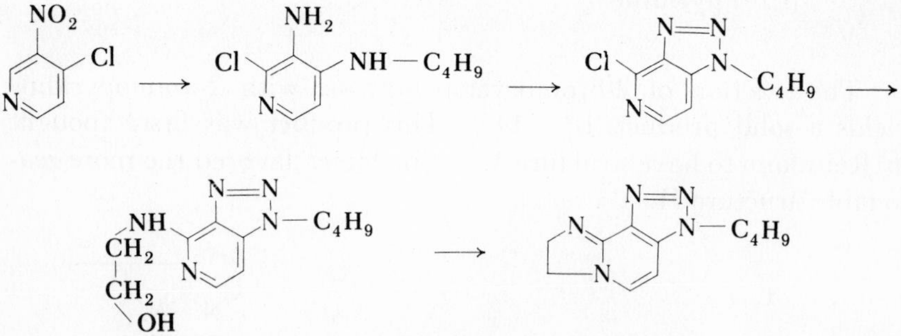

(II)

Reference

1. Bremer, *Ann.*, **539,** 276 (1939).

A-274. Pyrido[1,2-*a*]benzimidazole.
R.I. 1576

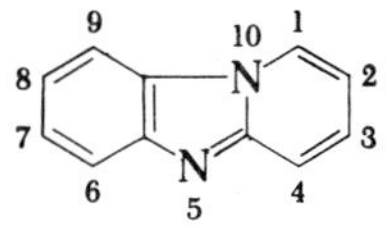

This nucleus has also been named *pyrido(1′:2′-1:2)benziminazole* (I), *1,2-pyrido-4,5-benz-1,3-diazaline* (II) and *benzimidazoperidine.*

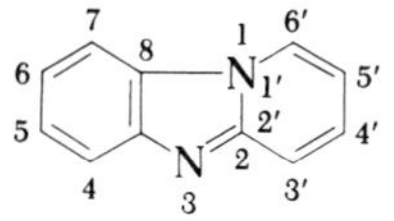

(I) 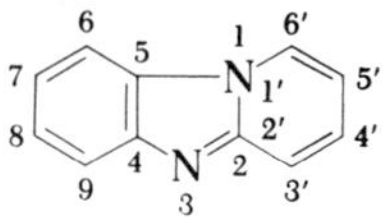 (II)

The condensation of 2-pyridylamine with benzo- and toluquinones was recently reported by Schmid and Czerny[1] to yield IIIa, although structure IIIb was not to be excluded. Where R = CH_3, two products were obtained, presumably the 6- and 7-methyl-8-hydroxy compounds. Xyloquinone, naphthoquinone and chloranil were reported[1] not to react with 2-pyridylamine. Azo dyes have been formed[15] by coupling into phenols such as III.

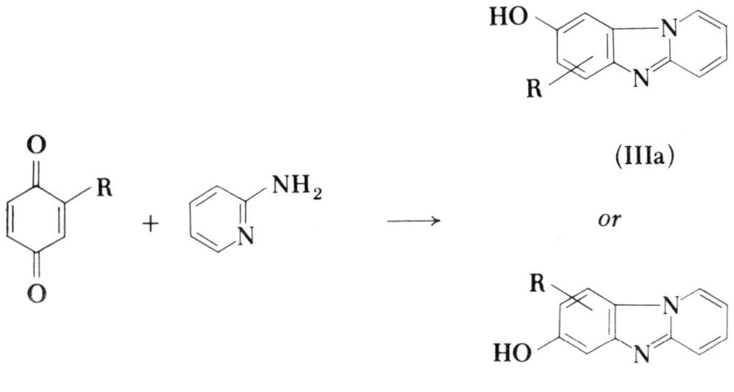

(IIIa)

or

(IIIb)

While investigating the applicability of the Pschorr synthesis to the preparation of α-carbolines (e.g., VI), Abramovich, Hey and Mulley[2] found that heating an aqueous solution of the diazonium salt of IV yielded 84% of V and 7% of VI.

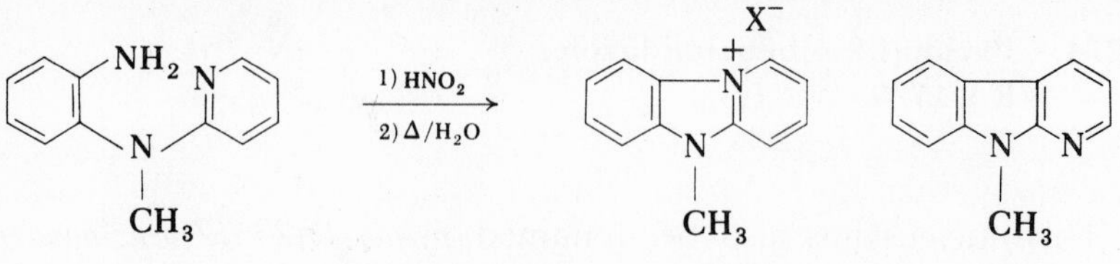

NH_2 N N CH_3

1) HNO_2 2) Δ/H_2O

X^- + N N CH_3

N N CH_3

(IV) (V) (VI)

The condensation of picryl chloride with 2-pyridylamine and related compounds was studied at length by Morgan and Stewart.[3-7] These authors assigned structure VIII to their product, with VII as its probable precursor, but offered no real evidence to refute the possibility that it might have structure X (formed from IX). However, the probable accuracy of Morgan and Stewart's structure as-

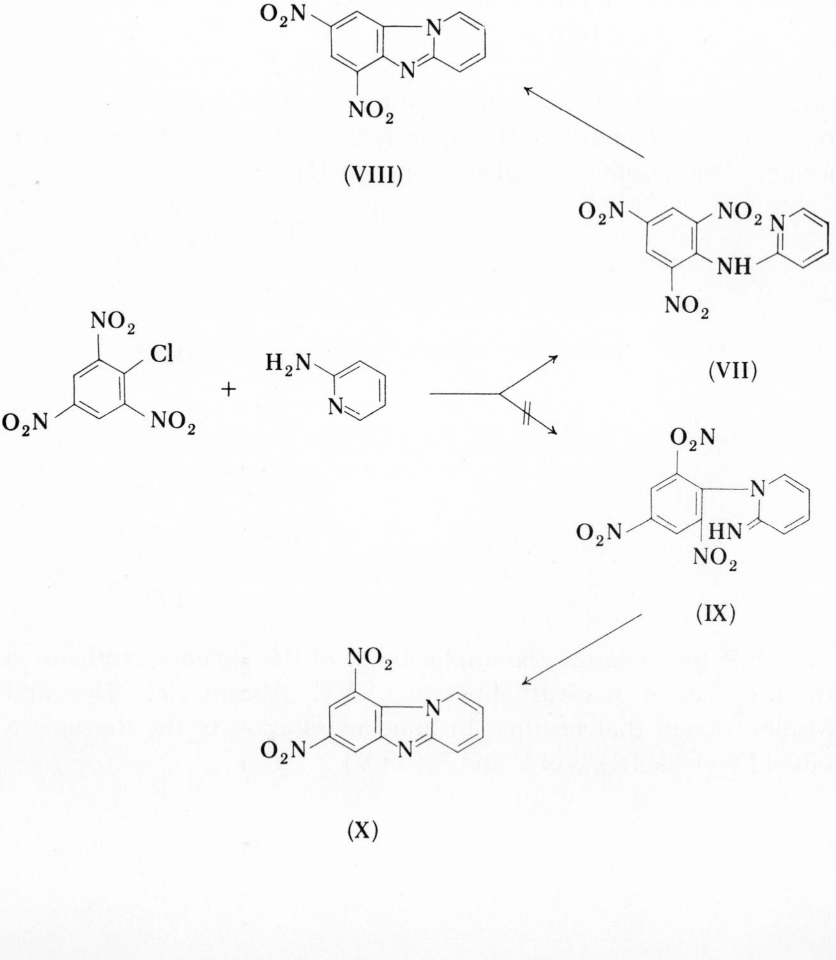

O_2N N N NO_2

(VIII)

O_2N NO_2 N NH NO_2

(VII)

NO_2 Cl O_2N NO_2 + H_2N N

O_2N N O_2N HN NO_2

(IX)

NO_2 N O_2N N

(X)

signment was adumbrated by the discovery of the structure of similar products obtained from 2-pyridylamine and 1-chloro-2,4-dinitronaphthalene (see Section A-283), and a body of evidence has slowly accumulated, which seems to indicate that the site of attack by activated aryl halides upon 2-pyridylamine is, indeed, the amino group.

Treatment of VIII with sodium sulfide gave[4] a monoamine formulated[6] as the 8-nitro-6-amine, since on deamination, the resulting product (XI, 8-nitropyrido[1,2-*a*]benzimidazole) was identical with that produced[5] by the condensation of 2-pyridylamine with 2,4-dinitrochlorobenzene. The 6-nitro analog has similarly been obtained[14] from 2,6-dinitrochlorobenzene. Mild catalytic reduction of VIII yielded the corresponding diamine, which upon deamination yielded XII, also prepared by the reduction and deamination of XI. The catalytic dehydrogenation of 1,2,3,4-tetrahydropyrido[1,2-*a*]benzimidazole at 300° also yielded[14] XII.

H_2/PtO_2

O_2N Na_2S_x O_2N H_2N

NO_2 NH_2 NH_2

(VIII)

O_2N

(XI) (XII)

O_2N NO_2 + N

Cl H_2N

Little is known concerning the products of substitution reactions upon this nucleus, although from its similarity to benzimidazole electrophilic substitution might be expected to occur at positions 7- or 8-. Nitration of XII has been reported[14] to yield the 8-nitro derivative (XI).

More drastic hydrogenation of VIII over Adams catalyst yielded XIII, which on deamination gave[4] XIV, a substance recently isolated by Huisgen and Rist[8] from the products of the reaction of lithium piperidine with nitrobenzene at −50°. Compound XIV is perhaps most conveniently obtained[17] by heating *o*-phenylenediamine with δ-valerolactone.

O_2N N N NO_2 $\xrightarrow{H_2/PtO_2}$ H_2N N N NH_2

(VIII) (XIII)

NO_2 + Li N → N N

(XIV)

O O $o\text{-}C_6H_4(NH_2)_2$

N N COC_6H_5

(XV)

In 1908, Spiegel and Kaufmann[9] isolated from the reduction products of 1-(2,4-dinitrophenyl)piperidine, a compound thought to have structure XVI. Although XIV gave[8] only a monobenzoyl derivative considered to have structure XV, benzoylation of XVI was reported[9] to yield a dibenzoyl derivative of structure XVII, which could be hydrolyzed to a phenyl ketone (XVIII).

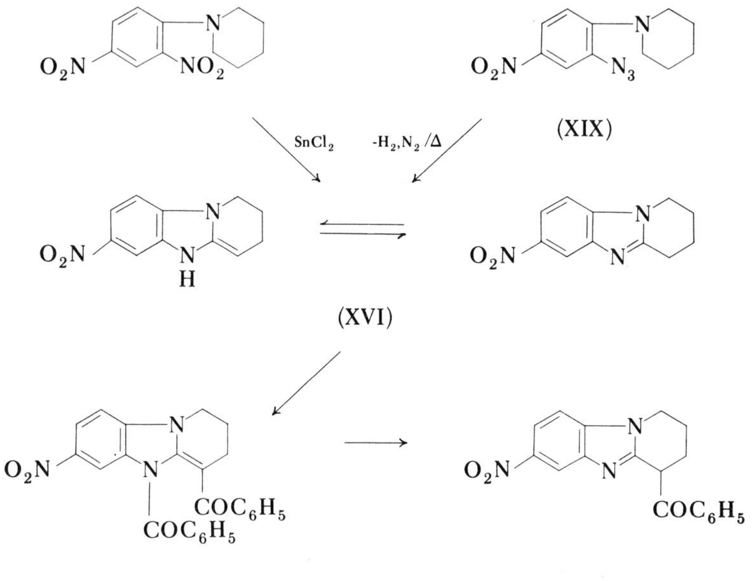

(XIX)

(XVI)

(XVII) (XVIII)

Recently Saunders[14] developed a much more convenient and general synthesis of 1,2,3,4-tetrahydropyrido[1,2-*a*]benzimidazoles from 1-(2-azidophenyl)piperidines. The azide was simply heated in nitrobenzene solution until gas evolution ceased, after which the product was isolated by removal of the solvent. Among other such compounds, Saunders prepared XVI from XIX, thus confirming the identity of Spiegel and Kaufmann's product. Although it was not found possible[9] to obtain XIV by the reduction of 1-(2-nitrophenyl)piperidine or by the oxidation of 1-(2-aminophenyl)piperidine, the pyrolysis of 1-(2-azidophenyl)piperidine readily yielded XIV. The 7-acetamido derivative of XIV was found[14] to nitrate in position 8.

In 1925, Chakravarti and Sen Gupta,[10] as part of a study of the color of various diazoles, prepared the isomeric compounds XXI and XXII by the reaction of *o*-phenylenediamine with camphoric anhydride (XX). Although these compounds are properly named (by

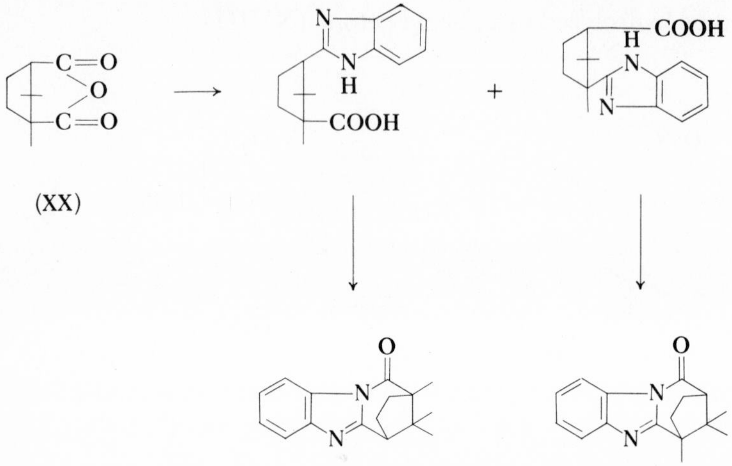

(XX)

(XXI) (XXII)

the *Ring Index*) as derivatives of 6,9-methano-6*H*-azepo[1,2-*a*] benzimidazole, they may also be considered as ethano-1,2,3,4-tetrahydropyrido[1,2-*a*]benzimidazoles, and for convenience are so included in the table.

Reitmann[11,12] described the condensation of several 2-chlorocyclohexanones with various 2-pyridylamines, and obtained a number of products to which he first[11] assigned the pyrid[2,3-*b*]indole structure (XXIII), and later[12] formulated as pyrido[1,2-*a*]benzimidazoles. It was recently demonstrated by Campbell and McCall[13] that Reitmann's products were actually 5,6,7,8-tetrahydropyrido[1,2-*a*]benzimidazoles (XXVI). By analogy to similar syntheses in imidazo[1,2-*a*]pyridine series (see Section A-271), the formation of XXVI would be expected to occur via the intermediate XXV. However, Campbell and McCall were able to show definitely that (at least 30% of) the precursor was XXIV. Thus syntheses involving substituted 2-chlorocyclohexanones might yield two possible isomeric derivatives of XXVI, and further exploration of this problem would seem useful.

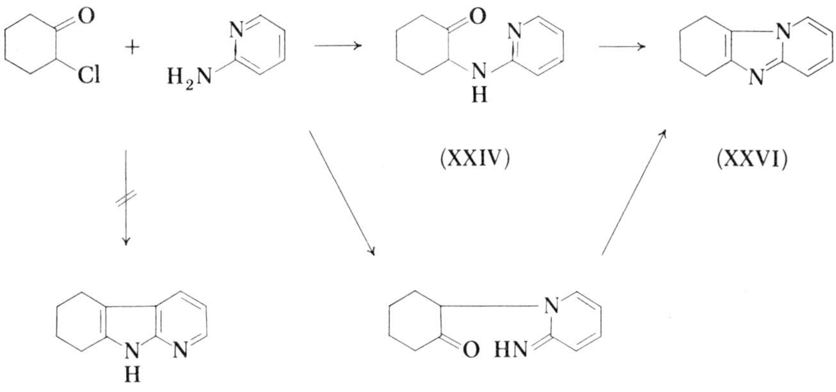

(XXIV) (XXVI)

(XXIII) (XXV)

Reitmann[11,12] also showed that 2-pyridylamine reacted with 1,2-dibromocyclohexane or with 2-methoxycyclohexanol to yield a product thought to be 5*a*,6,7,8,9,9*a*-hexahydropyrido[1,2-*a*]benzimidazole.

Pyrido[1,2-*a*]benzimidazoles

Empirical formula	Substituents	Properties and comments	Refs.
$C_{11}H_6N_4O_4$	6,8-Dinitro-	Brt. yel., m. > 300°.	3,4,6
$C_{11}H_6N_8$	6,8-Bis-triazo-	d. 167–70°.	4
$C_{11}H_7N_3O_2$	6-Nitro-	m. 272°.	14
	8-Nitro-	Yel., m. 268–9° (262–3°).	3-7,14
$C_{11}H_8N_2$	Unsubstituted	m. 178–9°. Methopicrate, m. 196–8°. Methiodide, m. 246–7°.	2-5,13,14
$C_{11}H_8N_2O$	8-Hydroxy-	Yel.-grn., d. 259–60°. Solns. fluoresce bl. HCl salt m. 243° d. *o*-Acetyl derivative, m. 209°; solns. fluoresce strongly. Picrate of *o*-acetyl derivative, m. 262° d.	1
$C_{11}H_8N_4O_2$	6-Amino-8-nitro-	Dk. red, m. > 280°.	3-5
$C_{11}H_9N_3$	6-Amino-	Yel., m. 133–4°. Acetyl derivative, m. 142–4°.	14
	8-Amino-	Yel., m. 230.0–0.5° (229–30°).	3-5,14

(continued)

Pyrido[1,2-*a*]benzimidazoles (*continued*)

Empirical formula	Substituents	Properties and comments	Refs.
$C_{11}H_{10}Br_2N_2$	2,4-Dibromo-6,7,8,9-tetrahydro-	m. 159–60°, λ_{max} 245, 290, 325 mμ (log ε 4.45, 3.68, 3.70). Picrate, m. 167–9°.	13
$C_{11}H_{10}N_4$	6,8-Diamino-	Yel., m. 204–5°.	4,6
$C_{11}H_{10}N_8$	1,2,3,4-Tetrahydro-6,8-bistriazo-	m. 132°.	4
$C_{11}H_{11}BrN_2$	2-Bromo-6,7,8,9-tetrahydro-	m. 148–9°; λ_{max} 245, 302, 332 mμ (log ε 4.45, 3.68, 3.70). HCl salt, m. 260–2°. Picrate, m. 264–5° d.	13
$C_{11}H_{11}ClN_2$	1,2,3,4-Tetrahydro-7-chloro-	m. 153–4°. HCl salt, m. 295–6°.	14
$C_{11}H_{11}IN_2$	6,7,8,9-Tetrahydro-2-iodo-	b_3 187–90°; m. 150°.	11,12
$C_{11}H_{11}N_3O_2$	6,7,8,9-Tetrahydro-2-nitro-	Yel., m. 214–5° (210°). Picrate, m. 216–9° d.	11–13
	1,2,3,4-Tetrahydro-7-nitro-	m. 219–20°. Dibenzoyl derivative with HCl gives monobenzoyl derivative, m. 178°, which gives oxime, m. 226°.	9,14
	1,2,3,4-Tetrahydro-8-nitro-	m. 217–9°.	14
	1,2,3,4-Tetrahydro-9-nitro-	m. 107–8°. Hydrochloride, m. 258–60° d.	14
$C_{11}H_{12}N_2$	1,2,3,4-Tetrahydro-	m. 107° (100–101)°; 101–2°). Picrate, m. 229–30°. Methiodide, m. 220–1°. I_2 complex, brn., m. 150°.	4,8,14,17
	6,7,8,9-Tetrahydro-	Hydrate, m. 56–8°. Anhydr., m. 95–6°. Picrate, m. 260–1°. Methiodide, m. 256–8°. (257°).	11–13
$C_{11}H_{12}N_4O_2$	7-Amino-1,2,3,4-tetrahydro-8-nitro-	Scarlet, m. 266–7°. Acetyl derivative, m. 199–200°.	14
$C_{11}H_{13}N_3$	2-Amino-6,7,8,9-tetrahydro-	m. 195°.	11
	7-Amino-1,2,3,4-tetrahydro-	m. 218–20°. Acetyl derivative, m. 219.5–20°.	14
	8-Amino-1,2,3,4-tetrahydro-	m. 198–200°.	14

Pyrido[1,2-*a*]benzimidazoles (*continued*)

Empirical formula	Substituents	Properties and comments	Refs.
	9-Amino-1,2,3,4-tetrahydro-	m. 186–7°. Acetyl derivative, m. 236–7°.	14
$C_{11}H_{14}N_2$	5*a*,6,7,8,9,9*a*-Hexahydro-	Probable structure of product b_3 122–5°; m. 94°.	11
$C_{11}H_{14}N_4$	6,8-Diamino-1,2,3,4-tetrahydro-	Yel.-grn., m. 201–2°.	4
$C_{11}H_{16}N_2$	1,2,3,4,6,7,8,9-Octahydro-	(Probable structure; shown as perhydrogenated in ref. 12.) b_4 160–3°, m. 58–9°. Methiodide, m. 248°.	11,12
$C_{12}H_8N_4O_4$	4-Methyl-6,8-dinitro-	m. 256–60°.	4
$C_{12}H_9N_3O_2$	4-Methyl-8-nitro-	m. 260–2°.	4
$C_{12}H_{10}N_2$	4-Methyl-	m. 162°.	4
$C_{12}H_{10}N_2O_2$	8-Hydroxy-6 (or 7?)-methyl-	m. 273° d. *O*-Acetyl derivative m. 203–4°.	1
	8-Hydroxy-7 (or 6?)-methyl-	m. 222° d. *O*-Acetyl derivative m. 139–40°.	1
$C_{12}H_{10}N_4O_2$	6-Amino-4-methyl-8-nitro-	m. 269–70°.	4
$C_{12}H_{11}N_3$	8-Amino-4-methyl-	Yel., m. 229–30°.	4
$C_{12}H_{12}N_4$	6,8-Diamino-4-methyl-	m. ~130°.	4
$C_{12}H_{14}N_2$	6,7,8,9-Tetrahydro-1-methyl-	b_2 159–60°; m. 56°. Methiodide, m. 302°.	11,12
	6,7,8,9-Tetrahydro-4-methyl-	Dihydrate, m. 60–1°. Anhydr., m. 85–7°. Picrate, m. 155–8°.	13
	6,7,8,9-Tetrahydro-8 (or 7?)-methyl-	b_3 150–4°. Methiodide, m. 270°.	11,12
$C_{12}H_{14}N_2O$	6,7,8,9-Tetrahydro-6 (or 9?)-methoxy-	b_3 140°.	11,12
$C_{15}H_{20}N_2$	7 (or 8?)-Isopropyl-9-(or 6?)-methyl-6,7,8,9-tetrahydro-	b_1 155–60°.	11,12

(*continued*)

Pyrido[1,2-*a*]benzimidazoles (*continued*)

Empirical formula	Substituents	Properties and comments	Refs.
$C_{16}H_{18}N_2O$	2,4-Ethano-1,2,3,4-tetrahydro-2,3,3-trimethyl-1-oxo-	(*Chem. Abstracts* Name: 10-Oxo-9,12,12-trimethyl-6,9-methano-6-azepo[1,2-*a*]benzimidazole. *Ring Index No.* 2275) m. 138°.	10
	2,4-Ethano-1,2,3,4-tetrahydro-3,3,4-trimethyl-1-oxo-	(*Chem. Abstracts* Name: 10-Oxo-6,12,12-trimethyl-6,9-methano-6-azepo[1,2-*a*]benzimidazole. *Ring Index No.* 2275) m. 132°.	10
$C_{16}H_{20}N_4O_2$	7-Nitro-8-(1-piperidino)-	Dimorphic; scarlet, m. 137–40°; orange, m. 155–6°.	14
$C_{16}H_{22}N_4$	7-Amino-8-(1-piperidino)-	m. 189–91°.	14
$C_{17}H_{20}N_2O$	2,4-Ethano-1,2,3,4-tetrahydro-2,3,3,8-tetramethyl-1-oxo-	(*Chem. Abstracts* Name: 10-Oxo-3,9,12,12-tetramethyl-6,9-methano-6-azepo[1,2-*a*]benzimidazole. *Ring Index No.* 2275) m. 93°.	10
	2,4-Ethano-1,2,3,4-tetrahydro-3,3,4,8-tetramethyl-1-oxo-	(*Chem. Abstracts* Name: 10-Oxo-3,6,12,12-tetramethyl-6,9-methano-6-azepo[1,2-*a*]benzimidazole. *Ring Index No.* 2275) m. 97°.	10
$C_{18}H_{16}N_2O$	5-Benzoyl-1,2,3,5-tetrahydro-	m. 162.5–3.5°.	8
$C_{18}H_{18}N_2$	8 (or 7?)-Benzyl-6,7,8,9-tetrahydro-	b_1 204–12°.	11,12
$C_{22}H_{14}N_4O_7S$	8-(1-Methyl-*x*,5-dinitro-4-naphthylsulfonoxy)-	Yel.-brn., chars < 190°.	16

References

1. Schmid and Czerny, *Monatsh.*, **83**, 31 (1952).
2. Abramovich, Hey and Mulley, *J. Chem. Soc.*, **1954**, 4263.
3. Morgan and Stewart, *Chem. and Ind.*, **1937**, 670.
4. Morgan and Stewart, *J. Chem. Soc.*, **1938**, 1292.

5. Morgan and Stewart, *J. Chem. Soc.*, **1939,** 1057.
6. Morgan and Stewart, Brit. Pat. 496,258; *Chem. Abstracts*, **33,** 3173 (1939).
7. Morgan and Stewart, Brit. Pat. 519,660; *Chem. Abstracts*, **36,** 784 (1942).
8. Huisgen and Rist, *Ann.*, **594,** 159 (1955).
9. Spiegel and Kaufmann, *Ber.*, **41,** 679 (1908).
10. Chakravarti and Sen Gupta, *Quart. J. Indian Chem. Soc.*, **1,** 329 (1925); *Chem. Zentr.*, **II,** 1864 (1925); *Chem. Abstracts*, **19,** 2493 (1925).
11. Reitmann, Ger. Pat. 547,985; *Frdl.*, **18,** 2782 (1933). Brit. Pat. 360,027; *Brit. Chem. Abstracts*, **B-III,** 252 (1932).
12. Reitmann, U. S. Pat. 2,057,978.
13. Campbell and McCall, *J. Chem. Soc.*, **1951,** 2411.
14. Saunders, *J. Chem. Soc.*, **1955,** 3275.
15. Rudner, U. S. Pat. 2,742,457.
16. Süs, Schmidt and Glos, U. S. Pat. 2,773,765.
17. Mosby, *J. Org. Chem.*, **24,** 419 (1959).

A-275. Dipyrido[1,2-*a*, 4′,3′-*d*]-imidazole

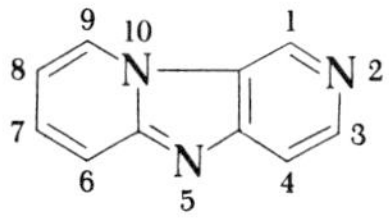

This nucleus has also been called *3,9,12-triazafluorene* and numbered as shown in I.

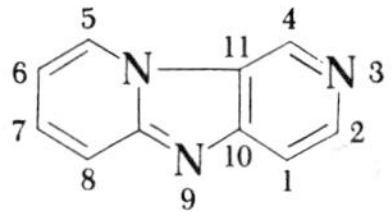

(I)

Only four compounds with this nucleus have been reported. They were obtained by Petrov and Saper[1] from the condensation of 2-aminopyridine and 3,5-dinitro-4-chloropyridine. Compound II is a yellow solid, m. 319°, which was reduced by iron and hydrochloric acid to corresponding amine (yellow, m. 256–7°), a convulsant poison with an LD_{50} (i.v./mice) of 60 mg./kg. The methiodide is yellow, m. 311°, and the acetyl derivative melts at 264–5°. Treatment of the amine with nitrous acid produces a normal diazonium salt (red dye with β-naphthol), which, when heated in solution, is converted into a compound (m.p. 311°) assigned structure III.

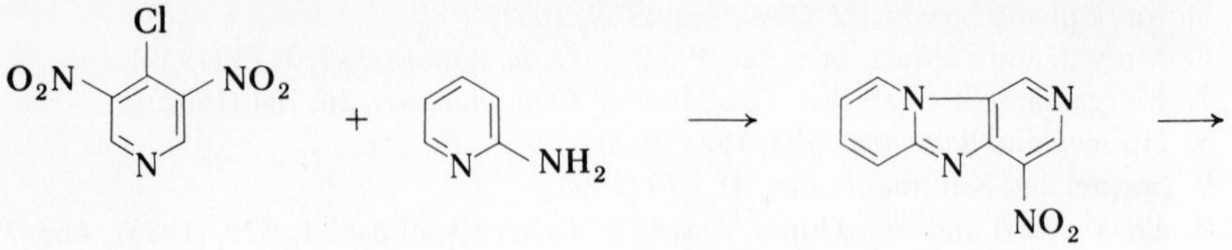

Cl
O_2N NO_2 N + N NH_2 → N N N NO_2 (II) →

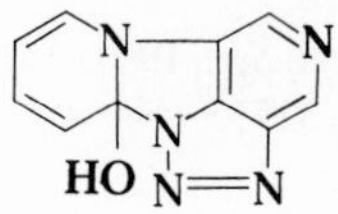

N N N HO N=N

(III)

Reference

1. Petrov and Saper, *J. Chem. Soc.*, **1946,** 588.

A-276. Imidazo[1,2-*a*]quinoline

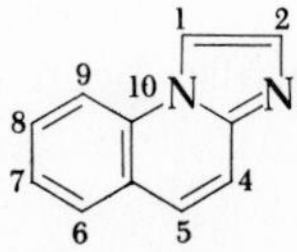

1 2 9 10 N N 3 8 7 4 6 5

This nucleus has also been called *glyoxalino[1′:2′-1:2]quinoline.*

Treatment of 2-quinolylamine (I) with phenacyl bromide, unlike the corresponding reactions with 2-pyridylamine or 2-thiazolylamine (see Sections A-131 and A-271), fails to stop with the formation of the imidazo compound (II), but yields only the quaternary salt III.[1] The action of bases converts III into the "enol-betaine" IV.[1] One example of the fully aromatic system is known, however, compound VI, which was prepared[1] by the acetylation of V under mildly basic conditions.

Osbond[2] has described the preparation of some 2,3-dihydro derivatives (e.g., VIII) of this nucleus by the dehydrohalogenation of compounds of type VII.

The first reference to this ring system occurs in a patent by Harriman,[3] who claimed to have prepared compounds of type IX by treatment of I with chloroacetyl chloride and a second acylating

(V) $\xrightarrow[KOAc]{Ac_2O}$ (VI)

p-$NO_2C_6H_4CH_2Br$

(I) $\xrightarrow{BrCH_2COC_6H_5}$ [(II)] $\longrightarrow$

(III) $\xrightarrow{-HBr}$ (IV)

(VII) $\xrightarrow{-HX}$ (VIII)

agent. However, no description of the techniques or of the products was given.

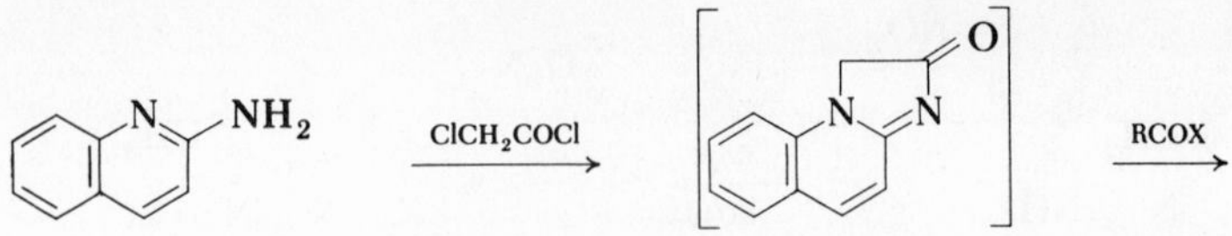

$ClCH_2COCl$ → RCOX →

(I)

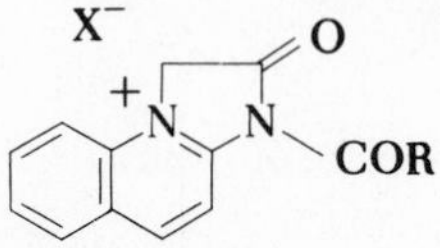

(IX)

Derivatives of Imidazo[1,2-*a*]quinoline

Empirical formula	Structure	Properties and comments	Refs.
$C_{13}H_{14}BrN_3$	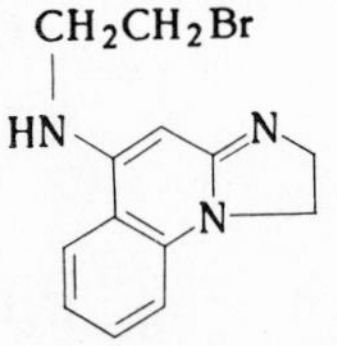 CH_2CH_2Br, HN, N, N	HBr salt, m. 292°.	2
$C_{13}H_{14}ClN_3$	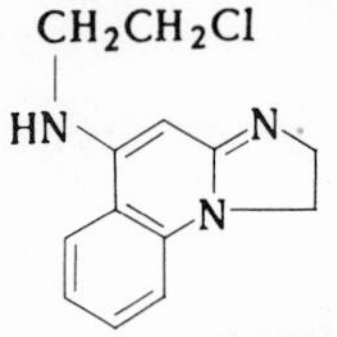 CH_2CH_2Cl, HN, N, N	Yel., m. >320°. HCl salt. m. 220–1°. Methiodide, m. 226°.	2
$C_{15}H_{14}N_2O_4$	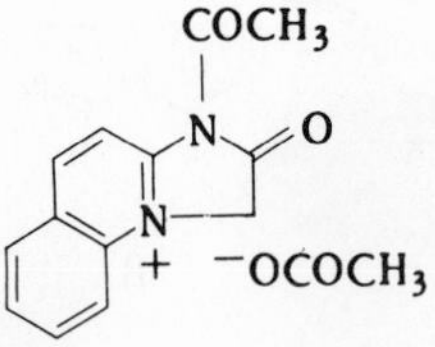 $COCH_3$, N, O, N, +, $^{-}OCOCH_3$	Structure correct?	3
$C_{16}H_{16}N_2O_4$	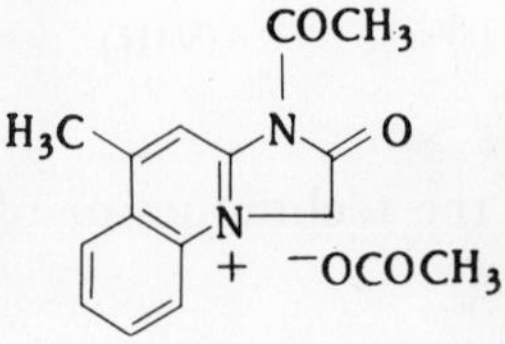 $COCH_3$, H_3C, N, O, N, +, $^{-}OCOCH_3$	Structure correct?	3

Derivatives of Imidazo[1,2-*a*]quinoline (*continued*)

Empirical formula	Structure	Properties and comments	Refs.
$C_{17}H_{22}N_4O$	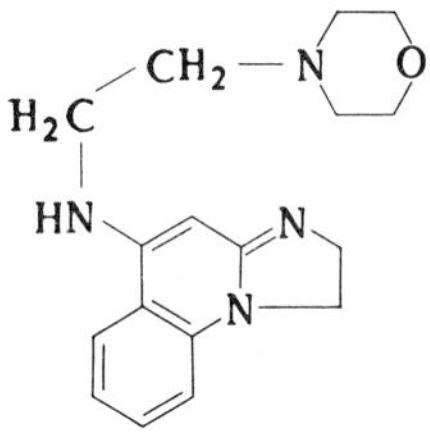	HCl salt, m. 290°.	2
$C_{18}H_{13}N_3O_2$	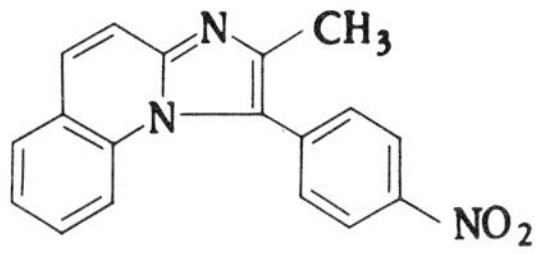	m. 183°; intense yellow fluorescence in UV. HBr salt, m. 318-9° d.	1
$C_{25}H_{19}N_2O$	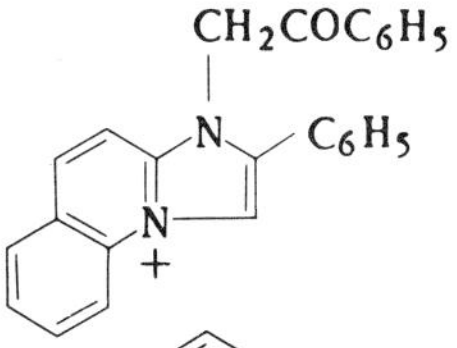	Bromide, m. 213-0-4.5°. "Enol-betaine," or., m. 194-5° d.	1
$C_{26}H_{26}N_6$	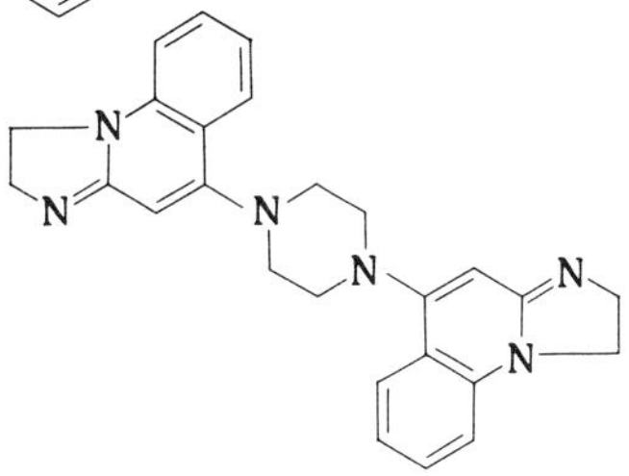	Yel., m. ca. 167°.	2
$C_{29}H_{45}ClN_2O$	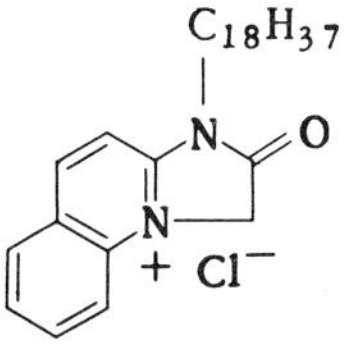	—	3

References

1. Kickhöfen, *Chem. Ber.*, **88,** 1114 (1955).
2. Osbond, *J. Chem. Soc.*, **1950,** 1853.
3. Harriman, U. S. Pat. 2,421,693.

A-277. Imidazo[1,2-*a*][1,8]naphthyridine

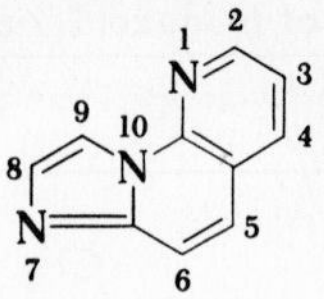

The name *3,9,11-triazapentanthrene* has been used.

The treatment of 2-amino-5,7-dimethyl-1,8-naphthyridine (I) with α-haloketones is reported by Schmid and Gründig[1] to give products of structure II (IIa, R = C_6H_5, m. 174° (vac.), $b_{0.05}$ 185–90°, HCl salt d. 200°; IIb, R = CH_3, m. 142–4° (vac.) $b_{0.05}$ 115–60°).

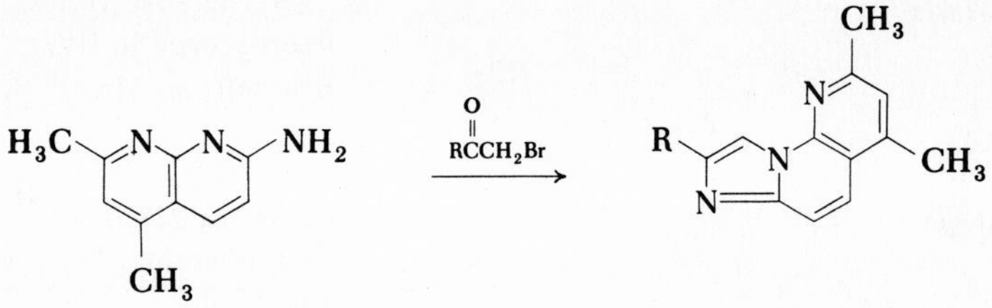

(I)

(IIa) R = C_6H_5
(IIb) R = CH_3

Reference

1. Schmid and Gründig, *Monatsh.*, **84,** 491 (1953).

A-278. Imidazo[2,1-*a*]isoquinoline

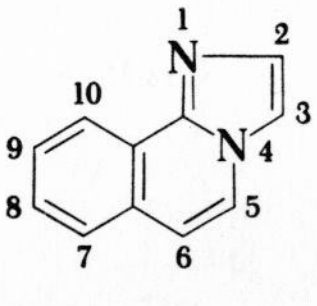

The only reference to this ring system occurs in a patent by Harriman,[1] which mentions compound I but gives no descriptive or experimental details.

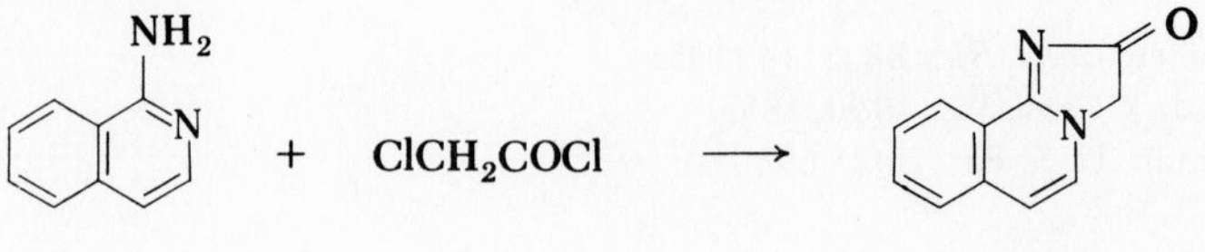

$ClCH_2COCl$

(I)

Reference

1. Harriman, U. S. Pat. 2,421,693.

A-279. Benzimidazo[1,2-*a*]quinoline.
R.I. 2389

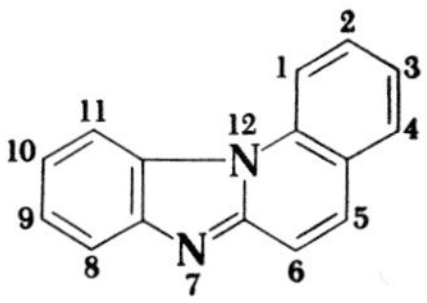

Derivatives of this nucleus were prepared by Morgan and Stewart[1-4] [who named the nucleus *quinolo(1′:2′-1:2)benziminazole* (I) or *1:2-quinolo-4:5-benz-1:3-diazaline* (II)], from the condensation of 2-

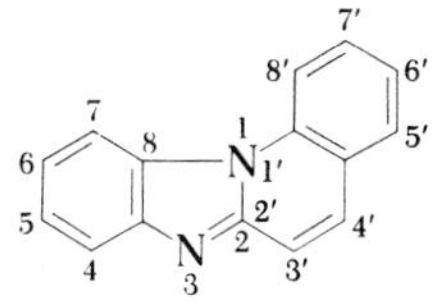

(I) 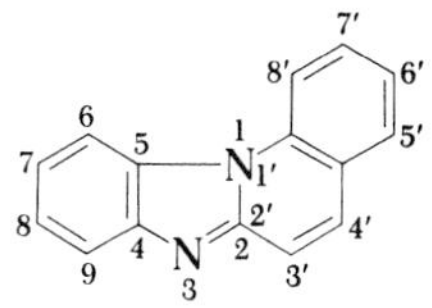 (II)

aminoquinoline with picryl chloride or 2,4-dinitrochlorobenzene. Stepwise reduction of IIIa followed by deamination also gave IIIb. This in turn on reduction and deamination yielded benzimidazo[1,2-*a*]quinoline (IV). A tetrahydro derivative of IV was obtained by

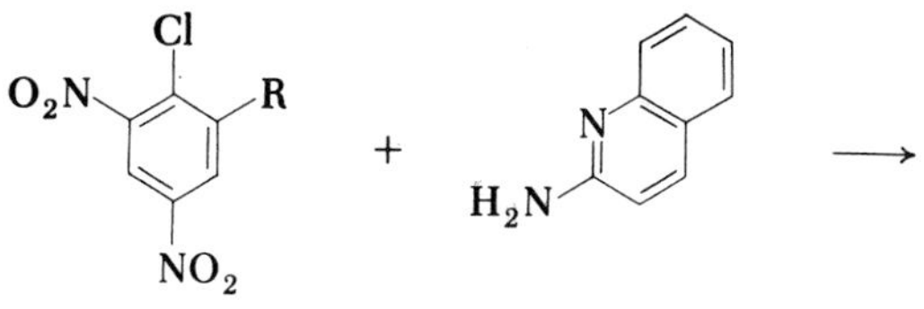

R = H or NO_2

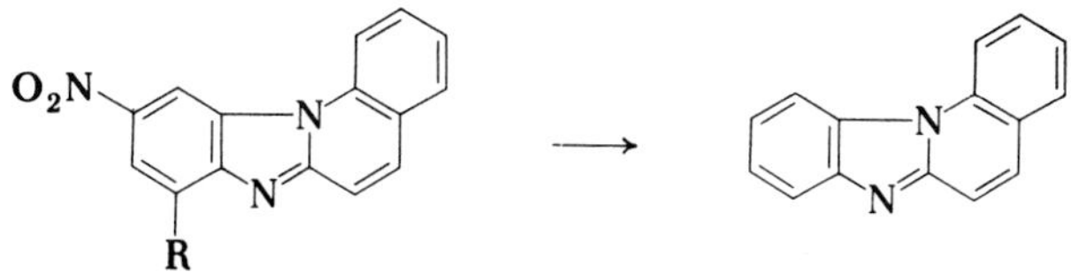

(IIIa) R = NO_2
(IIIb) R = H

(IV)

Reimann[5] from the reaction of 2-chlorocyclohexanone with 2-amino-6-methoxyquinoline.

Benzimidazo[1,2-*a*]quinolines

Empirical formula	Structure	Properties and comments	Refs.
$C_{15}H_8N_4O_4$	8,10-Dinitro-	m. >300°.	2,4
$C_{15}H_9N_3O_2$	10-Nitro-	m. 242–3°.	2,3
$C_{15}H_{10}N_2$	Unsubstituted	m. 102–3°.	2,3
$C_{15}H_{10}N_4O_2$	8-Amino-10-nitro-	m. >300°.	2
$C_{15}H_{11}N_3$	10-Amino-	m. 233° (223°?).	2
$C_{15}H_{12}N_4$	8,10-Diamino-	m. 273–4°.	2
$C_{16}H_{16}N_2O$	8,9,10,11-Tetrahydro-3-methoxy-	m. 153°. Hydrochloride, m. 265°.	5

References

1. Morgan and Stewart, *Chem. and Ind.*, **1937**, 670.
2. Morgan and Stewart, *J. Chem. Soc.*, **1938**, 1292.
3. Morgan and Stewart, *J. Chem. Soc.*, **1939**, 1057.
4. Morgan and Stewart, Brit. Pat. 519,660; *Chem. Abstracts*, **33**, 3173 (1939).
5. Reitmann, Ger. Pat. 547,985; *Frdl.*, **18**, 2782 (1933). U. S. Pat. 2,057,978.

A-280. Benzimidazo[1,2-*b*]isoquinoline*

From the reaction of homophthalic anhydride with *o*-phenylenediamine, Bistrzycki and Fässler[1] isolated a yellow substance (d. ~345°), to which they assigned structure I, although II remained an alternative choice. Recently Schroeder claimed[2] that this product is actually a 3:1 mixture of I and II (see Section A-281).

Condensation of this mixture (II fails to react) with glyoxal yielded[2] III (red crystals giving a red solution in sulfuric acid), while with terephthalaldehyde, IV (reddish orange, nonvattable) was obtained.[3] Oxidation (e.g., with manganese dioxide, etc.) of III in an aluminum chloride-sodium chloride melt yielded the bluish red V (green vat; violet solution in sulfuric acid). Dichloro and di-

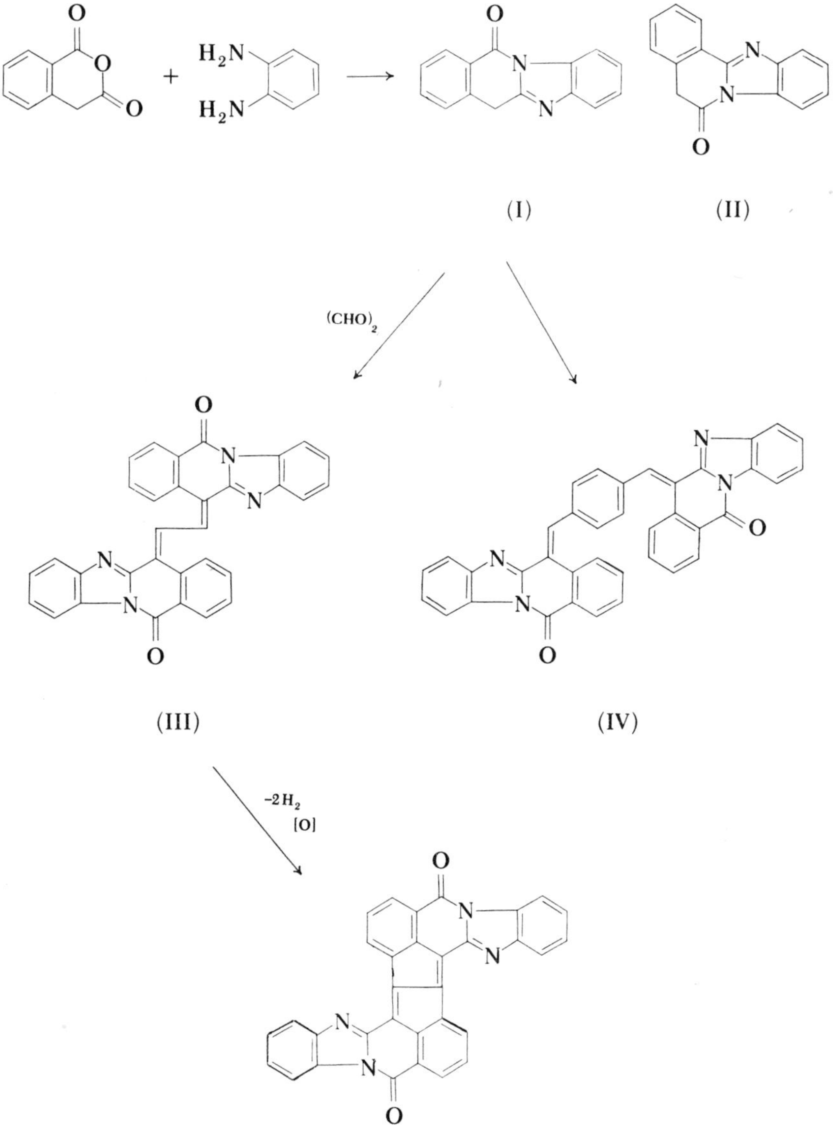

(I) (II)

$(CHO)_2$

(III) (IV)

$-2H_2$
[O]

(V)

bromo analogs of V, prepared[2] from 4-halo-*o*-phenylenediamines, had similar properties.

References

1. Bistrzycki and Fässler, *Helv. Chim. Acta*, **6,** 519 (1923).
2. Schroeder, U. S. Pat. 2,785,167.
3. Oken and Schroeder, U. S. Pat. 2,777,845.

A-281. Benzimidazo[2,1-*a*]isoquinoline.
R.I. 2386

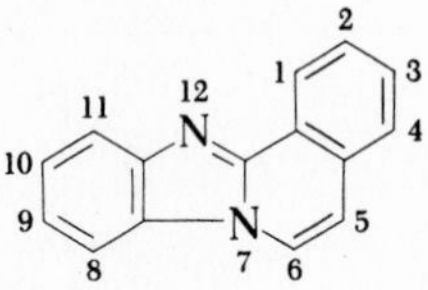

Other titles encountered are: *pyrido(1':2'-1:2)benziminazole* (I) and *1:2-pyrido-4:5-benz-1.3-diazaline* (II).

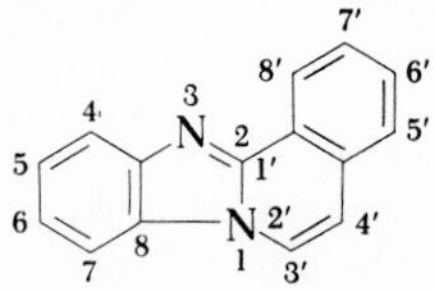

(I) 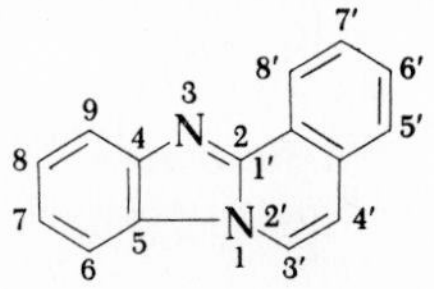 (II)

The product (see Section A-280) obtained by Bistrzycki and Fässler[1] from the condensation of homophthalic anhydride with *o*-phenylenediamine is claimed[2] to be a 1:3 mixture of III with the linear isomer.

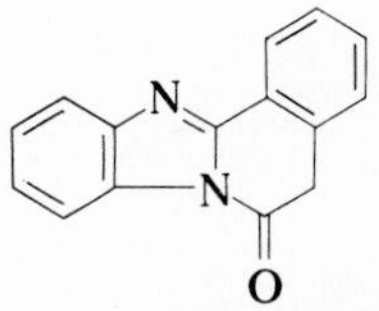

(III)

The condensation of picryl chloride, or of 2,4-dinitrochlorobenzene with 1-aminoisoquinoline is reported[3-5] to yield products of structure IV. Reduction followed by deamination converted IV into the parent compound of this nucleus.

Reitmann[6] prepared the 8,9,10,11-tetrahydro derivative by reacting 1-aminoisoquinoline with 2-chlorocyclohexanone.

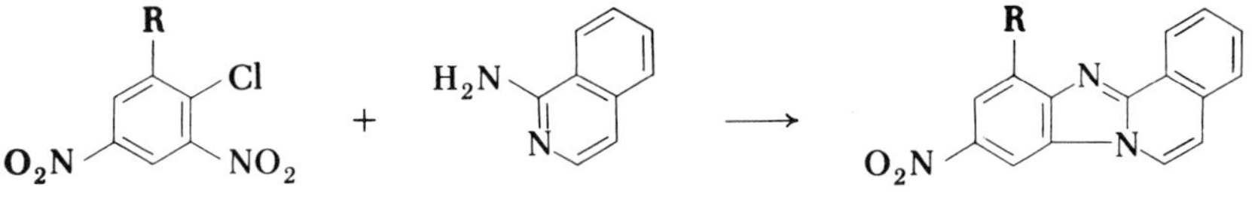

(IV)

Benzimidazo[2,1-*a*]isoquinolines

Empirical formula	Substituents	Properties and comments	Refs.
$C_{15}H_{10}N_2O$	5,6-Dihydro-6-oxo-	Yel., d. ~345°.	1
$C_{15}H_{10}N_4O_4$	9,11-Dinitro-	m. >280°.	2,3
$C_{15}H_{11}N_3O_2$	9-Nitro-	m. 271–2°.	4
$C_{15}H_{12}N_2$	Unsubstituted	m. 129°.	3
$C_{15}H_{12}N_4O_2$	11-Amino-9-nitro-	—	4
$C_{15}H_{13}N_3$	9-Amino-	m. 266–7°.	4
$C_{15}H_{14}N_4$	9,11-Diamino-	m. 249–50°.	3
$C_{15}H_{16}N_2$	8,9,10,11-Tetrahydro-	Solid, b_3 200–10°.	5

References

1. Bistrzycki and Fässler, *Helv. Chim. Acta*, **6,** 519 (1923).
2. Schroeter, U. S. Pat. 2,785,167.
3. Morgan and Stewart, *Chem. and Ind.*, **1937,** 670.
4. Morgan and Stewart, *J. Chem. Soc.*, **1938,** 1292.
5. Morgan and Stewart, *J. Chem. Soc.*, **1939,** 1057.
6. Reitmann, Ger. Pat. 547,985; *Frdl.*, **18,** 2782 (1933). U. S. Pat. 2,057,978.

A-282. 12*aH*-Pyrido[1,2-*a*]quin[1,2-*c*]-imidazole. R.I. 2385

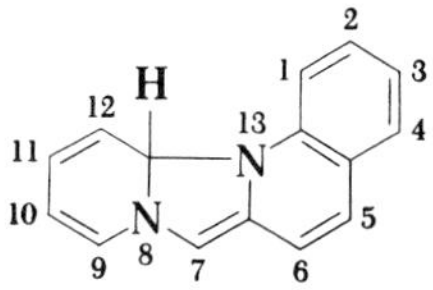

A red dye containing this nucleus was reported by Krollpfeiffer and Schneider[1] to be obtained by the action of quinaldic acid chloride on pyridine. This product (I) crystallized in red-brown needles, which sintered and darkened above 200°, and melted with decomposition at 238–40°. The yellow picrate melted at 193–4°; the greenish yellow methyl iodide addition compound at 190° d., and the methyl sulfate addition compound at 165–8°d. Vigorous treat-

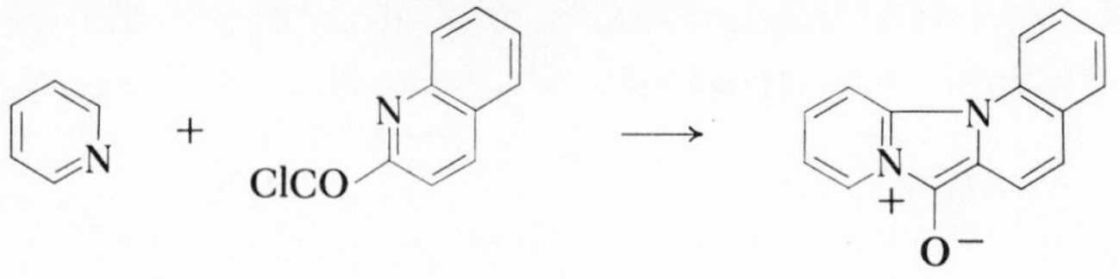

(I)

ment of the dye with 48% hydrobromic acid hydrolyzed it to pyridine and quinaldic acid. The structure of the dye is probably best represented by a mesoionic hydrid (to which formula I is a major contributor) similar to that postulated for Besthorn's Red (see Section A-291).

Recently Brown and Wild[2] prepared the oxygen-free salts II [X = picrate, m. 238–9°; X = bromide, in water λ_{max} 235, 275, 317, 334, 350, 370 and 380 mμ (log ϵ = 4.33, 4.28, 3.73, 3.92, 4.05, 4.07 and 3.94, respectively), and X = ClO_4^-], by two different routes, which demonstrate the involvement of the α-carbon atom of the pyridine nucleus, and effectively support structure II. Catalytic hydrogenation of the bromide of II over Raney nickel yielded the 9,10,11,12-tetrahydro derivative of II (picrate, m. 186–7°; the bromide and perchlorate salts were also prepared, but the melting points were not given).

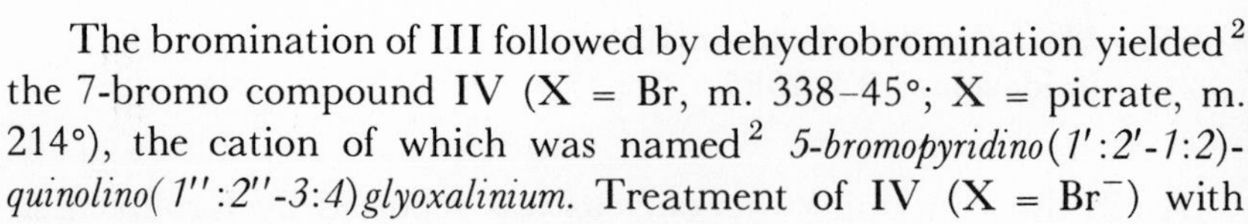

(II)

The bromination of III followed by dehydrobromination yielded[2] the 7-bromo compound IV (X = Br, m. 338–45°; X = picrate, m. 214°), the cation of which was named[2] *5-bromopyridino(1′:2′-1:2)-quinolino(1″:2″-3:4)glyoxalinium.* Treatment of IV (X = Br^-) with

(III)

(IV)

sulfuric acid at 100° did not remove the nuclear bromine atom, but yielded a sulfonic acid (picrate, m. 226°). Compound IV was also obtained[3] by brominating II in acetic acid.

References

1. Krollpfeiffer and Schneider, *Ann.*, **530,** 34 (1937).
2. Brown and Wild, *J. Chem. Soc.*, **1956,** 1158.
3. Brown and White, *J. Chem. Soc.*, **1957,** 1589.

A-283. Benzo[*e*]pyrido[*a*]-benzimidazole. R.I. 2386H

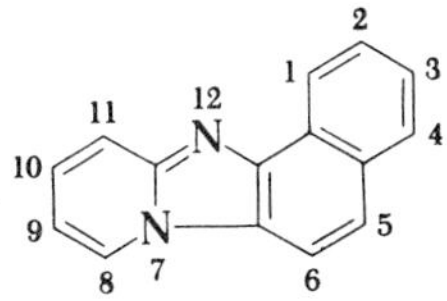

The name *1:2-pyrido-8:9-benzo-4:5-benz-1:3-diazaline* and the numbering shown in I have also been used.

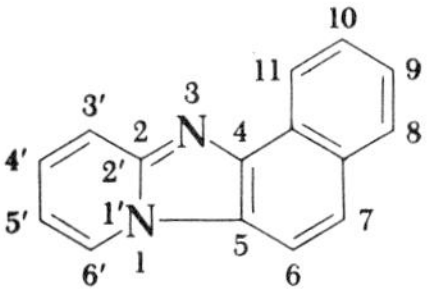

(I)

The condensation of 2-aminopyridine with 1-chloro-2,4-dinitronaphthalene yields a product which could, a priori, have either structure II or III. Morgan and Stewart assigned[1] structure III to the

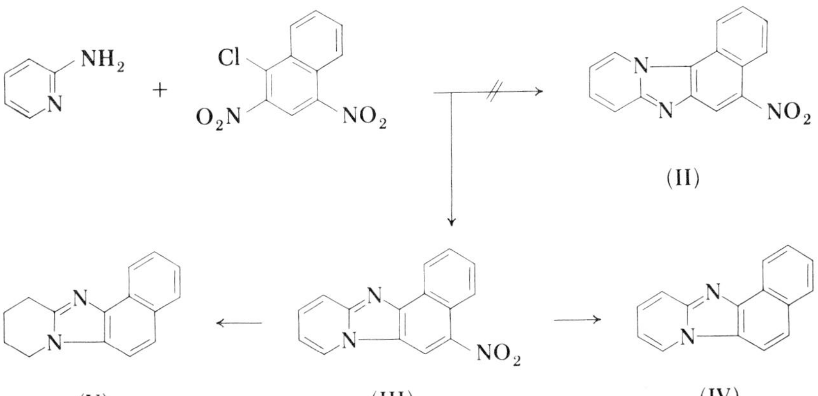

(II)

(V) (III) (IV)

$N \cdot SO_2C_6H_5$ / $N \cdot SO_2C_6H_5$ (VI) + 2-aminopyridine (NH_2, N) → $NHSO_2C_6H_5$ (VII)

(VI) ↓ pyridine / HCl

(VII) ↓ H_2/PtO_2, EtOH/HCl

$C_6H_5SO_2$–NH, N^+, $NHSO_2C_6H_5$, Cl^- (VIII)

H_2/ Raney Ni, EtOH/ NaOH →

H, N, N, $NHSO_2C_6H_5$ (X)

(VIII) ↘ H_2/PtO_2, Na_2CO_3

(VIII) ↓ $[HO]^-$

(IX) ↑ H_2/PtO_2, EtOH/HCl

$C_6H_5SO_2$–N, N, $NHSO_2C_6H_5$ (XI)

H, N, N, $NHSO_2C_6H_5$ (IX)

(XI) ↓ H_2/PtO_2, EtOH

$C_6H_5SO_2$–NH, N, $NHSO_2C_6H_5$ (XII)

product, although until very recently, without corroborative evidence. However, Adams and Pomerantz,[2] while investigating the reactions of VI with pyridine and with 2-aminopyridine, obtained compound VII, which, upon hydrolysis, yielded an amine identical with that prepared by Morgan and Stewart from III. Compound VII was reduced to X, which could also be obtained (via VIII and IX) from the reaction of VI with pyridine. These steps effectively demonstrate the skeleton present in these derivatives, and preclude the alternative skeleton present in II. Basification of VIII yielded XI, which could be reduced, depending upon the conditions, either to IX or to XII.

Chemical reduction[1] of III, followed by diazotization and removal of the amino group gave the parent compound IV. Its behavior in substitution reactions has not been described. Catalytic hydrogenation of III reduced[1] both the nitro group and also the pyridine ring, and subsequent deamination gave V.

The reaction of 2,3-dichloro-1,4-naphthoquinone with 2-aminopyridine yields a quinone incorrectly thought[3] to be XIII, but shown[4] to have structure XIV. When 2-aminopyridine reacted[4] with

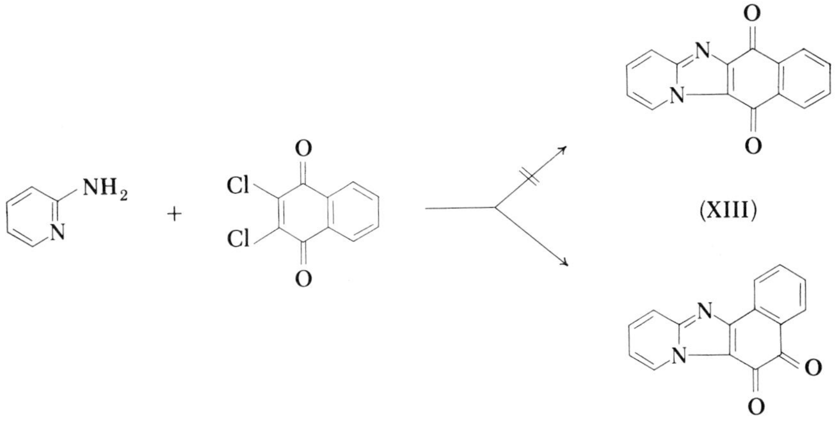

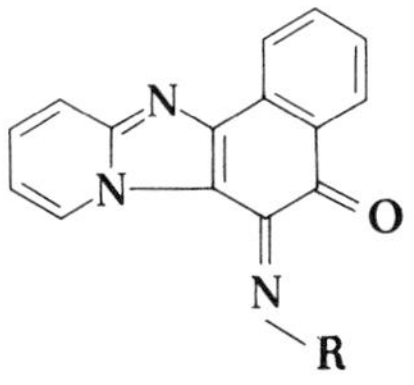

(XIII)

(XIV)

(XV)

2-acetamido-3-chloro-1,4-naphthoquinone in alcoholic solution, XIV was produced, while in chlorobenzene solution, XV (R = CH_3CO) was the product. The reaction of dichloronaphthoquinone with a large excess (four moles) of 2-aminopyridine in alcohol or in chlorobenzene, yielded[4] compound XV (R = 2-pyridyl). Nitration of XIV gave[4] a product thought to be the 3-nitro derivative. Several homologs of XIV were obtained[4] by analogous reactions.

Reitmann[5] condensed 2-bromo-1-tetralone with 2-aminopyridine and obtained a product to which he assigned structure XVI, although structure XVII was not invalidated. The accuracy of structure XVI was recently confirmed[6] by the isolation of XIV from the oxidation of Reitmann's product.

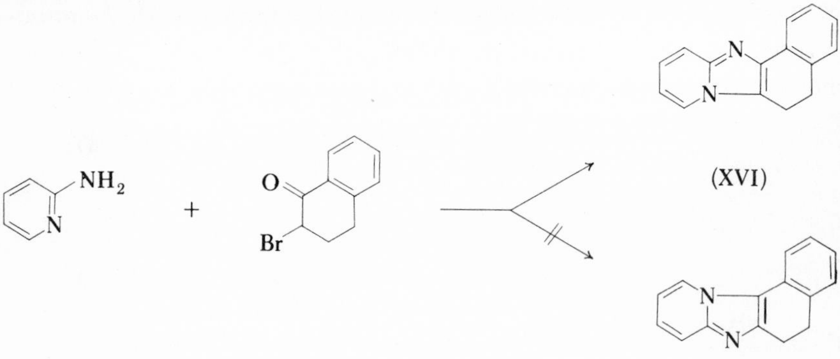

(XVI)

(XVII)

Tetrahydro compounds of type V may be prepared[6] by heating 1,2-naphthylenediamine with δ-valerolactone. The yield is less

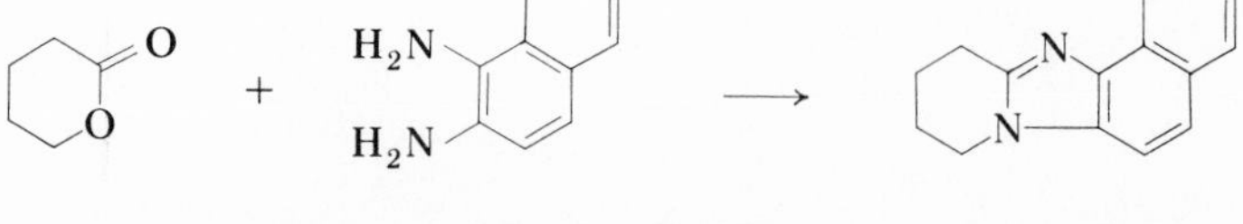

(V)

good than that obtained[6] in the case of homologous products (see Sections A-274, A-285 and A-789), and the product is accompanied by some 2-(γ-hydroxybutyl)-naphth[1,2-*d*]imidazole. Notwithstanding, it is, as is Reitmann's, one of the simplest syntheses of this ring system, and it utilizes readily obtainable materials.

Condensation of camphoric anhydride with 1,2-naphthylenediamine gave[7] two isomeric 2-(carboxytrimethylcyclopentyl)-naphthimidazoles, analogous to the isomers obtained from *o*-phenylenediamine (see Section A-274). Cyclization of one of these isomers yielded a product (XVIII), which may be regarded as a derivative of the benzo[*e*]pyrido[*a*]benzimidazole nucleus.

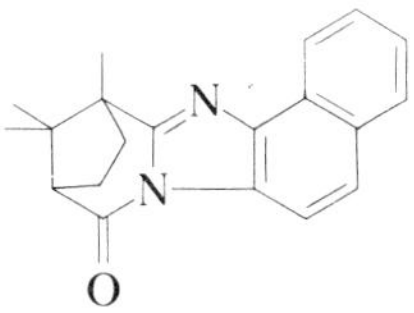

(XVIII)

Benzo[*e*]pyrido[*a*]benzimidazoles

Empirical formula	Substituents	Properties and comments	Refs.
$C_{15}H_6Cl_2N_2O_2$	1,4-Dichloro-5,6-dihydro-5,6-dioxo-	Or., m. 319.0–20.7°. Phenazine deriv., ochre, m. 313.0–4.2°.	4
$C_{15}H_7N_3O_3$	1 (or 4)-Nitro-5,6-dihydro-5,6-dioxo-	Or., m. 321.5–2.9°; red vat.	4
	4 (or 1)-Nitro-5,6-dihydro-5,6-dioxo-	Or.-brn., m. 301.5–3.5°; red vat.	4
	3-Nitro-5,6-dihydro-5,6-dioxo-	Brn., m. >360°d., red vat.	4
	9-Nitro-5,6-dihydro-5,6-dioxo-	Or.-yel., m. ~295°d.	4
$C_{15}H_8N_2O_3$	5,6-Dihydro-5,6-dioxo-	Brn.-or., m. 302–3°. Phenazine deriv. yel., m. 294.1–5.0°.	3,4
$C_{15}H_9N_3O_2$	5-Nitro-	m. 240–1°.	1
$C_{15}H_{10}N_2$	Unsubstituted	m. 195.2–6.2° (185°). Picrate, m. 258–61°.	1,4
$C_{15}H_{11}N_3$	5-Amino-	Yel., m. 238–40° (238–9°).	1,2

(*continued*)

Benzo[*e*]pyrido[*a*]benzimidazoles (*continued*)

Empirical formula	Substituents	Properties and comments	Refs.
$C_{15}H_{12}N_2$	5,6-Dihydro-	b_1 200–10°, m. 159.4–60.6° (157°). HCl salt, m. 307–8°d. Picrate, m. 249–50°.	5,6
$C_{15}H_{12}N_2O_2$	5,6,8,9,10,11-Hexahydro-5,6-dioxo-	m. 233.3–4.7°.	4
$C_{15}H_{14}N_2$	8,9,10,11-Tetrahydro-	m. 161.5–2.5° (158–9°). Picrate. m. 233.5–5.5°.	1,4
$C_{15}H_{15}N_3$	5-Amino-8,9,10,11-tetrahydro-	m. 228–30°.	1
$C_{16}H_{10}N_2O_2$	5,6-Dihydro-11-methyl-5,6-dioxo-	Yel., m. 281–3°.	4
$C_{17}H_{11}N_3O_2$	6-Acetimino-5,6-dihydro-5-oxo-	Brn.-or., m. 271.5–2.5°.	4
$C_{19}H_{14}N_2O_4$	5,6-Diacetoxy-	m. 233–4° (194°).	3,4
$C_{20}H_{12}N_4O$	5,6-Dihydro-5-oxo-6-(2-pyridyl)-imino-	Brn.-purple, m. 245.0–5.5°.	4
$C_{20}H_{20}N_2O$	9,11-Ethano-8,9,10,11-tetrahydro-10,10,11-trimethyl-8-oxo-	m. 80–2°.	7
$C_{21}H_{15}N_3SO_2$	5-Phenylsulfonamido-	m. 235–7° d.	2
$C_{21}H_{19}N_3SO_2$	*x*,*x*,11*a*,12-Tetrahydro-5-phenylsulfonamido-	m. 246.0–7.5°.	2
$C_{21}H_{21}N_3SO_2$	8,9,10,11,11*a*,12-Hexahydro-5-phenylsulfonamido-	HCl salt, m. 305–7° d.	2
$C_{22}H_{17}N_3SO_2$	10-Methyl-5-phenylsulfonamido-	m. 266° d.	2
$C_{24}H_{18}N_4O_3$	6-Acetoxy-5-[*N*-(2-pyridyl)-acetamino]-	m. 280° d.	4
$C_{27}H_{21}N_3S_2O_4$	11*a*,12-Dihydro-5-sulfonamido-12-phenylsulfonyl-	m. 220–1°.	2
$C_{27}H_{23}N_3S_2O_4$	*x*,*x*,11*a*,12-Tetrahydro-5-sulfonamido-12-phenylsulfonyl-	m. 247.5–8°.	2
$C_{27}H_{25}N_3S_2O_4$	8,9,10,11,11*a*,12-Hexahydro-5-sulfonamido-12-phenylsulfonyl-	m. 248°.	2

References

1. Morgan and Stewart, *J. Chem. Soc.*, **1939,** 1057.
2. Adams and Pomerantz, *J. Am. Chem. Soc.*, **76,** 702 (1954).
3. Truitt, Cooper and Wood, *J. Am. Chem. Soc.*, **79,** 5708 (1957).
4. Mosby and Boyle, *J. Org. Chem.*, **24,** 374 (1959).
5. Reitmann, U. S. Pat. 2,057,978.
6. Mosby, *J. Org. Chem.*, **24,** 419 (1959).
7. Chakravarti and Sen Gupta, *Quart. J. Indian Chem. Soc.*, **1,** 329 (1925); *Chem. Zentr.*, **II,** 1864 (1925); *Chem. Abstracts*, **19,** 2493 (1925).

A-284. Benzo[*g*]pyrido[*a*]-benzimidazole*

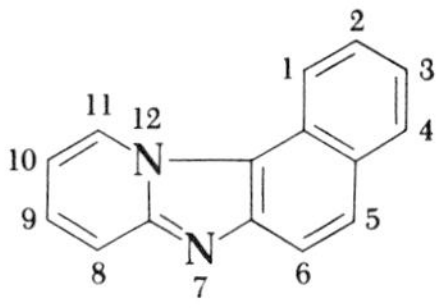

See under benzo[*e*]pyrido[*a*]benzimidazole (Section A-283).

A-285. Benzo[*f*]pyrido[*a*]-benzimidazole*

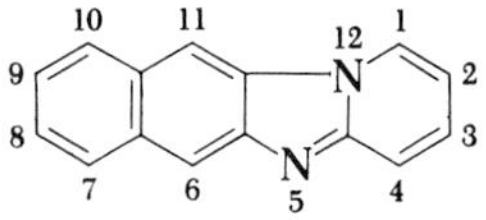

The reaction of 2,3-dichloro-1,4-naphthoquinone with 2-amino-pyridine yielded a product incorrectly thought[1] to be I, but shown[2] to have structure II (see Section A-283).

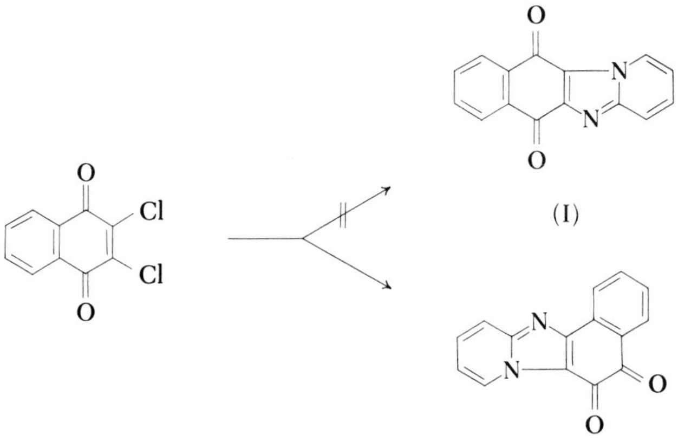

(I)

(II)

However, fusion of 2,3-diaminonaphthalene with δ-valerolactone afforded[3] a good yield of III (greenish-yellow, m. 190.5–2.5°; picrate, m. 271.5–2.0° d.), which was oxidized by chromic acid to IV (yellow, m. 250–1°, clear yellow vat). Efforts to aromatize III were not successful.

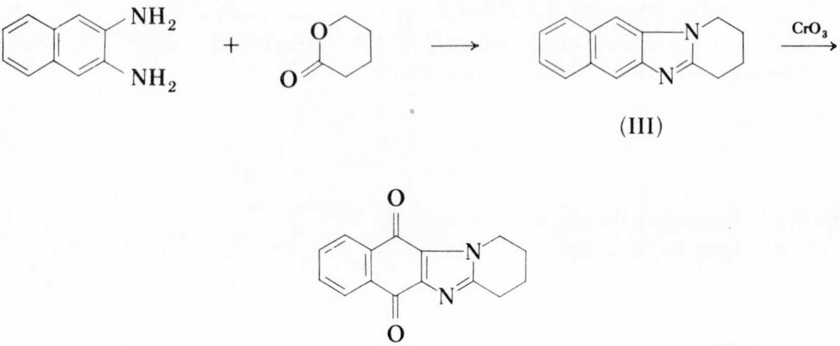

NH_2 NH_2 + O O → N N CrO_3 →

(III)

O N N O

(IV)

References

1. Truitt, Cooper and Wood, *J. Am. Chem. Soc.*, **79,** 5708 (1957).
2. Mosby and Boyle, *J. Org. Chem.*, **24,** 374 (1959).
3. Mosby, *J. Org. Chem.*, **24,** 419 (1959).

A-286. 7*H*-Benz[*de*]imidazo[2,1-*a*]isoquinoline. R.I. 2391

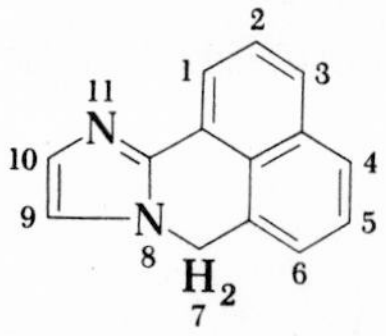

2 1 3 11 N 10 4 9 N 5 8 H_2 6 7

In continuation of his investigation[1] of the condensation of dicarboxylic acids and diamines, Bistrzycki[2] reacted ethylenediamine with naphthalic anhydride and obtained compound I. Fierz-David and Rossi[3] noticed that treatment of I with bromine in acetic acid produced a dissociable bromine addition complex, whereas chlorine in boiling trichlorobenzene simultaneously dehydrogenated and halogenated I to the x,9,10-trichloro compound (II), in which the location of one of the chlorine atoms is undetermined.

$(CH_2NH_2)_2$ (I) Cl_2 in $C_6H_3Cl_3$ (II)

Derivatives of 7*H*-Benz[*de*]imidazo[2,1-*a*]isoquinolin-7-one

Empirical formula	Substituents	Properties and comments	Refs.
$C_{14}H_5Cl_3N_2O$	*x*,9,10-Trichloro-	m. 308–9°	3
$C_{14}H_{10}N_2O$	9,10-Dihydro	Grn.-yel., m. 184–5° (179–80°). Picrate yel., m. 294–5° d. Ethiodide, or., m. 286–7°; with NaOH gives *N*-ethyl hydroxide, m. 92–3°. Br_2 complex, yel., sinters 222°, m. 297–300°.	2,3

References

1. Bistrzycki and Fässler, *Helv. Chim. Acta*, **6,** 519 (1923).
2. Bistrzycki and Risi, *Helv. Chim. Acta*, **8,** 810 (1925).
3. Fierz-David and Rossi, *Helv. Chim. Acta*, **21,** 1466 (1938).

A-287. Dipyrido[1,2-*a*, 1′,2′-*a*′]benzo-[1,2-*d*, 5,4-*d*′]bisimidazole*

The reaction[1] of 1,5-dichloro-2,4-dinitrobenzene with piperidine gave I, in which one of the nitro groups was reduced, diazotized and converted into the azide (II). Pyrolysis of II afforded a low yield of III, which was again subjected to a similar reaction sequence to yield IV (m. 279–80°).

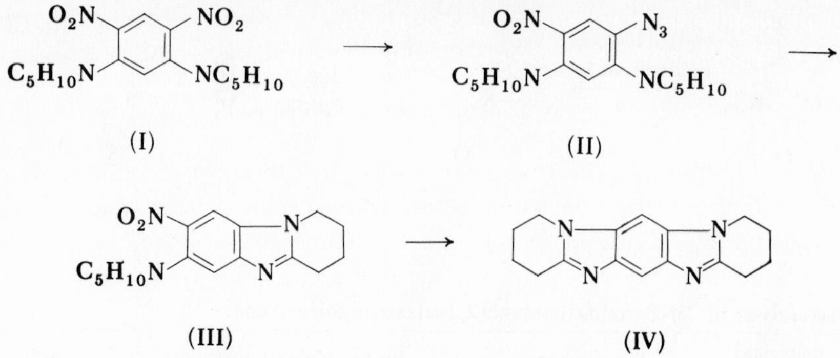

(I) → (II) →

(III) → (IV)

Reference

1. Saunders, *J. Chem. Soc.*, **1955,** 3275.

A-288. Dipyrido[1′,2′-*a*, 1″,2″-*a*′]-benzo[1,2-*d*, 4,5-*d*′]bisimidazole

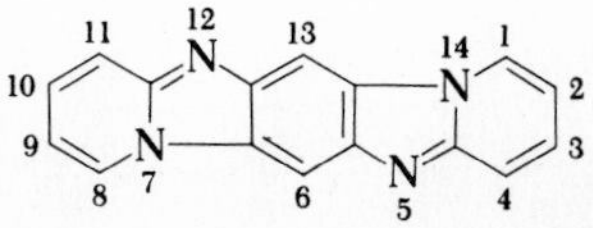

Although chloranil had been reported[1] not to condense with 2-aminopyridine, Boyle[2] obtained, in 33% yield, a product (red-brown, m. >360°) thought to have structure I (R = H). The dimethyl homolog I (R = CH_3, red-brown, m. >360°; red vat; yellow solution in sulfuric acid) was similarly prepared.

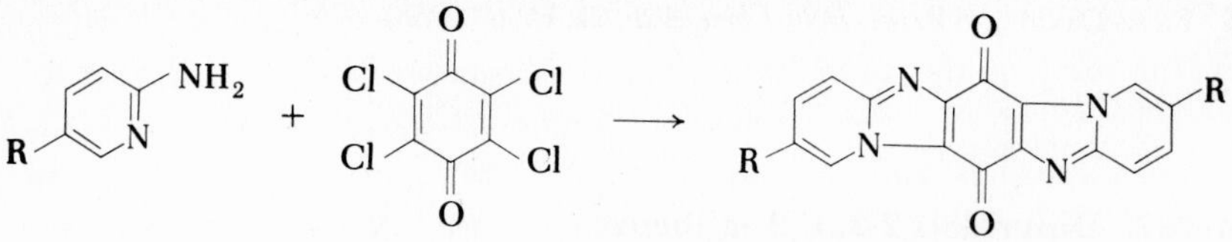

(I)

References

1. Schmid and Czerny, *Monatsh.*, **83,** 31 (1952).
2. Boyle, *Chem. and Ind.*, **1957,** 1069.

A-289. 14*H*-1,3-Dioxolo[5,6]indeno-[2,1-*d*][1,3]dioxolo[6,7]isoquinolo[2,3-*a*]imidazole. R.I. 3681

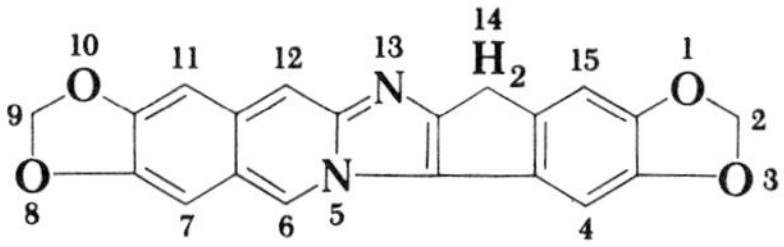

A red compound melting above 360°, and thought to have structure II, was obtained by Ruhemann[1] from action of ammonium hydroxide upon I. Evidence to support this structure is needed.

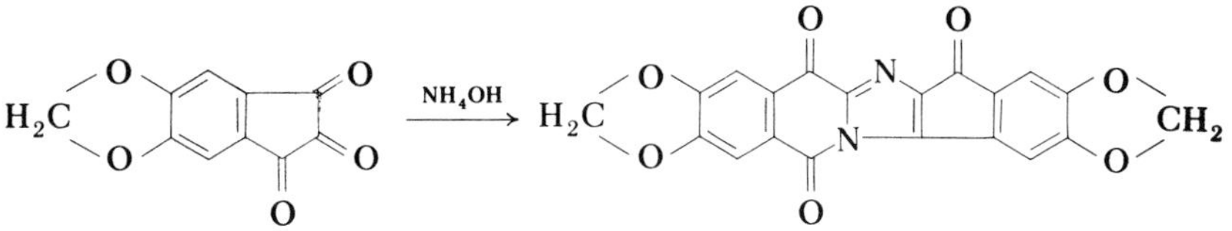

(I) (II)

Reference

1. Ruhemann, *J. Chem. Soc.*, **101,** 780 (1912).

A-290. Benzimidazo[1,2-*f*]phenanthridine. R.I. 3042

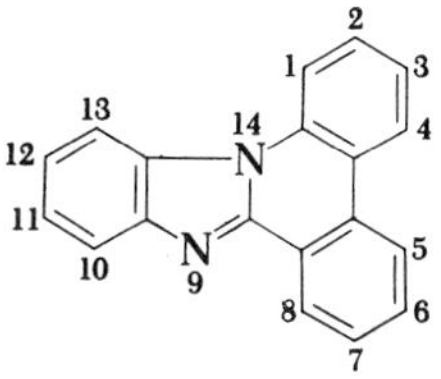

This nucleus has also been named *phenanthrido(10′:9′-1:2)benzimidazole* and *1:2(10′:9′)phenanthrido-4:5-benz-1:3-diazaline* (I). The only known examples were prepared by Morgan and Stewart[1] by the condensation of 6-aminophenanthridine with picryl chloride. As dis-

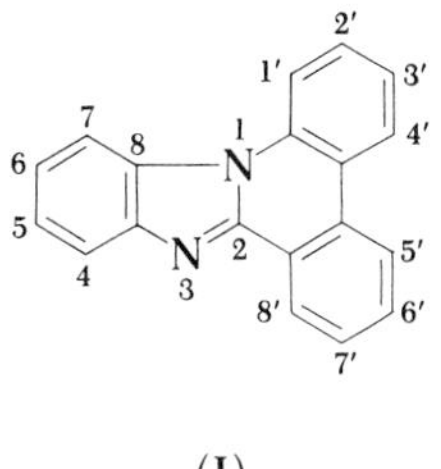

(I)

cussed previously in the case of the pyrido[1,2-*a*]benzimidazole nucleus (see Section A-274), condensation might occur at either the ring nitrogen or the amino group giving intermediates which, on cyclization, would yield either 10,12- or 11,13-dinitrobenzimidazo-[1,2-*f*]phenanthridine. Morgan and Stewart prefer the 10,12-dinitro structure (II) for their product (m. >280°) and, by analogy to related systems, they are probably correct in their choice.

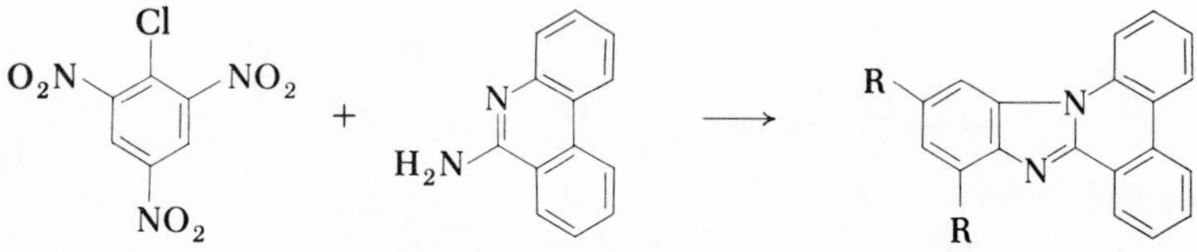

Cl
O_2N NO_2 + N H_2N → R N N R
NO_2

(II) R = NO_2
(III) R = H

Reduction of the dinitro compound II affords the yellow diamine, and, on diazotization and removal of the diazo groups, the unsubstituted parent substance (III, m. 153–4°), is obtained. Substitution reactions upon this ring system have not been described.

Reference

1. Morgan and Stewart, *J. Chem. Soc.*, **1938,** 1292.

A-291. 6*aH*-Diquin[1,2-*a*, 1′,2′-*c*]imidazole. R.I. 3040 and 3041

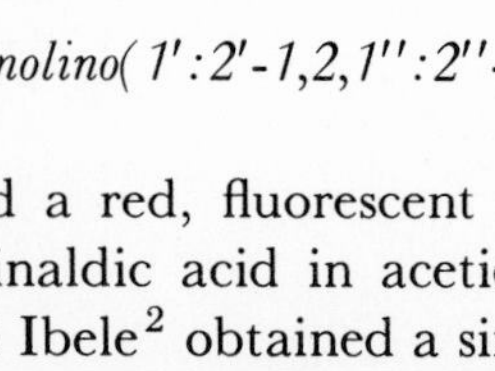

2 1 3 4 13 14 15 N 12 N 5 11 7 6 10 8 H 9

This nucleus has also been called *diquinolino(1′:2′-1,2,1″:2″-3:4)-glyoxaline.*

In 1894 Besthorn and Jaeglé[1] obtained a red, fluorescent compound by heating 4-(*p*-hydroxyphenyl)quinaldic acid in acetic anhydride. From quinaldic acid Besthorn and Ibele[2] obtained a similar red condensation product having the empirical formula $C_{19}H_{12}N_2O$ (Besthorn's Red), which they first thought to be di(2-quinolyl) ketone. This was soon shown to be untrue, and they then[3] proposed structure I for their product. The reaction was found to be general for

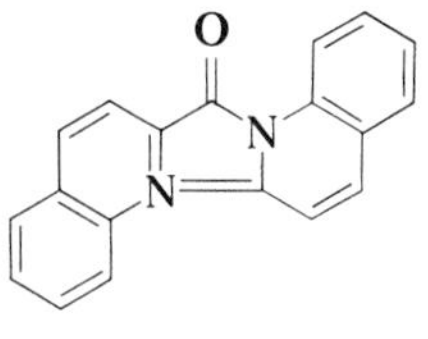

(I)

acids similar to quinaldic acid, and other methods were found for the preparation of these red dyes. Among these were: (1) the treatment of quinoline with quinaldic acid chloride; (2) heating quinaldic acid with benzoic anhydride and (3) heating quinaldic anhydride in water.

Wieland, Hettche and Hoshino[4] reinvestigated Besthorn's Red in 1928, and while they were displeased with a structure (I) containing a pentacovalent nitrogen atom, they were unable to disprove its validity. Almost a decade later, Krollpfeiffer and Schneider[5] corrected the erroneous valence state of the nitrogen and proposed formula II for Besthorn's Red, and, following a suggestion[12] of Wieland's, they disproved the possibility that the dye had a free radical structure by showing the molecule to be diamagnetic. As indicated by these authors,[5] the incursion of dipolar resonance forms of the type shown, might be expected to contribute materially to the stability of the molecule. The color and structure of Besthorn's Red have been considered[6] in relation to the structurally similar, but colorless "quinacolls," and support has recently been given[7] to the representation of such systems as "mesoionic"[9,10] compounds, essentially equivalent to structure IIa proposed by Krollpfeiffer[12] in 1936.

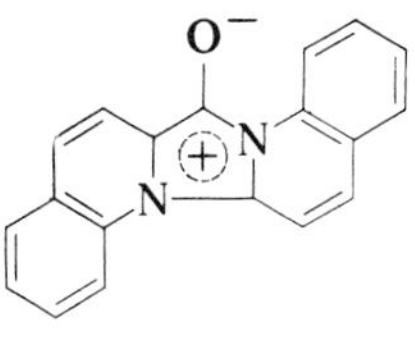

(IIa) 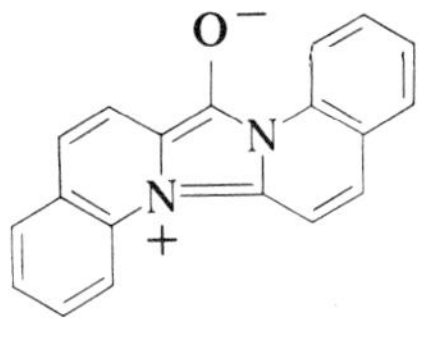 (IIb) 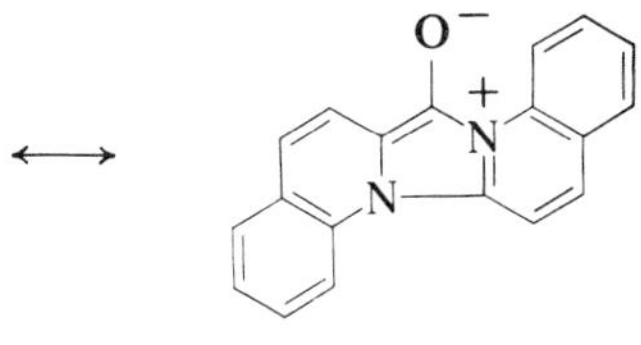 ⟷ (IIc)

Compound II sinters at about 200°, m. 230–40°. The ultraviolet absorption spectrum in benzene, measured by Krollpfeiffer and Schneider, showed maxima at 525 and 569 mμ (log K = 4.10 and 4.13, respectively). The red benzene solution rapidly became colorless in air and sunlight. The methyl sulfate addition compound III (yellow-brown, m. 179–80°d.), when heated with caustic, decomposed to yield a new substance: $C_{20}H_{16}N_2O_2$ (colorless needles, m. 213.5–4.5°), which was thought to have either structure IV or V, since when heated with 48% hydrobromic acid it yielded carbostyril and quinoline-2-carboxaldehyde. Recently structure V was shown[13] to be correct. Catalytic reduction of II consumed three moles of hydrogen and afforded two stereoisomeric 5,6,12,13,13a,14-hexahydro derivatives of II, m. 133–4° and 155° respectively.[4,8] Oxidation of the hexahydro compounds with chromic acid gave a red com-

(III)

Δ dil. NaOH

(IV) or (V)

Δ HBr

pound, presumably II, whereas peracetic acid gave quinaldic acid and hydrocarbostyril.[4]

Besthorn[7] also prepared some further derivatives of II. The reaction of quinaldic acid chloride with 4-carbethoxyquinoline gave VI (yellow prisms with a metallic reflex, m. 238°), and quinaldic

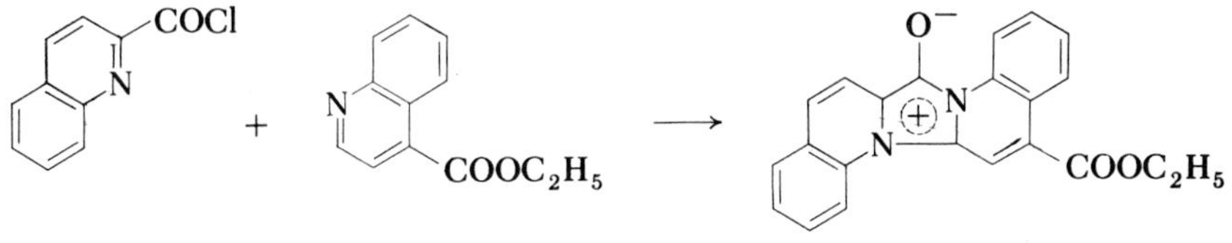

(VI)

acid chlorine with 4-phenylquinoline gave the dye VII (red-brown tablets melting indefinitely above 240°). The isomeric dye VIII,

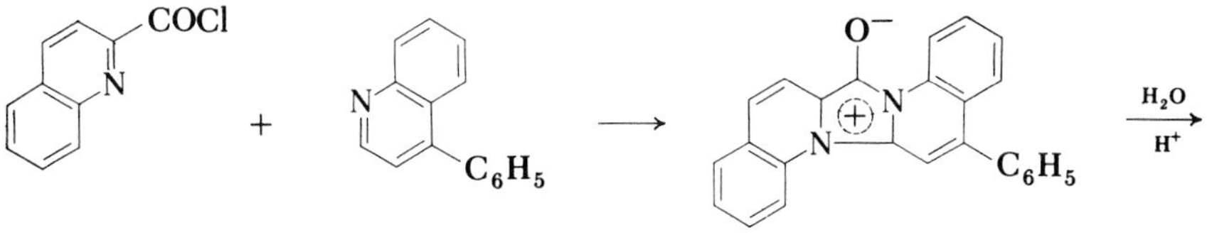

(VII)

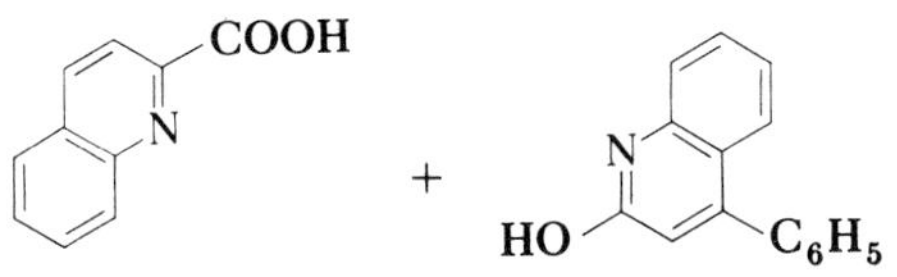

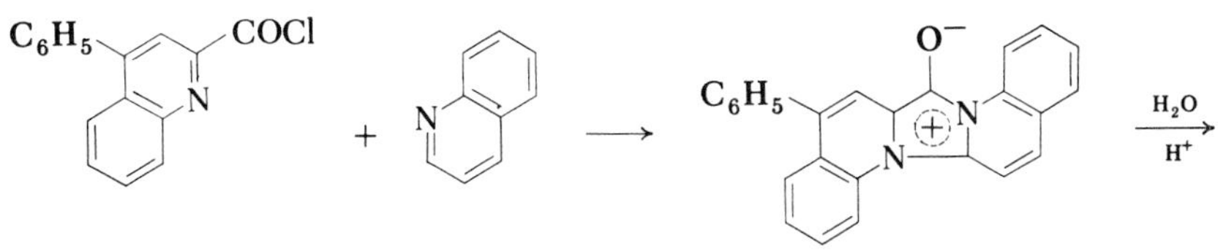

(VIII)

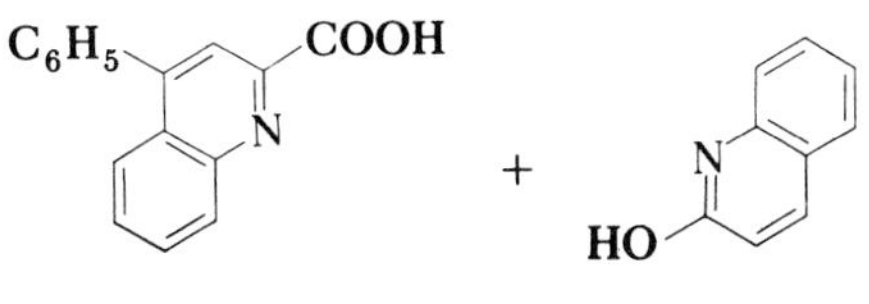

of similar color and melting point, was obtained from 4-phenylquinaldic chloride and quinoline. Dyes VII and VIII yielded, respectively, upon hydrolysis, 4-phenylcarbostyril and quinaldic acid, and carbostyril and 4-phenylquinaldic acid, as would be expected by analogy to the hydrolysis of III.

Recently the quaternary compound IX was prepared as shown.[11] The picrate (m. 261–2°) and the perchlorate form yellow needles. The bromide forms pale yellow crystals and its aqueous solutions show a strong blue fluorescence; in methanol λ_{max} = 225, 260, 300, 350, 370 and 390 mμ (log ε = 4.12, 4.30, 4.15, 3.94, 4.09, 4.02). Bromination of IX in aqueous acetic acid yielded[13] the 14-bromo derivative, isolated as the bromide, perbromide and perchlorate salts. Hot aqueous alkali decomposed IX, yielding[13] a product thought to be 1-(2-quinolylmethyl)carbostyril.

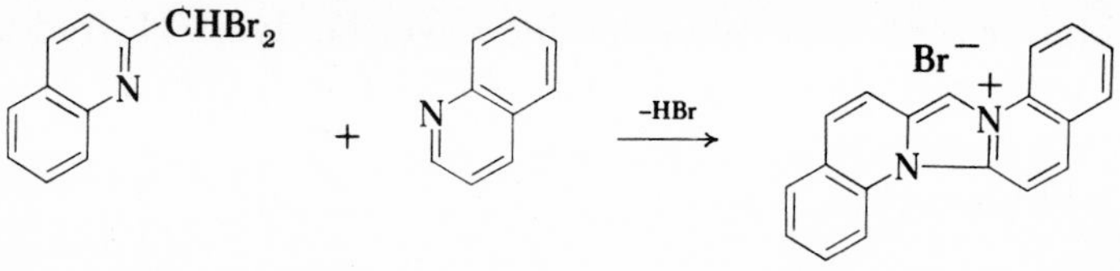

(IX)

References

1. Besthorn and Jaeglé, *Ber.*, **27,** 907 (1894).
2. Besthorn and Ibele, *Ber.*, **37,** 1236 (1904).
3. Besthorn and Ibele, *Ber.*, **38,** 2127 (1905).
4. Wieland, Hettche and Hoshino, *Ber.*, **61,** 2371 (1928).
5. Krollpfeiffer and Schneider, *Ann.*, **530,** 34 (1937).
6. Brown and Hammick, *J. Chem. Soc.*, **1950,** 628.
7. Hammick and Roe, *Chem. and Ind.*, **1953,** 900.
8. Besthorn, *Ber.*, **46,** 2762 (1913).
9. Katritzky, *Chem. and Ind.*, **1955,** 521.
10. Bieber, *Chem. and Ind.*, **1955,** 1055.
11. Brown and Wild, *J. Chem. Soc.*, **1956,** 1158.
12. Krollpfeiffer, *Angew. Chem.*, **49,** 550 (1936).
13. Brown and White, *J. Chem. Soc.*, **1957,** 1589.
14. Baker and Ollis, *Quart. Rev.*, **11,** 15 (1957).

A-292. 15*aH*-Isoquino[2,1-*a*]quin-[1,2-*c*]imidazole*

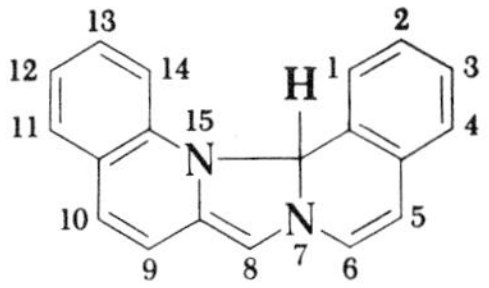

This nucleus was also named *quinolino(1′:2′-3:4)isoquinolino(1″:-2″-2:1)glyoxaline.*

Brown and Wild[1] obtained I as the yellow perbromide salt [in water λ_{max} = 285, 300, 315 and 370 mμ (log ε = 4.21, 4.19, 3.97 and 3.91)]. The picrate (m. 234°), bromide and perchlorate salts of I were also obtained.[2] These salts are decomposed to 1-(2-quinolylmethyl)-isocarbostyril by hot aqueous alkali.[2]

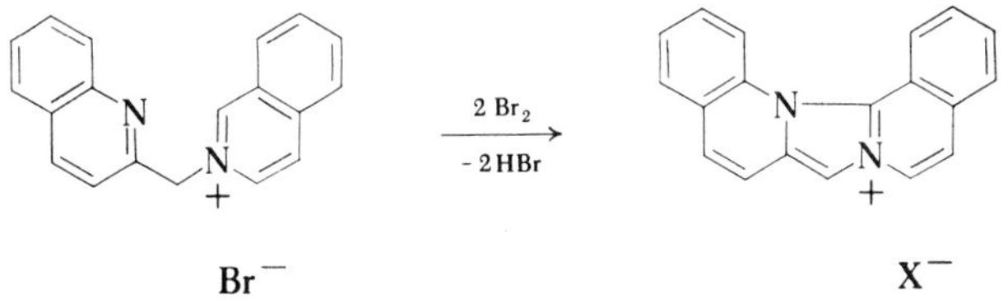

$$\xrightarrow[-\ 2HBr]{2\ Br_2}$$

Br⁻ X⁻

(I)

References

1. Brown and Wild, *J. Chem. Soc.*, **1956,** 1158.
2. Brown and White, *J. Chem. Soc.*, **1957,** 1589.

A-293. 12*bH*-Diisoquin[2,1-*a*, 2′,1′-*c*]-imidazole

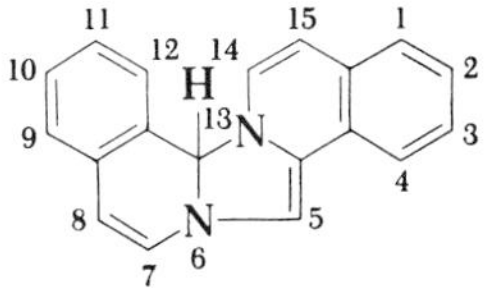

By heating isoquinaldic acid in acetic anhydride, Krollpfeiffer and Schneider[1] obtained a red dye (m. ~280°) similar to that ("Besthorn's Red") obtained under these conditions from quinaldic acid (see Section A-291). The dye, to which they assigned structure I, yielded a colorless derivative (II, d. 205–8°) when treated with methyl sulfate.

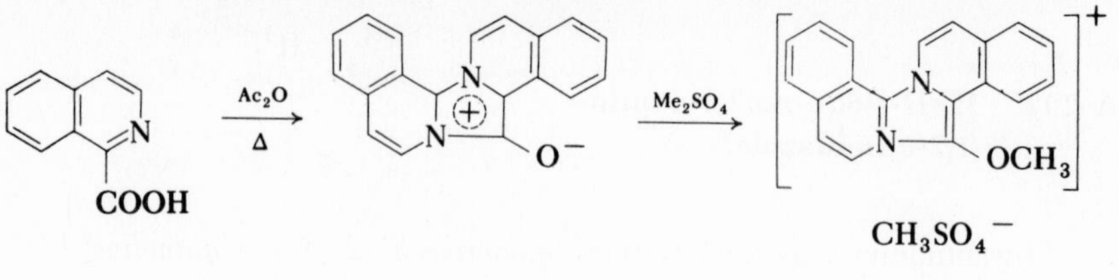

$$\text{isoquinoline-1-COOH} \xrightarrow[\Delta]{Ac_2O} \text{(I)} \xrightarrow{Me_2SO_4} \text{(II)}\ CH_3SO_4^-$$

(I) (II)

Reference

1. Krollpfeiffer and Schneider, *Ann.*, **530,** 34 (1937).

A-294. Benzo[*e*]quino[1,2-*a*]-benzimidazole. R.I. 3041M

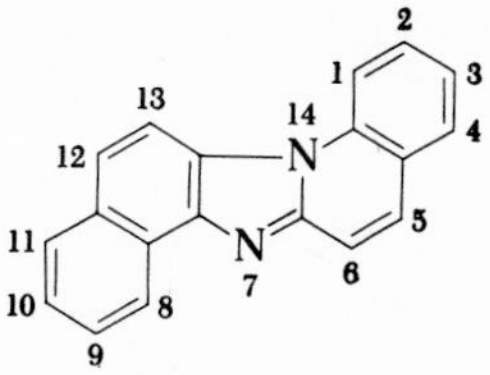

The name *1:2-quinolo-8:9-benzo-4:5-benz-1:3-diazaline* and the numbering shown in I have been used.

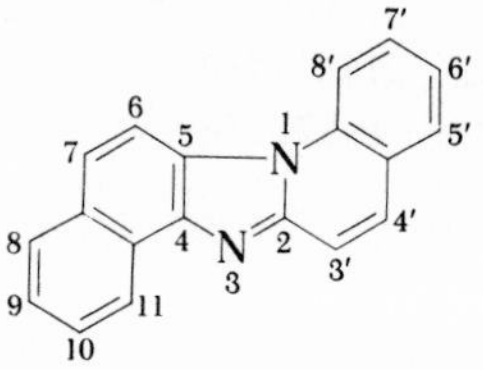

(I)

Condensation of 2-aminoquinoline with 1-chloro-2,4-dinitronaphthalene yielded[1] a product which could have either structure II or III (R = NO_2). Morgan and Stewart preferred structure II, and it seems probable by analogy with related systems (see Section A-274) that this choice is correct.

Reduction of IIa (m. >280°) to the corresponding amine (IIb, m. 166°) and removal of the amino group by diazotization gave the parent compound IIc (m. 244–5°). No information is available on the substitution reactions of IIc.

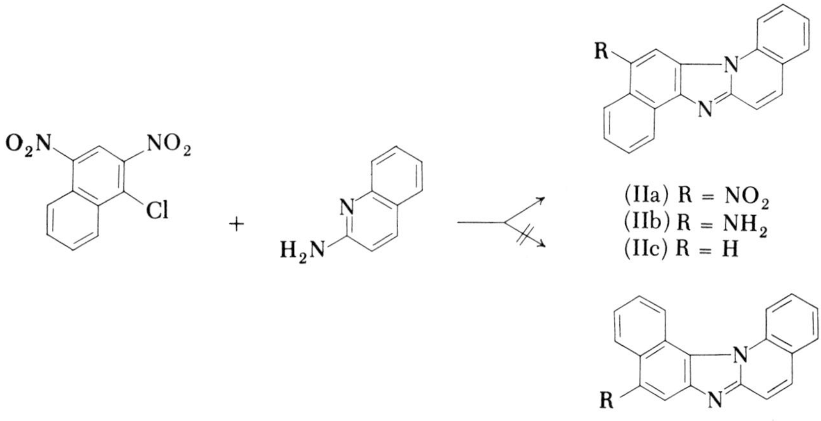

(IIa) R = NO_2
(IIb) R = NH_2
(IIc) R = H

(III)

The reaction of 2-aminoquinoline with 2,3-dichloronaphthoquinone yielded a brownish-yellow quinone (m. 327.5–8.5°) assigned[2] structure IV.

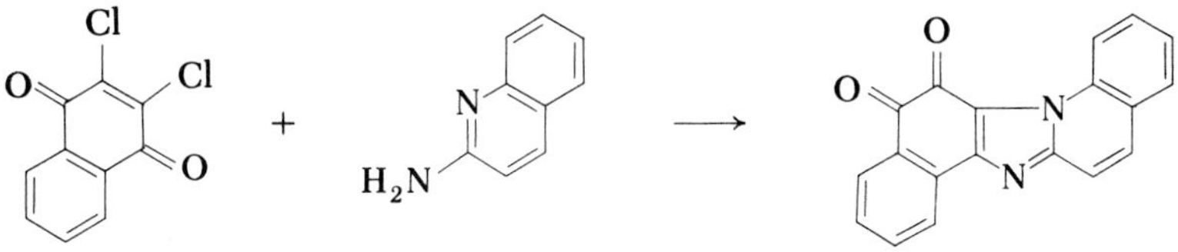

(IV)

References

1. Morgan and Stewart, *J. Chem. Soc.*, **1939,** 1057.
2. Mosby and Boyle, *J. Org. Chem.*, **24,** 374 (1959).

A-295. Benz[*e*]isoquino[1,2-*a*]-benzimidazole. R.I. 3041F

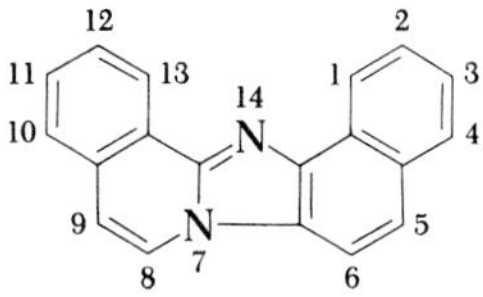

The alternate name *1:2(2′:1′)isoquinolo-8:9-benzo-4:5-benz-1:3-diazaline* (I) has been proposed for this nucleus. The only known examples (IIa, b and c) were reportedly obtained by Morgan and

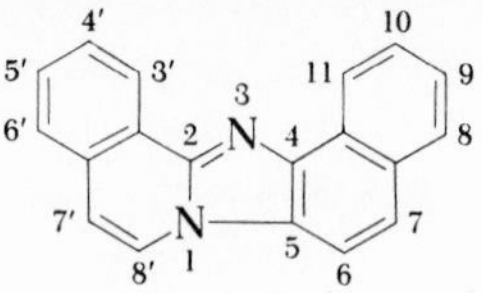

(I)

Stewart[1] from the condensation of 1-chloro-2,4-dinitronaphthalene with 1-aminoisoquinoline. Although no evidence was offered to show that the products do not have the alternative structure III, related reactions (see Section A-274) have yielded products analogous to II. The nitro compound IIa (m. > 280°) was reduced to the amine (IIb, shrinks at 170°, m. 184°), which, upon diazotization and removal

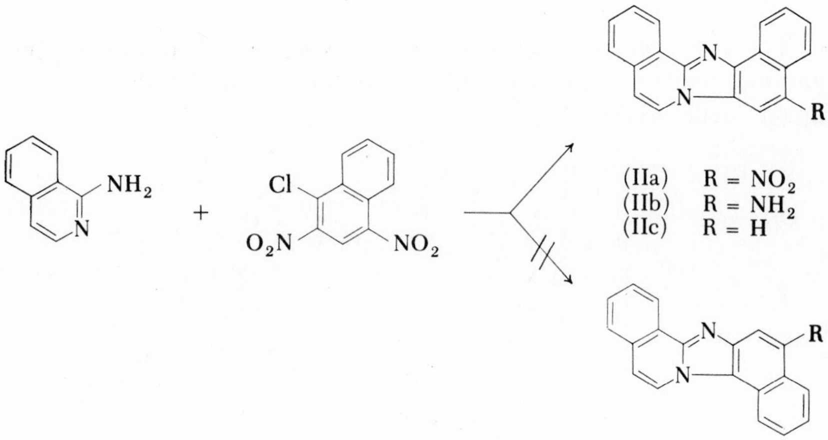

(IIa) R = NO_2
(IIb) R = NH_2
(IIc) R = H

(III)

of the diazo group, gave the unsubstituted compound (IIc, m. 252–253°). Nothing is known concerning the substitution reactions of this nucleus.

Reference

1. Morgan and Stewart, *J. Chem. Soc.*, **1939**, 1057.

A-296. 7*H*-Benzimidazo[2,1-*a*]benz-[*de*]isoquinoline. R.I. 3043

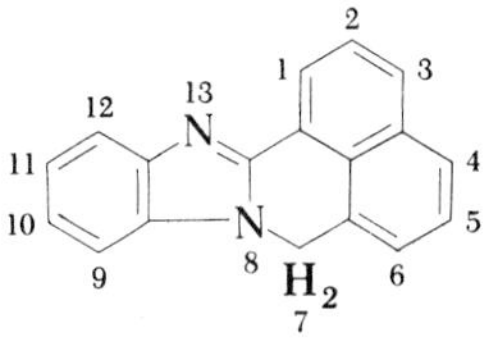

The 7-oxo derivative of this ring system has been called *1,2-(1′,8′)-naphthoylene-1,3-benzodiazole; 1′,8′-naphthoylene-1,2-benziminazole; 9′-keto-8′-azaphenalino(7′:8′:2:3)-ψ-indole* (I); *9′-keto-8′-azaphenalino(7′:8′:2:1)-benziminazole* (II) and *1′-keto-2′-azaperinaphthano(2′:3′-1:2)benziminazole* (III). The first example was the 7-oxo derivative, described by

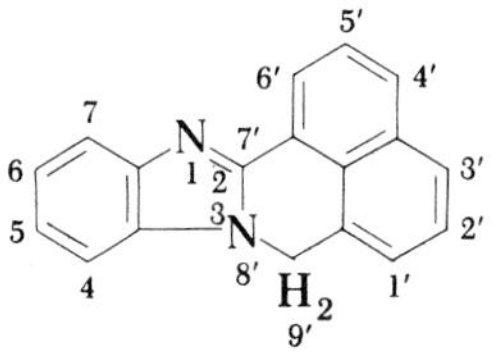

(I) 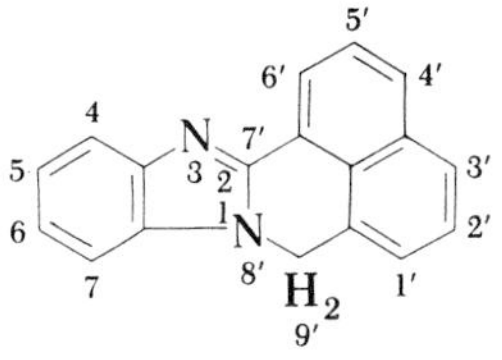 (II) 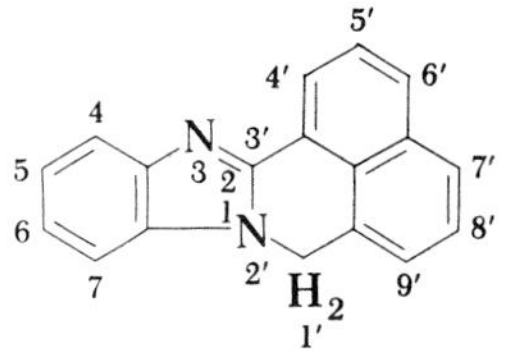 (III)

Chakravarti[1] in 1924, and obtained from the condensation of *o*-phenylenediamine and naphthalic anhydride. This synthesis was corroborated by Bistrzycki and Risi[2] and by Rule and Thompson.[3] The same product was shown by Stephenson[4] to result from the condensation of 1,8-naphthaldehydic acid and *o*-phenylenediamine with the possible formation of the 13,13*a*-dihydro compound as a labile intermediate.

Of particular interest are the dicarboxylic acids V, since they may be used to prepare a number of commercially valuable dyes (see Sections A-324/5). They are perhaps most easily prepared from the reaction[12,27] in buffered aqueous solution of the disodium salt of naphthalene-1,4,5,8-tetracarboxylic acid (VI) with *o*-phenylenediamines. They were also prepared[15,16] from IV as shown, or by the oxidation[13] of VII (see Section A-298).

The derivatives tabulated were usually obtained from the reaction of substituted naphthalic acids with *o*-phenylenediamine or substituted *o*-phenylenediamines. Several of the resulting product mixtures VIII have been separated into the isomeric (*cis-trans*)

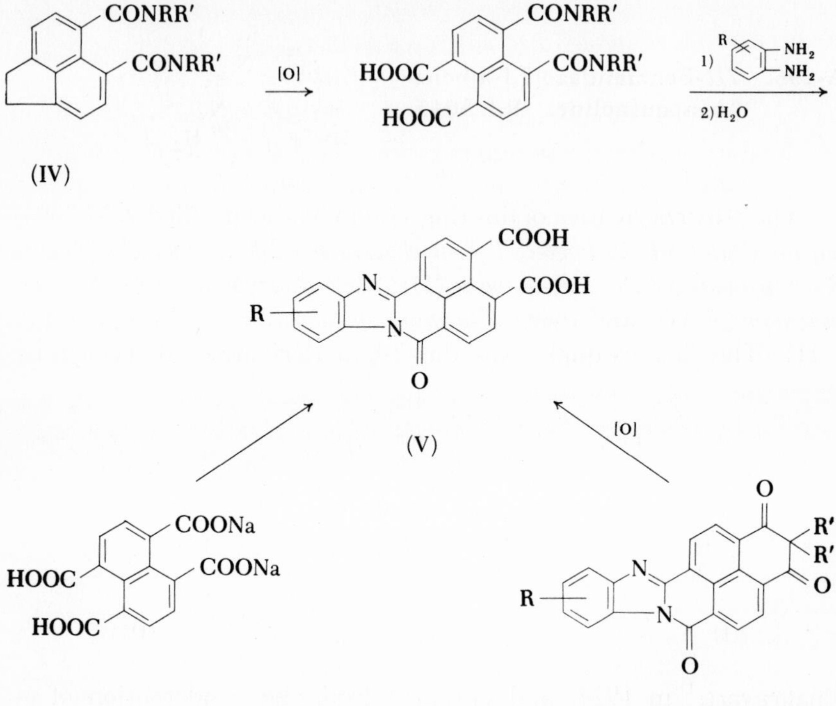

CONRR′ CONRR′ [O] → HOOC HOOC CONRR′ CONRR′ 1) R-C$_6$H$_3$(NH$_2$)$_2$ 2) H_2O →

(IV)

COOH COOH R N N O

(V)

[O]

COONa COONa HOOC HOOC

(VI)

O R′ R′ O R N N O

(VII)

components of the type shown. With symmetrically substituted reactants, of course, only one isomer is formed. Recently Okazaki *et al.*[31–34] studied the reaction of naphthalic acids with substituted

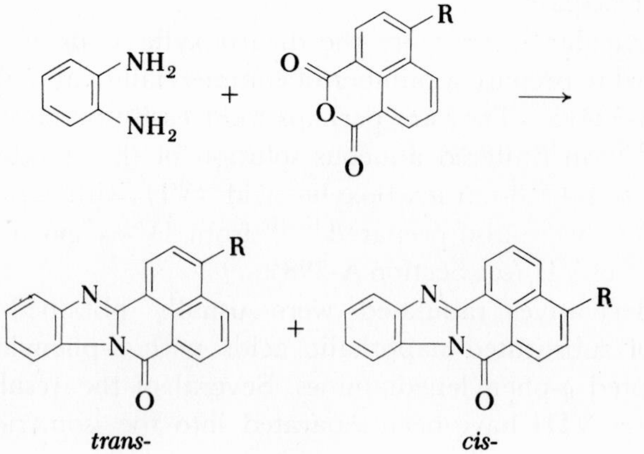

NH_2 NH_2 + O O O R →

R N N O *trans-* + N N O R *cis-*

(VIII)

o-phenylenediamines. It had previously been assumed that the benzimidazo[2,1-*a*]benz[*de*]isoquinolinone so obtained was substituted in the 11-position. However, they showed that nearly equal amounts of the 10- and 11-isomers were formed.

Nothing has been reported regarding substitution reactions in this ring system, probably because electrophilic attack might be expected to occur in the "benz-" ring rather than at more useful positions in the naphthalene nucleus. The 7-oxo derivative (VIII, where R = H) has been shown[5] not to undergo oxidative dimerization to a perylene derivative as naphthalimide does when fused with caustic.

Although several derivatives of VIII have been patented, none finds application at present as a dye for cotton or wool. However, several have recently been claimed[28-30] of value in the coloration of superpolyamide plastics.

Benzimidazo[2,1-*a*]benz[*de*]isoquinolin-7-ones

Empirical formula	Substituents	Properties and comments	Refs.
$C_{18}H_8BrClN_2O$	3(or 4)-Bromo-11-chloro-	Yel., m. 230°. (Mixture)	6
$C_{18}H_8N_4O_5$	2,5-Dinitro-	Or., m. 301°.	2,28
	3,4-Dinitro-	Bronze, m. 370°.	2
$C_{18}H_9BrN_2O$	3(or 4)-Bromo-	Yel., m. 283° (270–2°). Less sol. in C_6H_5Cl than isomer.	6–8
	4(or 3)-Bromo-	Yel., m. 223° (219–21°). More sol. in C_6H_5Cl than isomer.	6–8
$C_{18}H_9ClN_2O$	10-Chloro-	Yel., m. 232.5–4°.	34
	11-Chloro-	Yel., m. 234–5°.	28,34
$C_{18}H_9N_2O_4S$	2(or 5)-Sulfonic acid	—	28
$C_{18}H_9N_3O_3$	2(or 5)-Nitro-	—	28
	3(or 4)-Nitro-	—	28
$C_{18}H_{10}N_2O$	Unsubstituted	Deep yel., m. 206° (198°; 189°). Stable to hot aq. or alc. alkali.	1–3,26,31

(*continued*)

Benzimidazo[2,1-*a*]benz[*de*]isoquinolin-7-ones (*continued*)

Empirical formula	Substituents	Properties and comments	Refs.
$C_{18}H_{11}N_3O$	10-Amino-	Yel., m. 275°.	26
	11-Amino-	Red., m. 245–7°.	26
$C_{18}H_{11}N_3O_4S$	3(or 4)-Sulfamino-	(Mixture ?) Na salt, or.	9
	3(or 4)-Amino-x-sulfo-	(Mixture ?) dyes wool or.	9
$C_{19}H_9N_3O$	3(or 4?)-Cyano-	m. 257–60°.	35
$C_{19}H_{10}N_2O_3$	3(or 4?)-Carboxy-	—	35
$C_{19}H_{10}N_2O_7S$	3(or 4)-Carboxy-2(or 5)-hydroxy-11-sulfo-	(Mixture ?) dyes wool yel., which becomes brn.-yel. on "after-chroming."	10
	10(or 11)-Carboxy-11(or 10)-hydroxy-3(or 4)-sulfo-	(Mixture ?) "after-chroming" gives a red-yel. dye of fair moisture and light fastness.	11
	10(or 11)-Carboxy-11(or 10)-hydroxy-2(or 5)-sulfo-	"After-chroming" gives a red-yel. dye of fair moisture and light fastness.	11
$C_{19}H_{12}N_2O$	9(or 12)-Methyl-	(Mixture ?). Deep yel., m. 187°.	32
	10-Methyl-	Yel., m. 190–1°.	32
	11-Methyl-	Yel., m. 212–3°.	32
$C_{19}H_{12}N_2O_2$	10-Methoxy-	Or., m. 210–1°.	33
	11-Methoxy-	Or., yel., m. 192.5–3.5°.	33
$C_{20}H_8Br_2N_2O_5$	9,11(or 10,12)-Dibromo-3,4-dicarboxy-	Or.	12
$C_{20}H_8Cl_2N_2O_5$	3,4-Dicarboxy-10,11-dichloro-	Red. Anhydride, or., m. > 350°.	12,13,27
$C_{20}H_9BrN_2O_5$	11-Bromo-3,4-dicarboxy-	Or.	12
$C_{20}H_{10}N_2O_5$	3,4-Dicarboxy-	Or.-yel., m. > 350°. Anhydride (R.I. 3499). Imide, see Section A-300.	12,13,15,16,27

Benzimidazo[2,1-*a*]benz[*de*]isoquinolin-7-ones (*continued*)

Empirical formula	Substituents	Properties and comments	Refs.
$C_{20}H_{12}N_2O_3S$	3-Carboxymethylenethio-	Gives colorless alkali salts.	8
	4-Carboxymethylenethio	Gives colorless alkali salts.	8
$C_{21}H_{11}ClN_2O_5$	10(or 11)-Chloro-3,4-dicarboxy-11(or 10)-methyl-	(Mixture ?) yel.	12
$C_{21}H_{12}N_2O_5$	3,4-Dicarboxy-11-methyl-	Red.	12,27
$C_{22}H_{14}N_2O_6$	3,4-Dicarboxy-11-ethoxy-	Or.-red.	12,27
$C_{22}H_{16}Br_2N_2O$	2(or 5)-*t*-Butyl-3,4-dibromo-	(Mixture ?); yel., m. 250–1°.	18
$C_{25}H_{14}N_2O_2$	3(or 4)-Benzoyl-	(Mixture ?); yel.; red soln. in H_2SO_4.	19
$C_{25}H_{20}N_2O_4$	3(or 4)-Carboxy-4(or 3)-(α-ethylbutyryl)-	(Mixture ?), yel. amorph.	13
$C_{26}H_{14}N_2O_4$	3(or 4)-(2-Carboxybenzoyl)-	(Mixture ?), yel., m. 285–7°.	20,21
$C_{26}H_{25}N_3O_3$	2,5-Di-*t*-butyl-3(or 4)-nitro-	(Mixture ?), yel., m. 266–7°.	22
$C_{26}H_{25}BrN_2O$	3(or 4)-Bromo-2,5-di-*t*-butyl-	(Mixture ?), yel., m. 280–3°.	22
$C_{26}H_{25}ClN_2O$	2,5-Di-*t*-butyl-3-(or 4)-chloro-	(Mixture ?), yel., m. 270–2°.	18
$C_{26}H_{26}N_2O$	2,5-Di-*t*-butyl-	Grn.-yel., m. 278–9°.	23
$C_{30}H_{22}N_2O_4$	3(or 4)-(4-*t*-Butyl-2-carboxybenzoyl)-	(Mixture ?), or., m. 300–2°.	24
$C_{32}H_{16}ClN_3O_3$	3(or 4)-(1-Anthraquinonylamino)-11-chloro-	(Mixture ?), brn.	6
$C_{32}H_{17}N_3O_3$	3(or 4)-(1-Anthraquinonylamino)-	Red-brn., m. ca. 400°.	6
	4(or 3)-(1-Anthraquinonylamino)-	Red-brn., m. ca. 380°.	6
$C_{33}H_{19}N_3O_4$	3(or 4)-(1-Anthraquinonylamino)-2(or 5)-methoxy-	Not cyclized by caustic melt. Heated to 190° in H_2SO_4 → vt. vat dye.	5

(*continued*)

Benzimidazo[2,1-*a*]benz[*de*]isoquinolin-7-ones (*continued*)

Empirical formula	Substituents	Properties and comments	Refs.
$C_{35}H_{18}N_2O_2$	3(or 4)-(3-Benzanthronyl)-	(Mixture ?)	25
$C_{36}H_{16}Br_2N_4O_2$	3,3′(or 4,4′)-Dibromo-11,11′-bis-	(Mixture ?) red-brn. m. > 360°.	6
$C_{36}H_{18}N_4O_2$	11,11′-Bis-	—	28
$C_{36}H_{18}N_4O_4S$	2,2′(or 5,5′)-Sulfonylbis-	—	28
$C_{36}H_{28}N_4O_3$	3,4-Dicarboxethylanilide-	Or., m. 213–4°.	15,16

References

1. Chakravarti, *Quart. J. Indian Chem. Soc.*, **1**, 19 (1924); *Chem. Abstracts*, **19**, 830 (1925); *Chem. Zentr.*, **I**, 518 (1925).
2. Rule and Thompson, *J. Chem. Soc.*, **1937**, 1764.
3. Bistrzycki and Risi, *Helv. Chim. Acta*, **8**, 810 (1925).
4. Stephenson, *J. Chem. Soc.*, **1952**, 5024.
5. Gruschke and Quint, *I.G. Farbenindustrie A.G., 42 Wissenschaftlicher Austausch der Gruppe IX*, Feb. 16, 1940, Frankfurt; *PB Report No.* 73484, frames 816–828.
6. Wolfram, Nawiasky, Langbein and Elbs, Ger. Pat. 607,341; *Frdl.*, **21**, 1181 (1937). Fr. Pat. 753,185; *Chem. Zentr.*, **I**, 467 (1934); *Chem. Abstracts*, **28**, 906 (1934). U. S. Pat. 2,069,663.
7. Campbell, Easton, Rayment and Wilshire, *J. Chem. Soc.*, **1950**, 2784.
8. Braunsdorf, *I.G. Farbenindustrie A.G., 40 Wissenschaftlicher Austausch der Gruppe IX*, Dec. 15, 1938, Höchst; *PB Report Nos.* 70338, frames 10560–10565, and 73484, frames 802–808.
9. Eckert, U. S. Pat. 1,796,011.
10. Diefenbach, *I.G. Farbenindustrie A.G., 42 Wissenschaftlicher Austausch der Gruppe IX*, Feb. 15, 1940, Frankfurt; *PB Report Nos.* 70338, frames 10832–10838, and 73484, frames 836–842.
11. Quint, *I.G. Farbenindustrie A.G., 38 Wissenschaftlicher Austausch der Gruppe IX*, Dec. 8, 1937, Wolfen; *PB Report No.* 70338, frames 10343–10351.
12. Eckert and Braunsdorf, Ger. Pat. 553,629; *Frdl.*, **19**, 2194 (1934). U. S. Pat. 1,924,090.
13. Eckert and Braunsdorf, Ger. Pats. 552,173 and 523,521; *Frdl.*, **17**, 1415 and 1417 (1932). U. S. Pat. 1,910,465.
14. Höpff, Ger. Pat. Appln. I 51,838 Ne/1202; *PB Report No.* 73719, frame 2201.
15. Wyler and Kershaw, Fr. Pat. 793,576 and Brit. Pat. 442,529; *Chem. Abstracts*, **30**, 4693 (1936); *Chem. Zentr.*, **I**, 4805 (1936).

16. Wyler and Kershaw, U. S. Pat. 2,072,238.
17. Eckert and Braunsdorf, Ger. Pat. 547,924; *Frdl.*, **18,** 1501 (1933). Ger. Pat. 551,183; *Frdl.*, **19,** 2198 (1934). U. S. Pat. 1,935,945.
18. Nursten and Peters, *J. Chem. Soc.*, **1950,** 729.
19. Kränzlein, Greune and Vollmann, Ger. Pat. 494,111; *Frdl.*, **16,** 1441 (1931); *Chem. Zentr.*, **II,** 820 (1930).
20. Peters and Rowe, *J. Soc. Dyers and Colourists*, **59,** 52 (1943).
21. Heidenreich, Brit. Pat. 304,263; *Chem. Zentr.*, **I,** 2585 (1929). U. S. Pat. 1,847,561.
22. Peters, *J. Chem. Soc.*, **1947,** 742.
23. Peters, *J. Chem. Soc.*, **1942,** 562.
24. Larner and Peters, *J. Chem. Soc.*, **1952,** 1368.
25. Scheyer, Ger. Pat. 638,602; *Frdl.*, **23,** 1122 (1940).
26. Krasovitskiĭ and Matskevitch, *Zhur. Obshchei Khim.*, **24,** 2027 (1954). *Chem. Abstracts*, **49,** 14743 (1955).
27. Eckert and Fuchs, Ger. Pat. 1,005,969; Fr. Pat. 1,121,732. U. S. Pat. 2,835,674.
28. LeThierry d'Ennequin, *Teintex*, **20,** 879 (1955).
29. LeThierry d'Ennequin, Dassigny and Robin, *XIV Int. Congr. Pure and Appl. Chem. Handbook*, Zürich, 1955, p. 291.
30. Dassigny and Robin, Fr. Pat. 1,111,620.
31. Okazaki, *J. Soc. Org. Synthet. Chem. Japan*, **13,** 80 (1955); *Chem. Abstracts*, **51,** 2745 (1957).
32. Okazaki and Kasai, *J. Soc. Org. Synthet. Chem. Japan*, **13,** 175 (1955); *Chem. Abstracts*, **51,** 2746 (1957).
33. Okazaki, *J. Soc. Org. Synthet. Chem. Japan*, **13,** 228 (1955); *Chem. Abstracts*, **51,** 2746 (1957).
34. Okazaki, Kasai and Matsubara, *J. Soc. Org. Synthet. Chem. Japan*, **13,** 413 (1955); *Chem. Abstracts*, **51,** 2747 (1957).
35. Schmidt-Nickels, U. S. Pat. 2,820,037.

A-297. 1*H*-Benzimidazo[2,1-*a*]indeno[6,7,1-*def*]isoquinoline*

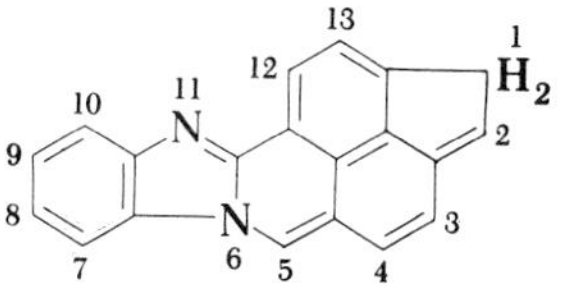

The only three representatives reported of this nucleus were obtained by the chemists of the I.G. Farbenindustrie A.G., from the reaction of acenaphthene-5,6-dicarboanhydrides with *o*-phenylenediamine. The 5-oxo compound[1,2] is yellow (m. 272–3°) and the

4(or 12)-amino-5-oxo derivative[3] is reported to be orange-yellow. Caustic fusion of a material thought to be the 5-oxo-3-(or possibly 13-) sulfonic acid (I) gave a product (mixture?) formulated[2] as II, presumably by analogy to the product obtained under similar circumstances from acenaphthene-3-sulfonic acid.

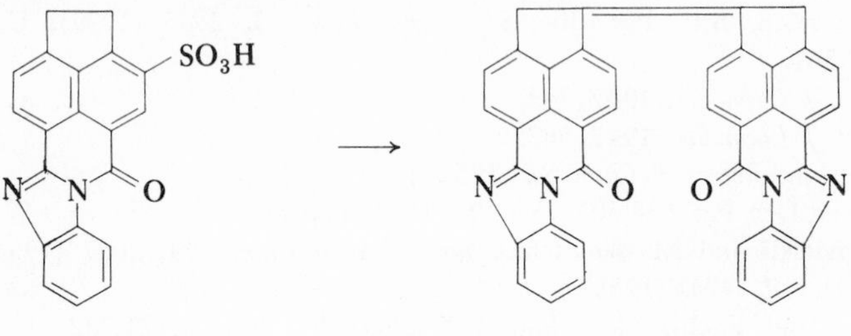

SO_3H N N O → N N O O N N

(I) (II)

References

1. Eckert and Brannsdorf, Ger. Pats. 522,173 and 523,521; *Frdl.*, **17,** 1415, 1417 (1932). U. S. Pat. 1,910,465.
2. Sieber, *I.G. Farbenindustrie A.G., 43 Wissenschaftlicher Austausch der Gruppe IX*, Leverkusen, April 25, 1941; *PB Report Nos*. 70338, frames 10875–10878 and 73484, frames,863–867.
3. Quint, *I.G. Farbenindustrie A.G., 38 Wissenschaftlicher Austausch der Gruppe IX*, Wolfen, Dec. 8, 1937; *PB Report No*. 70338, frames 10322–10329.

A-298. Benzimidazo[2,1-*a*]naphth-[2,1,8-*def*]isoquinoline. R.I. 3501

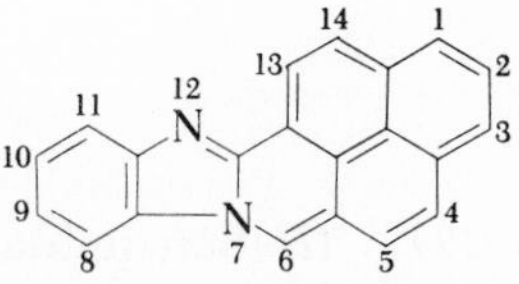

14 1 13 2 12 11 N 3 10 9 N 4 8 7 6 5

Three derivatives of this ring system have been reported. Sieber[1] prepared the red compound I, starting from pyrene. The other two representatives were obtained by Eckert and Braunsdorf[2] starting with acenaphthene. Compound IIa (R = H) is yellow, m. 254–6°; compound IIb (R = Cl) is also yellow, m. 325–7°.

CrO_3
HOAc

or

(I)

$Et_2C(COCl)_2$

$Na_2Cr_2O_7$

(IIa) R = H
(IIb) R = Cl

References

1. Sieber, *I.G. Farbenindustrie A.G.*, *33 Wissenschaftlicher Austausch der Gruppe IX*, Frankfurt, March 27, 1935; *PB Report No.* 70338, frames 9525–9527.
2. Eckert and Braunsdorf, Ger. Pats. 522,173 and 523,521; *Frdl.*, **17,** 1415 and 1417 (1932); U. S. Pat. 1,910,465.

A-299. 1*H*-[2]Benzopyrano[6,5,4-*def*]-benzimidazo[2,1-*a*]isoquinoline. R.I. 3499

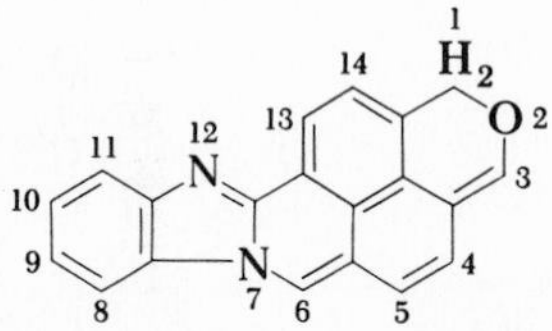

The only examples of this ring system are the anhydrides of benzimidazo[2,1-*a*]benz[*de*]isoquinol-7-one-3,4-dicarboxylic acids (see Section A-296).

A-300. Benzimidazo[2,1-*a*]isoquino-[6,5,4-*def*]isoquinoline. R.I. 3498

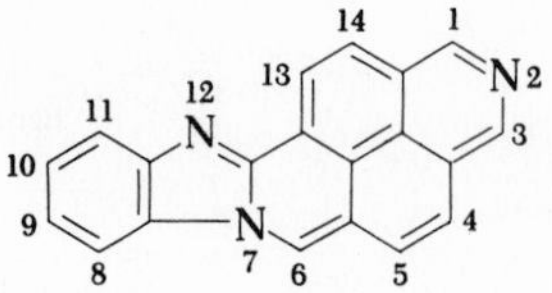

A number of dyes of types II and III have been prepared[1,2] by the reaction of I (see Section A-296) with various amines. They are, for the most part, yellows to oranges, although browns may be obtained by introduction of suitable (e.g., alkoxy) groups in position 10. An interesting characteristic which these dyes share with others (see Sections A-324/5) derived from naphthalene-1,4,5,8-tetracarboxylic acid, is the formation of a red-green dichroic vat solution.

The simplest imide of this series (V) was prepared by Höpff[3] from IV, which was obtained from the reaction of acenaphthene with carbamyl chloride under Friedel-Crafts conditions.

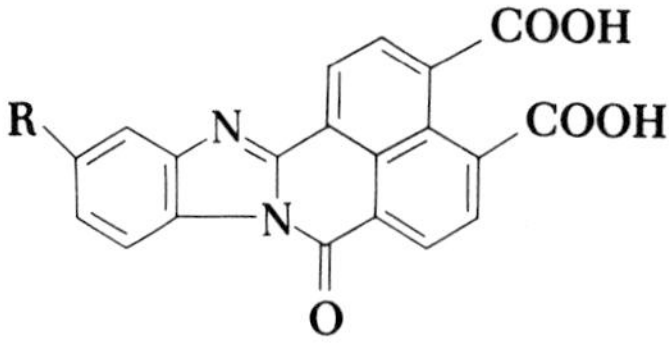

(I)

$R'NH_2$

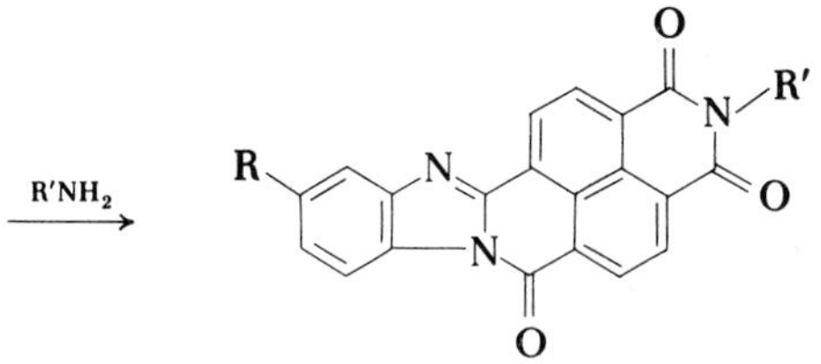

(II)

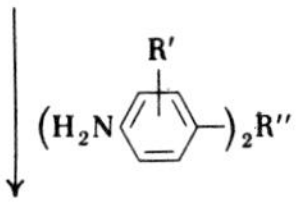

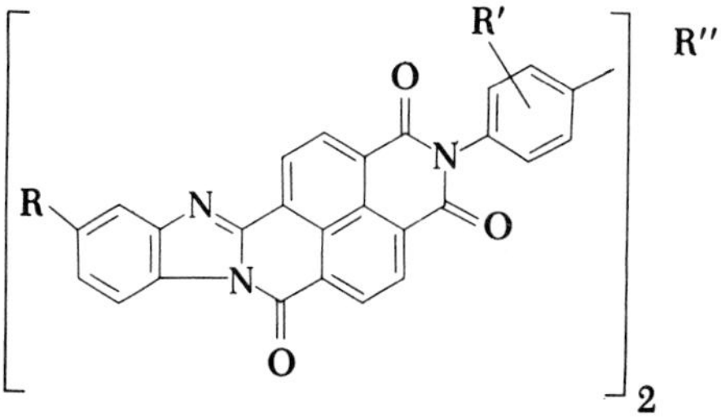

(III)

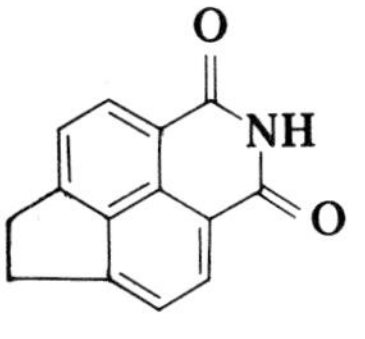

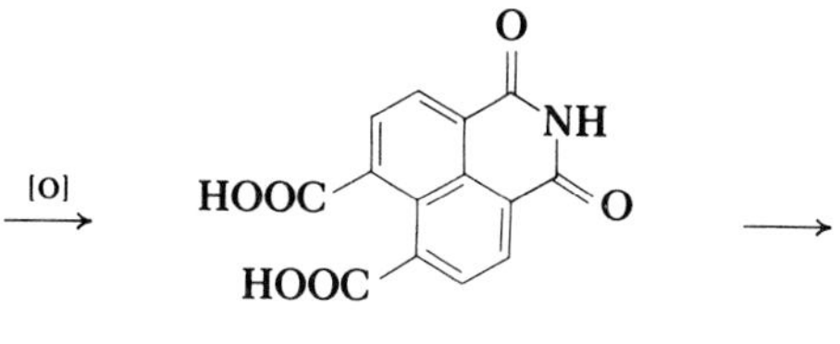

[O]

(IV)

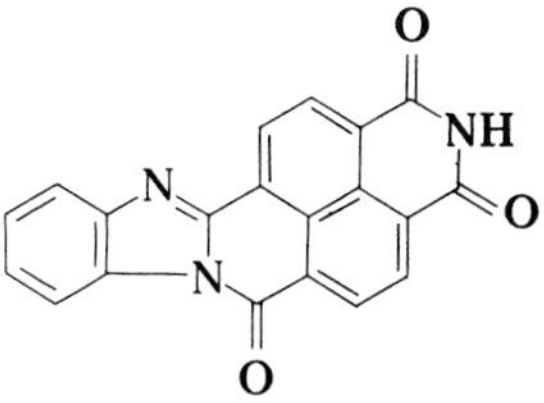

(V)

Dyes of Structure II

R	R′	Properties and comments	Refs.
H	H	Red. Dissolves unchanged in alkali; dyes cotton a weak orange (bl.-red vat).	3
H	NH_2-	Or., dyes cotton yel.-red.	1
H	$HOCH_2CH_2$-	Or., dyes cotton yel.	1,4
CH_3	$HOCH_2CH_2$-	Dyes cotton red-yel.	1
H	4-C_6H_4Cl-	Red, dyes cotton yel.	1
H	C_6H_5-	Yel., dyes cotton red-yel.	1
9,10-Br_2	C_6H_{11}-	Yel.	1
9,10-Cl,Br	C_6H_{11}-	(Mixture), yellow.	1
9,10-Cl_2	C_6H_{11}-	Yel.	1
H	$C_6H_5CH_2$-	Or., dyes cotton red.-yel.	1
H	2-$CH_3C_6H_4$-	Brn.-yel., dyes cotton yel.	1
H	2,4-$(CH_3)_2$-C_6H_3-	Yel.	1
H	2,5-$(CH_3)_2$-C_6H_3-	Yel.	1
CH_3	2-$CH_3C_6H_4$	Or., dyes cotton red-yel.	1
H	2-$C_{10}H_7$-	Yel.	1

Dyes of Structure III

R	R′	R″	Properties	Refs.
H	H	Nothing	Yel.	2
Cl	2-Cl	Nothing	Golden or.	2
Cl	3-Cl	Nothing	Golden yel.	2
H	3-OCH_3	Nothing	Yel.	2
H	H	CH_2	Yel.	2
H	H	CO	Golden or.	2
Cl	H	CH_2	Golden yel.	2
H	H	S	Yel.	2
H	H	NH	Yel.	2
OC_2H_5	H	Nothing	Brn.	2
H	H	CHC_6H_5	Golden yel.	2

References

1. Eckert and Braunsdorf, Ger. Pat. 547,924; *Frdl.*, **18,** 1501 (1933); Ger. Pat. 551,183; *Frdl.*, **19,** 2198 (1934); U. S. Pat. 1,935,945; Brit. Pats. 366,660 and 366,705.

2. Eckert and Fuchs, Ger. Pat. Appl'n. F. 15002 IVb/22e.
3. Höpff, Ger. Pat. Appl'n. I. 51838 IVe/1202; *PB Report No.* 73719, frame 2201.
4. LeThierry d'Ennequin, *Teintex*, **20,** 879 (1955).

A-301. 5*H*-Benzimidazo[1,2-*a*]naphtho-[1,2,3-*de*]quinoline*

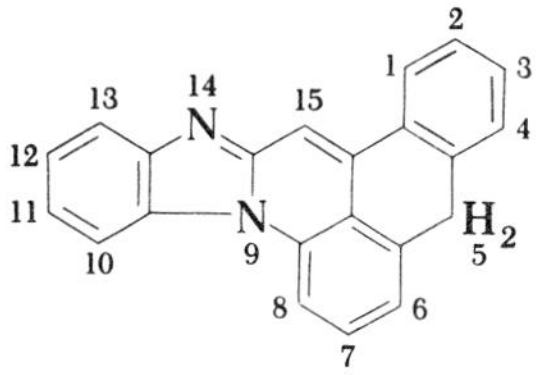

By the successive reduction, acetylation and cyclization of 1-(*o*-nitroanilino)-anthraquinone (I), Rösch[1] obtained the 5-oxo derivative (II) of this nucleus. Eckert[1] mentions that the *p*-toluidino

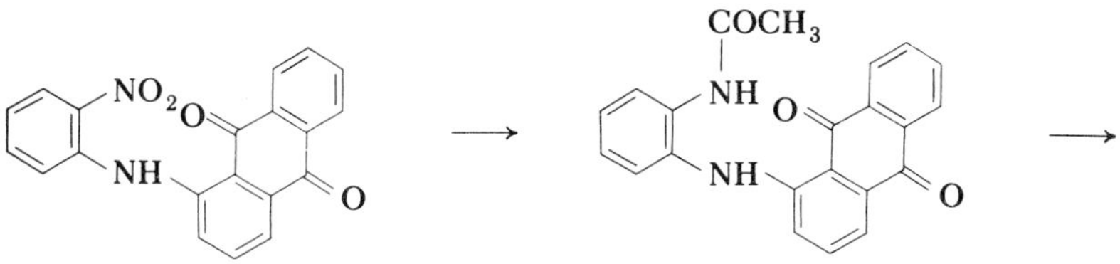

(I)

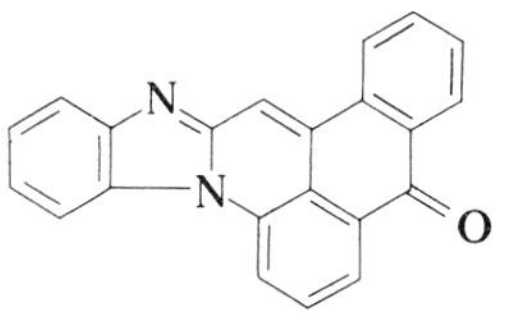

(II)

derivative (III) of II was prepared as shown from 2-methylbenzimidazole. Compound III was a red dye of no interest and, similarly, II showed poor light-fastness.

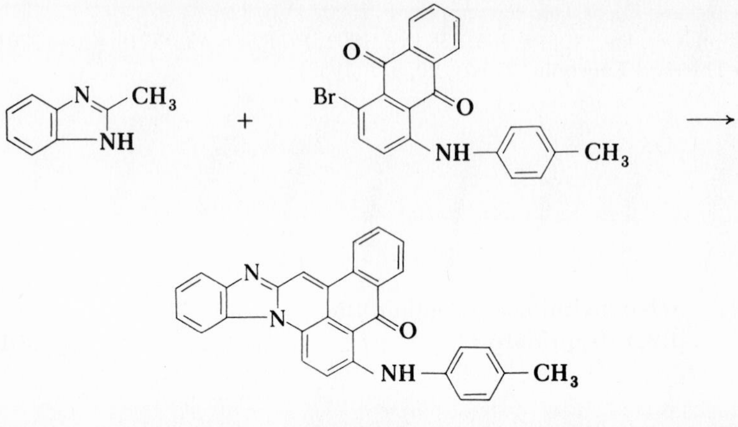

(III)

Reference

1. Eckert and Rösch, *I.G. Farbenindustrie A.G., 31 Wissenschaftlicher Austauch der Gruppe IX*, Frankfurt, June 20, 1934, and Höchst, July 17, 1934; *PB Report No.* 25632, frames 226–7.

A-302. 15*H*-Benzimidazo[2,1-*a*]naphtho-[1,2,3-*de*]isoquinoline

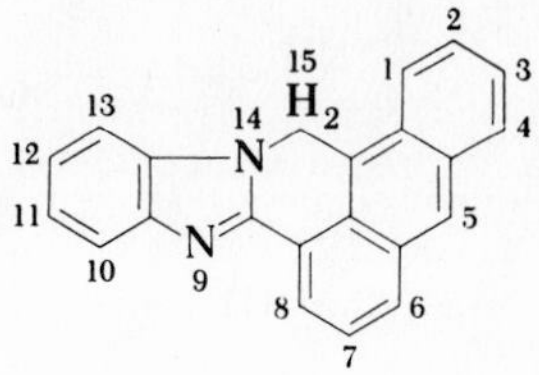

and/or

A-303. 9*H*-Benzimidazo[2,1-*a*]dibenzo-[*de,h*]isoquinoline*

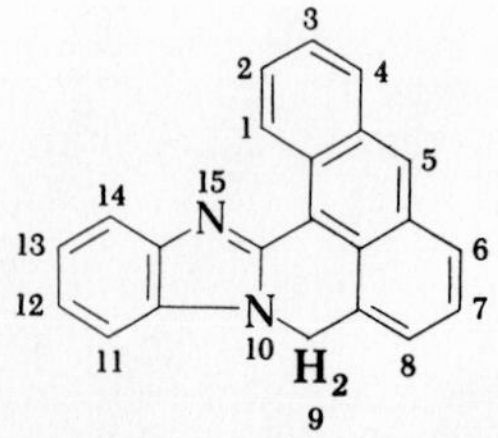

Compounds representing either one or the other of these nuclei (or possibly a mixture of both) have been obtained by Eckert and Braunsdorf.[1,2] The carboxyl group of compound(s?) I was converted into the acid chloride and this was allowed to react with benzene under Friedel-Crafts conditions to give the corresponding benzoyl

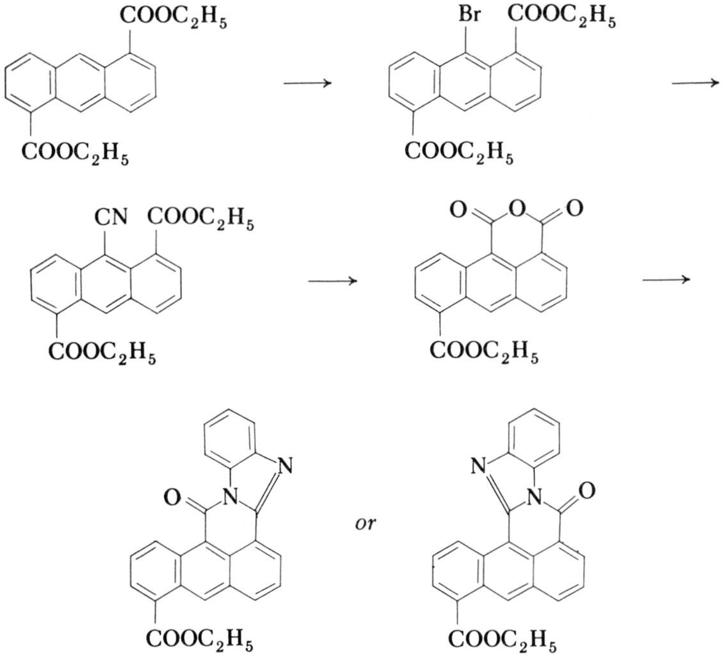

or

(I)

compound(s?). This product crystallized from acetic acid in red needles, m. 270–3°, and was claimed to dye violet from a blue vat.

References

1. Eckert and Braunsdorf, *I.G. Farbenindustrie A.G., 33 Wissenschaftlicher Austausch der Gruppe IX*, Frankfurt, March 29, 1935; *PB Report No.* 70338, frames 9533–9535.
2. Eckert and Braunsdorf, Ger. Pat. 637,091; *Frdl.*, **23,** 1124 (1940).

A-304. 14*H*-Benzo[*de*]naphth[2′,1′-4,5]-imidazo[1,2-*b*]isoquinoline. R.I. 3500

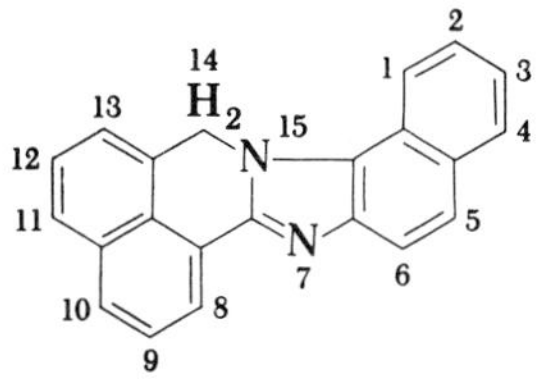

The 14-oxo derivative of this nucleus was described in 1924 by Chakravarti[1] as being the product of the condensation of naphthalic anhydride with 1,2-naphthylenediamine. He reported the compound to melt at 256°. The following year Bistrzycki and Risi[2] reported the same reaction to yield a product (m. 238–9°d.), which they considered to have structure I, and which they named *1′,8′-naphthoylen-α-naphthiminazole-1,2.* Their preference for structure I was based upon their observation that phthalic anhydride reacted with

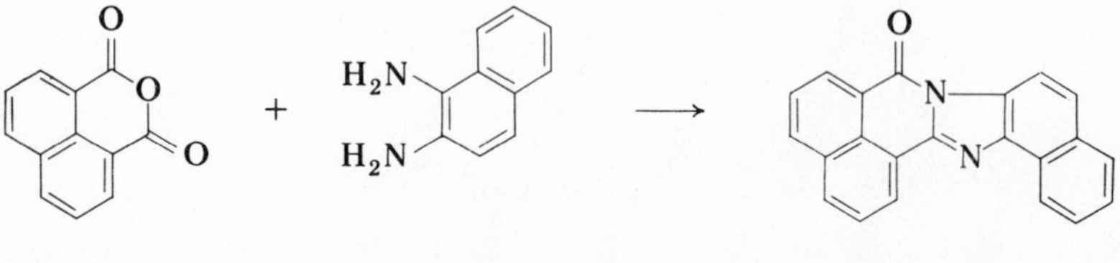

(I)

the 2-amino group of 1,2-naphthylenediamine and that the product could be converted (by deamination and hydrolysis) to 2-naphthylphthalamic acid (II) rather than the corresponding 1-isomer (III). The analogy between these reactions and the present condensation was felt by Bistrzycki and Risi to be sufficiently valid to support structure I over that suggested by Chakravarti. No direct evidence

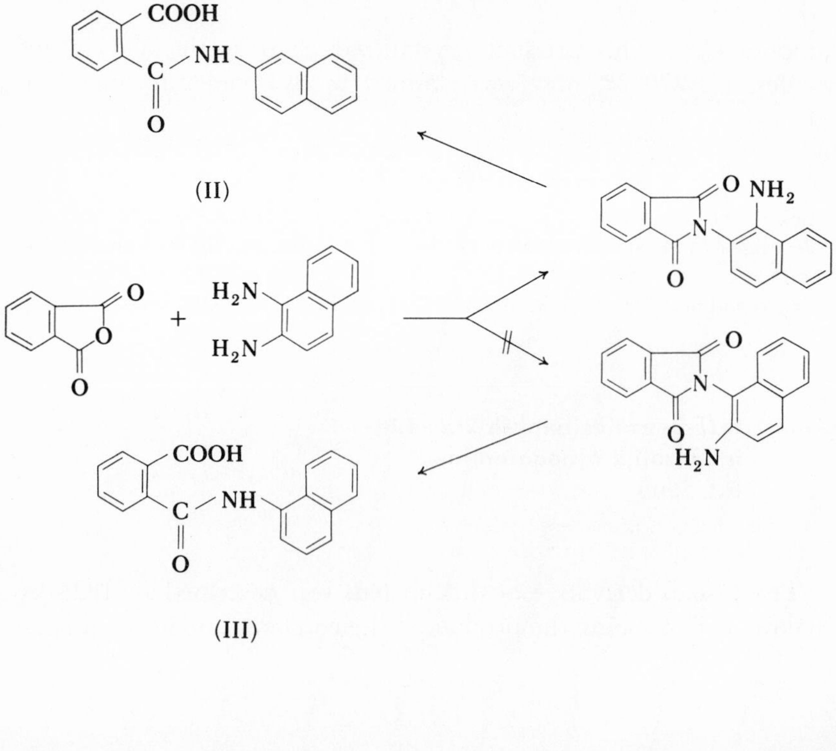

(II)

(III)

on the behavior of naphthalic acid is available however, and it has subsequently been claimed by Crippa and Galimberti,[3] that the condensation of phthalic anhydride and 1,2-naphthylenediamine (see Sections A-101/2) yields IV when run at 170°, but V when run at

170°

(IV)

270°

(V)

270°. A decision as to the exact structure of these products must therefore await further experimental evidence.

14H-Benzo[*de*]napth[2′,1′,4,5]imidazo[1,2-*b*]isoquinolin-14-ones

Empirical formula	Substituents	Properties and comments	Refs.
$C_{22}H_{12}N_2O$	Unsubstituted	Or.-red, m. 256° (238–9° d.).	1,2
$C_{22}H_{12}N_2O_2$	1-Hydroxy-	Or., m. 350°.	4
	4-Hydroxy-	Or., m. 323°.	4
	4,9(or 4,12)-Dihydroxy-	Or., m. >355°.	4
	4,10 (or 4,11)-Dihydroxy-	Or., m. >355°.	4
$C_{22}H_{12}N_2O_4S$	1-Sulfo-	—	4
	4-Sulfo-	—	4
$C_{22}H_{12}N_2O_5S$	4-Hydroxy-2-sulfo-	—	4
	1-Hydroxy-3-sulfo-	—	4
	10-Hydroxy-4-sulfo-	—	4
$C_{22}H_{13}N_2O_7S_2$	1,3-Disulfo-	—	4
	2,4-Disulfo-	—	4
	4,9 (or 4,12)-Disulfo-	—	4
$C_{24}H_{12}N_2O_5$	10,11-Dicarboxy-	Red	5,6

References

1. Chakravarti, *Quart. J. Indian Chem. Soc.*, **1,** 19 (1924); *Chem. Abstracts*, **19,** 830 (1925); *Chem. Zentr.*, **I,** 518 (1925).
2. Bistrzycki and Riši, *Helv. Chim. Acta*, **8,** 810 (1925).
3. Crippa and Galimberti, *Gazz. chim. ital.*, **59,** 510 (1929).
4. Neelmeier and Meiser, Ger. Pat. 519,052; *Frdl.*, **17,** 1423 (1932). U. S. Pat. 1,867,091.
5. Eckert and Braunsdorf, Ger. Pat. 553,629; *Frdl.*, **19,** 2194 (1934). U. S. Pat. 1,924,090.
6. Eckert and Fuchs, Ger. Pat. 1,005,969.

A-305. *7H*-Benzo[*de*]quinoxalo[2′,3′]-imidazo[1,2-*b*]isoquinoline. R.I. 3495

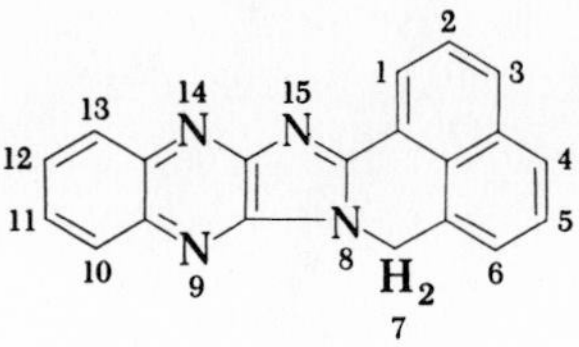

The 7-oxo derivative of this nucleus was briefly described as forming yellow needles, by Sircar and Pal,[1] who obtained it from the condensation of naphthalic anhydride with 2,3-diaminoquinoxaline.

Reference

1. Sircar and Pal, *J. Indian Chem. Soc.*, **9,** 527 (1932); *Chem. Zentr.*, **I,** 1947 (1933); *Chem. Abstracts*, **27,** 1882 (1933).

A-306. Benzo[*lmn*]bisimidazo-[1,2-*c*, 1′,2′-*j*][3,8]-phenanthroline. R.I. 3462

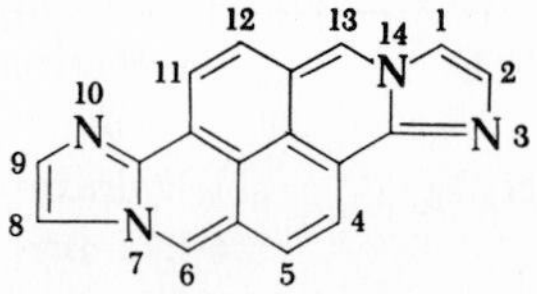

and/or

A-307. Benzo[*lmn*]bisimidazo-[1,2-*c*, 2′,1′-*j*][3,8]-phenanthroline

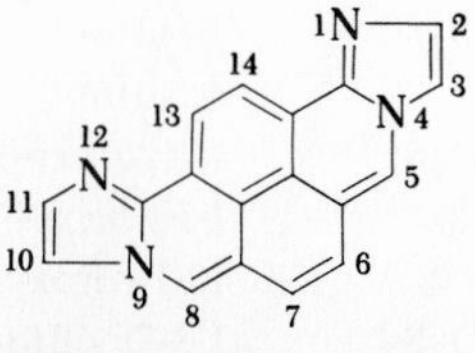

By condensing naphthalene-1,4,5,8-tetracarboxylic acid (I) with two moles of ethylenediamine, Fierz-David and Rossi[1] obtained a tetrahydrodioxo derivative (II and/or III) of one or both of these ring systems. The product was orange-yellow and very readily vatted, but so strongly basic that it possessed little vat dye character.

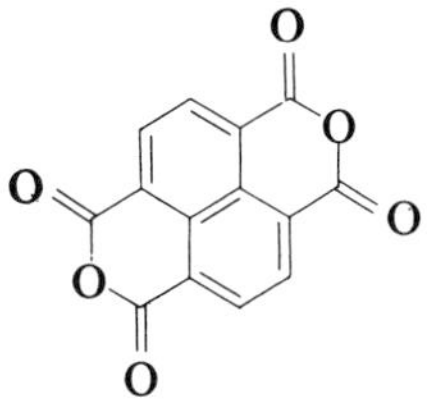

(I) →

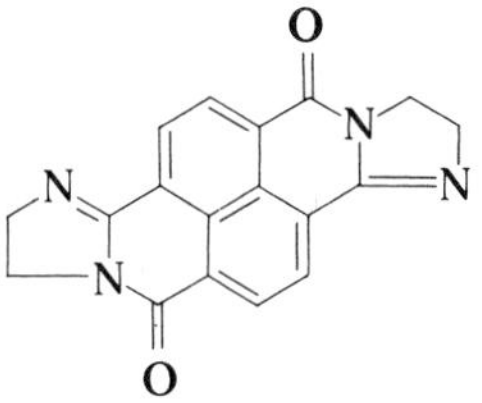

(II) *trans*

and/or

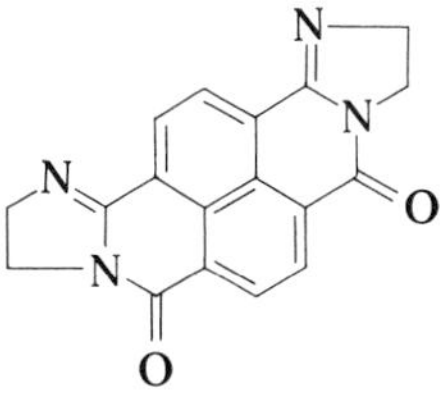

(III) *cis*

Treatment of this tetrahydro product in trichlorobenzene at 180–200° with bromine dehydrogenated and brominated it to the tetrabromo compound(s) (halogens in imidazole rings), which dyed cotton a yellow-brown from a red vat.

Reference

1. Fierz-David and Rossi, *Helv. Chim. Acta*, **21,** 1466 (1938).

A-308. *7H*-Benz[4,5]isoquino[1,2-*a*]quinoxalo[2,3-*f*]benzimidazole. R.I. 3713

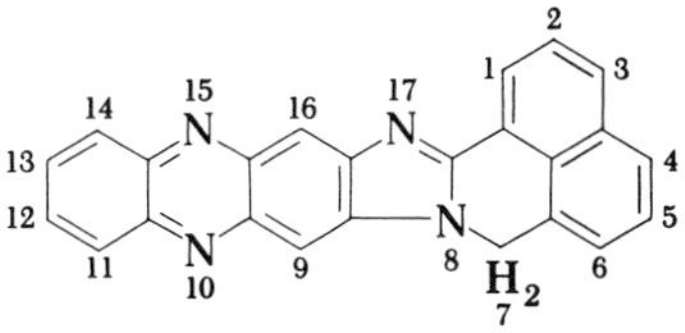

A yellow product (m. > 300°), thought to be the 7-oxo derivative, reportedly was obtained by Sircar and De[1] by condensing naphthalic anhydride with 2,3-diaminophenazine.

Reference

1. Sircar and De, *Quart, J. Indian Chem. Soc.*, **2,** 312 (1925); *Chem. Zentr.*, **I,** 2697 (1926); *Chem. Abstracts*, **20,** 1805 (1926).

A-309. 10*H*-Benzo[*de*]phenanthro-[9′,10′,4,5]imidazo[2,1-*a*]-isoquinoline*

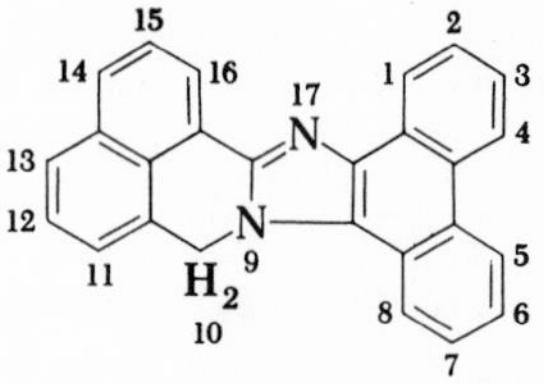

Treatment of 9,10-diaminophenanthrene with naphthalic acids (I, R = H, Br or NO_2) in hot acetic acid, was reported[1] to yield derivatives of structure II (R = H, yellow-orange, m. 326°, H_2SO_4 solution green; R = Br, bright orange, m. 273°, H_2SO_4 solution bright green; R = NO_2, bordeaux, m. 330°, H_2SO_4 solution violet). The substituent R is in either the 13 or 14 position, but was not located definitively.

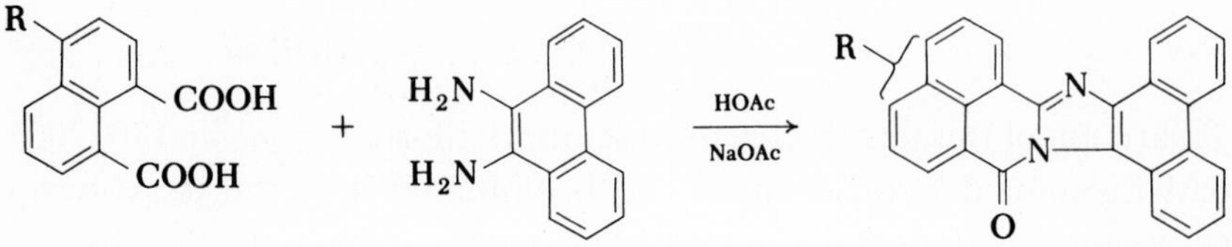

(I) (II)

Attempts by this method to prepare an amine of type II using 4-aminonaphthalic acid (I, R = NH_2) failed. To effect the condensation of this acid with 9,10-diaminophenanthrene it was necessary to resort to a high boiling solvent such as quinoline and a temperature of about 220°. However, the resulting product was not an imidazole such as II, but was thought to be 9,10-(*N*,*N*′-bis-4-aminonaphthalimido)phenanthrene.

Reference

1. Tsukerman and Krasovitski, *Ukrain. Khim. Zhur.*, **20,** 543 (1954).

A-310. 6*H*-Anthra[3,2,1-*de*]benz-imidazo[1,2-*b*]isoquinoline*

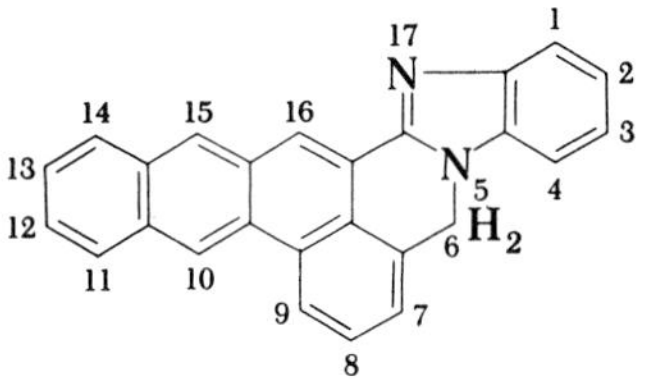

and/or

A-311. 10*H*-Anthra[3,2,1-*de*]benz-imidazo[2,1-*a*]isoquinoline*

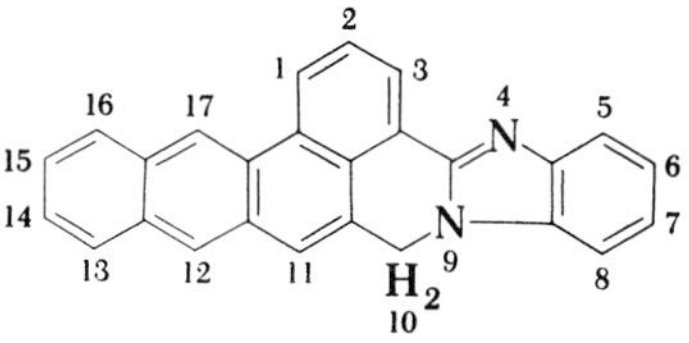

The name *9'-keto-4':5'(or 2':3')-o-phthaloyl-8'-aza-phenalino(7':8':-2:3)-ψ-indole* (I) was assigned by Peters and Rowe[1] to a product (ob-

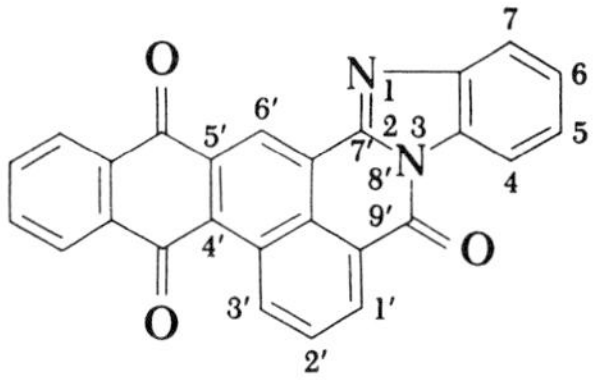

(I)

tained as shown), which is possibly a single component, but probably is a mixture of II and III. The same product was also obtained

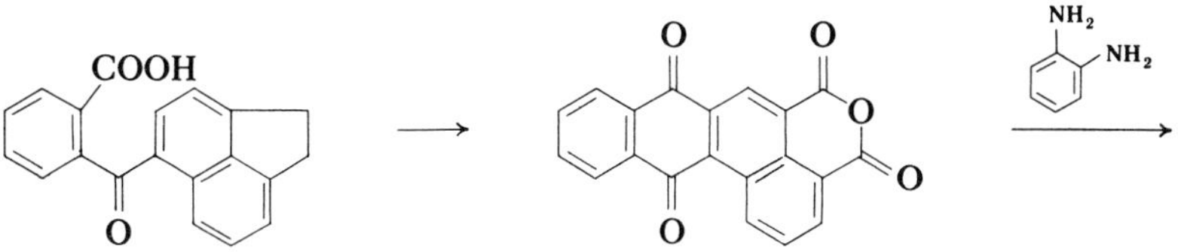

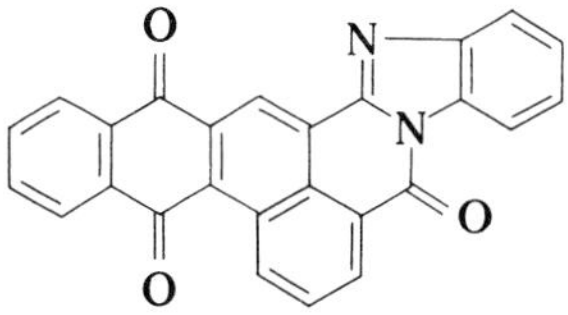

(II) (III)

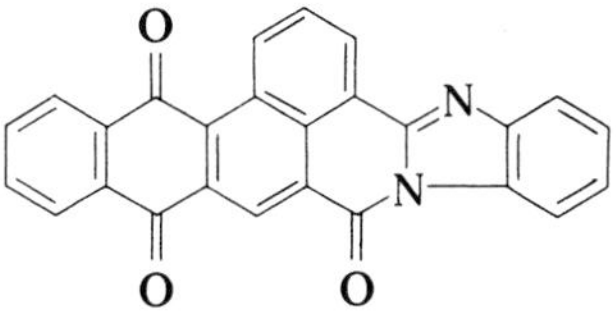

by Heidenreich[2] from IV. The product crystallizes in red plates, which shrink above 300° and melt at 320–5°. It dissolves in sulfuric acid with a yellow-brown color and dyes cotton orange from an olive green vat. The shade is yellower and brighter than that

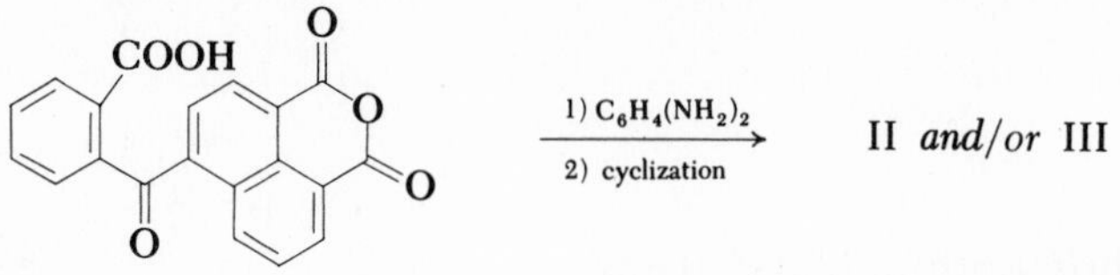

(IV)

of Indanthrene Golden Orange 2RT, but it is inferior to the latter dye in light- and wash-fastness.

References

1. Peters and Rowe, *J. Soc. Dyers and Colourists*, **59,** 52 (1943).
2. Heidenreich, Brit. Pat. 304,263; *Chem. Zentr.*, **I,** 2585 (1929); U. S. Pat. 1,847,561.

A-312. Benzimidazo[1,2-*b*]thioxantheno-[3,2,1-*de*]isoquinoline*

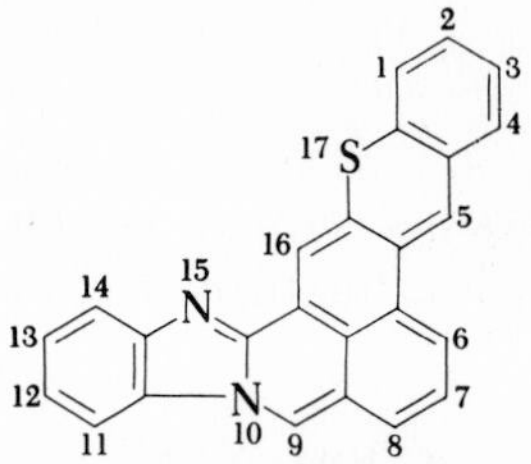

and/or

A-313. Benzimidazo[2,1-*a*]thioxantheno-[3,2,1-*de*]isoquinoline*

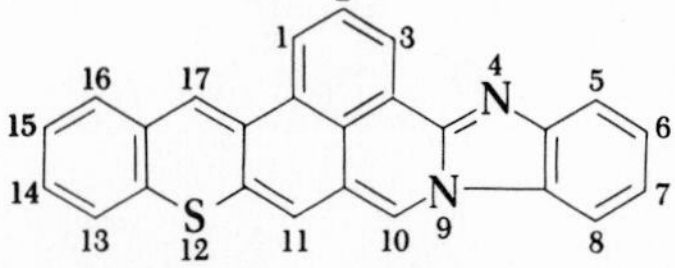

A product representing one or the other of these nuclei, or possibly a mixture of both, was described by Eckert and Quint.[1] The product crystallizes in yellow needles (m. 286–7°) and dissolves in sulfuric acid with an orange color. While the dye is stronger than the acridone analog (see Sections A-314/5), it is still appreciably weaker than, for example, Indanthrene Yellow GK, and inferior to it in light-fastness. The introduction of chlorine or of ethoxy groups into the benzimidazole ring failed to improve the strength of the dye.

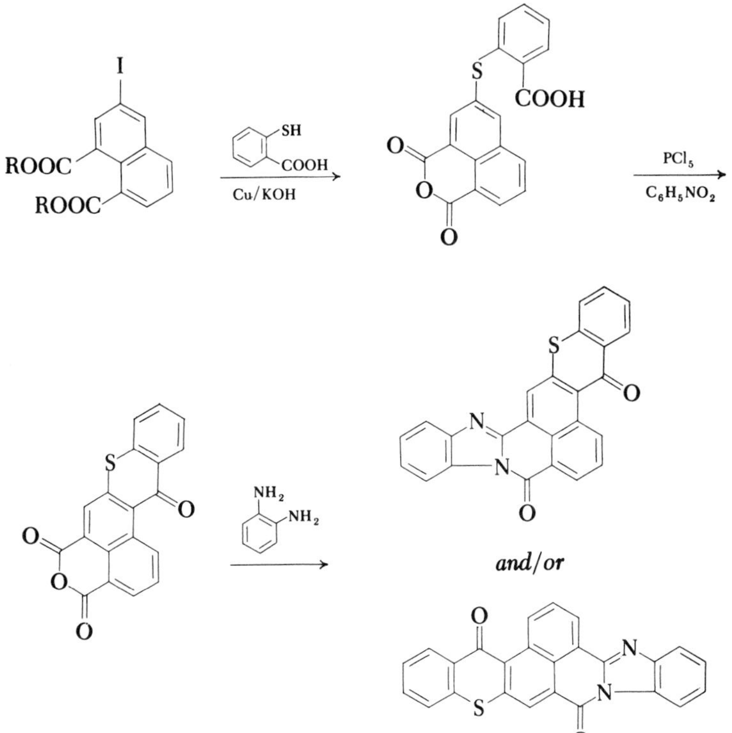

ROOC ROOC I SH COOH Cu/KOH S COOH O O O PCl_5 $C_6H_5NO_2$

S O O O O NH_2 NH_2 S O N N O *and/or* O N N S O

Reference

1. Eckert and Quint, *I.G. Farbenindustrie A.G.*, *35 Wissenschaftlicher Austausch der Gruppe IX*, March 13, 1936, Frankfurt, *PB Report No.* 70338, frames 9752–9757.

A-314. 9*H*-Benzimidazo[1′,2′,2,3]isoquin[5,4-*ab*]acridine*

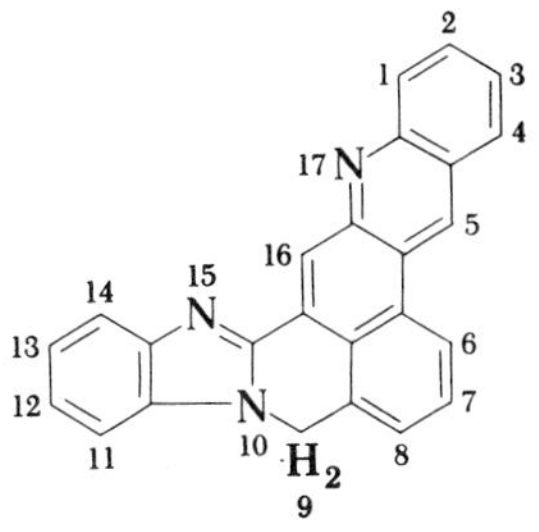

and/or

A-315. 10*H*-Benzimidazo[2′,1′,1,2]isoquin[5,4-*ab*]acridine*

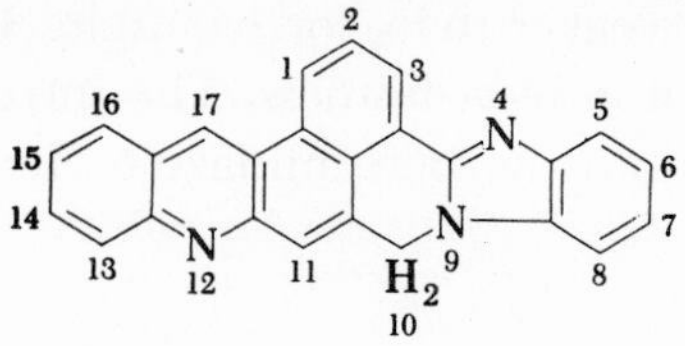

2
1 3
16 17 4 5
15 N 6
14 N 7
N
13 12 11 H_2 9 8
10

A product, which is probably a mixture of oxo derivatives of the above two isomers, was obtained by Eckert and Quint[1] via the route shown. It forms yellow needles, soluble in sulfuric acid with a yellow

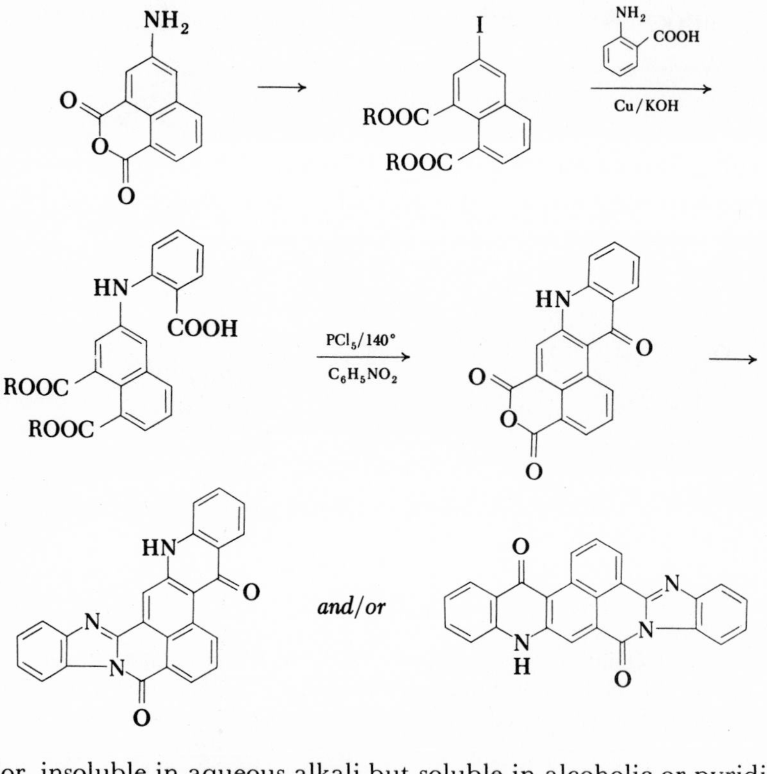

NH_2
O
O
O
→
I
ROOC
ROOC
NH_2
COOH
Cu/KOH

HN
COOH
ROOC
ROOC
PCl_5/140°
$C_6H_5NO_2$
HN
O
O
O
O
→

HN
O
N
N
O
and/or
O
N
N
N
H
O

color, insoluble in aqueous alkali but soluble in alcoholic or pyridine solutions of alkali. The product is a very weak yellow dye (orange vat) with poor soap-, wash- and soda-fastness.

Reference

1. Eckert and Quint, *I.G. Farbenindustrie A.G.*, *35 Wissenschaftlicher Austausch der Gruppe IX*, March 13, 1936, Frankfurt; *PB Report No.* 70338, frames 9752–9757.

A-316. Anthra[2,1,9-*def*]benzimidazo-[2,1-*a*]isoquinoline

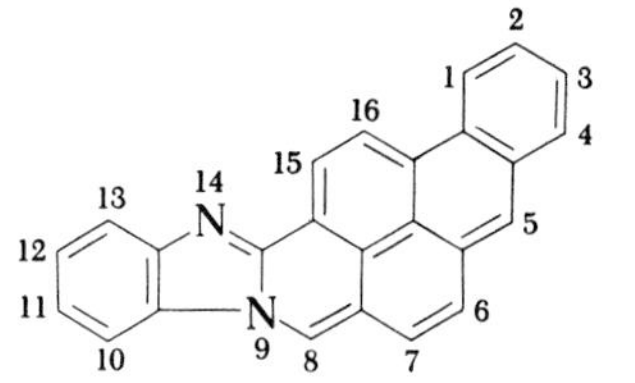

and/or

A-317. Anthra[2,1,9-*def*]benzimidazo-[1,2-*b*]isoquinoline*

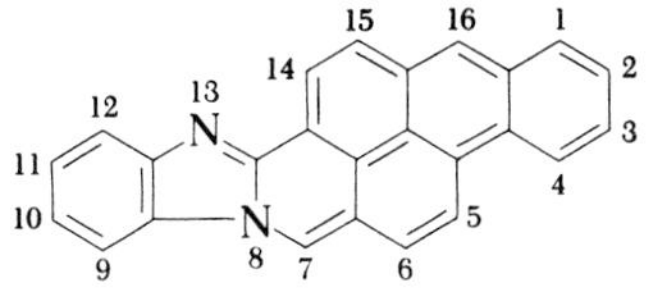

Derivatives of one or both of these nuclei are obtained by reacting benzanthrone-3,4-dicarboxylic acids with *o*-phenylenediamines[1-4] or with *o*-nitroanilines followed by reduction.[5] A further synthesis of these nuclei has been described briefly,[6] and consists in subjecting benzoylbenzimidazo[2,1-*a*]benz[*de*]isoquinolin-7-ones (e.g., III) to the Scholl condensation. While the colors of these various products range from orange through blue to brownish black, none has yet found commercial application. The separation of some of these dye mixtures into the isomeric components has been claimed.[7] For example, the mixture of the sulfates of I and II was fractionally

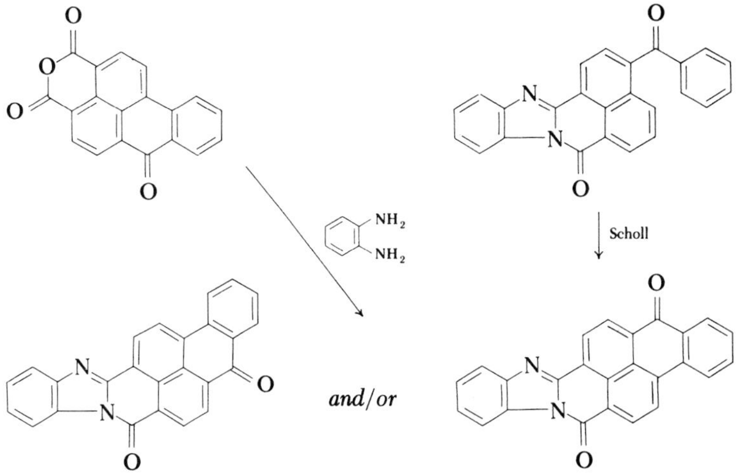

Scholl

and/or

(I)

(II)

crystallized from sulfuric acid, giving a less soluble (probably *trans*) isomer, which dyes cotton a clear fast orange from a red vat. The more soluble fraction dyes cotton red from a red vat.

Derivatives of I and II

Empirical formula	Substituents	Properties and comments	Refs.
$C_{25}H_{11}BrN_2O_2$	*x*-Bromo-*I* and/or *II* (possibly 3-Bromo-*I* and/or 2-bromo-*II*)	(Mixture?), dyes cotton red-or.	2,3
$C_{25}H_{11}ClN_2O_2$	2-Chloro-*I* and/or 3-chloro-*II*	(Mixture?), dyes cotton or.	2
	12-Chloro-*I* and/or 11-chloro-*II*	(Mixture?), dyes cotton or. from red vat.	2-4
$C_{25}H_{12}N_2O_2$	Unsubstituted *I* and/or *II*	(Mixture?), or.-red; fast or. dye.	1-4,6
$C_{26}H_{13}ClN_2O_2$	11(or 12)-Chloro-13(or 10)-methyl-*I* and/or 10(or 11)-chloro-12(or 9)-methyl-*II*	(Mixture?), or. dye.	2-4
	11(or 12)-Chloro-12(or 11)-methyl-*I* and/or 11(or 10)-chloro-10(or 11)-methyl-*II*	(Mixture?), brilliant or. dye.	2,3
$C_{26}H_{13}ClN_2O_3$	11(or 12)-Chloro-12(or 11)-methoxy-*I* and/or 10(or 11)-chloro-11(or 10)—methoxy-*II*.	(Mixture?), a clear brn. dye.	2,3
$C_{26}H_{14}N_2O_2$	10(or 13)-Methyl-*I* and/or 9(or 12)-methyl-*II*.	(Mixture?), dyes cotton a brilliant scarlet.	2-4
$C_{27}H_{16}N_2O_3$	11(or 12)-Ethoxy-*I* and/or 10(or 11)-ethoxy-*II*.	(Mixture?), dyes cotton a deep brn. from or.-red vat.	2-4
$C_{27}H_{16}N_2O_4$	11,12-Dimethoxy-*I* and/or 10,11-dimethoxy-*II*.	(Mixture?), dyes blk.-brn.	2,3
$C_{28}H_{18}N_2O_3$	11(or 12)-Ethoxy-2-methyl-*I* and/or 10(or 11)-ethoxy-3-methyl-*II*.	(Mixture?), dyes cotton bl.	4
$C_{50}H_{22}N_4O_4$	11(or 12), 11′(or 12′)-bis-*I*- and/or 10(or 11), 10′(or 11′)-bis-*II*.	(Mixture?), dyes vt.-brn.	4

References

1. Kränzlein, Greune and Langbein, Ger. Pat. 561,494; *Frdl.*, **18,** 1406 (1933). U. S. Pat. 1,856,711.
2. Kränzlein, Greune, Corell and Vollmann, Ger. Pat. 503,404; *Frdl.*, **17,** 1386 (1932). U. S. Pat. 1,921,360.
3. I.G. Farbenindustrie, A.G., Brit. Pat. 308,651; *Chem. Zentr.*, **II,** 662 (1929). Fr. Pat. 671,976.
4. I.G. Farbenindustrie, A.G., Fr. Pat. 39,499; *Chem. Zentr.*, **I,** 880 (1932).
5. Greune and Langbein, Ger. Pat. 531,014; *Frdl.*, **18,** 1406 (1933).
6. Kranzlein, Greune and Vollmann, Ger. Pat. 494,111; *Frdl.*, **16,** 1441 (1931); *Chem. Zentr.*, **II,** 820 (1930). U. S. Pat. 1,892,241.
7. Greune and Langbein, Ger. Pat. 563,493; *Frdl.*, **18,** 1407 (1933)

A-318. Benzimidazo[2,1-*a*]pyrido-[3′,2′,6,7]naphth[2,1,8-*def*]-isoquinoline*

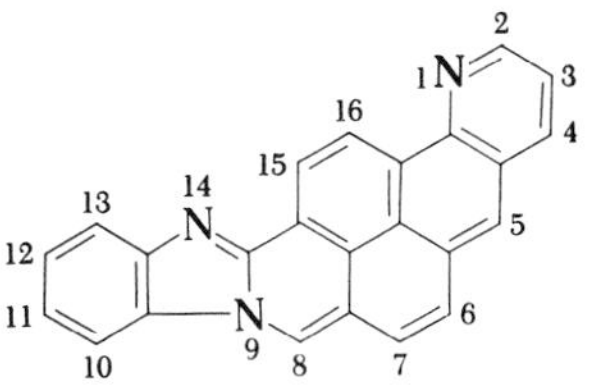

and/or

A-319. Benzimidazo[2,1-*a*]pyrido-[2′,3′,5,6]naphth[2,1,8-*def*]-isoquinoline*

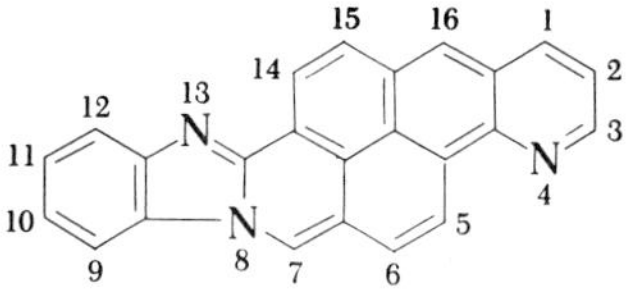

By the condensation of 11-azabenz[*de*]anthr-7-one-3,4-dicarboxylic acid (I) with *o*-phenylenediamine, Vollmann[1] obtained a product, which is probably a mixture of the dioxo derivatives of the above two nuclei. The dicarboxylic acid (I) was obtained as shown from 1-aminopyrene. The product dyes orange from a yellow-olive vat and gives a golden yellow solution in sulfuric acid. The shade is not appreciably different from that of the product formed by condensing benz[*de*]anthr-7-one-3,4-dicarboxylic acid with *o*-phenylenediamine (see Sections A-316/7), and the dye is inferior to this product in wash- and boil-fastness.

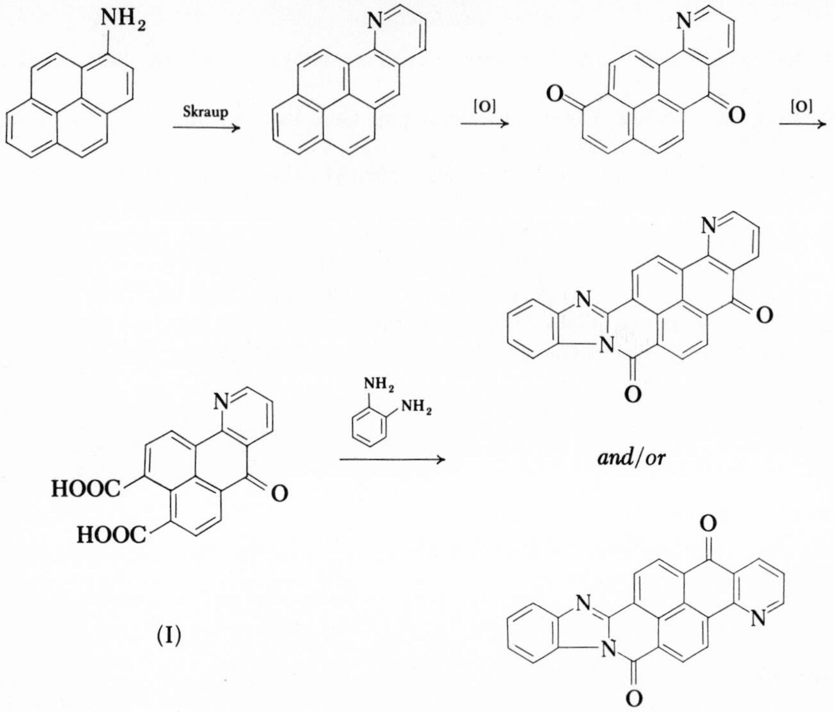

NH$_2$ Skraup [O] [O]

NH$_2$ NH$_2$

HOOC HOOC O

(I)

and/or

Reference

1. Vollmann, *I.G. Farbenindustrie A.G.*, *34 Wissenschaftlicher Austausch der Gruppe IX*, Oct. 25, 1935, Leverkusen; *PB Report No.* 70338, frames 9699–9700.

A-320. 8*H*-Benzimidazo[1,2-*a*]-pleiadeno-[3,4-*cd*]pyridine

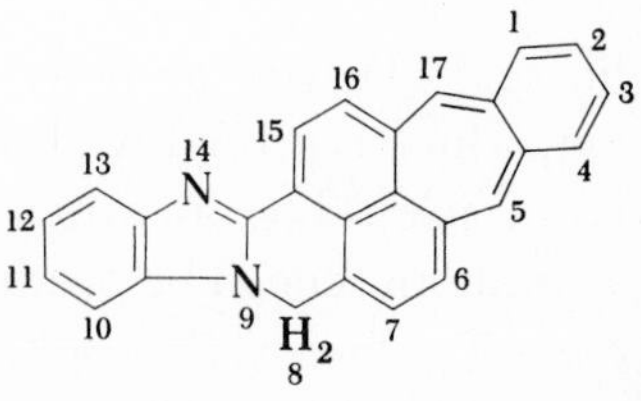

The trioxo derivative was obtained by Peters and Rowe,[1] who named it *9′-keto-3′,4′-phthaloyl-8-aza-phenalino(7′:8′:2:3)-ψ-indole* and numbered the nucleus as shown in I. Condensation of the anhydride II with *o*-phenylenediamine gave product III (orange needles, m. 380°, insoluble in aqueous alkali, but soluble with an orange-

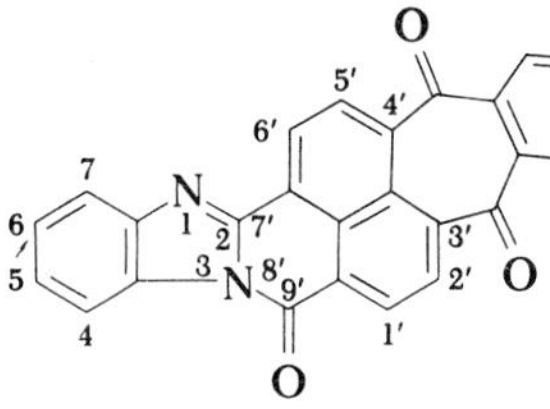

(I)

red color in sulfuric acid). It forms a deep red-violet vat and dyes a golden yellow, slightly redder and duller than Caledon Yellow 2RS, but a little greener and brighter than Indanthrene Golden Orange G, while inferior to the former in light- and wash-fastness.

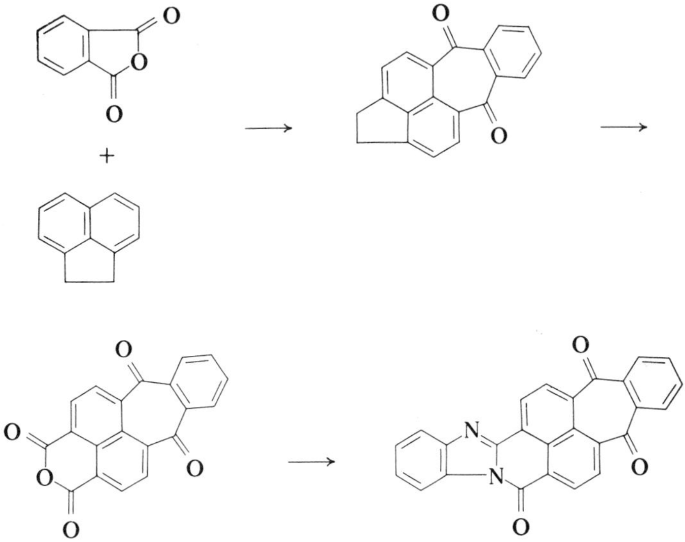

(II)

(III)

Reference

1. Peters and Rowe, *J. Soc. Dyers and Colourists*, **59,** 52 (1943).

A-321. Imidazo[2,1-*a*]quinoxalino-[2′,3′,6,7]naphth[2,1,8-*def*]-isoquinoline*

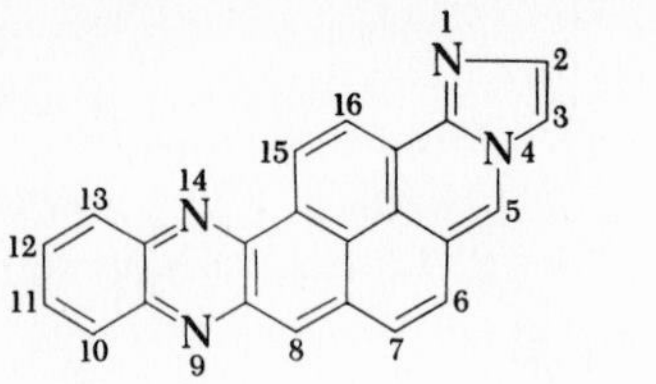

and/or

A-322. Imidazo[1,2-*b*]quinoxalino-[2′,3′,6,7]naphth[2,1,8-*def*]-isoquinoline*

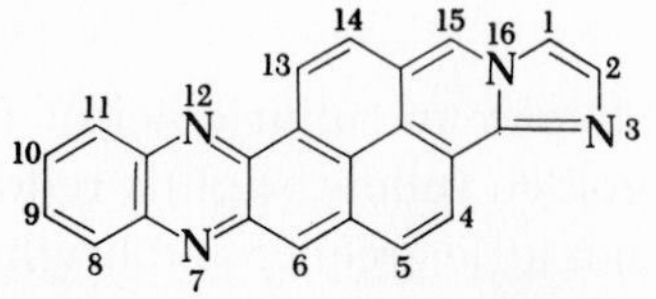

A yellow-brown dye (orange vat), probably a mixture of II and III, was prepared by Eckert and Sieber[1] by reacting the anhydride I with ethylenediamine.

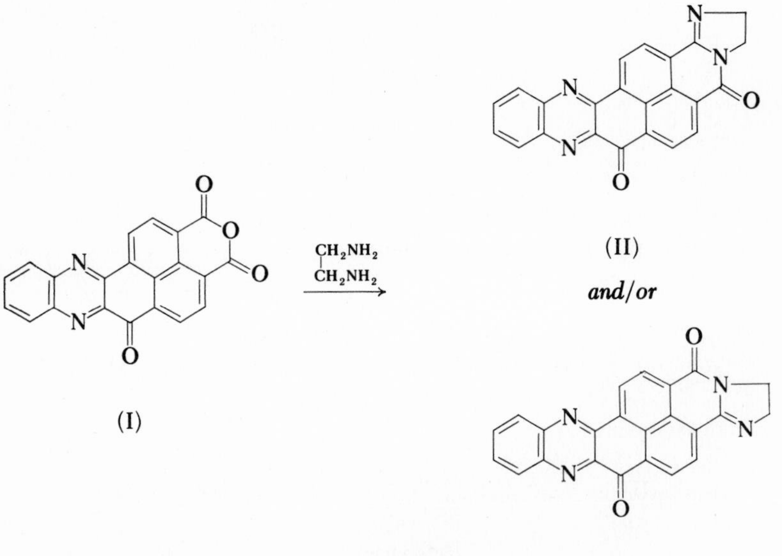

(I)

$\underset{CH_2NH_2}{\overset{CH_2NH_2}{|}}$ →

(II)

and/or

(III)

Reference

1. Eckert and Sieber, Ger. Pat. 659,095; *Frdl.*, **24,** 973 (1941).

A-323. Benzimidazo[2,1-*a*][1]benzothieno[3′,2′,5,6]naphtho[2,1,8-*def*]isoquinoline*

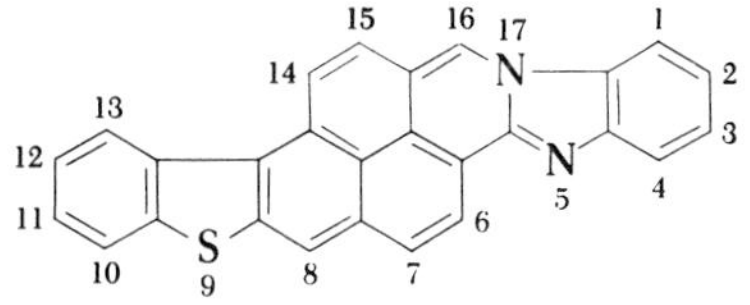

Acylation of benzo[*b*]thiophene with a product thought to be I (see Section A-296), followed by the Scholl condensation upon the intermediate ketone, yielded[1] a brown dye (red-brown vat) assigned structure II.

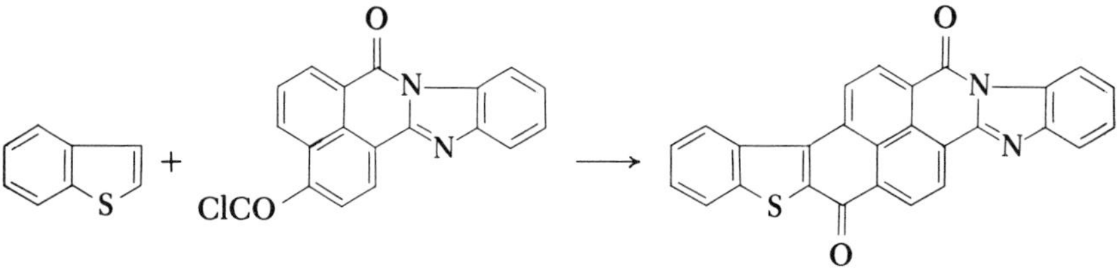

(I) (II)

Reference

1. Schmidt-Nickels, U. S. Pat. 2,820,036.

A-324. Bisbenzimidazo[2,1-*a*, 2′,1′-*h*][2,7]diazapyrene. R.I. 3855

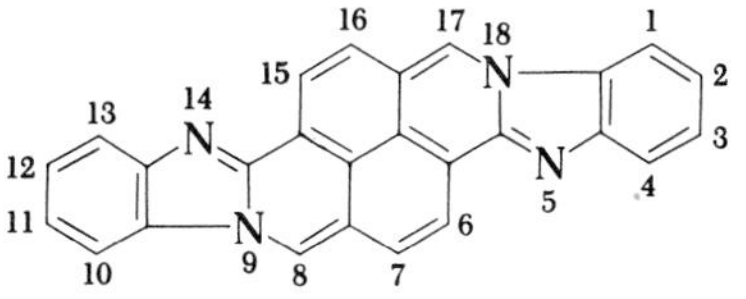

and

A-325. Bisbenzimidazo[2,1-*a*, 1′,2′-*i*][2,7]diazapyrene. R.I. 3856

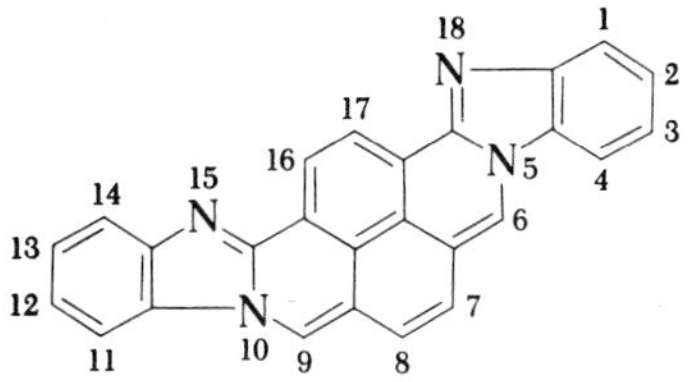

Derivatives of these two nuclei were among the first prepared and are the most important of the higher imidazo[1,2-*a*]pyridine ring systems.

The first commercial exploitation of compounds of this type occurred in 1926 when the I.G. Farbenindustrie A.G. marketed as "Indanthrenscharlach GG" the reaction product of *o*-phenylenediamine and naphthalene-1,4,5,8-tetracarboxylic acid dianhydride.[9] It was soon found that Indanthrene Scarlet GG was actually a mixture[10] of the two isomeric dyes I and II. Because of the juxtaposition of the carbonyl groups in compounds such as II, it is customary to refer to such structures as "*cis*" isomers, while those of type I are called "*trans*." Numerous methods were then patented for the separation of the *cis-trans* mixture, including extraction of

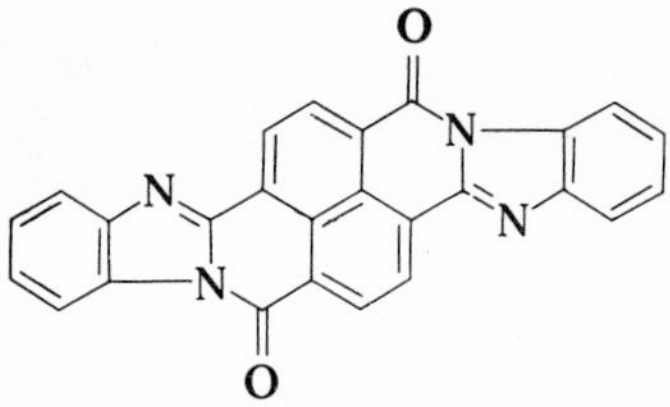

(I) *trans* 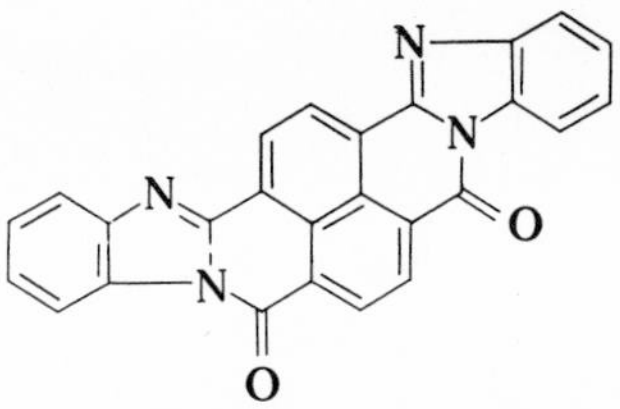 (II) *cis*

the product with hot chloroacetic acid[11] or sulfuric acid,[12] or treatment with sodium hydroxide, potassium hydroxide,[13] sodium alkoxides or sodamide,[14] aluminum or stannic chlorides,[15] or *p*-toluenesulfonic acid.[16] Once separated, the *trans* isomer (I) was marketed under the name of "Indanthrene Brilliant Orange GR" while the *cis* isomer (II) was called "Indanthrene Bordeaux RR." The ratio of the isomers produced changes somewhat with the solvent employed.[1] In acetic acid approximately equal amounts of the two dyes are formed, while in pyridine about 60% of the *trans* isomer (I) results.

Minor variations of this synthesis consist of condensing the tetracarboxylic acid or anhydride with an *o*-azo-[2] or *o*-nitroaniline[3] to give a bis-*N*-arylimide, followed by reducing the nitro- or azo-group to an amine and cyclizing the product. By refluxing the tetracarboxylic anhydride in ethanol with the diamine, it is possible to obtain the intermediate bis-(*o*-aminophenylimides),[4,5] which, when heated further in acetic acid or dimethylaniline,[6] or even with water in a sealed container at 150°,[6] give the two bisbenzimidazo compounds. The condensation[29] of 3,4-dicarboxybenzimidazo[2,1-*a*]-

benz[*de*]isoquinolin-7-one (see Section A-296) with *o*-phenylenediamine also gives a mixture of I and II. Evidence of the great stability of these compounds, and of the considerable driving force towards their formation, is found in the observations that they may be obtained also (1) by elimination of aniline in the treatment of the *N*,*N'*-bisphenyl-

1) $KCN-Cu_2(CN)_2$
2) H_2O/H^+

(II) (*cis*)

1) $KCN-Cu_2(CN)_2$
2) H_2O/H^+

(I) (*trans*)

imide of naphthalene-1,4,5,8-tetracarboxylic acid with *o*-phenylenediamine,[7] and (2) by elimination of a substituent in the condensation of the "tetra acid" with, e.g., *o*-H_2N-C_6H_4-$NHCH_3$ and *o*-H_2N-C_6H_4-$NHCONHC_6H_5$.[8]

The question of determining which dye corresponded to the *cis* or *trans* isomer was nicely answered by Eckert and Becker,[1,17] who synthesized each isomer by an unequivocal route. Generally, the *trans* isomer is lighter or yellower[21] than the (redder) *cis* isomer in any given pair of isomeric dyes of this type. Solutions of the leuco derivatives of I and II are peculiarly dichroic; thus the vat of I is green in transmitted light and red in reflected light, while that of II shows the same colors in reverse.[36] Most of the dyes derived from "tetra acid" are known for their dichroic vat solutions.

Dyes containing these nuclei are numbered among the most powerful vat dyes,[18] have good all-around fastness, and do not promote "tendering" of the textile fibers. Some representatives of the series have rather insoluble leuco derivatives, and to avoid this difficulty, analogs having —$SO_2C_6H_5$ and —$SO_2N(CH_3)_2$ groups in the naphthalene nucleus were prepared. They proved, however, to be greatly inferior in strength.[18] Black, gray and brown-black dyes have been obtained[19,20] by attaching anthraquinonylamino groups to the benz-rings of the parent nuclei. Treatment of Indanthrene Scarlet GG (I and II) with hydroxylamine and iron salts in sulfuric acid is reported[33] to give a blue-gray to black dye (green vat), which is probably an amino derivative.

Derivatives of I and II

Empirical formula	Substituents	Properties and comments	Refs.
$C_{26}H_8Br_2Cl_2N_4O_2$	3,12 (or 2,11)-Dibromo-2,11 (or 3,12)-dichloro-*I*-	(Mixture?), dyes cotton red-brn. from olive vat.	11
	2,13 (or 3,12)-Dibromo-3,12 (or 2,13)-dichloro-*II*-	(Mixture?), dyes brn. from olive green vat.	22
$C_{26}H_8Cl_4N_4O_2$	2,3,11,12-Tetrachloro-*I*-	Dyes a clear orange from olive grn. vat.	11,13,15, 18
$C_{26}H_{10}Br_2N_4O_2$	3,12-Dibromo-*I*-	Dyes copper-red from olive grn. vat.	11

Derivatives of I and II (*continued*)

Empirical formula	Substituents	Properties and comments	Refs.
	2,13-Dibromo-*II*-	Dyes brn. from olive grn. vat.	11
$C_{26}H_{10}Cl_2N_4O_2$	3,12-Dichloro-*I*-	Dyes scarlet from olive grn. vat.	11
	2,13-Dichloro-*II*-	Dyes brn. from olive grn. vat.	11
	3,12-Dichloro-*I*-and 2,13-dichloro-*II*-	(Mixture) "Indanthrene Printing Brown 5R." Dyes red-brn.	19,35
$C_{26}H_{10}N_6O_6$ See also $C_{26}H_{14}N_6O_2$	3,12-Dinitro-*I*-	Dyes bl.-gray from olive vat. Undoubtedly is reduced to the amine by vatting.	11
	2,13-Dinitro-*II*-	Dyes gray from olive vat. Is reduced to the amine by vatting.	11
$C_{26}H_{12}N_4O_2$	Unsubstituted *I*	"Indanthrene Brilliant Orange GR"	17,23,24
	Unsubstituted *II*	"Indanthrene Bordeaux RR"	1,23,24
	Unsubstituted *I* and *II*	(Mixture) "Indanthrene Scarlet GG"	2,4,7,9, 23–26, 28,29, 35
$C_{26}H_{14}N_6$	8,17-Di-imino-*I*-	—	17
	6,9-Di-imino-*II*-	Red, insol. in dil. soda solution.	1
$C_{26}H_{14}N_6O_2$	3,12-Diamino-*I* 2,13-Diamino-*II*	The dye colors listed under $C_{26}H_{10}N_6O_6$ (the corresponding nitro compounds) are no doubt those of these amines formed during the vatting operation.	11
	x,*x*-Diamino-*I* and *II*	Blue-grey (green vat).	33
$C_{28}H_{10}F_6N_4O_2$	1,10 (and/or 4,13)-bistrifluoro-methyl-*I* and/or 4,14 (and/or 1,11)-bis-trifluoro-methyl-*II*	(Mixture), much lighter in color than the corresp. methyl analog.	18

(*continued*)

Derivatives of I and II (*continued*)

Empirical formula	Substituents	Properties and comments	Refs.
$C_{28}H_{12}N_4O_6$	3,12-Dicarboxy-*I* and/or 2,13-dicarboxy-*II*	Olive grn. vat; yel.-brn. H_2SO_4 solution. Amides from aminoanthraquinones, *etc.*; or. to or.-red (brn. vat).	34
$C_{28}H_{15}BrN_4O_2$	6 (or 7)-Bromo-3,12-dimethyl-*I*-	(Mixture?), dyes scarlet.	14
	7 (or 17)-Bromo-2,13-dimethyl-*II*-	(Mixture?), dyes bordeaux.	14
$C_{28}H_{16}N_4O_2$	1,10 (and/or 4,13)-Dimethyl-*I*	(Mixture?) dyes yel.-scarlet from olive grn. vat.	15
	4,14 (and/or 1,11)-Dimethyl-*II*	(Mixture?) dyes bordeaux.	15
$C_{28}H_{16}N_4O_4$	3,12-Dimethoxy-*I*	Dyes red-brn. from olive vat.	11
	2,13-Dimethoxy-*II*	Dyes violet-brn. from olive vat.	11
$C_{28}H_{17}N_5O_4S$	6 (or 7)-Dimethyl-sulfamyl-*I* and/or 7 (or 17)-dimethyl-sulfamyl-*II*	(Mixture), dyes a brn.-red from grn. vat. Weaker than the dye without the Me_2NSO_2 group.	8,18
$C_{30}H_8F_{12}N_4O_2$	2,4,11,13 (or 1,3,10,12)-tetrakis(trifluoromethyl)-*I* and/or 1,3,11,13 (or 2,4,12,14)-tetrakis-(trifluoromethyl)-*II*	(Mixture), dyes much lighter color than the unsubstituted dye.	18
$C_{30}H_{14}F_6N_4O_4$	3,12-bis(2,2,2-trifluorethoxy)-*I* and/or 2,13-bis-(2,2,2-trifluorethoxy)-*II*	(Mixture), dull brn.-red.	31
$C_{30}H_{16}N_4O_4$	3,12-Diacetyl-*I*	Dyes yel.-brn. from olive grn. vat.	16
	2,13-Diacetyl-*II*	Dyes red-brn. from olive vat.	16

Derivatives of I and II (*continued*)

Empirical formula	Substituents	Properties and comments	Refs.
$C_{30}H_{19}BrN_4O_2$	6 (or 7)-Bromo-2,13-diethoxy-*I*	(Mixture?), dyes yel.-brn.	14
	7 (or 17)-Bromo-3,12-diethoxy-*II*	(Mixture?), dyes violet-brn.	14
$C_{30}H_{20}N_4O_2$	2,3,11,12-Tetramethyl-*I*	Dyes cotton bordeaux-red.	3,11,18
	2,3,12,13-Tetramethyl-*II*	Dyes cotton red from grn. vat.	3,11,18
	1,3,10,12 (or 2,4,11,13 or 1,3,11,13)-Tetramethyl-*I*	(Mixture?), dyes red-violet from olive grn. vat.	11
	2,4,12,14 (or 1,3,11,13 or 2,4,11,13)-Tetramethyl-*II*	(Mixture?), dyes bordeaux from olive grn. vat.	11
$C_{30}H_{20}N_4O_4$	3,12-Diethoxy-*I*	Dyes red-brn.from olive vat. λ_{max} 4700 A. (in H_2SO_4).	2,5,11
	2,13-Diethoxy-*II*	Dyes violet-brn. from olive vat. λ_{max} 5000 A. (in H_2SO_4).	2,5,11
	3,12-Diethoxy-*I* and 2,13-diethoxy-*II*	(Mixture) "Indanthrene Printing Brown B," dyes red-brown from green vat.	27,28,35
	3,12-Bis(methoxymethyl)-*I* and/or 2,13-bis(methoxymethyl)-*II*	(Mixture?), dyes a clear red.	18
	2,11-Dimethoxy-3,12-dimethyl-*I* and/or 3,12-dimethoxy-2,13-dimethyl-*II*	(Mixture), dyes cotton a fast bl.-red from a red vat.	3
$C_{32}H_{16}N_4O_4S$	6 (or 7)-Phenylsulfonyl-*I* and/or 7(or 17)-phenylsulfonyl-*II*	(Mixture), dyes brn.-red from vat. Color weaker than that of dye without the $C_6H_5SO_2$ group.	18
$C_{32}H_{20}N_4O_2$	2,3-11,12-Bis(trimethylene)-*I* and/or 2,3-12,13-bis(trimethylene)-*II*	(Mixture), shows v. poor light-fastness.	18

(*continued*)

Derivatives of I and II (*continued*)

Empirical formula	Substituents	Properties and comments	Refs.
	1,2(or 3,4)-10,11(or 12,13)-bis(trimethylene)-*I* and/or 3,4(or 1,2)-13,14(or 11,12)-bis(trimethylene)-*II*	(Mixture) shows v. poor light-fastness.	18
$C_{33}H_{18}N_4O_6$	2,11(or 3,12)-Dimethoxy-3,12(or 2,11)-diphenoxy-*I* and/or 3,12(or 2,13)-dimethoxy-2,13(or 3,12-diphenoxy-*II*		18
$C_{38}H_{20}N_4O_2$	3,12-Diphenyl-*I*	Dyes brn.-red from grn. vat.	16
	2,13-Diphenyl-*II*	Dyes violet-brn. from yel.-grn. vat.	16
$C_{38}H_{32}N_4O_2$	3,12-Di-cyclohexyl-*I* and/or 2,13-dicyclohexyl-*II*	(Mixture), dyes red, but leuco deriv. insol.	18
$C_{40}H_{22}N_6O_4$	3,12-Bisbenzoylamino-*I* and/or 2,13-bisbenzoylamino-*II*	(Mixture), dyes cotton bordeaux red.	19
$C_{53}H_{22}N_6O_6$	Tetraoxo-bis-naphthindolo-*II*	"Vat Black-Brown 133," a brn.-blk. dye obtained by carbazolizing $C_{53}H_{26}N_6O_6$.	20,30
$C_{53}H_{26}N_6O_6$	3,12-Bis(1′-anthraquinonylamino)-*I* and/or 2,13-bis-(1′-anthraquinonylamino)-*II*	(Mixture), dyes cotton a fast Corinth from grn. vat. From dibrom (*I* + *II*) and 1-aminoanthraquinone.	19,20
$C_{55}H_{30}N_6O_6$	3,12-Bis(2′-methyl-1′-anthraquinonylamino)-*I* and/or 2,13-bis-(2′-methyl-1′-anthraquinonylamino)-*II*	(Mixture), dyes an intense dull brn.	19

Derivatives of I and II (*continued*)

Empirical formula	Substituents	Properties and comments	Refs.
$C_{67}H_{36}N_8O_8$	3,12-Bis(4′-benzoyl-amino-1′-anthra-quinonylamino)-*I* and/or 2,13-bis-(4′-benzoylamino-1′-anthraquinonyl-amino)-*II*	(Mixture), dyes grn.-gray.	19
	2,11-Bis(5′-benzoyl-amino-1′-anthra-quinonylamino)-*I* and/or 3,12-bis-(5′-benzoylamino-1′-anthraquinonyl-amino)-*II*	(Mixture), dyes cotton a dull brn.	19
$C_{81}H_{40}N_8O_{10}$	1,3,11,13 (or 2,4,10,12)-Tetrakis-(1′-anthraquinonyl-amino)-*I* and/or 2,4,12,14 (or 1,3,11,13) tetrakis-(1′-anthraquinonyl-amino)-*II*	(Mixture), dyes gray-brn. from a brn. vat.	19

References

1. Becker, *I.G. Farbenindustrie A.G., 42 Wissenschaftlicher Austausch der Gruppe IX*, Feb. 15, 1940, Frankfurt a/M.; *PB Report No.* 70338, frames 10790–10793; *PB Report No.* 73484, frames 810–814; *PB Report No.* 70248, frames 2851–2854.
2. Eckert, Ger. Pat. 456,236; *Frdl.*, **16,** 1363 (1931). U. S. Pat. 1,690,775.
3. Eckert and Braunsdorf, Ger. Pat. 655, 652; *Frdl.*, **24,** 971 (1941). U. S. Pat. 2,143,830.
4. Eckert and Greune, U. S. Pats. 1,765,661/2.
5. Gratchev, *Prom. Org. Chem.*, **6,** 304 (1939); *Chem. Abstracts*, **34,** 2373 (1940); *Brit. Chem. Abstracts*, **B,** 1025 (1939).
6. Gratchev, *J. Chem. Ind. (U.S.S.R.)*, **18,** No. 2, 18 (1941); *Chem. Abstracts*, **38,** 2334 (1944); *Chem. Zentr.*, **II,** 2421 (1942).
7. Eckert, Ger. Pat. 571,737; *Frdl.*, **19,** 2193 (1934).
8. Eckert and Sieber, Ger. Pat. 659,843; *Frdl.*, **24,** 970 (1941).
9. Eckert and Greune, Ger. Pats. 430,632, 438,197; *Frdl.*, **15,** 788/9 (1928). U. S. Pat. 1,588,451 and Reissue 18,643.

10. Neresheimer and Eichholz, Ger. Pat. 507,832; *Frdl.*, **17,** 1421 (1932). U. S. Pat. 1,874,584.
11. Eckert and Braunsdorf, Ger. Pat. 538,314; *Frdl.*, **18,** 1499 (1933). U. S. Pat. 1,888,625; *Chem. Abstracts*, **27,** 1518 (1933).
12. Eckert, Greune and Eichholz, Ger. Pat. 536,911; *Frdl.*, **18,** 1497 (1933). U. S. Pat. 1,888,624; *Chem. Abstracts*, **27,** 1519 (1933).
13. Eckert and Sieber, Ger. Pat. 567,210; *Frdl.*, **19,** 2188 (1934). U. S. Pat. 1,927,928.
14. Eckert and Sieber, Ger. Pat. 638,339; *Frdl.*, **23,** 1116 (1940). U. S. Pat. 2,073,098.
15. Eckert and Gmelin, Ger. Pat. 607,945; *Frdl.*, **21,** 1179 (1937). U. S. Pat. 2,011,807.
16. Eckert, Fischer and Braunsdorf, Ger. Pat. 576,132; *Frdl.*, **19,** 2189 (1934). U. S. Pat. 1,952,661.
17. Eckert and Becker, *I.G. Farbenindustrie A.G.*, *43 Wissenschaftlicher Austausch der Gruppe IX*, April 25, 1941, Frankfurt a/M; *PB Report No.* 70339, frames 10900–10906; *PB Report No.* 70250, frames 3808–3815. Ger. Pat. 852,725.
18. Eckert and Sieber, *I.G. Farbenindustrie A.G.*, *34 Wissenschaftlicher Austausch der Gruppe IX*, Oct. 22, 1935, Höchst a/M; *PB Report No.* 70338, frames 9644–9650.
19. Eckert, Ger. Pat. 534,493; *Frdl.*, **18,** 1507 (1933). U. S. Pat. 1,928,719.
20. Eckert and Braunsdorf, Ger. Pat. 632,447; *Frdl.*, **23,** 1117 (1940). Fr. Pat. 786,782; *Chem. Zentr.*, **I,** 188 (1936). U. S. Pat. 2,026,026.
21. Friedländer, *Fortschritte der Teerfarbenfabrikation*, **21,** 1020 (1937).
22. Eckert and Sieber, Ger. Pat. 659,095; *Frdl.*, **24,** 973 (1941).
23. I.G. Farbenindustrie A.G.; *F.I.A.T. Report No.* 1313, Vol. II, pg. 168–9.
24. Grachev and Shchukevich, *J. Chem. Ind. (U.S.S.R.)*, **18,** No. 19, 4 (1941); *Chem. Abstracts*, **38,** 5818 (1944).
25. Eckert and Braunsdorf, U. S. Pat. 1,889,279.
26. Lyashchenko and Grachev, Russ. Pat. 55,969; *Chem. Abstracts*, **34,** 3100 (1940); *Chem. Zentr.*, **I,** 3988 (1940).
27. Fox, *J. Soc. Dyers Colourists*, **63,** 297 (1947).
28. Schultz, *Farbstofftabellen*, Springer, Berlin, 1923–1939; Vol. II, p. 132; 1st Suppl., p. 107; 2nd Suppl., p. 77.
29. Hopff, Ger. Pat. Apln. I 51,838 Ne/1202; *PB Report No.* 73719, frame 2201.
30. Eckert and Braunsdorf, *PB Report No.* 25632, frames 83, 109, 137 and 212; Ger. Pat. Apln. J 49,177.
31. Scherer, *I.G. Farbenindustrie A.G.*, *44 Wissenschaftlicher Austausch der Gruppe IX*, Leverkusen, May 13, 1942; *PB Report No.* 70339, frames 10931–6.
32. Eckert, Ger. Pat. 438,197; *Frdl.*, **15,** 789 (1928).
33. Eckert, Ger. Pat. 496,341; *Frdl.*, **16,** 857 (1931).
34. Honold, Ger. Pat. Apln. C8078 IVb/22e.
35. Farbwerke Hoechst, Fr. Pat. 1,121,722.
36. Mosby and Berry, unpublished observations.

A-326. Anthr[1′,2′,4,5]imidazo-[1,2-*a*]naphtho[2,3-*g*]quinoline*

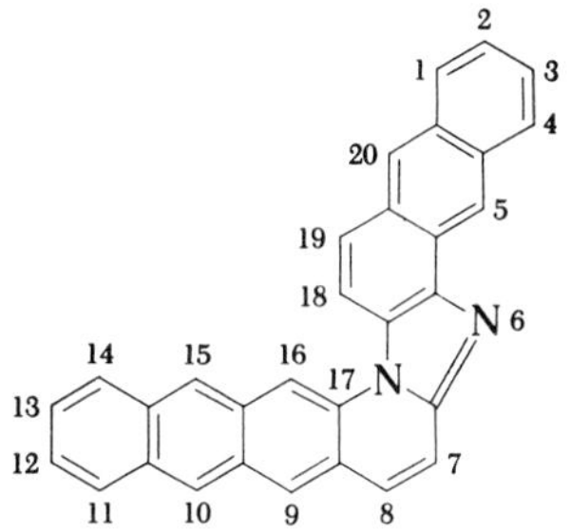

By treating I with aluminum chloride under mild conditions, Baumann and Schwechten[1] isolated a yellow dye, which they first thought to be II. However, because of the shade of the dye and its insensitivity to a pyridine-alkali solution, they finally decided in

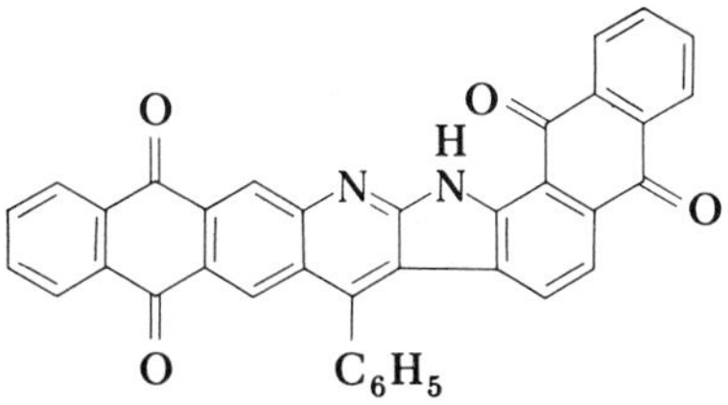

(II)

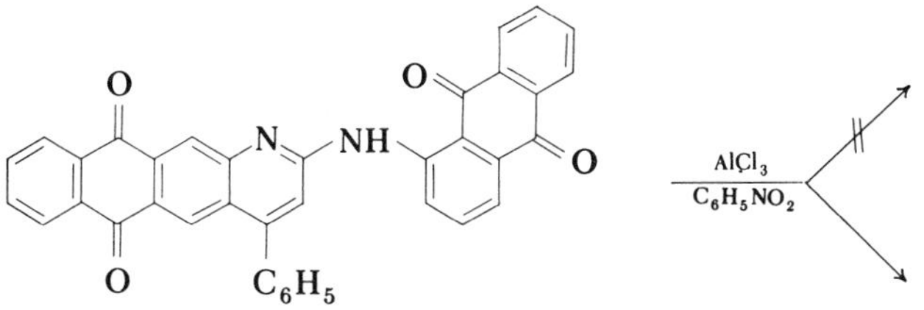

$\xrightarrow[C_6H_5NO_2]{AlCl_3}$

(I)

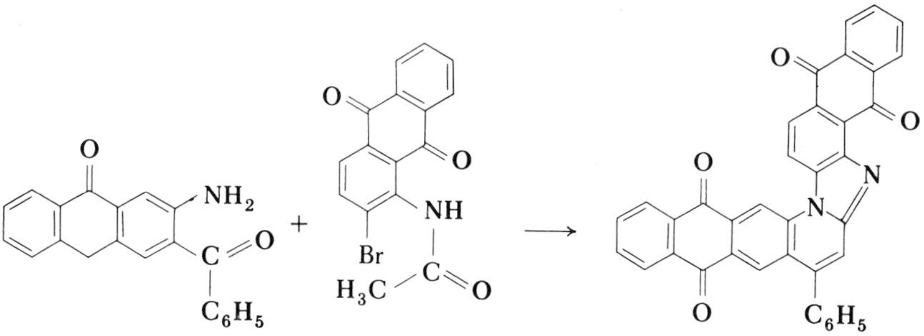

(IV) + (V) → (III)

favor of structure III. This was confirmed by an alternative synthesis of III from IV and V. The dye has several disadvantageous properties and is of no commercial value.

Reference

1. Baumann and Schwechten, *I.G. Farbenindustrie A.G., 37 Wissenschaftlicher Austausch der Gruppe IX*, Ludwigshafen, March 18 and 19, 1937; *PB Report No.* 70339, frame 11707.

A-327. Anthr[2′,3′,4,5]imidazo-[1,2-*a*]naphtho[2,3-*g*]quinoline*

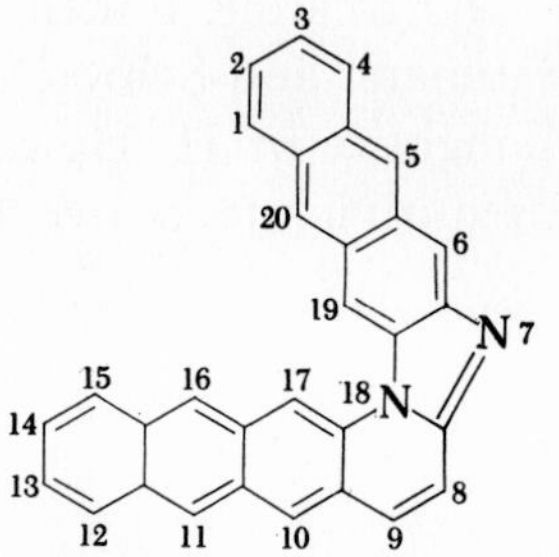

Baumann and Schwechten[1] prepared the yellow dye III by reacting I with II. They were unable to prepare III by cyclization of the β-anthrimide (analogous to compound I, Section A-326). The dye is of no commercial value.

$$\text{(I)} + \text{(II)} \xrightarrow{-2H_2O} \text{(III)}$$

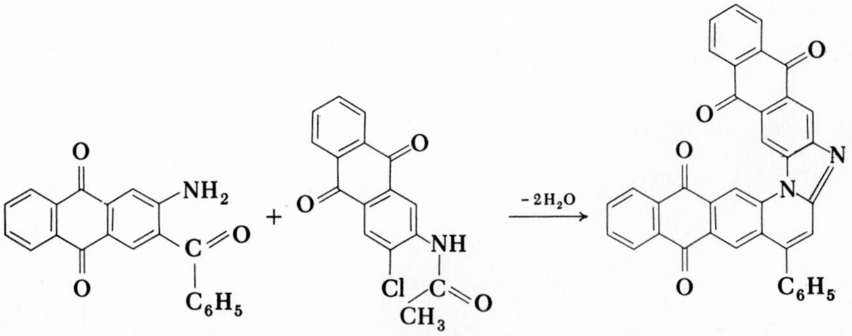

(I) (II) (III)

Reference

1. Baumann and Schwechten, *I.G. Farbenindustrie A.G., 37 Wissenschaftlicher Austausch der Gruppe IX*, Ludwigshafen, March 18, and 19, 1937; *PB Report No.* 70339, frame 11707.

A-328. 12*H*-Anthr[1′,2′,4,5]imidazo-[1,2-*a*]naphtho[1,2,3-*de*]-quinoline*

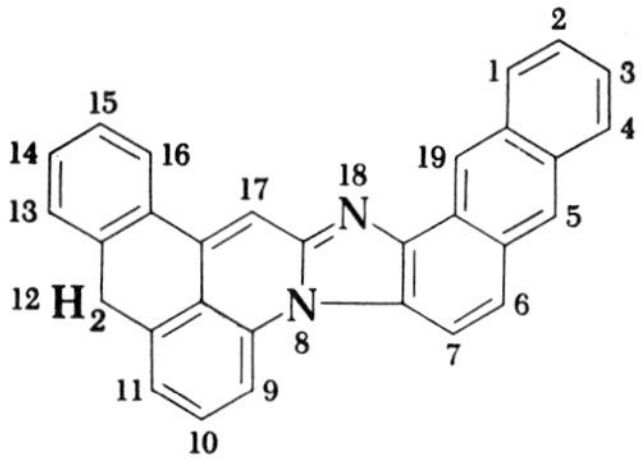

When I was condensed with 1-aminoanthraquinone in an Ullmann reaction, and the resulting anthrimide (II) was treated with aluminum chloride in nitrobenzene, there resulted a yellow dye,[1] which might have either structure III or IV. On the basis of the re-

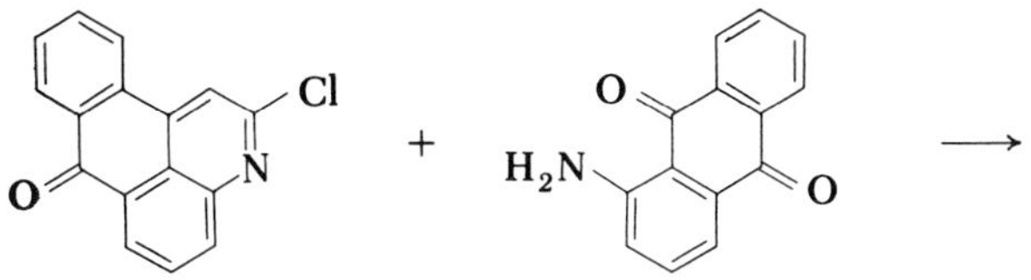

(I)

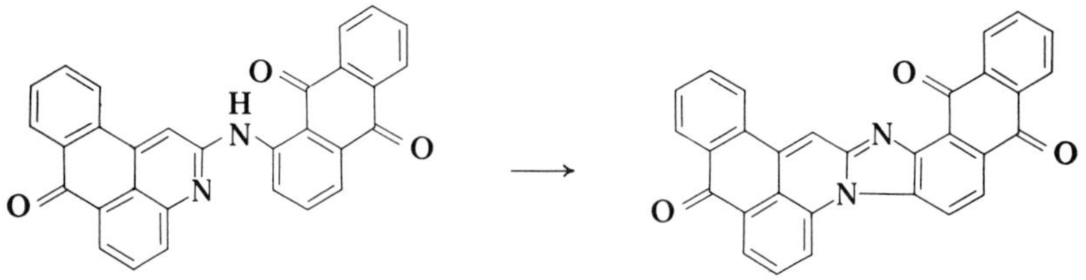

(II)

(III)

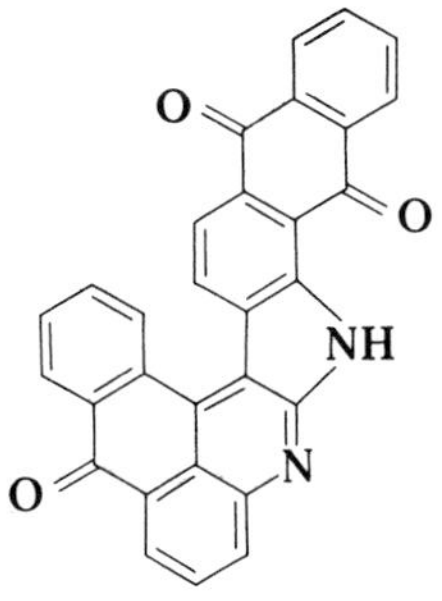

(IV)

semblance between the properties of this product and those of several similarly prepared imidazole dyes (see for example formula II, Section A-376, which could be only an imidazole and not a carbazole), Baumann and Schwechten[1] preferred structure III.

Recently an alternative synthesis of III (dyes orange from an orange-brown vat) from V via VI was presented.[2]

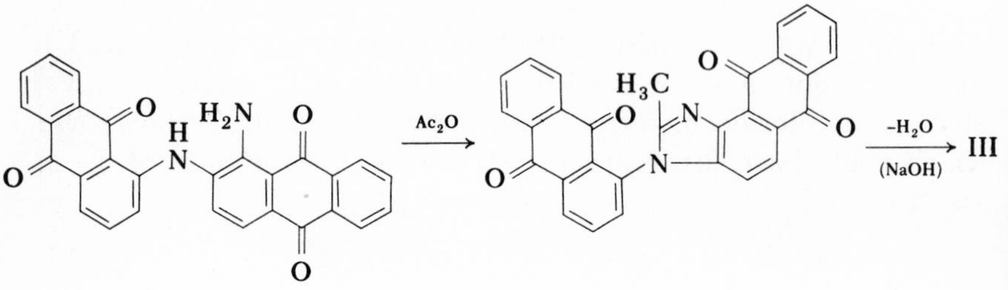

(V) (VI)

References

1. Baumann and Schwechten, *I.G. Farbenindustrie A.G., 37 Wissenschaftlicher Austausch der Gruppe IX*, Ludwigshafen, March 18 and 19, 1937; *PB Report No.* 70339, frame 11707.
2. Grelat and Jenny, U. S. Pat. 2,815,347. Brit. Pat. 787,311. Fr. Pat. 1,146,970.

A-329. *5H*-Anthr[2′,3′,4,5]-imidazo[1,2-*a*]naphtho-[1,2,3-*de*]quinoline*

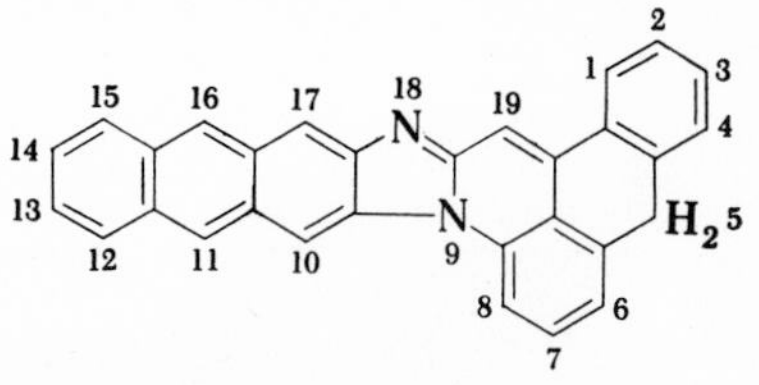

A yellowish orange dye of structure V, mentioned briefly by Rösch,[1] was probably obtained either from the condensation of I with II or of III with IV. Although the dye (V) was considered[1] insufficiently light-fast to be of value, V (and its 19-methyl, 19-phenyl, and its 4- or 6-methoxy or benzamido homologs, prepared from anthrimides such as VI) was the subject of a recent patent.[2] Com-

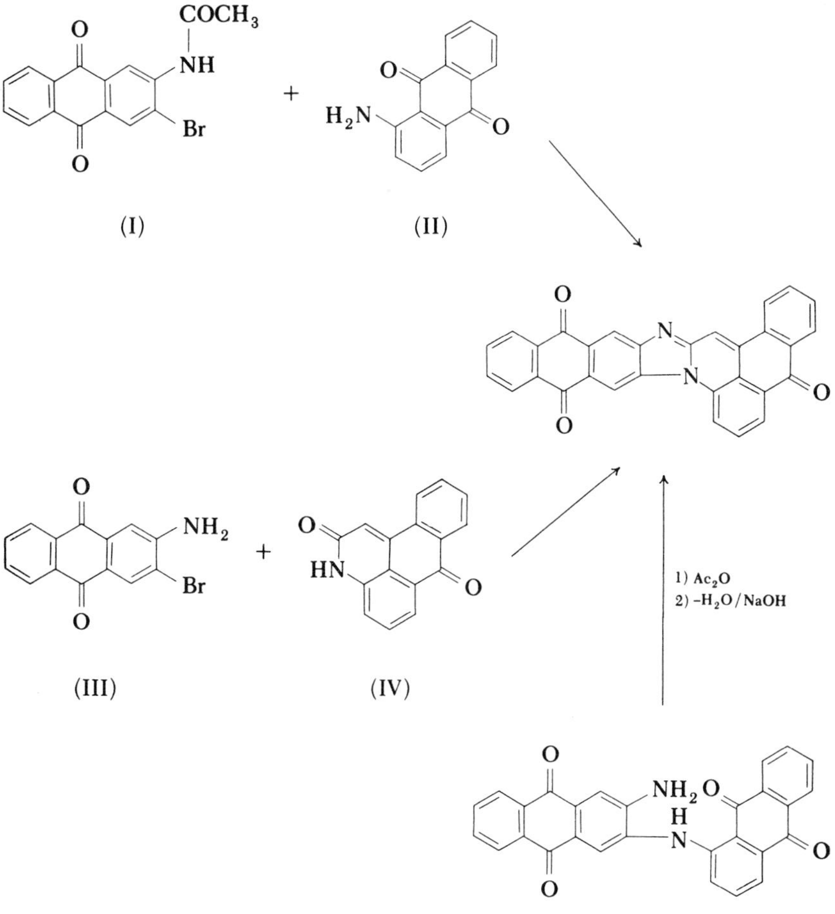

(I) (II)

(III) (IV)

1) Ac_2O
2) $-H_2O/NaOH$

(VI)

pound V was reported[2] to form an orange-brown vat. See Sections A-326/8.

References

1. Rösch, *I.G. Farbenindustrie, A.G., 31 Wissenschaftlicher Austausch der Gruppe IX*, Frankfurt, June 20, 1934 and Höchst, July 17, 1934; *PB Report No.* 25632, frames 174 and 226.
2. Grelat and Jenny, U. S. Pat. 2,815,347. Brit. Pat. 787,311. Fr. Pat. 1,146,970.

A-330. Anthra[2,1,9-*def*]naphth-[2',1',4,5]imidazo[2,1-*a*]-isoquinoline*

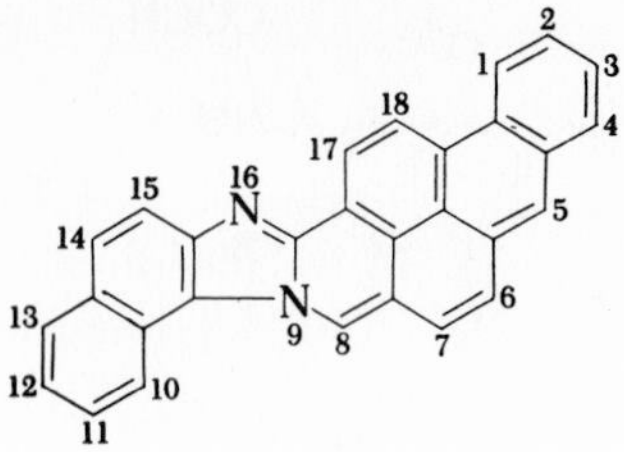

and/or

A-331. Anthra[2,1,9-*def*]naphth-[2',1',4,5]imidazo[1,2-*b*]-isoquinoline*

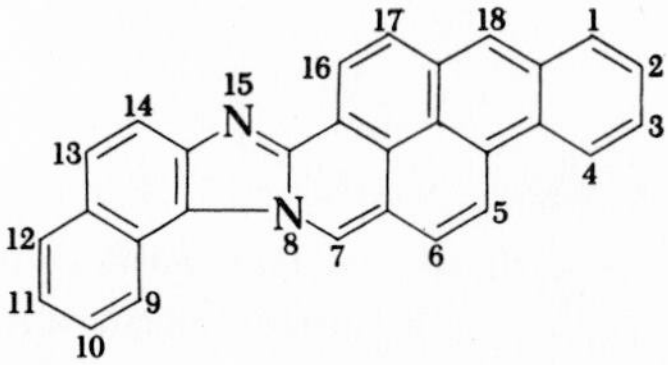

From the condensation of naphthylene-1,2-diamine with benzanthrone-3,4-dicarboxylic acid a product, consisting probably of a mixture of the two dioxo derivatives (5,8- and 7,18-, respectively) of these two ring systems, is obtained.[1,2,3,4] However, in view of the controversy over the structure of the reaction product of naphthalic anhydride and naphthylene-1,2-diamine (see Section A-304), structures I and II must also be considered. The product is described as dyeing cotton a strong brown from a red vat.

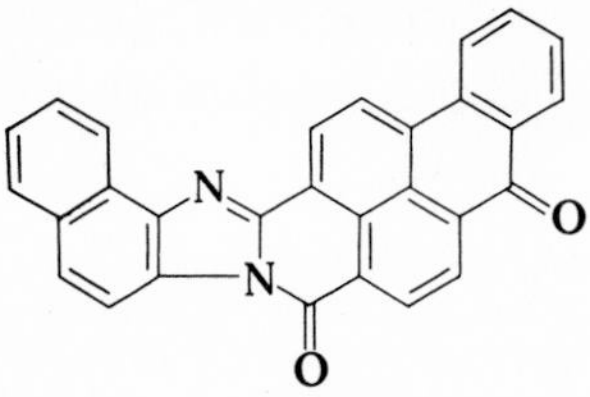

(I) 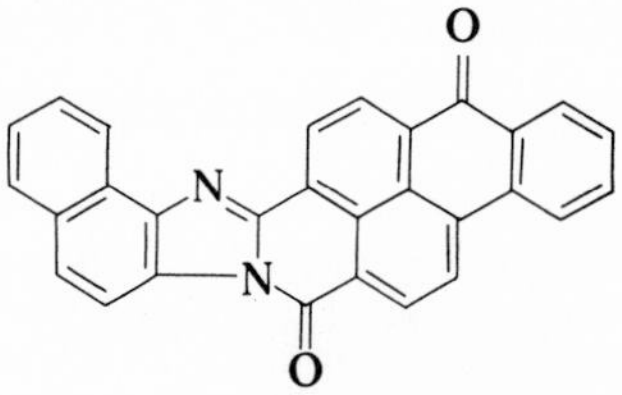 (II)

References

1. Kränzlein, Greune and Vollmann, Ger. Pat. 494,111; *Frdl.*, **16**, 1441 (1931); *Chem. Zentr.*, **II**, 820 (1930). U. S. Pat. 1,892,241.
2. Kränzlein, Greune, Corell and Vollmann, Ger. Pat. 503,404; *Frdl.*, **17**, 1386 (1932). U. S. Pat. 1,921,360.
3. I.G. Farbenindustrie, A.G., Brit. Pat. 308,651; *Chem. Zentr.*, **II**, 662 (1929). Fr. Pat. 671,976.
4. I.G. Farbenindustrie, A.G., Fr. Pat. 39,499; *Chem. Zentr.*, **I**, 880 (1932).

A-332. Naphth[2′,1′,4,5]imidazo-[2,1-*a*]pyrido[3′,2′,6,7]naphtho-[2,1,8-*def*]isoquinoline*

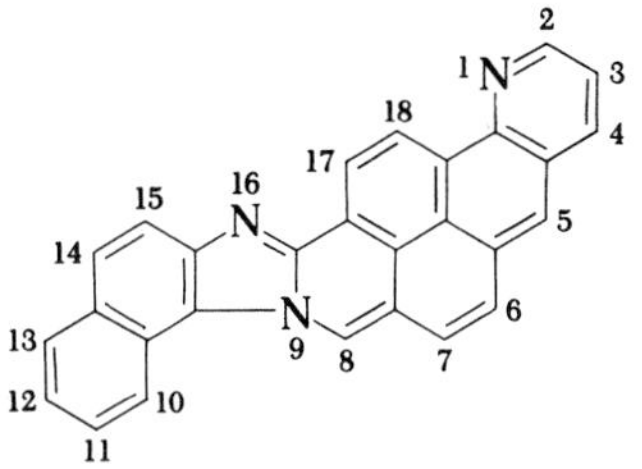

and/or

A-333. Naphth[2,1′,4,5]imidazo-[2,1-*a*]pyrido[2′,3′,5,6]naphtho-[2,1,8-*def*]isoquinoline*

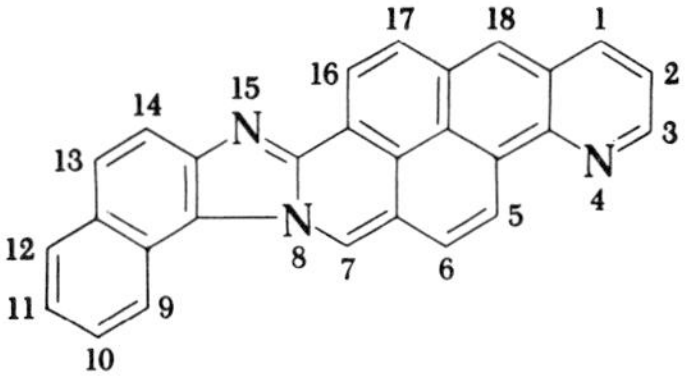

and/or

A-334. Naphth[1′,2′,4,5]imidazo-[2,1-*a*]pyrido[3′,2′,6,7]naphtho-[2,1,8-*def*]isoquinoline*

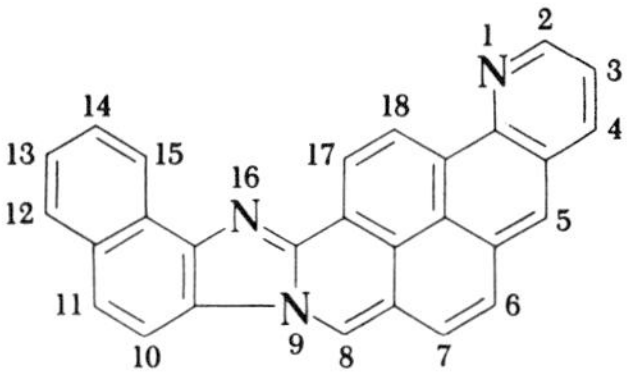

and/or

A-335. Naphth[1′,2′,4,5]imidazo-[2,1-*a*]pyrido[2′,3′,5,6]naphtho-[2,1,8-*def*]isoquinoline*

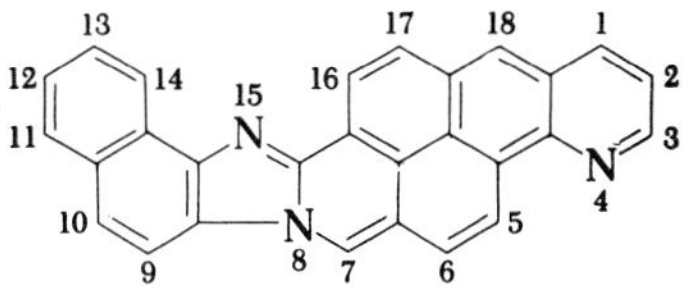

Condensation of 1,2-naphthylenediamine with 11-azabenz[*de*]-anthr-7-one-3,4-dicarboxylic acid afforded[1] a deep red-brown dye (reddish blue solution in sulfuric acid), which is probably the dioxo derivative of one or more of these nuclei.

Reference

1. Vollmann, *I.G. Farbenindustrie, A.G., 34 Wissenschaftlicher Austausch der Gruppe IX*, Leverkusen, Oct. 25, 1935; *PB Report No.* 70338, frame 9699.

A-336. 9*H*-Benzimidazo[1,2-*b*]benzo[6,7]phenanthr[3,4,5-*defg*]isoquinoline*

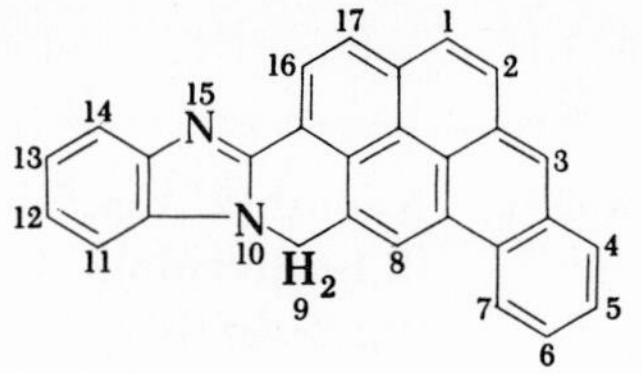

and/or

A-337. 10*H*-Benzimidazo[2,1-*a*]benzo[6,7]phenanthr[3,4,5-*defg*]isoquinoline*

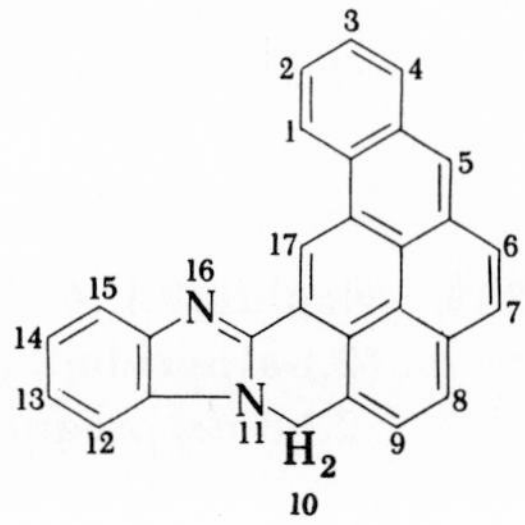

By treating I (see Section A-298) with aluminum chloride at 170°, Sieber[1] obtained a blue dye (emerald green vat), which may represent one or the other (or a mixture) of the two above-named nuclei. On methylation of the dye in nitrobenzene solution, there was obtained a blue product which no longer vatted.

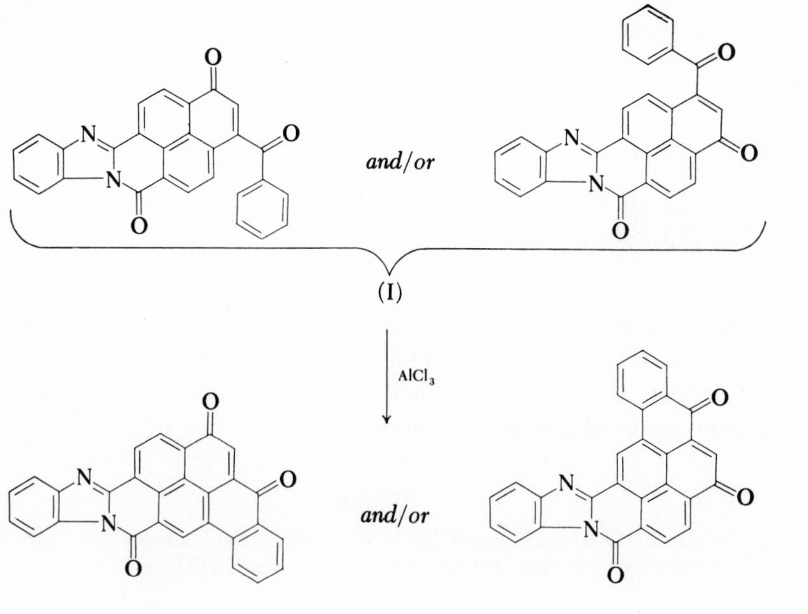

and/or

(I)

$AlCl_3$

and/or

trans *cis*

Reference

1. Sieber, *I.G. Farbenindustrie A.G.*, *33 Wissenschaftlicher Austausch der Gruppe IX*, March 27, 1935, Frankfurt; *PB Report No.* 70338, frames 9525–9527.

A-338. Anthra[9,1-*gh*]benzo[*de*]benzimidazo[1,2-*b*]isoquinoline*

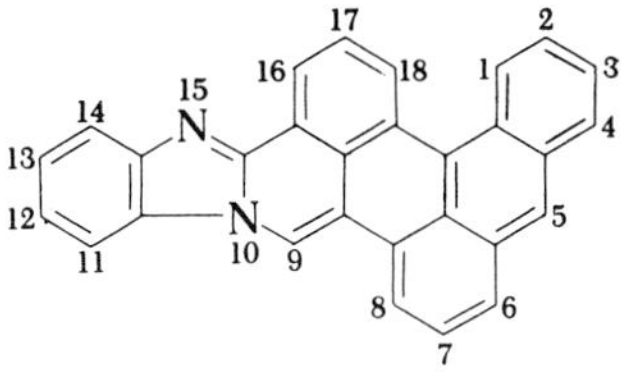

and/or

A-339. Anthra[9,1-*gh*]benzo[*de*]benzimidazo[2,1-*a*]isoquinoline*

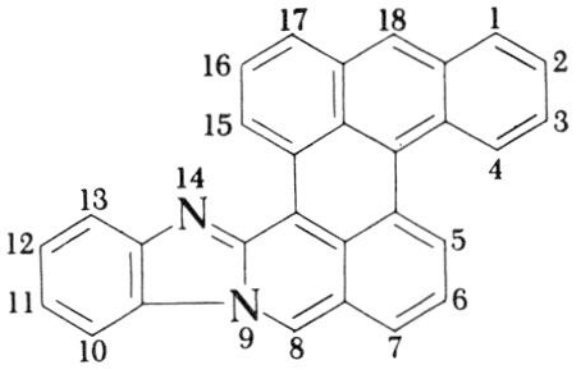

In Sections A-302/3, was described the preparation of a benzoyl derivative of benzimidazo[2,1-*a*]naphtho[1′,2′,3′-*de*]isoquinolin-7-one (I) and/or benzimidazo[1,2-*b*]naphtho[1′,2′,3′-*de*]isoquinolin-

(I) and/or (II)

$AlCl_3$–MnO_2

(III) *cis* and/or (IV) *trans*

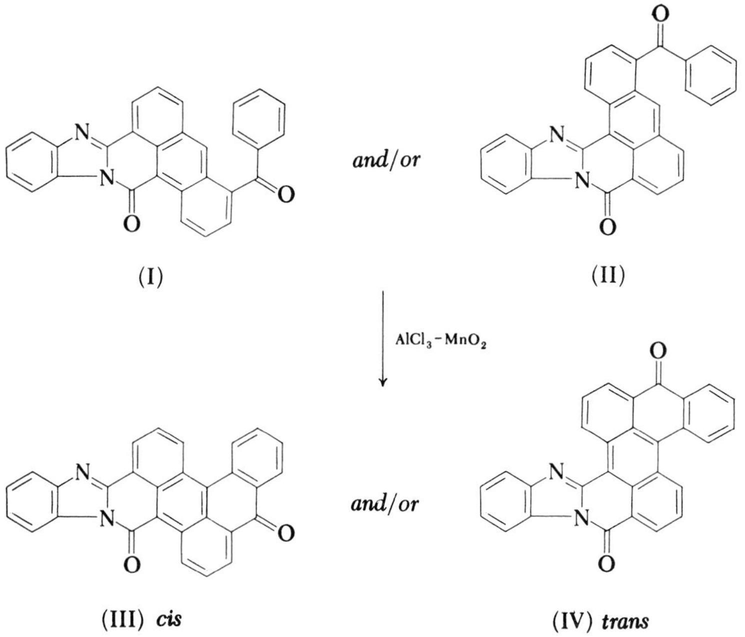

9-one (II). Treatment of this product (or mixture) with aluminum chloride alone, or in solvents, or in a melt with sodium chloride, gave no cyclization. However, treatment of the substance in an aluminum chloride melt with manganese dioxide gave a violet dye (blue vat) of rather poor light fastness. On the basis of the similarity in properties (color of vat; green color of sulfuric acid solution; vivid red fluorescence of solutions in organic solvents) of the dye to those of V, Eckert and Braunsdorf[1,2] felt that their dye had the "trans" configuration (IV).

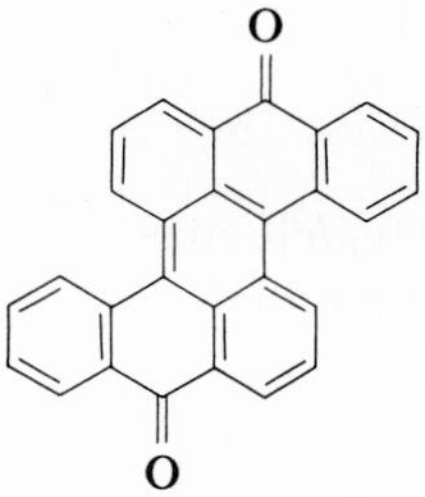

(V)

References

1. Eckert and Braunsdorf, *I.G. Farbenindustrie A.G., 33 Wissenschaftlicher Austausch der Gruppe IX*, March 29, 1935, Frankfurt; *PB Report No.* 70338, frames 9533–9535.
2. Eckert and Braunsdorf, Ger. Pat. 637,091; *Frdl.*, **23,** 1124 (1940).

A-340. Benz[7,8]anthra[2,1,9-*def*]-benzimidaz[2,1-*a*]isoquinoline*

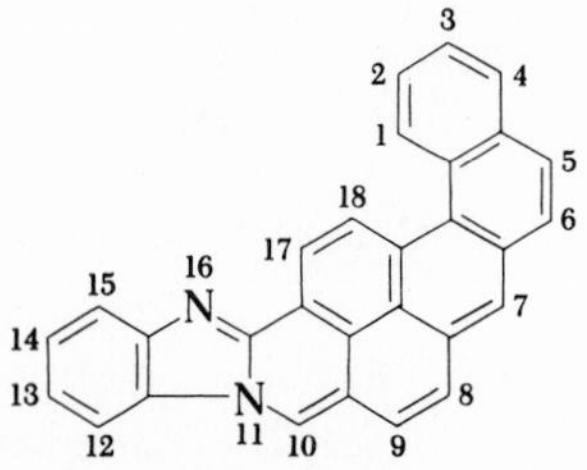

and/or

A-341. Benz[7,8]anthra[2,1,9-*def*]-benzimidaz[1,2-*b*]isoquinoline*

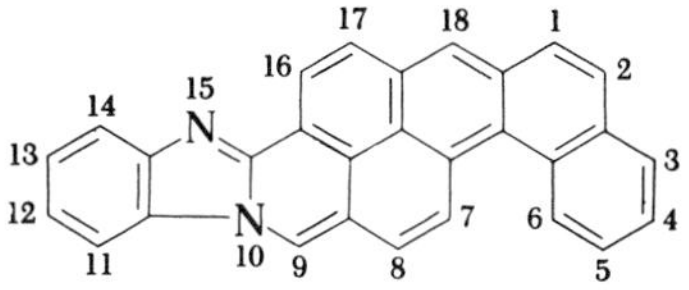

The dioxo derivative of one or the other of these two ring systems, or a mixture of the two, has been obtained[1,2] from the reaction of dibenz[*de,h*]anthr-7-one-3,4-dicarboxylic acid with *o*-phenylenediamine. The product is claimed to form red crystals, which dye a blue-red shade with good fastness.

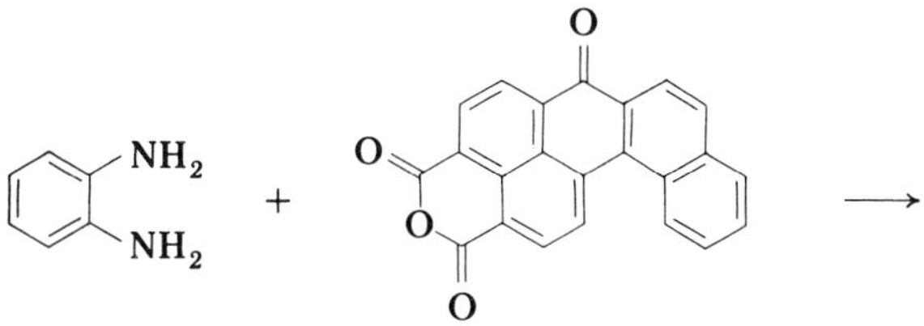

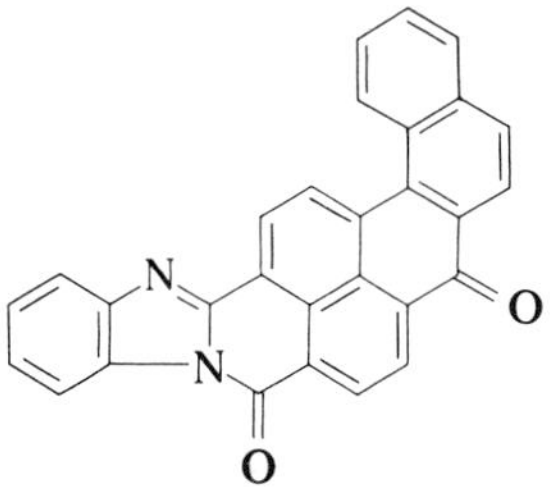

and/or

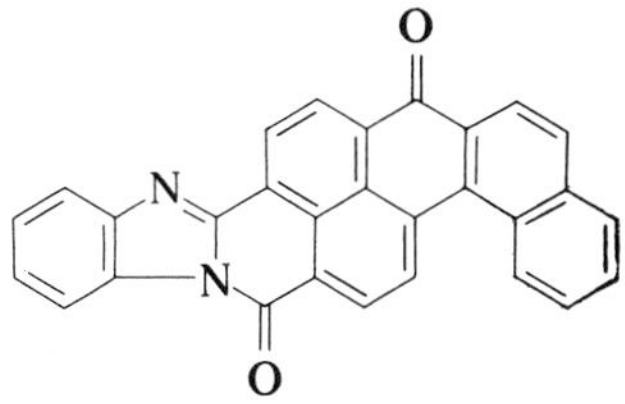

References

1. Kränzlein, Greune, Corell and Vollmann, Ger. Pat. 503,404; *Frdl.*, **17,** 1386 (1932). U. S. Pat. 1,921,360.
2. I.G. Farbenindustrie A.G., Fr. Pat. 39,499; *Chem. Zentr.*, **I,** 880 (1932).

A-342. Benzimidazo[1,2-*b*]chryseno-[2,1,12-*def*]isoquinoline*

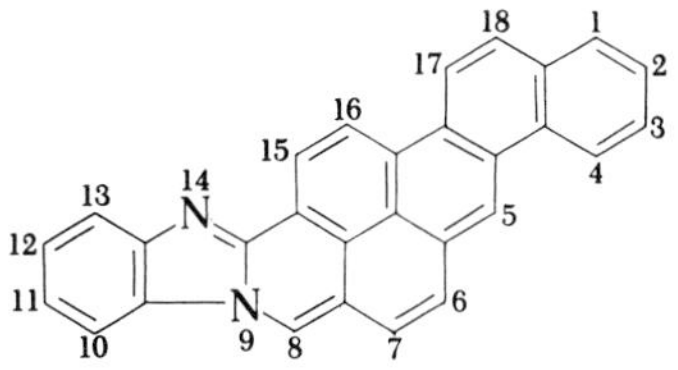

and/or

A-343. Benzimidazo[2,1-*a*]chryseno-[2,1,12-*def*]isoquinoline*

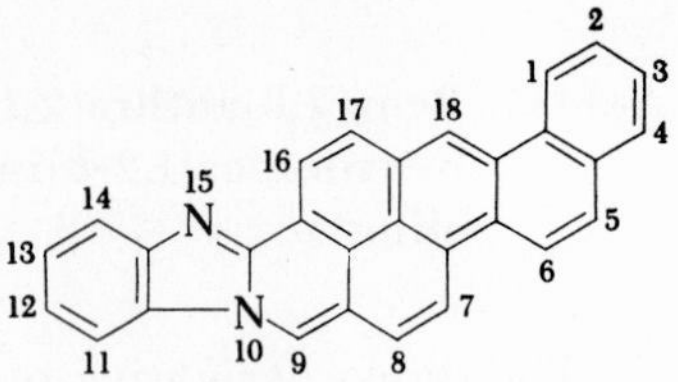

A product, probably the dioxo derivative of one or the other of the above two nuclei, or a mixture of both, has been obtained[1-3] from the condensation of dibenz[*de*, *j*]anthr-7-one-3,4-dicarboxylic acid with *o*-phenylenediamine. It dyes cotton a blue-red from an orange vat.

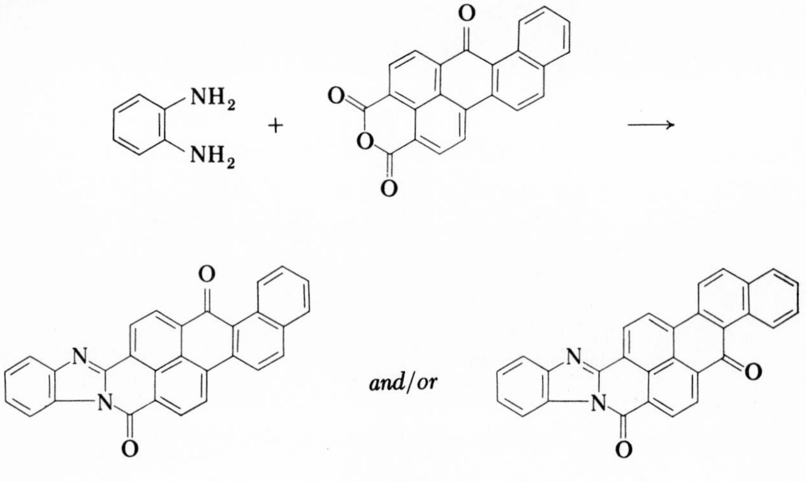

and/or

References

1. Kränzlein, Greune, Corell and Vollmann, Ger. Pat. 503,404; *Frdl.*, **17,** 1386 (1932). U. S. Pat. 1,921,360.
2. I.G. Farbenindustrie A.G., Fr. Pat. 39,499; *Chem. Zentr.*, **I,** 880 (1932).
3. I.G. Farbenindustrie A.G., Brit. Pat. 308,651; *Chem. Zentr.*, **II,** 662 (1929). Fr. Pat. 671,976.

A-344. Benzimidazo[2,1-*a*]quinoxalino[2′,3′,6,7]naphth-[2,1,8-*def*]isoquinoline*

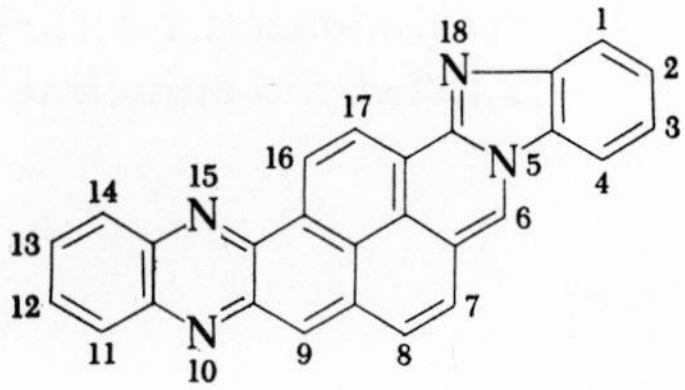

and/or

A-345. Benzimidazo[2,1-*a*]quinoxalino[2′,3′,5,6]naphth[2,1,8-*def*]isoquinoline*

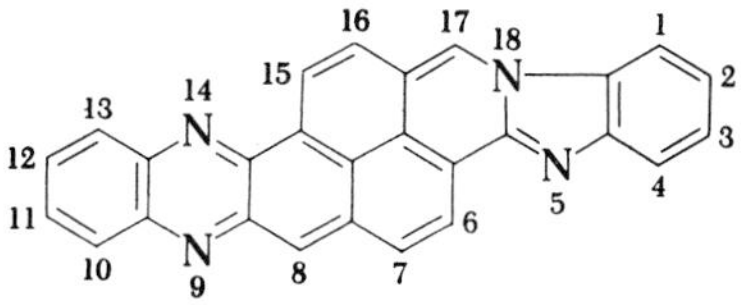

By the condensation of the anhydrides Ia-d with various *o*-phenylenediamines, Eckert and Sieber[1] prepared a series of red to brown-red dyes probably consisting of mixtures of derivatives (II and III). The dyes were insufficiently soda-fast.[2]

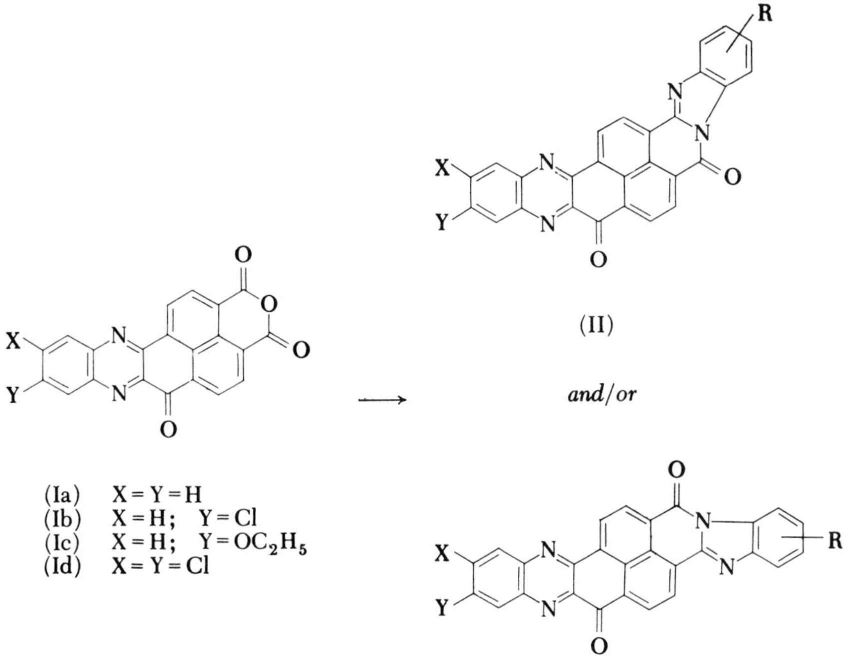

(Ia) X = Y = H
(Ib) X = H; Y = Cl
(Ic) X = H; Y = OC_2H_5
(Id) X = Y = Cl

(II)

and/or

(III)

References

1. Eckert and Sieber, Ger. Pat. 659,095; *Frdl.*, **24,** 973 (1941).
2. Greune, *PB Report No.* 25632, frame 42ff.

A-346. Bisbenzimidazo-[2,1-*a*, 2′,1′-*a*′]benzo-[1,2,3-*de*, 4,5,6-*d*′*e*′]-diisoquinoline*

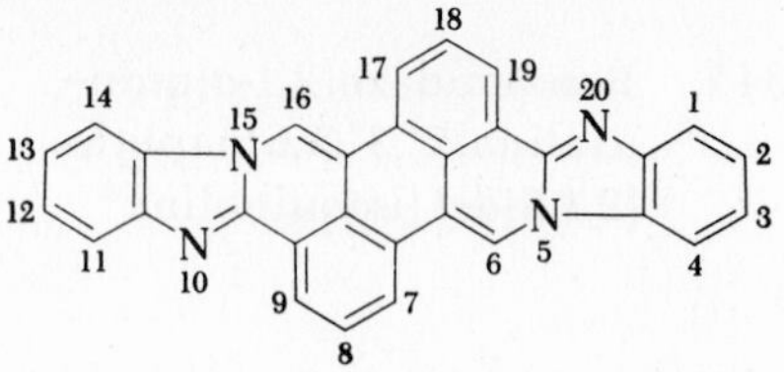

and/or

A-347. Bisbenzimidazo-[1,2-*b*, 1′,2′-*b*′]benzo-[1,2,3-*de*, 4,5,6-*d*′*e*′]-diisoquinoline*

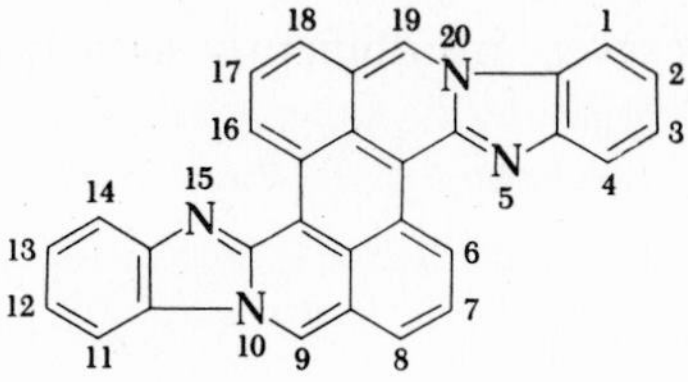

and/or

A-348. Bisbenzimidazo-[2,1-*a*, 1′,2′-*b*′]benzo-[1,2,3-*de*, 4,5,6-d′*e*′]-diisoquinoline*

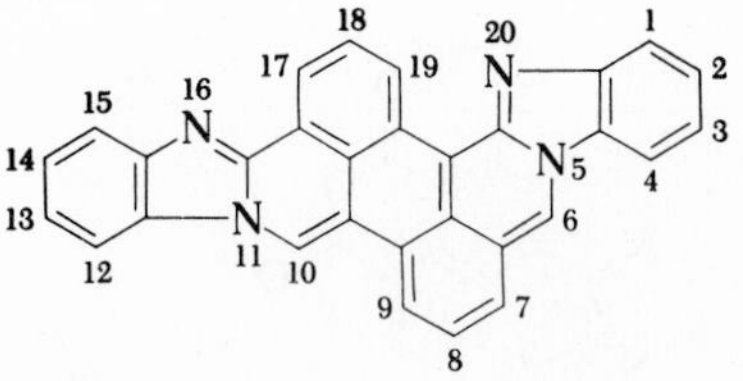

The condensation of anthracene-1,5,6,10-tetracarboxylic acid with o-phenylenediamine was shown by Becker[1] to yield blue-black needles of a dye, which is probably a dioxo derivative of one or more of the above ring systems. The product dyes cotton violet from a red-violet vat and exhibits poor wash- and soda-fastness.

Reference

1. Becker, *I. G. Farbenindustrie A. G., 42 Wissenschaftlicher Austausch der Gruppe IX*, Feb. 15, 1940, Frankfurt a/M.; PB Report No. 70338, frames 10784–10788; *PB Report No.* 70248, frames 2846–2850; *PB Report No.* 73484, frames 829–834.

A-349. Bisbenzimidazo[1,2-*c*, 1′,2′-*j*]-naphtho[1,2,3,4-*lmn*][3,8]-phenanthroline*

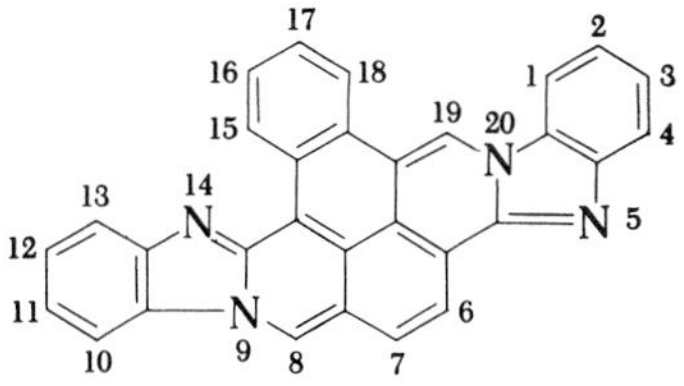

and/or

A-350. Bisbenzimidazo[2,1-*b*, 1′,2′,-*j*]-naphtho[1,2,3,4-*lmn*][3,8]-phenanthroline*

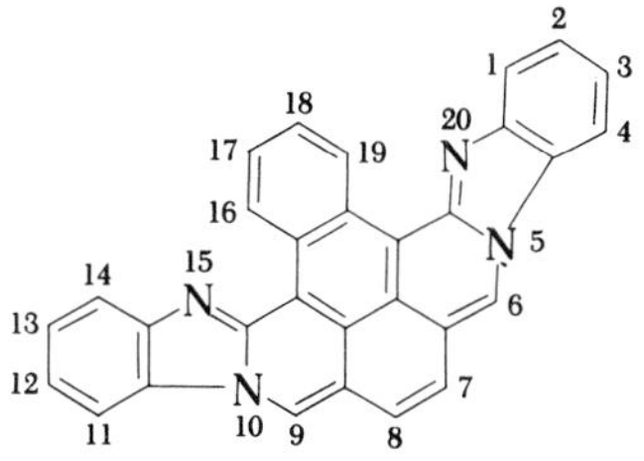

and/or

A-351. Bisbenzimidazo[2,1-*b*, 1′,2′-*j*]-dibenzo[*f*, *lmn*][3,8]-phenanthroline*

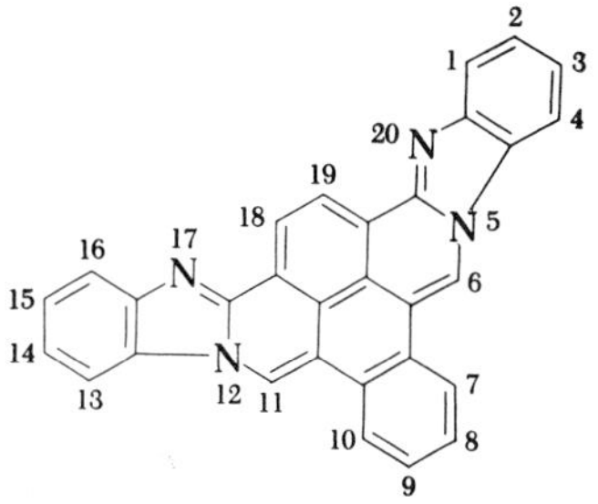

By reacting anthracene-1,4,9,10-tetracarboxylic acid with *o*-phenylenediamine[1,2] or 4-ethoxy-*o*-phenylenediamine,[2,3] blue dyes (red vats) of excellent light-, chlorine- and soda-fastness[4,5] were obtained. These dyes are presumably mixtures of two or more of compounds I, II and III (or their ethoxy homologs). The dyes give green solutions in sulfuric acid.[2] Attempts, by the usual methods, to separate into isomers the gray-blue dye obtained from *o*-phenylenediamine, were unsuccessful,[4] indicating either failure of the separation techniques in this case, or the substantial homogeneity of the dye.

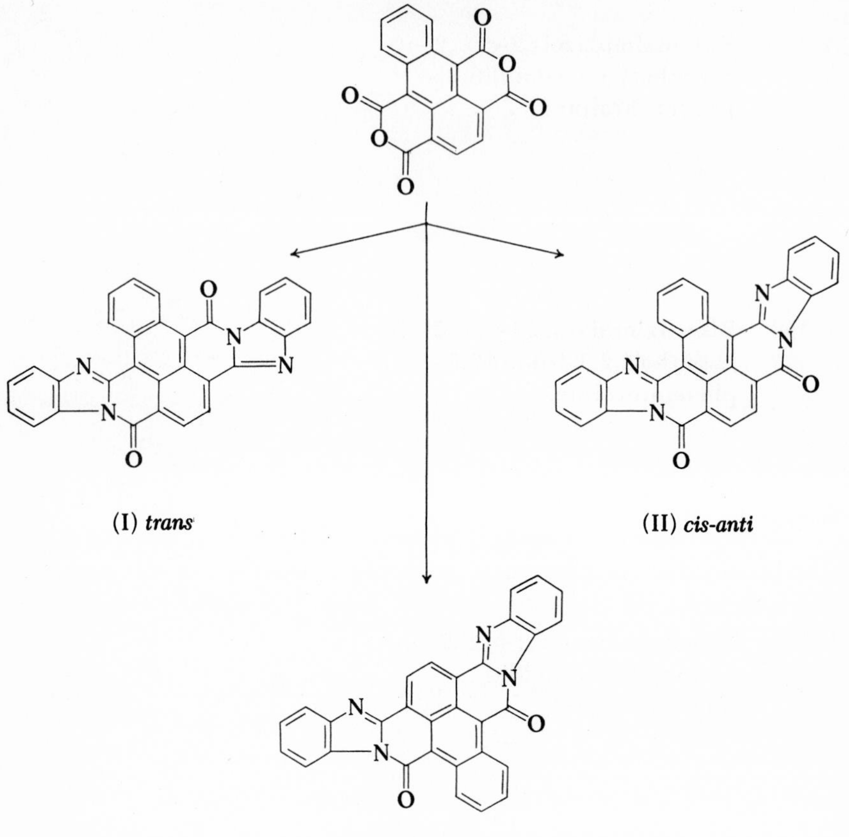

(I) *trans*

(II) *cis-anti*

(III) *cis-syn*

References

1. Becker, *I.G. Farbenindustrie A.G., 42 Wissenschaftlicher Austausch der Gruppe IX*, Feb. 15, 1940, Frankfurt a/M.; *PB Report No.* 70338, frames 10784–10788; *PB Report No.* 70248, frames 2846–2850; *PB. Report No.* 73484, frames 829–834.
2. Eckert and Braunsdorf, U. S. Pat. 2,028,384. Ger. Pat. 600,092; *Frdl.*, **21,** 1184 (1937). Ger. Pat. 612,930; *Frdl.*, **22,** 1158 (1939).
3. I.G. Farbenindustrie A.G., *F.I.A.T. Report No.* 1313, Vol. 3, p. 39.
4. Eckert and Braunsdorf, *I.G. Farbenindustrie A.G., 34 Wissenschaftlicher Austausch der Gruppe IX*, October 25, 1935, Leverkusen; *PB Report No.* 70338, frames 9639–9643.
5. I. G. Farbenindustrie A. G., Brit. Pat. 416,385; French Pat. 765, 974; Swiss Pat. 167,174; *Chem. Zentr.*, **II,** 3186 (1934).

A-352. Naphth[2′,1′,4,5]imidazo-[2,1-*a*]quinoxalino-[2′,3′,6,7]naphth[2,1,8-*def*]-isoquinoline*

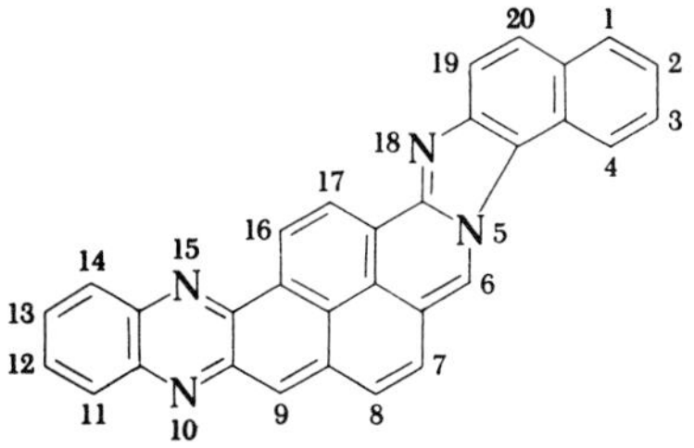

and/or

A-353. Naphth[2′,1′,4,5]imidazo-[2,1-*a*]-quinoxalino-[2′,3′,5,6]naphth[2,1,8-*def*]-isoquinoline*

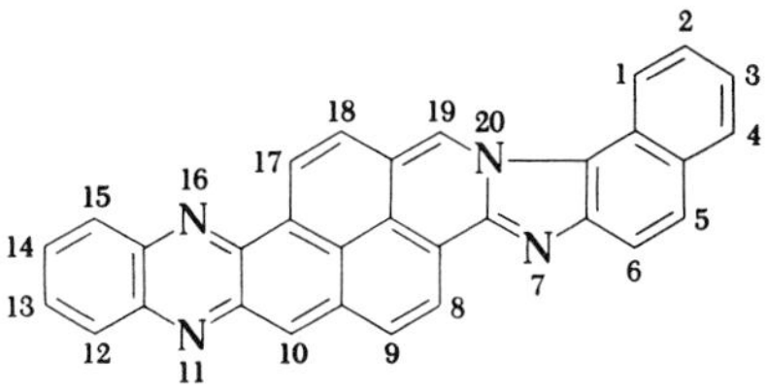

The only reported example of either of these ring systems is the blue-brown dye (orange vat), probably a mixture of II and III, which Eckert and Sieber[1] obtained from 1,2-naphthylenediamine and the anhydride I.

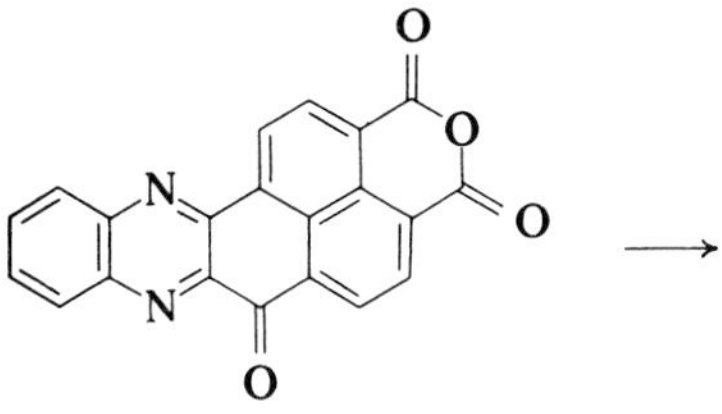

(I)

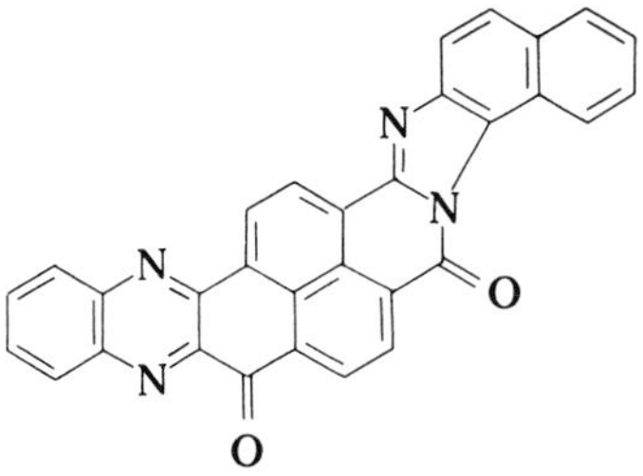

(II)

and/or

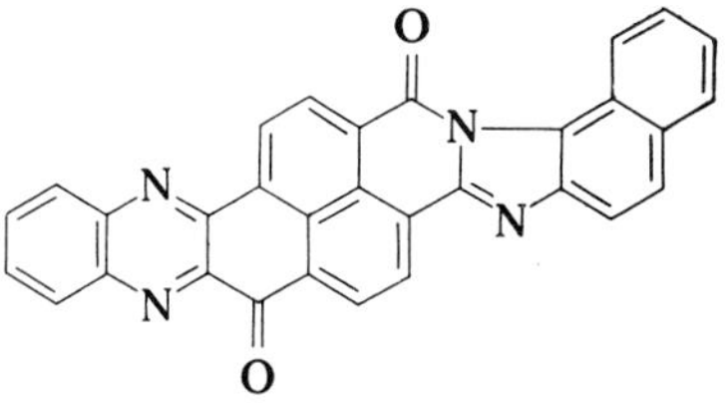

(III)

Reference

1. Eckert and Sieber, Ger. Pat. 659,095; *Frdl.*, **24,** 973 (1941).

A-354. Benzimidazo[1′,2′,2,3]isoquino[6,5,4-*mna*]naphth[2,3-*h*]acridine*

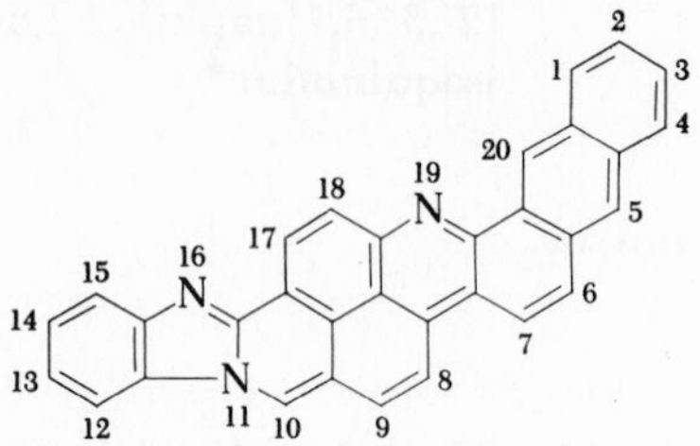

and

A-355. Benzimidazo[2′,1′,1,2]isoquino[6,5,4-*mna*]naphth[2,3-*h*]acridine*

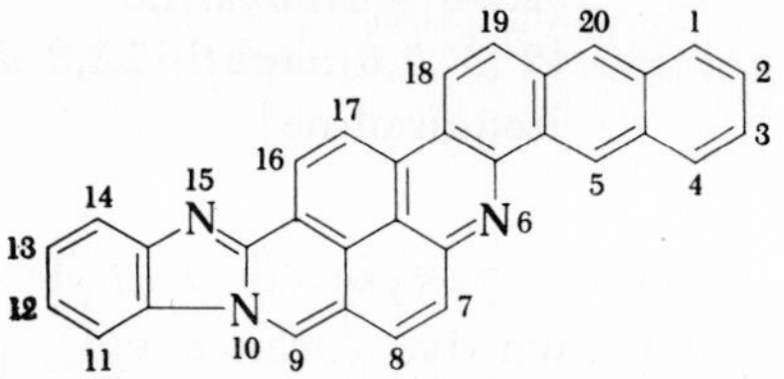

Derivatives of each of these nuclei were obtained[1,2] from the condensation of 3- and 4-bromobenzimidazo[2,1-*a*]benz[*de*]isoquino-

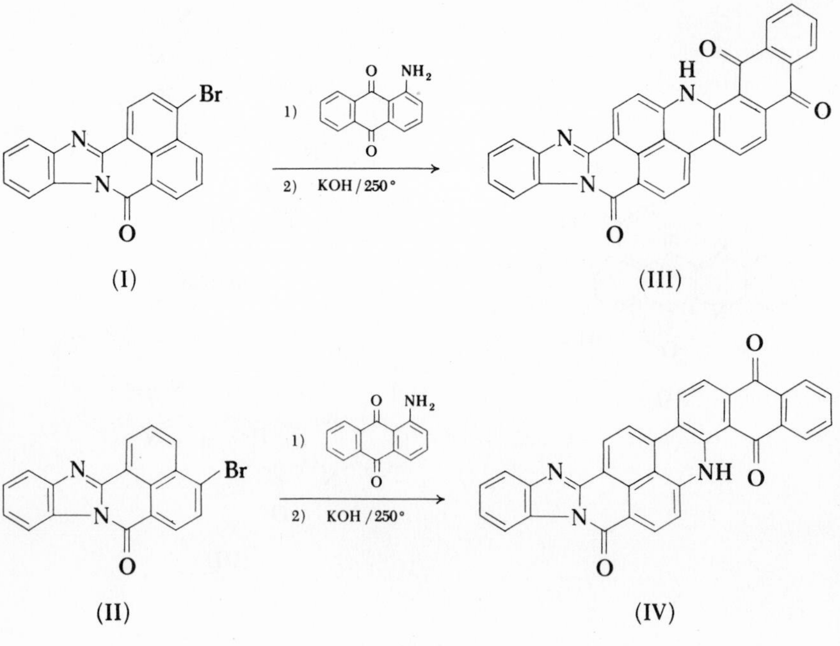

(I) → 1) 1-aminoanthraquinone; 2) KOH/250° → (III)

(II) → 1) 1-aminoanthraquinone; 2) KOH/250° → (IV)

lin-7-ones (I and II), respectively, with 1-aminoanthraquinone, followed by cyclodehydrogenation of the resulting anthrimides in a caustic melt. The former product III is a yellow-green dye (violet vat), m. 363°, whereas the latter (IV) is a green dye (red-violet vat), m. 342–3°. Neither is sufficiently chlorine-fast.[4] A green dye, a mixture of compounds III and IV, was obtained[1] by a similar reaction sequence starting from 4-bromonaphthalic anhydride. Introduction of a chlorine atom into the benzimidazole moiety of the nucleus, deepens the shade to a dark green[1] (the product thus described was a mixture of two isomers of types III and IV) without improving the fastness.[3] A yellow-green dye (red-violet vat) was similarly obtained from 3,3′,4,4′-tetraaminobiphenyl and 4-bromonaphthalic anhydride.

References

1. Wolfram, Nawiasky, Langbein and Elbs, Ger. Pat. 607,341; *Frdl.*, **21,** 1181 (1937). Fr. Pat. 753,185 and Brit. Pat. 399,724; *Chem. Zentr.*, **I,** 467 (1934); *Chem. Abstracts*, **28,** 906 (1934). U. S. Pat. 2,069,663.
2. Braunsdorf, *I. G. Farbenindustrie A. G., 40 Wissenschaftlicher Austausch der Gruppe IX*, December 15, 1938, Höchst; *PB Report Nos.* 70338, frames 10560–10565 and 73484, frames 802–808.
3. Wolfram, *PB Report No.* 25630, frames 680–683.
4. Greune, *PB Report No.* 25632, frames 41–42.

A-356. 12*H*-Benzimidazo[1′,2′,2,3]-isoquino[5,4-*ab*]naphth-[2,3-*h*]acridine*

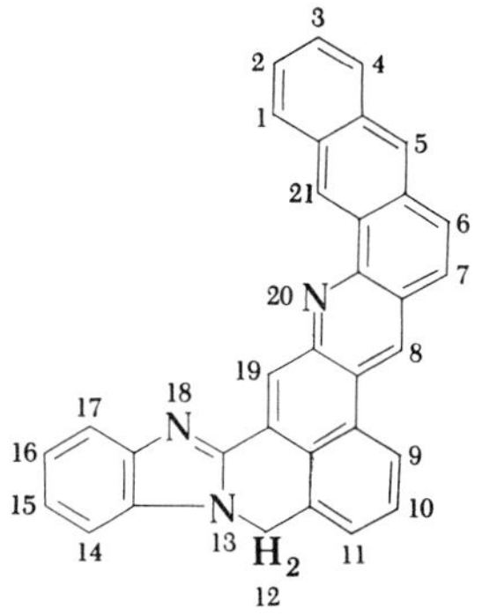

1 2 3 4 5 6 7 8 9 10 11 12 13 14 15 16 17 18 19 20 21 N N N H_2

and/or

A-357. 18*H*-Benzimidazo[2′,1′,1,2]-isoquino[5,4-*ab*]naphth-[2,3-*h*]acridine*

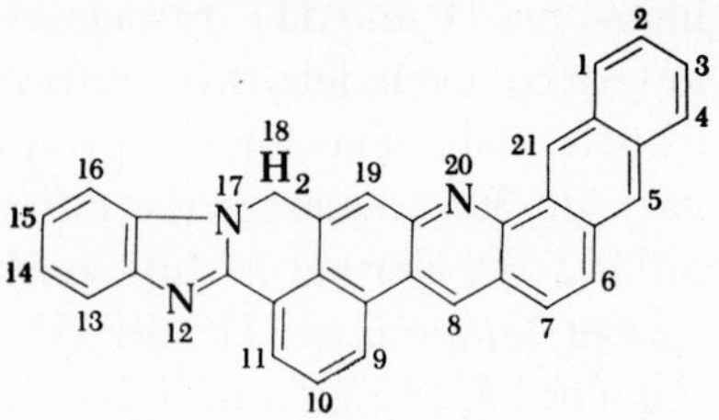

Condensation of 1-chloro(or nitro)-2-carboxyanthraquinone with 3-aminonaphthalic anhydride and cyclization of the resulting product with chlorosulfonic acid gave the dicarboxylic anhydride (I), which Eckert and Quint[1] reacted with *o*-phenylenediamine. The

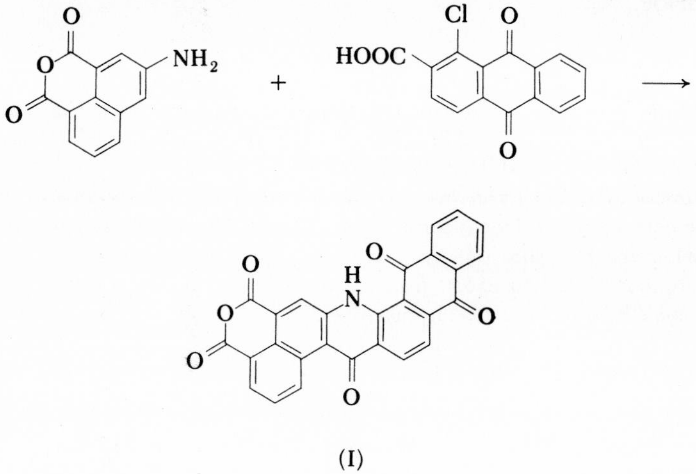

(I)

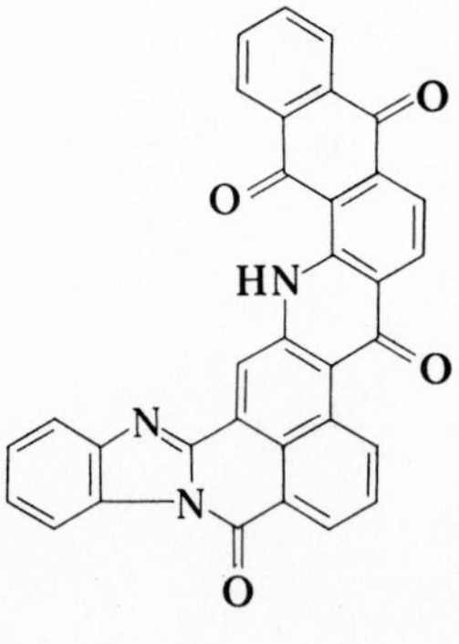

and/or

(II)

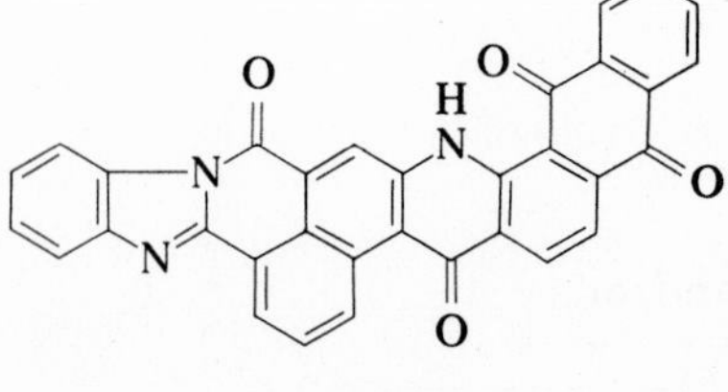

(III)

product they obtained was probably a mixture of II and III, and was a feeble orange-brown dye.

Reference

1. Eckert and Quint, *I. G. Farbenindustrie A. G., 35 Wissenschaftlicher Austausch der Gruppe IX*, March 13, 1936, Frankfurt; *PB Report No.* 70338, frames 9752–9757.

A-358. Benzimidazo[2,1-*a*]anthra-[2,1,9-*def*, 6,5,10-*d'e'f'*]bisisoquinoline*

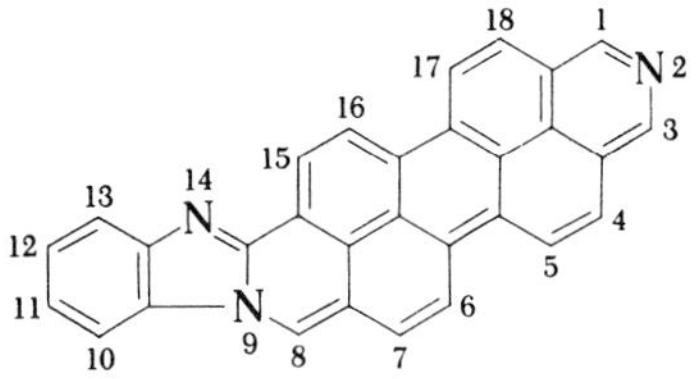

By the condensation of perylene-3,4,9,10-tetracarboxylic acid with *o*-phenylenediamines at 190°, Maki and Hashimoto[1,2] were able to obtain compounds of type I. The product, where R = H, is readily soluble in 90% sulfuric acid and in alkaline hydrosulfite solutions, dyes cotton a deep violet from a violet-red vat, and was named "Acenaphthene Violet" by its discoverers. The dye has a light-fastness of 8, a wash-fastness of 4–5 and a chlorine-fastness of 5. When the

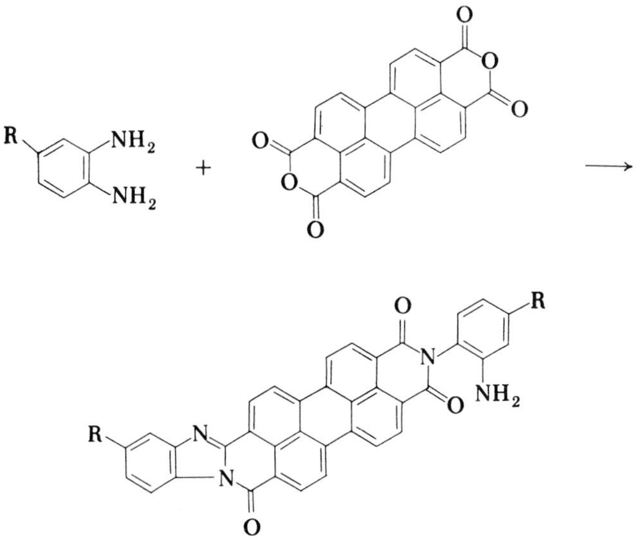

(I)

free amino group was diazotized and the product coupled with β-naphthol, the dye produced was a redder shade and of greatly inferior light-fastness. The *N*-benzoyl derivative of I is stated[1] not to vat. Other violet dyes of type I, in which R = Cl and OCH_3 have also been described.[2]

References

1. Maki and Hashimoto, *Bull. Chem. Soc. Japan*, **25**, 411 (1952); *Chem. Abstracts*, **48,** 1687 (1954).
2. Maki and Hashimoto, *Bull. Chem. Soc. Japan*, **27**, 602 (1954); *Chem. Abstracts*, **49,** 7857 (1955).

A-359. Acenaphtho[1′,2′,6,7]-phenanthro[2,1,10-*def*]-benzimidazo[2,1-*a*]-isoquinoline*

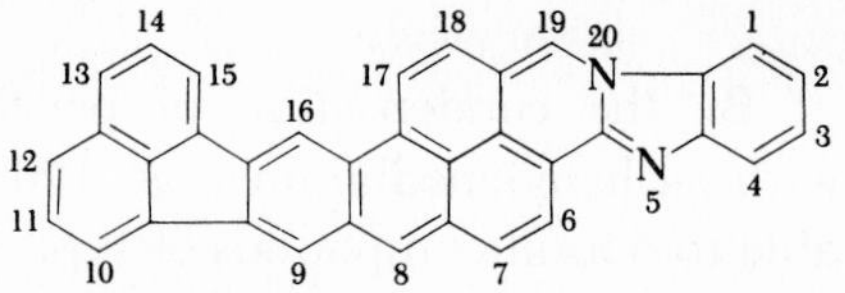

Acylation of fluoranthene with a product (see Section A-296) thought to be I, followed by a Scholl condensation upon the intermediate ketone, yielded[1] a chocolate-brown vat dye considered to be II.

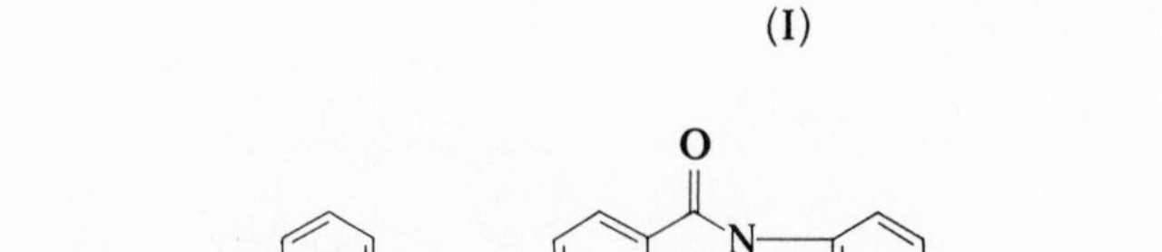

ClCO

(I)

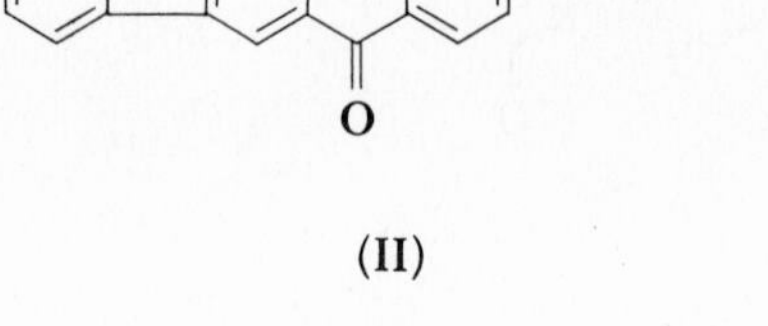

(II)

Reference

1. Schmidt-Nickels, U. S. Pat. 2,820,036.

A-360. Bisbenzimidazo-[2,1-*a*, 2′,1′-*a*′]naphtho-[2,1,8-*def*, 6,5,4-*d*′*e*′*f*′]-diisoquinoline*

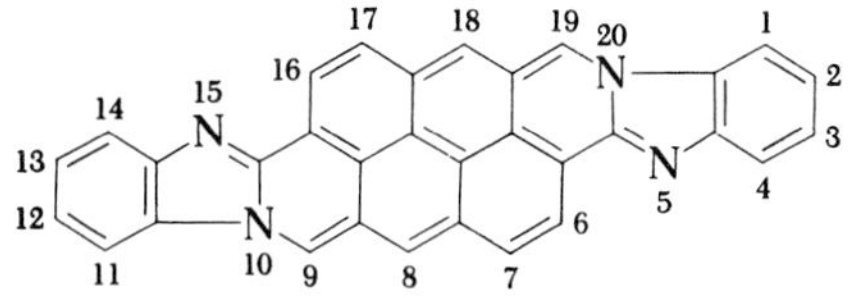

and/or

A-361. Bisbenzimidazo-[2,1-*a*, 1′,2′-*b*′]naphtho-[2,1,8-*def*, 6,5,4-*d*′*e*′*f*′]-diisoquinoline*

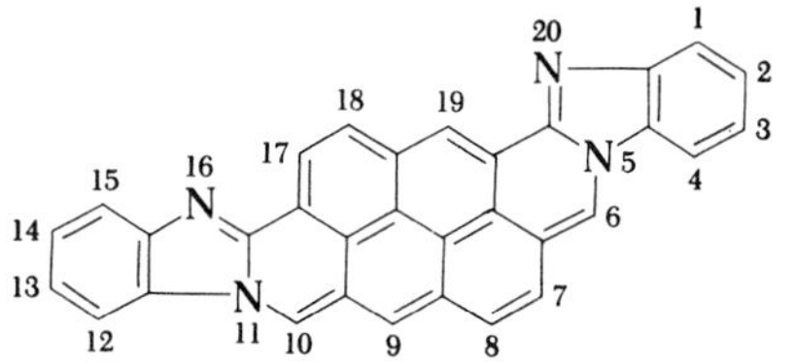

Vat dyes containing one or both of these nuclei were obtained[1] from the condensation of I with *o*-phenylenediamines. These dyes, of types I and/or II, were scarlet to brown shades rather similar to their

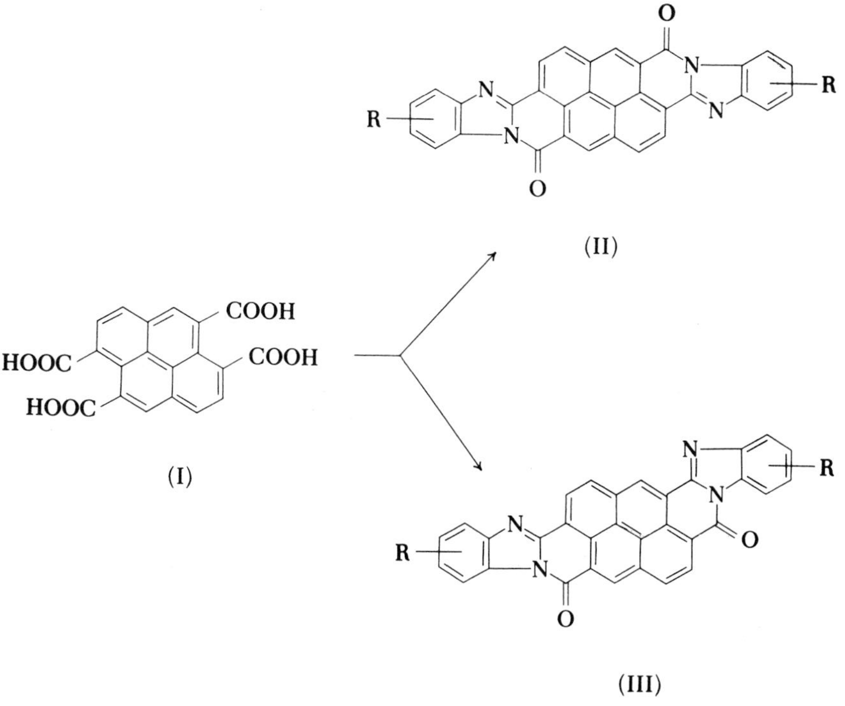

(II)

(I)

(III)

analogs obtained from naphthalene-1,4,5,8-tetracarboxylic acid (see Sections A-324/5).

Reference

1. Eckert and Greune, *I. G. Farbenindustrie, A. G., 33 Wissenschaftlicher Austausch der Gruppe IX*, March 29 and May 24, 1935, Frankfurt a/M.; *PB Report No.* 25632, frame 396.

A-362. Benzo[*lmn*]bisnaphth-[2′,1′,4,5]imidazo-[1,2-*c*, 1′,2′-*j*][3,8]-phenanthroline*

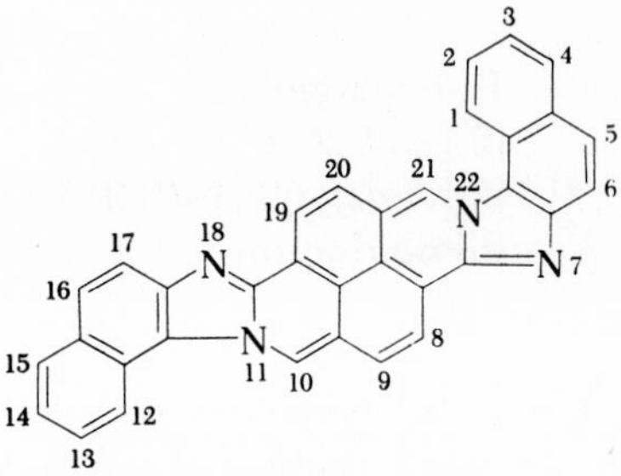

and

A-363. Benzo[*lmn*]bisnapth-[2′,1′,4,5]imidazo-[2,1-*b*, 1′,2′-*j*][3,8]-phenanthroline*

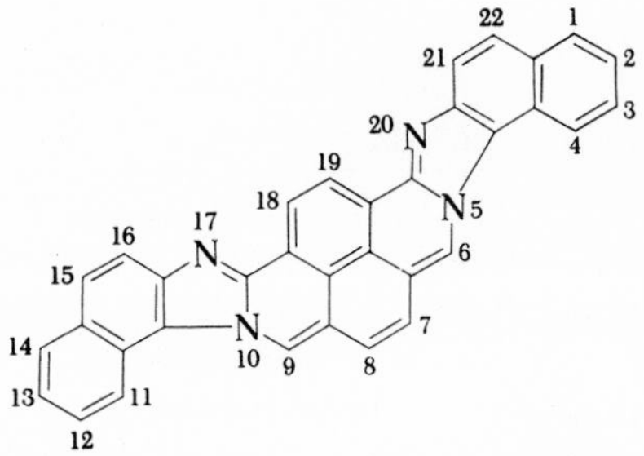

Derivatives of these nuclei were prepared by Eckert[1-3] and co-workers by the condensation of naphthalene-1,4,5,8-tetracarboxylic acid dianhydride with naphthylene-1,2-diamines. A mixture of I and II undergoes nitration,[3] presumably in what would be the 4-position of the two naphthalene nuclei (arrows). It would be gratifying to have more evidence for the accuracy of the structures assigned to these two ring systems, in view of the controversy over the reaction products from 1,2-naphthylenediamine and naphthalic anhydride (see Section A-304).

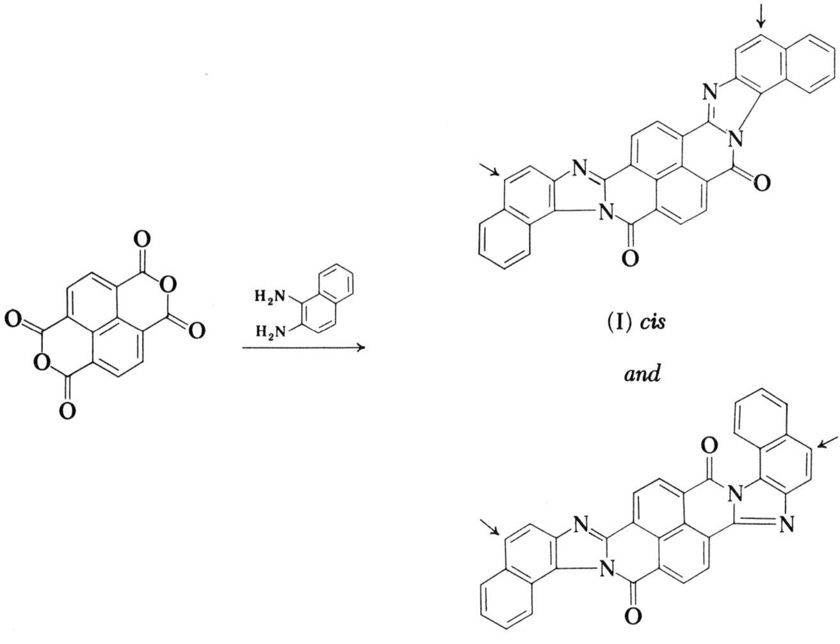

(I) *cis*

and

(II) *trans*

Derivatives of I and II

Empirical formula	Substituents	Properties and comments	Refs.
$C_{34}H_{14}Cl_2N_4O_2$	5,16-Dichloro-*II* and/or 15,22-dichloro-*I*	—	2
$C_{34}H_{16}N_4O_2$	Unsubstituted *II*-	Dyes cotton violet (or vt.-grey) from grn.-brn. vat.	1,4
	Unsubstituted *I*-	Dyes a "currant" (or violet) color from grn.-brn. vat.	1,4
$C_{34}H_{18}N_6O_2$	5,16(??)-Diamino-*II* and/or 15,22(??)-diamino-*I*-	Dyes cotton olive grn. Obt. by nitration of *I* and/or *II* followed by reduction with alk. hydrosulfite.	3

(*continued*)

Derivatives of I and II (*continued*)

Empirical formula	Substituents	Properties and comments	Refs.
$C_{36}H_{20}N_4O_2$	5,16-Dimethyl-*II* and/or 15,22-dimethyl-*I*	—	2
$C_{34}H_{24}N_4O_2$	1,2,3,4,12,13,14,15-Octahydro-*II* and/or 1,2,3,4,11,12,13,14-octahydro-*I*	—	2

References

1. Eckert and Braunsdorf, Ger. Pat. 538,314; *Frdl.*, **18,** 1499 (1933). U. S. Pat. 1,888,625; *Chem. Abstracts*, **27,** 1519 (1933).
2. Eckert and Sieber, *I. G. Farbenindustrie A.G.*, *34 Wissenschaftlicher Austausch der Gruppe IX*, October 22, 1935, Höchst a/M; *PB Report No.* 70338, frames 9644–9650.
3. Eckert, U. S. Pat. 1,819,082.
4. Tsukerman and Krasovitski, *Ukrain. Khim. Zhur.*, **20,** 543 (1954).

A-364. Benzo[*lmn*]bisnaphtho[2′,3′,4,5]imidazo[1,2-*c*, 1′,2′-*j*][3,8]phenanthroline*

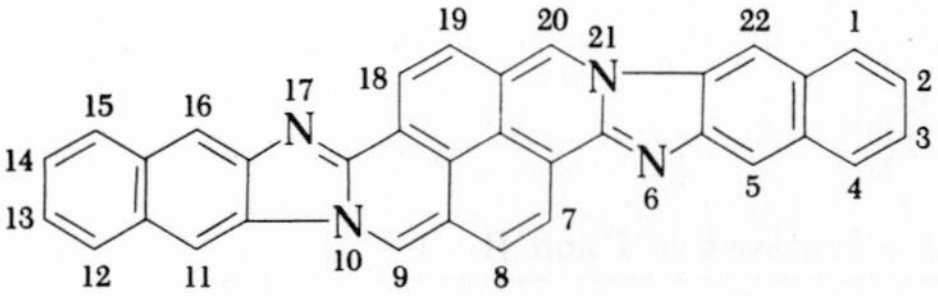

and/or

A-365. Benzo[*lmn*]bisnaphtho[2′,3′,4,5]imidazo[2,1-*b*, 1′,2′-*j*][3,8]phenanthroline*

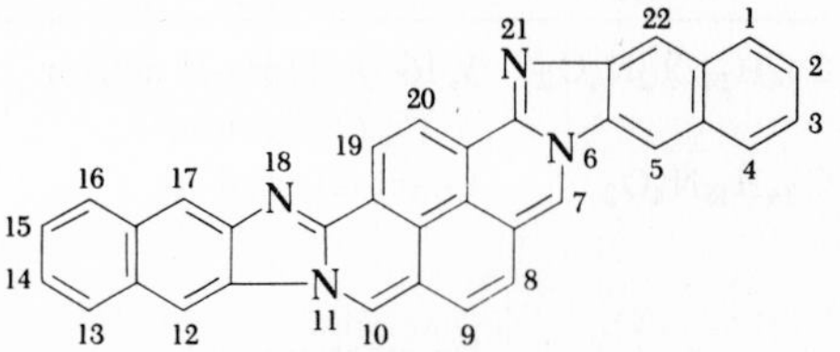

The only reported derivative of these nuclei is one which is probably a mixture of the two octahydrodioxo compounds, obtained by Eckert and Sieber[1] by reacting 1,2,3,4-tetrahydronaphthylene-6,7-diamine with naphthalene-1,4,5,8-tetracarboxylic acid.

Reference

1. Eckert and Sieber, *I. G. Farbenindustrie A. G.*, *34 Wissenschaftlicher Austausch der Gruppe IX*, Oct. 22, 1935, Höchst a/M.; *PB Report No.* 70338, frames 9644–9650.

A-366. Benzimidazo[1′,2′,2,3]isoquino[6,5,4-*mna*]benz[6,7]indazolo[2,3,4-*fgh*]acridine*

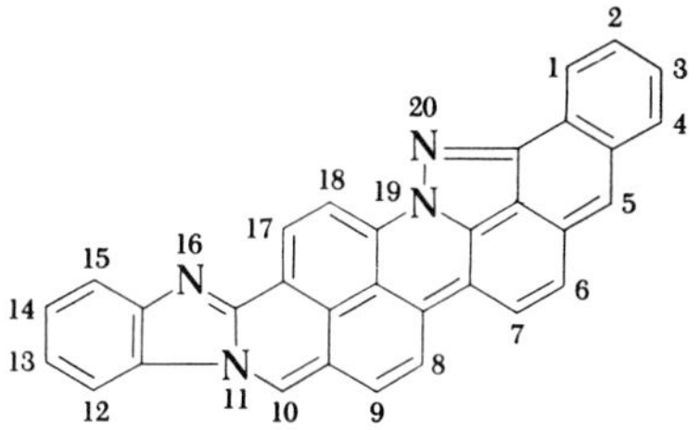

and/or

A-367. Benzimidazo[2′,1′,1,2]isoquino[4,5,6-*anm*]benz[6,7]indazolo[2,3,4-*fgh*]acridine*

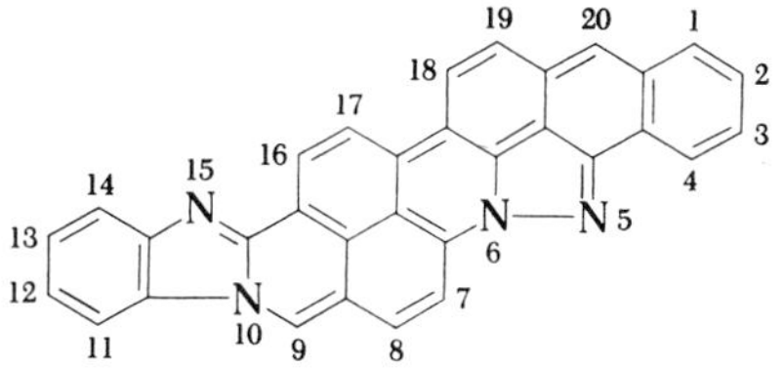

A blue dye, probably a mixture of compounds I and II, was mentioned briefly by Braunsdorf.[1]

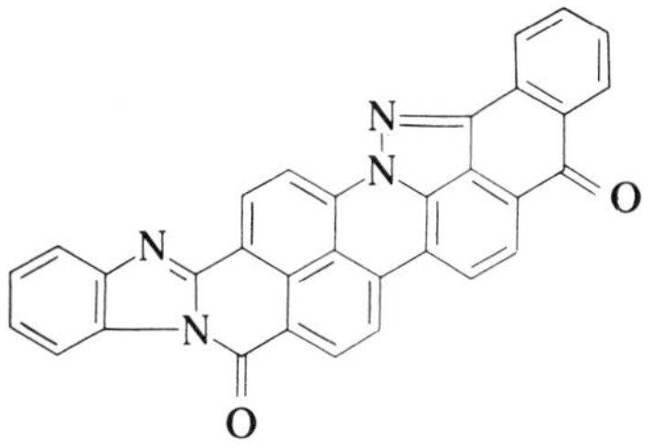

(I) 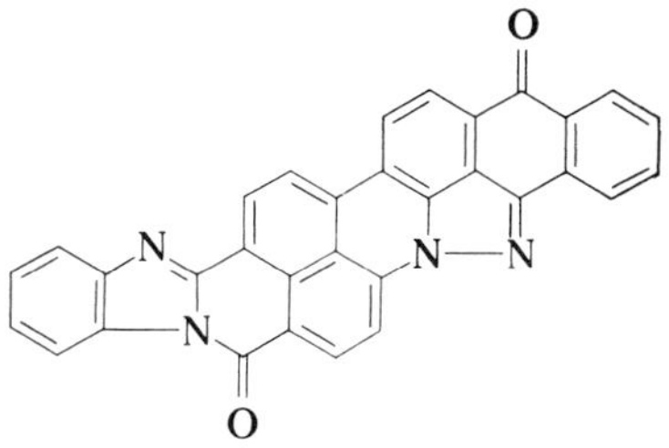 (II)

Reference

1. Braunsdorf, *I. G. Farbenindustrie A. G.*, *40 Wissenschaftlicher Austausch der Gruppe IX*, Dec. 15, 1938, Höchst; *PB Report Nos.* 70338, frames 10560–10565, and 73484, frames 802–808.

A-368. Anthra[2′,1′,9′,10,5,6]anthra[2,1,9-*def*]benzimidazo[1,2-*b*]isoquinoline*

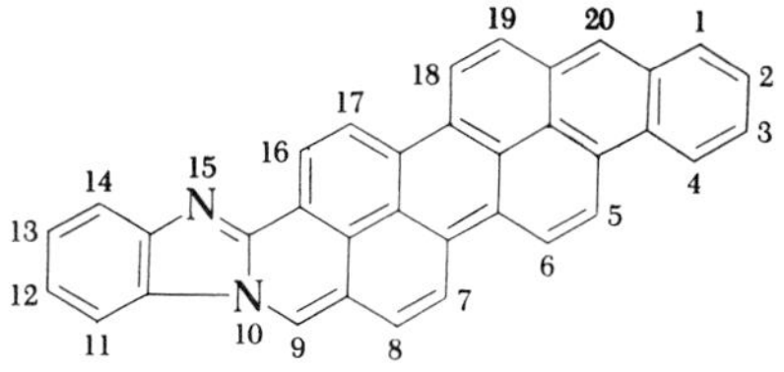

and/or

A-369. Anthra[2′,1′,9′,10,5,6]-anthra[2,1,9-*def*]benzimidazo-[2,1-*a*]isoquinoline*

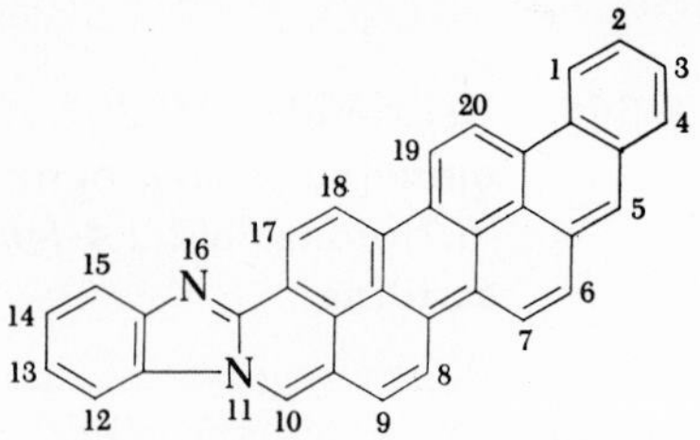

By subjecting to caustic fusion a product which was either 4- or 3-(3-benzanthronyl)-benzimidazo[2,1-*a*]benz[*de*]isoquinolin-7-one (I and II, respectively) or a mixture of both. Scheyer[1] obtained a blue-violet dye (violet vat) representing probably one or the other (or a mixture of both) of the above-named ring systems.

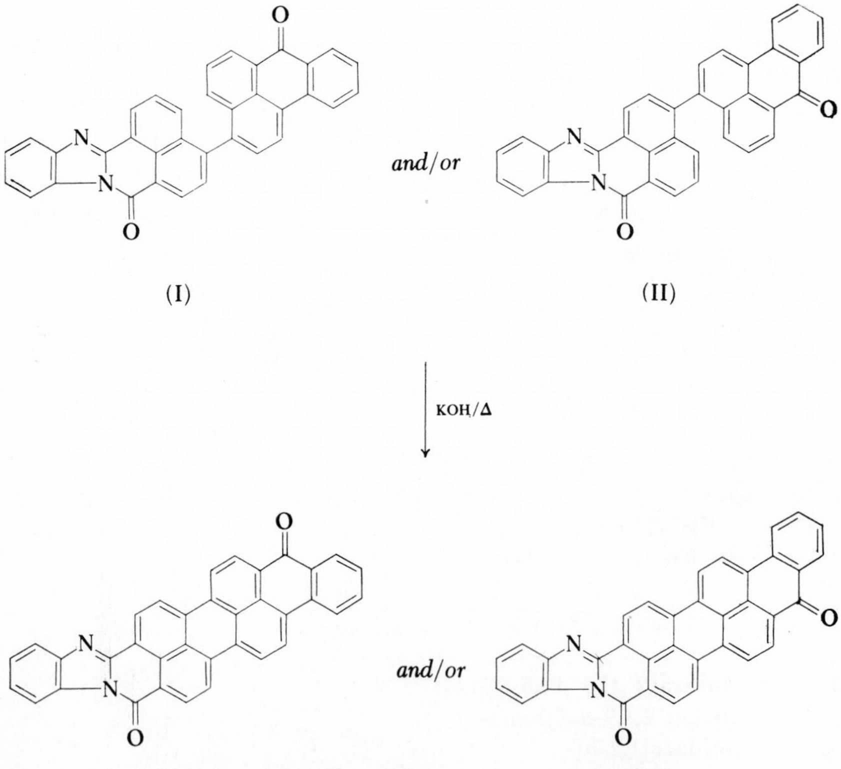

(I) *and/or* (II)

KOH/Δ

(III) *trans* *and/or* (IV) *cis*

Reference

1. Scheyer, Ger. Pat. 638,602; *Frdl.*, **23,** 1122 (1940); *Chem. Zentr.*, **I,** 2466 (1937).

A-370. Bisbenzimidazo-[2,1-*a*, 2′,1′-*a*′]anthra-[2,1,9-*def*, 6,5,10-*d*′*e*′*f*′]-diisoquinoline*

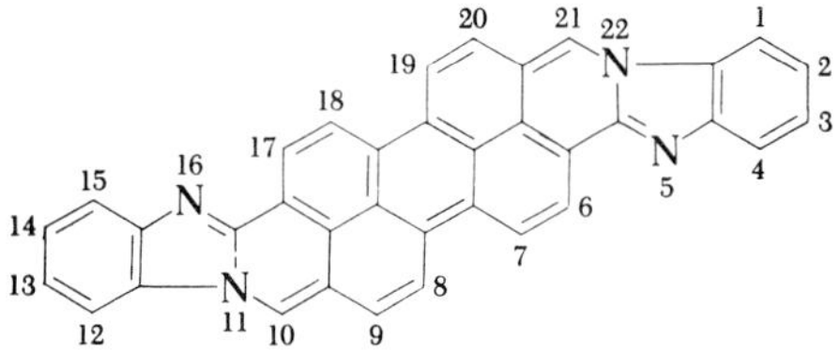

and/or

A-371. Bisbenzimidazo-[2,1-*a*, 1′,2′-*b*′]anthra-[2,1,9-*def*, 6,5,10-*d*′*e*′*f*′]-diisoquinoline*

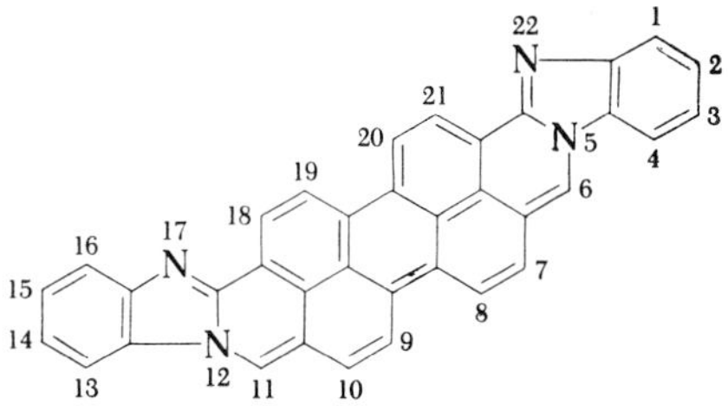

Considerable attention has been devoted to compounds having these ring systems because of their possible value as dyes. In 1924, Kalle and Company secured a patent [1] on the reaction of perylene-3,4,9,10-tetracarboxylic acid (prepared by the oxidative dimerization of naphthalimide in a caustic melt, followed by acid hydrolysis of the perylenetetracarboximide) with *o*-phenylenediamine. Numerous variations using substituted perylenetetracarboxylic acids and/or substituted *o*-phenylenediamines have since been reported.

The exact nature of the products has not been demonstrated conclusively, since in those cases where separation of the dye products into *cis* and *trans* isomers (such as I and II) has been attempted, it has not been successful. While this does not eliminate the possibility that the dyes are mixtures, Maki and Hashimoto [12] are of the opinion that these dyes are the *trans* isomers exclusively, because of the very limited solubility of their leuco derivatives.

An attempt to synthesize these nuclei by the caustic fusion of benzimidazo[2,1-*a*]benz[*de*]isoquinolin-7-one (see Section A-296), failed.[2]

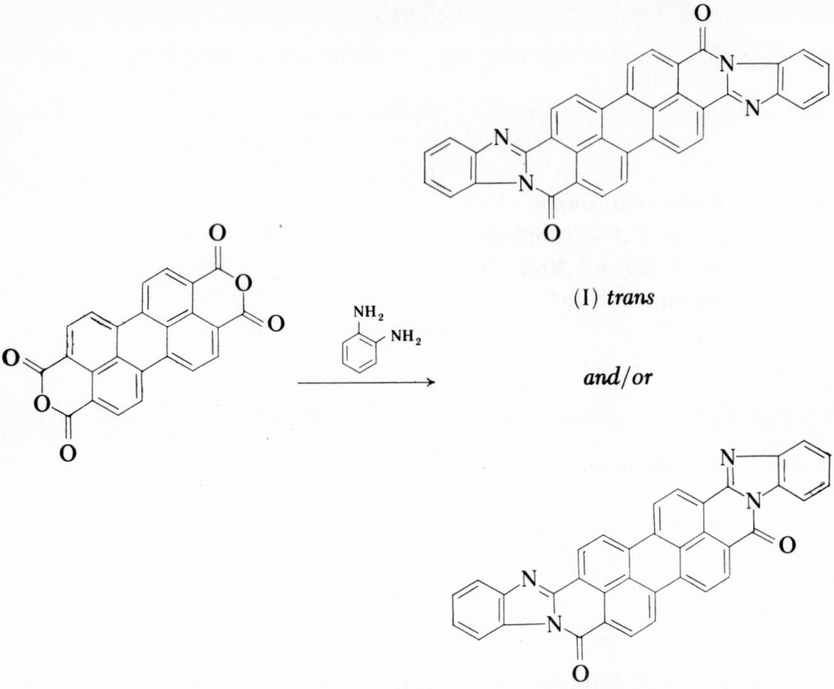

NH_2

NH_2

(I) *trans*

and/or

(II) *cis*

Dyes of this series range from green-blue, gray-blue and navy, to violet, and many exhibit outstanding fastness. The usefulness of these dyes is greatly impaired by the limited solubility of the leuco derivatives, and a tendency of the dyeings to waterspot.

Derivatives of I and II

Empirical formula	Substituents	Properties and comments	Refs.
$C_{36}H_{12}Cl_4N_4O_2$	6(or 7), 8(or 9), 17(or 18), 19(or 20)-Tetrachloro-*I* and/or 7(or 8), 9(or 10), 18(or 19), 20(or 21)-tetrachloro-*II*.	(Mixture?), dyes bl.-vt. with poor soda- and boil-fastness.	3,4
$C_{36}H_{14}Cl_2N_4O_2$	(6 or 7 or 19 or 20), (8 or 9 or 17 or 18)-dichloro-*I* and/or (7 or 8 or 20 or 21), (9 or 10 or 18 or 19)-dichloro-*II*.	(Mixture?), violet dye, soda- and boil-fast.	3,4
$C_{36}H_{16}N_4O_2$	Unsubstituted *I* and/or *II*.	(Mixture?), violet dye; leuco deriv. poorly soluble.	1,4,5
$C_{36}H_{16}N_4O_4$	7,8(or 18?)-Dihydroxy-*I* and/or 8,9(or 19?)-dihydroxy-*II*.	(Mixture?), gives redder shades than the methoxy analog.	7
$C_{38}H_{12}Br_4N_4O_2$	1,3(or 2,4),12,14(or 13, 15)-Tetrabromo-*I* and/or 1,3-(or 2,4),13,15(or 14, 16)-tetrabromo-*II*.	(Mixture?), a fast bl. dye, sl. greener than dibromo analog.	6
$C_{38}H_{14}Br_2N_4O_2$	1,12(or 4,15)-Dibromo-*I* and/or 1,13(or 4,16-dibromo-*II*.	(Mixture?), H_2SO_4 soln. grn. Dyes cotton a fast bl. from bl. vat.	6
$C_{38}H_{16}N_4O_6$	3,14-Dicarboxy-*I* and/or 2,15-dicarboxy-*II*.	(Mixture?), vt.; red-vt. vat; bl. H_2SO_4 soln. Amides from aminoanthraquinones, *etc.*, navy-blues.	13
$C_{38}H_{18}Cl_2N_4O_4$	3,14-Dichloro-7,18(or 8, 19)-dimethoxy-*I* and/or 2,14-dichloro-8,19-dimethoxy-*II*.	(Mixture?), similar to Indanthrene Dark Blue BO.	6,8
$C_{38}H_{20}N_4O_4$	7,8-Dimethoxy-*I* and/or 8, 9-(and/or 19,20)-dimethoxy-*II*.	(Mixture?), difficulty vattable grn. dye. Could not be separated into *cis-trans* isomers by standard methods.	7,8,11

(*continued*)

Derivatives of I and II (*continued*)

Empirical formula	Substituents	Properties and comments	Refs.
	7,18(and/or 8,19)-Dimethoxy-*I* and/or 8,19-dimethoxy-*II*.	(Mixture?), readily vatted navy blue. Could not be separated into *cis-trans* isomers by standard methods.	6,8
$C_{40}H_{18}F_6N_4O_4$	7,18(and/or 8,19)-Dimethoxy-3,14-bis-(trifluoromethyl)-*I* and/or 8,19-dimethoxy-2,15-bis-(trifluoromethyl)-*II*.	(Mixture?), very fast gray-blue dye.	6,8
$C_{40}H_{24}N_4O_4$	7,8-Diethoxy-*I* and/or 8,9-(and/or 19,20)-dimethoxy-*II*.	(Mixture?), a fast blue dye.	6
$C_{42}H_{16}F_{12}N_4O_4$	1,3,12,14-(or 2,4,13,15)-Tetrakis-(trifluoromethyl)-7,18-(and/or 8,19)-dimethoxy-*I* and/or 1,3,14,16-(or 2,4,13,15)-tetrakis(trifluoromethyl)-8,19-dimethoxy-*II*.	(Mixture), similar to the bis-trifluoromethyl analog in shade.	6
$C_{42}H_{28}N_4O_6$	3,14-Diethoxy-7,18 (and/or 8,19)dimethoxy-*I* and/or 2,15-diethoxy-8,19-dimethoxy-*II*.	(Mixture?), dye similar to Indanthrene Navy Blue R.	6,8
$C_{43}H_{22}N_5O_2$	(6 or 7 or 19 or 20)-Chloro-(8 or 9 or 17 or 18)-*p*-tolylamino-*I* and/or (7 or 8 or 20 or 21)-chloro-(9 or 10 or 18 or 19)-*p*-tolylamino-*II*.	(Mixture?), dyes violet-bl. from bl. vat.	3
$C_{48}H_{22}Cl_2N_4O_4$	3(or 2) 14(or 13)-Dichloro (6 or 7 or 8 or 9 or 17 or 18 or 19 or 20)-diphenoxy-*I* and/or 2(or 3) 15(or 14)-dichloro-(7 or 8 or 9 or 10 or 18 or 19 or 20 or 21)-diphenoxy-*II*.	(Mixture), redder than the corresponding dye lacking the chlorine atoms.	3

Derivatives of I and II (*continued*)

Empirical formula	Substituents	Properties and comments	Refs.
$C_{48}H_{24}N_4O_4$	(6 or 7 or 8 or 9 or 17 or 18 or 19 or 20)-diphenoxy-*I* and/or (7 or 8 or 9 or 10 or 18 or 19 or 20 or 21)-diphenoxy-*II*.	(Mixture), dyes a fast bl. from a violet vat; rather less light-and moisture-fast than the dimethoxy analog.	2,3,9
$C_{60}H_{32}N_4O_6$	(6 or 7 or 8 or 9 or 17 or 18 or 19 or 20)-tetraphenoxy-*I* and/or (7 or 8 or 9 or 10 or 18 or 19 or 20 or 21)-tetraphenoxy-*II*.	(Mixture), violet dye.	3,10

References

1. Kalle & Co., Fr. Pat. 555,954; *Chem. Zentr.*, **I,** 447 (1924). Brit. Pat. 201,786.
2. Gruschke and Quint, *I.G. Farbenindustrie A.G., 42 Wissenschaftlicher Austausch der Gruppe IX*, Feb. 16, 1940; Frankfurt a/M; *PB Report No.* 73484, frames 816–828.
3. Schmidt and Neugebauer, Ger. Pat. 412,122; *Frdl.*, **15,** 778 (1928). U. S. Pat. 1,878,986.
4. Schmidt and Neugebauer, Ger. Pat. 502,352; *Frdl.*, **17,** 1395 (1932). U. S. Pat. 1,808,260.
5. Maki and Hashimoto, *Bull. Chem. Soc. Japan*, **25,** 411 (1952); *Chem. Abstracts*, **48,** 1687 (1954).
6. I.G. Farbenindustrie A.G., Fr. Pat. 852,254; *Chem. Abstracts*, **36,** 2158 (1942); *Chem. Zentr.*, **II,** 1948 (1940).
7. Eckert and Quint, *I.G. Farbenindustrie A.G., 41 Wissenschaftlicher Austausch der Gruppe IX*, June 16/17, 1939, Leverkusen; *PB Report No.* 70338, frames 10679–10687; *PB Report No.* 70248, frames 2576–2583; *PB Report No.* 73484, frames 890–897.
8. Eckert and Quint, *I.G. Farbenindustrie A.G., 39 Wissenschaftlicher Austausch der Gruppe IX*, June 21/22, 1938, Mainkur; *PB Report No.* 70338, frames 10415–10420.
9. I.G. Farbenindustrie A.G., *F.I.A.T. Report No.* 1313, Vol. 3, p. 37–8.
10. Schmidt and Neugebauer, U. S. Pat. 1,715,430.
11. Blümmel, *I.G. Farbenindustrie A.G., 32 Wissenschaftlicher Austausch der Gruppe IX*, Nov. 9, 1934, Ludwigshaven; *PB Report No.* 70340, frames 12975–12980.
12. Maki and Hashimoto, *Bull. Chem. Soc. Japan*, **27,** 602 (1954); *Chem. Abstracts*, **49,** 7857 (1955).
13. Honold, Ger. Pat. Apln. C8078 IVb/22e.

A-372. Bisanthra[2′,1′,4,5]-imidazo[1,2-*c*, 1′,2′-*j*]-benzo[*lmn*][3,8]-phenanthroline*

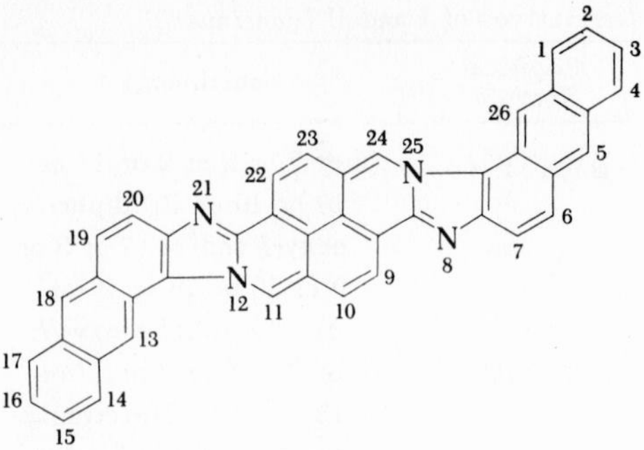

and/or

A-373. Bisanthra[2′,1′,4,5]-imidazo[2,1-*b*, 1′,2′-*j*]-benzo[*lmn*][3,8]-phenanthroline*

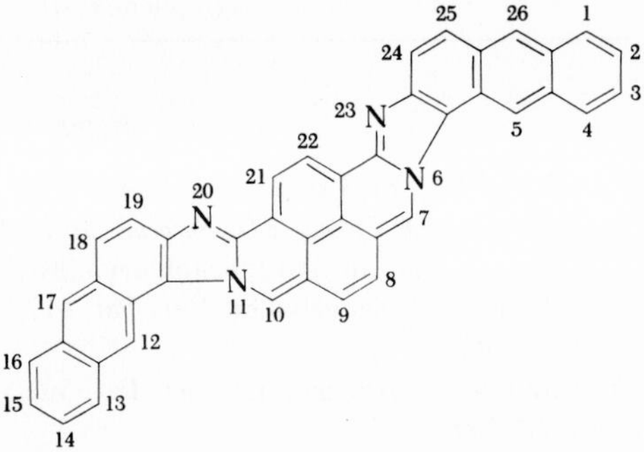

A dye (mixture?), thought to contain one (or both?) of these nuclei, was prepared[1] by the condensation of naphthalenetetracarboxylic acid (I) with anthracene-1,2-diamine. The product (II) gave (with difficulty) a greenish yellow vat, from which cotton was dyed a weak orange.

Oxidation of the dye (II) with chromic acid converted the two anthracene nuclei into anthraquinone groups, and simultaneously effected cleavage of the two pyridone rings to yield a base-soluble yellow-brown dye (red vat) of type III. This same dye (III) resulted from all efforts to condense I with 1,2-diaminoanthraquinone, showing the apparent instability of the diquinone analog of II.

H_2N NH_2

+

HOOC COOH

HOOC COOH

(I)

+

NH_2 H_2N

→

N N O N N O

and/or

O N N N N O

(II)

O H_2N NH_2 O $\xrightarrow{(I)}$

O O N NH O COOH COOH N NH O O O

and/or

O O N NH O COOH HOOC N NH O O O

Reference

1. Ritter, *I.G. Farbenindustrie A.G.*, *10 Tätigkeitsbericht*, July 1930-January 1931; *PB Report No.* 74203, frame 6853.

A-374. Benz[*lmn*]bisphenanthro-[9′,10′,4,5]imidazo-[1,2-*c*, 1′,2′-*j*][3,8]-phenanthroline*

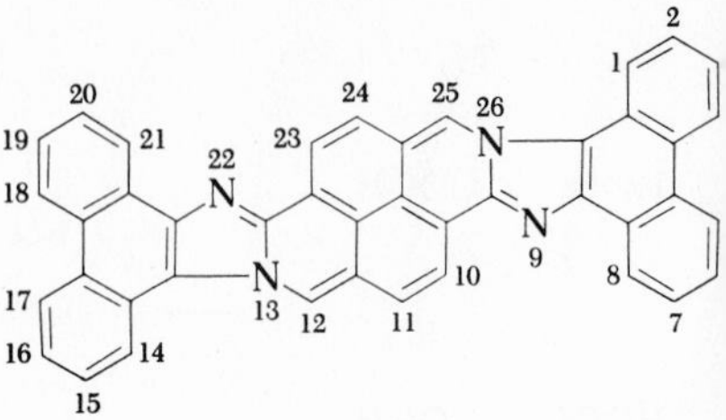

and

A-375. Benz[*lmn*]bisphenanthro-[9′,10′,4,5]imidazo-[2,1-*b*, 1′,2′-*j*][3,8]-phenanthroline*

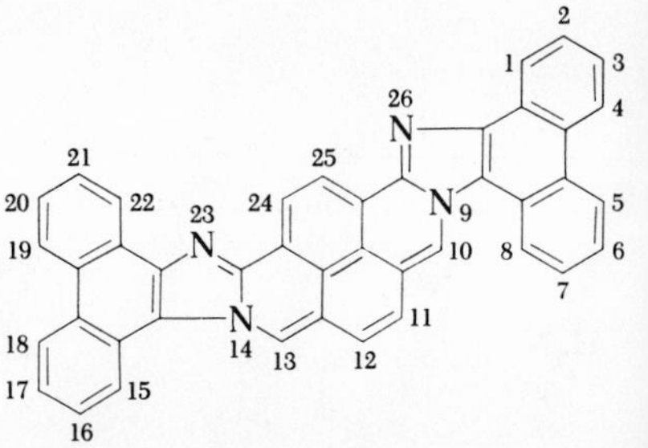

The condensation of naphthalene-1,4,5,8-tetracarboxylic acid with 9,10-diaminophenanthrene was found[1] to yield a mixture (dark

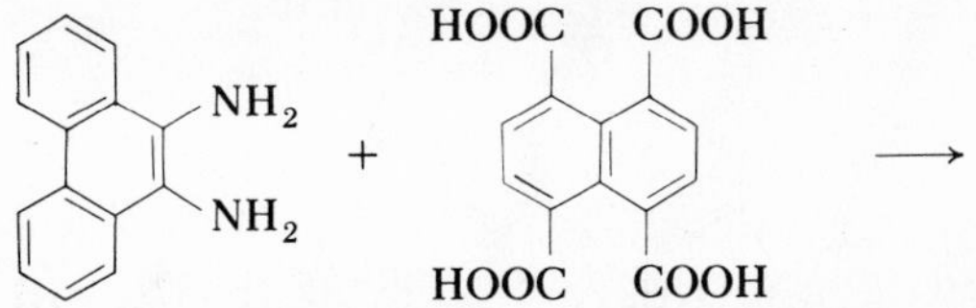

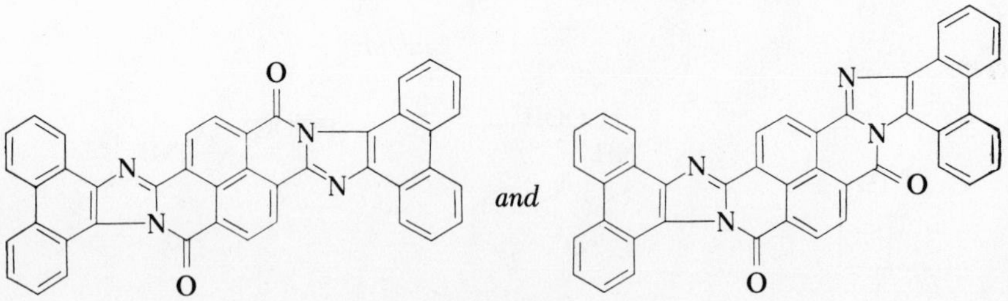

(I) and (II)

brown, d. about 400°) of the two dyes I and II. Separation of the mixture into pure I (red-violet) and II (brown) was accomplished by treatment with hot alcoholic potassium hydroxide, whereupon the colorless potassium derivative of I remains insoluble, while the salt of II dissolves. These dyes are difficultly vattable and show little affinity for cotton.

Reference

1. Tsukerman and Krasovitski, *Ukrain. Khim. Zhur.*, **20,** 543 (1954).

A-376. 12*H*-Anthra[1,9,8-*cdef*]bis-anthr[1′,2′,4,5]imidazo-[2,1-*a*, 1′,2′-*h*][2,7]-naphthyridine*

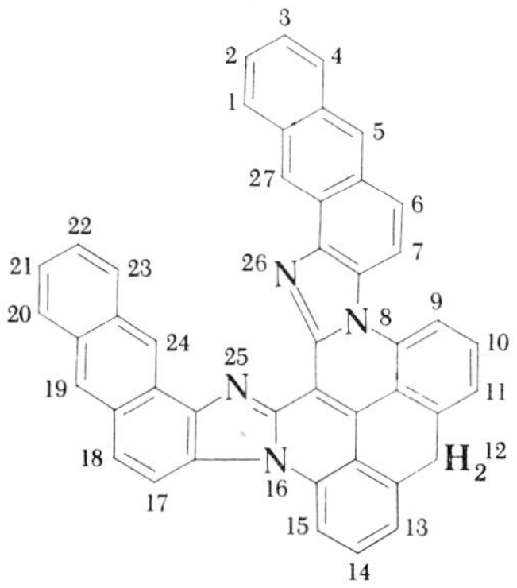

A yellow vat dye, presumably II, was obtained by Baumann and Schwechten[1] from the mild treatment of I with aluminum chloride. The cyclization of the anthrimid (I) cannot lead to a carbazole-like structure as could other related examples (see Sections A-326/9), and the assignment to the dye of structure II seems reasonable. This

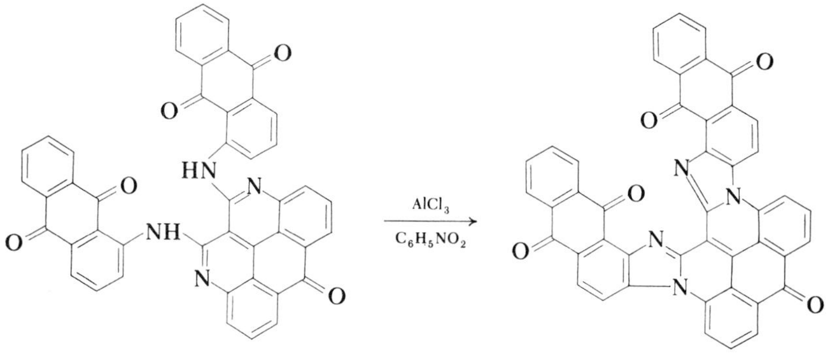

$AlCl_3$, $C_6H_5NO_2$

(I) (II)

series of dyes is characterized by the formation of insoluble and quite stable leuco derivatives, and the dyes have no practical value.

Reference

1. Baumann and Schwechten, *I.G. Farbenindustrie A.G., 37 Wissenschaftlicher Austausch der Gruppe IX*, Ludwigshafen, March 18 and 19, 1937; *PB Report No.* 70339, frame 11707.

A-377. Bisbenzimidazo[2,1-*a*, 2′,1′-*a*′]thieno[2″,3″,2,3:5″,4″,2′,3′]-diindeno[6,7,1-*def*, 6′,7′,1′-*d*′*e*′*f*′]diisoquinoline*

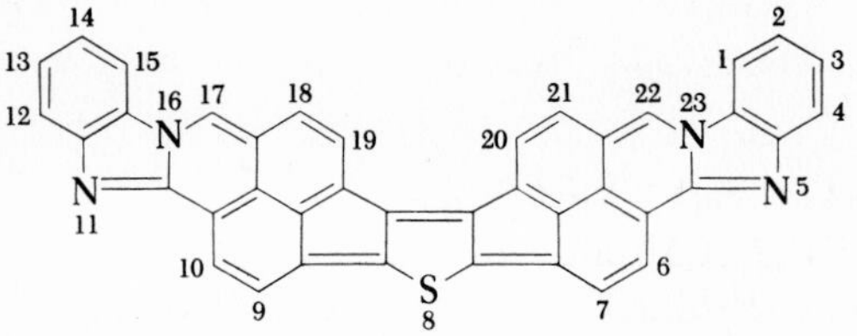

A dioxo derivative of this or of one of the other two possible isomeric nuclei, was prepared[1] by condensing *o*-phenylenediamine with acenaphthiophenetetracarboxylic acid. The product is a difficultly vatted, weak brown dye.

Reference

1. Sieber, *I.G. Farbenindustrie, A.G., 43 Wissenschaftlicher Austausch der Gruppe IX*, April 25, 1941, Leverkusen; *PB Report No.* 70338, frames 10875–8; *PB Report No.* 73484, frames 863–7.

A-378. Bisbenzimidazo[2,1-*a*, 2′,1′-*a*′]dibenzo[*h*,*h*′]anthra-[2,1,9-*def*, 6,5,10-*d*′*e*′*f*′]diisoquinoline*

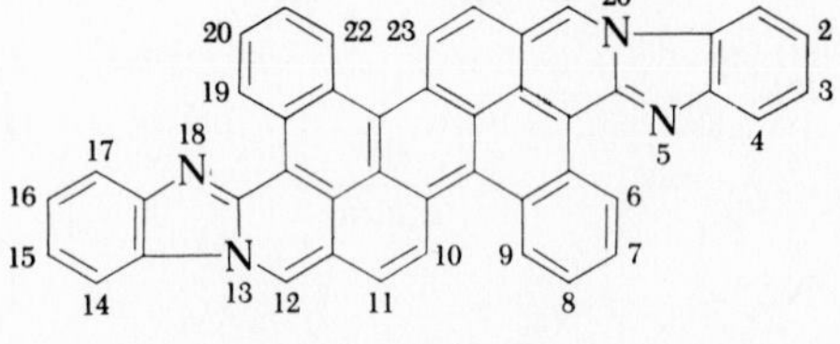

and/or

A-379. Bisbenzimidazo[1,2-*b*, 1′,2′-*b*′]dibenzo[*h*,*h*′]anthra-[2,1,9-*def*, 6,5,10-*d*′*e*′*f*′]diisoquinoline*

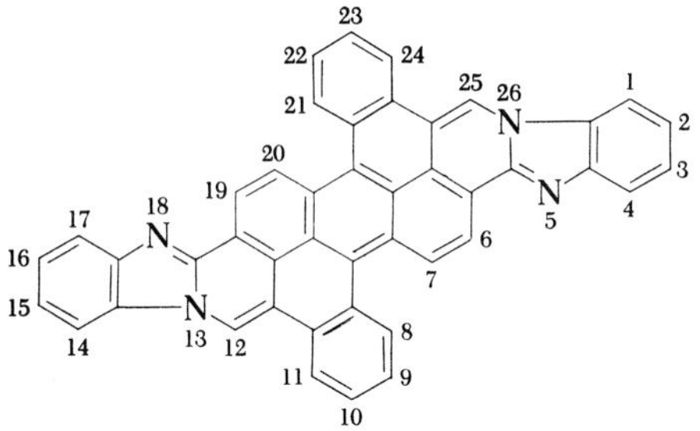

and/or

A-380. Bisbenzimidazo[2,1-*a*, 1′,2′-*b*′]dibenzo[*h*,*h*′]anthra-[2,1,9-*def*, 6,5,10-*d*′*e*′*f*′]diisoquinoline*

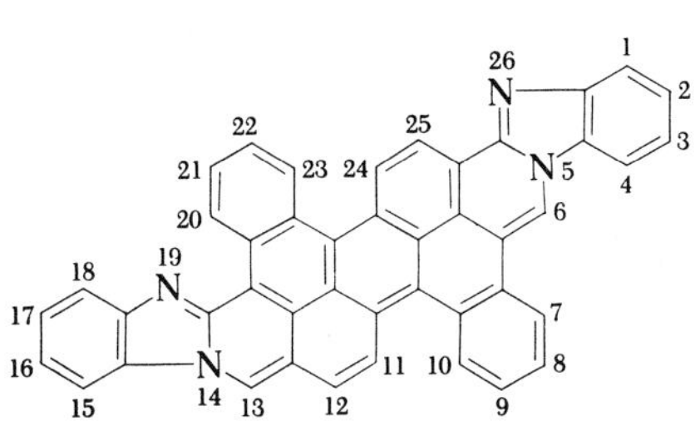

By condensing *o*-phenylenediamine with an acid thought to have structure I, Gruschke and Quint[1] obtained a low yield of dark-colored product. Recrystallization from nitrobenzene or 1-chloronaphthalene gave two isomers, presumably I, II or III. Both isomers are green vat dyes, the more insoluble of the two resembling Indanthrene Green GG.

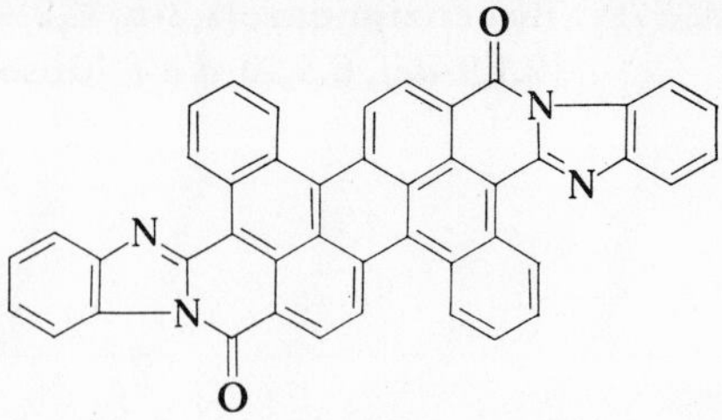

(II) *trans-anti*

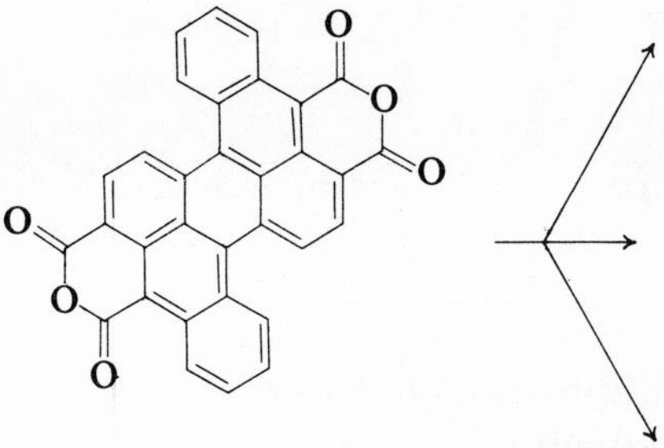

(I)

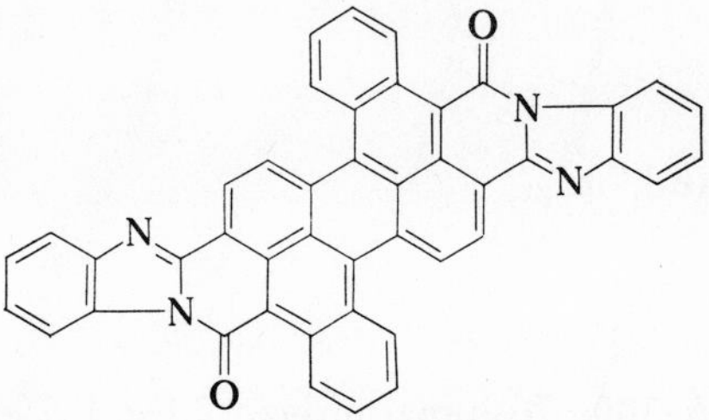

(III) *trans-syn*

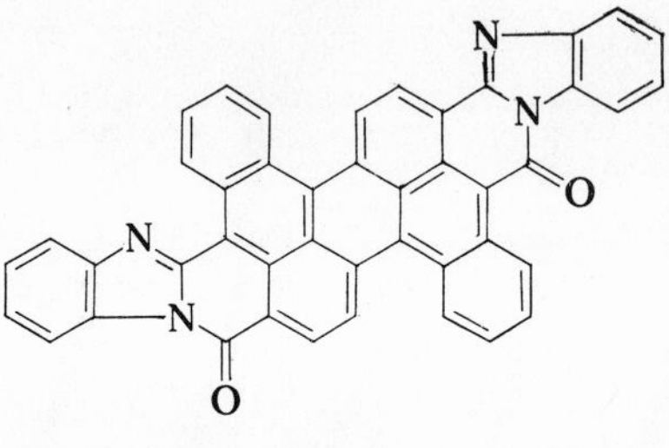

(IV) *cis*

Reference

1. Gruschke and Quint, *I.G. Farbenindustrie, A.G., 42 Wissenschaftlicher Austausch der Gruppe IX*, Feb. 16, 1940, Frankfurt a/M.; *PB Report No.* 73484, frames 816–28; *PB Report No.* 70248, frames 2834–45.

A-381. 23-Thia-5,14,18*b*,27*a*-tetraza-23*H*-diindeno[2,1,-*h*,2′,1′-*h*]-fluoreno[2,3-*a*, 7,6-*a*′]dipyrene*

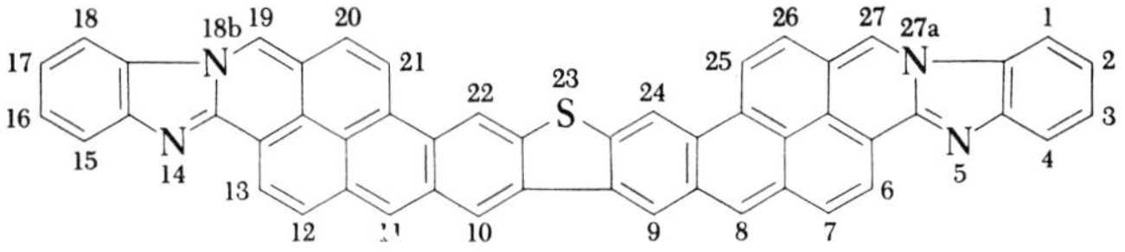

Acylation of dibenzothiophene with a substance thought to be I (see Section A-296), followed by a double Scholl condensation upon the intermediate diketone, yielded[1] a red-brown vat dye considered to be II.

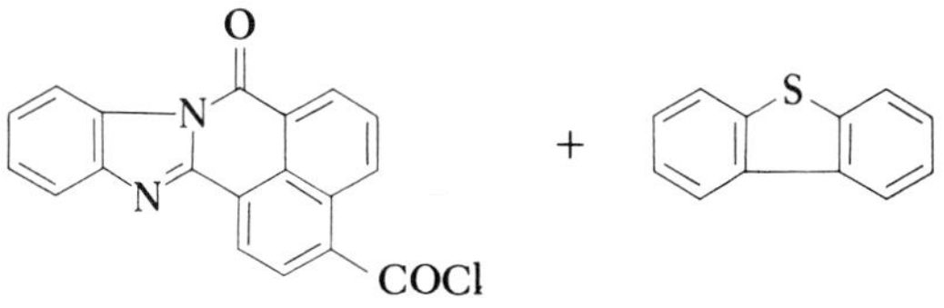

(I)

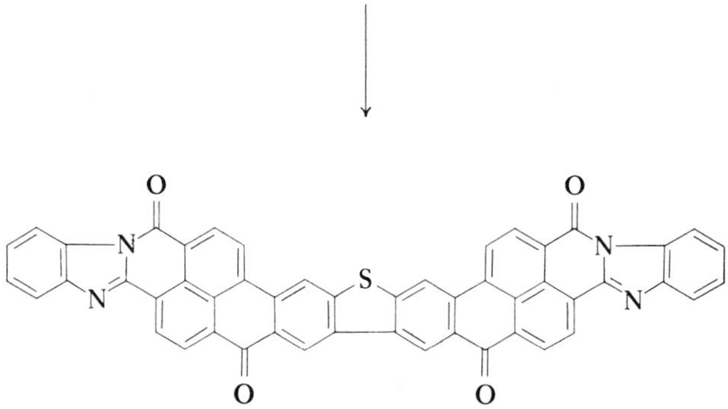

(II)

Reference

1. Schmidt-Nickels, U. S. Pat. 2,820,036.

A-382. 5,14,18*b*,23,27*a*-Pentaza-23*H*-diindeno[2,1-*h*, 2',1'-*h*']fluoreno-[2,3-*a*, 7,6-*a*']dipyrene*

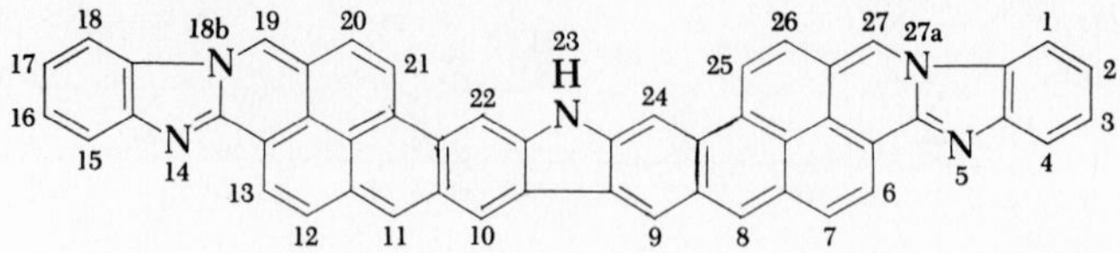

Acylation of carbazole with two moles of a product thought to be I (see Section A-296), followed by a Scholl condensation upon the intermediate diketone, yielded[1] a red-brown dye (red-brown vat) assigned structure II.

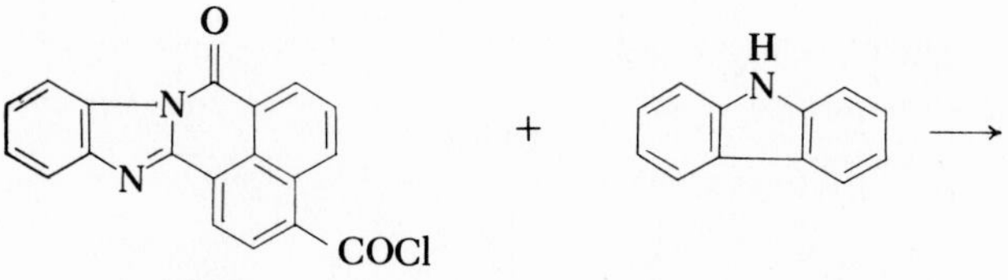

(I)

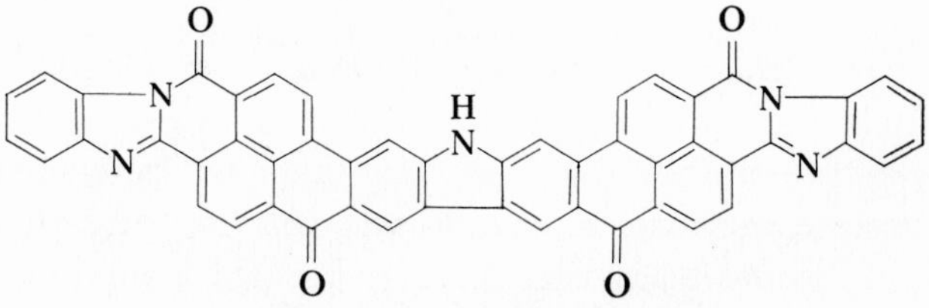

(II)

Reference

1. Schmidt-Nickels, U. S. Pat. 2,820,036.

A-383. Bisphenanthro[9′,10′,4,5]-imidazo[1,2-*b*, 1′,2′-*b*′]anthra-[2,1,9-*def*, 6,5,10-*d*′*e*′*f*′]-diisoquinoline*

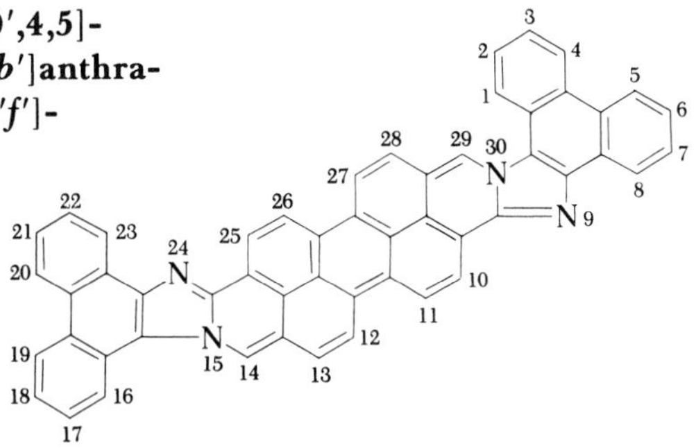

and

A-384. Bisphenanthro[9′,10′,4,5]-imidazo[2,1-*a*, 1′,2′-*b*′]anthra-[2,1,9-*def*, 6,5,10-*d*′*e*′*f*′]-diisoquinoline*

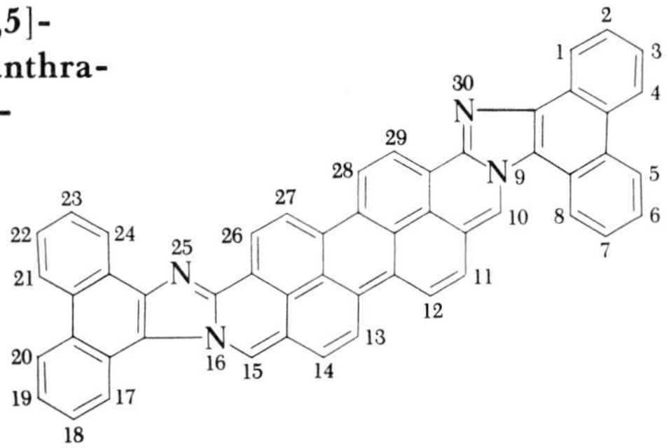

While perylene-3,4,9,10-tetracarboxylic acid (I) does not condense with 9,10-diaminophenanthrene even after prolonged refluxing in either nitrobenzene, pyridine, quinoline or in an acetic acid–sodium acetate mixture, it was found[1] that heating the reactants in a flux of sodium acetate at 340–70° yielded a mixture of II and III (dark brown with a violet cast, decomposes above 400°; sulfuric acid solution exhibits a red-violet fluorescence). The mixture was separated into pure II (violet) and III (brown) by treatment with alcoholic potassium hydroxide (a standard technique, see Sections A-325/6). These dyes proved rather difficult to vat and showed poor substantivity for cotton.

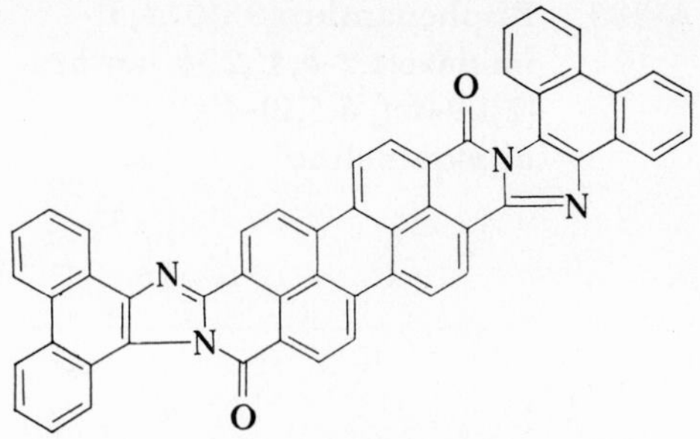

(II)

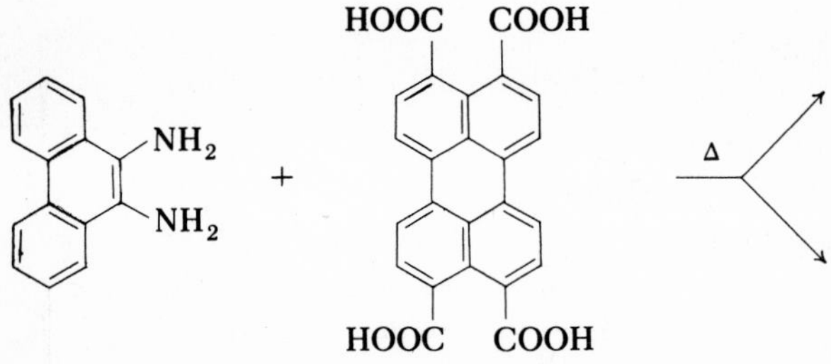

HOOC COOH

NH_2

NH_2

+

HOOC COOH

(I)

Δ

and

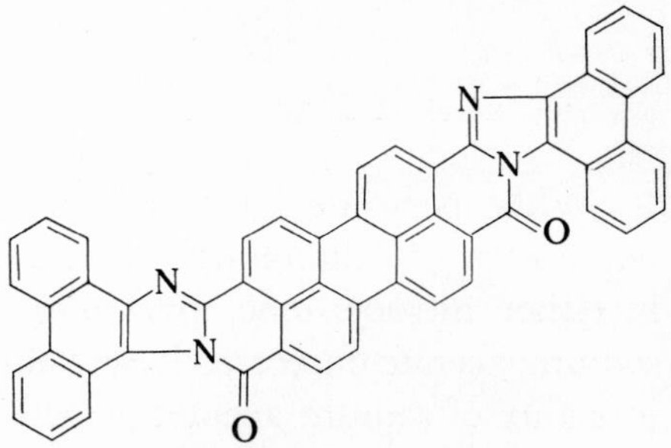

(III)

Reference

1. Tsukerman and Krasovitski, *Ukrain. Khim. Zhur.*, **20,** 543 (1954).

A-385. *3H*-Oxazolo[3,4-*a*]pyridine.
R.I. 726

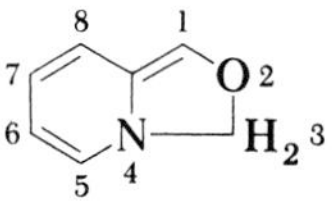

The pyrolysis of I yielded[1] II (b_{14} 164°), and a group of products of structure IV were obtained[1,2] by treating piperidines of type III with formaldehyde. Some of the products acted as stimulants to the central nervous system.

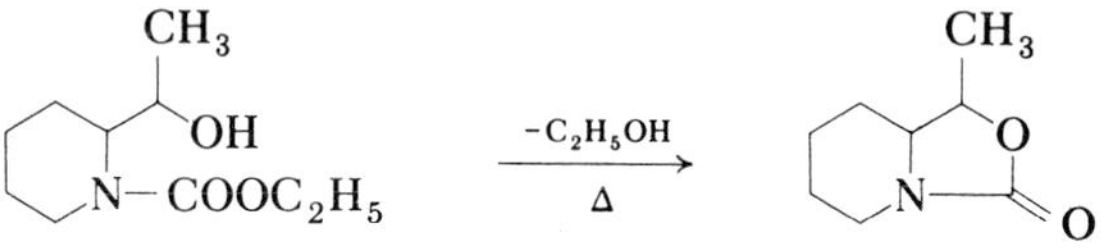

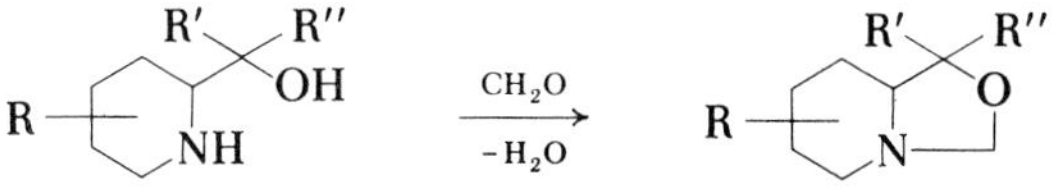

$$\text{(I)} \xrightarrow[\Delta]{-C_2H_5OH} \text{(II)}$$

$$\text{(III)} \xrightarrow[-H_2O]{CH_2O} \text{(IV)}$$

Compounds of Structure IV

R	R′	R″	Properties	Refs.
H	H	CH_3	b_{18} 79–81°. Picrate, m. 163°.	1
H	2-Thienyl	2-Thienyl	HCl salt, m. 211–2°.	2
H	9-Fluorenylidene		m. 96–8°.	2
H	C_6H_5	m-C_6H_4Cl	m. 83–5°.	2
H	C_6H_5	p-C_6H_4Cl	m. 99–100°.	2
H	p-C_6H_4Cl	p-C_6H_4Cl	m. 169–71°. Acid maleate salt, m. 132–4°.	2
H	C_6H_5	C_6H_5	m. 117–21°. HCl salt m. 312–24. Acid maleate salt, m. 158–9°.	2

(continued)

Compounds of Structure IV (*continued*)

R	R′	R″	Properties	Refs.
H	1-Indanylidene		m. 150–1°.	2
H	9-Anthrylidene		m. 162–4°. Acid maleate salt, m. 168–9°.	2
5-CH_3	C_6H_5	C_6H_5	m. 121–3°. HCl salt, m. 220–2°.	2
H	C_6H_5	2,5-$(CH_3)_2C_6H_3$	m. 116–7°. Acid maleate salt, m. 200–3°.	2
H	*o*-CH_3-C_6H_4	*o*-CH_3-C_6H_4	HCl salt, m. 224–6°.	2
7-CH_3	*p*-$CH_3C_6H_4$	*p*-$CH_3C_6H_4$	HCl salt, m. 295°.	2
H	C_6H_5	*m*-C_6H_4Cl	Acid maleate salt, m. 126–8°.	2
H	C_6H_5	$C_6H_5CH_2$	Acid maleate salt, m. 114–6°.	2
H	C_6H_5	*m*-$C_6H_4CH_3$	Acid maleate salt, m. 134–6°.	2
H	C_6H_5	Bicyclo [2.2.1]-2-heptyl	Acid maleate salt, m. 129–32°.	2
H	C_6H_5	Cycloheptyl	Neutral maleate salt, m. 140–2°.	2

References

1. Hess and Corleis, *Ber.*, **54,** 3010 (1921).
2. McCarty, Tilford and Van Campen, *J. Am. Chem. Soc.*, **79,** 472 (1957).

A-386. 1*H*-Oxazolo[3,4-*a*]quinoline. R.I. 1517

The anhydride I (m. 155–6°)[1] is the only actual example of this nucleus, although structures such as III have been postulated to exist

$COOC_2H_5$ ... COOH —$SOCl_2$→

(I)

as intermediates in the hydrolysis of Reissert compounds (e.g., II).[2,3]

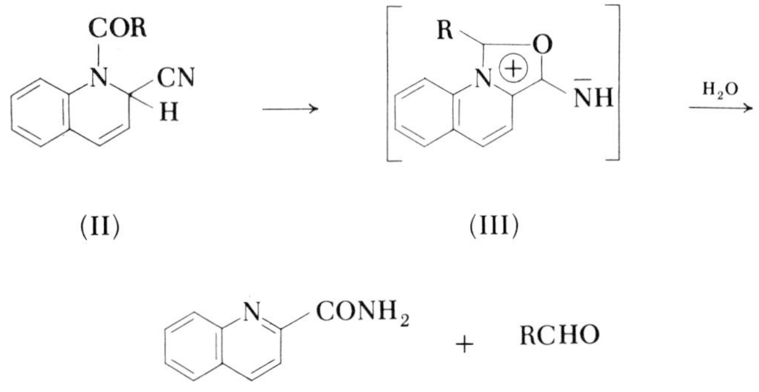

(II) (III)

$\xrightarrow{H_2O}$ + RCHO

References

1. Wieland, Hettche and Hoshino, *Ber.*, **61,** 2371 (1928).
2. McEwen and Cobb, *Chem. Rev.*, **55,** 511 (1955).
3. Cobb and McEwen, *J. Am. Chem. Soc.*, **77,** 5042 (1955).

A-387. 2*H*,4*H*-Oxazolo[*ij*]quinoline

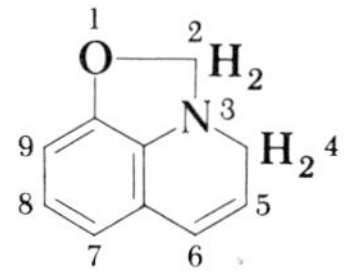

Schwarz and Schouwenaars[1] heated I with acetyl chloride and obtained II (X = Br, m. 121°), which was used to prepare photographic sensitizing dyes.[1,2]

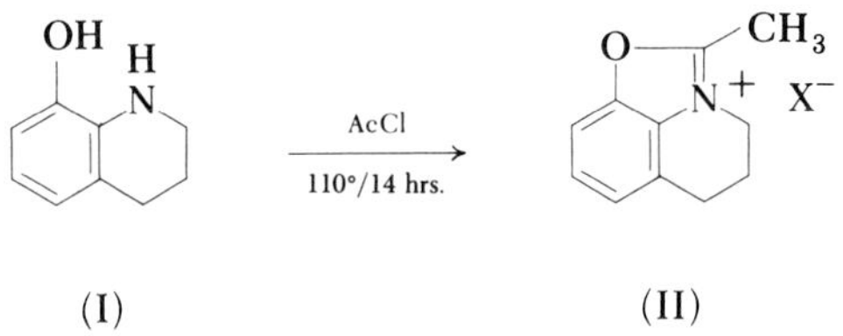

AcCl, 110°/14 hrs.

(I) (II)

References

1. Schwarz and Schouwenaars, Brit. Pat. 625,245; *Chem. Abstracts*, **45,** 3269 (1951).
2. Schwarz and Schouwenaars, Ger. Pat. 741,071 and Fr. Pat. 870,563; *Chem. Abstracts*, **40,** 2752 (1946).

A-388. *3H*-Pyrido[1,2-*c*]thiazole

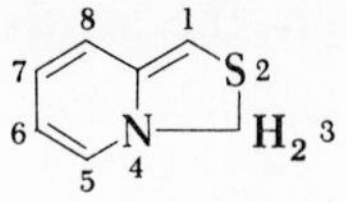

The reaction of 2-carbethoxypiperidine with phenyl isothiocyanate yielded a product (m. 159.0–9.5°; λ_{max} 232 and 271 mμ) thought probably to be I, although structure II is not impossible (see Section A-390).

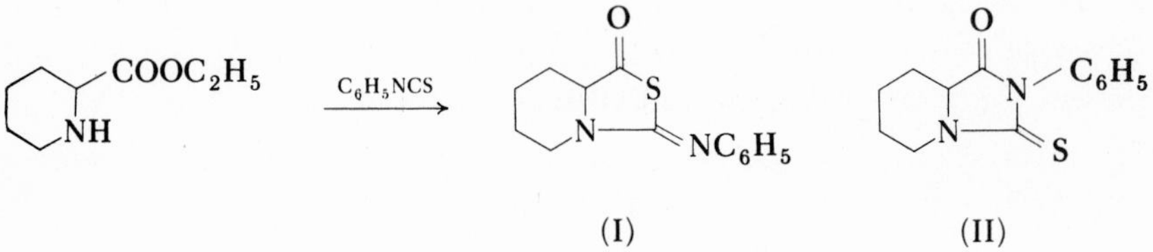

(I) (II)

Reference

1. Reckhow and Tarbell, *J. Am. Chem. Soc.*, **74,** 4960 (1952).

A-389. *2H,4H*-Thiazolo[*ij*]quinoline. R.I. 1538

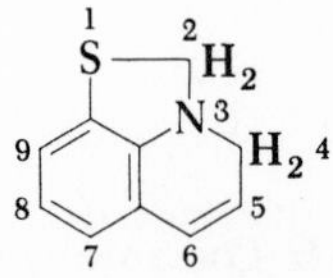

The only examples of this ring system are the 5,6-dihydro derivatives, often referred to as *1,7-trimethylenebenzothiazolines*, which have

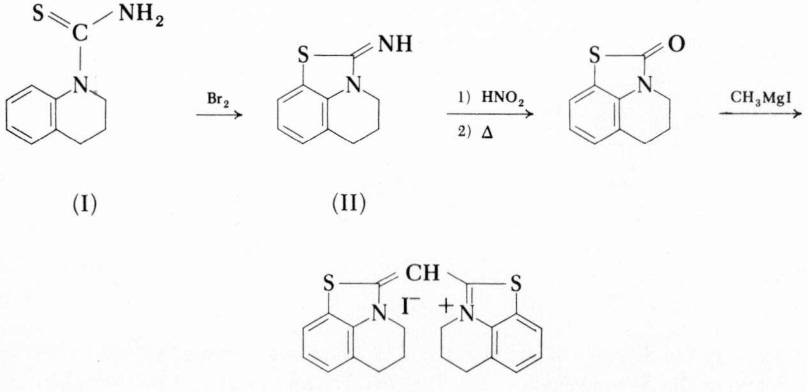

(I) (II)

(III)

been prepared in connection with the synthesis of photographic sensitizing dyes.

König, Kleist and Gotze[1] found that oxidation of the thiourea I with bromine produced II, which they converted, as shown, into the methine dye III.

Similarly, it was found[2] that thioacetyl derivatives of suitable aromatic amines (e.g., IV) could be oxidized to benzothiazole derivatives such as V by iodine[2] or bromine[3] in dilute acetic acid. When iodine is used, the initial product is the triiodide (I_3^-) salt, which is reduced to the normal iodide salt by sulfurous acid. Compound V and several of its homologs were also obtained[14] from VI.

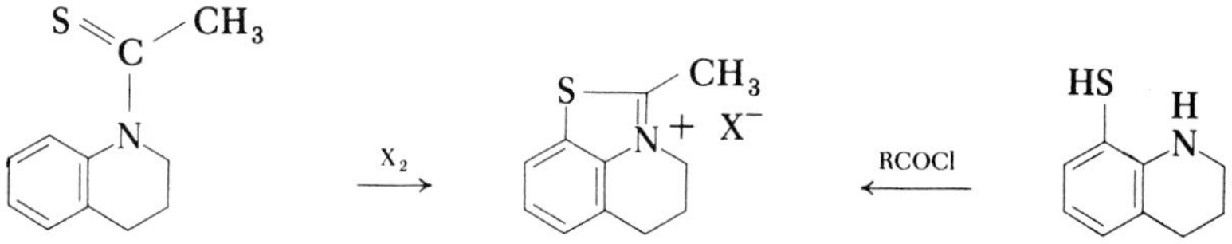

(IV) (V) (VI)

From V and its 8-methoxy analog a number of cyanine, merocyanine, styryl, etc., dyes have been prepared. Many of these are listed in the table, but others,[3,9-12] which were inadequately characterized, have been omitted.

The cyclodehydration of VII to VIII (R = H or Cl) was reported[13] recently.

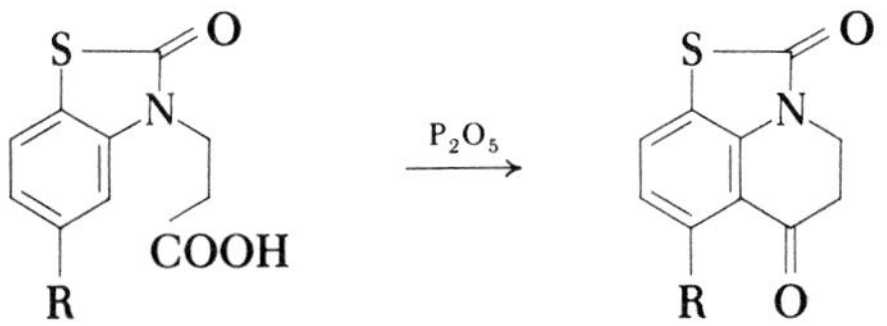

(VII) (VIII)

5,6-Dihydro-4*H*-thiazolo[*ij*]quinolines

Empirical formula	Structure	Properties	Refs.
$C_{10}H_6ClNO_2S$	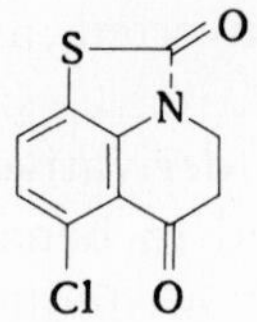	Yel., m. 236–8°.	13
$C_{10}H_7NO_2S$	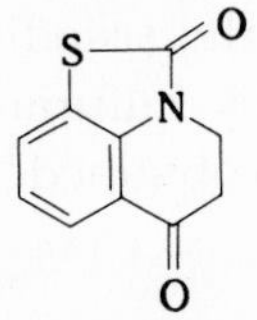	m. 153–4°.	13
$C_{10}H_9NOS$	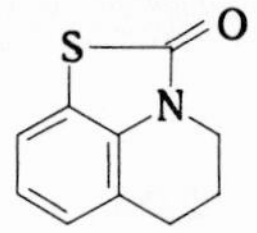	m. 77°.	1
$C_{10}H_9N_3OS$	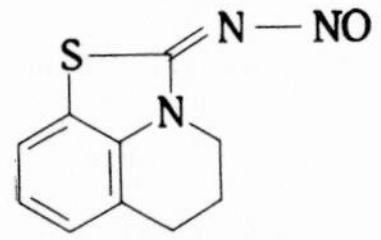	Or.-red, m. 149° d. on slow heating, or 154° on rapid.	1
$C_{10}H_{10}N_2S$	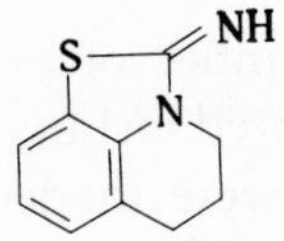	HBr salt, m. 328°.	1
$C_{11}H_{12}NS$	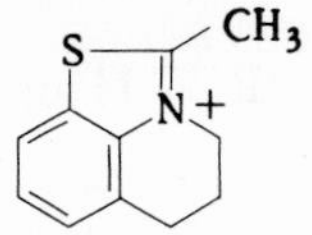	Bromide, m. 247°. Iodide, m. 257–60° d. (254–6°, 247°). Triiodide, yel., m. 121–3° d.	2,3,7, 14
$C_{12}H_{14}NS$	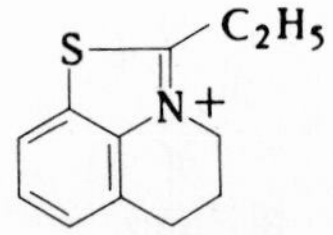	Iodide, m. 234–5°.	14
$C_{12}H_{14}NOS$	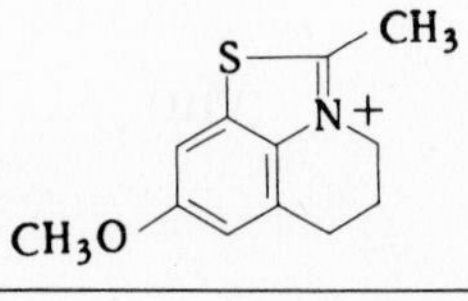	Bromide, m. 249°.	3

5,6-Dihydro-4*H*-thiazolo[*ij*]quinolines (*continued*)

Empirical formula	Structure	Properties	Refs.
$C_{13}H_{16}NS$	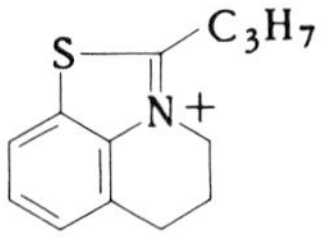	Iodide, m. 225–6°.	14
$C_{14}H_{18}NS$	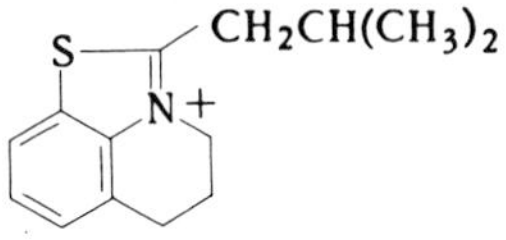	Iodide, m. 197–8°.	14
$C_{16}H_{13}N_3O_2S_2$	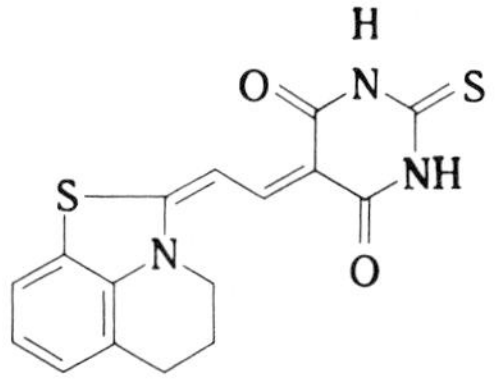	Or., m. >325°.	8
$C_{17}H_{16}NS$	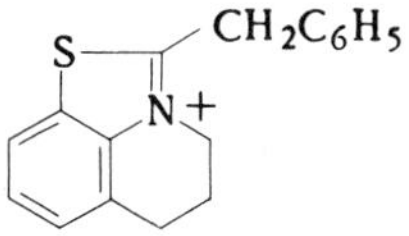	Iodide, m. 165–6°.	14
$C_{17}H_{16}N_2OS_3$	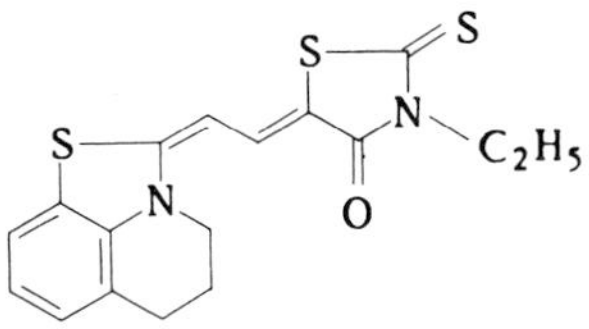	Red, m. 288–9° d.	5–8
$C_{17}H_{16}N_2O_2S_2$	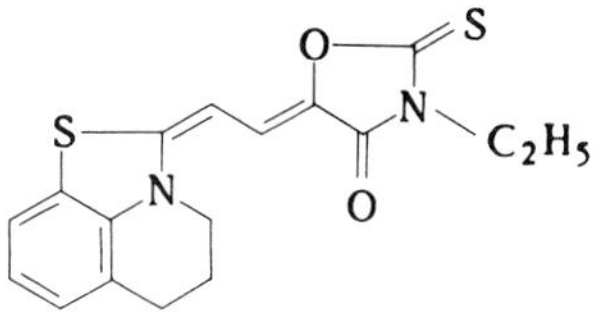	Red, m. 287–8° d.	6,7
$C_{19}H_{18}N_2OS_3$	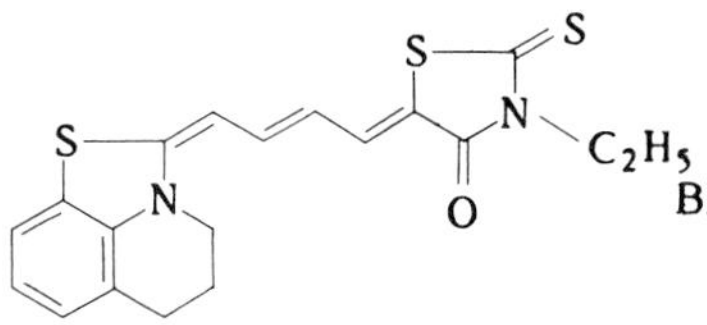	Bl.-grey, m. 260–2° d.	7
$C_{20}H_{19}N_2S$	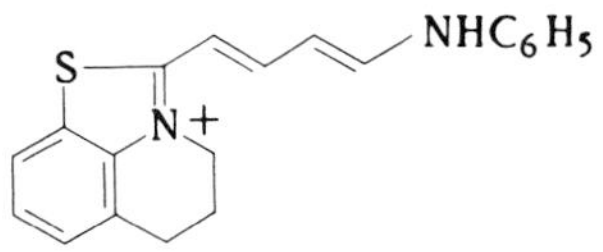	Iodide, brn., m. 247–8° d.	6

(*continued*)

5,6-Dihydro-4*H*-thiazolo[*ij*]quinolines (*continued*)

Empirical formula	Structure	Properties	Refs.
$C_{20}H_{19}N_2OS$	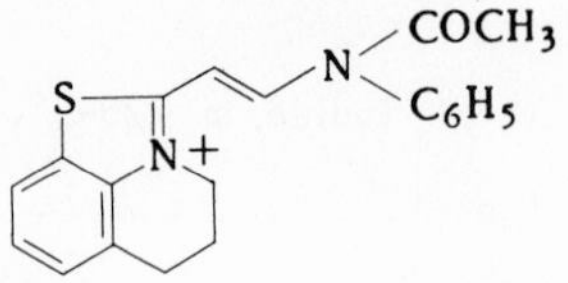	Iodide, dk. brn.	6,8
$C_{20}H_{21}N_2S$	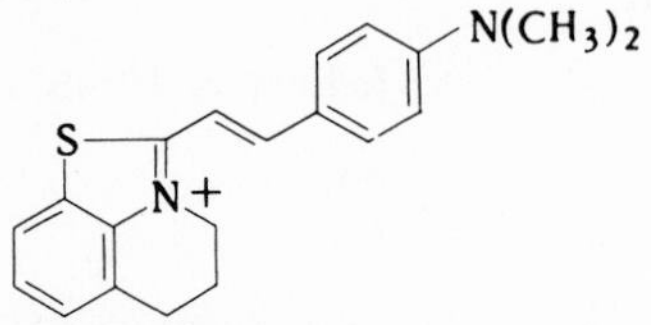	Iodide, purple, m. 293–4° (d. 292°); λ_{max} 528 mμ.	4,6,7, 14
$C_{21}H_{19}N_2S_2$	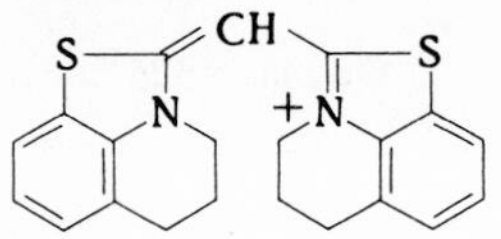	Iodide, yel., m. >360°. Perchlorate, m. >360°.	1
$C_{21}H_{19}N_3OS$	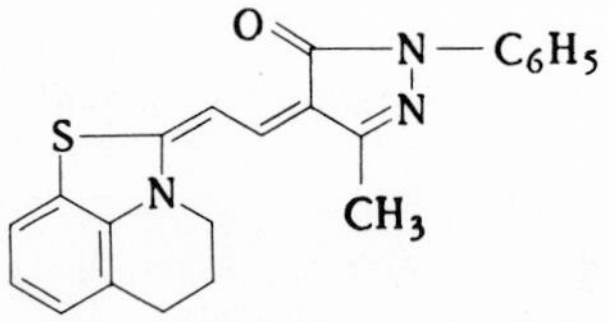	Red, m. 238–9°.	6
$C_{21}H_{23}N_2S$	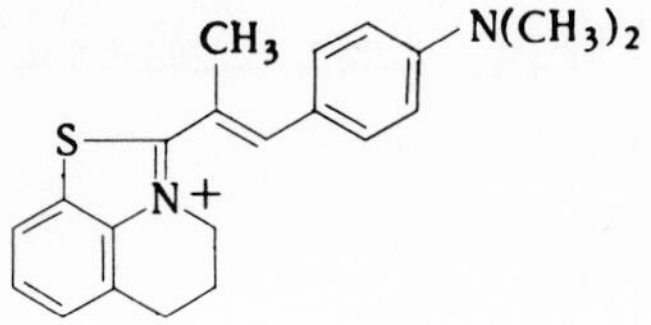	Perchlorate, m. 187°; λ_{max} 468 mμ.	14
$C_{22}H_{21}N_2OS$	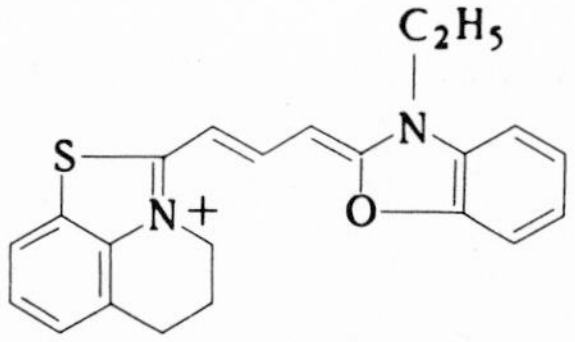	Iodide, red, m. 258–9° d.	6,7
$C_{22}H_{21}N_2S$	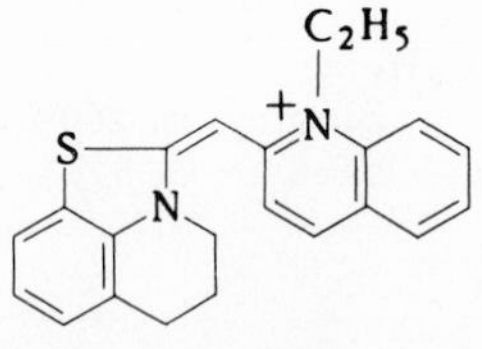	Iodide, or., m. 286–7° d.	6,7

5,6-Dihydro-4*H*-thiazolo[*ij*]quinolines (*continued*)

Empirical formula	Structure	Properties	Refs.
$C_{22}H_{25}N_2S$	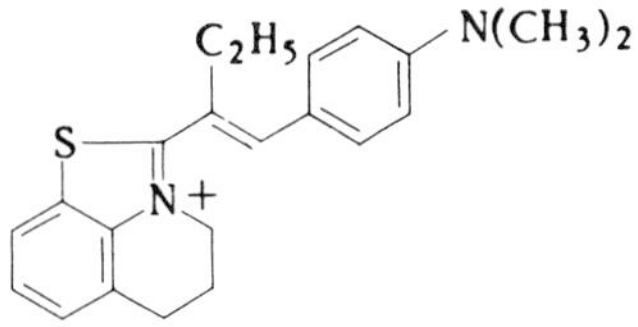 C_2H_5; $N(CH_3)_2$; S; N+	Perchlorate, d. 171–2°; λ_{max} 465 mμ.	14
$C_{23}H_{21}N_2S$	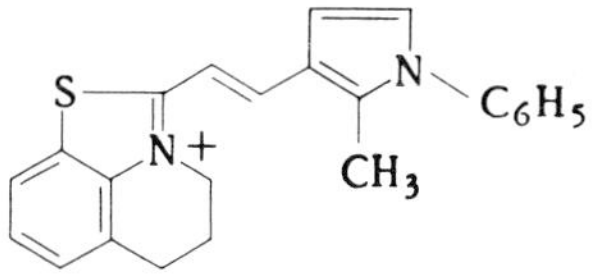 S; N+; N; C_6H_5; CH_3	Perchlorate, vermilion, m. 264–5° d. λ_{max} 459.5 mμ (MeOH).	4
$C_{23}H_{21}N_2S_2$	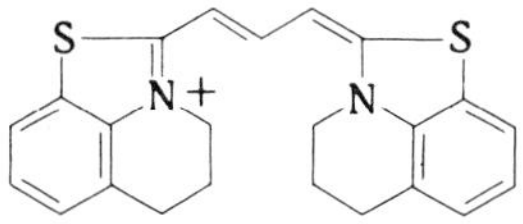 S; N+; S; N	Iodide, purple, m. 308–9° d. λ_{max} 555.5 mμ (CH_3OH), or 558.0 mμ (CH_3NO_2).	2,4,6, 7,14
$C_{23}H_{21}N_3OS_2$	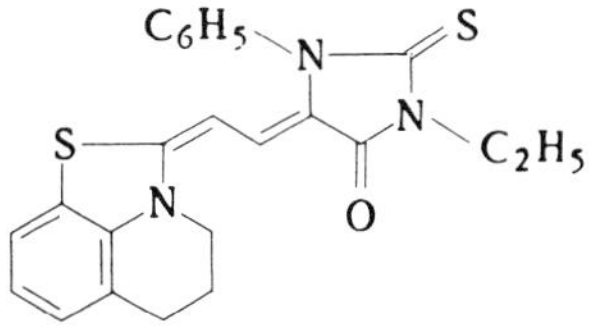 C_6H_5; N; S; N; C_2H_5; O; S; N	Purple, m. 246–7°.	8
$C_{23}H_{24}N_2S_2$	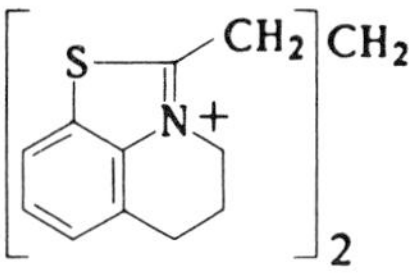 [S; N+; CH_2]$_2$ CH_2	Diiodide, m. 150°.	14
$C_{23}H_{27}N_2S$	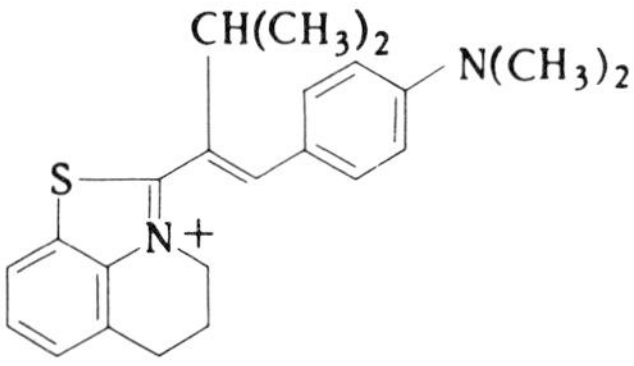 $CH(CH_3)_2$; $N(CH_3)_2$; S; N+	Perchlorate, d. 155°, λ_{max} 430 mμ.	14
$C_{24}H_{26}N_2S_2$	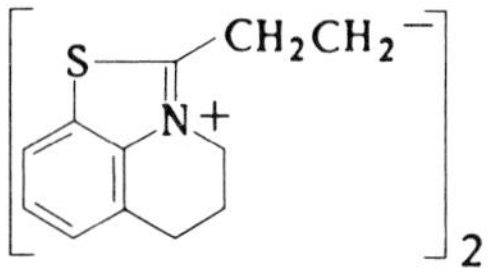 [S; N+; CH_2CH_2–]$_2$	Diiodide, d. 305°.	14

(*continued*)

5,6-Dihydro-4*H*-thiazolo[*ij*]quinolines (*continued*)

Empirical formula	Structure	Properties	Refs.
$C_{25}H_{23}N_3OS_2$	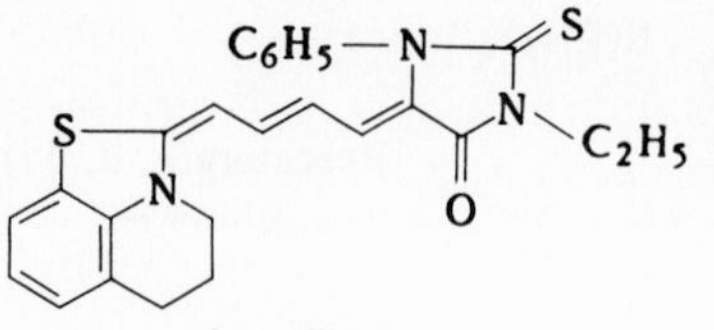	Blue, m. 265–6°.	8
$C_{25}H_{25}N_2S_2$	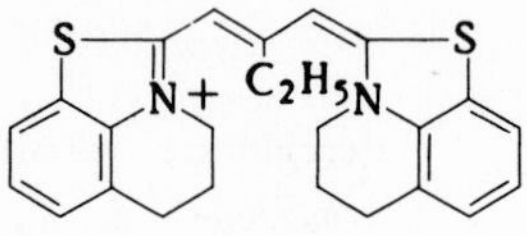	Iodide, m. 285°; λ_{max} 545 mμ.	14
	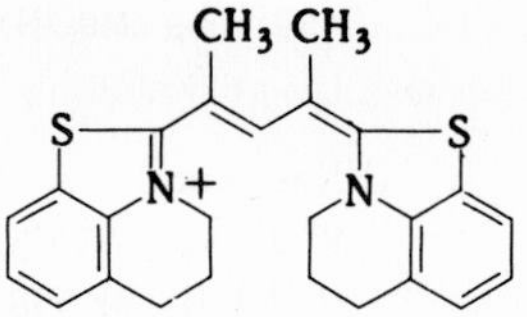	Iodide, m. 248–9°; λ_{max} 575 mμ.	14
$C_{26}H_{25}N_2S$	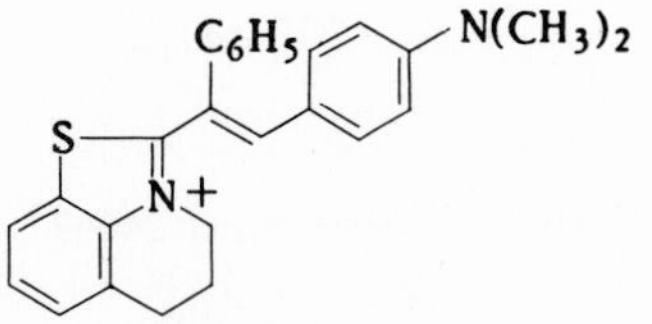	Iodide, m. 275°; λ_{max} 509 mμ.	14
$C_{27}H_{29}N_2S$	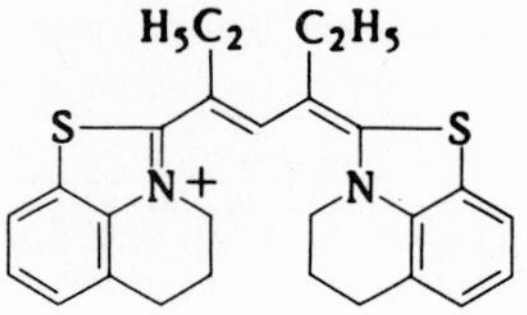	Iodide, m. 214°; λ_{max} 576 mμ.	14

References

1. König, Kleist and Götze, *Ber.*, **64,** 1664 (1931).
2. Brooker and Cressman, *J. Am. Chem. Soc.*, **67,** 2046 (1945).
3. Schwarz and Schouwenaårs, Brit. Pat. 625,245; *Chem. Abstracts*, **45,** 3269 (1951).
4. Brooker, Sklar, Cressman, Keyes, Smith, Sprague, Van Lare, Van Zandt, White and Williams, *J. Am. Chem. Soc.*, **67,** 1875 (1945).
5. Brooker, Keyes, Sprague, Van Dyke, Van Lare, Van Zandt, White, Cressman and Dent, *J. Am. Chem. Soc.*, **73,** 5332 (1951).
6. Brooker and Cressman, U. S. Pat. 2,398,999.
7. Brooker and Cressman, U. S. Pat. 2,317,357.
8. Brooker and Cressman, U. S. Pat. 2,409,189.
9. Kodak Ltd., Brit. Pat. 556,266; *Chem. Abstracts*, **39,** 2411 (1945); *Brit. Chem. Abstracts*, **BII,** 10 (1944).

10. Schwarz and Schouwenaars, Ger. Pat. 741,071; Fr. Pat. 870,563; *Chem. Abstracts*, **40,** 2752 (1946).
11. Gevaert Photo-Producten N.V., Brit. Pat. 633,824; *Chem. Abstracts*, **44,** 9840 (1950).
12. Van de Straete and Schouwenaars, U. S. Pat. 2,557,806.
13. Fujii, *Yakugaku Zasshi*, **77,** 1065 (1957); *Chem. Abstracts*, **52,** 5417 (1958).
14. Ushenko and Portnyagina, *Ukrain. Khim. Zhur.*, **21,** 738 (1955); *Chem. Abstracts*, **50,** 16753 (1956).

A-390. Imidazo[1,5-*a*]pyridine. R.I. 766

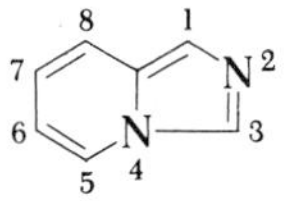

This ring system has also been called *2,3a-diazaindene* (I), *2-azaindolizine* and *2,4-imidazopyridine.*

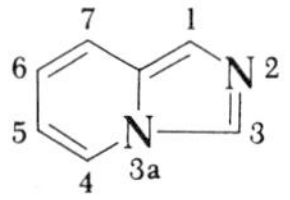

(I)

Although derivatives of this ring system were mentioned in the older literature (v.i.) the only well authenticated examples are of recent origin. Bower and Ramage[1] prepared the prototype and several homologs (III) by the cyclization of II. Compound III (R = R′ = H) was found to acetylate under Friedel-Crafts conditions in the 1-position, or if this were blocked (III, R = CH_3, R′ = H), in the 3-position.

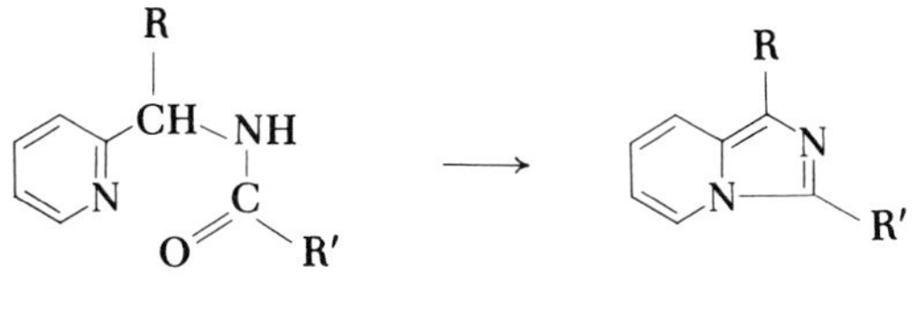

(II) (III)

Demethylation of methylisopelletierine with cyanogen bromide yielded[2] a cyanamide derivative which underwent cyclization when its hydrolysis was attempted. At that time, methylisopelletierine was thought to have structure IV, hence Hess[2] considered the cyanamide derivative to be V and the cyclized product either VI or VII. However, methylisopelletierine was subsequently shown[3,4] to have structure VIII, so the cyclized hydrolysis product is more apt to have structure IX (see Section A-827).

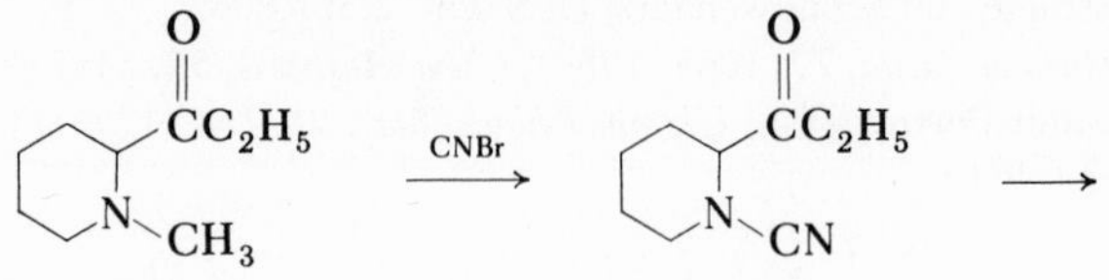

CNBr

(IV) (V)

C_2H_5 C_2H_5

or

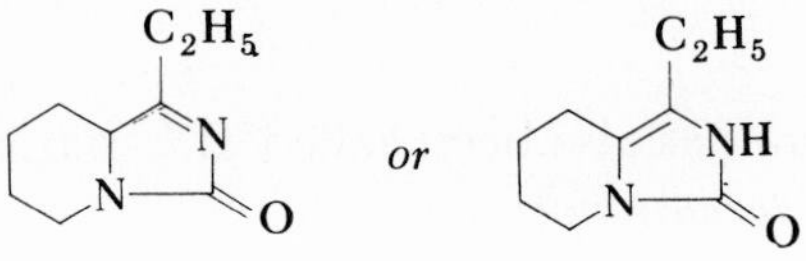

(VI) (VII)

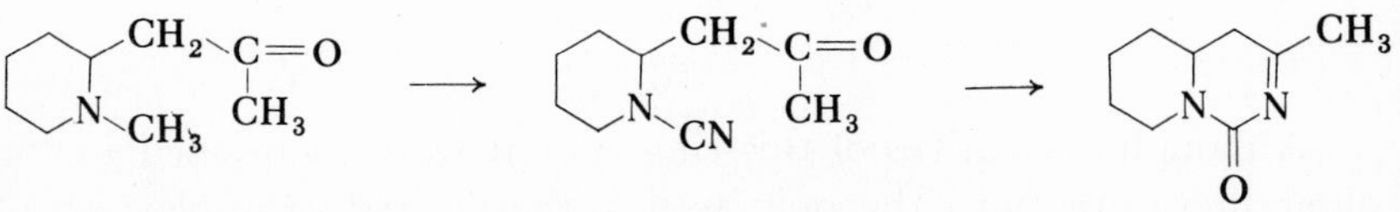

(VIII) (IX)

By treating ethyl pipecolate (X) with phenyl isothiocyanate, Reckhow and Tarbell[5] isolated a product, which might, a priori,

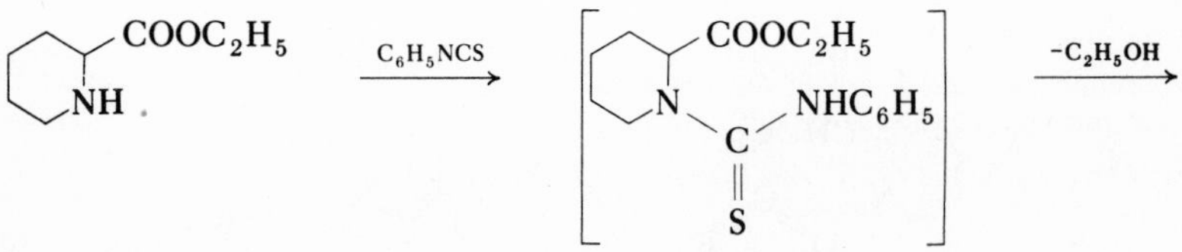

C_6H_5NCS $-C_2H_5OH$

(X)

or

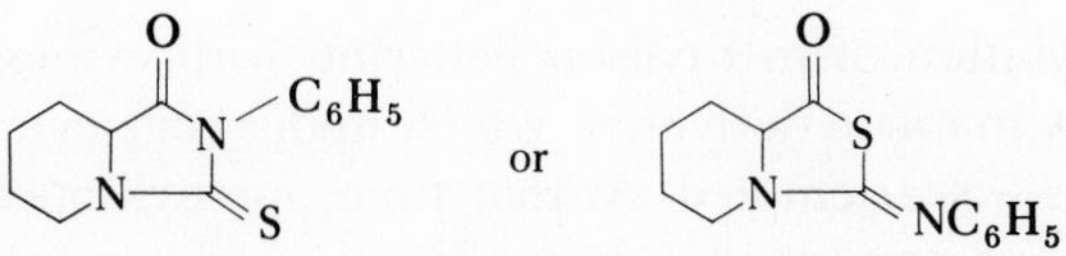

(XI) (XII)

have either structure XI or XII, although evidence in favor of structure XII was presented (see Section A-388).

The ultraviolet spectra of III (R = R′ = H and R = H, R′ = C_6H_5) have been compared[6] with those of related polyazaindenes.

Derivatives[1] of Imidazo [1,5-*a*] pyridine

Substituents	Properties
Unsubstituted	m. 54–5°. b_3 120–5°. Strong blue fluorescence. Picrate, m. 216°. $B_2 \cdot AgNO_3$, m. 178°.
1-Methyl-	m. 64–5°. Methiodide, m. 209°.
3-Methyl-	m. 55°. Picrate, m. 221°. Methiodide, m. 184°. $B_2 \cdot AgNO_3$, m. 189–90°.
1-Acetyl-	m. 129°; strong vt. fluorescence.
1,3-Dimethyl-	b_5 120–5°. Picrate, m. 254° d.
1-Ethyl-	b_2 116°. Picrate, m. 203° d. Picrolonate, m. 222°. $B_2 \cdot AgNO_3$, m. 152–3°.
1-Acetyl-3-methyl-	m. 139°, vt. fluorescence.
3-Acetyl-1-methyl-	m. 66–7°, vt. fluorescence.
1-Ethyl-3-methyl-	b_2 120°. Picrate, m. 258–9°. Methiodide, m. 200°. $B \cdot HgCl_2$, m. 210–11°.
3-Ethyl-1-methyl-	b_5 130°. $B \cdot HgCl_2$, m. 203–4° d. $B_2 \cdot AgNO_3$, m. 175° d.
3-Phenyl-	m. 109°. Picrate, m. 185–6°.
1-Methyl-3-phenyl-	m. 120°.

References

1. Bower and Ramage, *J. Chem. Soc.*, **1955**, 2834.
2. Hess, *Ber.*, **52**, 964 (1919).
3. Meisenheimer and Mahler, *Ann.*, **462**, 301 (1928).
4. Hess and Littman, *Ann.*, **494**, 7 (1932).
5. Reckhow and Tarbell, *J. Am. Chem. Soc.*, **74**, 4962 (1952).
6. Bower, *J. Chem. Soc.*, **1957**, 4510.

A-391. 3*H*-Imidazo[3,4-*a*]pyrrolo-[2,3-*e*]pyridine

1 N2 9N $H_2$3 8 7 N 6 5 4

De Jong and Wibaut[1] found that treatment of 2,6-lutidine with two moles of phenyl lithium followed by two moles of benzonitrile, gave a product ($C_{21}H_{19}N_3$, m. 165°), for which they proposed, tentatively, structure I.

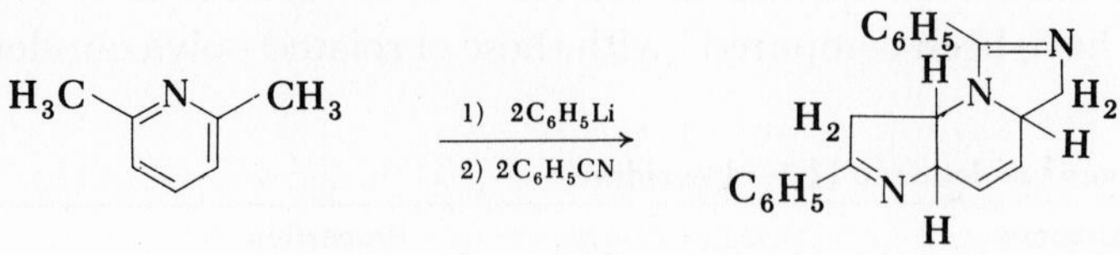

H_3C N CH_3 1) $2C_6H_5Li$ 2) $2C_6H_5CN$ → C_6H_5 N H N H_2 H H_2 C_6H_5 N H

(I)

The product is largely unchanged by dilute acids but is cleaved to ammonia, benzoic acid and phenyl-α-(2,6-lutidyl)ketone by boiling concentrated hydrochloric acid. Treatment of I with nitrous acid gives a new oxygen-containing substance which, however, seems not to contain more than the original number of nitrogen atoms. Compound I adds bromine and iodine, but the accompanying resinification prevented characterization of the halo derivatives. Further work is needed to clarify the structure of these compounds.

Reference

1. de Jong and Wibaut, *Rec. trav. chim.*, **70,** 962 (1951).

A-392. Imidazo[1,5-*a*]quinoline

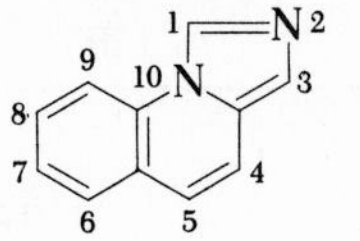

1 N 2 3 4 5 6 7 8 9 10 N

Bidder and Rupe[1] prepared 3,3*a*,4,5-tetrahydroimidazol[1,5-*a*]-quinolin-1 (2*H*)one (II, b_{10} 245–7°, m. 197°) by the reaction of 2-aminomethyltetrahydroquinoline (I) with ethyl chlorocarbonate in refluxing benzene, or with phosgene in ether solution.

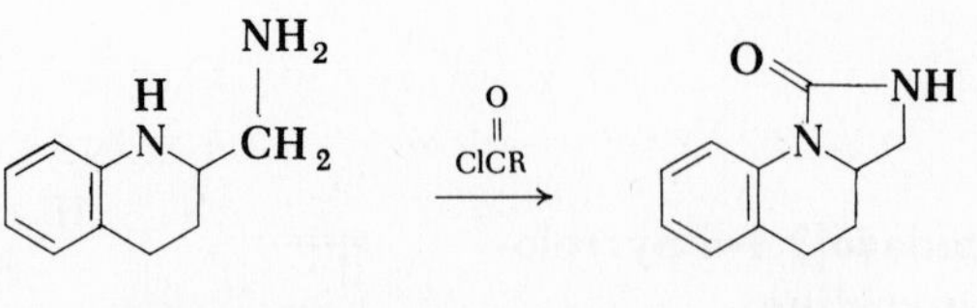

NH_2 H N CH_2 O ‖ ClCR → O NH N

(I) (II)

Reference

1. Bidder and Rupe, *Helv. Chim. Acta*, **22,** 1268 (1939).

A-393. Imidazo[5,1-*a*]isoquinoline. R.I. 1583

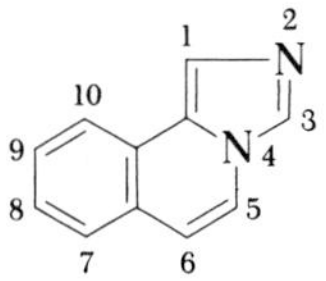

This ring system also has been called *benzoglyoxalocoline* and numbered as shown in I. The parent compound is unknown, but a number of 5,6-dihydro derivatives and one tetrahydro derivative have been reported.

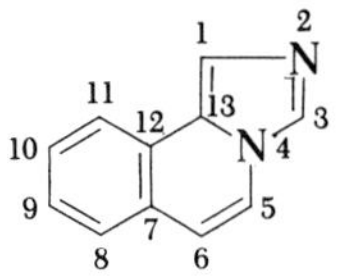

(I)

While attempting to prepare 1-benzamidomethyl-3,4-dihydro-6,7-dimethoxyisoquinoline by the cyclodehydration of *N*-homoveratrylhippuramide (II) with phosphorus oxychloride, Child and Pyman[1] obtained instead, compound III. This synthesis has been employed by Kametani and his collaborators[2-11] to prepare a number of 3-aryl-5,6-dihydroimidazo[5,1-*a*]isoquinolines.

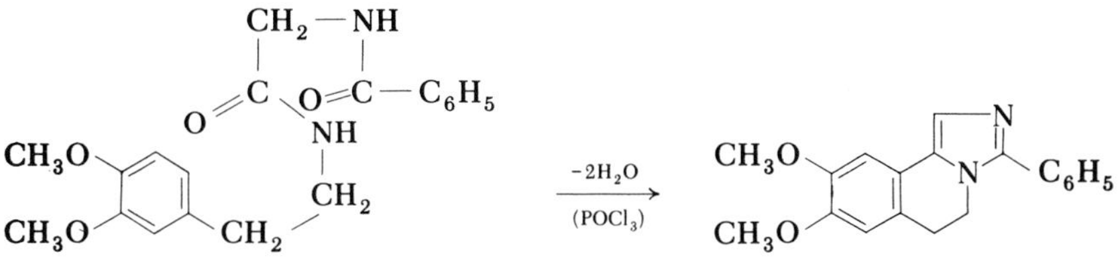

$$\text{(II)} \xrightarrow[(POCl_3)]{-2H_2O} \text{(III)}$$

(II) (III)

Rupe and Frey[12] obtained V by treating 1-aminomethyl-1,2,3,4-tetrahydroisoquinoline (IV) with phosgene or ethyl chlorocarbonate.

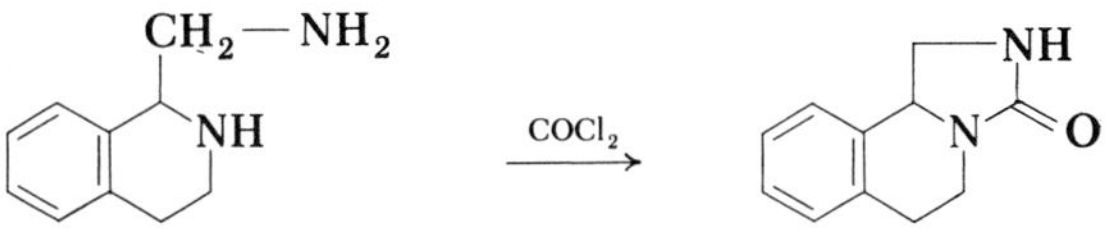

$$\text{(IV)} \xrightarrow{COCl_2} \text{(V)}$$

(IV) (V)

Several of the 5,6-dihydro derivatives were evaluated[13] in the treatment of amoebic dysentery.

Imidazo[5, 1-*a*]isoquinolines

Empirical formula	Substituents	Properties	Refs.
$C_{11}H_{12}N_2O$	1,2,3,5,6,10*b*-Hexahydro-3-oxo-	m. 148°.	12
$C_{17}H_{14}N_2O_2$	5,6-Dihydro-8,9-dihydroxy-3-phenyl-	m. 293°.	1
$C_{17}H_{16}N_2O_3$	3-(2-Furyl)-5,6-dihydro-8,9-dimethoxy-	m. 149–50°. Picrate, m. 224°.	11
$C_{18}H_{17}N_3O_2$	5,6-Dihydro-8,9-dimethoxy-3-(2-pyridyl)-	m. 171–2°. Picrate, d. 272°.	8
	5,6-Dihydro-8,9-dimethoxy-3-(3-pyridyl)-	m. 165–6°.	6
	5,6-Dihydro-8,9-dimethoxy-3-(4-pyridyl)-	Picrate, m. 114°.	7
$C_{19}H_{15}N_3O_4$	5,6-Dihydro-5-methyl-8,9-methylenedioxy-3-(4-nitrophenyl)-	Softens at 258°, darkens at 270°, chars at 278°.	8
$C_{19}H_{17}N_3O_4$	5,6-Dihydro-8,9-dimethoxy-3-(4-nitrophenyl)-	m. 243–7° d.	2
$C_{19}H_{18}N_2O_2$	5,6-Dihydro-8,9-dimethoxy-3-phenyl-	m. 187°. HCl salt, m. 286–7° d. HBr salt, m. 293°. Methiodide, m. 255°. Picrate, m. 226–7°. *x*-Nitro deriv., m. 202°.	1
$C_{19}H_{19}N_3O_3$	3-(4-Aminophenyl)-5,6-dihydro-8,9-dimethoxy-	Picrate, m. 147°.	2
$C_{20}H_{16}N_2O_4$	5,6-Dihydro-5-methyl-8,9-methylenedioxy-3-(3,4-methylenedioxyphenyl)-	m. 135–40°. HCl salt, d. 295°. Picrate, d. 227–8°.	5
$C_{20}H_{18}N_2O_4$	5,6-Dihydro-8,9-dimethoxy-3-(3,4-methylenedioxyphenyl)-	m. 177° d. HCl salt, d. 263°. Picrate, m. 228°.	4

Imidazo[5,1-*a*]isoquinolines (*continued*)

Empirical formula	Substituents	Properties	Refs.
$C_{21}H_{20}N_2O_4$	5,6-Dihydro-5-methyl-3-(3,4-dimethoxy-phenyl)-8,9-methyl-enedioxy-	Yel., m. 138–43°. Picrate, m. 96°.	5
$C_{21}H_{22}N_2O_4$	5,6-Dihydro-8,9-di-methoxy-3-(3,4-dimethoxy-phenyl)	m. 186.5°. Picrate, m. 235.5°.	3
$C_{22}H_{19}N_3O_2$	5,6-Dihydro-8,9-di-methoxy-3-(4-quino-lyl)-	d. 85°. HCl salt, m. 120–9°. Picrate, d. 206°.	10
$C_{26}H_{26}N_4O_4$	5,5′,6,6′-Tetrahydro-8,8′,9,9′-tetramethoxy-3,3′-bis-	m. 198° d. Picrate, d. 150°.	9

References

1. Child and Pyman, *J. Chem. Soc.*, **1931,** 36.
2. Kametani and Iida, *J. Pharm. Soc. Japan*, **70,** 258 (1950); *Chem. Abstracts*, **45,** 6205 (1951).
3. Kametani and Iwakata, *J. Pharm. Soc. Japan*, **70,** 261 (1950); *Chem. Abstracts*, **45,** 6205 (1951).
4. Kametani and Iwakata, *J. Pharm. Soc. Japan*, **70,** 263 (1950); *Chem. Abstracts*, **45,** 6205 (1951).
5. Kametani, Iida, and Iwakata, *J. Pharm. Soc. Japan*, **71,** 325 (1951); *Chem. Abstracts*, **46,** 4546 (1952).
6. Kametani and Iida, *J. Pharm. Soc. Japan*, **71,** 995 (1951); *Chem. Abstracts*, **46,** 8119 (1952).
7. Kametani and Iida, *J. Pharm. Soc. Japan*, **71,** 998 (1951); *Chem. Abstracts*, **46,** 8119 (1952).
8. Kametani and Iida, *J. Pharm. Soc. Japan*, **71,** 1000 (1951); *Chem. Abstracts*, **46,** 8119 (1952).
9. Kametani and Iwakata, *J. Pharm. Soc. Japan*, **71,** 1002 (1951); *Chem. Abstracts*, **46,** 8119 (1952).
10. Kametani and Iida, *J. Pharm. Soc. Japan*, **71,** 1004 (1951); *Chem. Abstracts*, **46,** 8120 (1952).
11. Iida and Kametani, *Yakagaku Kenkyu*, **27,** 774 (1955); *Chem. Abstracts*, **51,** 13865 (1957).
12. Rupe and Frey, *Helv. Chim. Acta*, **22,** 673 (1939).
13. Kametani and Katagi, *J. Pharm. Soc. Japan*, **75,** 709 (1955); *Chem. Abstracts*, **50,** 3460 (1956).

A-394. 4*H*-Imidazo[*ij*]quinoline.
R.I. 1584

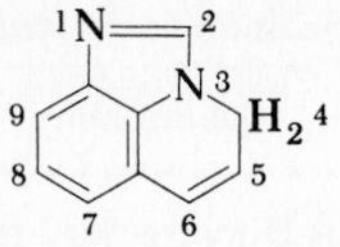

The names *quinimidazole*, peri-*quinolinazole* and *imidazo[4,5,1-ij]-quinoline* have been used for this ring system, and 5,6-dihydro derivatives have been referred to as *1,7-trimethylenebenzimidazoles*.

Bamberger and Wulz[1,2] prepared the first imidazo[*ij*]quinolines by heating 8-amino-1,2,3,4-tetrahydroquinolines with acetic acid, acetic anhydride and sodium acetate. A number of dihydro imidazo-

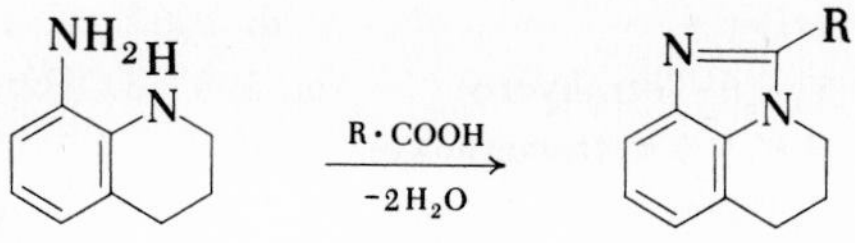

$$\xrightarrow[-2H_2O]{R\cdot COOH}$$

[*ij*]quinolines have thus been prepared,[3-8,12] using several substited 8-aminotetrahydroquinolines and a variety of acids including formic, acetic, propionic, lactic, glycollic, mandelic, phenylacetic and benzilic acids. In some cases esters may replace acids in these reactions.[5,6]

Elderfield and his collaborators,[9,10] in studies on the synthesis of the antimalarial "Plasmochin," found that in the reductive alkylation of I by II with Raney nickel catalyst in methanol, III was formed in about 50% yield and Plasmochin (IV) in only 25–29% yield.

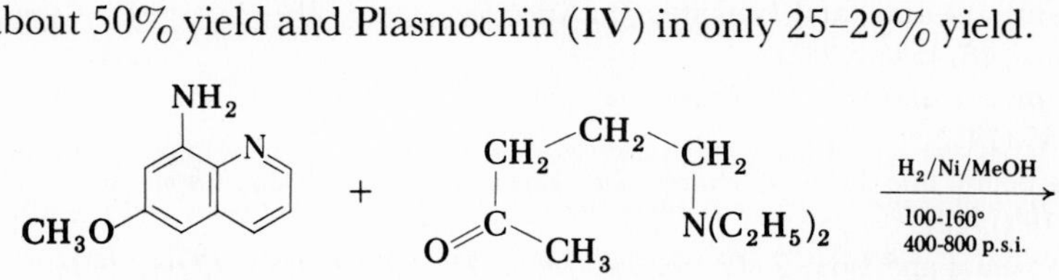

NH_2 CH_3O (I) + CH_2–CH_2–CH_2–$N(C_2H_5)_2$, O=C–CH_3 (II) $\xrightarrow[100\text{-}160°,\ 400\text{-}800\ p.s.i.]{H_2/Ni/MeOH}$

CH_3 CH_3O (III) + $CH_3CHCH_2CH_2CH_2N(C_2H_5)_2$ NH (IV)

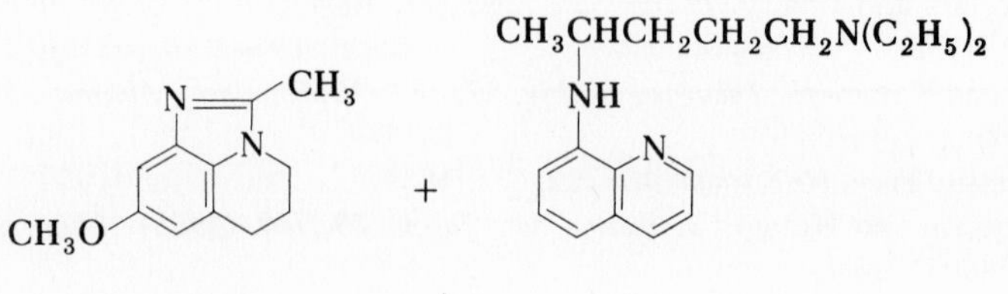

The formation of III is not confined to the reaction of I with II, but occurs[11] when I is heated at 150–200° with any of a variety of methyl ketones. In these reactions, it was invariably the 2,3 bond of the ketone which cleaved, and no other 2-alkylimidazo[*ij*]quinolines were detected. In the reaction of I with cyclopentanone, scission of the ketone ring produced V. Pyrolysis of VI (produced[6] from the reaction of I with acetone) resulted in the formation[9,11] of III by the elimination of methane.

Nitration of III was reported[10] to give a mononitro derivative, possibly the 7 isomer. Oxidation of 5,6-dihydro-4*H*-imidazo[*ij*]quinolines with potassium permanganate produced benzimidazole-4-carboxylic acids.

4*H*-Imidazo[*ij*]quinolines

Empirical formula	Substituents	Properties and derivatives	Refs.
$C_{10}H_{10}N_2$	5,6-Dihydro-	m. 148°.	5
$C_{11}H_{11}N_2Br$	8-Bromo-5,6-dihydro-2-methyl-	m. 165°. HCl salt, m. 253°; chloroplatinate, m. >300°.	3

(*continued*)

4H-Imidazo[*ij*]quinolines (*continued*)

Empirical formula	Substituents	Properties and derivatives	Refs.
$C_{12}H_{12}N_2$	5,6-Dihydro-2-methyl-	m. 128°.	5,13
	5,6-Dihydro-8-methyl-	b_{18} 210–20°, m. 82–3°. Perchlorate, m. 240° d.	4
$C_{11}H_{12}N_2O$	5,6-Dihydro-2-hydroxymethyl-	m. 183°.	5
	5,6-Dihydro-8-hydroxy-2-methyl-	d. 295–305°.	10
$C_{12}H_{13}N_3O_3$	5,6-Dihydro-8-methoxy-2-methyl-7(or 9)-nitro-	m. 238–40° d.	10
$C_{12}H_{13}N_2$	2-Ethyl-5,6-dihydro-	b_{20} 195°, m. 86°.	5
$C_{12}H_{14}N_2$	5,6-Dihydro-2,4-dimethyl-	m. 110°.	1
	5,6-Dihydro-2,8-dimethyl-	m. 163°.	2
$C_{12}H_{14}N_2O$	5,6-Dihydro-2-(α-hydroxyethyl)-	Pink, m. 142°.	5
	5,6-Dihydro-8-methoxy-2-methyl-	m. 119.5–20° (120–1°). HCl salt, m. 233–3.5°; HBr salt, m. 242°; picrate, d. 248–53°, m. 253–4°; methiodide, d. 285–90°; *p*-toluenesulfonate, m. 139.5–40.5°; perbromide, d. 285°.	6,7,10
$C_{13}H_{16}N_2O_2$	1,2,5,6-Tetrahydro-8,9-dimethoxy-	m. 105.0–5.5°. Picrate, m. 193–5°.	12
$C_{13}H_{18}N_2O$	1,2,5,6-Tetrahydro-8-methoxy-2,2-dimethyl-	m. 119°.	6
$C_{15}H_{20}N_2O$	2-Butyl-5,6-dihydro-8-methoxy-	m. 60–1°. Picrate, m. 172–3°.	11
$C_{17}H_{16}N_2$	2-Benzyl-5,6-dihydro-	m. 109°.	5
$C_{17}H_{16}N_2O$	5,6-Dihydro-2-(α-hydroxybenzyl)-	m. 205°.	5
$C_{17}H_{24}N_2O$	2-Hexyl-5,6-dihydro-8-methoxy-	m. 27°. Picrate, m. 127°.	11
$C_{18}H_{19}N_3O$	7-Anilino-5,6-dihydro-8-methoxy-2-methyl-	m. 222–4°.	8
$C_{23}H_{20}N_2O$	5,6-Dihydro-2-(α-hydroxybenzhydryl)-	m. 275°.	5

References

1. Bamberger and Wulz, *Ber.*, **24,** 2051 (1891).
2. Bamberger and Wulz, *Ber.*, **24,** 2055 (1891).
3. Kunckell, *Ber. pharm. Ges.*, **20,** 214 (1910); *Chem. Zentr.*, **II,** 94 (1910).
4. Ing and Cahn, *J. Chem. Soc.*, **1931,** 2195.
5. Hazlewood, Hughes, and Lions, *J. Proc. Roy. Soc. N.S. Wales*, **71,** 462 (1938); *Chem. Zentr.*, **II,** 4242 (1938); *Chem. Abstracts*, **33,** 610 (1939).
6. Barber and Wragg, *J. Chem. Soc.*, **1946,** 610.
7. Price and Herbrandson, *J. Am. Chem. Soc.*, **68,** 910 (1946).
8. Snyder and Easton, *J. Am. Chem. Soc.*, **68,** 2641 (1946).
9. Elderfield, Kreysa, Dunn, and Humphreys, *J. Am. Chem. Soc.*, **69,** 186 (1947).
10. Elderfield, Kreysa, Dunn and Humphreys, *J. Am. Chem. Soc.*, **70,** 40 (1948).
11. Elderfield and Kreysa, *J. Am. Chem. Soc.*, **70,** 44 (1948).
12. Elderfield and Krueger, *J. Org. Chem.*, **17,** 358 (1952).
13. Elderfield and Claffin, *J. Am. Chem. Soc.*, **74,** 2953 (1952).

A-395. 1*H*-Benz[*f*]imidazo[*ij*]-quinoline. R.I. 2390

Bamberger and Strasser[1] found 5-amino-1,2,3,4,7,8,9,10-octahydro-3-methylbenzo[*f*]quinoline (I) to react with an acetic acid-acetic anhydride-sodium acetate mixture to yield II (HCl salt, m. 262° d.).

$$\text{(I)} \xrightarrow[-H_2O]{HOAc} \text{(II)}$$

(I) (II)

Reference

1. Bamberger and Strasser, *Ber.*, **24,** 2662 (1894).

A-396. 2*H*-Isoxazolo[2,3-*a*]pyridine*

Adams and Reifschneider[1] found that 2-bromopyridine *N*-oxides (I) condense with certain active methylene compounds to give products of type II (R = H, R′ = $COOC_2H_5$, m. 181°; R = H, R′ = $COCH_3$, m. 188–90°; R = H, R′ = COC_6H_5, m. 193–4°; R = CH_3, R = $COOC_2H_5$, m. 175–6°; R = CH_3, R′ = $COCH_3$, m. 200°; R = CH_3, R′ = COC_6H_5, m. 208–9°). With cyanoacetic ester in benzene solution, I (R = CH_3) yielded a mixture of III (yellow, m. 128° d.), IV (m. 217–9° d.) and V (m. 209–12° d.), while in dioxane solution only the latter two products were isolated. Compound V was also obtained from the reaction of I with β-imino-α-cyanoglutaric ester. Hydrogenation of II (R = H, R′ = $COOC_2H_5$) over a platinum oxide catalyst yielded VI (m. 157–8°).

(I) —$R'CH_2COOC_2H_5$→ (II) —H_2→ (VI)

(I) → (III) + (IV) + (V)

Treatment of VII with hydrobromic acid yielded[2] VIII (X = Br, m. 152–5°; X = picrate, m. 94–7°).

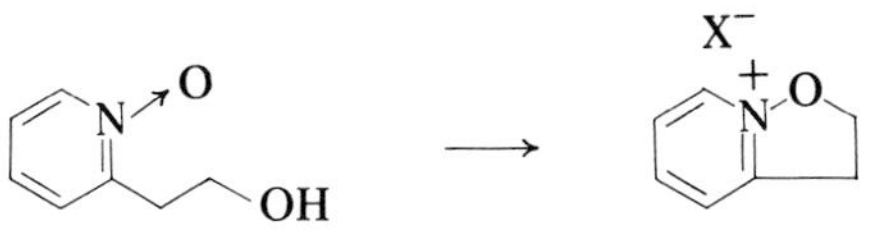

(VII) (VIII)

References

1. Adams and Reifschneider, *J. Am. Chem. Soc.*, **79,** 2236 (1957).
2. Boekelheide and Feely, *J. Am. Chem. Soc.*, **80,** 2217 (1958).

A-397. 10*H*-Isoxazolo[2,3-*a*]quinoline. R.I. 1516

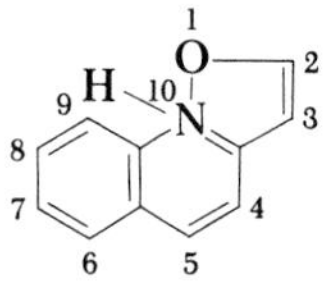

No true isoxazolo[2,3-*a*]quinolines are known, but condensation of 2-quinolylacetonitrile with formic acid or acetic anhydride yielded products, which, because of their amphoteric nature and lack of carbonyl character, were formulated[1] as I.

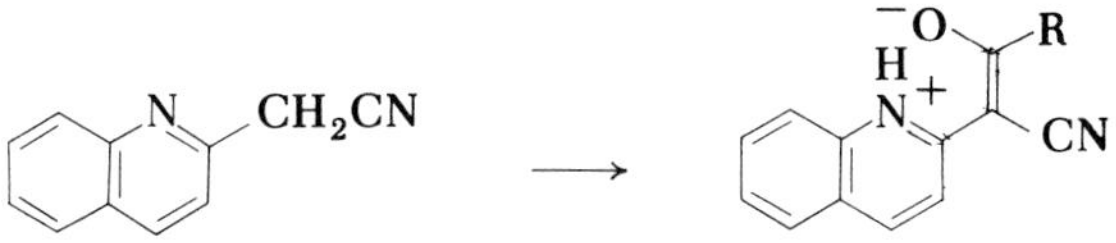

CH_2CN

(I)

Reference

1. Borsche and Manteuffel, *Ann.*, **526,** 22 (1936).

A-398. 10*bH*-Isoxazolo[3,2-*a*]isoquinoline*

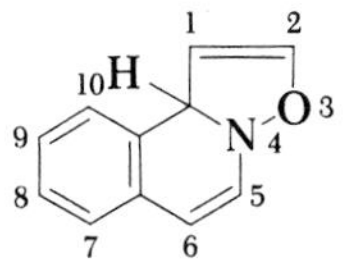

Treatment of I in benzene solution with phosphorus oxychloride was reported[1] to yield II (no details given).

$$\text{(I)} \xrightarrow[\Delta]{POCl_3} \text{(II)}$$

Reference

1. Itoh and Sugasawa, *Tetrahedron*, **1,** 45 (1957).

A-399. 2*H*-Isothiazolo[2,3-*a*]pyridine. R.I. 735

The reaction of I (prepared by the treatment of α-picoline methiodide with caustic) with carbon disulfide yielded[1] a yellow product assigned structure II containing a pentacovalent nitrogen atom. Mumm,[2] however, correctly formulated the product as III. See Section A-400.

(II) $\overset{CS_2}{\nleftarrow}$ (I) $\xrightarrow{CS_2}$ (III)

References

1. Schneider, Gaertner and Jordan, *Ber.*, **57,** 522 (1924).
2. Mumm, *Ann.*, **443,** 272 (1925).

A-400. 2*H*-Isothiazolo[2,3-*a*]quinoline. R.I. 1537

The reaction of I (R = CH_3 or C_2H_5) with carbon disulfide yielded products assigned structure II having a pentacovalent nitrogen atom. The correct structure (III) was proposed by Mumm.[2]

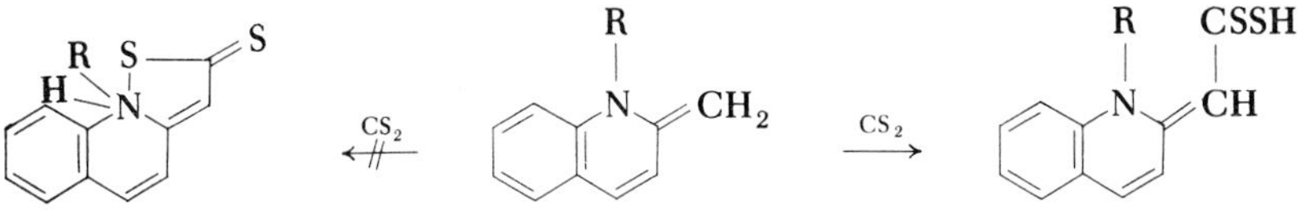

(II) (I) (III)

References

1. Rosenhauer, *Ber.*, **57**, 1291 (1924).
2. Mumm, *Ann.*, **443**, 272 (1925).

A-401. Diisothiazolo[*def,qrs*]flavanthrene

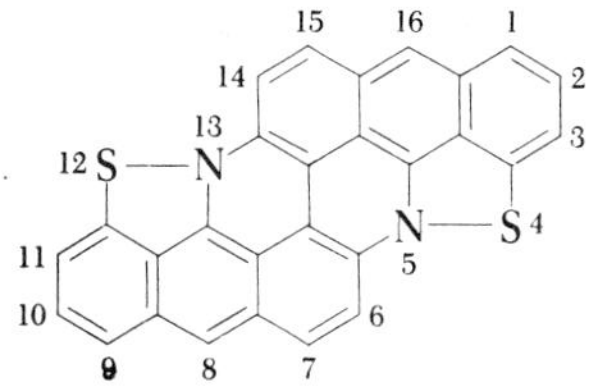

When I was heated in amyl alcohol with potassium hydroxide, a blue-black mixture resulted from which, after oxidation, a yellow dye was obtained.[1] This dye gave a blue vat and an orange-red sulfuric acid solution, and had the "same" nitrogen and sulfur content as I. The dye was thought to be analogous in structure to *Pyrazolan-*

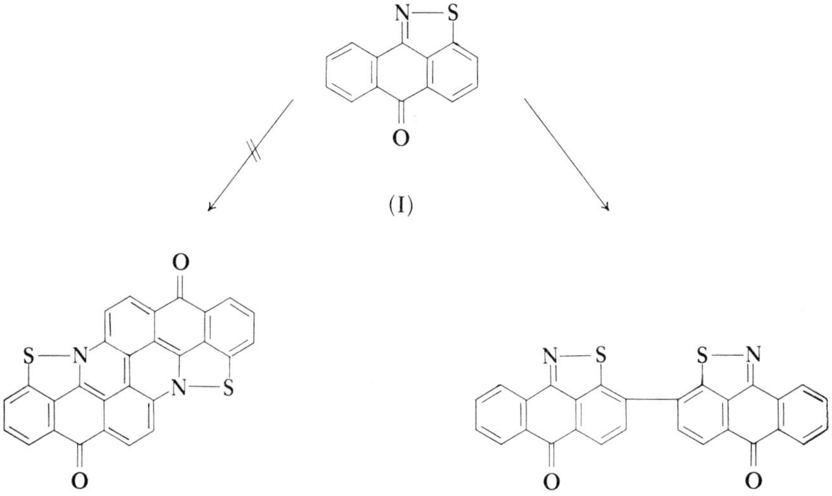

(I)

(II) (III)

throne Yellow (see Section A-559). No formula was given in the patent, but Houben[2] assigned the product structure II. However, as a result of the structure now assigned to *Pyrazolanthrone Yellow*, II is almost certainly incorrect, and formula III is more likely. Thus there are no examples known of this nucleus.

References

1. Chemische Fabrik Griesheim-Elektron, Ger. Pat. 343,065; *Frdl.*, **13**, 411 (1923).
2. Houben, *Das Anthracen und die Anthrachinone*, G. Thieme, Leipzig, 1929, p. 769.

A-402. Pyrazolo[1,5-*a*]pyridine*

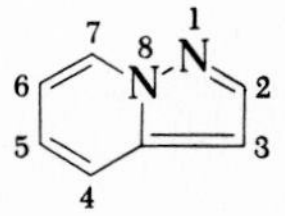

The name *1,7a-diazaindene* has also been used.

Oxidation of I with alkaline ferricyanide solutions gave[1] II (R = H, b_{25} 108°, picrate, m. 151°d.; R = C_6H_5, m. 109°). The

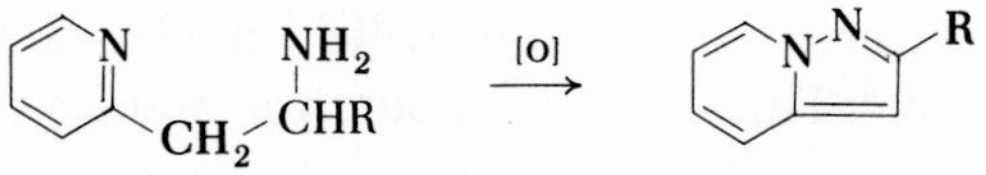

(I) (II)

ultraviolet spectra of these products were compared[2] with those of related polyazaindenes.

References

1. Bower and Ramage, *J. Chem. Soc.*, **1957**, 4506.
2. Bower, *J. Chem. Soc.*, **1957**, 4510.

A-403. Pyrid[1,2-*b*]indazole

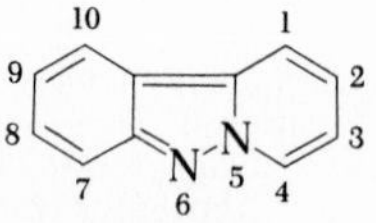

When I was heated with ferrous oxalate at 300°, a product (m. 83–4°; hydrochloride, m. 165–6°; picrate, m. 205°; methiodide, m. 208–9°) of the formula $C_{11}H_8N_2$ was obtained.[1] The infrared and ultraviolet spectra were discussed. Although the product was considered to be represented best by the mesoionic structure II, there seems no reason to exclude structure III as a contributor.

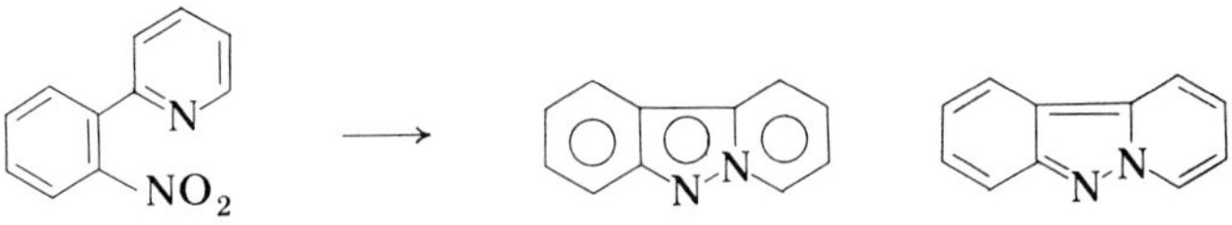

(I) (II) (III)

Reference

1. Abramovich, *Chem. and Ind.*, **1957**, 422.

A-404. 4*H*-Pyrazolo[4,5,1-*ij*]quinoline*

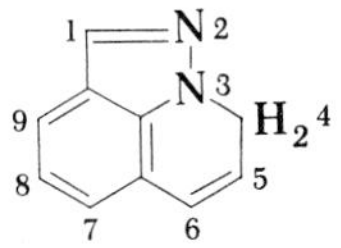

The name *periquinazolineazole* has also been used.

Attempts to cyclize I (R = H or C_6H_5) to II, by treatment with phosphorus oxychloride in toluene or phosphorus pentoxide in xylene, proved unsuccessful.[1]

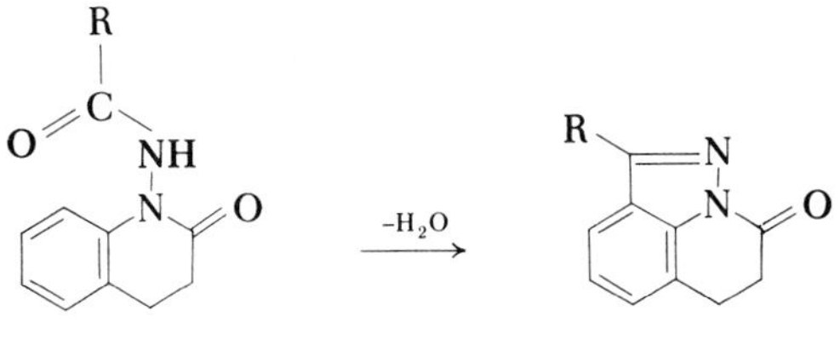

$-H_2O$

(I) (II)

Reference

1. Chakravarti and Ganapati, *J. Annamalai Univ.*, **3**, 223 (1934); *Chem. Zentr.*, **I**, 1875 (1935); *Chem. Abstracts*, **29**, 1090 (1935).

A-405. Indazolo[2,3-*a*]quinoline*

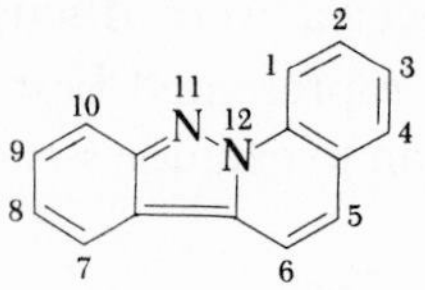

When the sydnone I (see Section A-532) was refluxed with benzoquinone in tetrahydrofuran for forty-eight hours, a 63% yield of a yellow crystalline product (m. ~202°, varies with rate of heating) was obtained.[1] This product had the empirical formula $C_{15}H_{10}N_2O_2$ and was thought to have structure II. See Sections A-407 and A-411.

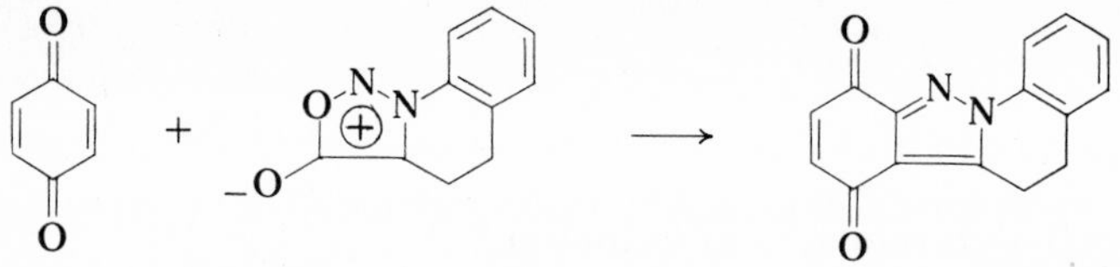

(I) (II)

Reference

1. Hammick and Voaden, *Chem. and Ind.*, **1956**, 739.

A-406. Pyrazolo[2,3-*f*]phenanthridine

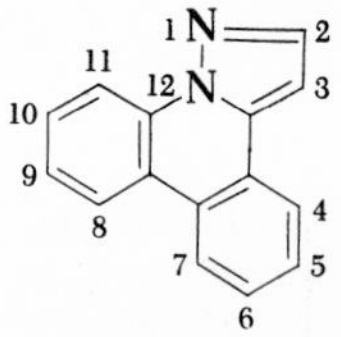

This nucleus has also been called *pyrazolo(5′:1′-9:10)phenanthridine*.

Reduction of I with metallic sodium in boiling ethanol was reported[1,2] to yield II (R = SO_2H; converted by alkaline hypochlorite solution into the sulfonyl chloride, m. 165°), which lost sulfur dioxide readily under acidic aqueous conditions, giving II (R = H, m. 123–4°). Compound II (R = H) was readily converted[1] into the 3-bromo (m. 142–3°) and into the green 3-nitroso (m. 202–3°) derivatives. Independent syntheses of II (R = H) from III (R = R′ =

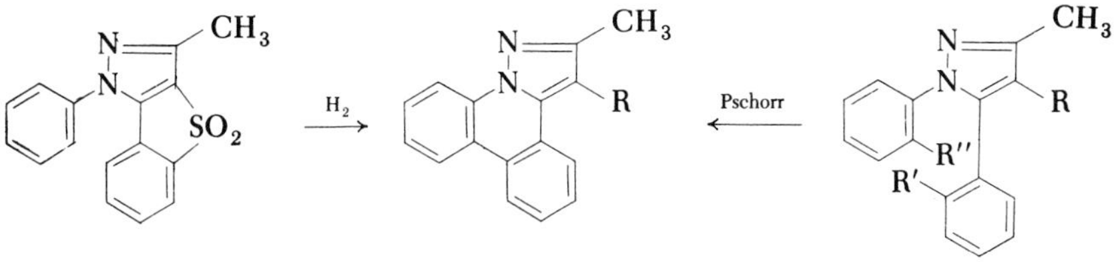

(I) (II) (III)

H,R″ = NH_2)[2] and of II (R = Br) from III (R = Br, R′ = NH_2, R″ = H)[4] confirm the structure assigned.

The reaction of diazofluorene (IV) with acetylenedicarboxylic ester yielded V, which, when heated in acetic acid or with maleic anhydride, rearranged[3] to give VI (m. 136°) and VII. Alkaline hydrolysis of VI gave a resinous acid, which resisted decarboxylation. The product of type V formed from the reaction of IV with methyl phenylpropiolate, gave[3] only a derivative of type VII upon rearrangement.

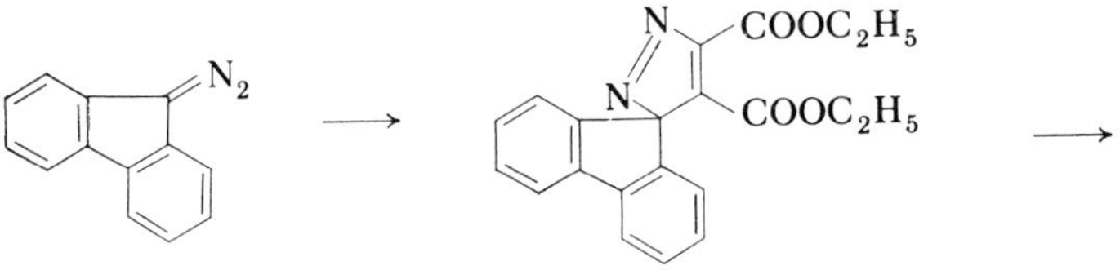

(IV) (V)

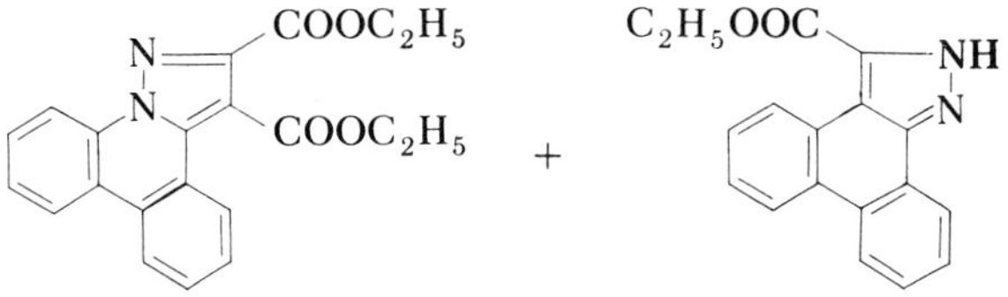

(VI) (VII)

References

1. Barry and McClelland, *J. Chem. Soc.*, **1935,** 471.
2. Barry, Finar and Simmonds, *J. Chem. Soc.*, **1956,** 4974.
3. Van Alphen, *Rec. trav. chim.*, **62,** 491 (1943).
4. Finar and Simmonds, *J. Chem. Soc.*, **1958,** 200.

A-407. Benzo[*f*]pyrid[*b*]indazole*

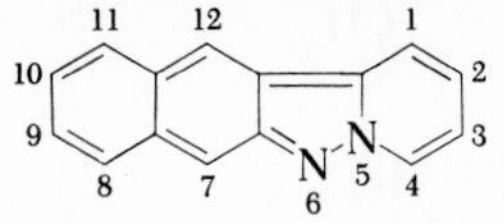

The reaction of the sydnone I (see Section A-531) with 1,4-naphthoquinone yielded[1] a pale cream-colored substance (m. 278–9°), thought to be II. See Sections A-405 and A-411.

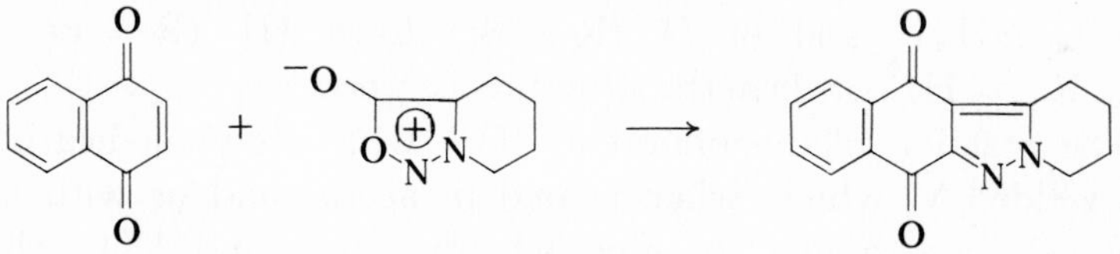

(I) (II)

Reference

1. Hammick and Voaden, *Chem. and Ind.*, **1956,** 739.

A-408. Isoquino[2,1-*b*]naphtho[1,2-*d*]-pyrazole. R.I. 3041J

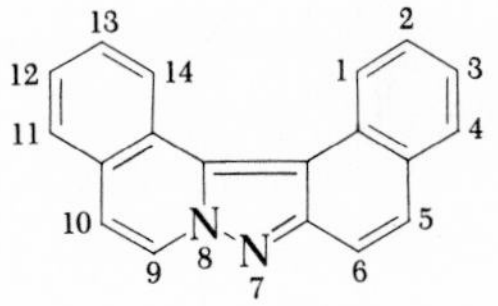

By refluxing I with thionyl chloride, Corbellini, Botrugno and Capucci[1] obtained a product ($C_{20}H_{11}ClN_2O$, m. ~250°d.), which was hydrolyzed to the carboxylic acid $C_{20}H_{12}N_2O_2$ (m. 273.5°; amide, m. 274°; methyl ester, m. 238°; ethyl ester, m. 234°). Structure II was proposed[2] for this acid, but III would seem to be a more satisfactory representation of the bond structure. Esters of III were obtained either directly from III, or by oxidation of I with lead tetraacetate.[2]

Reduction of III (or its esters) with zinc dust and acetic acid gave I (or its esters). Chromic acid oxidation of the methyl or ethyl esters of III gave IVa (R = CH_3, orange-yellow, m. 235–8° d.; phenazine derivative, red, m. 327°) or IVb (R = C_2H_5, orange, m. 327° d.; phenazine derivative, yellow, m. 281°) respectively. A product thought to be the ester V was obtained when IVa was reduced with zinc dust and acetic acid. In view of the peculiar ring

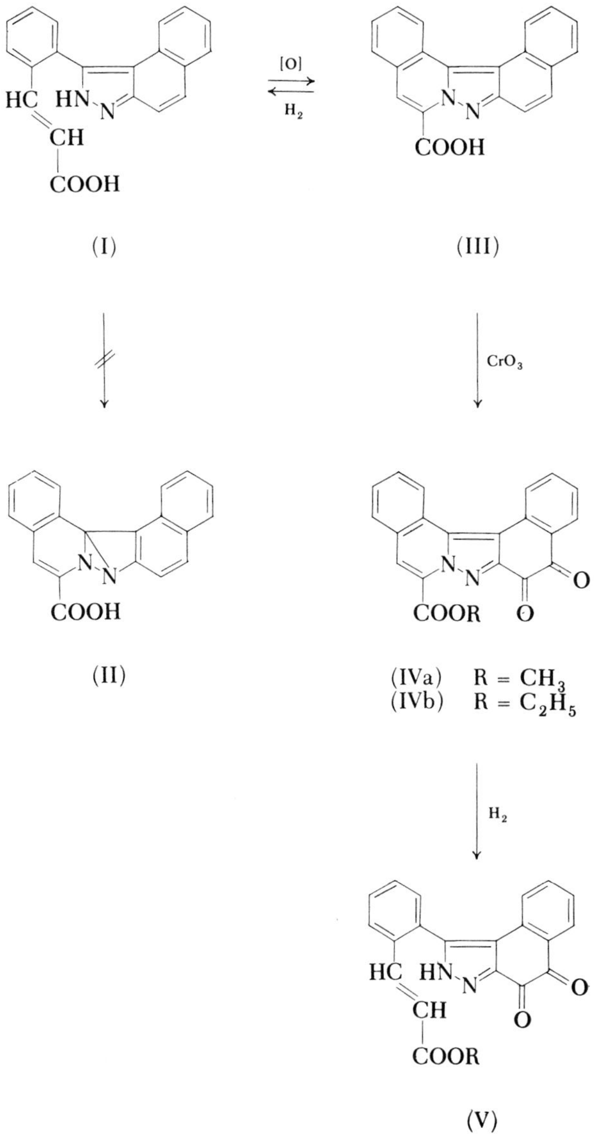

(I) (III)

(II)

(IVa) R = CH_3
(IVb) R = C_2H_5

(V)

scissions postulated, further study of these compounds would seem desirable.

References

1. Corbellini, Botrugno and Capucci, *Rend. ist. lombardo sci.*, [2] **66,** 477 (1936); *Chem. Abstracts*, **33,** 7780 (1939).

2. Corbellini, Capucci and Tommasini, *Gazz. chim. ital.*, **69**, 137 (1939); *Chem. Abstracts*, **33**, 7780 (1939).

A-409. Naphtho[1,2,3-*cd*]quin[3,2,1-*hi*]-indazole*

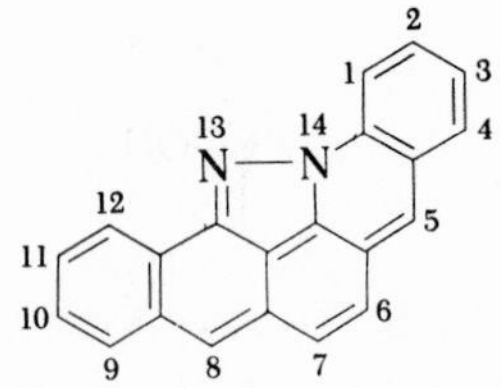

Fusion of I with potassium hydroxide at 120–140° for an hour yielded[1] II, which dyed cotton yellowish-orange from a blue-red vat, and gave a dark blue solution in sulfuric acid.

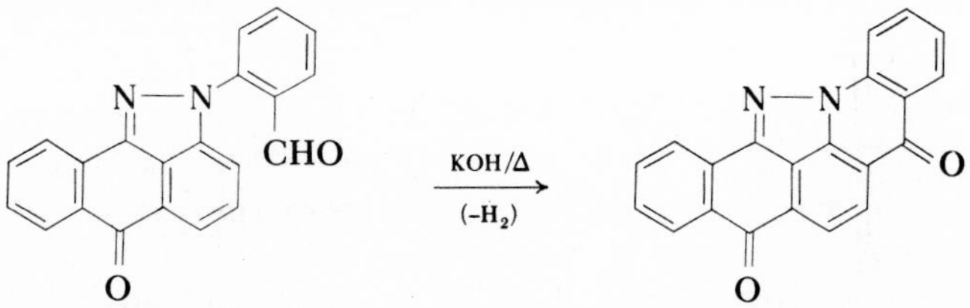

KOH/Δ
($-H_2$)

(I) (II)

KOAc/Cu^{++}
(-HCl)

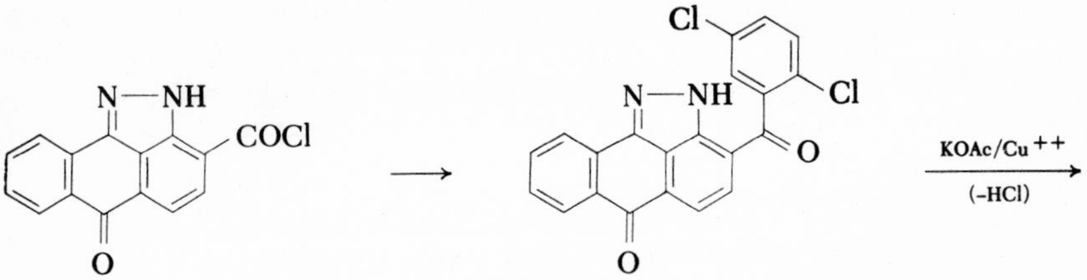

(III)

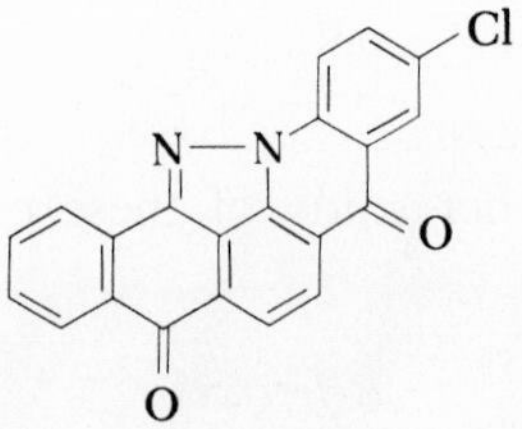

(IV)

A further synthesis of this system was achieved[2] by cyclizing III to IV, which dyed reddish-yellow from a violet vat and gave a green solution in sulfuric acid.

References

1. Kalischer, Bayer and Ritter, Ger. Pat. 525,217; *Frdl.*, **17,** 1295 (1932). Fr. Pat. 686,341. Brit. Pat. 344,558.
2. Scheyer, Ger. Pat. 522,689; *Frdl.*, **16,** 3035 (1931). U. S. Pat. 1,793,138. Fr. Pat. 674,562. Brit. Pat. 332,316.

A-410. 9*H*-14,14*a*-Diazabenzo[*de*]-cyclopenta[*rst*]pentaphene

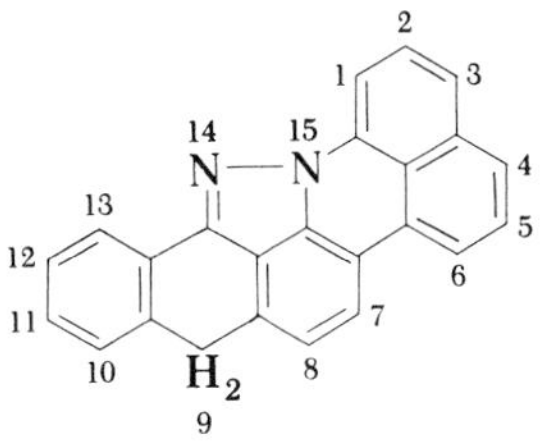

Fusion of I with potassium hydroxide at 115–120° for half an hour converts[1-3] it into II, which dyes cotton a violet-red from a blue vat (sulfuric acid solution blue). Treatment of II with appropriate toluenesulfonic acid esters replaces the imide hydrogen atom with various groups, yielding dyes not greatly different from II. Somewhat yellower shades are produced[1] by chlorinating or brominating II.

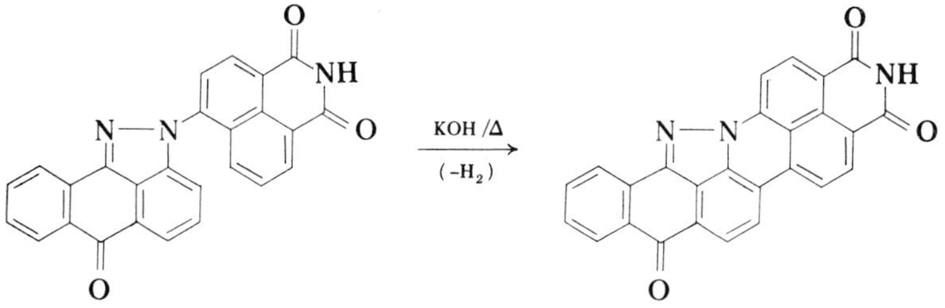

KOH /Δ (−H_2)

(I) (II)

In a very similar synthesis, IV was obtained[2] by fusing III with caustic and then oxidizing the methylene group. The anhydride IV was condensed with *o*-phenylenediamine to form blue vat dyes (see Sections A-366/7).

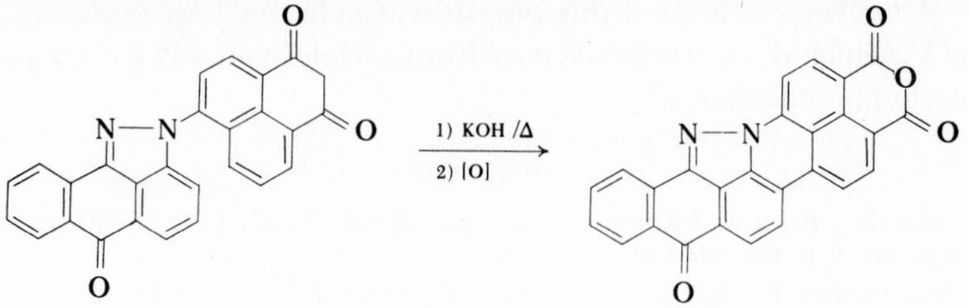

(III) 1) KOH /Δ 2) [O] (IV)

References

1. Nawiasky, Ger. Pat. 491,429; *Frdl.*, **16,** 1365 (1931). Brit. Pat. 321,703.
2. Gruschke and Quint, *I.G. Farbenindustrie, A.G., 42 Wissenschaftlicher Austausch der Gruppe IX*, February 15, 1940, Frankfurt; *PB Report No.* 70248, frame 2834.
3. Akiyoshi and Tsuge, *J. Chem. Soc. Japan*, Ind. Chem. Sect., **57,** 296 (1954); *Chem. Abstracts*, **49,** 4297 (1955).

A-411. *7H,16H*-Diquino[1,2-*b*, 1′,2′-*b*′]-benzo[1,2-*d*, 4,5-*d*′]dipyrazole*

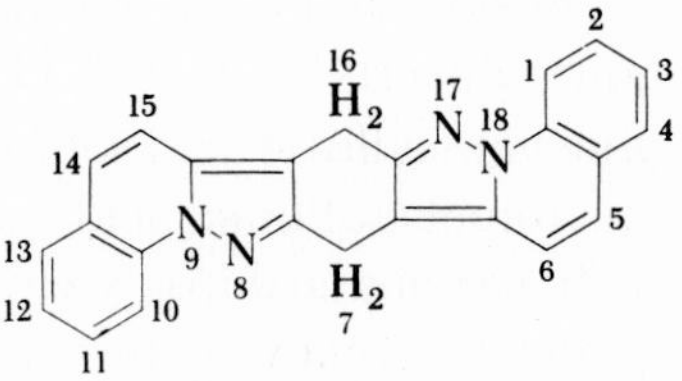

From the reaction of I (see Section A-532) with benzoquinone in refluxing tetrahydrofuran, Hammick and Voaden[1] isolated a pale yellow product ($C_{24}H_{16}N_4O_2$, m. >335°) thought to have structure II. See Sections A-405 and A-407.

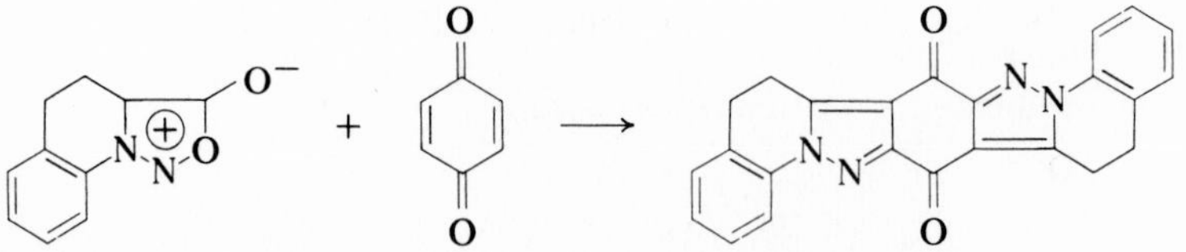

(I) (II)

Reference

1. Hammick and Voaden, *Chem. and Ind.*, **1956,** 739.

A-412. Benz[*a*]isoquino[2′,1′,1,5]-pyrazolo[4,3-*c*]phenazine. R.I. 3712M

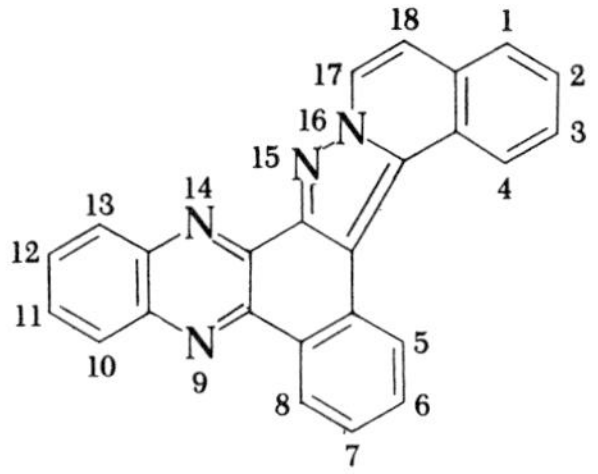

The phenazine derivatives of the isoquino[2,1-*b*]naphtho[1,2-*d*]pyrazole-5,6-diones (see Section A-408) prepared by Corbellini, Capucci and Tommasini[1] are represented by I. Two such compounds were obtained, the methyl (I, R = CH_3, yellow, m. 327°) and ethyl (I, R = C_2H_5, yellow, m. 281°) esters.

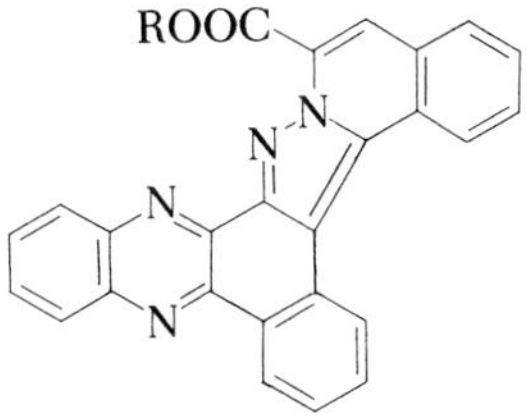

ROOC

(I)

Reference

1. Corbellini, Capucci and Tommasini, *Gazz. chim. ital.*, **69**, 137 (1939).

A-413. Benz[6,7]indazolo[4,3,2-*cde*]-naphtho[2,3-*i*]phenanthridine*

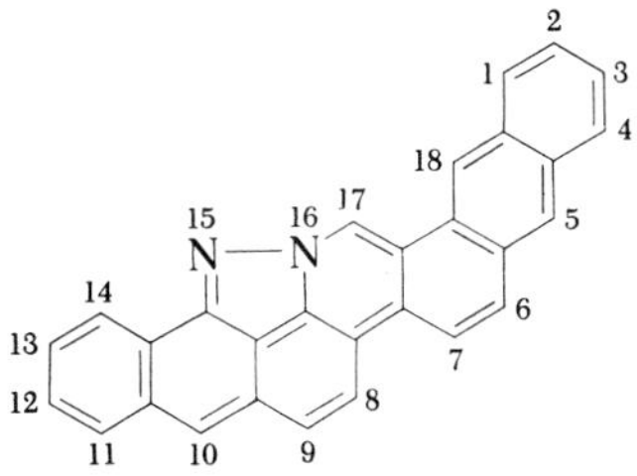

This nucleus could also be named *naphth[1′,2′,3′-3,4]indazolo-[1,7-bc]naphth[2,3-h]isoquinoline**.

Oxidation of Navy Blue R (I, see Section A-416) in 60–65% sulfuric acid with chromic acid at 50–60° yielded[1] the yellow product

II. The pyridone ring of II was readily opened by warm dilute aqueous alkali, and the product had no substantivity for cotton.

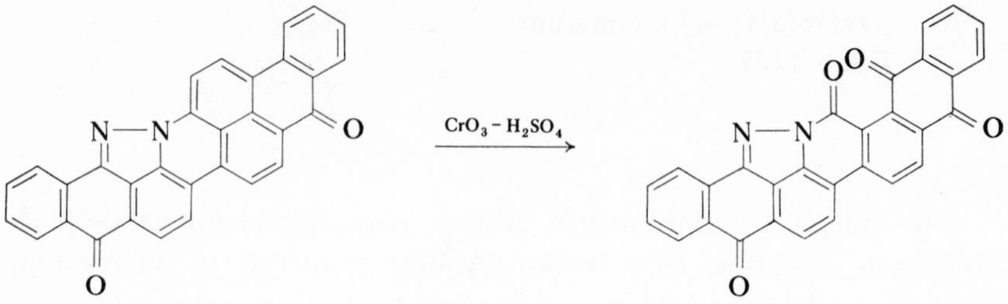

$CrO_3 - H_2SO_4$

(I) (II)

Reference

1. Neresheimer and Böhner, Ger. Pat. 499,352; *Frdl.*, **17,** 1384 (1932). U. S. Pat. 1,897,439.

A-414. 10*H*-Benz[6,7]indazolo-[4,3,2-*cde*]naphth[3,2,1-*kl*]-acridine*

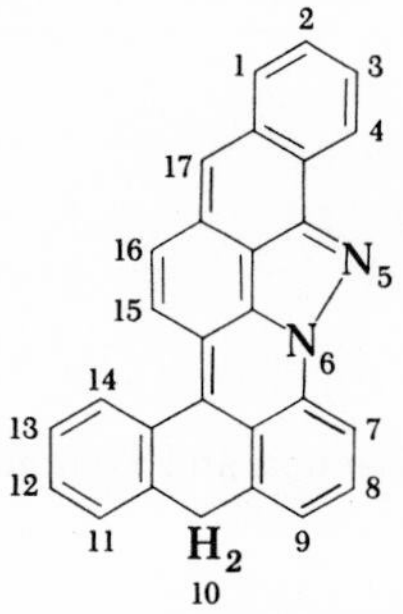

While attempts to cyclize I under acidic conditions (e.g., in an aluminum chloride-sodium chloride melt) were unsuccessful, under alkaline conditions a deep green product, thought to be II (or III), was obtained.[1] This substance forms deep blue salts with acids, and (in pyridine) olive-brown salts with alkalies. It is unchanged by air oxidation, but upon recrystallization from nitrobenzene, or upon oxidation of an alkaline solution with hydrogen peroxide or with potassium ferricyanide, there is formed an olive-green solid thought[1] to be a resonance-stabilized free radical produced by abstraction of H$^{\cdot}$ from II (and/orIII).

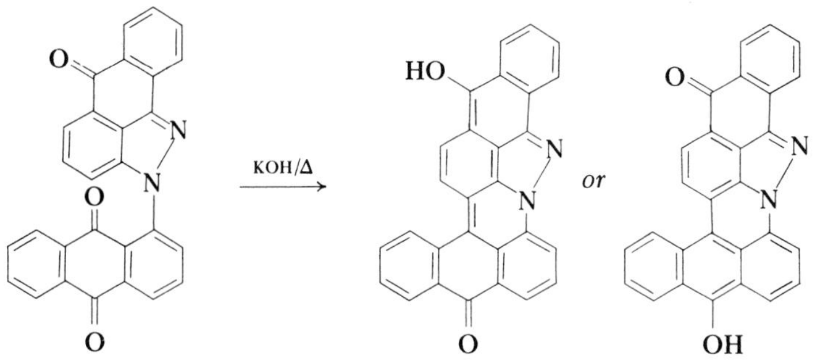

(I) $\xrightarrow{KOH/\Delta}$ (II) *or* (III)

When sodium hydrosulfite is added to an olive solution of II in aqueous alkali, the initially green vat changes to violet-blue, and a violet solid may be isolated (solution in sulfuric acid, olive-green). This product is a powerful violet dye, but is not chlorine-fast; it possesses the formula $C_{28}H_{14}N_2O$, and is thought[1] to be the des-hydroxy derivative of structure II.

Reference

1. Baumann and Schwechten, *I.G. Farbenindustrie, A.G., 35 Wissenschaftlicher Austausch der Gruppe IX*, Frankfurt, March 13–14, 1936; *PB Report No.* 70339, frames 11484–7.

A-415. Indazolo[4,3,2-*bed*]phenanthro[2,1,10-*fgh*]thebenidine. R.I. 3920

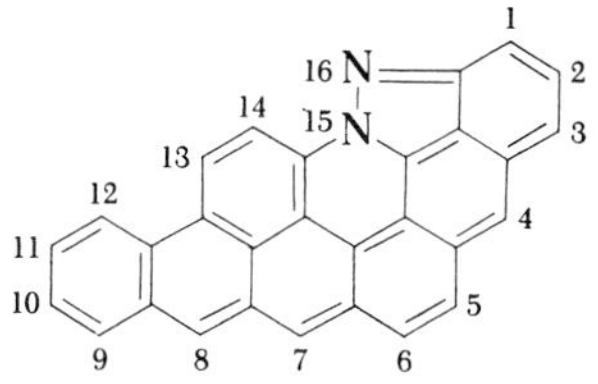

As the result of an error, this ring system has found its way into *Chemical Abstracts* and into the *Ring Index*. In fact, no products of this type are known and the vat dyes assigned this structure are actually anthra[9,2,1-*jkl*]benz[6,7]indazolo[4,3,2-*cde*]acridines (see Section A-416).

A-416. Anthra[9,1,2-*jkl*]benz[6,7]-indazolo[4,3,2-*cde*]acridine. R.I. 3919

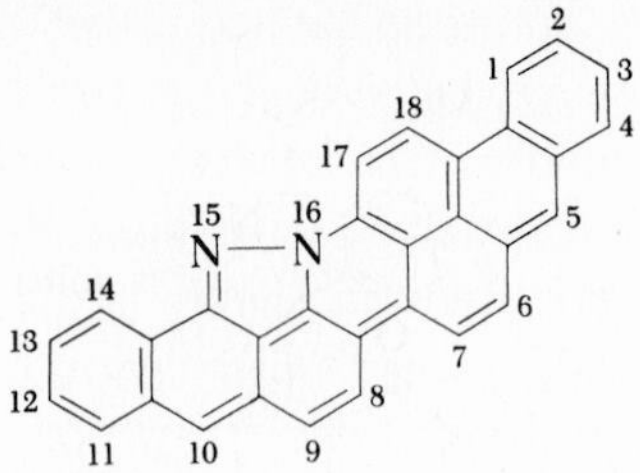

The numerous examples reported of this ring system are all 5,10-dioxo derivatives, prepared as potential vat dyes. These dioxo compounds (often called *benzanthrone-pyrazolanthrones*, after the method of their preparation) are all deeply colored: dark-blue to green or black.

These dyes are readily made by heating the pyrazolanthrone (I) in a solvent such as dichlorobenzene or nitrobenzene with potassium carbonate to form the potassium salt of I, then adding the 3-halo- or 3-nitrobenzanthrone (II) together with a copper catalyst. After refluxing the mixture for several hours, the intermediate anthrimide (III) is isolated and heated for several hours more in an alcoholic potash melt at about 100°, to effect the cyclization to IV.

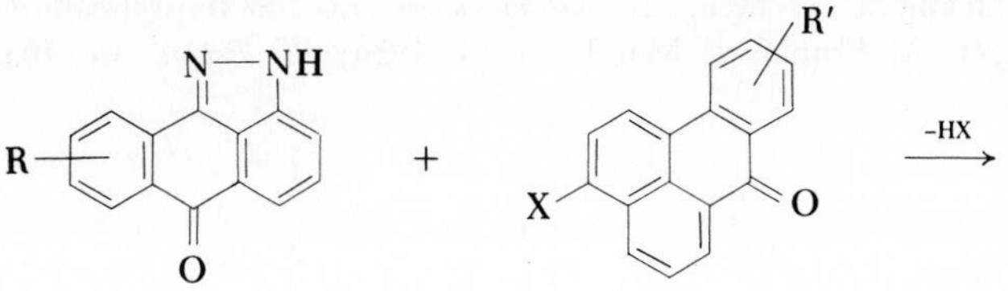

(I) (II)

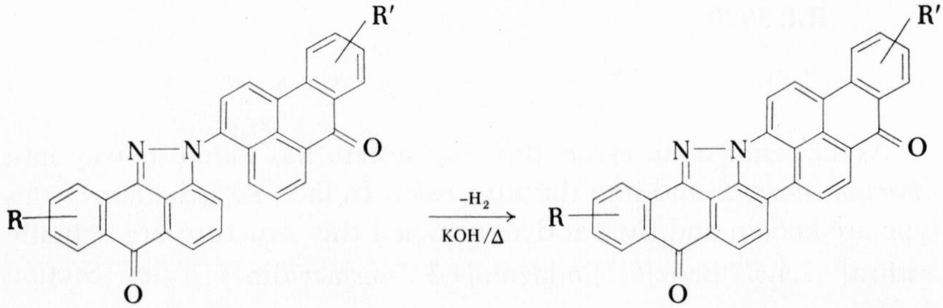

(III) (IV)

The simplest example of this class (IV, R = R′ = H) was discovered by Wilke[1] in the I.G. Farbenindustrie laboratories. It has been used as a vat dye under the name Navy Blue R, but the tendency of fabrics dyed with Navy Blue R to "waterspot" has greatly reduced its commercial value.[2] In efforts to overcome this defect, numerous homologs and substitution products were prepared.[1,3–18] Some were prepared by substitution reactions upon Navy Blue R itself; others were obtained by utilizing substituted pyrazolanthrones or benzanthrones. In this latter category two dyes were studied extensively: Vat Blue P-113 and Vat Blue Hö 259. The former is a monochloro-17-phenyl homolog of Navy Blue R, obtained by mild chlorination[11,12,13,27,35] of the 17-phenyl compound. The location of the halogen atom is unknown, and it may be in the phenyl group[11] or possibly in the 18-position. Vat Blue Hö 259 was prepared[12] from 10-chloropyrazolanthrone and 2-phenylbenzanthrone.

Little definite information exists concerning the location of entering substituents in IV (R = R′ = H). Nitration is said[4,20] to occur in the 17-position, and probably other electrophilic monsubstitution reactions occur at this most reactive position (e.g. halogenation[1,3,4,6–9] and hydroxylation by manganese dioxide in sulfuric acid[5,9]). However, as many as six chlorine atoms have been introduced[9,20] into IV (R = R′ = H), and the location of the second and subsequent entering groups is unproven. One might expect positions 1,3,9 and 17 to be amongst those most readily substituted. Chloromethylation is thought[15] to occur first in the 17 and then in the 3-position. Oxidation of Navy Blue R in 60–65% sulfuric acid with chromic acid yielded[21] compound V, which underwent scission of the lactam ring in the presence of alkali.

(IV) R = R′ = H $\xrightarrow[H_2SO_4]{CrO_3}$

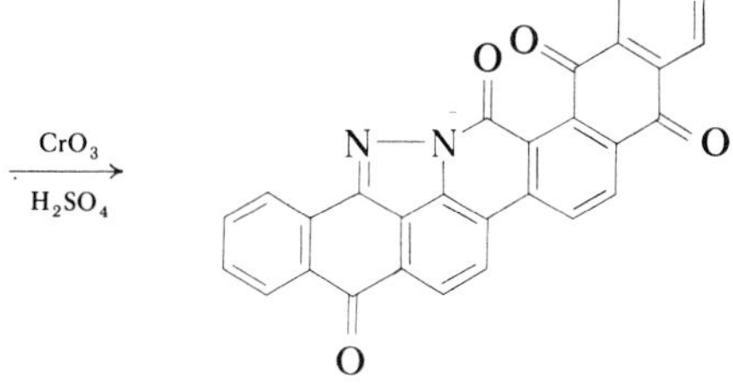

(V)

At present, the most important dye, commercially, of this class is Vat Grey M [IV, R = H, R′ = 3-(1-anthraquinonylamino)].[20,22-25] It is prepared by condensing 3,9-dibromobenzanthrone first with a mole of pyrazolanthrone, then with a mole of 1-aminoanthraquinone and subjecting the intermediate dianthrimide to a caustic fusion.[24] Numerous variations upon and derivatives of Grey M were prepared.[20,22-26,28,29] Related dyes were obtained by condensing halogenated Navy Blue R with various amines such as aminothiophthanthraquinone,[33] aminodibenzanthrone,[32] etc. Many of the dyes thus prepared are of rather large molecular weight, and being quite complex and of limited interest, are not included in the table of derivatives of Navy Blue R, althought the patents concerning them are listed with the other references. Black dyes are reported to result from the acylation of amines of the Navy Blue R class with 1-nitroanthraquinone-2-carbonyl chloride.[34]

Anthra[9,1,2-*jkl*]benz[6,7]indazolo[4,3,2-*cde*]acridine-5,10-diones

Substituents	Properties	Refs.
x,x,x,x,x,x-Hexachloro-	Brn.; diff. to vat; olive-brn. in H_2SO_4.	9
x,x,x,x,x,x-Hexachloro-*x,x*-dihydroxy-	Bl.-grn.	9
x,x,x-Tribromo-*x,x*-dichloro-	Vt.-bl.; diff. to vat.	6
x,x,x,x,x-Pentabromo-	Bl.; vt. in H_2SO_4.	6
x,x,x,x,x-Pentachloro-*x,x*-dihydroxy-	Bl.-grn.; wine-red in H_2SO_4.	9
x-Bromo-*x,x,x*-trichloro-	Bl.-vt.	8
x,x-Dibromo-*x,x*-dichloro-	Vt.-bl.; grn.-bl. vat; vt. in H_2SO_4.	7
x,x-Dibromo-*x*-chloro-	Navy bl.	9
x,x-Dibromo-*x*-chloro-*x,x*-dihydroxy-	—	9
x,x,x-Tribromo-	Dk. bl.; blue vat; vt. in H_2SO_4.	6
x,x,x-Trichloro-	Bl.-vt.; grn.-bl. vat.	8,9
x,x,x-Trichloro-*x*-hydroxy-	—	9
x,x,x-Trichloro-*x,x*-dihydroxy-	Bl.-grn.	9
x,x-Dibromo-	Bl.; bl. vat; vt. in H_2SO_4.	6,7,30
x,x-Dibromo-*x,x*-dihydroxy-	Grn.	9

Anthra[9,1,2-*jkl*]benz[6,7]indazolo[4,3,2-*cde*]acridine-5,10-diones (*continued*)

Substituents	Properties	Refs.
x,x-Dichloro-	Bl.; bl. vat; vt. in H_2SO_4.	7
x,x-Dichloro-*x*-hydroxy-	Vt.; bordeaux in H_2SO_4.	9
x,x-Dichloro-*x,x*-dihydroxy-	Grn.-bl.	9
3-Bromo-	Red-vt. in H_2SO_4.	18,20,22
x-Bromo-	Bl. vat; vt. in H_2SO_4.	6,30
9-Chloro-	Vt.-bl. vat; olive in H_2SO_4.	23
11-Chloro-	Bl.-Grey vat; grey-grn. in H_2SO_4.	23
14-Chloro-	Grn.-grey-bl. vat; H_2SO_4 sol'n. wine-red.	23
x-Chloro-	Dk. bl.; grn.-bl. vat; vt. in H_2SO_4.	7,9,20
14-Chloro-*x,x*-dihydroxy-	Olive-grn.	9
x-Chloro-*x,x*-dihydroxy-	Grn.-bl.	9
3-Nitro-	Bl. vat; brn.-yel. in H_2SO_4.	1
17-Nitro-	Vt.-blk.; bl. vat; green in H_2SO_4.	4,20,22
Unsubstituted	Vt.-bl.; grn.-bl. vat; vt.-red in H_2SO_4. (Vat Navy Blue R.)	1
x-Hydroxy-	Vt.-bl.; wine-red in H_2SO_4.	5
x,x-Dihydroxy-	Bl. vat; yel.-grn. in caustic.	5
3-Amino-	Dyes cotton grey-grn. from grey-bl. vat; brn.-yel. in H_2SO_4.	1,22,34
9-Amino-	—	34
14-Amino-	—	34
17(?)-Amino-	Acetyl deriv., bl. vat, red in H_2SO_4. Benzoyl deriv., bl. vat, brn.- red in H_2SO_4.	20
x,x,x-Trichloro-*x*-methoxy-	Brn.-red in H_2SO_4.	9
x,x-Dichloro-*x*-methoxy-	Bl. vat; vt.-red in H_2SO_4.	9
3-Chloromethyl-	—	15
3-Methyl-	Dyes cotton blue.	16
9-Methyl-	Grn.-bl. vat.	1
17-Methyl-	Blue vat.	14
3-Methoxy-	—	18
x-Methoxy-	Vt.-bl.	5

(*continued*)

Anthra[9,1,2-*jkl*]benz[6,7]indazolo[4,3,2-*cde*]acridine-5,10-diones (*continued*)

Substituents	Properties	Refs.
x,x,x,x,x,x-Hexachloro-*x,x*-dimethoxy-	Bordeaux in H_2SO_4.	9
x,x,x,x,x-Pentachloro-*x,x*-dimethoxy-	Low strength as a dye.	9
x,x-Dibromo-*x*-chloro-*x,x*-dimethoxy-	Wine-red in H_2SO_4.	9
x,x,x-Trichloro-*x,x*-dimethoxy-	Wine-red in H_2SO_4.	9
x,x-Dibromo-*x,x*-dimethoxy-	Wine-red in H_2SO_4.	9
3,17-Bis-chloromethyl-	Grn.-bl. on cotton.	15
x,x-Dichloro-17-ethyl-	—	14
x,x-Dichloro-*x,x*-dimethoxy-	Bl. vat; wine-red in H_2SO_4.	9
14-Chloro-17-ethyl-	Bl. vat.	14
14-Chloro-*x,x*-dimethoxy-	Bl.-grn. on cotton.	9
x-Chloro-*x,x*-dimethoxy-	Wine-red in H_2SO_4.	9
3,17-Dimethyl-	—	16
17-Ethyl-	Bl. vat.	14
x,x-Dimethoxy-	Grn.-bl. on cotton.	5
x-Chloro-*x*-dimethylamino-	Bl. vat; grn. in H_2SO_4.	22
17-*i*-Propyl-	Bl. vat.	14
x-Bromo-17-phenyl-	—	13
14-Chloro-17-Phenyl-	Grn.-blk. in H_2SO_4. (Vat Blue Hö 259.)	12,13
x-Chloro-17-phenyl-	Vt.-red in H_2SO_4. (Vat Blue P-113.)	11–13,27
17-Phenyl-	Grn.-bl. vat; vt.-red in H_2SO_4.	1,10,11,13
x-Phenoxy-	Bl. in H_2SO_4.	30
17(?)-Benzylamino-	Bl. vat; olive-brn. in H_2SO_4.	20
3-(1-Anthraquinonylamino)-	Bl. grey vat; grn. in H_2SO_4. (Vat Greys M and MG.)	20,22,24,25,30
3-(2-Anthraquinonylamino)-	Grey-bl. vat.	22
8-(1-Anthraquinonylamino)-	Vt.-bl. vat; brn.-olive in H_2SO_4.	23
11-(1-Anthraquinonylamino)-	Bl.-grey vat; grey-grn. in H_2SO_4.	23
14-(1-Anthraquinonylamino)-	Grn.-bl.-grey vat; red in H_2SO_4.	23
3,17-Bisphenoxymethyl-	—	17

Anthra[9,1,2-*jkl*]benz[6,7]indazolo[4,3,2-*cde*]acridine-5,10-diones (*continued*)

Substituents	Properties	Refs.
3-(1-Nitroanthraquinone-2-carboxamido)-	Black vat. Also prepared the 9-, 11-, and 14-isomers.	34
3-(1-Anthraquinonylamino)-9-methyl-	"Anthrasolgrau AL 14841."	26
Note: Numerous more complex derivatives have also been prepared.		22,23,25, 28 30–34

References

1. Wilke, Ger. Pat. 490,723; *Frdl.*, **16,** 1368 (1931). Brit. Pat. 298,284. Fr. Pat. 640,939. U. S. Pat. 1,790,780.
2. I.G. Farbenindustrie, A.G., *B.I.O.S. Report 1493*, p. 26.
3. Wilke, Ger. Pat. 492,274; *Frdl.*, **16,** 1374 (1931). Fr. Pat. 640,939.
4. Wilke, Ger. Pat. 492,275; *Frdl.*, **16,** 1373 (1931). Fr. Pat. 640,939.
5. Wilke, Ger. Pat. 507,560; *Frdl.*, **18,** 1424 (1933). Fr. Pat. 640,939.
6. Kunz, Köberle and Berthold, Ger. Pat. 516,313; *Frdl.*, **17,** 1285 (1932). Brit. Pat. 341,884. Fr. Pat. 692,869. U. S. Pat. 1,846,121.
7. Kunz, Köberle and Berthold, Ger. Pat. 531,102; *Frdl.*, **18,** 1421 (1933). Brit. Pat. 341,884. Fr. Pat. 692,869. U. S. Pat. 1,846,122.
8. Kunz and Köberle, Ger. Pat. 535,092; *Frdl.*, **18,** 1422 (1933).
9. Wilke, Ger. Pat. 538,480; *Frdl.*, **18,** 1425 (1933). Brit. Pat. 360,776. Fr. Pat. 39,807 add'n. to 640,939. U. S. Pat. 1,878,050.
10. Wilke, *I.G. Farbenindustrie, A.G., 36 Wissenschaftlicher Austausch der Gruppe IX*, Oct. 2/3, 1936, Frankfurt a/M., *PB Report No.* 70338, frame 9906.
11. Wilke, *I.G. Farbenindustrie, A.G., 42 Wissenschaftlicher Austausch der Gruppe IX*, June 16/17, 1939, Leverkusen; *PB Report No.* 70338, frame 10688. *PB Report No.* 70248, frame 2584ff.
12. Wilke, *I.G. Farbenindustrie, A.G., 43 Wissenschaftlicher Austausch der Gruppe IX*, April 25, 1941, Frankfurt a/M., *PB Report No.* 70338, frame 10885. *PB Report No.* 70350, frame 3826ff.
13. Farbwerke Höchst, A. G., Brit. Pat. 766,345. Fr. Pat. 1,098,937.
14. Schlichenmaier and Pohlmann, Ger. Pat. 1,005,665.
15. Randall, U. S. Pat. 2,619,487.
16. Randall, U. S. Pat. 2,647,899.
17. Randall and Martin, U. S. Pat. 2,703,321.
18. Scalera and Westlake, U. S. Pat. 2,673,851, Fr. Pat. 1,084,058.
19. Thiess, Meissner and Wilke, Ger. Pat. 500,520; *Frdl.*, **17,** 1283 (1932). Fr. Pat. 35,598, add'n. to 640,939.
20. Wilke, Stock and Schubert, Ger. Pat. 516,698; *Frdl.*, **17,** 1287 (1932). Brit. Pat. 344,057. Fr. Pat. 685,867. U. S. Pat. 1,938,059.

21. Neresheimer and Böhner, Ger. Pat. 499,352; *Frdl.*, **17,** 1384 (1932). U. S. Pat. 1,897,439.
22. Wilke, Stock and Schubert, Ger. Pat. 518,335; *Frdl.*, **17,** 1290 (1932). Brit. Pat. 344,147. Fr. Pat. 685,867. U. S. Pat. 1,938,059.
23. Wilke, Stock and Schubert, Ger. Pat. 520,395; *Frdl.*, **17,** 1291 (1932). Brit. Pat. 345,728. Fr. Pat. 38,112, add'n. to 640,939. U. S. Pat. 1,943,710.
24. I.G.Farbenindustrie, A.G., *F.I.A.T. Report* 1313, vol. 2, p. 111. *B.I.O.S. Report* 987, p. 109.
25. Wilke, *I.G. Farbenindustrie, A.G., 39 Wissenschaftlicher Austausch der Gruppe IX*, June 21/2, 1938, Mainkur; *PB Report No.* 70338, frame 10393ff.
26. Bortl, *I.G. Farbenindustrie, A.G., 44 Wissenschaftlicher Austausch der Gruppe IX*, May 3, 1942, Ludwigshafen; *PB Report No.* 70342, frame 14921ff.
27. I.G. Farbenindustrie, A.G., *F.I.A.T. Report* 1313, vol. 3, p. 28.
28. Braun, *I.G. Farbenindustrie, A.G., 43 Wissenschaftlicher Austausch der Gruppe IX*, March 20, 1941, Frankfurt a/M., *PB Report No.* 70342, frame 14665.
29. Slinger, Brit. Pat. 633,502.
30. Kunz and Köberle, Ger. Pat. 534,933; *Frdl.*, **18,** 1428 (1933). Brit. Pat. 345,651. Fr. Pat. 700,603. U. S. Pat. 1,857,553.
31. Kunz and Köberle, U. S. Pat. 1,901,308.
32. Kunz and Köberle, U. S. Pat. 1,909,690.
33. Schroeder and Ringrose, U. S. Pat. 2,559,676.
34. Irving and Livingston, Brit. Pat. 716,558. U. S. Pat. 2,709,170. Ger. Pat. Apln. I 6266 IVd/22b, Gr. 3/13. Fr. Pat. 1,099,348.
35. Wilke, Greune, Schlichenmaier and Pohlmann, Ger. Pat. Apln. F 10236 IVb/22b.
36. Fairweather and Coffey, Brit. Pat. 743,865; *Chem. Abstracts*, **50,** 16125 (1956).

A-417. Benz[6,7]indazolo[2,3,4-*fgh*]-phenanthro[2,1,10-*mna*]acridine*

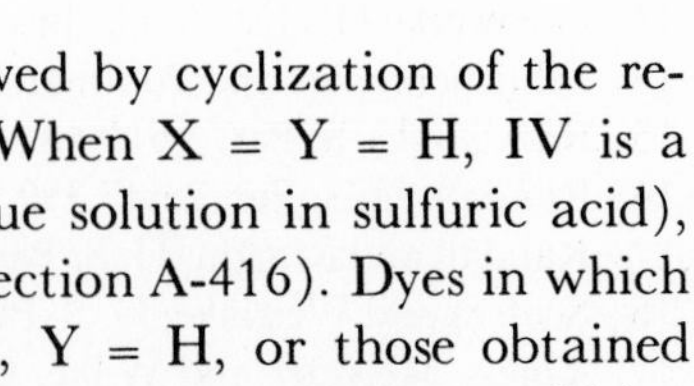

The condensation of I with II, followed by cyclization of the resulting anthrimide (III), yielded[1] IV. When X = Y = H, IV is a red-violet dye (with a blue vat and a blue solution in sulfuric acid), which is an isomer of Navy Blue R (see Section A-416). Dyes in which X = H, Y = C_6H_5CONH, or X = Cl, Y = H, or those obtained by chlorinating IV (X = Y = H), are violet with violet vats and blue solutions in sulfuric acid.

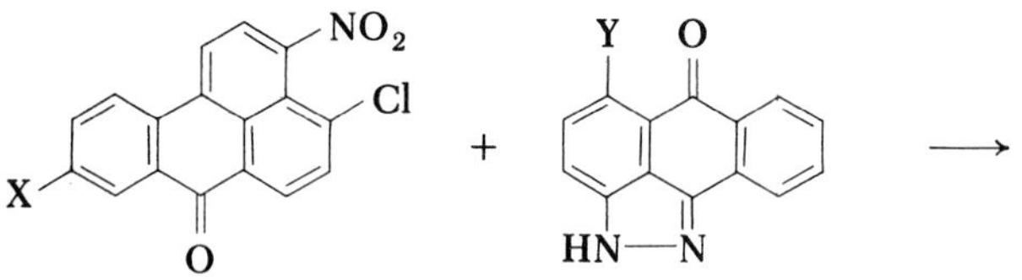

(I) (II)

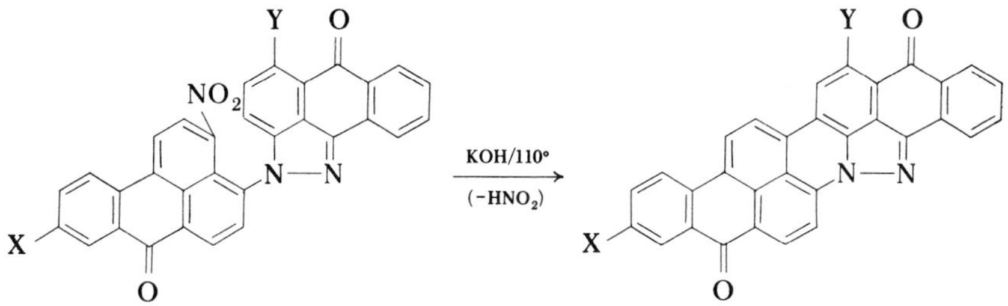

(III) (IV)

KOH/110° ($-HNO_2$)

Reference

1. Neresheimer and Schneider, Ger. Pat. 497,825; *Frdl.*, **17,** 1284 (1932). U. S. Pat. 1,846,139. Fr. Pat. 682,057. Brit. Pat. 326,268.

A-418. Benz[6,7]indazolo[2,3,4-*fgh*]-pyrido[3′,2′,6,7]naphth-[2,1,8-*mna*]acridine*

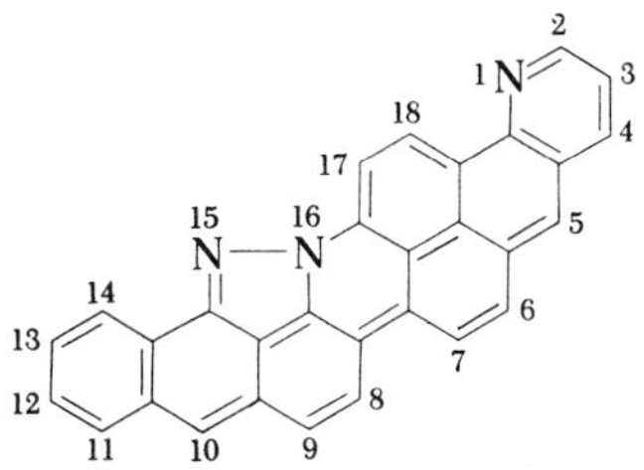

From the condensation of I (R = H) with pyrazolanthrone, followed by a caustic-melt treatment of the intermediate anthrimide, the bluish-violet dye II (R = H, green vat and green solution in sulfuric acid) was obtained.[1,2] It is more violet than Navy Blue R (the isostere having carbon in place of the nitrogen in the 1-position), and upon chlorination, somewhat clearer shades are obtained.[1]

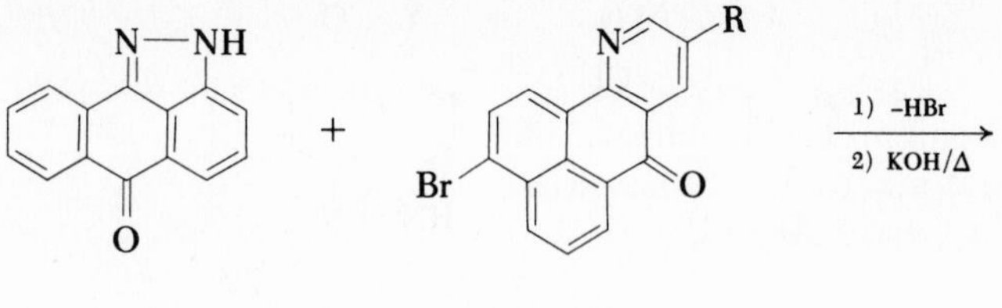

N—NH

O

\+

N R

Br O

1) -HBr
2) KOH/Δ

(I)

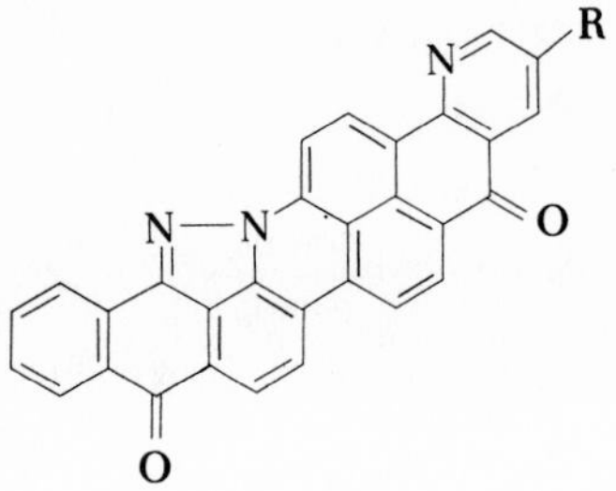

N R

N—N O

O

(II)

Dyes of type II, in which R is represented by III or IV, are grey vat dyes (light-fastness 7–8, soda-fastness 4) similar to Indanthrene Grey M (see Section A-416).

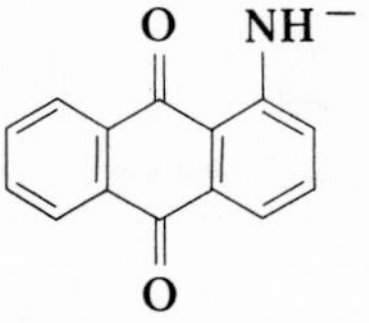

O NH⁻

O

O NH⁻

N N

(III) 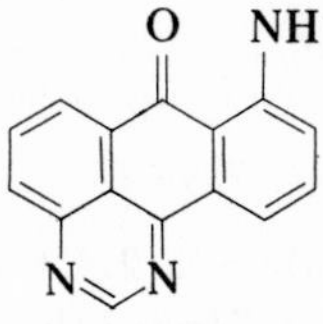 (IV)

References

1. Kunz, Köberle, Ebel and Kochendörfer, *I.G. Farbenindustrie, A.G.*; *PB Report No.* 70340, frame 12922.
2. Kunz, Köberle and Kochendörfer, Ger. Pat. 654,617; *Frdl.*, **23,** 1086 (1940). U. S. 2,023,479.

A-419. Benz[6,7]indazolo[4,3,2-*hij*]-naphth[1′,2′,3′,1,8]isoquino-[4,5-*bc*]quinoline*

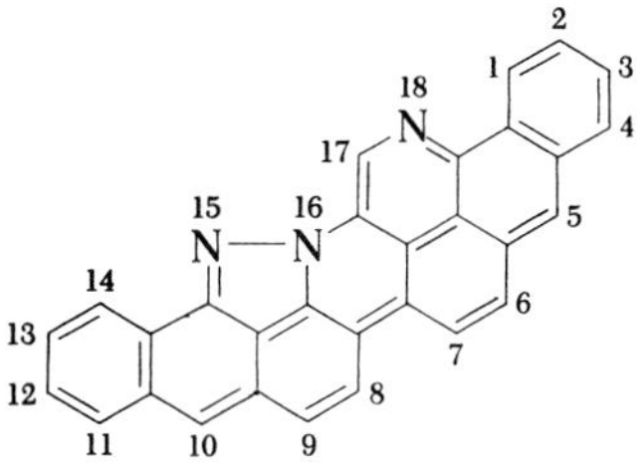

The violet vat dye (blue-green vat, green sulfuric acid solution) II was prepared[1,2] as shown from I and pyrazolanthrone.

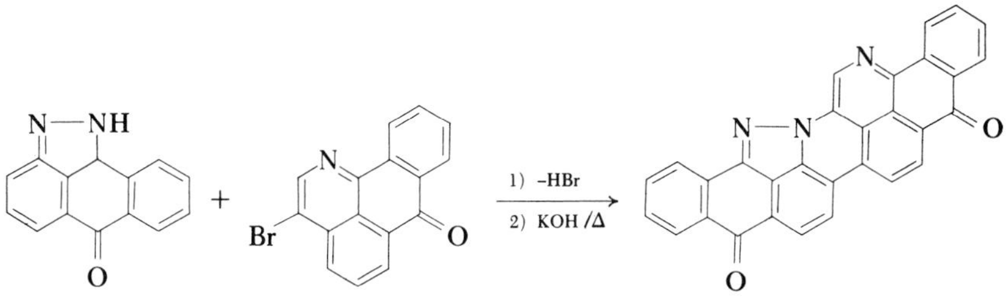

1) −HBr
2) KOH /Δ

(I) (II)

References

1. Kunz, Köberle, Ebel and Kochendörfer, *I.G. Farbenindustrie, A.G.*; *PB Report No.* 70340, frame 12922.
2. Kunz, Köberle and Kochendörfer, Ger. Pat. 655,593; *Frdl.*, **23,** 1091 (1940).

A-420. 9*H*,18*H*-Diquino-[3,2,1-*hi*, 3′,2′,1′-*h′i′*]benzo-[1,2,3-*cd*, 4,5,6-*c′d′*]diindazole*

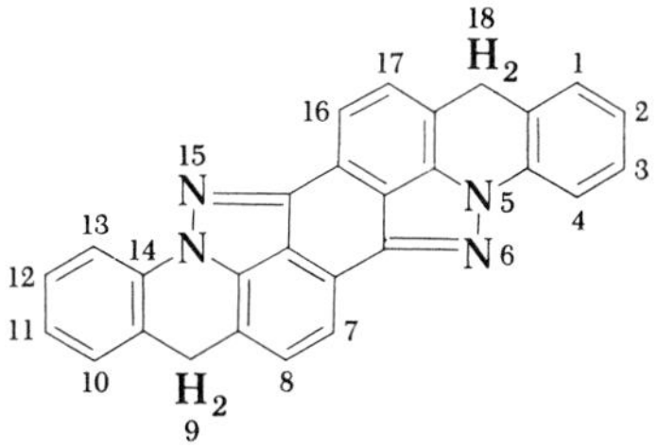

Fusion of I (R = H) with potassium hydroxide yielded[1] the difficulty vattable, olive-green dye II (green vat and intense green solution in sulfuric acid).

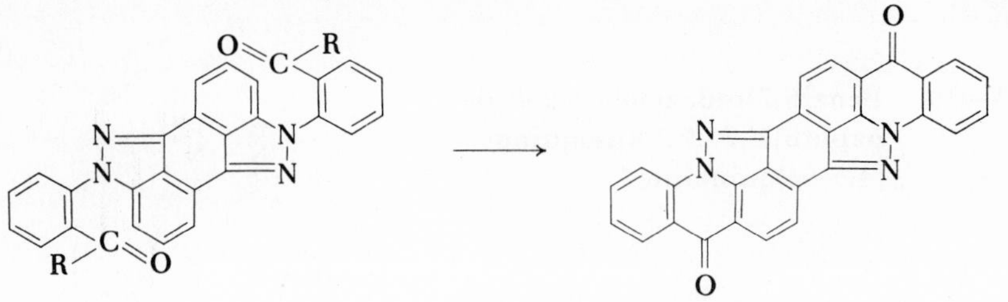

(I) (II)

Treatment of I (R = OH) with chlorosulfonic acid gave a product[2] for which no structure or properties were disclosed, but which may also be II.

References

1. Kalischer, Bayer and Ritter, Ger. Pat. 525,217; *Frdl.*, **17,** 1295 (1932). Brit. Pat. 344,558. Fr. Pat. 686,341.
2. Thiess, Braunsdorf and Wilke, Ger. Pat. 504,240; *Frdl.*, **16,** 3032 (1931). U. S. Pat. 1,772,620. Brit. Pat. 298,775. Fr. Pat. 644,589.

A-421. 8*H*,16*H*-Dipyrazolo[*def, qrs*]-flavanthrene. R.I.3955

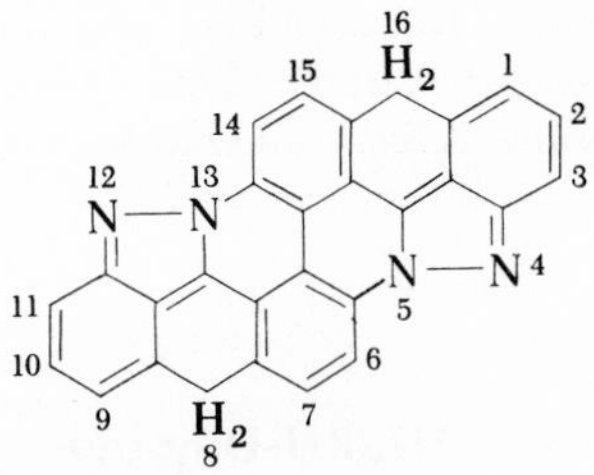

The *Ring Index* name omitted the 8*H*,16*H* prefix.

The vat dye "pyrazolanthrone yellow" was once thought to be the 8,16-dioxo derivative of this nucleus, but is now known to have a different structure. See Section A-559.

A-422. Benz[6,7]indazolo[2,3,4-*mna*]-quino[3′,2′,6,7]naphth-[2,1,8-*fgh*]acridine*

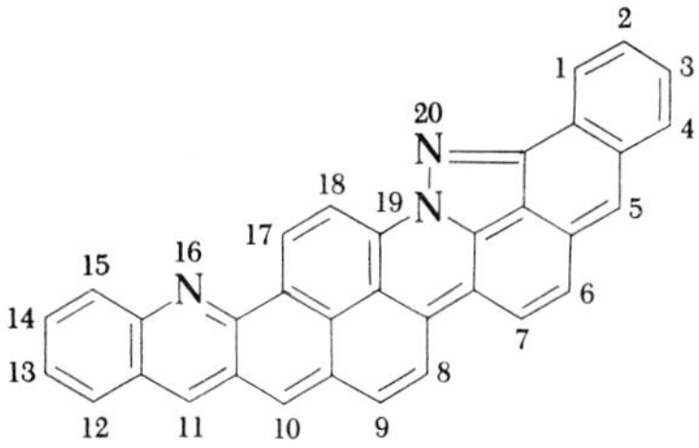

The reaction[1] of 2-aminobenzaldehyde with I yielded II, which was converted by the action of a caustic melt into a green dye of structure III. Replacement of 2-aminobenzaldehyde with 1-aminoanthraquinone-2-aldehyde yielded an olive-green homolog of III.

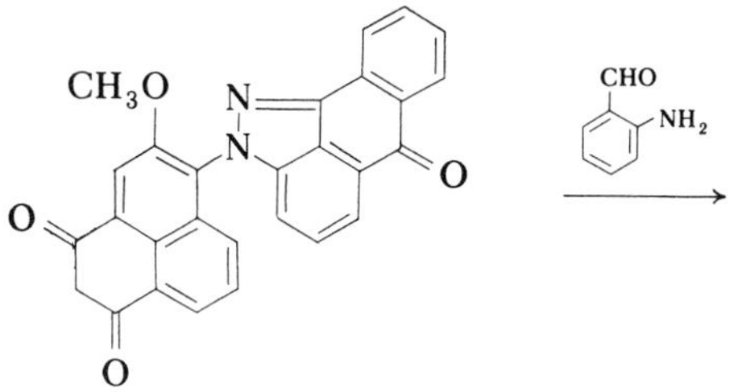

(I)

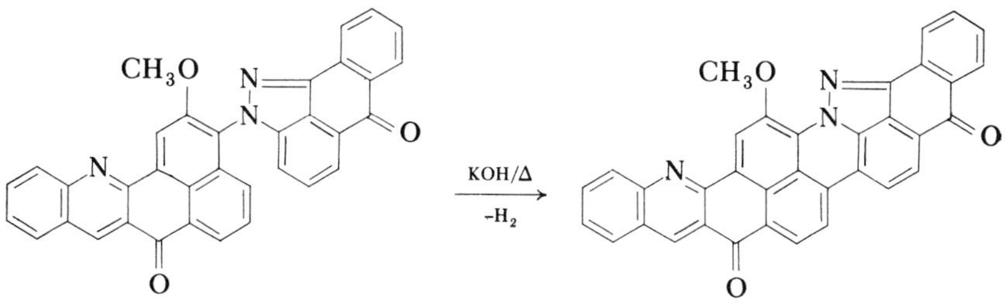

(II)

(III)

Reference

1. Gruschke and Quint, *I.G. Farbenindustrie, A.G., 42 Wissenschaftlicher Austausch der Gruppe IX*, Frankfurt a/M., February 15, 1940; *PB Report No.* 70248, frame 2834.

A-423. Bisbenz[6,7]indazolo-[4,3,2-*hij*, 4′,3′,2′-*h′i′j′*]benzo-[1,2-*b*, 4,5-*b′*]diquinoline*

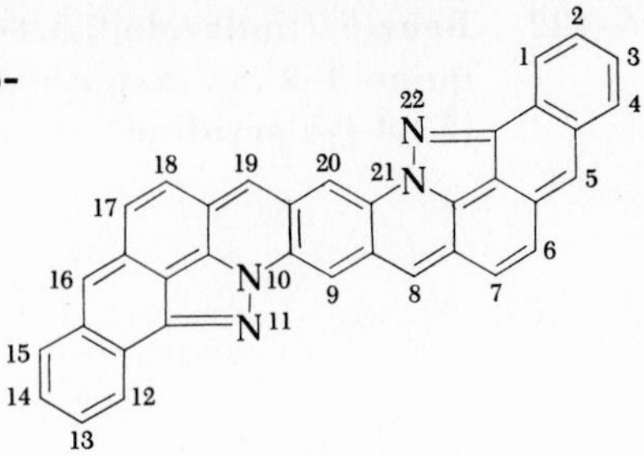

Fusion of I with caustic yielded[1] the yellowish brown dye II (violet-red vat).

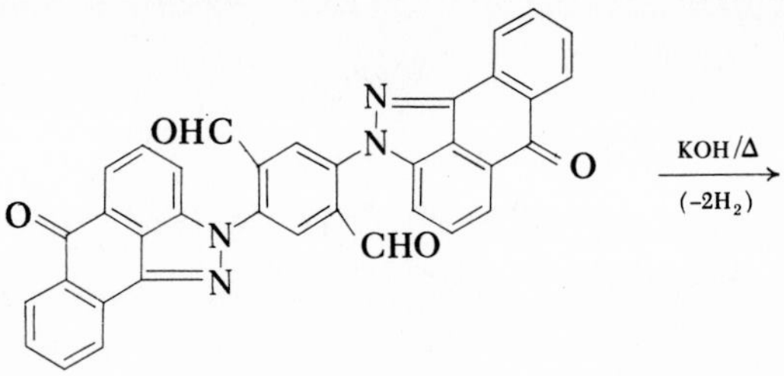

$\xrightarrow[(-2H_2)]{KOH/\Delta}$

(I)

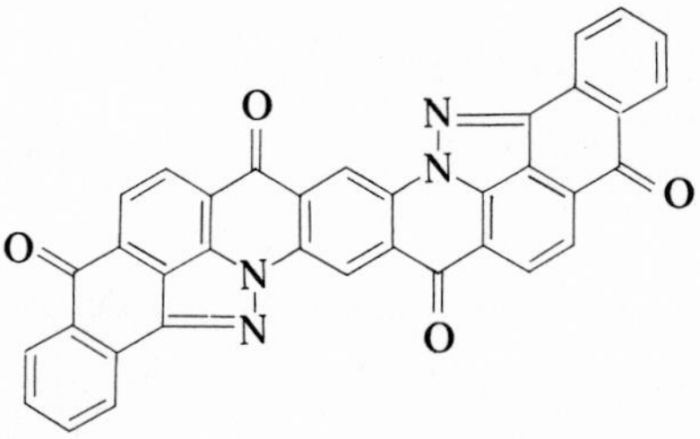

(II)

Reference

1. Kalischer, Bayer and Ritter, Ger. Pat. 525,217; *Frdl.*, **17,** 1295 (1932). Brit. Pat. 344,558. Fr. Pat. 686,341.

A-424. 13*H*,26*H*-Bisanthra[2,1,9, 4,5,6]-quino[3,2,1-*hi*, 3′,2′,1′-*h′i′*]benzo-[1,2,3-*cd*, 4,5,6-*c′d′*]diindazole*

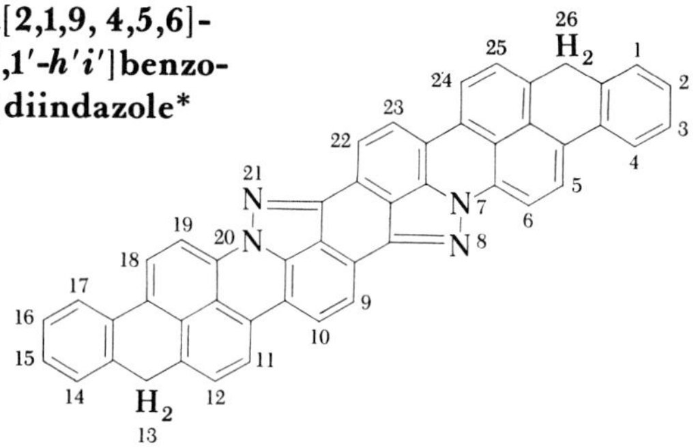

An Ullmann reaction between I and 3-bromobenzanthrone yielded[1] II, which was cyclized to III by caustic fusion. Compound

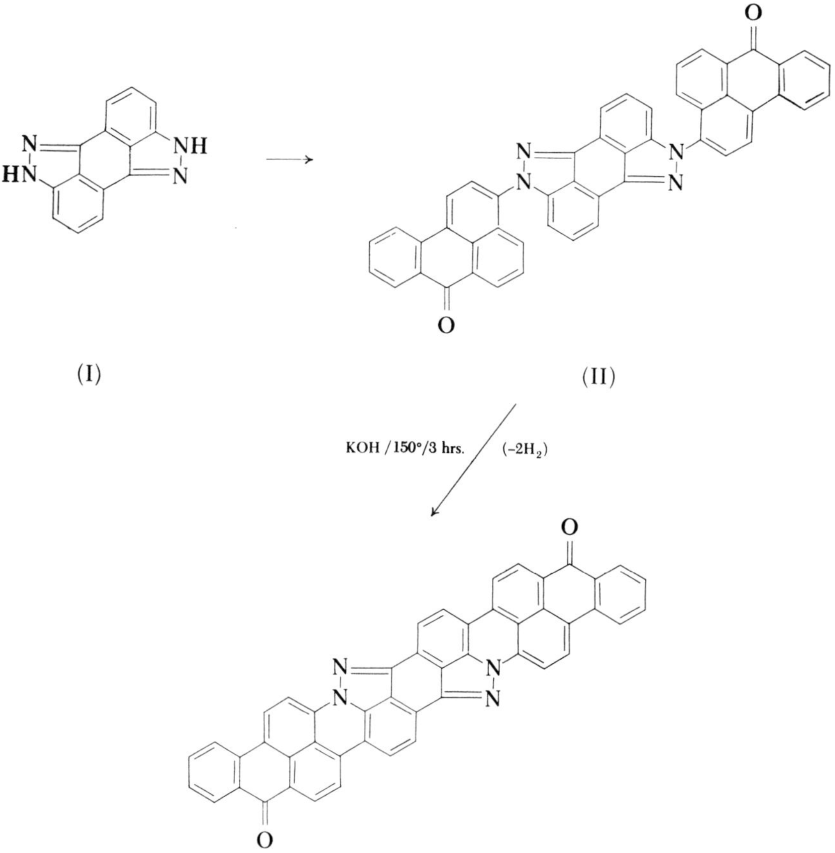

(I)

(II)

KOH / 150°/3 hrs. $(-2H_2)$

(III)

III was described as a dark brown solid (olive-green solution in sulfuric acid), which dyed cotton a reddish-blue shade from a violet-red vat.

Reference

1. Wilke, Ger. Pat. 490,723; *Frdl.*, **16,** 1368 (1931). U. S. Pat. 1,790,780. Fr. Pat. 640,939; *Chem. Zentr.*, **II,** 1947 (1928). Brit. Pat. 298,284; *Brit. Chem. Abstracts*, **B,** 9 (1928).

A-425. *5H*-Bisbenz[6,7]indazolo[4,3,2-*cde*, 4′,3′,2′-*c′d′e′*]-phenaleno[2,1,9-*ghi*, 5,6,7-*g′h′i′*]diphenanthridine*

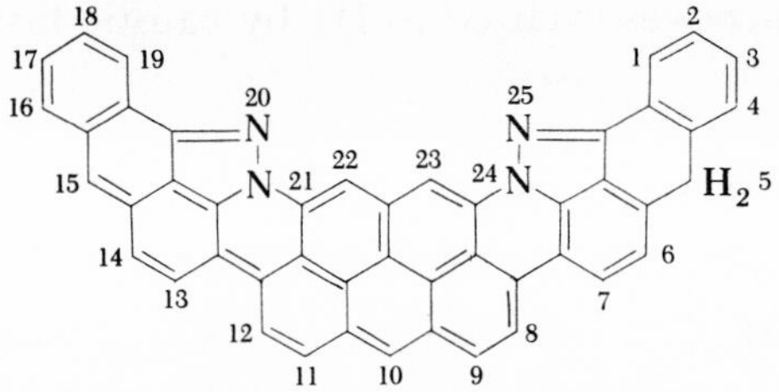

By subjecting I to an Ullmann reaction with two moles of pyrazolanthrone, Corell and Eichler[1] obtained II, which was cyclized to III

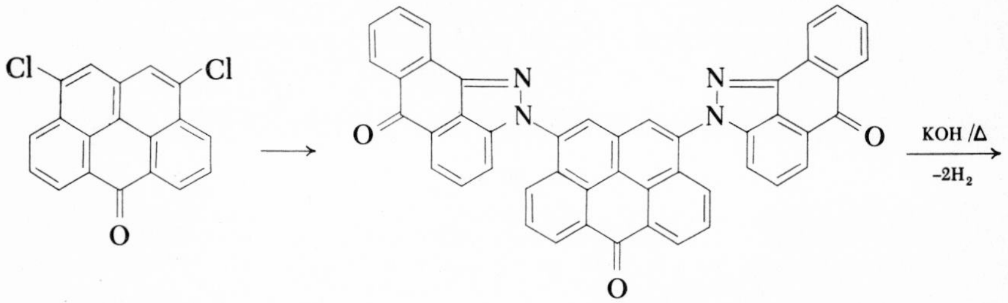

KOH /Δ
$-2H_2$

(I)

(II)

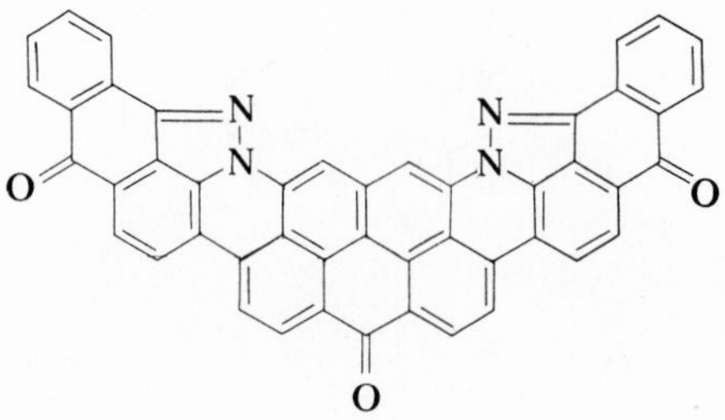

(III)

(violet needles, m. 372°; sulfuric acid solution black-violet; blue vat). While III dyed cotton a navy blue of good wash- and soda-fastness, it readily water-spotted.

Reference

1. Corell and Eichler, *I.G. Farbenindustrie, A.G., 39 Wissenschaftlicher Austausch der Gruppe IX*, Mainkur, June 21–2, 1938; *PB Report No.* 70338, frame 10381.

A-426. Pyrrolo[1,2-*b*]pyridazine

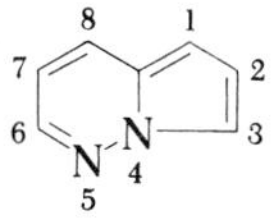

The numbering shown in I also has been used.

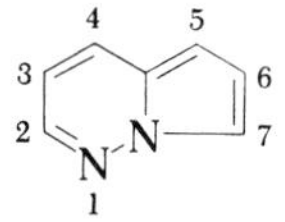

(I)

By treating pyrroylpyruvic ester with hydroxylamine, Angeli obtained a product (m. 123–4°) to which he at first[1] gave structure IIa, but later[2] considered IIIa an alternative possibility. Hydrolysis of the ester gave the acid (IIb or IIIb, m. 179°d.). The infrared spectrum of the product should readily distinguish between structures II and III.

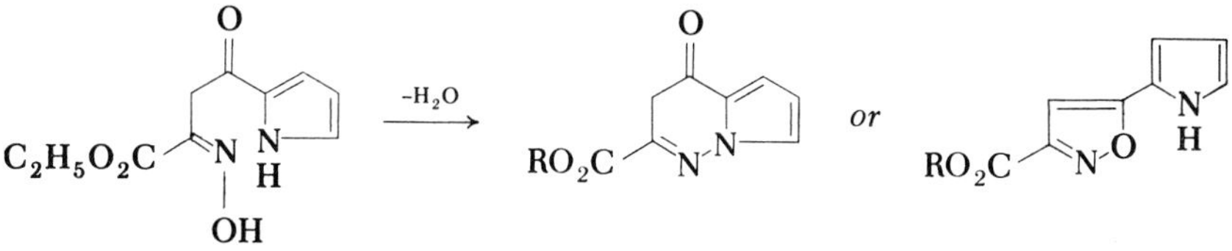

$-H_2O$ *or*

(IIa) $R = C_2H_5$
(IIb) $R = H$

(IIIa) $R = C_2H_5$
(IIIb) $R = H$

In an extension of the work of Diels *et al.* in the pyridine series (see Sections A-721, A-725, A-729, etc.), Letsinger and Lasco[3] condensed pyridazine and 3-methylpyridazine (IVa and IVb) with methyl acetylenedicarboxylate. In methanol solution a 26% (R = H) to 37% (R = CH_3) yield of V (a, R = H, m. 160–1°; b, R = CH_3, m. 164.5–5°) was formed. The ester V was saponified to the tricarboxylic acid (R = H, m. 223°), which could be reesterified to V by reaction with diazomethane. Heating the tricarboxylic acid with hydrochloric acid readily afforded VI (a, R = H, m. 243°; b, R = CH_3, m. 225.5–6°). Esterification of VI to VII (a, R = H, R′ = CH_3, m. 93–4°; b, R = CH_3, R′ = CH_3, m. 84–5°; c, R = CH_3, R′ = C_2H_5, m. 67.5–8°) was accomplished by treatment with diazomethane or by the Fischer-Speier technique.

(IVa) R = H
(IVb) R = CH_3

$(\equiv C-COOCH_3)_2$

(Va) R = H
(Vb) R = CH_3

(VI) R = H
(VI) R = CH_3

(VIIa) R = H, R′ = CH_3
(VIIb) R = R′ = CH_3
(VIIc) R = CH_3, R′ = C_2H_5

$BrCH_2COCOOC_2H_5$

(VIII)

In an alternative synthesis, which demonstrates the structure of the nucleus, VIIc was obtained[3] from the reaction of VIII with ethyl bromopyruvate.

References

1. Angeli, *Ber.*, **23,** 1793 (1890).
2. Angeli, *Ber.*, **23,** 2154 (1890).
3. Letsinger and Lasco, *J. Org. Chem.*, **21,** 764 (1956).

A-427. Pyrrolo[1,2-*c*]pyrimidine

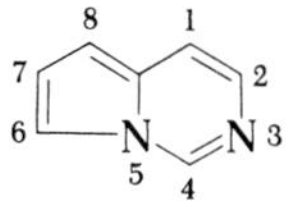

While studying the preparation of 2-pyrrolealanine by the azlactone synthesis from 2-pyrrolealdehyde, Herz[1] isolated two azlactones, one of which, with base, gave a product $C_{14}H_{10}N_2O_2$ (m.p. 182–3°) thought to have structure I. Treatment with diazomethane gave a methyl ester (m. 107°).

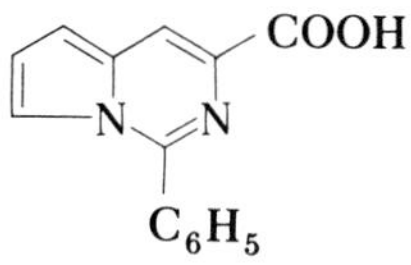

(I)

Reference

1. Herz, *J. Am. Chem. Soc.*, **71,** 3982 (1949).

A-428. Indolo[1,2-*c*]quinazoline

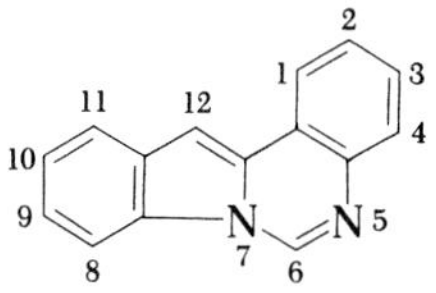

This nucleus was also named *indolo-1′:2′-3:4-quinazoline*.

The reaction of I under various conditions with acylating agents was studied recently.[1] Under the mildest conditions II was produced, but under increasingly severe conditions III and IV were formed, the latter generally being obtained under vigorous acidic conditions. For example, I with acetyl cyanide in chloroform and dry hydrogen chloride at 15° gave II together with III (R = CH_3), while at 50° the same reactants yielded IV (R = CH_3, pale yellow, m. 115–6°). Benzoyl chloride in pyridine or benzoyl cyanide in chloroform at 60° reacted with I to yield II, while with benzoyl cyanide and hydrogen chloride in chloroform at 60° III was produced, and IV (R = C_6H_5, m. 197–8°) was formed from I with benzoyl chloride in boiling chloroform. The benzyl derivative of type IV (R = $C_6H_5CH_2$, m. 194–7°) was obtained similarly. Heating I with formic acid or acetic anhydride yielded exclusively IV (R = H, m. 200–1°), as did heating II under acidic conditions.

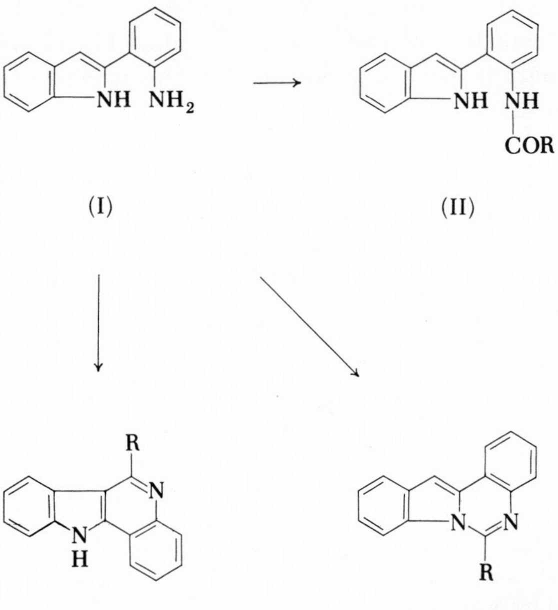

NH NH_2 → NH NH COR

(I) (II)

R N N H

N N R

(III) (IV)

Quaternization of IV (R = CH_3) yielded[2] the bright yellow 5-methyl *p*-toluenesulfonate salt (m. 258–60°), which could not be induced to yield cyanine dyes.

References

1. Kiang, Mann, Prior and Topham, *J. Chem. Soc.*, **1956,** 1319.
2. Mann and Prior, *J. Chem. Soc.*, **1956,** 1331.

A-429. Indolo[2′,3′-5,6]pyrido[1,2-*a*]-pyrrolo[*c*]pyrimidine

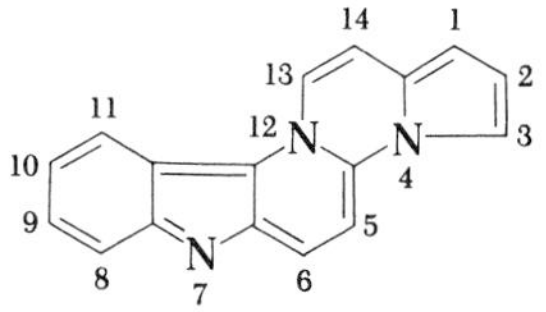

Eiter and Svierak proposed[1,2] structure I for the alkaloid *folicanthine*, although this has been questioned,[3] and other, quite different structures recently have been suggested.[4,5]

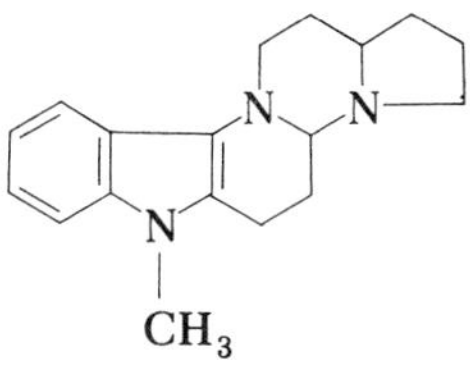

(I)

References

1. Eiter and Svierak, *Monatsh.*, **82,** 186 (1951).
2. Eiter and Svierak, *Monatsh.*, **83,** 1453 (1952).
3. Saxton, *Quart. Rev.*, **10,** 120 (1956).
4. Hodson and Smith, *Chem. and Ind.*, **1956,** 740.
5. Hodson and Smith, *J. Chem. Soc.*, **1957,** 1877.

A-430. 1*H*-Pyrrolo[2,1-*c*]oxazine. R.I. 799

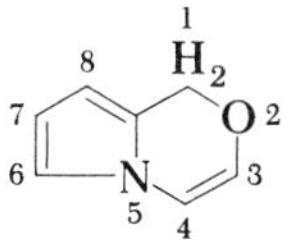

Fischer and Abderhalden[1] dehydrated what they thought was *dl*-leucylproline (I, R = NH_2) and obtained a product, to which they assigned the lactam structure II. However, Fischer and Ref[2] later showed that the starting compound was a hydroxy acid (I, R = OH) instead of an amino acid, and that the product (m. 124°) actually is the lactone III. When the *l*-isomer of I (R = OH) was used, *l*-III (m. 164°, $[\alpha]_D^{20}$ −166.7°) was obtained.[2]

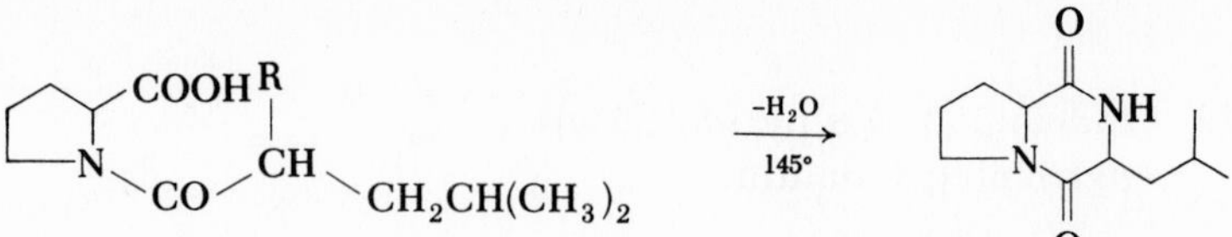

COOH R | N CO CH $CH_2CH(CH_3)_2$ $\xrightarrow[145°]{-H_2O}$ O NH N O

(I) (II)

O O N O

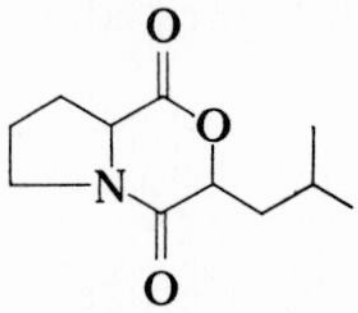

(III)

The acid IV, obtained as the product after several degradative reactions upon the alkaloid *monocrotaline*, was dehydrated[3] to V (oil; picrate, m. 169–70°; methiodide, 242–3°, $[\alpha]_D^{29}$ −15.02°).

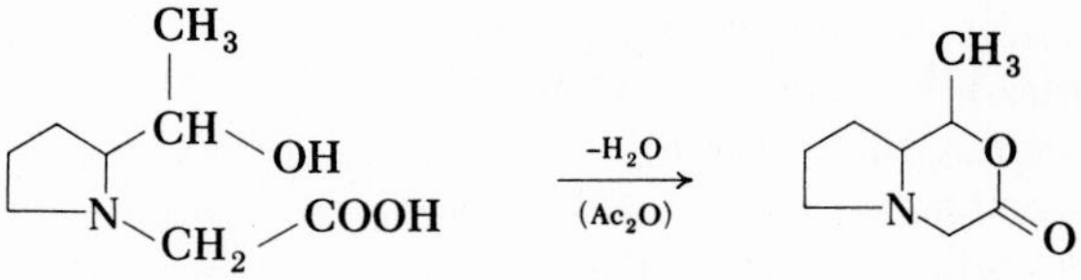

CH_3 | CH OH N CH_2 COOH $\xrightarrow[(Ac_2O)]{-H_2O}$ CH_3 O N O

(IV) (V)

References

1. Fischer and Abderhalden, *Ber.*, **37**, 3071 (1904).
2. Fischer and Reif, *Ann.*, **363**, 118 (1908).
3. Adams and Mahan, *J. Am. Chem. Soc.*, **65**, 2009 (1943).

A-431. 1*H*-*p*-Oxazino[4,3-*a*]indole

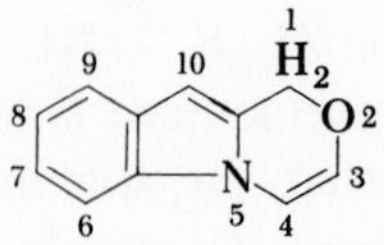

1 9 10 H_2 8 O 2 7 N 3 6 5 4

This nucleus has also been called *indolo(1′2′-3:4)morpholine*.

The anhydride II (m. 237–8°) has been obtained[1] from the thermal dehydration of I.

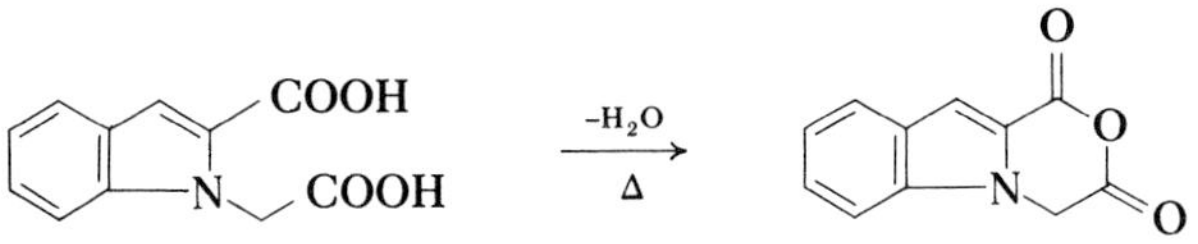

(I) (II)

Elvidge and Spring[2] heated III with sodium methoxide in benzene, hoping thereby to prepare IV, but instead they obtained V (m. 204°; O-acetyl derivative, m. 141°).

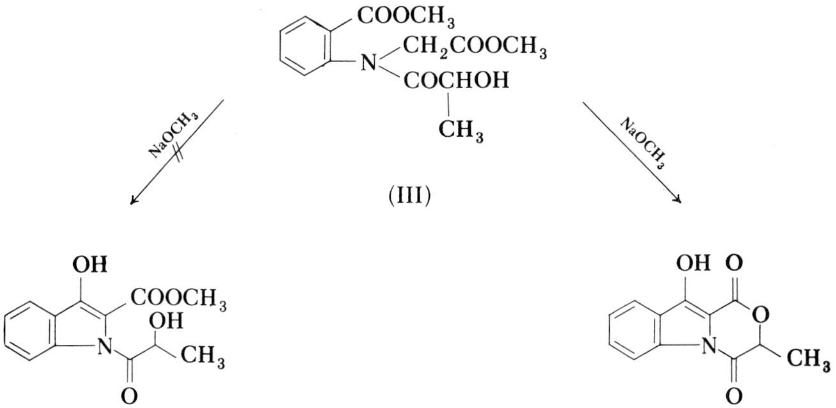

(III)

(V)

References

1. Smith and Moir, *Can. J. Chem.*, **30,** 411 (1952); *Chem. Abstracts*, **47,** 3296 (1953).
2. Elvidge and Spring, *J. Chem. Soc.*, **1949,** 2935.

A-432. Pyrrolo[1,2-*a*]pyrazine. R.I. 805

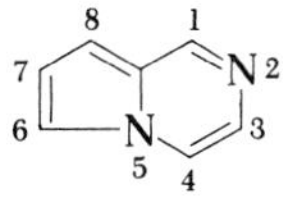

This nucleus has been called *2,5-pyrrolopyrazine*, and the octahydro derivatives have been referred to as *1,2-trimethylenepiperazines* (I).

Condensation of pyrrole-2-aldehyde or of 2-acetylpyrrole with aminoacetal yielded II, which was cyclized[1] to III (R = H or CH_3) by the action of a mixture of polyphosphoric acid and phosphorus oxychloride.

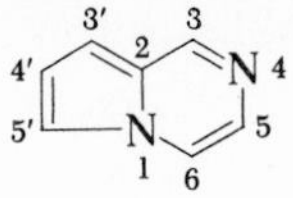

(I)

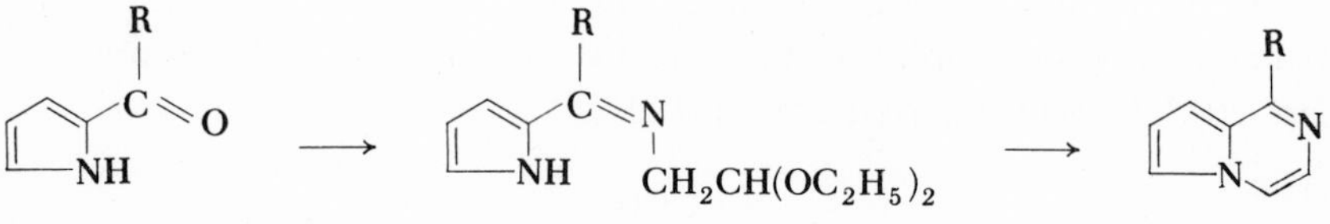

(II) (III)

The 3,4-dihydro compound IV was prepared[2] by heating 2-acetylfuran with ethylenediamine.

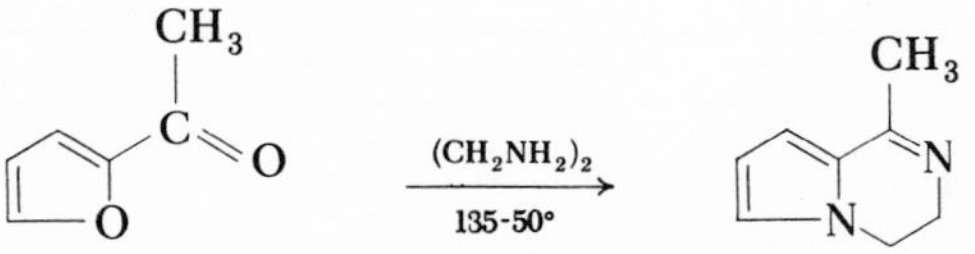

$(CH_2NH_2)_2$
135-50°

(IV)

Most of the work on these compounds has been devoted to the octahydro-1,4-dioxo derivatives (V), which are dipeptide lactams derived from proline or hydroxyproline with another amino acid. Products of type V are generally named from the amino acid components; thus V, without the hydroxy group and where R = methyl,

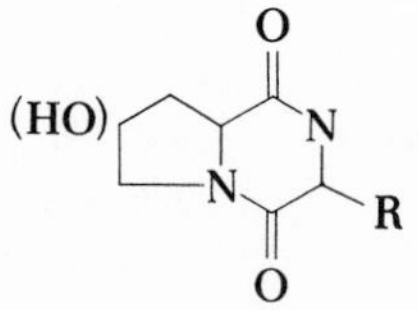

(V)

might be called *d*-alanyl-*l*-proline lactam. These lactams have been isolated from many types of proteinaceous material such as extracts of silkworm pupa,[3] extracts of streptomyces[4] and rhizopus[5] molds, and hydrolysates of casein[6] and edestin.[7] A favorite source is gelatin, degraded either by tryptic digestion,[8] pyrolysis[9] or acidic hydrolysis.[10] Quite a few (e.g., VI) have been prepared[11-17] synthetically from the component amino acids. Several have been isolated from the products of cleavage of the ergot alkaloids by heat[18-20] or the action of hydrazine,[21] or caustic.[22]

COCl NH + H_2N–C–$CH_2CH(CH_3)_2$ | $COOC_2H_5$ ⟶ O NH N O

(VI)

Perhydro derivatives of this nucleus have been obtained in two ways: treatment of gelatin with sodium and alcohols,[24,25] and reduction of products of type V (or of the ergot alkaloids) with lithium aluminum hydride.[26,27]

Several complex derivatives containing this nucleus have been obtained in connection with studies[23] upon the ergot alkaloids and these are not included in the tables.

Pyrrolo[1,2-*a*]pyrazines

Empirical formula	Substituents	Properties	Refs.
$C_7H_6N_2$	Unsubstituted	b_2 71°; n_D^{20} 1.6176; λ_{max} 230, 280, 330 and 372 mμ (log ε 3.50, 2.70, 2.52 and 2.02). Picrate, m. 212°.	1
$C_7H_{10}N_2O_2$	Perhydro-1,4-dioxo-	L-Form: m. 180–3° (182–3°, 188°, 203–13°); $[\alpha]_D^{20}$ –202° (–217.4°).	7,8,10, 13,28
$C_7H_{14}N_2O$	Perhydro-7-hydroxy-	HCl salt, d. 190°. *N*-Carbanilino deriv., d. 198°.	24
$C_8H_8N_2$	1-Methyl-	$b_{1.5}$ 82°; n_D^{20} 1.6910; λ_{max} 230, 280, 330 and 360 mμ (log ε 3.45, 3.58, 3.30 and 1.95). Picrate, m. 230°.	1

(*continued*)

Pyrrolo[1,2-*a*]pyrazines (*continued*)

Empirical formula	Substituents	Properties	Refs.
$C_8H_{10}N_2$	3,4-Dihydro-1-methyl-	$b_{1.8-2.5}$ 84–9°.	2
$C_8H_{12}N_2O_2$	Perhydro-3-methyl-1,4-dioxo-	m. 126–9°. *dl*-L-Form: m. 114–5°.	3,11,15
$C_8H_{16}N_2O$	Perhydro-7-methoxy-	m. 195°.	24
$C_{10}H_{16}N_2O_2$	Perhydro-3-(2-propyl)-1,4-dioxo-	L,D-Form: m. 147–9°, $[\alpha]_D^{20°}$ 88° (H_2O).	19
$C_{11}H_{18}N_2O_2$	Perhydro-3-isobutyl-1,4-dioxo-	L,L-Form: m. 170–1° (158–9°, 150–60°, 158–61°); $[\alpha]_D^{20°}$ −142.4° (3.33, ethanol) or −144° (0.4, water) or −146.7 (1, water).	3–5,13, 14,17, 26
		L,D-Form: m. 148–50° (148°), $[\alpha]_{5461}^{20°}$ + 105° (H_2O).	18,19
		dl,*dl*-Form: m. 117–21°.	12
$C_{11}H_{22}N_2$	Perhydro-3-isobutyl-	Oil, b 228°; b_{15} 110°. Chloroaurate, m. 197°.	24,25
		L,L-Form: b_{12} 95–100°, $[\alpha]_D^{20°}$ 15° (ethanol). Dipicrate, m. 185–6°.	26,27
		L,D-Form: oil, $[\alpha]_D^{20°}$ 28° (0.3, ethanol). Dipicrate, m. 222–4°.	26
$C_{14}H_{14}N_2O_2$	3-Benzylidene-perhydro-1,4-dioxo-	L-Form: m. 177–80°, $[\alpha]_D^{25°}$ 284.7 (5, pyridine).	16
$C_{14}H_{16}N_2O_2$	3-Benzyl-perhydro-1,4-dioxo-	L,L-Form: m. 135–6°, $[\alpha]_D^{20°}$ −107.6°.	16
		L,D-Form: m. 150°; $[\alpha]_D^{20°}$ 92°, $[\alpha]_{5451}^{20°}$ 110°.	20,26
		dl-Forms: m. 149° (130–2°, 146–8°, 117–23°) $[\alpha]_D^{20°}$ 23 to −35° (0.2, ethanol).	16,21,22
$C_{14}H_{16}N_2O_3$	Perhydro-2-(4-hydroxybenzyl)-1,4-dioxo-	Two forms: m. 187°, $[\alpha]$ −10.25°; m. 226–8°, $[\alpha]$ 67.1°.	6
$C_{14}H_{20}N_2$	3-Benzyl-perhydro-	L,L-Form: oil, $[\alpha]_D^{20°}$ −17° (0.3, pyridine). Dipicrate, m. 258°.	26

Pyrrolo[1,2-*a*]pyrazines (*continued*)

Empirical formula	Substituents	Properties	Refs.
		L,D-Form: m. 63–5°, $[\alpha]_D^{20}$ 24° (ethanol). Dipicrate, m. 257–8°.	26
$C_{15}H_{18}N_2O_3$	Perhydro-3-(4-methoxybenzyl)-1,4-dioxo-	m. 156–7°.	6
$C_{16}H_{16}N_2O_3$	2-Acetyl-3-benzylidene-perhydro-1,4-dioxo-	D-Form: m. 172–3°, $[\alpha]_D^{25°}$ 49.3° (5, pyridine). *dl*-Form: m. 149–51°.	6
$C_{16}H_{18}N_2O_3$	2-Acetyl-3-benzyl-perhydro-1,4-dioxo-	L,L-Form: m. 123–5°, $[\alpha]_D^{25}$ 202.6° (5, pyridine).	16

References

1. Herz and Tocker, *J. Am. Chem. Soc.*, **77,** 6355 (1955).
2. Dunlop and Swadesh, U. S. Pat. 2,655,512.
3. Butenandt, Karlson and Zillig, *Z. physiol Chem.*, **288,** 279 (1951); *Chem. Abstracts*, **49,** 2628 (1955).
4. Johnson, Jackson and Eble, *J. Am. Chem. Soc.*, **73,** 2947 (1951).
5. Eppstein, Peterson, Leigh, Murray, Weintraub, Reincke and Meister, *J. Am. Chem. Soc.*, **75,** 421 (1953).
6. Abderhalden and Sickel, *Z. physiol. Chem.*, **153,** 16 (1926); *Chem. Abstracts*, **20,** 3169 (1926).
7. Abderhalden and Komm, *Z. physiol. Chem.*, **149,** 308 (1925); *Chem. Abstracts*, **19,** 2810 (1925).
8. Levene and Beatty, *Ber.*, **39,** 2060 (1906).
9. Fodor and Kuk, *Koll. Zeitschr.*, **74,** 66 (1936); *Chem. Zentr.*, **I,** 103 (1937).
10. Gawrilow and Lawrowsky, *Biochem. Z.*, **190,** 278 (1927); *Chem. Abstracts*, **22,** 1593 (1928).
11. Fischer and Suzuki, *Ber.*, **37,** 2842 (1904).
12. Fischer and Abderhalden, *Ber.*, **37,** 3071 (1904).
13. Fischer and Reif, *Ann.*, **363,** 118 (1908).
14. Abderhalden and Sickel, *Z. physiol. Chem.*, **159,** 163 (1926); *Chem. Abstracts*, **21,** 390 (1927).
15. Abderhalden and Zumstein, *Fermentforschung*, **12,** 1 (1930); *Chem. Abstracts*, **25,** 77 (1931).
16. Bergmann and Tietzman, *J. Biol. Chem.*, **155,** 535 (1944); *Chem. Abstracts*, **39,** 930 (1945).
17. Neuman and Smith, *J. Biol. Chem.*, **193,** 97 (1951); *Chem. Abstracts*, **46,** 5037 (1952).

18. Smith and Timmis, *J. Chem. Soc.*, **1937**, 396.
19. Stoll, Hofmann and Becker, *Helv. Chim. Acta*, **26**, 1602 (1943).
20. Stoll, *Helv. Chim. Acta*, **28**, 1283 (1945).
21. Stoll, Petrzilka and Becker, *Helv. Chim. Acta*, **33**, 57 (1950).
22. Stoll and Hofmann, *Helv. Chim. Acta*, **33**, 1705 (1950).
23. Marion, in Manske and Holmes, *The Alkaloids*, Academic Press, New York, 1952, Vol. 2, p. 375.
24. Abderhalden and Schwab, *Z. physiol. Chem.*, **148**, 254 (1925); *Chem. Zentr.*, **I**, 1192 (1926); *Chem. Abstracts*, **20**, 55 (1926).
25. Wrede, Burch and Feuerriegel, *Z. physiol. Chem.*, **214**, 63 (1933); *Chem. Abstracts*, **27**, 983 (1933).
26. Stoll, Hofmann and Petrzilka, *Helv. Chim. Acta*, **34**, 1544 (1951).
27. Stoll and Petrzilka, U. S. Pat. 2,673,850; Brit. Pat. 728,968.
28. Smith, *J. Chem. Soc.*, **1957**, 3985.

A-433. 5*H*,10*H*-Dipyrrolo[*a*,*d*]pyrazine. R.I. 1394

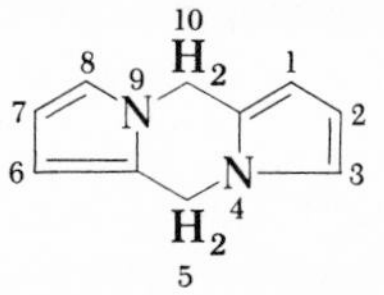

The *Ring Index* name lacks the 5*H*,10*H* prefix. The numbering systems I–III have also been used, and the trivial name *pyrocoll* is often applied to the 5,10-dioxo derivatives. *Chemical Abstracts* still indexes compounds under this heading.

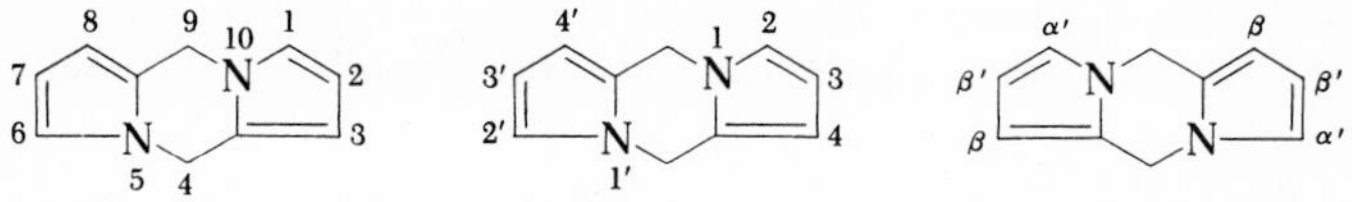

(I) (II) (III)

From the destructive distillation of gelatin, Weidel and Ciamician[1–4] isolated a nearly colorless crystalline substance, which they called *pyrocoll* (IV). It sublimes at high temperatures without melting, but in a sealed capillary melts at 268–9°. Concentrated alkali hydrolyzes pyrocoll to pyrrole-2-carboxylic acid, and treatment with ammonia in a sealed tube yields the corresponding amide. Zinc dust distillation of pyrocoll yields pyrrole.

Pyrocoll was also prepared[7] by heating pyrrole-2-carboxylic acid in acetic anhydride, and most of the substituted pyrocolls re-

Gelatin $\xrightarrow{\Delta}$ (IV) $\xleftarrow[\Delta]{-2H_2O}$ NH, COOH

O, N, N, O

(IV)

ported have been prepared in this manner. Formation of the high melting pyrocoll provides a convenient method for characterizing pyrrole-2-carboxylic acids.

The direct bromination of pyrocoll yields[5-8] mono-, di- or tetra-bromo derivatives, while treatment with phosphorus pentachloride gave[6] perchloropyrocoll. More drastic conditions produced more highly chlorinated products (e.g. $C_{10}Cl_{14}N_2O_2$) thought[6] to be addition compounds, but of unproven structure.

Nitration of pyrocoll at 4–10°C. gives chiefly the 1,6-dinitro derivative,[6,9,10] as shown by degradation to 3-nitro-2-pyrrolecarboxylic acid,[6,9] while at −10° to −4°C. the major product is 3,8-dinitropyrocoll.[10] The two dinitropyrocolls were also prepared[10] by dehydration of the appropriate nitropyrrole-2-carboxylic acids.

Molecular weight determinations[11] show that, in solution, 2-pyrrolecarboxaldehyde is associated, and isolation of a dibenzoate (m. 178°) supports structure V for the aldehyde.

Harrell and Corwin[12] describe the preparation of products of type VI (R = C_2H_5, R′ = 4-carbethoxy-3,5-dimethyl-2-pyrryl-,

H, OH, N, N, HO, H

(V)

R′CH_2, CH_3, HO, OR, C_2H_5OOC, N, N, $COOC_2H_5$, CH_3, HO, OR, CH_2R'

(VI)

cis, m. 195.0–6.5°, *trans*, m. 236.0–7.5°) from the catalytic reduction of 3,5,4′-tricarbethoxy-4,3′,5′-trimethylpyrromethene, or (where R of VI is H, and R′ is 3,5-dicarbethoxy-4-methyl-2-pyrryl-, m. 203–4°) by heating 3,3′,5′-tricarbethoxy-4,4′-dimethyl-5-carboxypyrromethane with acetic anhydride.

When glutamic acid is heated[13] with acetic anhydride and pyridine, amongst the resulting products is a high-melting solid of structure VII. This structure was confirmed by an alternative synthesis from VIII.

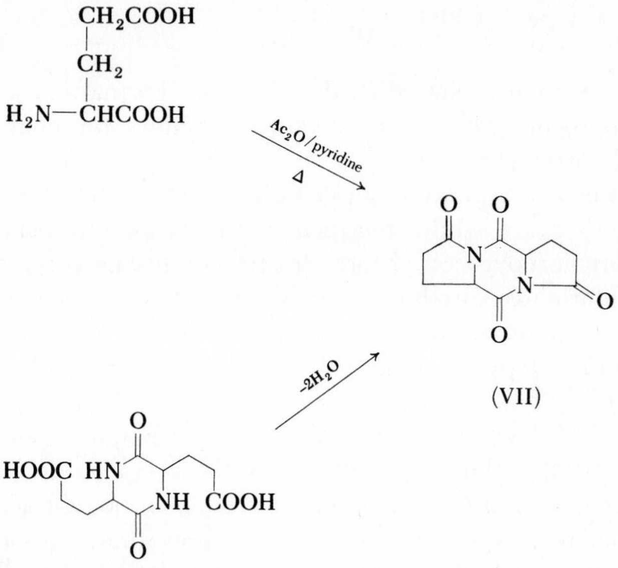

$$\begin{array}{l} CH_2COOH \\ | \\ CH_2 \\ | \\ H_2N-CHCOOH \end{array} \xrightarrow[\Delta]{Ac_2O/pyridine} \text{(VII)}$$

(VII)

$$\text{(VIII)} \xrightarrow{-2H_2O} \text{(VII)}$$

HOOC HN NH COOH

(VIII)

The dimeric lactams[14-18] of proline and hydroxyproline have structure IX. These lactams are present in the crude proline fractions

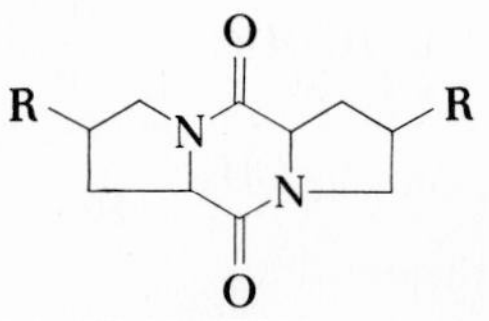

(IX)

from the acid hydrolysis of gelatin,[14] and they may be obtained by allowing proline hydrochloride to stand in ether,[15] or proline (or hydroxyproline) esters to stand in ethanol.[16-18] While these lactams are relatively stable to aqueous acids, they are readily hydrolyzed by dilute alkali.[20] The metabolism of the proline lactams has been studied.[20-22]

Hydrogenation of butyl pyroglutamate (X) over a copper chromite catalyst at about 200° yielded butanol and 5-hydroxymethylpyrrolidone, while at about 250° 1-butyl-2-hydroxymethylpyrrolidine and compound XI (m. 84.0–4.5°) were formed.[23,24] Further hydrogenation of pure 5-hydroxymethylpyrrolidone gave an excellent yield of XI, free of byproducts.

$COOC_4H_9$ ... NH ... O $\xrightarrow{H_2/Cu_2Cr_2O_5}$ [CH_2OH ... NH ... O] $\longrightarrow$ (XI)

(X) (XI)

Recently, pyrrole-2-aldehyde was found[34] to condense with piperidine, morpholine or pyrrolidine to yield products of structure XII (R = piperidyl, m. 160°; R = morpholinyl, m. 197–8°; R = pyrrolidyl, m. 93–4°).

NH, CHO $\longrightarrow$ R, N, N, R

(XII)

5*H*,10*H*-Dipyrrolo[*a*,*d*]pyrazine-5,10-diones

Empirical formula	Substituents	Properties	Refs.
$C_{10}Cl_6N_2O_2$	1,2,3,6,7,8-Hexachloro-	Yel., m. > 320° d. Octachloride, subl. 100°.	6,8
$C_{10}Cl_{10}N_2O$	Structure unknown.	m. 195–7°.	6
$C_{10}H_2Br_4N_2O_2$	*x*,*x*,*x*,*x*-Tetrabromo-	Yel., d. 250°.	8
$C_{10}H_4Br_2N_2O_2$	*x*,*x*-Dibromo-	Yel., m. 288–90°.	5,6

(*continued*)

$5H,10H$-Dipyrrolo[*a,d*]pyrazine-5,10-diones (*continued*)

Empirical formula	Substituents	Properties	Refs.
$C_{10}H_4N_4O_6$	1,6-Dinitro-	Yel., d. 315–20°.	6,10
	3,8-Dinitro-	Yel., d. 240–5°.	10
$C_{10}H_5BrN_2O_2$	*x*-Bromo-	Yel., m. 190–2°.	5–7
$C_{10}H_6N_2O_2$	Unsubstituted.	Lt. yel., m. 267°.	2,3,7
$C_{10}H_{10}N_2O_4$	1,2,6,7-Tetrahydro-3,8-dioxo-	m. 340° d.	13
$C_{10}H_{14}N_2O_2$	Octahydro-	*ll*-Form: m. 156° (149°, 143°); $[\alpha]_D^{20}$ −151.15 *dl*-Form: m. 183–4°.	15–19
$C_{10}H_{14}N_2O_3$	Octahydro-2-hydroxy-	*ll*-Form: m. 102–3° (from ether) or 135–40° (from H_2O). $[\alpha]_D^{20}$ −142° (H_2O).	14
$C_{10}H_{14}N_2O_4$	Octahydro-2,7-dihydroxy-	*ll*-Form: m. 245–6° d., $[\alpha]_D^{18}$ − 153.44°.	18
$C_{14}H_{14}N_2O_2$	1,3,6,8-Tetramethyl-	Lt. yel., m. 272.0–2.5°.	25
$C_{16}H_{14}N_2O_6$	2,7-Dicarboxy-1,3,6,8-tetramethyl-	Lt. yel., d. >350°.	25,26
$C_{16}H_{16}N_2O_2$	2,7-Di-2-propyl-	m. 156–7°.	33
$C_{18}H_{18}N_2O_6$	1,6-Dicarbethoxy-2,7-dimethyl-	Lt. yel., m. 168°.	27
$C_{20}H_{22}N_2O_6$	2,7-Dicarbethoxy-1,3,6,8-tetramethyl-	Lt. yel., m. ~270°. (257–8°).	25,30
	1,6-Dicarbethoxy-2,3,7,8-tetramethyl-	Lt. yel., m. 169°.	28
$C_{22}H_{26}N_2O_6$	1,6-Dicarbethoxy-2,7-diethyl-3,8-dimethyl-	Lt. yel., m. 159°.	29
	3,8-Dicarbethoxy-1,6-diethyl-2,7-dimethyl-	Lt. yel., m. 150°.	31
$C_{24}H_{28}Br_2N_2O_8$	3,8-Bisbromomethyl-2,7-dicarbethoxy-1,6-dimethyl-	m. 205.5–7°.	12
$C_{24}H_{30}N_2O_8$	2,7-Dicarbethoxy-3,8-bisethoxymethyl-1,6-dimethyl-	m. 158.0–9.5°.	12
$C_{26}H_{24}N_4O_6$	2,7-Bis(2-carbethoxy-2-cyanovinyl)-1,3,6,8-tetramethyl-	Red, m. 276°.	32

References

1. Weidel and Ciamician, *Monatsh.*, **1,** 279 (1880).
2. Weidel and Ciamician, *Ber.*, **14,** 1108 (1881).
3. Weidel and Ciamician, *Monatsh.*, **2,** 279 (1881).
4. Weidel and Ciamician, *Gazz. chim. ital.*, **11,** 28 (1881).
5. Ciamician and Danesi, *Gazz. chim. ital.*, **11,** 330 (1881); *Ber.*, **15,** 373 (1882).
6. Ciamician and Danesi, *Gazz. chim. ital.*, **12,** 28 (1882); *Ber.*, **15,** 1082 (1882).
7. Ciamician and Silber, *Ber.*, **17,** 103 (1884).
8. Ciamician and Silber, *Ber.*, **16,** 2388 (1883).
9. Hale and Hoyt, *J. Am. Chem. Soc.*, **37,** 2538 (1915).
10. Hale and Hoyt, *J. Am. Chem. Soc.*, **38,** 1065 (1916).
11. Emmert and Diehl, *Ber.*, **64,** 130 (1931).
12. Harrell and Corwin, *J. Am. Chem. Soc.*, **78,** 3135 (1956).
13. King and McMillan, *J. Am. Chem. Soc.*, **74,** 2859 (1952).
14. Dakin, *J. Biol. Chem.*, **44,** 499 (1920).
15. Abderhalden and Sickel, *Z. Physiol. Chem.*, **152,** 95 (1926); *Chem. Zentr.*, **I,** 2697 (1926).
16. Putochin, *Ber.*, **59,** 1987 (1926).
17. Abderhalden and Nienburg, *Fermentforschung*, **13,** 573 (1933); *Chem. Abstracts*, **27,** 2953 (1933).
18. Kapfhammer and Matthes, *Z. physiol. Chem.*, **223,** 43 (1933); *Chem. Abstracts*, **28,** 2353 (1934).
19. Stoll, Rutschmann and Schlientz, *Helv. Chim. Acta*, **33,** 375 (1950).
20. Abderhalden and Parshin, *Z. Vitamin-, Hormon-, u. Fermentforsch.*, **1,** 21 (1947); *Chem. Abstracts*, **42,** 4865 (1948).
21. Schultz, *Z. physiol. Chem.*, **280,** 16 (1944); *Chem. Abstracts*, **38,** 5926 (1944).
22. Parshin and Nikolaeva, *Biolchimiya*, **12,** 179 (1947); *Chem. Abstracts*, **41,** 6907 (1947).
23. Segel, *J. Am. Chem. Soc.*, **74,** 851 (1952).
24. Segel, U. S. Pat. 2,673,203. Brit. Pat. 711,651.
25. Magnani, *Ber.*, **21,** 2874 (1888); **22,** 35 (1889).
26. Erlenmeyer, *Ber.*, **22,** 792 (1889).
27. Fischer and Wiedemann, *Z. physiol. Chem.*, **155,** 52 (1926); *Chem. Abstracts*, **20,** 3455 (1926).
28. Piloty and Wilke, *Ber.*, **45,** 2586 (1912).
29. Piloty, Wilke and Blömer, *Ann.*, **407,** 1 (1914).
30. Küster, Weber, Maurer, Schlack, Niemann, Schlayerbach and Schlayerbach, *Z. physiol. Chem.*, **121,** 135 (1922); *Chem. Zentr.*, **III,** 1086 (1922).
31. Fischer, Sturm and Friedrich, *Ann.*, **461,** 244 (1928).
32. Fischer and Wesenegger, *Ann.*, **461,** 277 (1928).
33. Ueno, Nawa, Uenayagi, Morimoto, Nakamori and Matsuoka, *J. Pharm. Soc. Japan*, **75,** 814 (1956); *Chem. Abstracts*, **50,** 4116 (1956).
34. Herz and Brasch, *J. Org. Chem.*, **23,** 711 (1958).

A-434. Dipyrrolo[*a,c*]pyrazine. R.I. 1395

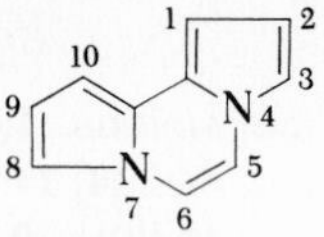

1 2 3 N 4 5 6 7 N 8 9 10

Oxidation of I with ferric chloride yielded[1] a red product (chars >200°; dark green solution in sulfuric acid), which was assigned structure II. Treatment of II with nitrous acid gave a product thought to be the dinitroso derivative of I. Further evidence for these structures would be welcome.

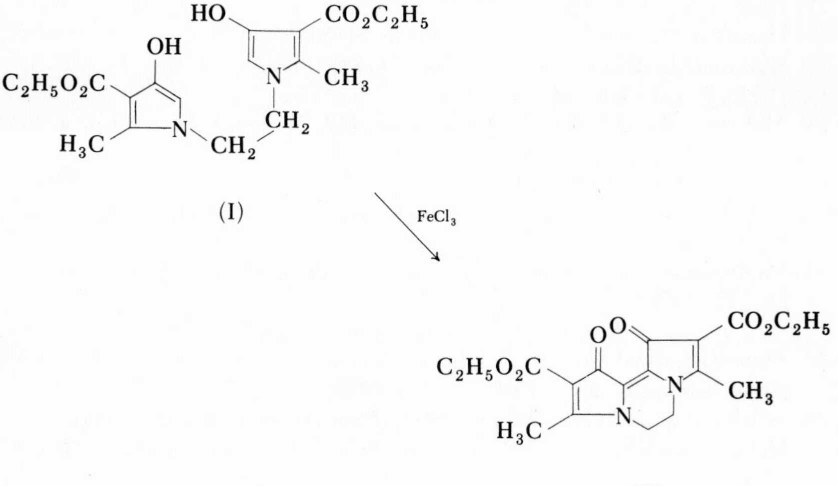

HO $CO_2C_2H_5$ OH $C_2H_5O_2C$ N CH_3 CH_2 H_3C N CH_2

(I)

$FeCl_3$

O O $CO_2C_2H_5$ $C_2H_5O_2C$ N CH_3 H_3C N

(II)

Reference

1. Benary, *Ber.*, **60,** 1826 (1927).

A-435. Pyrazino[1,2-*a*]indole. R.I. 1630

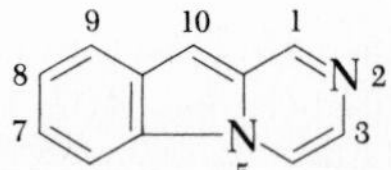

9 10 1 8 N 2 7 N 3 6 5 4

The names *α-pyrazindole*, *indolediazine(1:4)* and *indole-1,4-diazine*, and the numbering shown in I have also been employed.

During their investigations of the harmine alkaloids, Perkin *et al.*[1-3] studied the cyclization of indole derivatives such as II. When R = R′ = R″ = H or R = R′ = H, R″ = CH_3 the pyrazino[1,2-*a*]indolone (III) was the sole product, while the pyridindo-

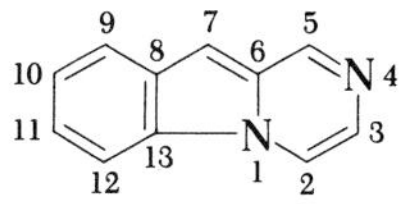

(I)

lone (IV) alone was formed[3,4] from the tertiary amine (II, R = R″ = H, R′ = CH_3). Similarly, the 4-, 5-, 6- and 7-methoxy homologs (II, R′ = R″ = H, R = CH_3O) gave III (R′ = R″ = H, R = CH_3O) when the nitrogen was unsubstituted, but the methyl homologs (II, R = CH_3O, R′ = CH_3, R″ = H) yielded[3] mixtures of III and IV (except the 4-methoxy isomer, which gave exclusively IV).

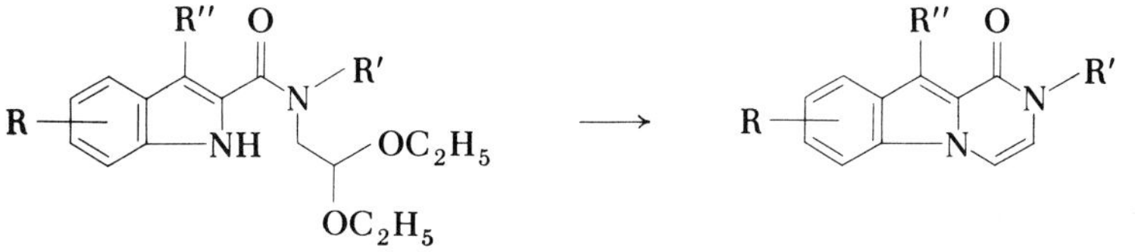

(II) (III)

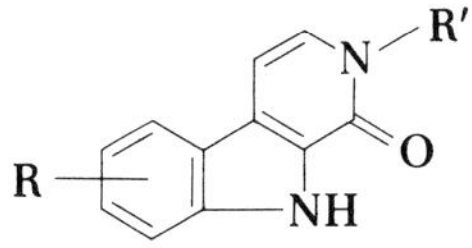

(IV)

A number of derivatives of this nucleus were obtained during work upon the structure of the antibiotic mold metabolite *gliotoxin.* The simpler derivatives are included in the table, but as the chemistry of gliotoxin was recently reviewed, and a complete bibliogra-

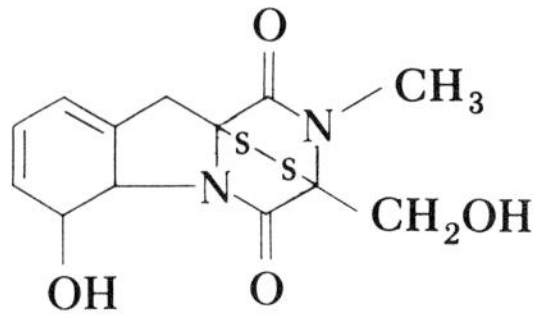

(V)

phy given,[5] no purpose would be served by repeating this information here. The new structure V was recently proposed[11] for gliotoxin, and some additional degradation products were described.

Pyrazino[1,2-*a*]indoles

Empirical formula	Substituents	Properties	Refs.
$C_{11}H_8N_2O$	1,2-Dihydro-1-oxo-	Pale yel., m. 250–1° (247°).	1,4
$C_{12}H_8N_2O_3$	1,2,3,4-Tetrahydro-2-methyl-1,3,4-trioxo-	Pale yel., m. 254–5°.	7,8
$C_{12}H_{10}N_2O$	1,2-Dihydro-2-methyl-1-oxo-	m. 147–8°.	4
	1,2-Dihydro-3-methyl-1-oxo-	Pale yel,, m. 253–4°.	4
	1,2-Dihydro-10-methyl-1-oxo-	Yel. m. 212–3° (210°).	1,4
$C_{12}H_{10}N_2O_2$	1,2,3,4-Tetrahydro-2-methyl-1,4-dioxo-	m. 204.5–5.5°.	9
	1,2-Dihydro-7-methoxy-1-oxo-	Yel., m. 253°.	1
	1,2-Dihydro-8-methoxy-1-oxo-	Yel., sinters 265°, m. 280°.	3
$C_{13}H_{10}N_2O_3$	1,2,3,4-Tetrahydro-2,10-dimethyl-1,3,4-trioxo-	m. 209–10°; λ_{max} 265, 340–5 mμ (log ϵ 4.2–4.3, 4.1).	8
	2-Carboxymethyl-1,2-dihydro-1-oxo-	m. 275–7° d.	4
$C_{13}H_{11}ClN_2O_2$	9-Chloro-1,2-dihydro-6-methoxy-10-methyl-1-oxo-	m. 190°.	3
$C_{13}H_{12}N_2O$	1,2-Dihydro-2,3-dimethyl-1-oxo-	Pale yel., m. 206–7.5°.	4
	1,2-Dihydro-2,10-dimethyl-1-oxo-	Pale yel., m. 160–1° (159°).	2,4
$C_{13}H_{12}N_2O_2$	1,2-Dihydro-7-methoxy-2-methyl-1-oxo-	Yel., m. 205°.	2
	1,2-Dihydro-8-methoxy-2-methyl-1-oxo-	m. 243°.	3
	1,2,3,4-Tetrahydro-2,3-dimethyl-1,4-dioxo-	m. 123.5–4° (121–2°).	6,8–10
$C_{14}H_{14}N_2O$	1,2-Dihydro-2,3,10-trimethyl-1-oxo-	Yel., m. 201–2.5°.	4
$C_{14}H_{14}N_2O_2$	1,2,3,4-Tetrahydro-2,3,10-trimethyl-1,4-dioxo-	Pale yel., m. 117.5–8.5°.	8
$C_{17}H_{23}N_3O$	2-(2-Diethylaminoethyl)-1,2-dihydro-10-methyl-1-oxo-	HCl salt, m. 173–4°.	4

References

1. Kermack, Perkin and Robinson, *J. Chem. Soc.*, **119,** 1602 (1921).
2. Kermack, Perkin and Robinson, *J. Chem. Soc.*, **121,** 1872 (1922).
3. Blaikie and Perkin, *J. Chem. Soc.*, **125,** 296 (1924).
4. Johnson, Larsen, Holley and Gerzon, *J. Am. Chem. Soc.*, **69,** 2364 (1947).
5. Johnson, in Marvel, editor, *The Roger Adams Symposium*, John Wiley & Sons, New York, 1955, p. 60.
6. Dutcher, Johnson and Bruce, *J. Am. Chem. Soc.*, **66,** 617 (1944).
7. Dutcher, Johnson and Bruce, *J. Am. Chem. Soc.*, **66,** 619 (1944).
8. Johnson, Hasbrouck, Dutcher and Bruce, *J. Am. Chem. Soc.*, **67,** 423 (1945).
9. Johnson, Andreen and Holley, *J. Am. Chem. Soc.*, **69,** 2370 (1947).
10. Johnson and Buchanan, *J. Am. Chem. Soc.*, **75,** 2103 (1953).
11. Bell, Johnson, Wildi and Woodward, *J. Am. Chem. Soc.*, **80,** 1001 (1958).

A-436. Pyrrolo[1,2-*a*]quinoxaline

Hydrogenation of Ia over a copper-chromite catalyst afforded IIa ($b_{0.5}$ 75°; $n_D^{20°}$ 1.5033; $d_{4°}^{20°}$ 0.981; dipicrate, m. 245–6°) in 46% yield. Similar treatment of Ib gave a 66% yield of a mixture of IIb (picrolonate, m. 213–32°) and III ($b_{0.5}$ 84–7°; $n_D^{20°}$ 1.5080; $d_{4°}^{20°}$ 0.997; dipicrate, m. 260–3°d.). The latter product was presumably formed by alkylation of IIb with the ethanol formed during reductive cyclization of the ester.

H_2 / $Cu_2Cr_2O_5$

(Ia) R = CH_3
(Ib) R = H

(IIa) R = CH_3
(IIb) R = H

(III)

A stepwise degradation of peptides was developed[2] in which the component amino acids are isolated as 3-substituted-7-carbomethoxy-3,4-dihydro-2(1*H*)quinoxalones. As standards, a group of these derivatives was prepared by the reaction of methyl 4-fluoro-3-nitrobenzoate (IV) with various amino acids. For example, with L-proline (Va) and L-hydroxyproline (Vb) the products VIa (m. 182–92° d., $[\alpha]_D^{23°}$ –270°) and VIb (m. 227–35°, $[\alpha]_D^{23°}$ –270°) were obtained.

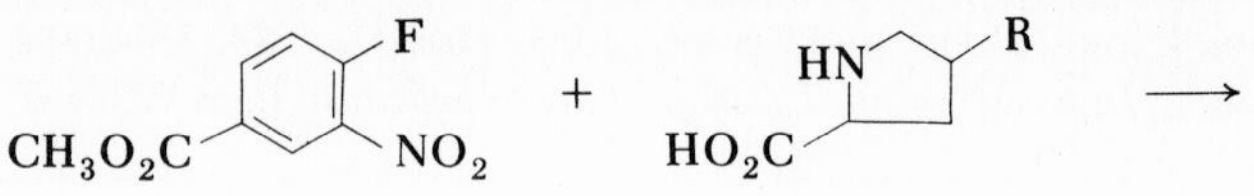

(IV)

(Va) R = H
(Vb) R = OH

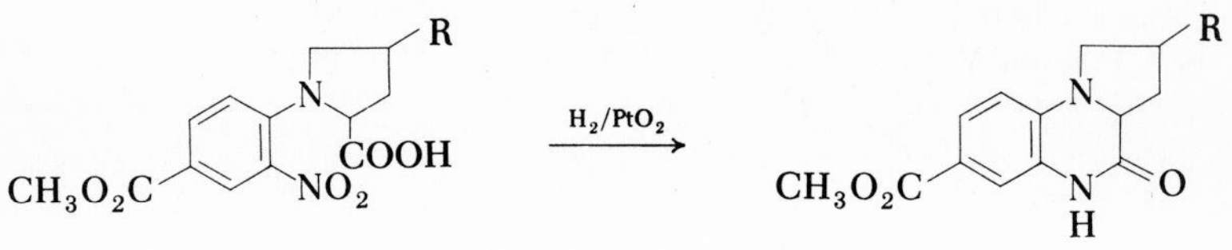

H_2/PtO_2

(VIa) R = H
(VIb) R = OH

References

1. Leonard and Boyer, *J. Am. Chem. Soc.*, **72,** 2980 (1950).
2. Holley and Holley, *J. Am. Chem. Soc.*, **74,** 5445 (1952).

A-437. 1*H*-Pyrazino[3,2,1-*jk*]carbazole. R.I. 2418

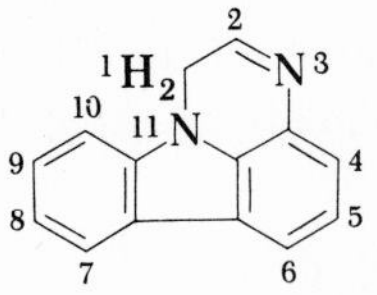

The names *carbazolo-1,9-piperazine* and *6H-peripyrazinocarbazole* (I) are also encountered.

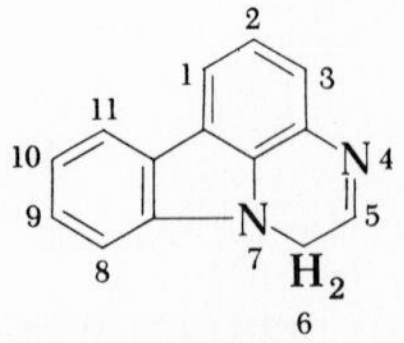

(I)

Quinoxaline derivatives of type II undergo the Fischer indole reaction with cyclohexanone to yield[1,2] III (R = H, m. 285°; R = o-$C_6H_4COOC_2H_5$, m. 172°). While Perkin and Riley[1] were unable to effect the cyclodehydration of IV, dehydrohalogenation of V (R = H or Br) readily yielded[3,4] VI (R = H, m. 255°; R = Br, m. 333°).

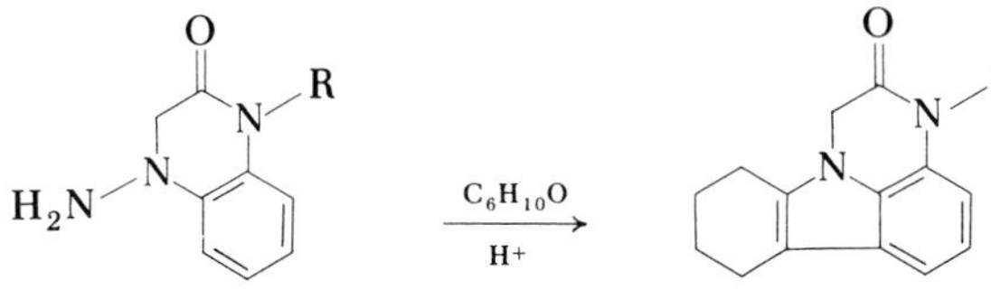

(II) $\xrightarrow[H^+]{C_6H_{10}O}$ (III)

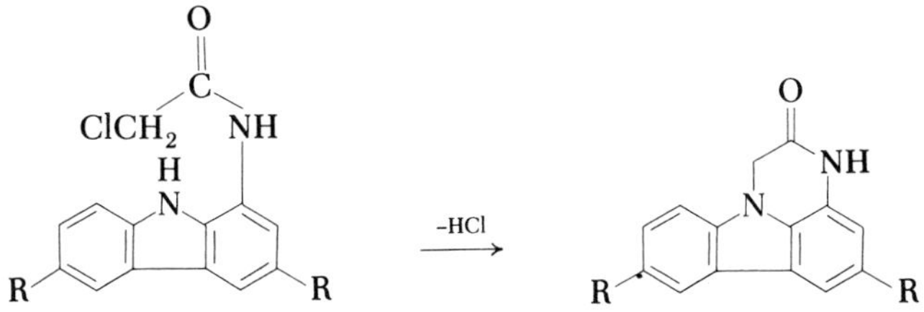

(V) $\xrightarrow{-HCl}$ (VI) $\xrightarrow{HNO_2 / HOAc}$ (VII)

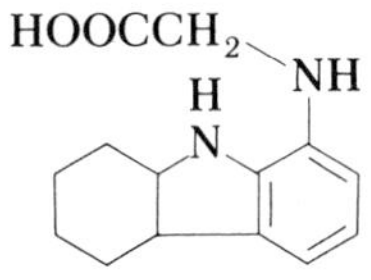

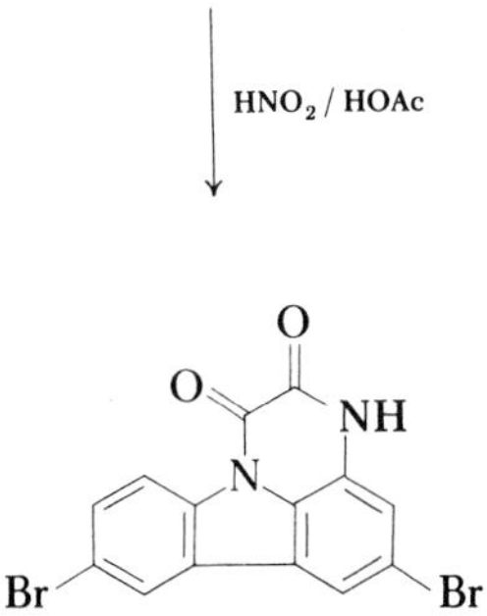

(IV)

Alcoholic caustic cleaved[1] the amide bond in III, although treatment of VI (R = Br) with nitrous acid yielded[3] VII (m. 435°). See Section A-443.

References

1. Perkin and Riley, *J. Chem. Soc.*, **123,** 2399 (1923).
2. Clemo, Perkin and Robinson, *J. Chem. Soc.*, **125,** 1751 (1924).
3. Lindemann and Muhlhaus, *Ber.*, **58,** 2371 (1925).
4. Campbell and MacLean, *J. Chem. Soc.*, **1942,** 504.

A-438. Pyrazino[2,1-*a*, 3,4-*a*′]diisoindole. R.I.2964

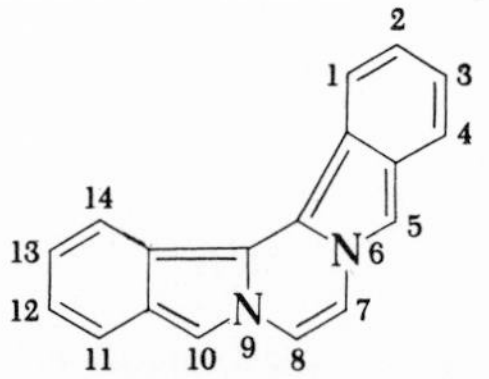

The name *diisoindo[2,1-*a*,1′,2′-*c*]pyrazine* has also been used.

Bistrzycki and Schmutz[1] condensed phthalide with ethylenediamine and obtained product I. When this was heated with sulfur a brownish-orange substance (m. 202–3°) thought to be II was obtained. Why further dehydrogenation of II did not occur under these conditions, is unexplained. See Sections A-442 and A-446.

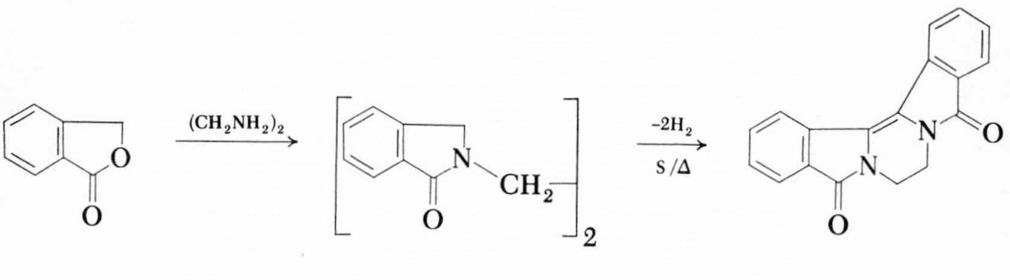

$(CH_2NH_2)_2$; $-2H_2$, S/Δ

(I) (II)

Reference

1. Bistrzycki and Schmutz, *Ann.*, **415,** 1 (1917).

A-439. 6*H*,13*H*-Pyrazino[1,2-*a*, 4,5-*a*′]-diindole. R.I. 2961

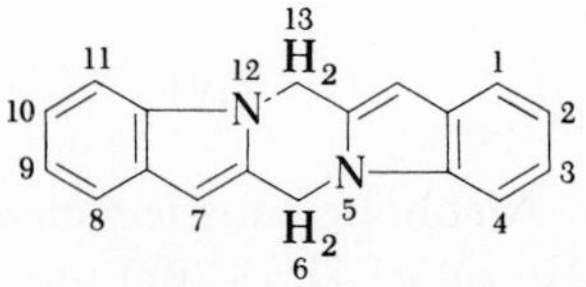

The name *diindolo[1,2-*a*,1′,2′-*c*]pyrazine* has been used. The *Ring Index* name lacks the 6*H*,13*H* prefix.

Several pale yellow, high melting (>300°) products of structure II (R = H or CH_3; R′ = H or C_6H_5) have been obtained[1,2,3] from the intermolecular dehydration of indole-2-carboxylic acids (I).

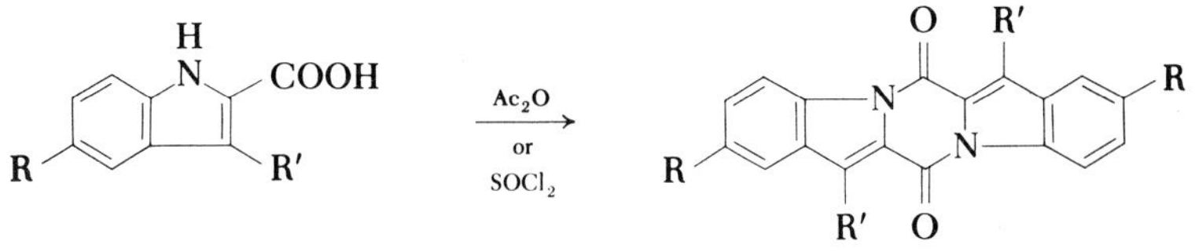

(I) (II)

In a closely related synthesis, the pyrolysis of arylaminomalonic esters (III) is reported[4,5] to yield V (R = H or CH_3, pale yellow, high melting), presumably via IV.

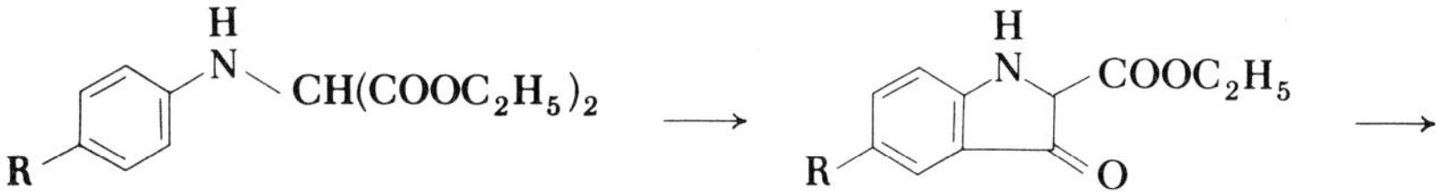

(III) (IV)

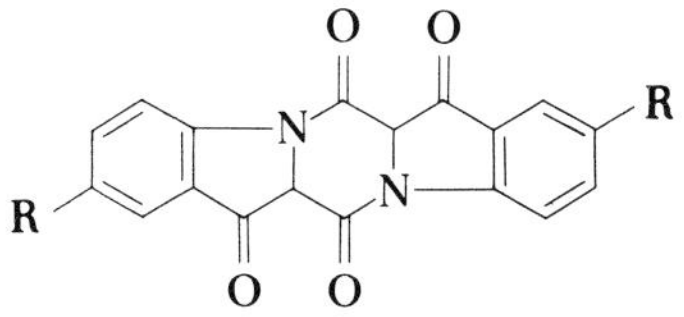

(V)

References

1. Ciamician and Zatti, *Ber.*, **21,** 1929 (1888).
2. Reissert, *Ber.*, **29,** 639 (1896).
3. Borsche and Klein, *Ann.*, **548,** 64 (1941).
4. Conrad and Reinbach, *Ber.*, **35,** 511 (1902).
5. Badische Anilin- und Soda-Fabrik, Ger. Pat. 129,001; *Frdl.*, **6,** 557 (1904). U. S. Pat. 644,326. Brit. Pat. 21,157. Fr. Pat. 282,083.

A-440. Pyrazino[1,2-*a*, 4,3-*a*′]diindole.
R.I. 2963

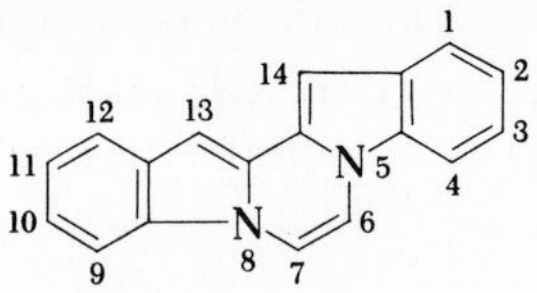

The name *diindolo*[*1,2*-a, *2*′,*1*′-c]pyrazine has also been used.

Friedländer and Sander found[1] that treatment of indigo with oxalyl chloride in nitrobenzene yielded oxalylindigo (I, yellow, m. >300°). The same product is produced[2] by treatment of indigo with monoethyl oxalyl chloride followed by partial saponification and cyclization of the intermediate *N*,*N*′-diacylindigo. Since oxalylindigo is necessarily a derivative of *cis*-indigo, its spectrum is of interest[3,4] (λ_{max} 436 mμ). While stable to acids, I is attacked at the amide linkages by dilute caustic solutions; it is sulfonated by hot sulfuric acid[5] and yields, with nitric acid, the 2,11-dinitro derivative (yellow, m. >300°).[2]

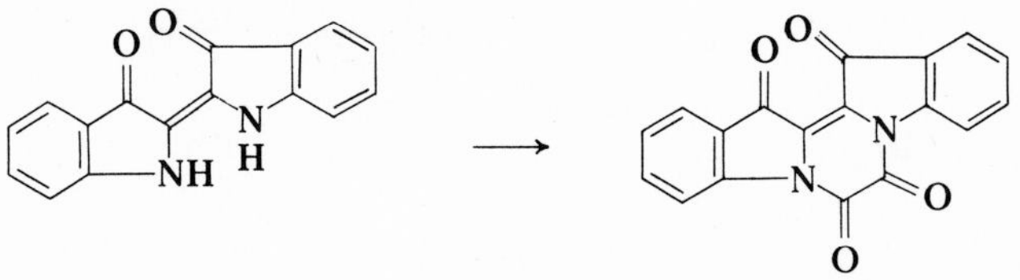

(I)

Van Alphen attempted unsuccessfully to prepare[7] IV by oxidizing II. However, Pummerer and his associates[8-12] obtained IV by the addition of various dienophiles (e.g. styrene, safrole, acrylic ester, etc.) to dehydroindigo (III). The products of type IV (R = C_6H_5, m. 228–9°; R = *p*-$CH_3OC_6H_4$, m. 164–5°; R = $COOCH_3$, m. 209°) are blue to violet vat dyes (yellow vats), but are not of adequate fastness to be of interest. Saponification and decarboxylation of the ester (IV, R = $COOCH_3$) gave IV (R = H), which was extremely air-sensitive. From the mother liquors of the preparation of the ester, however, a red-violet product (m. 325–30°), thought to be V, was obtained.[12] Oxidation of V with nitric acid yielded I, whereas oxidation of IV yields[9,11] VI. Recently a convenient synthesis of IV was disclosed[13] in which the leuco ester of indigo (VII, the so-called "Indigosol") was alkylated with ethylene bromide.

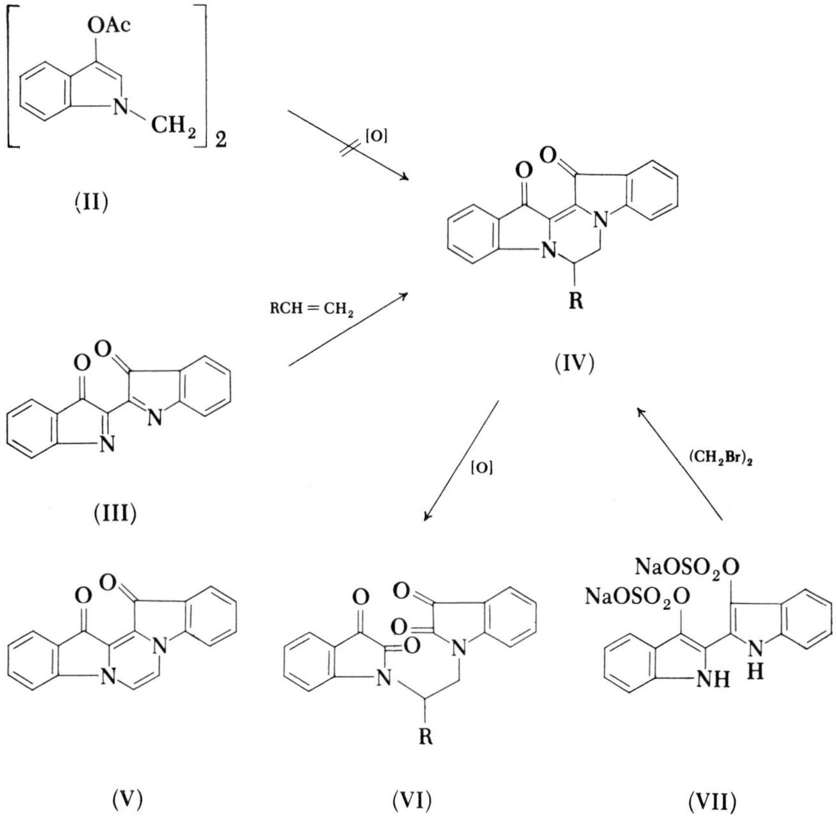

(II) (IV) (III) (V) (VI) (VII)

References

1. Friedlander and Sander, *Ber.*, **57,** 637 (1924).
2. Van Alphen, *Rec. Trav. Chim.*, **58,** 378 (1939).
3. Scheibe, Dörfling and Assmann, *Ann.*, **544,** 240 (1940).
4. Brode, Pearson and Wyman, *J. Am. Chem. Soc.*, **76,** 1034 (1954).
5. Heller, *Ber.*, **77,** 165 (1944).
6. Van Alphen, *Rec. Trav. Chim.*, **60,** 138 (1941).
7. Van Alphen, *Rec. Trav. Chim.*, **61,** 481 (1942).
8. Pummerer, *I.G. Farbenindustrie, A.G., Semesterberichte*, April 29, 1934; *PB Report No.* 73911, frame 4782.
9. Pummerer, *Angew. Chem.*, **49,** 327 (1936).
10. Pummerer and Fiesselmann, *Ann.*, **544,** 206 (1940).
11. Pummerer and Stieglitz, *Ber.*, **75,** 1072 (1942).
12. Pummerer and Reuss, *Ber.*, **80,** 242 (1947).
13. Pummerer and Meininger, *Ann.*, **590,** 173 (1954).

A-441. 8*H*-Indolo[3,2,1-*de*]phenazine

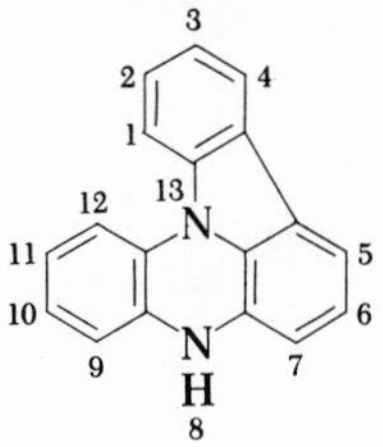

When I was heated at 225° for fifteen minutes with five times its weight of ferrous oxalate, a 40% yield was obtained[1] of a substance assigned structure II and named *1,9-dihydrophenazinocarbazole*. No description of the product or evidence for its structure were presented, although similar cyclizations have been described.[2]

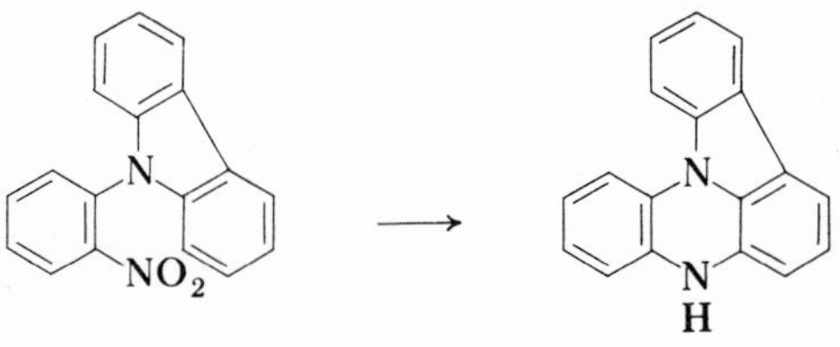

(I) (II)

References

1. Waterman and Vivian, U. S. Pat. 2,292,808.
2. Waterman and Vivian, *J. Org. Chem.*, **14,** 289 (1949).

A-442. Diisoindolo[2,1-*a*, 1′,2′-*c*]-quinoxaline. R.I. 3470

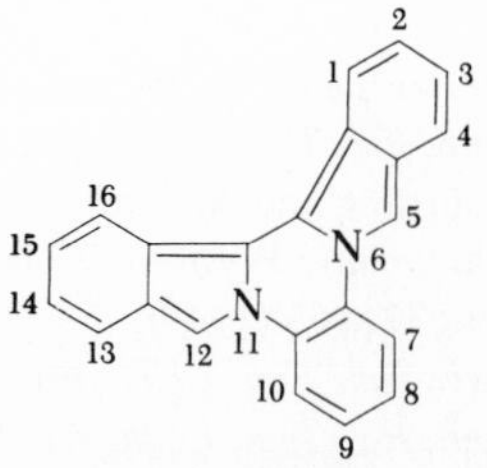

The name *1,2,3,4-dibenzylene-1,4-dihydroquinoxaline* has been used.

Lieb[1] investigated the zinc-acetic acid reduction of 1,2-bis-phthalimidobenzene (I), and obtained a product (m. 275–7°) thought to be II. When melted, II changes to a red crystalline product (m. 278°), which was assigned structure III. Attempts to prepare III from biphthalyl (IV) and *o*-phenylenediamine gave only *o*-phenylenebisbenzimidazole. Further study of these substances seems warranted. See Sections A-438 and A-446.

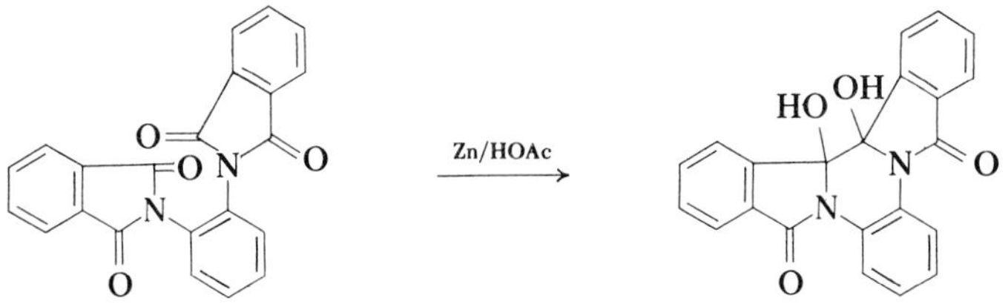

Zn/HOAc

(I)

(II)

Δ

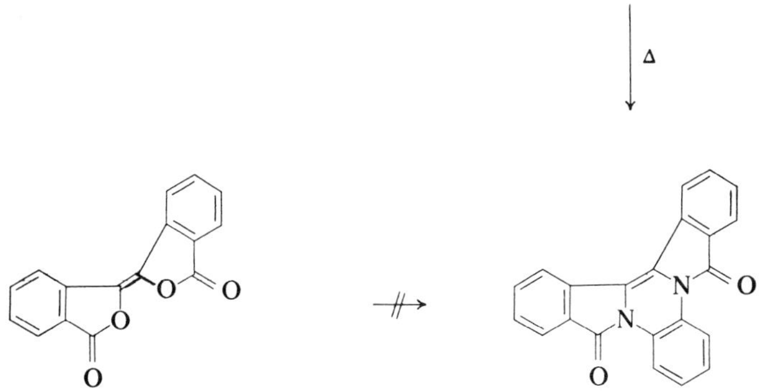

(IV)

(III)

Reference

1. Lieb, *Monatsh.*, **39,** 883 (1918).

A-443. 15*H*-Pyrazino[*qrs*]acrindoline. R.I. 3505

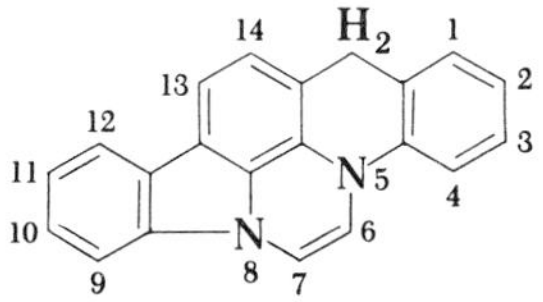

The name *10:21-etheno-acrindoline* (I) has been used.

While investigating the structure of the strychnine alkaloids, Clemo, Perkin and Robinson[1] prepared the pale yellow III (m. 206°)

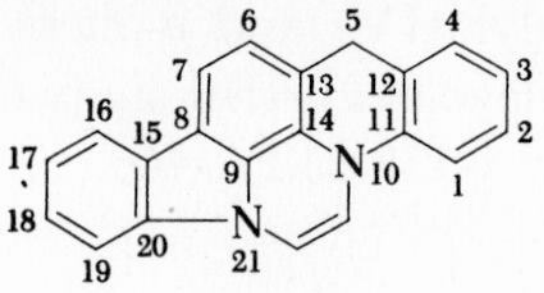

(I)

by condensing II with cyclohexanone under acidic reductive conditions. Distillation of III from zinc dust gave a bright yellow substance (m. 182°) thought to be IV, which yielded V (m. 209°) when treated with sodium amalgam. Electrolytic reduction of V probably causes scission of the ethylene bridge between the nitrogen atoms, as the product obtained gave an *N*-acetyl derivative.

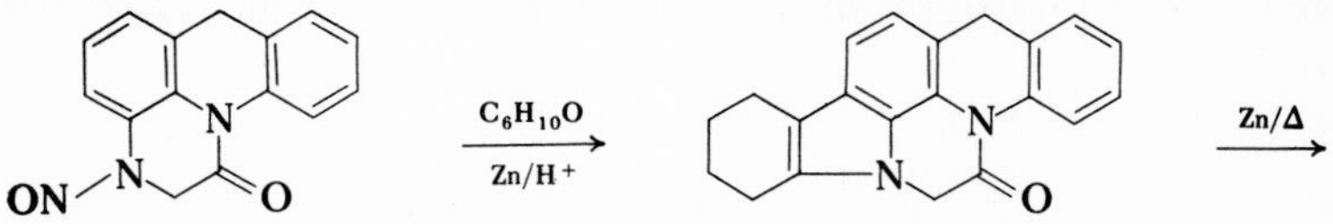

(II) (III)

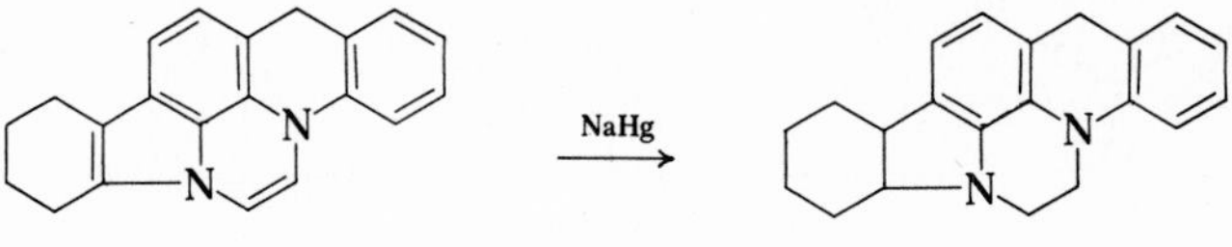

(IV) (V)

The ester VI (see Section A-437) could not be cyclized by treatment[1] with sulfuric acid, phosphorus oxychloride or thionyl chloride, etc.

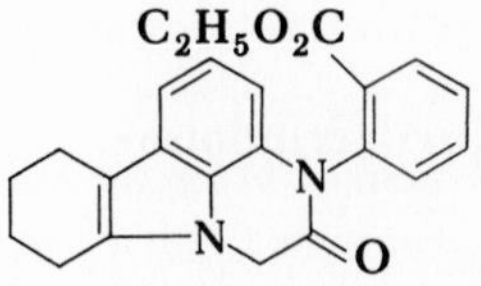

(VI)

Reference

1. Clemo, Perkin and Robinson, *J. Chem. Soc.*, **125,** 1751 (1924).

A-444. 6*H*-Triindolo-[1,2-*a*, 2′,1′-*c*, 2″,3″-*e*]pyrazine. R.I. 3685

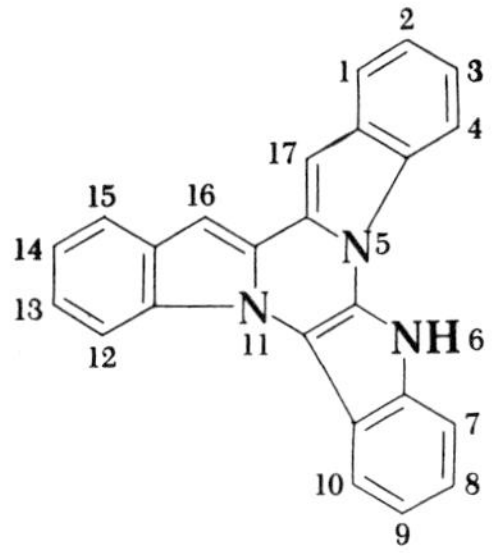

This ring system was proposed[1] as the nucleus of indole trimer ("triindole"), but this is known now to be incorrect (see Section A-262).

Reference

1. Tschelinzew, Tronow and Woskressenski, *J. Russ. Phys. Chem. Soc.*, **47,** 1224 (1915); *Chem. Zentr.*, **I,** 1246 (1916).

A-445. Diindolo[3,2,1-*de*, 3′,2′,1′-*kl*]-phenazine

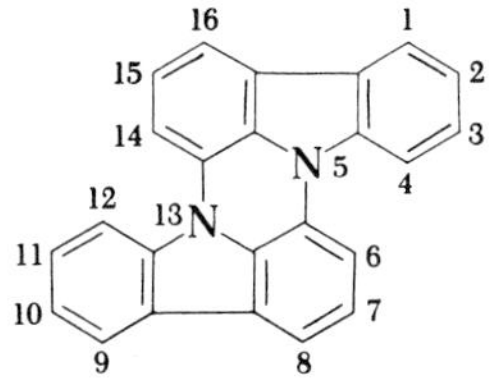

When either I or II is dehydrated, for example by heating with acetic anhydride, compound III (m.p. given variously as 293–5° or 255° with resolidification and further melting at 313°) is produced.[1,2] Dehydrogenation of III with sulfur, chloranil or palladium charcoal yielded IV (greenish-yellow, m. 337°; exhibits a brilliant violet fluorescence in benzene or toluene solution). Attempts to prepare IV from V or VI were reported[3] unsuccessful.

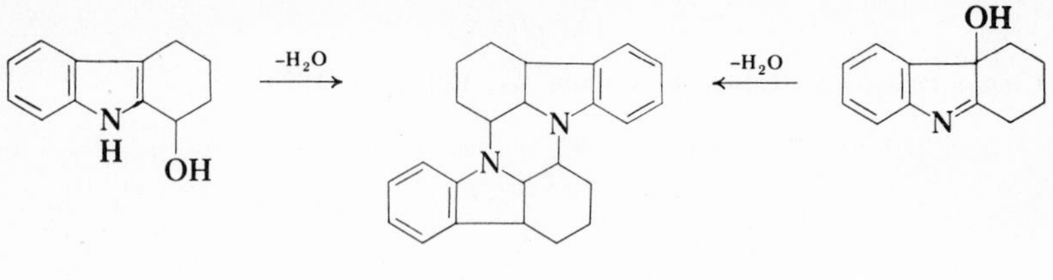

(I) (III) (II)

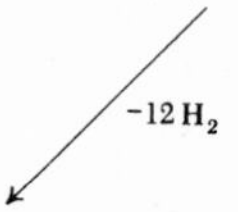

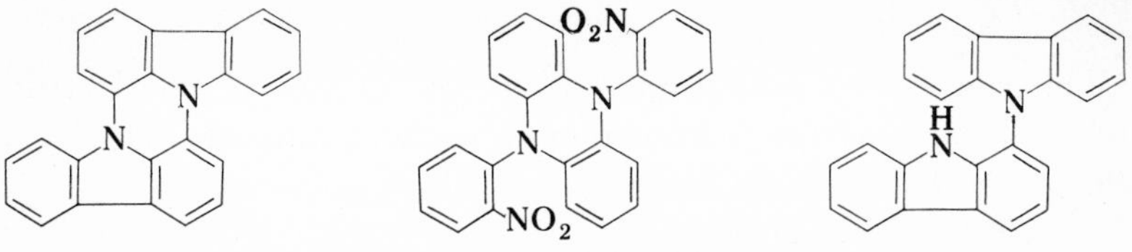

(IV) (V) (VI)

References

1. Plant, Robinson and Tomlinson, *Nature*, **165,** 928 (1950).
2. Plant and Tomlinson, *J. Chem. Soc.*, **1950,** 2127.
3. Geale, Linnell and Tomlinson, *J. Chem. Soc.*, **1956,** 1124.

A-446. Benzo[*f*]diisoindolo-[2,1-*a*, 1′,2′-*c*]quinoxaline. R.I. 3697

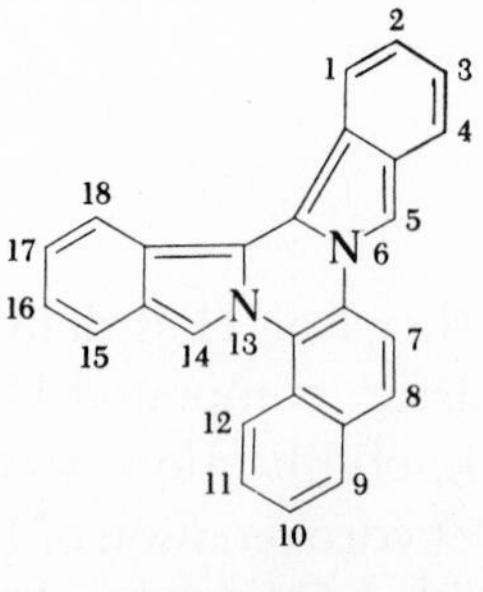

Reduction of I with zinc and acetic acid yielded[1] a substance $C_{26}H_{16}N_2O_4$ (m. 280–4°), which was converted by heat into a red product (m. 323–4°) thought to be II. Further evidence would be welcome. See Sections A-438 and A-442.

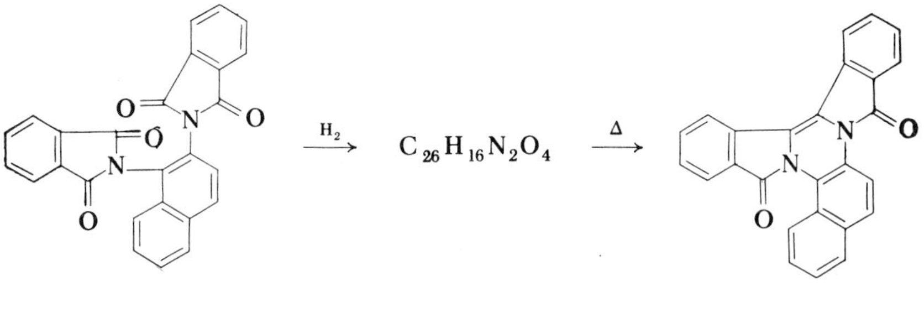

$\xrightarrow{H_2}$ $C_{26}H_{16}N_2O_4$ $\xrightarrow{\Delta}$

(I) (II)

Reference

1. Lieb, *Monatsh.*, **39,** 883 (1918).

A-447. 8*H*,17*H*-Bisbenz[4,5]indolo-[1,2-*a*, 1′,2′-*d*]pyrazine. R.I. *3696*

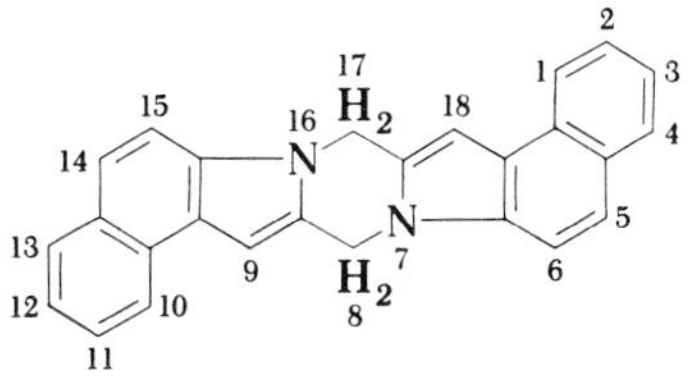

The *Ring Index* name lacks the 8*H*,17*H* prefix.

The preparation of II from the pyrolysis of I has been reported.[1,2] No properties were given. See Sections A-439 and A-450.

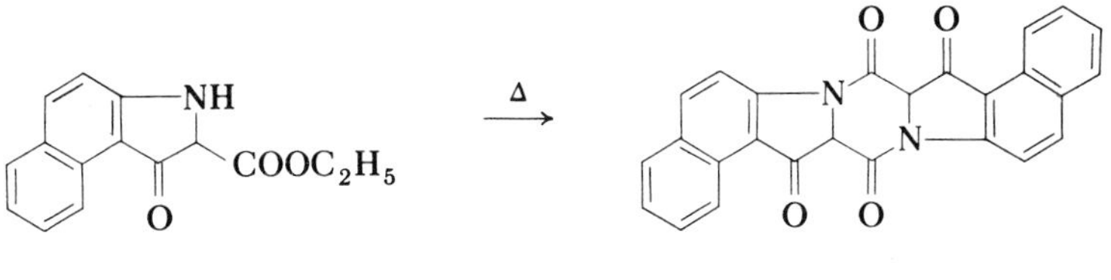

$\xrightarrow{\Delta}$

(I) (II)

References

1. Conrad and Reinbach, *Ber.*, **35,** 511 (1902).
2. Badische Anilin- und Soda-Fabrik, Ger. Pat. 129,001; *Frdl.*, **6,** 557 (1904). U. S. Pat. 644,326. Brit. Pat. 21,157. Fr. Pat. 282,083.

A-448. 17*H*-Indolo[1,2,3-*fg*]naphtho-[2,3-*a*]phenazine*

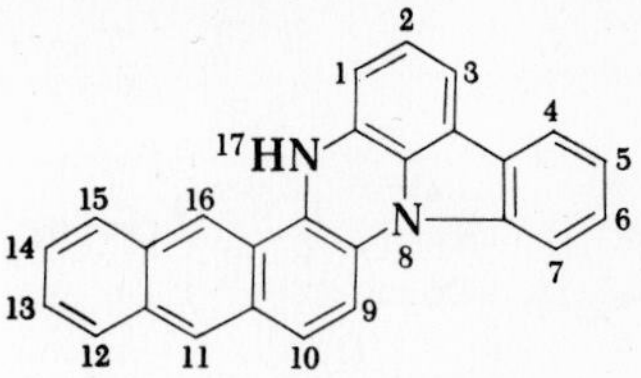

Fusion of the anthrimide I (R = H or Cl) with caustic yielded[1,2] blue dyes of structure II (R = Cl, sulfuric acid solution: brown). When R = Cl, the dye gives a red-brown vat only in the presence of pyridine and is not, therefore, of practical value, although it has excellent (8+) light-fastness;[2] when R = H, the dye has low affinity for cotton.

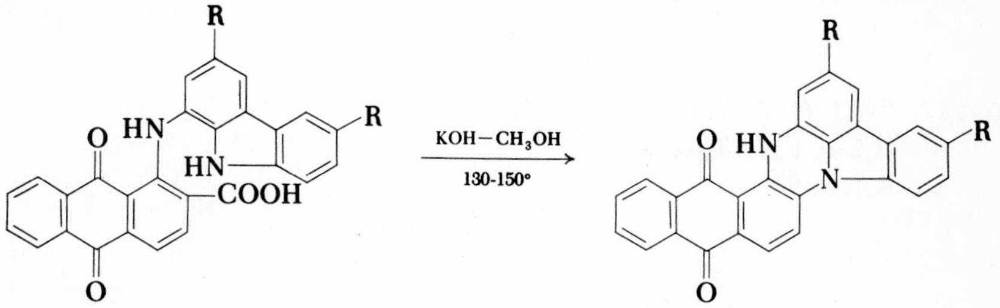

KOH—CH_3OH

130-150°

(I) (II)

References

1. Krämer, *I.G. Farbenindustrie, A.G., 43 Wissenschaftlicher Austausch der Gruppe IX*, Leverkusen, April 25–6, 1941; *PB Report No.* 70340, frame 12630.
2. I.G. Farbenindustrie, A. G., *F.I.A.T. Report No.* 1313, Vol. III, pp. 31–3.

A-449. Benz[4,5]isoindolo[2,1,7-*fgh*]-naphtho[2,3-*a*]phenazine*

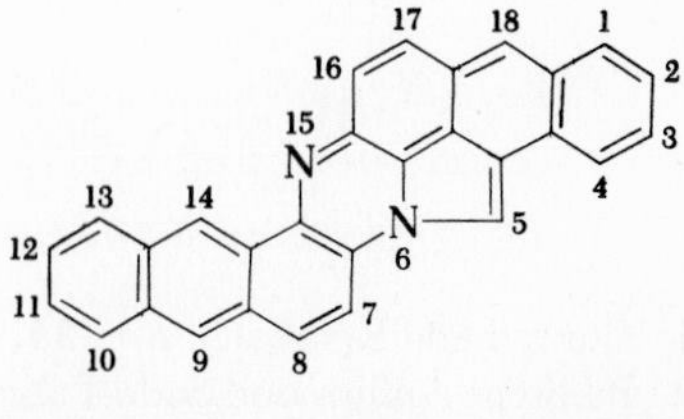

During the methylation of indanthrone (I) with methyl *p*-toluenesulfonate and potassium carbonate in hot trichlorobenzene, in addition to the expected *N,N'*-dimethylindanthrone, a small amount of an additional product was isolated.[1] Structure II was tentatively advanced[1] for this material, although further evidence is needed to establish it solidly, especially since the elemental analyses reported for the product are not in very close accord with the theoretical values for structure II.

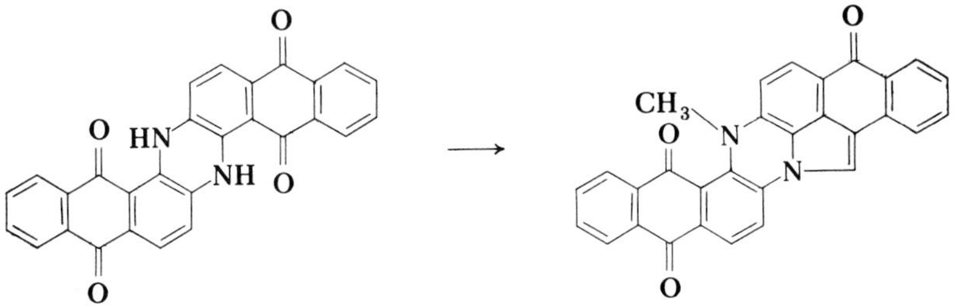

(I) → (II)

Reference

1. Bradley and Leete, *J. Chem. Soc.*, **1951,** 2129.

A-450. 9*H*,20*H*-Dinaphtho[2,3-*e*, 2',3'-*e*']-pyrazino[1,2-*a*, 4,5-*a*']bisindole*. R.I. 3912

The *Ring Index* name: *bisnaphth*[*1'',2'',4,5*]*indolo*[*1,2*-a,*1',2'*-d]*pyrazine* is evidently an error.

The pyrolysis of I is reported[1] to yield about 5–15% of III (m. >450°) together with II.

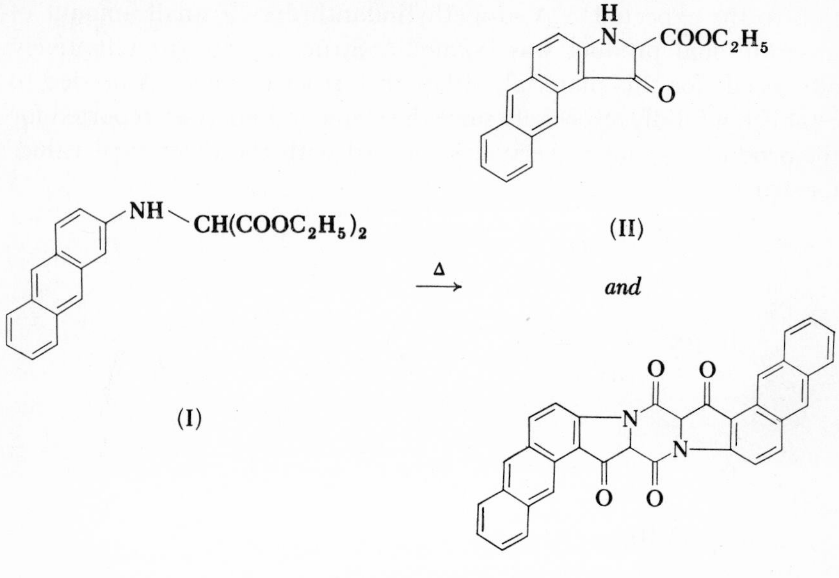

H
N COOC$_2$H$_5$
O

NH CH(COOC$_2$H$_5$)$_2$

$\xrightarrow{\Delta}$

(II)

and

(I)

O O
N
N
O O

(III)

Reference

1. Ruggli and Henzi, *Helv. Chim. Acta*, **13**, 409 (1930).

A-451. 5*H*-Isoindolo[2,1-*a*][3,1]-benzoxazine. R.I. 2408

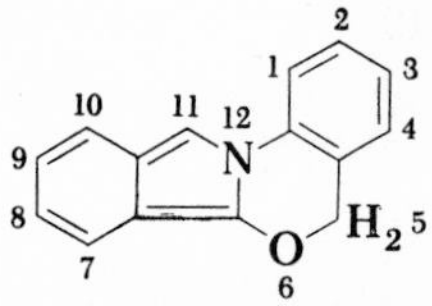

From the degradation of the dye Höchst Yellow R (see Section A-210), Hope, Kersey and Richter[1] obtained a lactone (m. 216–7°), to which they assigned structure I. While some of the other degradation products were not correctly formulated, the propriety of assigning structure I to the lactone was demonstrated by de Diesbach, Heppner and Siegwart,[2] who prepared it as shown.

By reacting II with anthranilic acid, Honzl[3] obtained III (m. 150°). Treatment of III, in the cold, with ammonia or amines yielded products thought to be either of type IV or V, which could be dehydrated to VI (see Section A-459). However, hot alcoholic ammonia converted III into VII.

COBr CHBr$_2$ + H_2N HOOC → O NH CHBr$_2$ COOH

$-2HBr$

Höchst Yellow R → O N O O

(I)

H_2N HOOC + O O COOH

(II)

$-CO_2$ / $-2H_2O$ → O N O O H_3C

(III)

NH_3 / 120° → N N H O COCH$_3$

(VII)

RNH_2 / 25°

O N CONHR H_3C OH

(IV)

or

O NH O CONHR CH$_3$

(V)

HOAc/Δ

O N N O H_3C R

(VI)

References

1. Hope, Kersey and Richter, *J. Chem. Soc.*, **1933,** 1000.
2. de Diesbach, Heppner and Siegwart, *Helv. Chim. Acta*, **31,** 724 (1948).
3. Honzl, *Collection Czechoslov. Chem. Communs.*, **21,** 725 (1956); *Chem. listy*, **49,** 1671 (1955); *Chem. Abstracts*, **50,** 5621 (1956).

A-452. 2*H*-[1,3]Thiazino[2,3-*a*]isoindole*

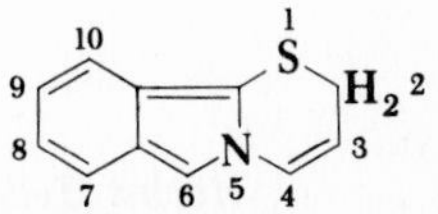

Condensation of homocysteine (I) with phthalaldehydic acid yielded[1] II (m. 230–1°), while with *o*-cyanobenzaldehyde the zwitterionic form of III (m. 228° d.) was formed. See Sections A-83/6.

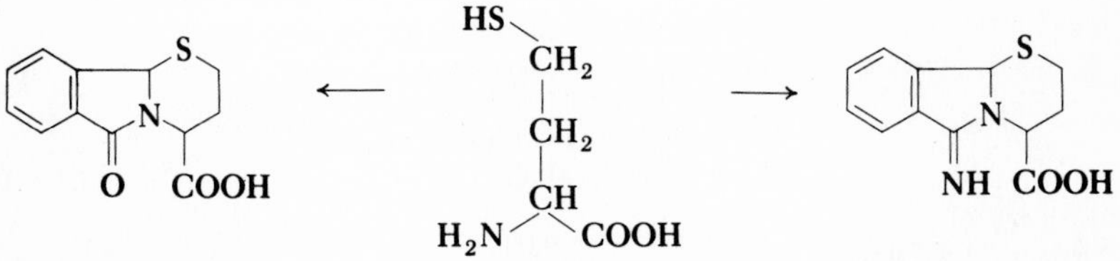

(II) (I) (III)

Reference

1. Oliver, Dann and Gates, *J. Am. Chem. Soc.*, **80,** 702 (1958).

A-453. Pyrrolo[1,2-*a*]pyrimidine. R.I. 803M

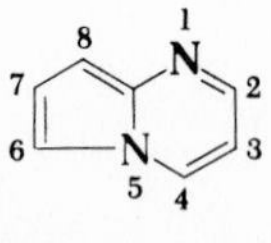

The name *pyrimidino-(1',2'-1,2)-pyrrole* has also been used.

Very few examples of this nucleus have been reported. Ochiai and Yanai[1] treated trimethylpyrimidine with phenacyl bromide and obtained I ($b_{0.005}$ 180–200°; picrate, d. 220–3°). Catalytic hydrogenation of IIa and IIb (using a Raney cobalt catalyst in the case of IIb) yielded, respectively, IIIa (m. 44°)[2] and IIIb (picrate, m. 315° d.).[3]

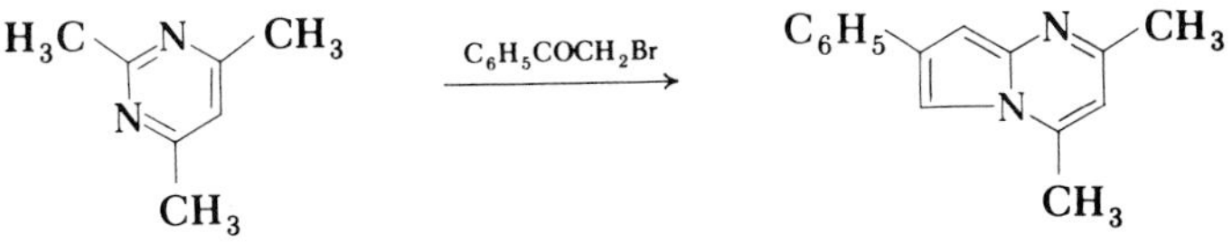

(I)

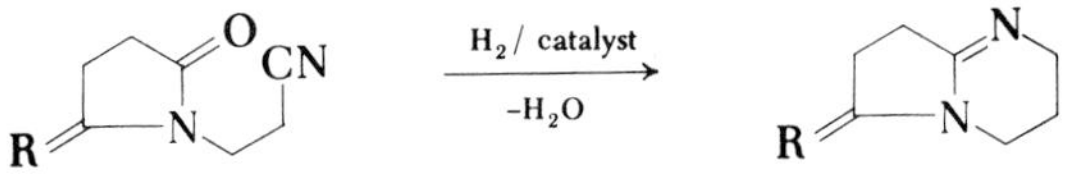

(IIa) R = O
(IIb) R = H_2

(IIIa) R = O
(IIIb) R = H_2

References

1. Ochiai and Yanai, *J. Pharm. Soc. Japan*, **59,** 18 (in Japanese) or 97 (in German) (1939); *Brit. Chem. Abstracts*, **AII,** 451 (1939); *Chem. Abstracts*, **33,** 3791 (1939).
2. Schröter, *I.G. Farbenindustrie,A.G.*; *F.I.A.T. Review of German Science*, "Preparative Organic Chemistry," 1948, Pt. I, p. 194.
3. Reppe, *et al.*, *Ann.*, **596,** 158 (1955).

A-454. Pyrimid[1,2-*a*]indole

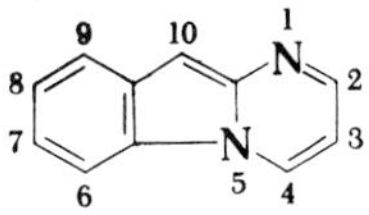

Birr states[1] that I may be obtained from the condensation of 2-aminoindole with acetoacetic ester, but gives no details. The use of 4-sulfophenylazoacetoacetic ester is claimed[2] to yield the yellow dye II, which could also, presumably, be obtained by coupling into I.

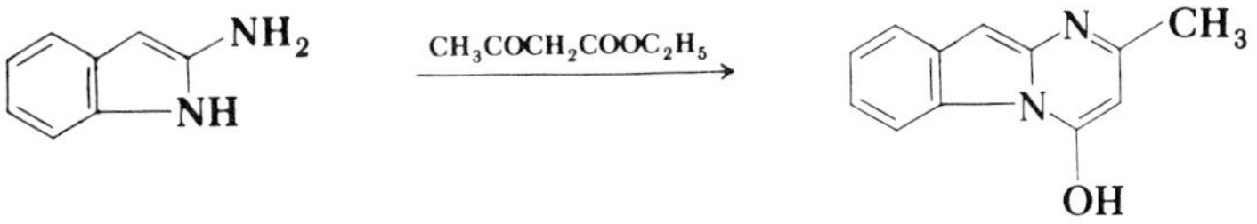

(I)

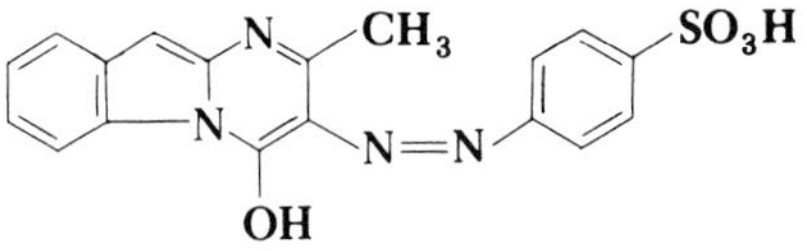

(II)

References

1. Birr, *Z. wiss. Phot.*, **47**, 2 (1952).
2. Heimbach, U. S. Pat. 2,432,419. Ger. Pat. 882,883.

A-455. Pyrrolo[1,2-*a*]quinazoline. R.I. 1633

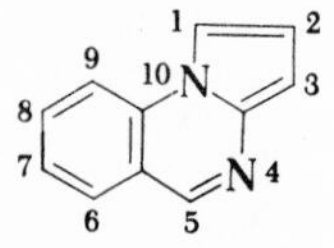

Condensation of 2-nitrobenzylamine with succinic anhydride, followed by reduction of the nitro group with ferrous ammonium sulfate, yielded[1] I, which was dehydrated to II (m. 192°) by heating in acetic acid. The linear isomer of II, the formation of which from I might also be envisioned, was obtained otherwise (see Section A-456). Electrolytic reduction of II gave III (dipicrolonate, m. 203–10°d.).

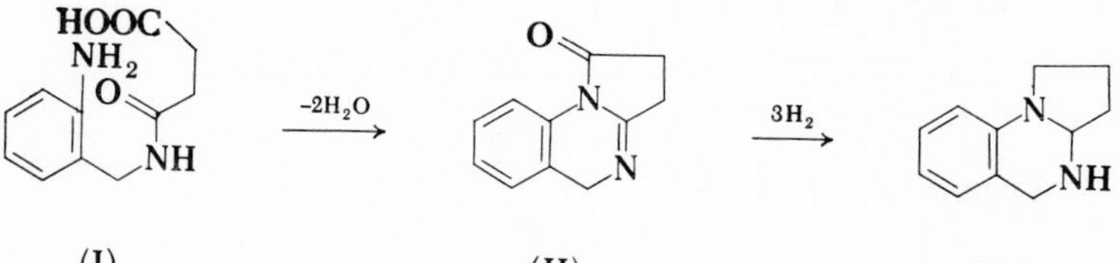

(I) —$-2H_2O$→ (II) —$3H_2$→ (III)

Reference

1. Juneja, Narang and Rây, *J. Chem. Soc.*, **1935**, 1277.

A-456. Pyrrolo[2,1-*b*]quinazoline. R.I. 1628.

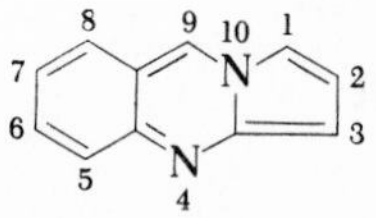

10(1)-Pyrrolo[2,1-b]quinazolinium (I, *R.I.* 1629) and *1,3-dioxolo-*[g]*pyrrolo*[b]*quinazoline* (II, *R.I.* 2279) will also be considered under this heading. The name *pegan*, and the numbering shown in III have been proposed for the 1,2,3,3*a*,4,9-hexahydro derivative.

While Gabriel[1] prepared the first example of this nucleus, the ketone IV [and named it (*oxo-trimethylene*)-*dihydroquinazoline*], by the reduction of *N*-(*o*-nitrobenzyl)-succinimide, the chief interest in this

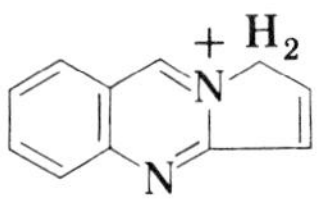

+ H_2 N N

8 9 10 11 1 O N 7 2 6 O 3 N 5 4

7 8 11 1 N 6 2 5 3 N 10 4 H 9

(I) 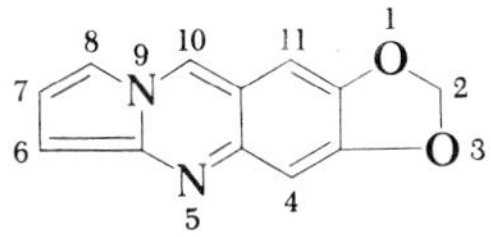 (II) 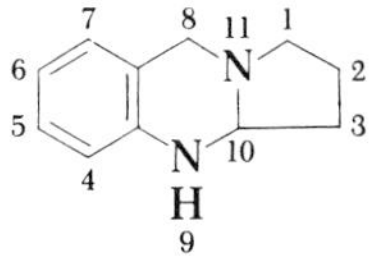 (III)

nucleus arises from its presence in the alkaloid *vasicine*[2] (*peganine*, or 3-hydroxy-1,2,3,9-tetrahydropyrrolo[2,1-*b*]quinazoline).

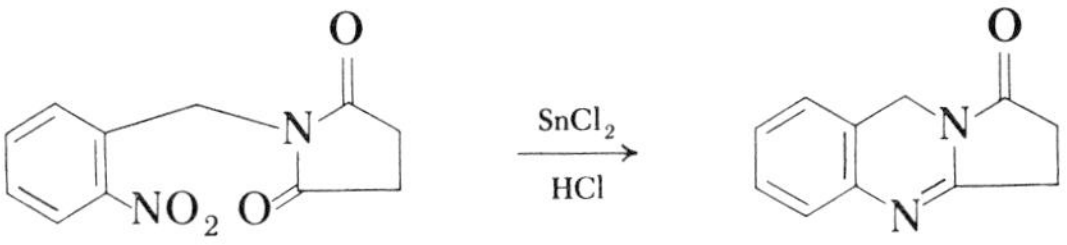

O N NO_2 O

$SnCl_2$ / HCl

O N N

(IV)

Späth and Platzer[3] prepared V by the reaction of pyrrolidone with isatoic anhydride, while the same product was also obtained[4] by the cyclodehydrobromination of VI.

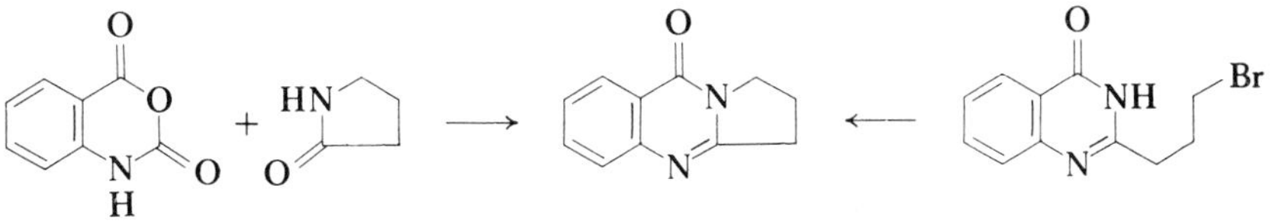

O O N H O + HN O → O N N ← O NH Br N

(V) (VI)

Compound VII was obtained both by the condensation of *o*-nitrobenzyl chloride with γ-aminobutyric esters (R = H or OH) followed by reduction of the nitro group[5,6] and, directly, by the condensation[7] of *o*-aminobenzylamine with γ-butyrolactones (R = H or OH). While heat alone failed[8] to dehydrate VII to VIII, the use of phosphorus oxychloride was successful. Dehydrobromination of IX also produced[8] VIII. Oxidation of VIII with hydrogen peroxide yielded[4] V.

From the condensation of *o*-aminobenzaldehyde with γ-aminobutyraldehyde in a citrate buffer at pH 5.0, Schopf and Oechler[9] isolated salts of X. Lead tetraacetate oxidized X to XI, while chromic

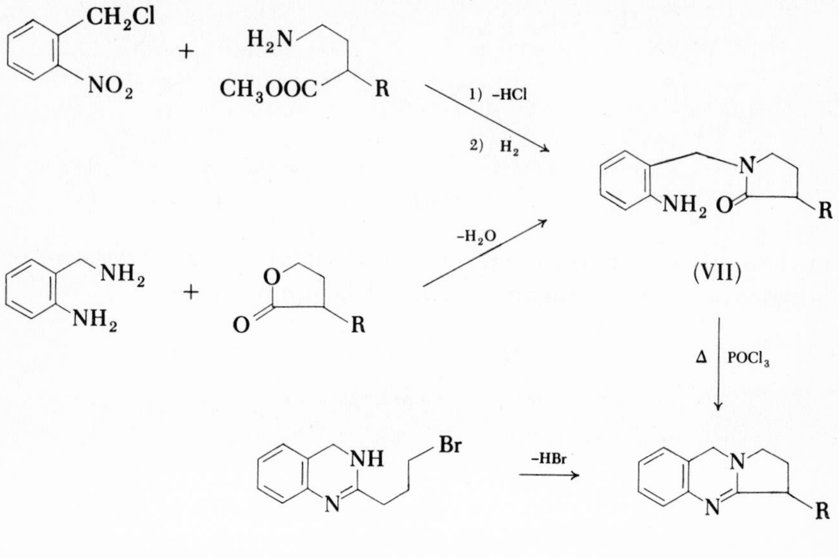

(VII)

(IX)

(VIII)

acid converted X into V. Interaction with a palladium sponge catalyst isomerized X to VIII (R = H).

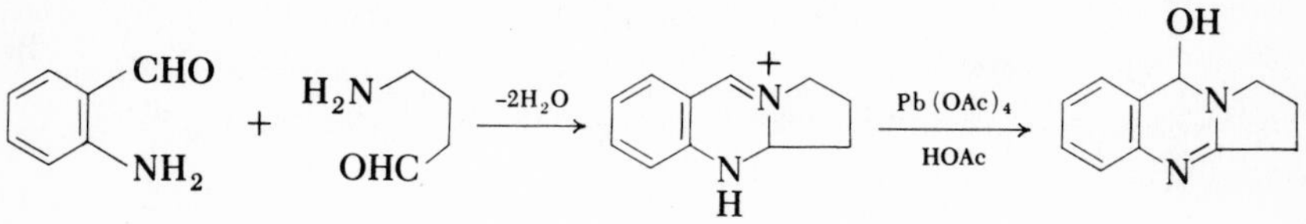

(X)

(XI)

Both V and VIII (R = H) condense in the 3-position with benzaldehyde.[4,8] Electrolytic reduction of either IV or V yielded[3,10] *N*-(*o*-aminobenzyl)-pyrrolidine, while sodium in alcohol reduced both IV and VIII (R = H) to 1,2,3,3*a*,4,9-hexahydropyrrolo[2,1-*b*]-quinazoline.[5,10] Quaternization of vasicine (VIII, R = OH) with methyl iodide and reduction of this salt with sodium borohydride gave[11] the 3-hydroxy-4-methyl-1,2,3,3*a*,4,9-hexahydro derivative.

Many of the syntheses and reactions of these products resemble those of the pyrido[1,2-*b*]quinazolines (see Section A-781).

Pyrrolo[2,1-*b*]quinazolines

Empirical formula	Substituents or structure	Properties	Refs.
$C_{11}H_{10}N_2O$	1,2,3,9-Tetrahydro-1-oxo-	m. 191° (183–4°).	1,10
	1,2,3,9-Tetrahydro-9-oxo-	m. 110–1°. Benzal deriv., m. 137–9°.	3,4,9
$C_{11}H_{10}N_2O_2$	1,2,3,9-Tetrahydro-3-hydroxy-9-oxo-	m. 214°.	13
$C_{11}H_{12}N_2$	1,2,3,9-Tetrahydro-	m. 99–100° (96.5–7.5°). HCl salt, m. 260° (in capillary) or 246° (on a block). Picrate, m. 205–6°. Oxalate, m. 234° (on a block). Benzal deriv., m. 161–3°.	5,7-9
	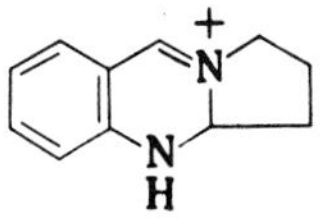 [structure: N⁺, N–H]	Picrate, or.-yel., m. 170–1°.	9,17
$C_{11}H_{12}N_2O$	1,2,3,9-Tetrahydro-3-hydroxy- (Vasicine or Peganine)	m. 211–2° (209–10°d.). Methiodide, m. 191.0–1.5°. HCl salt, m. 206–8° (205–7°) d.	6,7,11,16
	1,2,3,9-Tetrahydro-9-hydroxy-	m. 176–7°. Picrate, m. 146–7°.	9
$C_{11}H_{14}N_2$	1,2,3,3*a*,4,9-Hexahydro-	m. 71–3°. Picrolonate, m. 195–7°.	5,10
$C_{12}H_{10}N_2O_3$	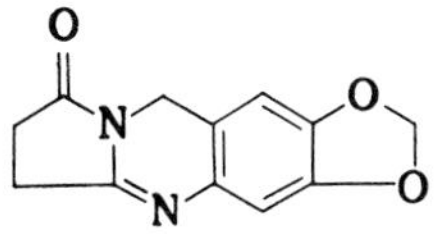 [structure: O, N, N, O, O]	m. 267°.	14
$C_{12}H_{14}N_2O_2$	1,2,3,9-Tetrahydro-3-hydroxy-6-methoxy-	m. 223–4° d.	16
$C_{12}H_{16}N_2O$	1,2,3,3*a*,4,9-Hexahydro-3-hydroxy-4-methyl-	Oil. Methiodide, m. 180–1°.	11
$C_{13}H_{12}N_2O$	4-Acetyl-4,9-dihydro-	m. 164°.	13,15
$C_{13}H_{14}N_2O_3$	1,2,3,9-Tetrahydro-6,7-dimethoxy-1-oxo-	Yel., m. 226–7°.	12

References

1. Gabriel, *Ber.*, **45,** 713 (1912).
2. Openshaw, "The Quinazoline Alkaloids," in Manske and Holmes, *The Alkaloids*, Academic Press, New York, N. Y., Vol. III, 1953, p. 102.
3. Späth and Platzer, *Ber.*, **68,** 2221 (1935).
4. Morris, Hanford and Adams, *J. Am. Chem. Soc.*, **57,** 951 (1935).
5. Späth, Kuffner and Platzer, *Ber.*, **68,** 497 (1935).
6. Späth, Kuffner and Platzer, *Ber.*, **68,** 699 (1935).
7. Späth and Platzer, *Ber.*, **69,** 255 (1936).
8. Hanford and Adams, *J. Am. Chem. Soc.*, **57,** 921 (1935).
9. Schöpf and Oechler, *Ann.*, **523,** 1 (1936).
10. Späth and Platzer, *Ber.*, **69,** 387 (1936).
11. Witkop and Patrick, *J. Am. Chem. Soc.*, **75,** 4474 (1953).
12. Downes and Lions, *J. Am. Chem. Soc.*, **72,** 3053 (1950).
13. Ghose, Krishna, Narang and Rây, *Current Sci.*, **4,** 158 (1935); *Chem. Abstracts*, **30,** 1060 (1936).
14. Ahmed, Narang and Rây, *J. Indian Chem. Soc.*, **15,** 152 (1938); *Chem. Zentr.*, **II,** 2935 (1938); *Chem. Abstracts*, **32,** 7040 (1938).
15. Späth, Kuffner and Platzer, *Ber.*, **68,** 935 (1935).
16. Southwick and Casanova, *J. Am. Chem. Soc.*, **80,** 1186 (1958).
17. Hasse and Maisack, *Biochem. Z.*, **327,** 296 (1955); *Chem. Abstracts*, **50,** 7162 (1956).

A-457. [1,3]Dioxolo[*g*]pyrrolo[*b*]-quinazoline. R.I. 2279

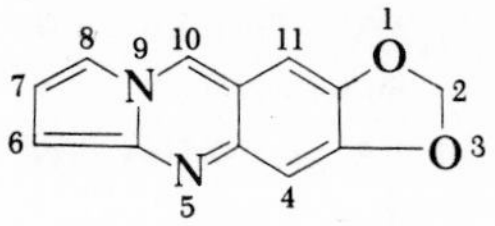

See pyrrolo[2,1-*b*]quinazoline (Section A-456).

A-458. Isoindolo[1,2-*b*]quinazoline. R.I. 2410.

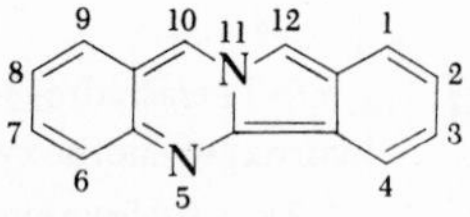

and

A-459. Isoindolo[2,1-*a*]quinazoline. R.I. 2416.

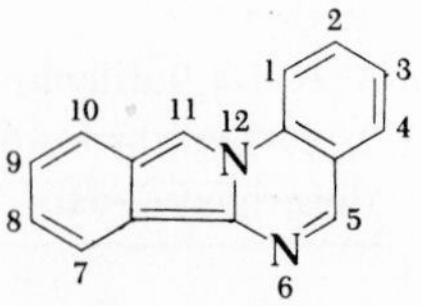

Current *Chemical Abstracts* and *Ring Index* numbering is shown above, but the first nucleus was numbered as shown in I by the

Chemical Abstracts 3rd Decennial Index, and as shown in II by the *1st Decennial Index*. The names *isoquinazindoline* and *benzylenedihydroquinazoline* have been applied to 10,12-dihydroisoindolo[1,2-*b*]-quinazolines.

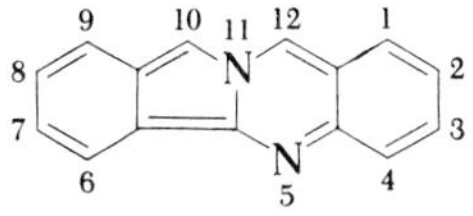

(I) 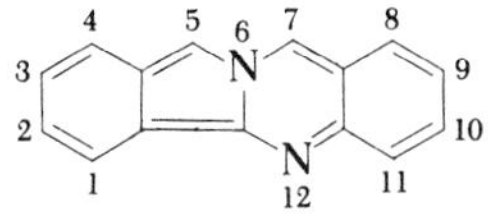 (II)

Reduction of III (R = H) with tin and hydrochloric acid yielded[1] IV (yellow, sinters ~155°, m. 162–4°; HCl salt, d. ~230°), while the use of stannous chloride and hydrochloric acid in acetic acid gave[1,7] V (R = H, yellow, m. 182–3°). Hydrogenation of III (R = OCH_3) over a Raney nickel catalyst yielded[2] V (R = OCH_3, m. 245–6°; HCl salt, red, m. 235–6° d.).

Hydrolytic reduction of V (R = H) with sodium amalgam produced[1] VI, which Gabriel reported to lose water when heated in vacuo and give a new product (m. 216–8°) thought to be either VII or VIII. Stephenson[3] was not able to duplicate this experiment, but found that VI was dehydrated by warm sulfuric acid to a substance (m. 204.5–5.5°; acetyl derivative, m. 163.0–4.5°; nitroso derivative, m. 212.5–3.5°) also obtainable by heating phthalaldehydic acid with 2-aminobenzylamine. This product was presumably also either VII or VIII, and she favored structure VIII because the N-nitroso derivative of VII might be expected to rearrange to a *para* nitroso derivative of VII. Thus the exact nature of Gabriel's product (m. 216–8°) remains unexplained.

The reaction of methyl anthranilate with phthalimidine in excess phosphorus trichloride is reported[4] to yield IX (m. 205–6°).

Crippa and Caracci[5] studied the reaction of phthalic anhydride with anthranilamide and found that fusion of the reactants at 135–160° for two hours yielded a product ($C_{15}H_{10}N_2O_3$, m. 225°), which could be either X or XII. This product lost water when heated in acetic anhydride, or simply upon standing in a desiccator or in warm air, giving a substance (m. 242°) considered to be either XI or XIII. That the two products obtained had structures XII and XIII, respectively, was demonstrated[5] by the preparation of XII from XIV (itself obtained from anthranilic acid and phthalic anhydride).

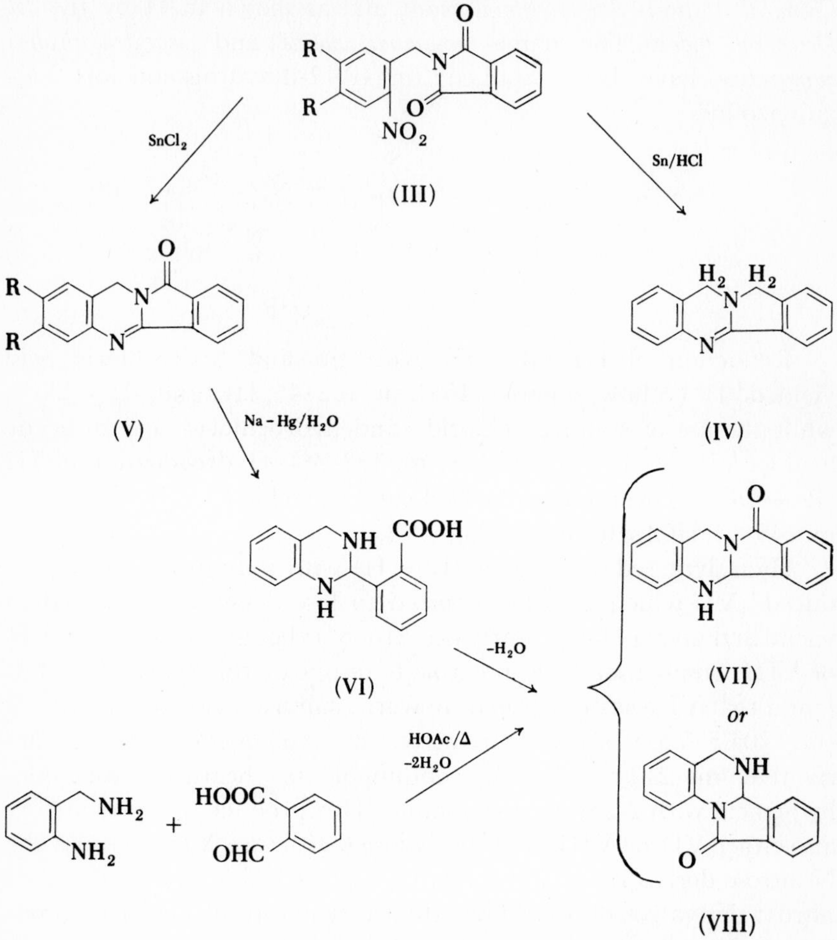

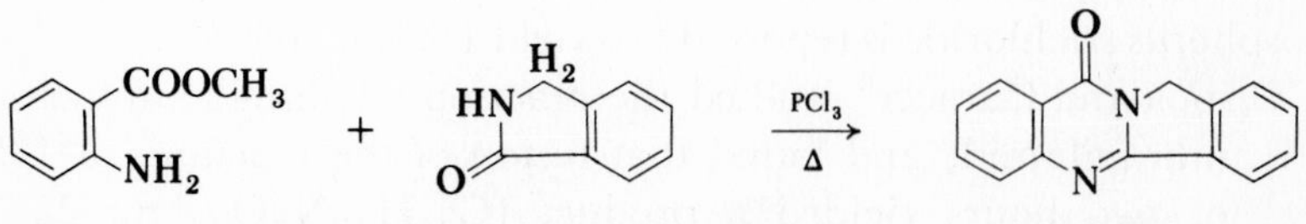

O R N R O NO_2

SnCl$_2$ Sn/HCl

(III)

O R N R N

H_2 H_2 N N

(V) Na - Hg/H_2O (IV)

O N N H

NH COOH N H

(VI) $-H_2O$ (VII) *or*

HOAc /Δ $-2H_2O$

NH N O

NH_2 NH_2 + HOOC OHC

(VIII)

$COOCH_3$ NH_2 + H_2 HN O PCl$_3$ Δ O N N

(IX)

The treatment of XV (see Section A-451) with ammonia or methylamine in ethanolic solution at room temperature yielded[6] intermediates (presumably either XVI or XVII), which could be dehydrated by hot acetic acid to XVIII (R = H, m. 215°; R = CH_3, m. 186°).

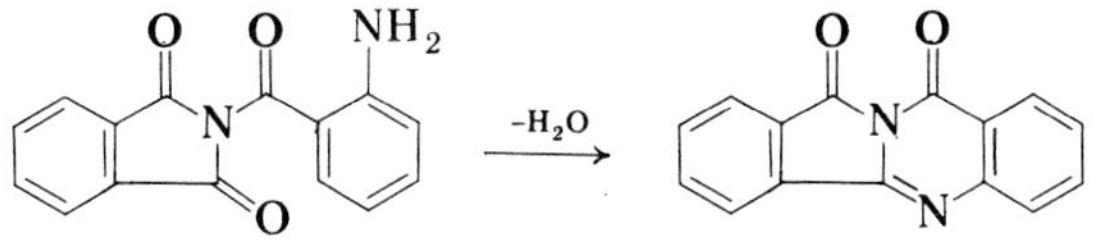

(X) (XI)

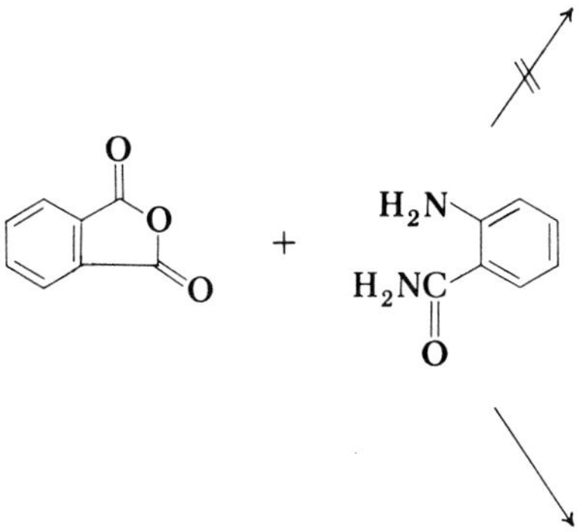

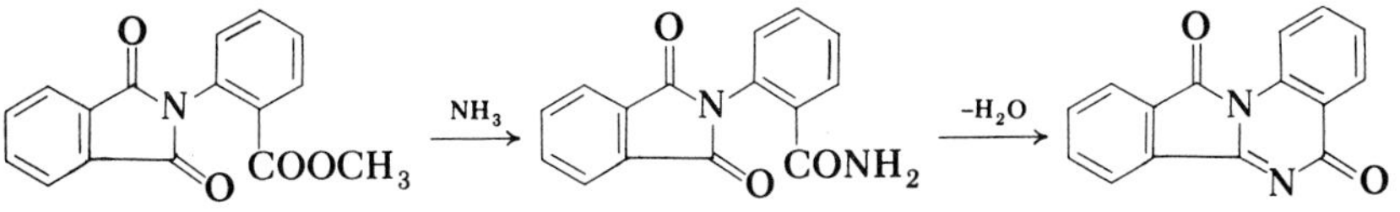

(XIV) (XII) (XIII)

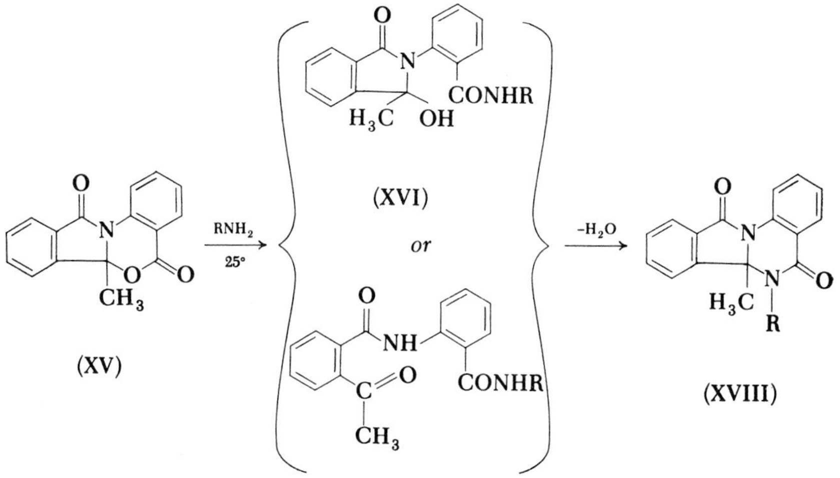

(XVI) (XVII) (XV) (XVIII)

References

1. Gabriel, *Ber.*, **45,** 713 (1912).
2. Downes and Lions, *J. Am. Chem. Soc.*, **72,** 3053 (1950).
3. Stephenson, *J. Chem. Soc.*, **1954,** 2354.
4. Asahina, Manske and Robinson, *J. Chem. Soc.*, **1927,** 1708.
5. Crippa and Caracci, *Gazz. chim. ital.*, **68,** 109 (1938).
6. Honzl, *Collection Czechoslov. Chem. Communs.*, **21,** 725 (1956); *Chem. listy*, **49,** 1671 (1955); *Chem. Abstracts*, **50,** 5622 (1956).
7. Barnes and Godfrey, *J. Org. Chem.*, **22,** 1038 (1957).

A-460. Indolo[2,1-*b*]quinazoline. R.I. 2415

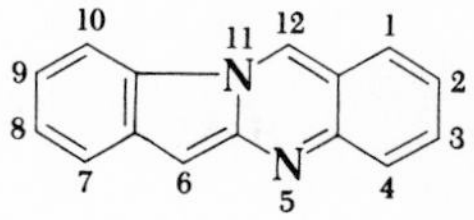

In 1892, O'Neill reported[1] the isolation of a yellow product from the oxidation of indigo (I) with potassium permanganate. The same product was obtained by Perkin[2] as the result of air-oxidation during the vacuum sublimation of indigo. The preparation of similar yellow products from the oxidation of isatin[3] (II) or of indigo[4] (and its homologs) with hot aqueous potassium permanganate was patented. Finally, Friedländer and Roschdestwensky[5] studied the subject in detail, and showed that the various methods yielded the same yellow product for which they confirmed Perkin's formula ($C_{15}H_8N_2O_2$), and for which they proposed structure III. This product has been named *anhydro-α-isatin anthranilide* and *9,10-dicarbonyl-[(indolenin-3')-1',2':3,2-(3,4-dihydroquinazoline)]*.

A convenient synthesis of III from IV by condensation with anthranilic acid was described[6,7] and this method was utilized to prepare homologs of III. Compound III was also obtained as one of the oxidation[8] products of V, and from the air oxidation of an indigo-pyridine-potash-copper mixture.[9] Furthermore, Heller and Benade[10,11] found that certain derivatives of indigo and isatin, which they called *isatols* and *isatoids*, were converted, in alkaline solution, into III by the action of sunlight. The structures of the starting materials were disputed by Hantzsch, although he confirmed their conversion[12,13] into III. Treatment of *β*-methyl isatoids (which may have structure VI, see Section A-46) with hot acetic acid gave[14,15] products thought to have structure VII, and which were oxidized by

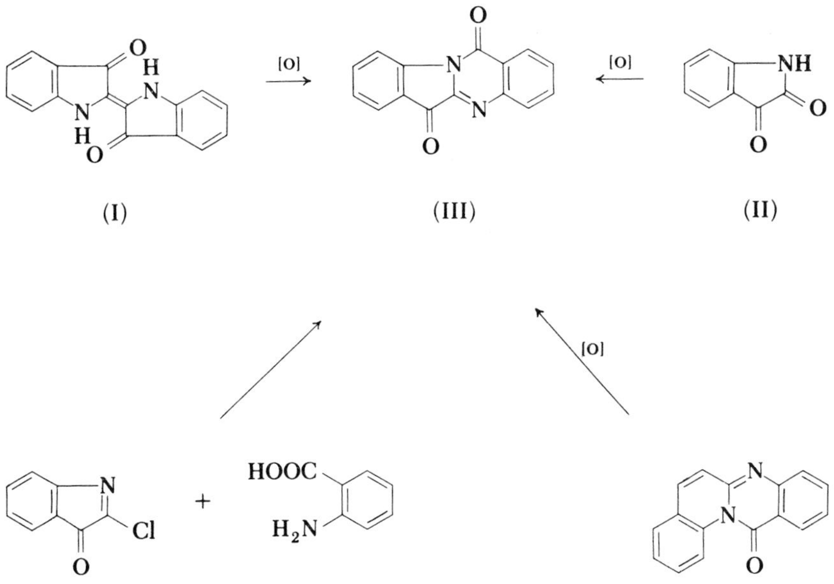

(I) (III) (II)

(IV) (V)

chromic acid to analogs of III. Finally, Heller also claimed to have prepared III by oxidizing α-isatol with chromic acid,[16] or indigo with silver acetate.[17]

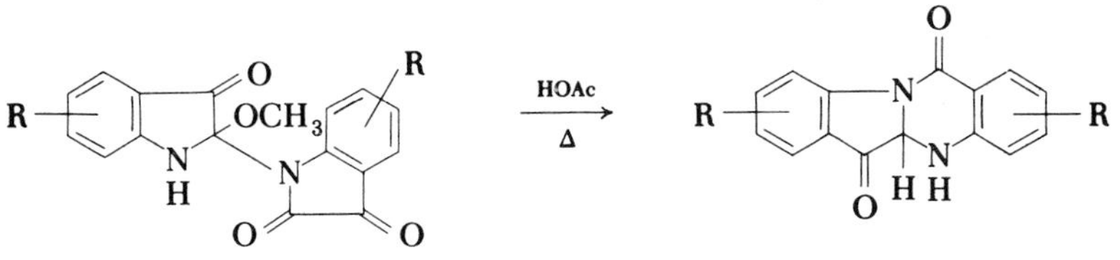

(VI) (VII)

Compound III yields[5] an oxime and a phenylhydrazone, and may be reduced[2] by tin and hydrochloric acid to a product ($C_{15}H_{12}N_2O$), which is probably the 5,5*a*,6,12-tetrahydro-12-oxo derivative. While III is cleaved by hot concentrated caustic to isatin and anthranilic acid, under mild conditions it gives a dark brown vat. The anhydro-α-isatin anthranilides were reviewed by Martinet and Grosjean.[18]

Indolo[2,1-*b*]quinazolines

Substituents or structure	Properties	Refs.
2,8-Dibromo-6,12-dihydro-6,12-dioxo-	Yel., m. 325° (318°, 310°).	4,9,14
2,2'-Bis(6,12-dihydroindolo-[2,1-*b*]quinazoline-6,12-dione)	Yel., m. 259°.	6
7-Chloro-6,12-dihydro-6,12-dioxo-	Yel.	6
2,8-Dibromo-5,5*a*,6,12-tetrahydro-6,12-dioxo-	m. 309–10° d.	14
6,12-Dihydro-6,12-dioxo-	Yel., m. 262° (261°, 260°, 258–9°). Oxime, m. ~265° d. Phenylhydrazone, m. 242°.	1–13,16–18
5,5*a*,6,12-Tetrahydro-12-oxo-(?)	m. 190–3°.	2
6,12-Dihydro-2,8-dimethyl-6,12-dioxo-	Yel., m. 242°.	4
6,12-Dihydro-2,4,8,10-tetramethyl-6,12-dioxo-	Yel., m. 245°.	15
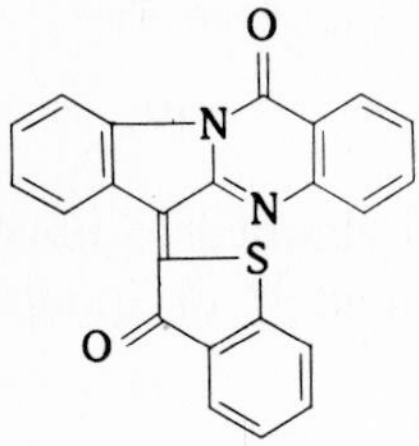		19

References

1. O'Neill, *Chem. News*, **65,** 124 (1892); *J. Chem. Soc.* (*Abstracts*), **62,** 991 (1892).
2. Perkin, *Proc. Chem. Soc.*, **22,** 198 (1906); *Chem. Zentr.*, **II,** 1434 (1906).
3. Farbwerke vorm. Meister Lucius & Brünning, Ger. Pat. 276,808; *Frdl.*, **12,** 259 (1917).
4. Farbwerke vorm. Meister Lucius & Brünning, Ger. Pat. 281,050; *Frdl.*, **12,** 260 (1917).
5. Friedländer and Roschdestwensky, *Ber.*, **48,** 1841 (1915).
6. Badische Anilin- und Soda-Fabrik, Ger. Pat. 287,373; *Frdl.*, **12,** 261 (1917).
7. Badische Anilin- und Soda-Fabrik, Ger. Pat. 288,055; *Frdl.*, **12,** 263 (1917).
8. Seide and Tschelinzew, *J. Gen. Chem.* (*U.S.S.R.*), **7,** 2318 (1937); *Chem. Zentr.*, **I,** 601 (1938); *Chem. Abstracts*, **32,** 572 (1938).
9. Machemer, *Ber.*, **63,** 1341 (1930).
10. Heller, *Ber.*, **52,** 437 (1919).
11. Heller and Benade, *Ber.*, **55,** 1006 (1922).
12. Hantzsch, *Ber.*, **54,** 1221 (1921).

13. Hantzsch and Kröber, *J. prakt. Chem.*, **115,** 126 (1927).
14. Heller and Lauth, *Ber.*, **56,** 1591 (1923).
15. Heller and Lauth, *J. prakt. Chem.*, **112,** 331 (1926).
16. Heller and Siller, *J. prakt. Chem.*, **123,** 257 (1929).
17. Heller, *Ber.*, **69,** 563 (1936).
18. Martinet and Grosjean, *Rev. gen. mat. color.*, **28,** 3 (1923).
19. Badische Anilin- und Soda-Fabrik, Ger. Pat. Appln. B 76,941; *Frdl.*, **13,** 459 (1923).

A-461. 5*H*-4*a*,9*b*-Diazabenzo[*f*]-cyclopent[*cd*]indene*

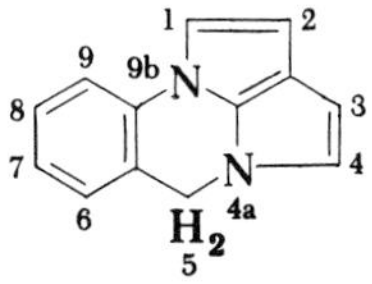

This nucleus was listed (*R.I.* 2284) but not named by the *Ring Index*.

A product (m. 164°) claimed to be II was obtained[1] from vasicine (I) by acetylation. However, this product was subsequently shown[2] to have structure III.

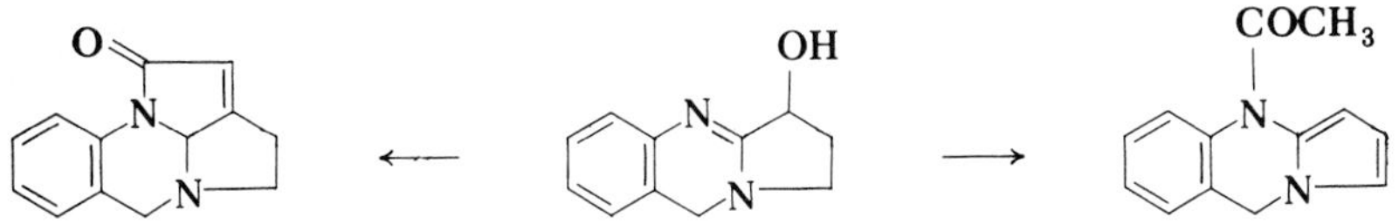

(II) (I) (III)

References

1. Ghose, Krishna, Narang and Ray, *Current Sci.*, **4,** 158 (1935); *Chem. Zentr.*, **II,** 3919 (1935); *Chem. Abstracts*, **30,** 1060 (1936).
2. Späth, Kuffner and Platzer, *Ber.*, **68,** 935 (1935).

A-462. 10*H*-Pyrrolo[1,2-*a*]perimidine. R.I. 2419

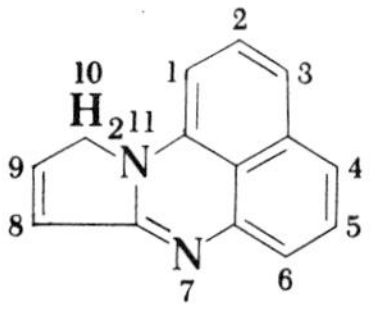

Condensation of 1,8-naphthylenediamine with suitable carboxylic acids yielded[1,2] several derivatives of this nucleus. Compounds I (grey-violet, m. 159–60°, H_2SO_4 solution green), II (violet-brown, m. 161°, H_2SO_4 solution blue) and III (red, m. 187–9°, H_2SO_4 solution green, KOH solution brown) were patented[2] as dye intermediates.

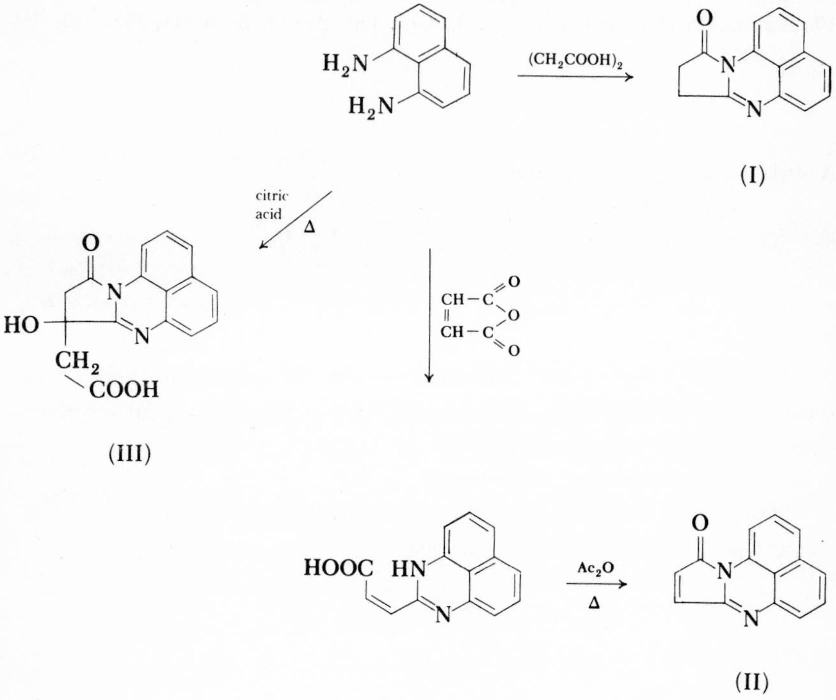

(I)

(III)

(II)

References

1. Sachs, *Ann.*, **365,** 53 (1909).
2. Bayer and Co., Ger. Pat. 202,354; *Frdl.*, **9,** 187 (1911). Fr. Pat. 388,955. Brit. Pat. 7575.

A-463. 12*H*-Phthaloperine. R.I. 3064

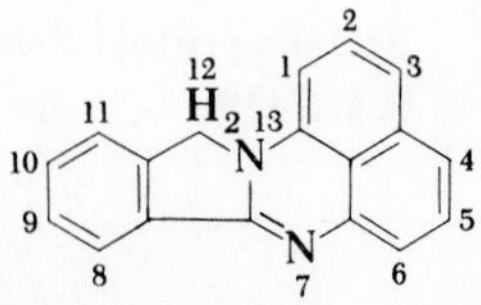

The name *2-benzyleneperimidine* has been used, but the name phthaloperine was proposed by Sachs (although he suggested the now obsolete numbering shown in I), and it now seems universally adopted.

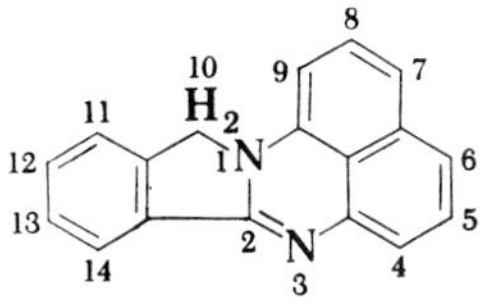

8
10 9 7
11 H_2
12 1N 6
13 2 N 5
14 3 4

(I)

Evidently the first synthesis of this system was accomplished by Pollack,[1] who heated phthalic anhydride with 1,8-diaminonaphthalene-3,6-disulfonic acid, and obtained a yellow dye of unknown structure. The first systematic work however, was done by Sachs.[2] He showed that phthaloperinones of structure II resulted from the condensation of phthalic acid (or substituted phthalic acids) with 1,8-naphthylenediamine. Replacement of phthalic anhydride by phthalaldehydic acid[5] also gives II (in low yield) instead of the 7,7*a*-dihydro derivative of II.

The lactam bond of II is cleaved[3] by alcoholic caustic and by concentrated hydrochloric acid. Bromination and nitration of II

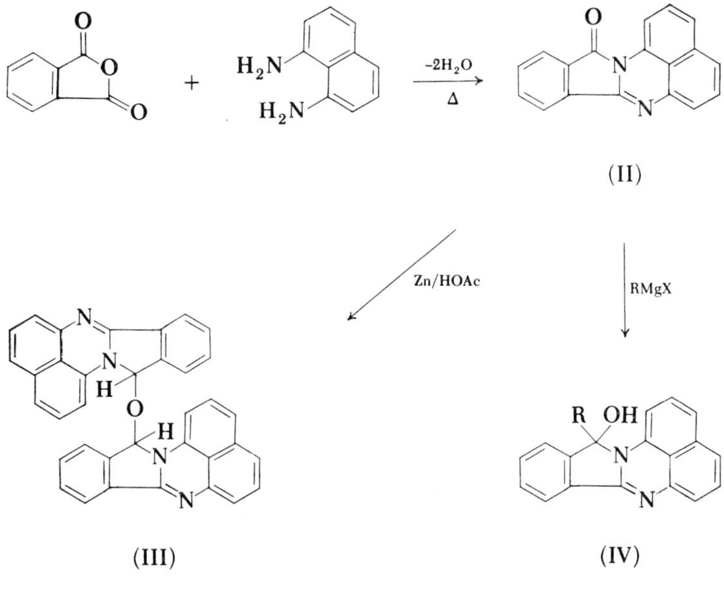

O
O
O
\+
H_2N
H_2N
$-2H_2O$
Δ
O
N
N

(II)

Zn/HOAc

RMgX

N
N
H
O
H
N
N

(III)

R OH
N
N

(IV)

yield[2] disubstituted derivatives, presumably the 3,4-isomers. Reduction of II by zinc and acetic acid afforded[2] a very stable yellow product, which was assigned structure III. Grignard reagents attack the carbonyl group of II, giving carbinols of type IV, which (when R = benzyl) may be dehydrated to benzylidenephthaloperine. A number of substituted phthaloperinones (II) have been described.[2,4,7-12]

Phthaloperinone, under the name "Orange 1584," was manufactured[14] for use in colored signal smokes[13] by the Wehrmacht in World War II. Recently, a number of phthaloperinones have been utilized[9-12] in the mass coloring of polyamide plastics and have been claimed[19] as dyes for polyester fibers. The condensation of II or its derivatives with copper, sulfur and sodium sulfide yields[15,16] brown to bordeaux sulfur dyes of unknown constitution (e.g., "Immedial Brown 3274").[17]

12*H*-Phthaloperines

Empirical formula	Substituents	Properties	Refs.
$C_{18}H_6Cl_4N_2O$	8,9,10,11-Tetrachloro-12-oxo-	m. 312–15°. Sold as "Aminoid Red JL."	9,10,18
$C_{18}H_8Br_2N_2O$	3,4-Dibromo-12-oxo	Red-brn., d. > 240°.	2
$C_{18}H_8Cl_2N_2O$	8,11-Dichloro-12-oxo-	m. 325–8°.	9,10
	9,10-Dichloro-12-oxo-	H_2SO_4 solution: bl.-vt.	9,10,18
	8,9- and/or 10,11-Dichloro-12-oxo-	m. 236°.	9,10,18
	x,*x*-Dichloro-12-oxo-	m. 235–7°.	2
$C_{18}H_8N_4O_5$	3,4-Dinitro-12-oxo-	Red, m. 247°.	2
	8,11-Dinitro-12-oxo-	m. > 340°.	9
	9,10-Dinitro-12-oxo-	m. > 340°.	9
$C_{18}H_9BrN_2O$	3- and/or 4-Bromo-12-oxo-	Red, m. 214°.	8
$C_{18}H_9ClN_2O$	3- and/or 4-Chloro-12-oxo-	Scarlet, m. 212°.	8
	8- and/or 11-Chloro-12-oxo-	m. 241°.	9,10,18
	9- and/or 10-Chloro-12-oxo-	m. 204°.	9,10,11
$C_{18}H_9N_3O_3$	8- and/or 11-Nitro-12-oxo-	Dk. red, m. 210–5°.	9

12*H*-Phthaloperines (*continued*)

Empirical formula	Substituents	Properties	Refs.
	9- and/or 10-Nitro-12-oxo-	Red, m. 278–80°.	9
$C_{18}H_{10}N_2O$	12-Oxo-	Red, m. 232° (229–30°).	2,3,5, 6,10
$C_{18}H_{10}N_2O_4S$	12-Oxo-*x*-sulfonic acid	—	4
$C_{18}H_{10}N_2O_7S_2$	12-Oxo-2,5-disulfonic acid	Or.-brn.	1
$C_{18}H_{12}N_4O$	2,4-Diamino-12-oxo-	m. 255–60°.	2
$C_{19}H_{14}N_2O$	12-Hydroxy-12-methyl-	Olive-brn., m. 241°. HI salt, m. 324°. Picrate, m. 220°d.	2
$C_{20}H_{10}N_2O_5$	3,4-Dicarboxy-12-oxo-	Yel., m. > 300°.	7
$C_{20}H_{16}N_2O$	12-Ethyl-12-hydroxy-	m. 243°.	2
$C_{24}H_{16}N_2O$	12-Hydroxy-12-phenyl-	m. 282–4°.	2
$C_{25}H_{16}N_2$	12-Benzylidene-	Purp.-red, m. 191°.	2
$C_{25}H_{18}N_2O$	12-Benzyl-12-hydroxy-	m. 258–9°.	2

References

1. Pollack, Ger. Pat. 122,854; *Frdl.*, **6,** 517 (1904).
2. Sachs, *Ann.*, **365,** 53 (1909).
3. Bayer & Co., Ger. Pat. 202,354; *Frdl.*, **10,** 187 (1911). Fr. Pat. 388,955. Brit. Pat. 7575.
4. Bayer & Co., Brit. Pat. 22,528; *Chem. Abstracts*, **9,** 865 (1915).
5. Stephenson, *J. Chem. Soc.*, **1952,** 5024.
6. Wanag, *Ber.*, **75,** 719 (1942).
7. Crippa and Galimberti, *Gazz. chim. ital.*, **63,** 81 (1933).
8. Hodgson and Hathway, *J. Chem. Soc.*, **1945,** 543.
9. Jones, Brit. Pat. 730,692. Fr. Pat. 1,075,110.
10. LeThierry d'Ennequin, *Teintex*, **20,** 879 (1955).
11. Dassigny and Robin, Fr. Pat. 1,111,620.
12. LeThierry d'Ennequin, Dassigny and Robin, *XIVth. Int. Congr. Pure and Appl. Chem., Handbook*, Zürich, 1955, p. 291.
13. Strauss and Pflaumer, *I.G. Farbenindustrie, A.G.*, "Smoke Dyes," *C.I.O.S. Report No.* 385, p. 61.
14. I.G. Farbenindustrie, A.G., *PB Report No.* 73726, frame 373.
15. Bayer & Co., Ger. Pat. 253,239; *Frdl.*, **11,** 495 (1915). U. S. Pats. 1,081,601/2. Brit. Pats. 12,163 and 22,414. Fr. Pat. 453,026.
16. Bayer & Co., Ger. Pat. 263,903; *Frdl.*, **11,** 496 (1915). Brit. Pat. 22,414.
17. I.G. Farbenindustrie, A.G., *PB Report No.* 74181, frame 2628 and *PB Report No.* 74026, frame 2584.

18. Robin, Fr. Pat. 1,108,109.
19. Sandoz, Fr. Pat. 1,155,008.

A-464. 12*H*-Pyrido[2′,3′,3,4]pyrrolo-[1,2-*a*]perimidine*

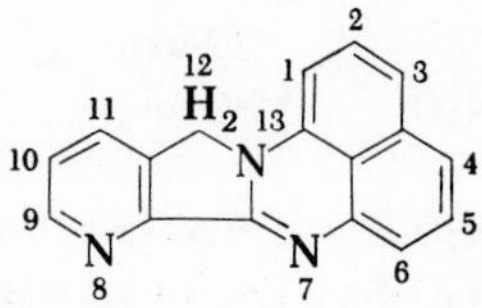

Reaction of 1,8-naphthylenediamine (II) with quinolinic acid (I) in refluxing toluene yielded[1] a mixture of III and IV. The identity of the former product was demonstrated by decarboxylation, which gave 2-(2-pyridyl)perimidine (V, alternatively prepared from picolinic acid and II). Dehydration of III, or simply fusion of I with II produced VI (m. 253–4°).

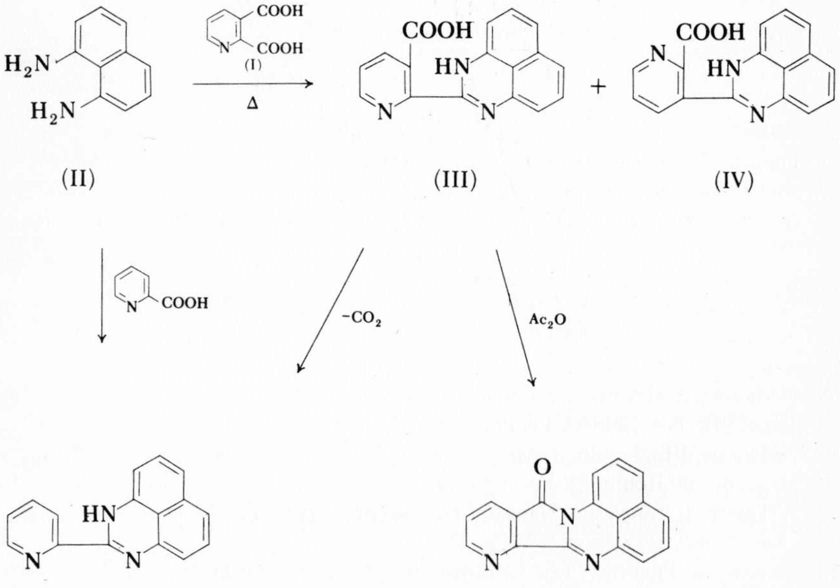

(II) (III) (IV)

$-CO_2$ Ac_2O

(V) (VI)

Reference

1. Bastic and Golubovic, *Bull. soc. chim. Belgrade*, **20,** 317 (1955).

A-465. 10*H*-Indeno[6,7,1-*def*]isoindolo-[2,1-*a*]quinazoline. R.I. 3477

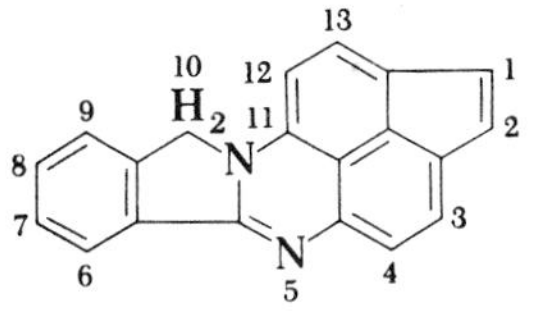

The name *phthaloaceperine* has been used.

Condensation of phthalic anhydride with 5,6-diaminoacenaphthene (I) yields[1,2] II (red, m. >300°[2] (m. 290°)[1]), together with some 5,6-diphthalimidoacenaphthene.[2] Chromic acid oxidation of II gives[2] phthaloperinone-3,4-dicarboxylic acid (see Section A-463).

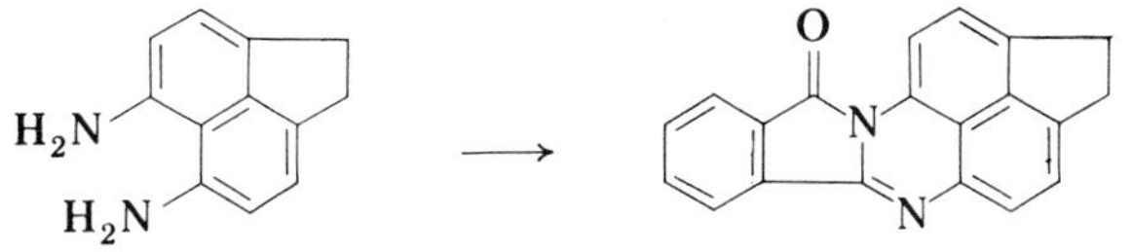

(I) (II)

References

1. Sachs and Mosebach, *Ber.*, **44**, 2852 (1911).
2. Crippa and Galimberti, *Gazz. chim. ital.*, **63**, 81 (1933); *Chem. Zentr.*, **II**, 217 (1933); *Chem. Abstracts*, **27**, 3463 (1933).

A-466. 10*H*-Isoindolo[2,1-*a*]pyrrolo-[2,3,4-*gh*]perimidine*

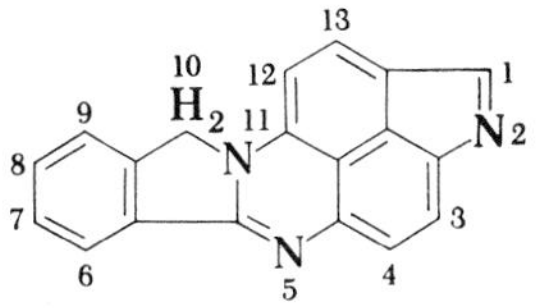

From the nitration of I, followed by reduction of the nitro derivative with alkaline hydrosulfite, a yellowish brown crystalline product, thought to be II was obtained.[1] It is reported to cleave, probably at one of the lactam bonds, under alkaline conditions.

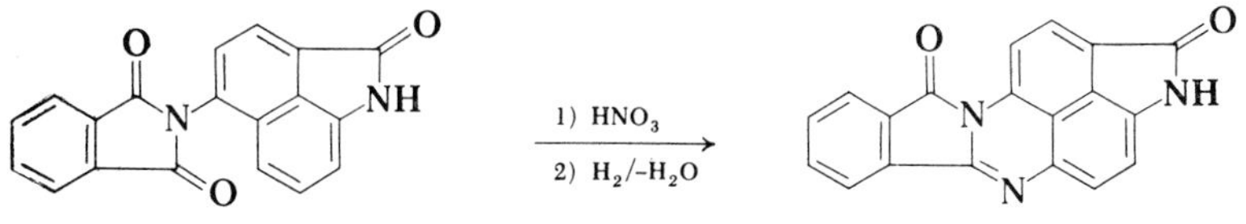

1) HNO_3
2) $H_2/-H_2O$

(I) (II)

Reference

1. Rösch, *I.G. Farbenindustrie, A.G., 33 Wissenschaftlicher Austausch der Gruppe IX*, Frankfurt, March 21, 1935; *PB Report No.* 70339, frame 11245; *PB Report No.* 25632, frame 449.

A-467. Indolo[2,1-*b*]naphtho[2,3-*h*]-quinazoline*

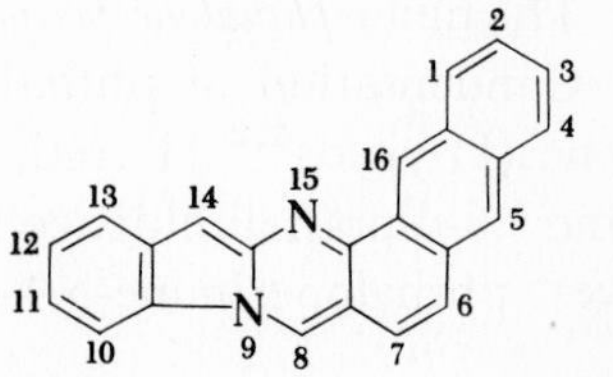

A brown vat dye of structure II was reported[1] to result from the condensation of I with isatin chloride. During the vatting operation the nitro group was, of course, reduced, so that the brown color actually represents the amino analog of II.

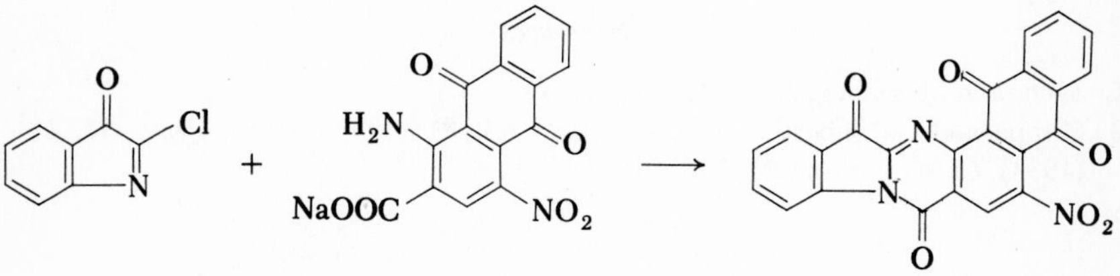

(I) (II)

Reference

1. Berthold, Rohland and Böttcher, *I.G. Farbenindustrie, A.G., 40 Wissenschaftlicher Austausch der Gruppe IX*, Ludwigshafen, Dec. 1, 1938; *PB Report No.* 70342, frame 14379.

A-468. 8*H*-Naphtho[2,3-*l*]-phthaloperine*

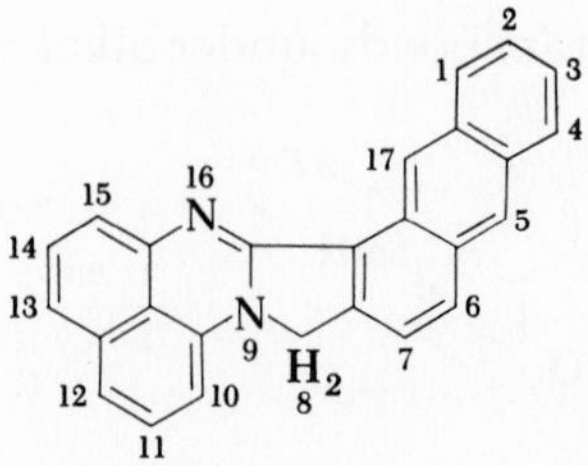

and/or

A-469. 16*H*-Naphtho[2,3-*n*]-phthaloperine*

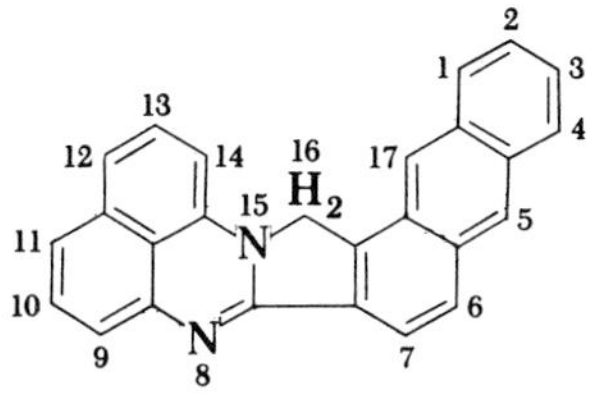

A product (m. 374°, sulfuric acid solution blue-black), presumably either I or II or a mixture of both, was obtained[1,2] as shown.

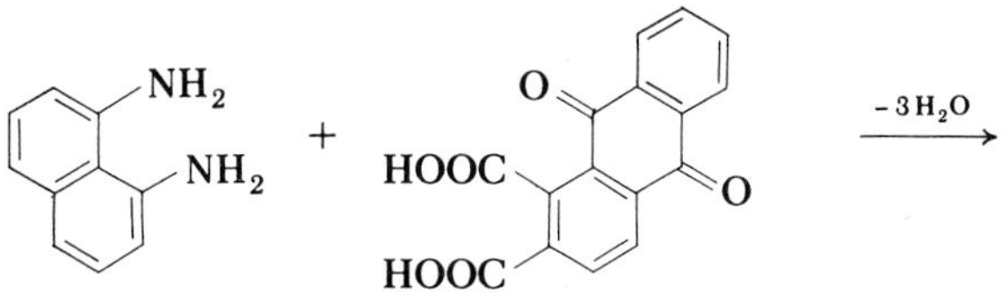

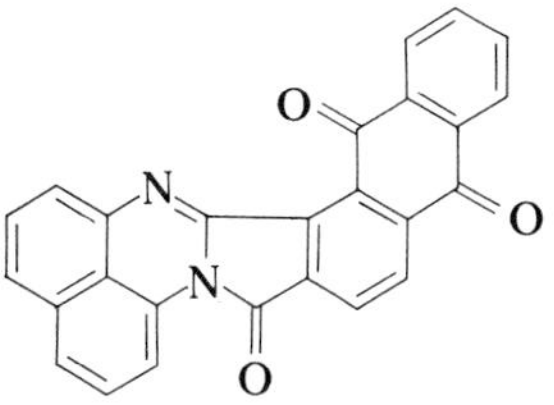

$-3H_2O$

and/or

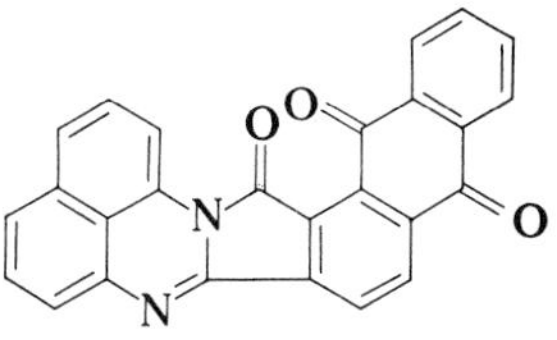

(I) (II)

References

1. Jones, Brit. Pat. 730,692. Fr. Pat. 1,075,110.
2. Robin, Fr. Pat. 1,108,109.

A-470. 16*H*-Naphtho[2,3-*m*]-phthaloperine*

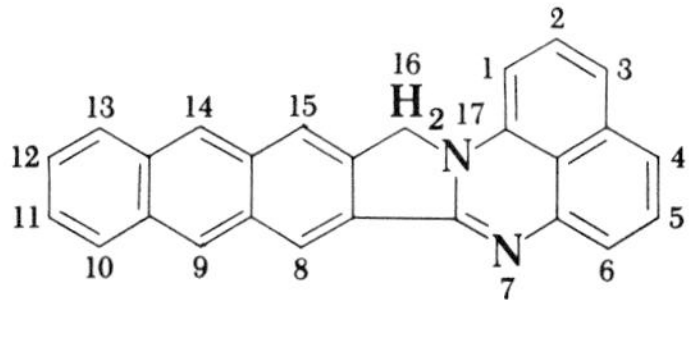

The condensation of anthraquinone-2,3-dicarboxylic acid with 1,8-naphthylenediamine yielded[1,3] I (m. >370°), which dissolved in sulfuric acid with a greenish-blue color, changing after half an hour to reddish-blue.

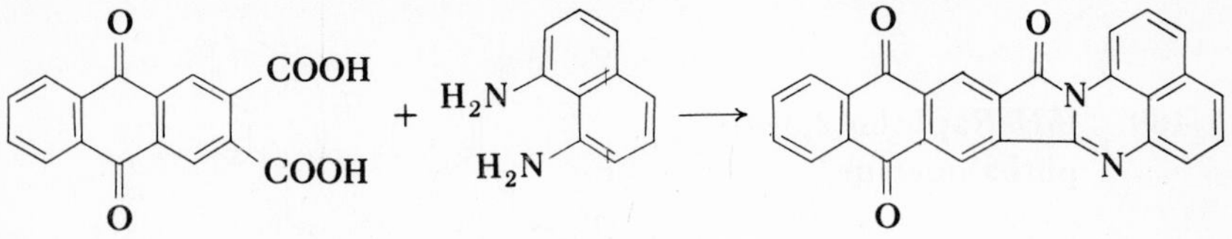

(I)

Vat dyes of structure III (IIIa, R = R′ = H, blue, dull violet solution in sulfuric acid; IIIb, R = H, R′ = Cl, blue, blue vat, olive-green solution in sulfuric acid; IIIc, R = NO_2, R′ = H, violet, dyes grey-blue from a blue-green vat) were obtained[2] by heating the imides IIa–IIc with 1,8-naphthylenediamine. The possibility of isomer formation from IIc was not discussed.

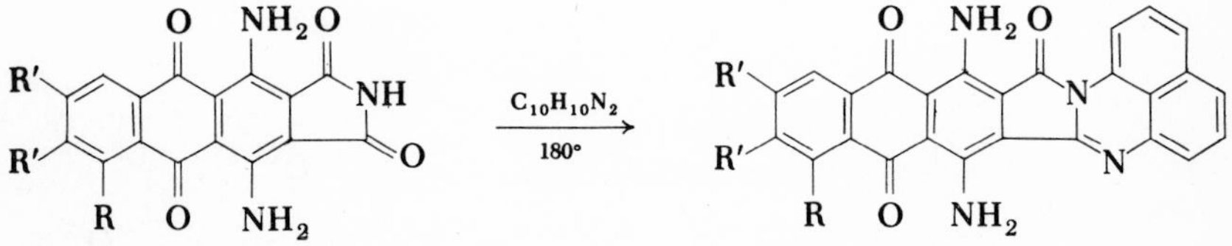

$C_{10}H_{10}N_2$, 180°

(IIa) R = R′ = H
(IIb) R = H, R′ = Cl
(IIc) R = NO_2, R′ = H

(IIIa) R = R′ = H
(IIIb) R = H, R′ = Cl
(IIIc) R = NO_2, R′ = H

References

1. Jones, Brit. Pat. 730,692. Fr. Pat. 1,075,110.
2. Baumann, U. S. Pat. 2,770,625. Fr. Pat. 1,104,697. Ger. Pat. Apln. F 12413 IVb/22b. Brit. Pat. 773,212.
3. Robin, Fr. Pat. 1,108,109.

A-471. 8bH,16H-Naphth[2′,1′,4,5]-indeno[1,7a-c]quinazolino-[3,2-a]pyrrole*

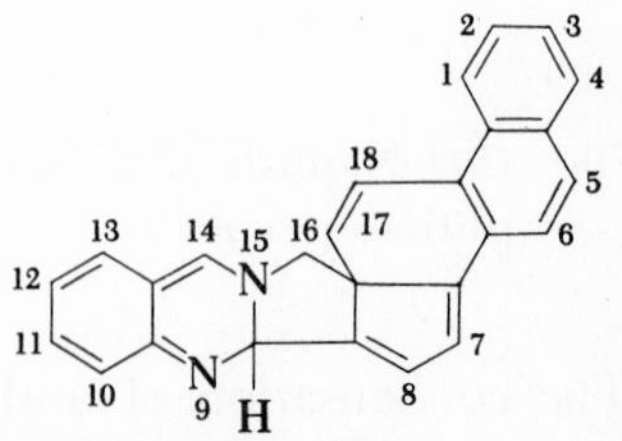

Products thought[1] to be of structure I (R = H or CH_3) were obtained[1,2] from the condensation of 2-aminobenzaldehyde with the alkaloids *conkurchine* and *conessidine*.

NHR

CH_3

$\overset{+}{N}$

N

H CH_3

(I)

References

1. Tschesche and Roy, *Chem. Ber.*, **89,** 1288 (1956).
2. Bertho, *Ann.*, **573,** 210 (1951).

A-472. 16*H*-Acenaphtho[1,2-*m*]-phthaloperine. R.I. 3858

13 12 14 16 1 2 3 15 H_2 17 N 11 4 10 5 9 8 N 7 6

The name *3,4-(1,8-naphthylene)phthaloperine* has been used.

Condensation of the anhydride I with 1,8-naphthylenediamine yielded[1] II (red, m. 362°).

C_6H_5 O O O C_6H_5

$\xrightarrow{C_{10}H_{10}N_2}$

C_6H_5 O N N C_6H_5

(I) (II)

Reference

1. Dilthey and Henkels, *J. prakt. Chem.*, **149,** 85 (1937).

A-473. 18*H*-Phenanthro[9,10-*m*]-phthaloperine. R.I. 3869

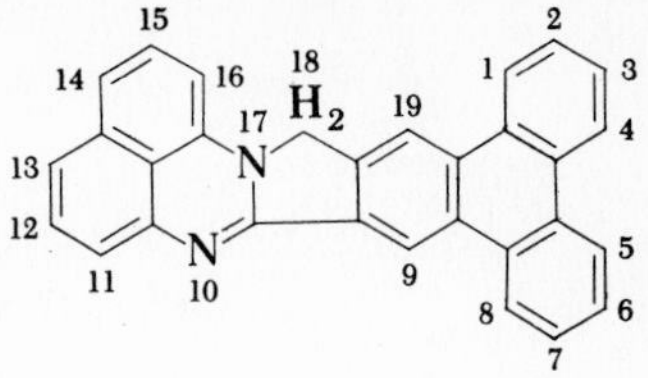

The name *4,5-(o,o'-biphenylene)-phthaloperine* also has been used.

Condensation of the anhydride I with 1,8-naphthylenediamine yielded[1] II (red, m. 319°).

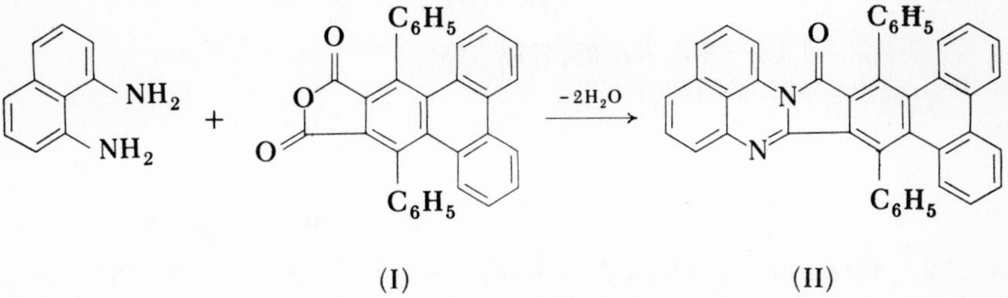

$\xrightarrow{-2H_2O}$

(I) (II)

Reference

1. Dilthey, ter Horst and Schaefer, *J. prakt. Chem.*, **148,** 53 (1937).

A-474. Diperimidino-[1,2-*a*, 1′,2′-*a*′]benzo-[1,2-*c*, 4,5-*c*′]dipyrrole*

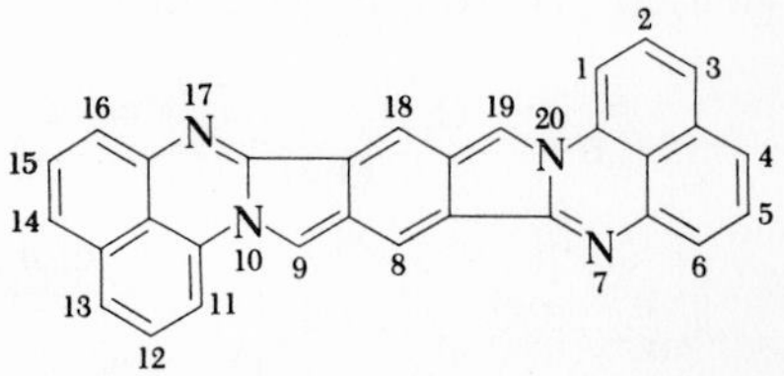

and

A-474. Diperimidino-[1,2-*a*, 1′,2′-*a*′]benzo-[1,2-*c*, 4,5-*c*′]dipyrrole*

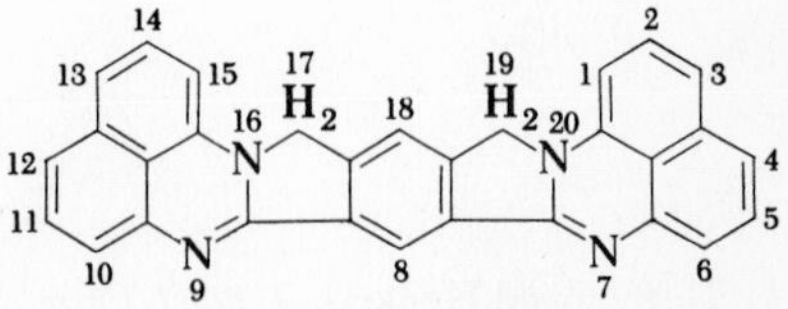

The condensation of pyromellitic anhydride with 1,8-naphthylenediamine yields[1,2,3] the dark violet product I, which gives a green, scarcely soluble vat and a blue-green solution in sulfuric acid.

While not reported by Bayer,[1] the formation of a certain amount of II might also be expected in this reaction. However, II would not be expected to vat, and thus might be separated from I. Jones[2] and Robin[3] indicate the reaction product to be a mixture.

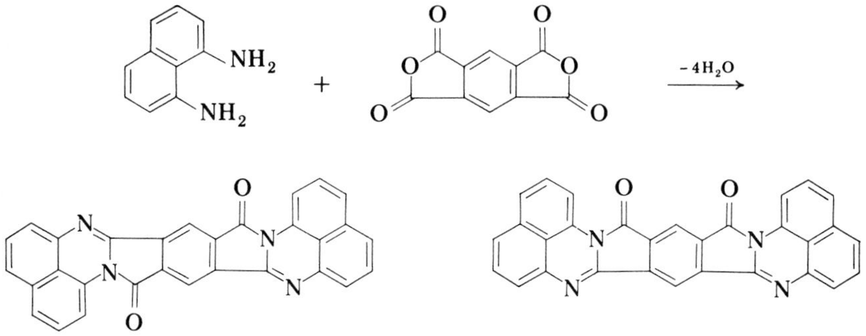

$$-4H_2O$$

(I) (II)

References

1. Bayer, *I.G. Farbenindustrie, A.G., 11 Wissenschaftlicher Sitzung*, Höchst, May 23 and June 28, 1933; *PB Report No.* 25630, frame 683.
2. Jones, Brit. Pat. 730,692. Fr. Pat. 1,075,110.
3. Robin, Fr. Pat. 1,108,109.